standard catalog of

CHEVROLET

1912-1990

by Pat Chappell

Published by

700 E. State Street • Iola, WI 54990-0001
Telephone: 715/445-2214

Please call or write for our free catalog of automotive publications. Our toll-free number to place an order or obtain a free catalog is 800-258-0929 or please use our regular business telephone 715-445-2214 for editorial comment and further information.

Library of Congress Catalog Number: 90-60576
ISBN: 0-87341-141-2

Printed in the United States of America

First Printing October 1990
Second Printing April 1995

CATALOG STAFF

PUBLISHER: John A. Gunnell
EDITOR: James T. Lenzke
PHOTO RESEARCH: Kenneth Buttolph
DATA PROCESSING: Bruce Denny
COVER DESIGN: Paul Tofte
BOOKS MANAGER: Pat Klug

CONTENTS

FOREWORD

Traditionally, the concept behind Krause Publications' Standard Catalogs is to compile massive amounts of information about motor vehicles and present it in a standard format which the hobbyist, collector or professional dealer can use to answer some commonly asked questions.

Those questions include: What year, make and model is the vehicle? What did it sell for new? How rare is it? What is special about it? Some answers are provided by photos and others by the fact-filled text.

Chester L. Krause of Krause Publications is responsible for the overall concept of creating the Standard Catalog series covering American automobiles. David V. Brownell, editor of *Special-Interest Autos* undertook preliminary work on the concept while serving as editor of *Old Cars Weekly* in the 1970s. Then editor John A. Gunnell assumed the project in 1978. The first Standard Catalog, covering postwar models (1946-1975) was published in 1982, while Beverly Rae Kimes continued writing and researching *The Standard Catalog of American Cars* (1805-1942), which was published in 1985. In 1987 *The Standard Catalog of Light Duty American Trucks* (1900-1986), was published by John Gunnell, while the second edition of the 1946-1975 volume was printed. In 1988, the 1805-1942 volume by Kimes appeared in second edition form. Also in 1988, James M. Flammang authored *The Standard Catalog of American Cars* (1976-1986), which went into its second edition in 1990. Currently the four-volume set of Standard Catalogs enjoys good sales in the automotive/truck collector hobby, and provides a wealth of detailed information that car and truck collectors, hobbyists, restorers and investors will not find from any other publishing house.

The scope of these catalogs has been to cover the major manufacturers, which have survived into the Nineties: Chrysler, Ford and General Motors as well as companies they have absorbed and companies no longer with us today. Independent companies such as Checker, Hudson, Kaiser-Frazer, Nash, Packard, Studebaker and Willys are included in the earlier catalogs, as well as some 200 producers of low-volume nameplates from Airscoot to Yenko. In each case, the data compiled encompasses a physical description; list of known equipment and original specifications; technical data; historical footnotes and appraisal of the car's current 'ballpark value'.

In each catalog, all compilations were made by an experienced editiorial team consisting of the Automotive Staff of Krause Publications and numerous contributors who are recognized experts on a certain marque or specific area of automotive history. A major benefit of combining teamwork with expertise has been the gathering of many significant facts about each model.

No claims are made about the catalogs being history textbooks or encyclopedias. Nor are they repair manuals or "bibles" for motor vehicle enthusiasts. They are, rather, intended as a contribution to the pursuit of greater knowledge about the many wonderful automobiles and trucks built in the United States since 1805. They are much larger in size, broader in scope and more deluxe in format than any previously published collectors' guides, buyers' digests or pricing guides.

The long-range goal of Krause Publications is to make all of the these catalogs as nearly perfect as possible. At the same time, we expect such catalogs will always raise new questions and bring forth new facts that were not previously unearthed in the countless hours of research by our team. All contributors are requested to maintain an ongoing file of new research, corrections and additional photos which can be used to refine and expand future editions.

With this *Standard Catalog of Chevrolet,* we begin a new venture into researching a single automotive marque which has been responsible for millions of production vehicles since the early 1900s. And we thank the editors and contributors to the three volume *Standard Catalog of American Cars* for providing much of the material herein. For it is through their research and editing effort that we produce this *Catalog of Chevrolet,* with an assurance that most of the information which we've combined herewith from those three catalogs is accurate and well-researched. Additionally, we have included some of the best Chevrolet-oriented articles from past issues of *Old Cars Weekly* authored by experts in the field. Should you, as an individual Chevy enthusiast, member of a Chevy club, or historian, have access to expanded information that you wish to share, please don't hesitate to contact the editors, in care of Krause Publications, *Standard Catalog of Chevrolet,* 700 East State Street, Iola, WI 54990.

Other catalogs currently available are: *The Standard Catalog of American Cars 1805-1942; The Standard Catalog of American Cars 1946-1975; The Standard Catalog of American Cars 1976-1986;* and *The Standard Catalog of Light Duty American Trucks 1900-1986.*With the publication of this *Standard Catalog of Chevrolet,* simultaneously Krause Publications is releasing *The Standard Catalog of Chrysler Corporation 1934-1990* by John Lee, and *The Standard Catalog of Ford Motor Company 1903-1990* by Bob Lichty. For ordering information and current prices write: Krause Publications/Old Cars Weekly, 700 East State Street, Iola, WI 54990.

ABBREVIATIONS

A/C	Air conditioning
A.L.A.M.	Assoc. of Licensed Automobile Mfgs.
Adj.	Adjustable
Aero.	Fastback
AM, FM, AM/FM	Radio types
Amp.	Amperes
Approx.	Approximate
Auto.	Automatic
Auxil.	Auxiliary
Avail.	Available
Avg.	Average
BxS	Bore x Stroke
Base	Base (usually lowest-priced) model
Bbl.	Barrel (carburetor)
B.H.P.	Brake horsepower
BSW	Black sidewall (tire)
Brk/Brkwd/Brkwood	Brookwood
Brdcl.	Broadcloth
Bus.	Business (i.e. Business Coupe)
C-A	Carryall
C.C.	Close-coupled
Cabr.	Cabriolet
Carb.	Carburetor
Capr.	Caprice
Cass.	Cassette (tape player)
Cav	Cavalier
CB	Citizens Band (radio)
Celeb	Celebrity
CEO	Chief Executive Officer
CFI	Cross Fire (fuel) Injection
Chvt.	Chevette
C.I.D.	Cubic inch displacement
Cit.	Citation
Clb	Club (Club Coupe)
Clth.	Cloth-covered roof
Col.	Colonnade (coupe body style)
Col.	Column (shift)
Conv/Conv.	Convertible
Conv. Sed.	Convertible Sedan
Corp Limo	Corporate Limousine
Cpe	Coupe
Cpe P.U.	Coupe Pickup
C.R.	Compression ratio
Crsr.	Cruiser
Cu. In.	Cubic Inch (displacement)
Cust.	Custom
Cyl.	Cylinder
DeL.	DeLuxe
DFRS	Dual facing rear seats
Dia.	Diameter
Disp.	Displacement
Dr.	Door
Ea.	Each
E.D.	Enclosed Drive
E.F.I.	Electronic Fuel Injection
E.W.B.	Extended Wheelbase
Eight	Eight-cylinder engine
8-tr.	Eight-track
Encl.	Enclosed
EPA	Environmental Protection Agency
Equip.	Equipment
Est. Wag.	Estate Wagon
Exc.	Except
Exec.	Executive
F.	Forward (3F - 3 forward speeds)
F.W.D.	Four-wheel drive
Fam.	Family
Fml.	Formal
"Four"	Four-cylinder engine
4WD	Four-wheel drive
4-dr.	Four-door
4-spd.	Four-speed (transmission)
4V	Four-barrel carburetor
FP	Factory Price
Frsm.	Foursome
Frt.	Front
FsBk	Fastback
Ft.	Foot/feet
FWD	Front wheel drive
G.B.	Greenbrier
GBR	Glass-belted radial (tire)
Gal.	Gallon
GM	General Motors (Corporation)
GT	Gran Turismo
G.R.	Gear Ratio
H	Height
H.B.	Hatchback
H.D.	Heavy Duty
HEI	High Energy Ignition
H.O.	High-output
H.P.	Horsepower
HT/HT Hdtp.	Hardtop
Hr.	Hour
Hwg.	Highway
I	Inline
I.D.	Identification
Imp	Impala
In.	Inches
Incl.	Included or Including
Int.	Interior
King/Kingwd.	Kingswood
Lan	Landau (coupe body style)
Lb. or Lbs.	Pound-feet (torque)
LH	Left hand
Lift.	Liftback (body style)
Limo	Limousine
LPO	Limited production option
Ltd.	Limited
Lthr. Trm.	Leather Trim
L.W.B.	Long Wheelbase
Mag.	Wheel style
Mast.	Master
Max.	Maximum
MFI	Multi-port Fuel Injection
M.M.	Millimeters
Monte	Monte Carlo
MPG	Miles per gallon
MPH	Miles per hour
Mstr.	Master
N/A	Not available (or not applicable)
NC	No charge
N.H.P.	Net horsepower
No.	Number
Notch or N.B.	Notchback
OHC	Overhead cam (engine)
OHV	Overhead valve (engine)
O.L.	Overall length
OPEC	Organization of Petroleum Exporting Countries
Opt.	Optional
OSRV	Outside rear view
O.W. or O/W	Opera window
OWL	Outline White Letter (tire)
Oz.	Ounce
P	Passenger
Park/Parkwd	Parkwood
PFI	Port fuel injection
Phae.	Phaeton
Pkg.	Package (e.g.option pkg)
Prod.	Production
Pwr.	Power
R	Reverse
RBL	Raised black letter (tire)
Rbt.	Runabout
Rds.	Roadster
Reg.	Regular
Remote	Remote control
Req.	Requires
RH	Right-hand drive
Roch.	Rochester (carburetor)
R.P.M.	Revolutions per minute
RPO	Regular production option
R.S. or R/S	Rumbleseat
RV	Recreational vehicle
RVL	Raised white letter (tire)
S	Gm lowtrim model designation
S.A.E.	Society of Automotive Engineers
SBR	Steel-belted radials
Sed.	Sedan
SFI	Sequential fuel injection
"Six"	Six-cylinder engine
S.M.	Side Mount
Spd.	Speed
Spec.	Special
Spt.	Sport
Sq. In.	Square inch
SR	Sunroof
SS	Super Sport
Sta. Wag.	Station wagon
Std.	Standard
Sub.	Suburban
S.W.B.	Short Wheelbase
Tach.	Tachometer
Tax.	Taxable (horsepower)
TBI	Throttle body (fuel) injection
Temp.	Temperature
THM	Turbo Hydramatic (transmission)
3S	Three-seat
Trans.	Transmission
Trk.	Trunk
2-Dr.	Two-door
2 V	Two-barrel (carburetor)
2WD	Two-wheel drive
Univ.	Universal
Utl.	Utility
V.	Venturi (carburetor)
V-6, V-8	Vee-type engine
VIN	Vehicle Identification Number
W.	With
W/O	Without
Wag.	Wagon
w (2w)	Window (two window)
W.B.	Wheelbase
Woodie	Wood-bodied car
WLT	White-lettered tire
WSW	White sidewall (tire)
W.W.	Whitewalls
W. Whl.	Wire wheel

PHOTO CREDITS

Whenever possible, throughout the Catalog, we have strived to picture all cars with photographs that show them in their most original form. All photos gathered from reliable outside sources have an alphabetical code following the caption which indicates the photo source. An explanation of these codes is given below. Additional photos from Krause Publications file are marked accordingly. With special thanks to the editors of the previous *Standard Catalogs of American Cars* for their original research and obtaining many of these photos of Chevrolet over the years.

(AA)	Applegate & Applegate
(CH)	Chevrolet
(CP)	Crestline Publishing
(GM)	General Motors
(HAC)	Henry Austin Clark, Jr.
(HFM)	Henry Ford Museum
(IMSC)	Indianapolis Motor Speedway Corporation
(JAC)	John A. Conde
(JG)	John Gunnell
(NAHC)	National Automotive History Collection
(OCW)	Old Cars Weekly
(PC)	Pat Chappell
(PH)	Phil Hall
(WLB)	William L. Bailey

INTRODUCTION

By PAT CHAPPELL

One supposes an author's introduction is the place to comment on the saga of putting a book or catalog together. Immediately, I want to publicly thank four people for tremendous energy and fortitude displayed — Beverly Rae Kimes, Henry Austin Clark, Jr., John Gunnell and Jim Flammang — in the original writing of the three *Standard Catalogs of American Cars.* And also I want to thank them for continuation of their dedication in seeing the second editions were properly updated.

These four writers and historians took on a monumental task tracing U.S. automotive history from the very beginning to the present. As pioneers in the compiling of data about all of the American cars ever manufactured, the foundation they have laid has made it now possible for an author to break out one — or several — automotive marques.

I also want to thank Pinky Randall — "Mr. Chevrolet" as he is known in the hobby — for his help and support with the early Chevrolets. And Tony Hossain, for his input throughout the Chevrolet history, and particularly that interesting Corvair introduction. I want to thank Charles Webb for his insight into Corvettes. And I want to thank John Gunnell for encouraging me at the Society of Automotive Historians banquet during Fall Hershey, 1989, to put this catalog together in the first place.

For me, this Chevrolet Catalog has been nurtured by desire and drive to put together the best catalog of its kind available. In all fairness, I owe that to the original authors and staff. Above all, I owe it to Krause Publications, and to Chet Krause, a friend for many years. I have literally lived on a daily basis with the cross-examination of Chevrolet and its long history, and during these four months I've developed even more of an appreciation for Chevrolet's past and its present. And I've felt a concern mixed with great hopes for its future in these relatively new times of "world cars".

When I think of Chevrolet, immediately I hear the echo of Dinah Shore's catch ditty, "See the U.S.A. in your Chevrolet. . ." More recently there is that haunting refrain, "The Heartbeat of America, Today's Chevrolet. . ." which for us old enthusiasts is so easily translated into thoughts of "yesterday's Chevrolet." Somewhere in between I am reminded of the U.S.A. and patriotism, based on "baseball, hot dogs, apple pie and Chevrolet".

I think these phrases — how utterly simple they are — help convey to several generations of Americans an image, be it the Chevy Suburban in the driveway or the '55 Bel Air sport coupe in the garage. Or the first Camaro ever owned, or one of a multitude of Chevy Impalas — indeed Everyman's car. Or is it a Chevelle, a Nova, a Chevette, or perhaps a brand-new Corvette that comes to mind? Or maybe there's a little yellow Corvair Monza convertible you can't get out of your dreams? Or is it a hot Chevy Super Sport from the Sixties with a fire-breathing dragon of an engine under the hood?

It has been a pleasure to work with Pat Klug, Books Manager. Ours has been a long-distance relationship, but it's been a good one. It's been comforting to visit by phone, to help each other and compare notes, with John Lee who now has the Chrysler Catalog added to his list of accomplishments, and Bob Lichty who has just completed the Ford Catalog in the same time span.

The words of someone I admire so tremendously, Beverly Rae Kimes, come to mind: "And so we shall ever continue". That, alas, is the role of an automotive historian. We do hope our readers will recall some of these wonderful years of Chevrolet history as they page through this catalog. But we also hope to hear from those who have *more* information, *more* corrections and *more* updated material.

History is never complete. Indeed, it is an ongoing process. Even as I write this, the Chevrolet Berettas and Corsicas roll off the Delaware Boxwood Plant Assembly Line just south of our home here in Wilmington.

Pat Chappell
April 16, 1990
Wilmington, Delaware

ABOUT THE AUTHOR

Pat Chappell has been a contributor to *Old Cars Weekly* for over 15 years. Since January, 1986 she has written a monthly column for *Old Cars Weekly* called *Speaking of Chevys.* Her specialty is Chevrolet, particularly postwar models. In 1977 she authored *The Hot One,* the history of 1955-56-57 Chevrolet, published by Dragonwyck Publishing. With over 25,000 copies printed, it is now in its third edition, fifth printing.

Currently, she serves as contributing editor and writes a regular column for *Classic Chevy World,* publication of the 30,000 member Classic Chevy International (1955-57); she is also a regular columnist for *Late Great Chevys,* published by the 10,000 member Late Great Chevy Association (1958-64). Additionally, Pat serves as contributing editor for *The Nomad Post,* which is edited by John Lee for Chevrolet Nomad Association.

In the past two decades she has contributed to many automotive publications, among them *Car Collector & Car Classics, Rod Action, Street Machine, Super Chevy, Hot Rod, Cars & Parts, Automotive Fine Arts Society Quarterly* and *Automotive Investor.*

She is a member of the Society of Automotive Historians, the Auburn-Cord-Duesenberg Club, Antique Automobile Club of America, Vintage Chevrolet Club of America, Classic Chevy International, Late Great Chevy Association, National Chevy/GMC Truck Association, Chevrolet Nomad Association, National Corvette Restorers Society, Corvair Society of America, and The Mid-Atlantic Nomad Association of which she was a co-founder in 1971. Pat serves as Delaware State Representative for Classic Chevy International, and is East Coast Publicity Director for the St. Ignace Auto Show.

Pat and her husband, Richard, presently own a 1955 Bel Air sport coupe, a 1956 Bel Air Nomad station wagon and a 1959 Impala convertible, the latter which they've owned since 1960.

HOW TO USE THIS CATALOG

APPEARANCE AND EQUIPMENT: Word descriptions identify cars by styling features, trim and (to a lesser extent) interior appointments. Most standard equipment lists begin with the lowest-priced model, then enumerate items added by upgrade models and option packages. Most lists reflect equipment available at model introductions.

I.D. DATA: Information is given about the Vehicle Identification Number (VIN) found on the dashboard. VIN codes show model or series, body style, engine size, model year and place built. Beginning in 1981, a standardized 17 symbol VIN is used. Earlier VINs are shorter. Locations of other coded information on the body and/or engine block may be supplied. Deciphering those codes is beyond the scope of this catalog.

SPECIFICATIONS CHART: The first column gives series or model numbers. The second gives body style numbers revealing body type and trim. Not all cars use two separate numbers. Some sources combine the two. Column three tells number of doors, body style and passenger capacity ('4-dr Sed-6P' means four-door sedan, six-passenger). Passenger capacity is normally the maximum. Cars with bucket seats hold fewer. Column four gives suggested retail price of the car when new, on or near its introduction date, not including freight or other charges. Column five gives the original shipping weight. The sixth column provides model year production totals or refers to notes below the chart. In cases where the same car came with different engines, a slash is used to separate factory prices and shipping weights for each version. Unless noted, the amount on the left of the slash is for the smallest, least expensive engine. The amount on the right is for the least costly engine with additional cylinders. 'N/A' means data not available.

ENGINE DATA: Engines are normally listed in size order with smallest displacement first. A 'base' engine is the basic one offered in each model at the lowest price. 'Optional' describes all alternate engines, including those that have a price listed in the specifications chart. (Cars that came with either a six or V-8, for instance, list the six as 'base' and V-8 'optional'). Introductory specifications are used, where possible.

CHASSIS DATA: Major dimensions (wheelbase, overall length, height, width and front/rear tread) are given for each model, along with standard tire size. Dimensions sometimes varied and could change during a model year.

TECHNICAL DATA: This section indicates transmissions standard on each model, usually including gear ratios; the standard final drive axle ratio (which may differ by engine or transmission); steering and brake system type; front and rear suspension description; body construction; and fuel tank capacity.

OPTIONAL EQUIPMENT LISTS: Most listings begin with drivetrain options (engines, transmissions, steering/suspension and mechanical components) applying to all models. Convenience/appearance items are listed separately for each model, except where several related models are combined into a single listing. Option packages are listed first, followed by individual items in categories: comfort/convenience, lighting/mirrors, entertainment, exterior, interior, then wheels/tires. Contents of some option packages are listed prior to the price; others are described in the Appearance/Equipment text. Prices are suggested retail, usually effective early in the model year. ('N/A' indicates prices are unavailable.) Most items are Regular Production Options (RPO), rather than limited-production (LPO), special-order or dealer-installed equipment. Many options were available only on certain series or body types or in conjunction with other items. Space does not permit including every detail.

HISTORY: This block lists introduction dates, total sales and production amounts for the model year and calendar year. Production totals supplied by auto-makers do not always coincide with those from other sources. Some reflect shipments from the factories rather than actual production or define the model year a different way.

HISTORICAL FOOTNOTES: In addition to notes on the rise and fall of sales and production, this block includes significant statistics, performance milestones, major personnel changes, important dates and places and facts that add flavor to this segment of America's automotive heritage.

1979 CORVETTE

SERIES Z — V-8 — "The Corvette evolution continues," declared this year's catalog. Not much of that evolution was visible, however, after the prior year's massive restyle. Under the hood, the base engine got the dual-snorkel air intake introduced in 1978 for the optional L82 V-8. That added 10 horsepower. The L82 V-8 had a higher-lift cam, special heads with larger valves and higher compression, impact-extruded pistons, forged steel crankshaft, and finned aluminum rocker covers. The "Y" pipe exhaust system had new open-flow mufflers, while the automatic transmission got a higher numerical (3.55:1) rear axle ratio. All Corvettes now had the highback bucket seats introduced on the 1978 limited-edition Indy Pace Car. A high pivot point let the seat backrest fold flat on the passenger side, level with the luggage area floor. An AM/FM radio was now standard. Of ten body colors, only one (dark green metallic) was new this year. The others were Classic white, black and silver, plus Corvette dark or light blue, yellow, light beige, red, and dark brown. Interiors came in black, red, light beige, dark blue, dark brown, oyster, or dark green. Corvettes had black roof panel and window moldings. Bolt-on front and rear spoilers (also from the Pace Car) became available. Buyers who didn't want the full Gymkhana suspension could now order heavy-duty shocks alone. Standard equipment include the L48 V-8 with four-barrel carb, either automatic transmission or four-speed manual gearbox (close-ratio version available), power four-wheel disc brakes, and limited-slip differential. Other standards: tinted glass; front stabilizer bar; concealed wipers/washers; day/night inside mirror; wide outside mirror; anti-theft alarm system; four-spoke sport steering wheel; electric clock; trip odometer; heater/defroster; bumper guards; and luggage security shade. Tires were P225/70R15 steel-belted radial blackwalls on 15 x 8 in. wheels. Corvettes had four-wheel independent suspension. Bucket seats came with cloth/leather or all-leather trim. The aircraft-type console held a 7000 R.P.M. tachometer, voltmeter, oil pressure, temp and fuel gauges. Seat inserts could have either leather or cloth trim.

I.D. DATA: Coding of the 13-symbol Vehicle Identification Number (VIN) was similar to 1978. Engine codes changed to '8' base L48 and '4' optional L82. Model year code changed to '9' for 1979. Serial numbers began with 400001.

CORVETTE

Model Number	Body/Style Number	Body Type & Seating	Factory Price	Shipping Weight	Production Total
1Y	Z87	2-dr. Spt Cpe-2P	10220	3372	53,807

ENGINE DATA: BASE V-8: 90-degree, overhead valve V-8. Cast iron block and head. Displacement: 350 cu. in. (5.7 liters). Bore & stroke: 4.00 x 3.48 in. Compression ratio: 8.2:1. Brake horsepower: 195 at 4000 R.P.M. Torque: 285 lbs.-ft. at 3200 R.P.M. Five main bearings. Hydraulic valve lifters. Carburetor: 4Bbl. RPO Code: L48. VIN Code: 8. OPTIONAL V-8: Same as above, except C.R.: 8.9:1. B.H.P.: 225 at 5200 R.P.M. Torque: 270 lbs.-ft. at 3600 R.P.M. RPO Code: L82. VIN Code: 4.

CHASSIS DATA: Wheelbase: 98.0 in. Overall length: 185.2 in. Height: 48.0 in. Width: 69.0 in. Front Tread: 58.7 in. Rear Tread: 59.5 in. Wheel Size: 15 x 8 in. Standard Tires: P225/70R15 SBR. Optional Tires: P225/60R15.

TECHNICAL: Transmission: Four-speed manual transmission (floor shift) standard. Gear ratios: (1st) 2.85:1; (2nd) 2.02:1; (3rd) 1.35:1; (4th) 1.00:1; (Rev) 2.85:1. Close-ratio four-speed manual trans. optional: (1st) 2.43:1; (2nd) 1.61:1; (3rd) 1.23:1; (4th) 1.00:1; (Rev) 2.35:1. Three-speed automatic optional: (1st) 2.52:1; (2nd) 1.52:1; (3rd) 1.00:1; (Rev) 1.93:1. Standard final drive ratio: 3.36:1 w/4spd, 3.55:1 w/auto. Steering: Recirculating ball. Front Suspension: Control arms, coil springs and stabilizer bar.

Rear Suspension: Independent, with single transverse leaf spring and lateral struts. Brakes: Four-wheel disc (11.75 in. disc dia). Ignition: Electronic. Body construction: Fiberglass, on separate frame. Fuel tank: 24 gal.

CORVETTE OPTIONS: L82 350 cu. in., 4Bbl. V-8 engine ($565). Close-ratio four- speed manual transmission (NC). Turbo Hydra-matic (NC). Highway axle ratio ($19). Gymkhana suspension ($49). H.D. shock absorbers ($33). Heavy-duty battery ($21). Trailer towing equipment inc. H.D. radiator and Gymkhana suspension ($98). California emissions system (N/A). High-altitude emissions (N/A). Four season air cond. ($635). Rear defogger, electric ($102). Cruise-master speed control ($113). Tilt/telescopic leather-wrapped steering wheel ($190). Power windows ($141). Power windows and door locks ($272). Convenience group ($94). Sport mirrors, left remote ($45). AM/FM stereo radio ($90); with 8track or cassette player ($228-$234). AM/FM stereo radio w/CB and power antenna ($439). Dual rear speakers ($52). Power antenna ($52). Removable glass roof panels ($365). Aluminum wheels ($380). P225/70R15 SBR WL tires ($54). P225/60R15 Aramid-belted radial WL tires ($226).

HISTORY: Introduced: Sept. 25, 1978. Model year production: 53,807 (Chevrolet initially reported a total of 49,901 units.) Calendar year production: 48,568. Calendar year sales by U.S. dealers: 38,631. Model year sales by U.S. dealers: 39,816.

Historical Footnotes: For what it's worth, 7,949 Corvettes this year were painted in Classic White, while 6,960 carried silver paint. Only 4,385 Corvettes had the MM4 four-speed manual gearbox, while 4,062 ran with the close-ratio M21 version.

BODY STYLES

Body style designations describe the shape and character of an automobile. In earlier years automakers exhibited great imagination in coining words to name their products. This led to names that were not totally accurate. Many of those **'car words'** were taken from other fields: mythology, carriage building, architecture, railroading, and so on. Therefore, there was no 'correct' automotive meaning other than that brought about through actual use. Inconsistences have persisted into the recent period, though some of the imaginative terms of past eras have faded away. One manufacturer's 'sedan' might resemble another's 'coupe.' Some automakers have persisted in describing a model by a word different from common usage, such as Ford's label for Mustang as a 'sedan.' Following the demise of the true pillarless hardtop (two- and four-door) in the mid-1970s, various manufacturers continued to use the term 'hardtop' to describe their offerings, even though a 'B' pillar was part of the newer car's structure and the front door glass may not always have been frameless. Some took on the description 'pillared hardtop' or 'thin pillar hardtop' to define what observers might otherwise consider, essentially, a sedan. Descriptions in this catalog generally follow the manufacturers' choice of words, except when they conflict strongly with accepted usage.

One specific example of inconsistency is worth noting: the description of many hatchback models as 'three-door' and 'five-door,' even though that extra 'door' is not an entryway for people. While the 1976-1986 domestic era offered no real phaetons or roadsters in the earlier senses of the words, those designations continue to turn up now and then, too.

TWO-DOOR (CLUB) COUPE: The Club Coupe designation seems to come from club car, describing the lounge (or parlor car) in a railroad train. The early postwar club coupe combined a shorter-than-sedan body structure with the convenience of a full back seat, unlike the single-seat business coupe. That name has been used less frequently in the 1976-86 period, as most notchback two-door models (with trunk rather than hatch) have been referred to as just 'coupes.' Moreover, the distinction between two-door coupes and two-door sedans has grown fuzzy.

TWO-DOOR SEDAN: The term sedan originally described a conveyance seen only in movies today: a wheelless vehicle for one person, borne on poles by two men, one ahead and one behind. Automakers pirated the word and applied it to cars with a permanent top, seating four to seven (including driver) in a single compartment. The two-door sedan of recent times has sometimes been called a pillared coupe, or plain coupe, depending on the manufacturer's whim. On the other hand, some cars commonly referred to as coupes carry the sedan designation on factory documents.

TWO-DOOR (THREE-DOOR) HATCHBACK COUPE: Originally a small opening in the deck of a sailing ship, the term 'hatch' was later applied to airplane doors and to passenger cars with rear liftgates. Various models appeared in the early 1950s, but weather-tightness was a problem. The concept emerged again in the early 1970s, when fuel economy factors began to signal the trend toward compact cars. Technology had remedied the sealing difficulties. By the 1980s, most manufacturers produced one or more hatchback models, though the question of whether to call them 'two-door' or 'three-door' never was resolved. Their main common feature was the lack of a separate trunk. 'Liftback' coupes may have had a different rear-end shape, but the two terms often described essentially the same vehicle.

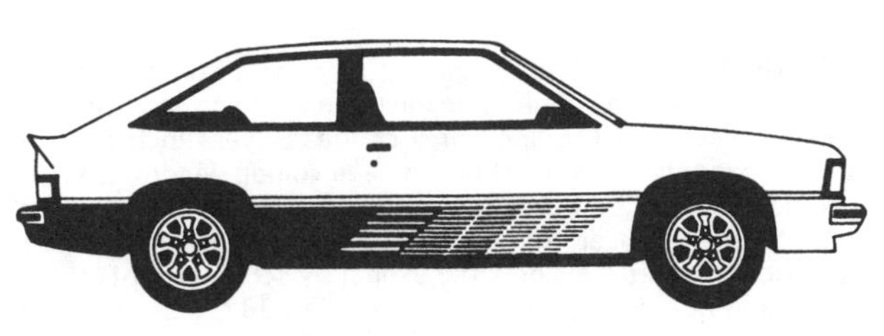

TWO-DOOR FASTBACK: By definition, a fastback is any automobile with a long, moderately curving, downward slope to the rear of the roof. This body style relates to an interest in streamlining and aerodynamics and has gone in and out of fashion at various times. Some (Mustangs for one) have grown quite popular. Others have tended to turn customers off. Certain fastbacks are, technically, two-door sedans or pillared coupes. Four-door fastbacks have also been produced. Many of these (such as Buick's late 1970s four-door Century sedan) lacked sales appeal. Fastbacks may or may not have a rear-opening hatch.

TWO-DOOR HARDTOP: The term hardtop, as used for postwar cars up to the mid-1970s, describes an automobile styled to resemble a convertible, but with a rigid metal (or fiberglass) top. In a production sense, this body style evolved after World War II, first called 'hardtop convertible.' Other generic names have included sports coupe, hardtop coupe or pillarless coupe. In the face of proposed rollover standards, nearly all automakers turned away from the pillarless design to a pillared version by 1976-77.

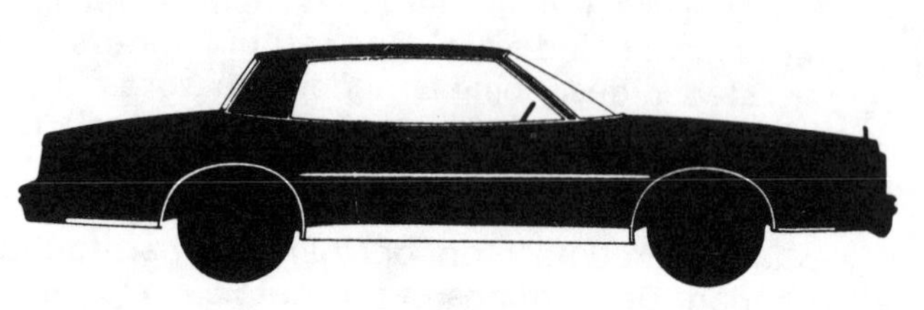

COLONNADE HARDTOP: In architecture, the term colonnade describes a series of columns, set at regular intervals, usually supporting an entablature, roof or series of arches. To meet Federal rollover standards in 1974 (standards that never emerged), General Motors introduced two- and four-door pillared body types with arch-like quarter windows and sandwich type roof construction. They looked like a cross between true hardtops and miniature limousines. Both styles proved popular (especially the coupe with louvered coach windows and canopy top) and the term colonnade was applied. As their 'true' hardtops disappeared, other manufacturers produced similar bodies with a variety of quarter-window shapes and sizes. These were known by such terms as hardtop coupe, pillared hardtop or opera-window coupe.

FORMAL HARDTOP: The hardtop roofline was a long-lasting fashion hit of the postwar car era. The word 'formal' can be applied to things that are stiffly conservative and follow the established rule. The limousine, being the popular choice of conservative buyers who belonged to the Establishment, was looked upon as a formal motorcar. So when designers combined the lines of these two body styles, the result was the Formal Hardtop. This style has been marketed with two or four doors, canopy and vinyl roofs (full or partial) and conventional or opera-type windows, under various trade names. The distinction between a formal hardtop and plain pillared-hardtop coupe (see above) hasn't always followed a strict rule.

CONVERTIBLE: To Depression-era buyers, a convertible was a car with a fixed-position windshield and folding top that, when raised, displayed the lines of a coupe. Buyers in the postwar period expected a convertible to have roll-up windows, too. Yet the definition of the word includes no such qualifications. It states only that such a car should have a lowerable or removable top. American convertibles became extinct by 1976, except for Cadillac's Eldorado, then in its final season. In 1982, though, Chrysler brought out a LeBaron ragtop; Dodge a 400; and several other companies followed it a year or two later.

ROADSTER: This term derives from equestrian vocabulary where it was applied to a horse used for riding on the roads. Old dictionaries define the roadster as an open-type car designed for use on *ordinary* roads, with a single seat for two persons and, often, a rumbleseat as well. Hobbyists associate folding windshields and side curtains (rather than roll-up windows) with roadsters, although such qualifications stem from usage, not definition of term. Most recent roadsters are either sports cars, small alternative-type vehicles or replicas of early models.

RUNABOUT: By definition, a runabout is the equivalent of a roadster. The term was used by carriage makers and has been applied in the past to light, open cars on which a top is unavailable or totally an add-on option. None of this explains its use by Ford on certain Pinto models. Other than this inaccurate usage, recent runabouts are found mainly in the alternative vehicle field, including certain electric-powered models.

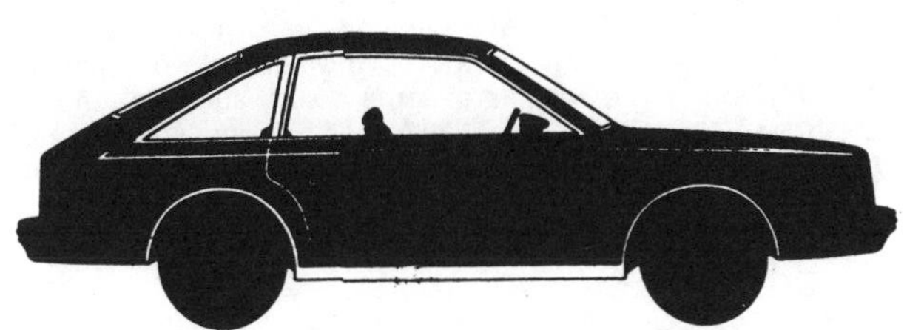

FOUR-DOOR SEDAN: If you took the wheels off a car, mounted it on poles and hired two weightlifters (one in front and one in back) to carry you around in it, you'd have a true sedan. Since this idea isn't very practical, it's better to use the term for an automobile with a permanent top (affixed by solid pillars) that seats four or more persons, including the driver, on two full-width seats.

FOUR-DOOR HARDTOP: This is a four-door car styled to resemble a convertible, but having a rigid top of metal or fiberglass. Buick introduced a totally pillarless design in 1955. A year later most automakers offered equivalent bodies. Four-door hardtops have also been labeled sports sedans and hardtop sedans. By 1976, potential rollover standards and waning popularity had taken their toll. Only a few makes still produced a four-door hardtop and those disappeared soon thereafter.

FOUR-DOOR PILLARED HARDTOP: Once the 'true' four-door hardtop began to fade away, manufacturers needed another name for their luxury four-doors. Many were styled to look almost like the former pillarless models, with thin or unobtrusive pillars between the doors. Some, in fact, were called 'thin-pillar hardtops.' The distinction between certain pillared hardtops and ordinary (presumably humdrum) sedans occasionally grew hazy.

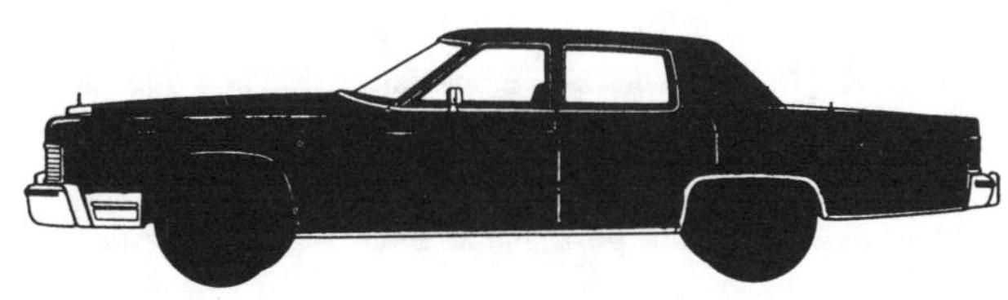

FOUR-DOOR (FIVE-DOOR) HATCHBACK: Essentially unknown among domestic models in the mid-1970s, the four-door hatchback became a popular model as cars grew smaller and front-wheel-drive versions appeared. Styling was similar to the orignal two-door hatchback, except for — obviously — two more doors. Luggage was carried in the back of the car itself, loaded through the hatch opening, not in a separate trunk.

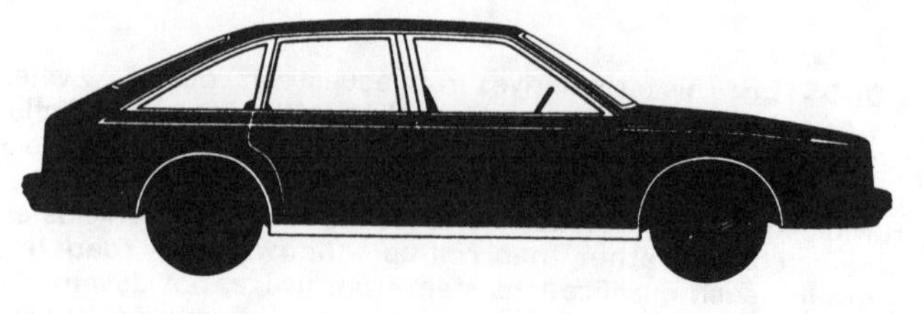

LIMOUSINE: This word's literal meaning is 'a cloak.' In France, Limousine means any passenger vehicle. An early dictionary defined limousine as an auto with a permanently enclosed compartment for 3-5, with a roof projecting over a front driver's seat. However, modern dictionaries drop the separate compartment idea and refer to limousines as large luxury autos, often chauffeur-driven. Some have a movable division window between the driver and passenger compartments, but that isn't a requirement.

TWO-DOOR STATION WAGON: Originally defined as a car with an enclosed wooden body of paneled design (with several rows of folding or removable seats behind the driver), the station wagon became a different and much more popular type of vehicle in the postwar years. A recent dictionary states that such models have a larger interior than sedans of the line and seats that can be readily lifted out, or folded down, to facilitate light trucking. In addition, there's usually a tailgate, but no separate luggage compartment. The two-door wagon often has sliding or flip-out rear side windows.

FOUR-DOOR STATION WAGON: Since functionality and adaptability are advantages of station wagons, four-door versions have traditionally been sales leaders. At least they were until cars began to grow smaller. This style usually has lowerable windows in all four doors and fixed rear side glass. The term 'suburban' was almost synonymous with station wagon at one time, but is now more commonly applied to light trucks with similar styling. Station wagons have had many trade names, such as Country Squire (Ford) and Sport Suburban (Plymouth). Quite a few have retained simulated wood paneling, keeping alive the wagon's origin as a wood-bodied vehicle.

LIFTBACK STATION WAGON: Small cars came in station wagon form too. The idea was the same as bigger versions, but the conventional tailgate was replaced by a single lift-up hatch. For obvious reasons, compact and subcompact wagons had only two seats instead of the three that had been available in many full-size models.

DIMENSIONS

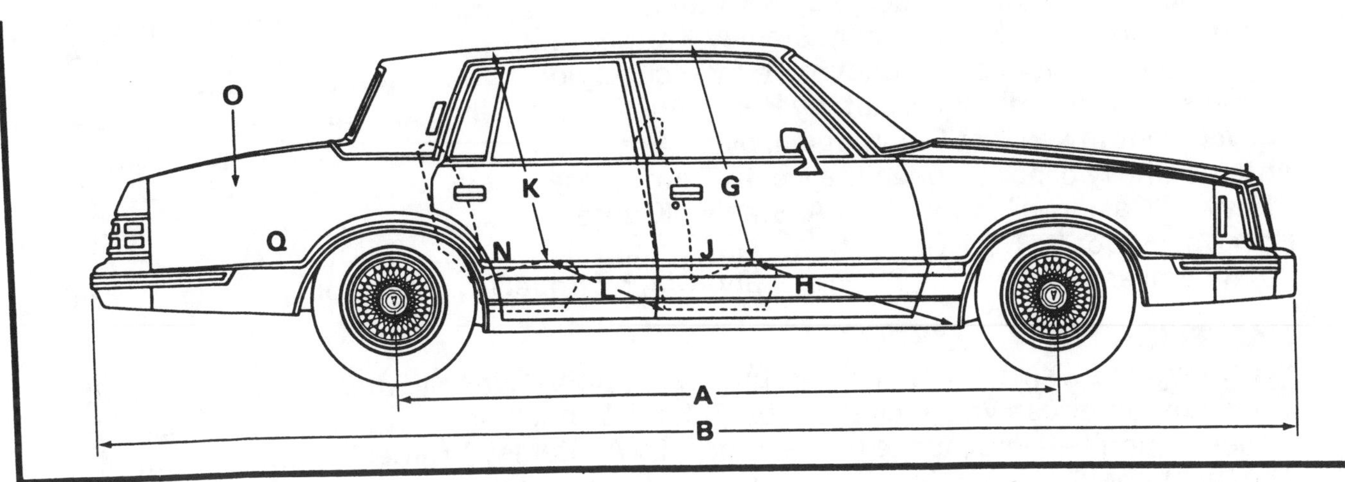

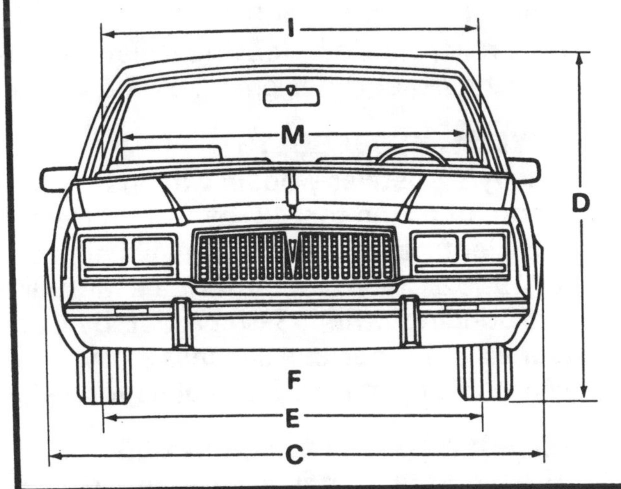

DIMENSIONS
Exterior:
A Wheelbase
B Overall length
C Width
D Overall height
E Tread, front
F Tread, rear
Interior—front:
G Headroom
H Legroom
I Shoulder room
J Hip room
Interior—rear:
K Headroom
L Legroom
M Shoulder room
N Hip room
O Trunk capacity (liters/cu. ft.)
P Cargo index volume (liters/cu. ft.)
Q Fuel tank capacity (liters/gallons)

INDEX TO ARTICLES

LATE-GREAT LEGACY

THE LONG AND SHORT OF IT

CORVETTE

CORVAIR

SPEAKING OF CHEVYS

CHEVROLET DREAM CARS

RACING AND PACING

INTRODUCTION TO THE BEST OF OLD CARS WEEKLY CONTRIBUTIONS

Over the years, many contributors to *Old Cars Weekly* have written numerous articles about Chevrolet — from the early Chevy "490" to the latest ZR-1 Corvette. From Bob Ackerson to Paul Zazarine, the history of Chevrolet has been looked at, dissected, analyzed, criticized, laughed at and praised to the nth degree.

We have a wonderful selection of Chevy stories gathered together here for the reader, stories which range from dead serious history to downright hilarious adventures.

Travel with us then, via this cast of veteran automotive writers whose contributions have graced not only the pages of *Old Cars Weekly* but numerous automotive magazines as well, and whose hearts encourage their pens, typewriters and word processors to engrave some wonderful tales on paper for posterity.

Some of these names are familiar as past and present *Old Cars Weekly* columnists: Terry Boyce, Henry Austin Clark, Jr., John Gunnell, Phil Hall, Bob Hovorka, Tim Howley, Rich Taylor, Peter J. Winnewisser and Perry Zavitz.

Bob Ackerson will fill our minds with a wonderful melange of Chevrolet history; Phil Hall will keep us up-to-speed on tons of checkered flag Chevy accomplishments;

Tim Howley will reminisce as he looks back to the early times "Somewhere West of Laramie" where he's talking '55 Chevy not Jordan Playboy; Bob Hovorka will spin wonderful tales with marvelous illustrations. Linda Clark will specialize in Caprice, Chevelle and Camaro; Tony Hossain will analyze Corvair in depth.

One of Corvette's finest historians and aficionados that had ever lived, Sam Folz, will remind us of Chevy's amazing sports cars; Terry Boyce will cover the Chevy waterfront in some interesting "Speaking of Chevys" columns. And much, much more will follow. It is with pride we introduce this remarkable potpourri of Chevrolet stories from a rather gigantic cross-section of *Old Cars Weekly* contributors over the past two decades. Enjoy!

CONTRIBUTORS TO CHEVROLET CATALOG from BEST OF OLD CARS WEEKLY

Robert C. Ackerson, Bill Artzberger, Terry J. Berkson, Terry Boyce, Henry Austin Clark Jr., Linda Clark, Sam Folz, John Gunnell, Phil Hall, Paul Holt, Tony Hossain, Bob Hovorka, Tim Howley, Wick Humble, A. Stanley Kramer, Tom LaMarre, John Lee, Bill and Mary Mason, Alan Mende, Gerald Perschbacher, David Reed, Tom Reese, Ed Robinson, Bill Siurv, Rich Taylor, Peter J. Winnewisser, Wally Wyss, Perry Zavitz, and Paul Zazarine.

Promising Beginnings

Louis Chevrolet and William Durant.

Happy Birthday Louis Chevrolet

By John Gunnell

Louis Chevrolet (circled in white duster at left) surveys the very first Chevrolet designed and built under his direction.

While the first Chevrolet motorcar did not appear until November 3, 1911, the history of the "Chevy" nameplate can be viewed as a Christmas tale, or at least as a story which began on Christmas Day in 1873.

For it was on that joyous holiday, 106 years ago, that Louis Joseph Chevrolet was born in Switzerland.

At the age of 27, Chevrolet was sent to America by the DeDion-Bouton people, for whom he worked in France, to set up that companys's branch in New York City. After arriving in the United States, his brothers Arthur and Gaston joined him there.

The three brothers became fascinated with the infant automobile manufacturing industry and all three entered the automobile business. Arthur and Gaston remained minor figures in the field, but Louis went on to greater fame.

His first recognition came, not as a manufacturer or businessman but as a mechanic for the Fiat Motor Company of New York, five years after the turn of the century. His shining performance as a top quality mechanic led to the company offering him sponsorship as a race driver. Remember that these were the very early days of automobile racing and most drivers were expected to have mechanical skills and know-how, as well as the ability to whip a car around the track at the highest possible speeds.

Chevrolet proved his worth in both capacities, turning in consistantly excellent performances in contests like the Vanderbilt Cup Race. His driving record shows that Chevrolet actually outran the great Barney Oldfield to the finish line three times in 1905 and championed in various important road races between 1906 and 1908. At the same time, Arthur and Gaston Chevrolet also proved to be excellent drivers who contributed to the Chevrolet family's racing reputation.

It was in 1907 that the Chevrolet name came to the attention of William C. Durant who was, at that point, busy building General Motors Corporation on a Buick foundation. Durant hired Arthur and Louis to be drivers for Buick's proposed racing team.

Suddenly, Durant's plans took an abrupt about face, when he lost financial, and then corporate control of the GM empire. This turnabout did not, however, delete the Durant energies and he turned to other automotive ventures.

Durant purchased the Little Motor Car Co. and the Mason Motor Co., both of which were to become a part of Chevrolet.

In 1909 Durant hired Louis Chevrolet to design the engine for a new automobile which would bear the Swiss racer's name. Durant felt that the combination of a European-sounding name and the family's racing reputation would be beneficial to the sale of the new car.

After two years of experiments and tests, the assembly of the new automobile began in a small shop on Detroit's Grand River Avenue in March of 1911. After the completion of four test cars, which were made to work out all the "bugs", the 1912 Chevrolet "Classic Six" began to roll off the assembly line in the Fall of 1911, as a 1912 model.

Louis Chevrolet stayed with the company until early in 1914, at which time certain differences with Durant's business philosophies led to his departure. Chevrolet favored a high-quality car with a resultant high list price. Durant, on the other hand, saw the Chevrolet as a competitor with the low-cost Model T Ford. Unfortunately for Louis, Durant held the rights to the Chevrolet nameplate, which became a product of General Motors in 1918 when Durant took control of the firm for the second time.

Of course, Durant left the firm again in later years, but the Chevrolet went on to become a major force in the U.S. automobile industry and ultimately, America's Number 1 selling car.

Today, most Americans consider Chevrolet as a car that's as much a part of their national heritage as baseball, hot dogs and apple pie. Yet, to old car lovers, the company's success story is a Christmas tale that started to unfold on a snowy Yuletide afternoon in Switzerland, in 1873.

Chevrolet...The car and the driver — Little is it known by the millions of Chevrolet drivers around the world that the man for whom their car was named was famed not only as a car builder but also was the greatest race driver of his day. Louis Chevrolet, the driver, sits at the wheel of one of his early racers (above) accompanied by a riding mechanic. Louis competed in four Indianapolis 500 races and, though he never won one, built the car that won two successive Indianapolis classics, including 1920 when his brother, Gaston, drove to victory.

Chevrolet—First With Low Cost

Luxury

Chevrolet for 1932 was a luxury revolution on wheels. It was, indeed, a mini-Cadillac.

Chevrolet got off to a wobbly start in 1913, couldn't seem to find its reach, and by 1921 sales had dropped to a trickle. Losses that year almost reached $10 million, a vast sum in those days. Model T was out-selling Chevrolet 16 to one and gaining.

The Chevrolet got up from this front seat on Death Row and built the broad base on which the modern General Motors was founded. Since GM came to be the mainstream of the US auto industry, Chevrolet led the United States, indeed the World in auto production.

This magnificent feat of imagination and courage perhaps unprecedented in American business, rests squarely on two Chevrolets—1925 Model K and 1932 Model named strangely Confederate Series BA. They were the beginning and the end of an automobile revolution.

In the beginning the small car production trouble was two-fold. When cars were built like birds' nests, one at a time, the way Rolls-Royce still is, only rich people could afford them. This method didn't produce many cars, but there weren't many rich people, either, so until World War I there was a nice balance in the business between supply and demand with little incentive to upset it. The only lower priced cars the established industry could conceive were still costly. Packard Single Six of 1921 sold for $2795, half the price of its big brother Twin Six but still five times too much for average Americans.

The looks of a low priced car before World War I weighed heavily against it. The deep rutted roads of the day demanded high wheels, and the body, set on a straight rail frame built up a high edifice. A long wheelbase car could carry this off, but foreshortened such a car looked awkward. That small cars should be ugly was taken for granted then. Henry Leland, past master of mechanical excellence, founder of Cadillac drove for his personal transportation a 1907 one cylinder Cadillac Model M Coupe that looked for all the world like a traveling telephone booth.

Henry Ford solved half of this small car dilemma. Nineteen twenty five was the year he dropped his price to $290 for a new touring car. If you wanted a low priced car, here it was. Like a mule it had no pride of ancestry, no hope of posterity. But nobody ever called it beautiful. It left the buyer with a crying psychological need. After World War I, the new motoring public wanted to take pride in its cars.

The Chevrolet stroke of genius was to understand this

1925 Chevrolet Coach

The 1924 Chevrolet was a most influential automobile. It showed that grace, style and color could be an integral part of the low-priced automobile. Prices started at $510 for the Touring Car.

1928 Chevrolet Coach

when Henry Ford didn't. Chevrolet set out to make the owner proud of his car. The sales record shows the result.

Henry Ford produced 1,749,827 units in 1924, compared to 262,100 for Chevrolet. Only three years later, these figures were almost exactly reversed. Chevrolet sales soared to 1,749,998 cars while Ford fell to an abysmal 356,188 and then he shut down the Model T production line forever. In 1925 buyers were no longer looking for bare bones transportation. They were looking for low cost luxury and Chevrolet undertook to give it to them.

Model K Chevrolet of 1926 may have revolutionized the industry, but there was nothing revolutionary about the car. It just looked better. A lot better.

The radiator shell used bright metal. Caddies waiting on the curb for a ride to a golf club I remember used to stand up when they saw a car coming with a shiny radiator, the mark of affluence. Now Chevrolet had one, too.

Duco made a great difference. You could have a Chevrolet in any color but black, and Chevrolets stood out in the drab traffic of the day in their bright coats of long lasting Duco paint.

The basics of Model K weren't so different. It was simply last year's car made more attractive. The body was longer, allowing more leg room. "All closed bodies featured a one-piece windshield with an automatic wiper, dome light and a Klaxon horn. The clutch was improved and a new rear end replaced the one that had given so much trouble," according to A. P. Sloan, GM President. Balloon tires, bumpers and moto-meters were available. The sedans normally featured disc wheels like Packard; nickel trim, a neat visor and cowl parking lights produced a stylish image entirely new to the low priced field.

Seven years later Chevrolet's low cost luxury revolution was complete. New models in 1932 joined the General Motors family with no more implications of inferiority than younger brothers. George Dammann's Chevrolet book pictures a 1932 Chevrolet Roadster without a background to betray its scale which could easily be taken for a Cadillac Sixteen. It could even be argued that the Chevrolet was the better automobile—simpler, easier to drive and take care of and a strong competitor on the highway. Chevrolet had proved a low cost car could be handsome, complete and capable.

Chevrolet had won for General Motors the ascendancy in the automobile world it has enjoyed ever since.

Chevrolets Are In My Blood
Says Pinky Randall

By Tony Hossain

"I've never owned a Chevrolet I didn't like." And Pinky Randall has owned a lot of them. He then adds: "The last Ford I owned was a '58. I didn't like it at all."

Pinky Randall, a resident of Houghton Lake, Mich., is known to antique and classic car enthusiasts all over the world as "Mr. Chevrolet." Pinky has an extensive collection of vintage Chevys. His area of specialization is the 1912-18 models and the classic 1932 models. Aiding Pinky in his restoration efforts is one of the world's largest collections of Chevy literature, service manuals and memorabilia.

Pinky's favorite, his 1932 Roadstar.

1914 Royal Mail Roadster

Pinky in his 1914 Baby Grand Chevrolet.

Pinky has been enthusiastic about Chevys ever since he was a five year old. On his way to school every day, Pinky would pass by a house with a brand new '32 Chevy parked in the driveway. He fell in love with that car and he has admired '32 Chevys ever since those days in the Houghton Lake area.

A member of the Vintage Chevrolet Club of America and the Antique Automobile Club of America, Pinky is active in both organizations and is often called to speak on the restoration of early Chevrolets. Pinky does all of his own woodwork, which can be a massive undertaking with a vintage Chevy. But skill and patience is evident in the work that is done in Pinky's shop. It's obviously a labor of love.

Pinky's collection of cars includes a dark maroon 1914 Royal Mail roadster, a rare 1918 V8 Chummy, a Mercury-bodied 1926 Chevy speedster and a Baby Grand touring car. Also part of the Randall collection is a 1932 phaeton and a '32 roadster. The '32 is his personal favorite.

The Randall collection does not end there, though. Pinky's interests span the whole gamut of Chevrolet history, from the earliest 1912 model to the latest 1982 Cavalier. Corvairs are among his favorites from the Sixties and he owns several.

Pinky has one of the last 1969 Monza convertibles..with only 27 miles on the odometer. Corvette enthusiasts would take a real interest in Pinky's red '54 model. Says Pinky: "I like to look at Vettes but I don't really like to drive 'em." Pinky has quite a collection of late Thirties and early Forties Chevys, including some very rare models, such as wood-bodied station wagons and panel wagons. The end of convertible production by Chevrolet is recognized in the Randall collection with a 1975 Caprice ragtop with only a few hundred miles on the odometer.

The 1975 Cosworth Vega is another one of Pinky's favorites.

"Everyday" cars currently sitting in the Randall driveway include a 1973 Caprice convertible and a '79 Caprice sedan. We asked Pinky to recall some of the cars out of his past. They include a 1967 Caprice hardtop, a 1953 210 sedan and a 1963 station wagon.

What are some other Chevys that Pinky really likes? "Well there are the '32 convertibles of course, I also like the 1938 convertibles, the 1941 Fleetline four-door sedan and the Aerosedan. Those '41 Fleetlines are just beautiful. I really fell in love with the 1955 Nomad when it was introduced." Other Randall favorites include the 1959 Impala four-door hardtops and the 1959 El Camino.

Randall says that "although car collecting won't be as easy as it was twenty years ago, the fun is still there. Years ago you could go where the people were and where the money was and you'd find some pretty sensational cars. Now everybody is excited by the old cars. I don't think all the rare cars have been found but I think that most of them have been."

In any event, for Pinky Randall, the excitement is still there. And it will be as long as people buy, collect and restore Chevys. And that looks like a long, long time.

Chevrolet 'Four-Ninety' VS Ford Model T

By A. Stanley Kramer

By 1914, Louis Chevrolet had departed in anger and W.C. Durant was in full control of the Chevrolet Motor Co.

In August, he bought the Tarrytown, N.Y. plant formerly occupied by Maxwell-Briscoe. He knew exactly what he wanted to do there: complete head-on with Ford's Model T.

Alfred Sturt, an old friend and a Buick alumnus, designed the low-priced Chevrolet. It was announced on Dec 16, 1914 and exhibited at the New York Auto Show that opened on New Year's Day. As soon as the assembly line could be rushed to completion, the car was put into production. Durant was ecstatic. At mid-year he wrote a friend, "I am pleased to report as follows: On June 1, 1915, the 'Four Ninety' was placed on sale. At the close of business, June 19, the Chevrolet Motor Co. had accepted orders from dealers and distributors—every contract secured by a cash deposit—for 46,611 cars, valued at $23,329,390 — a fairly good record for 17 working days. Since June 19, we have orders for more than 1,000 cars per day."

A great many Americans knew what "490" meant. It was the advertised price of a Model T Ford touring car. Now it was both the name and the price of the Chevrolet. But this apparently did not disturb Henry Ford. Six weeks after the Four-Ninety's appearance he cut his price to $440 and thereafter always managed to stay under Chevrolet's price.

Durant couldn't meet the cut. The Four-Ninety was already a car stripped to absolute essentials and on a shortened (102 inch) wheelbase. Like its competitor, it was offered in basic black only. The engine was Chevrolet's new Model H, with smaller main bearings and simplified design of the bottom end and elsewhere, in order to reduce manufacturing costs. At 20 h.p., it was neck and neck with Tin Lizzie, and, like it, had its own foibles.

Model T remained the better bargain. Durant wasn't able to hold his $490 price, although it had proven an effective gimmick for his car's introduction. Just two weeks after its presentation the price went to $550. Durant made a characteristic announcement, "Whenever the company's manufacturing facilities and production justify it, the price on this car, electrically equipped, will be $490."

At mid-year, the $490 was justified by the simple expedient of removing the electric equipment and offering it as a recommended option. It was a stout recommendation: "We strongly recommend the purchase of the Model Four-Ninety with electric lighting and starting equipment, as no car today is complete without it. If you buy a car without electric lights and starter you will make a mistake."

At the beginning of the next season, the starter was included at the $490 price, but only long enough for Chevrolet advertising to boast, "the lowest-priced electrically lighted and started automobile on the market today."

Durant was forced to raise his price. At $490 with a self-starter, Chevrolet couldn't make a reasonable profit. The price soon escalated to $550 and thereafter as the Model T's price went lower and lower, the price differential between the cars widened substantially.

A 1914 Chevy Baby Grand touring.

The Day Chevy Nearly Sank

By A. Stanley Kramer

For one tense moment, despite substantial sales, Chevrolet nearly went out of business. The year was 1920. As president of General Motors, W. C. Durant had expanded the company's operations tremendously from 1915 until then.

In 1915 Durant had moved Chevrolet's headquarters from Flint, Mich. to New York City. In the next few years he bought Maxwell's Terrytown, N.Y. assembly plant and made arrangements with investors in Canada and St. Louis, which made possible the assembly of the popular 490 Chevrolet in Flint, St. Louis, Tarrytown, Oshawa (Canada), Oakland, Calif., and Fort Worth, Texas. (The 490 got its name from the $490 Henry Ford charged for his Model T touring car, targeted as the competition. However, six weeks after the introduction of the 490, Ford lowered his price to $440.)

In 1916 factory sales soared to 70,701, then to 125,882 in 1917. They dropped slightly in 1918 and 1919 but bounced back to 150,226 in 1920—accounting for a large share of GM's total North American sales of 393,075 cars.

But Chevrolet's future was nowhere near as solid as these figures might indicate. As GM president, Durant had expanded GM's operations dazzlingly. But his entire personal fortune was committed to the support of its shares on Wall Street. When business fell off sharply in September 1920, Durant and his empire were in deep trouble. They were saved from disaster only through the intervention of the vast resources of the duPont family whose quick action alone kept GM alive. But at a price. Durant had to resign on Nov. 30, 1920 to be succeeded by Pierre S. duPont, who also made himself general manager of Chevrolet.

Alfred P. Sloan Jr. then became, as he wrote in *My Years with General Motors*, "sort of executive vice president in charge of all operations, reporting to Mr. duPont."

Sloan described the near debacle graphically. "Someone had the idea of having a survey made of the General Motors properties, with recommendations as to what might be done in the way of a reconstruction program. The job was entrusted to a firm of consulting engineers of high standing. The most illuminating recommendation was that the whole Chevrolet operation should be liquidated. There was no chance, they said, to make it a profitable business. We could not hope to compete. I was much upset because I feared the prestige of the authors might overcome our arguments to the contrary." Pierre duPont listened patiently and at length to Sloan's pleas to carry on the business. Sloan recalled, "I went to Mr. duPont and told him what we thought we might accomplish if we built a good product and sold it aggressively."

It was a tense moment. Millions of dollars and the working lives of thousands of people hung in the balance. President Pierre thought long and hard. Then he smiled, something he was not famous for.

"Forget the report," he said, "We will go ahead and see what we can do."

The rest is important American history. Like the bumblebee who flew very well despite aeronautic engineers' overwhelming proof that its wings were too small and its fuselage too thick for flight, Chevrolet flew too, and has been flying high ever since.

In 1912, famed racing driver Louis Chevrolet had completed two years of development work at the behest of W. C. Durant (standing on the far right with derby). Here they admire the result — the first Chevrolet, a 6-cylinder model with a folding top and adjustable windshields. At the wheel is Durant's son, Cliff, with his wife beside him. Chevrolet produced 2,999 vehicles in Detroit in 1912. The following year, Chevrolet moved to Flint, Mich., and began expanding.

1920 Chevrolet Coupe

Saga Of Copper Cooled Chevy

By Rich Taylor

Charles F. Kettering

Charles F. Kettering, the brilliant "boss Ket," figures prominently in the early history of General Motors, and indeed, the automobile. He invented the self-starter, the high-tension ignition system, the high-compression engine, freon refrigerant, the two-cycle Diesel and leaded gasoline. Indeed, Kettering had only one significant failure, and that was one that seems like it would have been the simplest of all...the air-cooled engine.

Boss Ket started work on his air-cooled engine in 1918. At that time he was the director of Daytona Engineering Laboratories, which was the research division of General Motors. Now in 1918, the air-cooled engine was nothing new ...Franklin was only the best known of dozens of air-cooled engine manufacturers.

Every air-cooled engine in production was made by laborously welding cooling fins onto the block, or carefully casting integral fins when the block was made. Either way was very expensive and time-consuming. Kettering wanted to invent a way to air-cool an engine that would be cheap enough for mass-production and more efficient than anything anybody else was doing.

His solution was to use cast iron cylinders that were smooth on the outside. Then he took sheet copper and pleated it into a series of continuous, vertical fins. These would be welded to the outside of the cast iron cylinders, and since copper transfers heat more efficiently than cast iron, Kettering figured his engine would be super-efficient and easy to build. The only problem was, he couldn't devise a way to weld the copper fins to the cast iron cylinders.

In 1919, Kettering reported to the new board of directors that he had solved the problem. A high-temperature bonding oven would literally fuse the fins to the cylinder at 1400 degrees. A year later, when Billy C. Durant was forced to leave GM and Pierre S. duPont took over, Kettering wrote to duPont. "The small air-cooled engine is now ready to push toward a production basis," he said.

duPont agreed. The Chevrolet Model 490 had been in production without change since 1913, and was desperately in need of sprucing up. duPont ordered Kettering to build a prototype four-cylinder "copper-cooled" engine that would fit into the existing Model 490 and share at least some parts with the existing 171 cubic inch Four. Kettering started work on a 135 cubic inch Four, with overhead valves borrowed from the water-cooled 490 and four individually-cast cylinders wrapped in copper fins. The bottom end was just a modified version of the existing engine.

In January of 1921, Pierre duPont decided that the new air-cooled engine deserved a whole new car, and he ordered Chevrolet general manager K. W. Zimmerschied to come up with a brand-new body and chassis for 1923. A month later, duPont decided that Oakland also needed to be revamped, and directed Kettering to simultaneously design a six-cylinder air-cooled engine for an all-new Oakland which would sell for around $1000..twice as much as the new Chevrolet.

In May, 1921, Kettering had test cars fitted with the new four and six-cylinder engines ready to run. Unfortunately, neither ran very well. The air flow around the vertical copper fins simply wasn't enough to cool the cylinders. Kettering designed a shroud to surround the cylinders and lead into a front-mounted fan. Air was sucked up beneath the car, flowed past the cylinders and exhausted out the sides of the hood. You'd think that Kettering would have designed it so the air would flow in the grille and be blown down and back by the fan, to be sucked out the bottom by the partial vacuum which exists beneath any moving car.

Chevrolet's Zimmerschied didn't have much faith in the four-cylinder air-cooled engine, so Kettering had switched his allegiance to George Hannum, the general manager of

Oakland, who was much more receptive to the whole idea. In October, 1921, Kettering shipped two six-cylinder test cars up to Hannum in Pontiac, Michigan.

After the cars had been driven for two weeks, Hannum sent a letter to Kettering, with a copy to Pierre duPont. "To get this car to the point where we are ready to put our OK on same, it will take at least six months. To bridge this time, we are planning on bringing in a complete new water-cooled line." Kettering was so furious that on the same day duPont indefinitely postponed the air-cooled Oakland project, he wrote a letter signed by all the members of the GM Executive Committee that reaffirmed their faith in Kettering, in the air-cooled concept and in the four-cylinder Chevrolet version.

duPont also ordered Kettering to try and get the air-cooled engine into production by September, 1922. And to help him, he gave an unprecedented order. The chief engineers of Chevrolet, Oakland and Buick were transferred to Dayton where they would work for Kettering. Pierre duPont was pinning everything on Kettering's untried engine.

Alfred Sloan was a member of the Executive Committee, as was Charles Mott. In January, 1922, they met with Chevrolet's Zimmerschied in the Hotel Statler in Detroit. The three men secretly decided that the copper-cooled motor was too much of a gamble for General Motors. They would let Kettering and duPont go along planning on the copper-cooled, but Sloan and Zimmerschied would secretly modernize the water-cooled Model 490, just in case.

General Motors was in a real mess. All sorts of corporate infighting was going on, and nobody knew exactly who was running the company. On February 1, 1922, duPont hired William S. Knudsen away from Ford and made him assistant to Charles Mott, with sweeping powers. Knudsen went down to Dayton, talked with Kettering and ordered that Chevrolet stop production of the water-cooled 490 and immediately start building the copper-cooled engine.

Zimmerschied told Knudsen where to get off. But Knudsen had Pierre duPont's backing, and Zimmerschied didn't. Knudsen was made vice-president of Chevrolet operations, and duPont named himself general manager of Chevrolet. Zimmerschied was given a vague executive post with no power.

Chevrolet began tooling up for production of the new engine in April of 1922, expecting to make ten per day by September and fifty per day by December. But Kettering wouldn't approve the tooling. He rightly claimed that the copper-cooled engine wasn't quite ready for production, and he needed just a little more time to work the bugs out.

By June, it was obvious even to duPont and Knudsen that the engine would never be ready. Sloan and Mott were allowed to take the lineup of bodies that had been designed for the new car and fit them to a spruced-up version of the Model 490 chassis. This would give them a new Superior 490 line for 1923. If and when the air-cooled engine was ready, it could be fitted to the Superior 490 without chassis modifications.

The Superior 490 used a longer 103 inch wheelbase version of the old 490 frame, with quarter-elliptic leaf springs front and rear, rigid axles, demountable rims on wooden spoke wheels and external contracting brakes on the rear wheels only. The engine was the tried and true water-cooled 490, now entering its tenth year, the transmission was the same old 3-speed, the differential a spiral bevel gear.

The Superior 490 line was priced from right around \$500, just upscale of the Model T, to just under \$900, or just downscale of the Oakland. The new line contained a two-passenger sedanette, a closed five passenger sedan and a closed two passenger coupe.

Throughout the summer of 1922, Pierre duPont kept putting off the introduction date of the copper-cooled motor, as Kettering kept asking for more development time. Finally, in November, 1922, duPont sent a letter to Kettering and the Executive Committee. "Chevrolet will proceed with the development of its Copper-Cooled model cautiously, in such a way that the hazard to the Corporation is at all times kept at a minimum."

Chevrolet was seemingly off the hook. But in the same letter, duPont now ordered Kettering to get back to work on the six-cylinder version and have it ready for Oldsmobile to start building by August of 1923. Indeed, he even ordered Oldsmobile—which had so far not been involved in the air-cooled debacle at all—not to do any development work on water-cooled engines starting from receipt of the letter on November 16, 1922. If you read between the lines, it's obvious that there was a terrific struggle going on for control of General Motor, with duPont and Knudsen on one side and Mott and Sloan on the other. The divisions were being swapped around, only pawns in their game.

Knudsen ordered Chevrolet to actually produce Copper-Cooled cars beginning in December, 1922. The price

William S. Knudsen

was set at \$200 more that the equivalent water-cooled model. The cars were identical except that the starter location was moved, the generator was belt-driven, the clutch used multiple discs instead of a single disc, the distributor had one of Kettering's automatic spark advancers and the emergency brake acted on the driveshalf.

Between December and May, Knudsen built only 759 Copper-Cooled cars. And on May 10, 1923, the executive battle over who would control GM was finally won by Alfred Sloan. Pierre duPont resigned. Sloan's first move was to ask for a status report on the six-cylinder Copper-Cooled engine that was supposedly being readied for Oldsmobile, duPont was so sure of Kettering's engine that he had ordered Oldsmobile to sell off its entire stock of water-cooled cars at a \$50 loss on each one, in order to clear the pipeline for fabulous new air-cooled cars which would come along in less than 3 months.

The engineer's report on the Copper-Cooled Six was exactly two paragraphs long.

"The Copper-Cooled Six preignites badly after driving at moderate speeds in air temperatures from sixty to seventy degrees. It shows a serious loss of compression and power when hot, though the power is satisfactory when the engine is warming up from a cold condition.

"These major difficulties plus several minor ones which

can be reported in detail, if you so desire, lead us to the conclusion that the job is not in shape for immediate production. We recommend that we set it aside for further development and it be left out of consideration as far as immediate production is concerned."

As a result of this devastating report, Sloan ordered Oldsmobile to get going on a water-cooled car. He also ordered Knudsen not only to stop building the four-cylinder air-cooled cars, but to buy back and destroy any 759 which had been sold. Knudsen scrapped 239 which were still on the production lines, plus about 150 cars that were being driven by Chevrolet managers and 300 that were bought back from dealer's showrooms.

Only 100 had actually been sold to retail customers, and Chevrolet field service men were able to buy back all but two coupes. One had been purchased in Detroit by Henry Ford, curiously enough, just to see what all the fuss was about. It's in the Henry Ford Museum at Greenfield Village today. The other coupe was bought by a Mr. Samuel Elliot of Boston, who being a typical crusty New Englander, simply refused to give it up. It's now in Harrah's collection.

Charles F. Kettering was understandably upset when he learned that Sloan had canned his car, and threatened to resign. Sloan handled him beautifully. He suggested that Kettering himself introduce a new line of cars, called Copper-Cooled, to be built in Dayton and distributed through General Motors dealers. Kettering diddled around all summer, and in September, 1923 he gave a number of test engines to the engineering department at the University of Michigan.

The student engineers discovered something that Kettering had overlooked. While the inlet manifold temperatures of the water-cooled 490 engine were 125 degrees at all four cylinders, the inlets of the Copper-Cooled were 134, 122, 127 and 160 degrees, front to back. And while the cylinder head temperature of the front cylinder was only 380 degrees, the back cylinder was 450 degrees.

The evidence is obvious. The reason the Copper-Cooled engine didn't work is because Kettering never figured out an adequate way to get equal amounts of cooling air to each cylinder. The uneven temperatures led to detonation, higher temperatures and eventually, piston seizure.

Faced with this thermodynamic evidence, and with no interest in the engine from GM, Kettering abandoned the Copper-Cooled. It's nothing more than a reminder of the way in which a few ambition-blinded executives in the wrong positions can make a total muddle of a large corporation within a matter of months. If not for Alfred Sloan, Pierre duPont and Charles Kettering might have totally bankrupt General Motors by selling a car that simply didn't run.

Curiously enough, it was while trying to find a way to stop the detonation which destroyed his copper-cooled engine that Kettering began investigating the properties of gasoline itself. He discovered that the addition of tetraethyl lead to the gasoline raised the octane rating and made the engine run cooler, with less detonation. In a well-cooled engine, it permitted higher compression ratios for much more power. So in two respects, really, the Copper-Cooled Chevrolet was a success. It helped put Alfred Sloan into the presidency of General Motors, and it led to the discovery of leaded gasoline. That's more than you can say for many more successful cars.

The brilliant Charles F. Kettering had only one significant failure . . . his air-cooled engine for the Chevrolet car.

Austie's "Air Cooled" Chevrolet

By Henry Austin Clark, Jr.

There was a time not long ago when we had two Chevrolets in the collection at the museum in Southhampton, and they were cooled by air, not water. In addition neither of them was a Corvair. Just what were they, you may well ask? Well, one of them was an experimental World War II airborne Jeep, powered by an Indian motorcycle engine, air cooled, of course. The other was a 1923 Chevrolet Copper-Cooled coupe.

Charles F. Kettering, the great General Motors genius, had ideas of introducing aircooling to the entire G.M. line of cars, starting with Chevrolet. He designed a four cylinder engine which had copper fins welded in some manner to the cast iron cylinders. Air was blown through these fins, which were encased in shrouds, in order to cool the engine more or less in the manner of the time-tested Franklin. The plan was well worked out, and there was no reason why it would not have worked just fine. The Copper-Cooled Chevrolet was introduced at the automobile shows in January of 1923, and a fine technical article appeared in **Automobile Industries**, the leading trade periodical.

Then, suddenly the Copper-Cooled Chevrolet was recalled in total. Few if any had been delivered, and these were exchanged or refitted with water-cooled engines. A very few did manage to escape the dragnet, however. One of these wound up in the collection of the Henry Ford Museum some years later. Another was located by Professor Dean Abner Fales, Assistant Professor of Automotive Engineering at the Massachusetts Institute of Technology. He passed it on some years later to his friend Samuel Eliot, and Sam squirreled it away in the barn. We had seen the example at Dearborn, and wanted one for our museum, but the chance of finding one seemed slight. Then in 1949 we found ourselves on a cruise on the old Mauretania to the Caribbean. As we boarded we ran across Sam Eliot, much to the disgust of my wife, who could predict seven days of having to listen to conversations about old cars, to the exclusion of most other activities. Sure enough, we mentioned our desire to find the elusive rare Chevy, and Sam said that he had one. Yes, he would sell it, and a deal was made in the aft smoking lounge. We also arranged the purchase of a much needed radiator for our fifty hp. Simplex, which was under restoration. All in all a very good cocktail hour.

After the cruise we went up to Massachusetts with our trailer, and retrieved both the Chevrolet and the radiator. The little coupe went to Reuter's Coachworks in the Bronx for a fresh black paint job, and a general cleaning up. The tires provided a problem as they were 30 x 3 1/2 straight side. As any Ford man call tell you, 30 x 3 1/2 clincher fits Model T's from 1909 to 1925. However, they are not interchangeable with the straight sides. The former have a beaded edge which slips into a groove on the rim, while the latter have wires in the straight bead to keep them on the rim. Fortunately we were able to find a set of new old stock tires of the correct size and type, so the car was now able to roll around on its own wheels.

We never did run the little car, but put it on display in the museum. There were still one or two minor items, including a fan belt which were missing. We had acquired most of a spare engine for the car, which a friend found in a Connecticut junk yard, and was able to purchase for us for the sum of $10., and this made a fine display to go with the car.

Back in 1962 we had to reduce the number of vehicles in our own collection, and the little Chevrolet had to be sold. It was loaded into the huge van from Reno, and went to join the world's largest automobile collection, belonging to William Harrah.

1923 Air-cooled Chevrolet, formerly of the Clark collection.

I Never Want To See That Chevy Again

By Ed Robinson

Parenting can be described as inflicting upon your own children all the unpleasant things which your parents did to you. Half the things which seem to me as a father to be excellent training turn out to be repetitions of training devices used on me by my Dad. His ideas of teaching me about cars I interpreted as delaying tactics, intentional frustrations, unearned punishments and general lack of understanding. Dad simply didn't know how badly I needed a car.

I made my son help me rebuild and repair his first car before he began to drive — primarily because my father did the same thing to me. My son is smarter than I was at his age. He did not "trade off" his first car without consulting me. My first "on my own" trade started a long list of cars about which I can only say "I'm sorry I bought it. I'm glad I sold it and I hope I never see that heap again."

I started my driving in a 1924 Essex six cylinder, two door sedan. It had about the same glass area as a telephone booth. Its general lines more nearly resembled a two hole outdoor privy. Its engine roared like a B29 under full power but the torque output was barely above that of a gasoline driven Maytag washing machine. The old Essex would get you there eventually but you used up lots of time in the process. About the only justification for teenage pride lay in the fact that you weren't walking. The principle problem with the Essex lay in the fact that it belonged to the boy friend of my older sister and he would only let me drive it after I spent a full afternoon pulling weeds and carrying water to his large vegetable garden. About the only thing the Essex and I had in common was our ages. It was nine years old. I was eleven.

Three years after I learned surreptitiously to drive, my father decided it was time for him to teach me. In those days teaching your son to drive was the Protestant equivalent of a Bar Mitzva. The drivers license was the ultimate verification of your having reached manhood. Dad had planned a leisurely two years of occasional lessons culminating in my acquisition of a drivers license at the earliest legal age — sixteen. During lesson number one I listened patiently to his explanation of the functions of the gear shift lever, the accelerator, the clutch and brake pedals. Then he said "put it in low gear, give it a little gas, let the clutch out slowly. Try not to kill the motor." I smugly dropped into first gear, revved the engine and smoked the rear tires. I laid rubber until I double clutched into second and slam speed shifted into third. I stopped just short of demonstrating a bootlegger's one eighty. I did leave broad tracks around the first corner we came to. I circled the block and quickly backed into a parallel parking slot in front of the house. It took Dad several minutes to get his mouth closed.

My next few lessons had nothing to do with learning to drive. I did some significent unlearning. I did discover a great deal about the inadvisability of "showing off" in front of the old man.

After the first lesson and demonstration Dad shifted tactics. It was obvious that he couldn't use the next two years teaching me the rudiments of driving. He started time consumer plan number two. He called it "fixing up a car for me to drive." I called it teaching me how to work on one. I realize now that the fix up period was meant to consume the full two years between me and the legal driving age. The car we worked on was a 1931 American Austin coupe. Less than two days after we purchased it, Dad had the Austin completely disassembled. It took me, all my friends, and my father almost two years to put it back together. Never in history have so many small pieces been so thoroughly sanded, buffed, and polished. When it was finished it was as perfect as we could make it. In retrospect I am amazed that Dad would give a fully restored car to a young kid. It was almost ideal for a teenager. It had only one intolerable weakness. It would not run as fast as the 1927 Model "T" coupe that my friend Jack had received from his father. It didn't matter how shiny the paint, how neat the wiring, how carefully the rings were fitted, how well the valves had been hand lapped — if you consistently came in second in the boulevard drag race that car was unacceptable.

Without consulting Dad, I traded cars. In return for my restored '31 Austin and fifteen dollars I got a 1927 Chevy coupe. That's the one I'm sorry I bought. It satisfied the immediate reason for changing — it would outrun Jack's "T". It had a few flaws that were not related to the top speed of 52 miles per hour.

When the '27 Chevy was new it had two wheel brakes. By the time I got mine it had no wheel brakes. To stop from cruising speed you did the following: turn off the ignition, grasp the bottom side of the large wooden steering wheel firmly with both hands, place both feet squarely upon the brake pedal, stand up and pull against the steering wheel with all your strength. If you weren't going over twenty miles an hour when you started this procedure, you could expect the forward motion to be slowed sufficiently to snub the car against a rock, a curb or a convenient tree, providing, of course, that the potential snub point was at least three miles downstream.

That vintage Chevy also had solid disk wheels with demountable split rims. If you snubbed her too enthusiastically the demountable rims dismounted. In addition to the split rims mine also had splittable tires. I quickly got very well acquainted with tire tools, patching kits, hand pumps and a heavy ball peen hammer.

By 1927, Chevrolets came equipped with self starters. The '27 also had an adjustable spark. If you got careless with the spark adjuster during starting maneuvers the car would frequently backfire and quite often flywheel teeth would disappear. An electric self starter which has no teeth with which to engage makes horrendous noises but starts nothing. Whoever owned my Chevy before I got it had been careless with the spark adjustment and the flywheel teeth. My starter only worked when I was alone. Any time I got a girl in the car that portion of the flywheel needing dentures was always opposite the starter gear. Fortunately the Chevy was not too hard to hand crank. I estimate its compression ratio to have been about one half to one. The only problem with hand cranking in front of a girl came from the one way door on the driver's side. In the twenties, General Motors used Bodies by Fisher. These later became quite famous. In 1927, they were infamous. The driver's side door post on my coupe had apparently been made of powdered Balsa wood and termite turds. The upper hinge screws were firmly anchored in thin air. You could, with careful lifting and pulling, open the driver's door from outside. Opening the door from the inside never happened. If you seated your girl friend, walked around and climbed in yourself, closed the door behind you, and then discovered that the starter had chosen not to work you were literally trapped. It is very difficult climb out the window with a crank in your hand and at the same time maintain the illusion of romance.

In addition to the one way door it also had a one way, vacuum operated, windshield wiper. If the rain was heavy enough to thoroughly wet the windshield glass the wiper blade would slowly move from left to right. There it stopped. You had to roll down the window, reach around and manually pull the blade from right to left. It is hard to be romantic when your entire left side is wringing wet.

These eccentricities I tolerated willingly. I faithfully hand-oiled the rocker arms. I regularly sucked on the vacuum tank. I even tried to polish the dull cadmium plated radiator shell. It was not a very good car for dating but I had purchased it for the primary purpose of outrunning Jack's "T". I came in first for about three weeks. I stopped winning our daily-after-school-races only when a connecting rod let loose ventilating the side of the Chevy block. The resulting gaposis could only be cured with an engine transplant. At this point, my father taught me another of life's major lessons. He said "You were big enough to trade for that thing without asking me, surely you are big enough to fix it yourself. Here's the tool box."

It took the better part of a school semester of late afternoons toiling under the backyard mulberry tree for me to install a used, junkyard motor. As soon as I got it running again I humbly asked Dad for his help in getting rid of it and getting something better to drive. He relented and helped. I was only sixteen years old when my first car trade taught me to say — "I'm sorry I bought it. I'm glad I sold it and I never want to see that car again."

Antique Chevy drops through the ice

By Tom Reese

It was Christmas Eve day. As befits a Minnesota winter, the temperature stood at 20 degrees below zero; the windchill index at 35 degress below zero.

The children were all home to spend the holidays. The lake ice out in front of the house had frozen glass smooth, with just fingers of the snow tracing outlines across the surface.

All afternoon the children had been skate sailing across the mile and a half of open ice from the house to the opposite shore. The trip over with the wind was exhilaratingly fun, while the return, pumping frozen legs against the wind, was purest work.

Rodney, the 1927 Chevrolet, in happier days. This was the first year that Chevy outsold Ford. Rodney was a peppy, reliable car, that was fun to drive. It was a good car, but it couldn't "walk" on water, as later events proved.

"Dad, can you give us rides back?" was the request, thinking that I would go "modern," complete with heater and enclosed accommodations. I was ready to pop my Christmas surprise.

Out in the somewhat heated garage stood Rodney, my 1927 Chevy roadster. A few turns of the starter brought the engine to life, and after letting it warm up I ventured out toward the lake, carefully skirting by some 75 feet the open water where a neighbor maintained a bubbler around his "permanent" dock.

Numerous cars of ice fishermen, plus some fleets of snowmobiles, had already passed that way, so I felt secure. The children and I then spent a couple of glorious hours, they blasting across the lake surface, propelled by the wind blowing into their tightly held blanket sails, and I sliding my Chevy around, eventually towing them back to the upwind side of the lake as they held tightly to the rear bumper of the car.

When we all agreed that the cold was getting the better of us, we called it quits. The children skated toward our house, while I headed back off the lake, again carefully skirting the open water.

At the nearest point to the open water and still about 75 yards from shore, I felt the front of the car slowly tilt forward. I watched in stunned disbelief as the ice parted, allowing the car and its driver to settle in four feet of the coldest water I have ever felt. I scrambled out of the car, and sought to climb up on the edge of the ice. Standing up, my clothes instantly froze solidly to my body. It was as though I were encased in an unjointed suit of armor.

My son noted my predicament from a distance, and skated home to tell my wife and to shed his skates. When he reported: "Mom, dad just fell though the ice in the car," she didn't know whether to grab for the will or the windbreaker.

A passing motorist took me home, which settled her decision. The family then mobilized for the effort to get Rodney free of the rapidly reforming ice. By now it was 4 p.m. on Christmas eve. The nearby service station was just closing for the holiday. I went to the owner and told him, "Duane, you know the old saying, 'a friend in need is a friend indeed.' Well, my '27 Chevy just dropped into four feet of water." He replied, "Just don't ask me to put my wrecker on the ice. I won't go closer than just near the ice with that unit."

Fifteen minutes later, following Duane's instructions, we were standing around Rodney amid a clutter of planks, chain saws and ice chisels. We sawed slots in the ice for 25 feet toward the shore, where Duane's wrecker stood, true to his word, "near the ice" with its winch pointed toward Rodney.

Taking the ice chisels, we broke up the ice between the slots until the whole water surface was filled with floating ice chunks. We put the planks down to form ramps upon which we could pull Rodney from the lake bottom. The moment of truth had arrived. Someone had to go swimming to attach the winch cable to the center of Rodney's front axle.

All of our respective teeth were chattering in unison at just the thought. Being the only two males, my son and I considered which would do it. (Male macho was still "in" then.) Doing the only decent thing (to my way of thinking), Andy took the cable end, popped into the water and did the attachment.

A few minutes with Duane's winch and Rodney stood shivering on the ice surface. The car instantly locked up in every moving part. We towed it home, sliding the tires on the ice slicked streets. I put it in the garage, and lit a couple of borrowed construction salamander stoves. I sadly closed the door to let Rodney commence his lonely fight back to operating condition, while we somehow found a way to celebrate Christmas.

I spent the rest of the winter putting Rodney back to some semblance of its prior good looks. The cold water had cracked the lacquer in several places. The ice chunks had bent the head and parking lights. The right front fender somehow got damaged in all the furor. There was water in every single cavity in the car, necessitating disassembly, drying and perhaps repair. This included not only the engine and gear boxes, but also such things as the instruments, lamps and space behind the upholstery.

By spring, Rodney was back among the running, but not back among the show cars. I just didn't have the heart to re-restore the car, so I found a kind man who promised to restore Rodney, so I sadly let him go to a more secure home — off the lake!

Chevy's "Cast Iron Wonder"

By A. Stanley Kramer

It was an uncomplicated six-cylinder engine, so strong and trouble-free that Chevrolet continued to use it for a quarter of a century with only occasional updating.

Its nickname was derived from the fact that it had cast iron pistons. It was also referred to as the "Stove Bolt Six" because it used quarter inch-20 slotted head bolts or "stove bolts" as they came to be called.

Designed by chief engineer, Ormond E. Hunt, Chevrolet introduced the durable power plant late in 1928, as an overhead valve engine with three main bearings, developing 46 b.h.p. at only 2600 r.p.m. While its basic design remained unchanged, its power was substantially increased over the years. And early in the '30s it was given a much fancier official name, "The Blue Flame Six." By 1934 it also had a re-designed combustion chamber, a longer stroke, and was churning out 80 b.h.p. at 3000 r.p.m.

The year 1937 saw the Cast Iron Wonder re-engineered, with bore and stroke nearly square: 3½x3¾ inches. In this version it produced 85 h.p. at 3200 r.p.m., had four main bearings instead of three and improved pumps for oil and water.

In 1939, in a "Master 85" coupe with softly sprung "kneeaction," a Cast Iron Wonder played a significant part in enhancing Chevrolet's reputation. A 28-year-old Argentine raced a Chevrolet for the first time that year — a used car given him by friends, who were unable to come up with the Ford he really preferred. Juan Manuel Fangio was his name. He didn't win his first race but his performance so impressed General Motors of Argentina that they gave him a car, a race-prepared '39 coupe with a solid front axle for better cornering.

Fangio became a national hero in 1940 when he won the car — destroying a 5,900-mile road race from Buenos Aires to Lima, Peru and back. He averaged 53.6 m.p.h. over roads whose surface could have destroyed a tank.

That was merely the beginning. Fangio and his Chevrolet won four consecutive major road races in the next two years. After World War II, he continued to race the same coupe, winning three more first places in important races. "Cast Iron" or not, the engine was a wonder.

Shortly thereafter he sold the most famous Chevrolet in South America, if not in the whole world, and went on to greater triumphs. By then no one anywhere who knew anything at all about automobiles had the slightest doubt about the power and reliability of the Cast Iron Wonder.

1928 Chevrolet

1937 Chevrolet

How Chevy Got Its Bow-Tie

When the first Chevrolet hit the market in 1912, it lacked its now world-famous insignia, commonly referred to as the "bow-tie."

We know that it was a W.C. Durant inspiration. Exactly where he got it is not so certain. According to Durant, he had been carrying the idea around in his head for "a long time." With the fast-moving Durant, anything over an hour would have fitted that time frame.

Durant's explanation of where he got it depended on to whom he was telling the story.

The Paris hotel version was his favorite and the one he told most frequently. It was, explained the romantic Billy, the motif on the wallpaper of a hotel suite he was staying in. It struck him instantly and he tore off a piece and put it in his wallet.

His widow remembered the bow-tie's genesis quite differently. She said her husband spotted the design in the rotogravure section of a Sunday newspaper he was reading in Hot Springs, Va.

In either event, Durant was very pleased with it.

A Milestone Year for Chevrolet and General Motors Corp.

By Robert C. Ackerson

Riding in any automobile that is older than you is almost by definition a humbling experience. And when the automobile is well over half a century in age it also becomes a memorable one. In the case of Laddie MacKenzie's 1928 National Series AB Chevrolet sedan (with barely 22,000 miles on the odometer) it assumes even additional importance since Chevrolets of this vintage are, in automotive history, significant vehicles.

The first Chevrolet of 1911 was powered by a six cylinder engine but three years later the "Chevrolet Four" debuted and that car says General Motors, "first made the Chevrolet name famous." The 1914 model was the first Chevrolet to wear the soon to be world famous bow-tie logo and began Chevrolet's long use of overhead valves. In a 1914 advertisement Chevrolet noted the advantages of this arrangement, explaining to readers, "Gasoline is introduced directly into the cylinder head and exploded there. The full force of the explosion comes in direct contact with the piston head. For this reason Chevrolet power is maximum with minimum fuel."

Chevrolet was as is common knowledge directly involved in the machinations of William Durant and his second coming as the master of General Motors. This colorful if ultimately tragic (for Durant) episode in automotive history has been, and appropriately so, well researched and recorded. But, in terms of its actual impact upon the development of the American automotive industry, Chevrolet, by the end of World War I was yet to be heard from. From that point events moved with great rapidity. While the Model T Ford was reaching its peak sales year in 1923 with 2,091,000 cars sold, Alfred Sloan was beginning his long tenure as General Motors president. Under Sloan and his immediate predecessor, Pierre S. duPont GM had become a corporation with clearly defined and clarified responsibilities for every key individual at each crucial level of operation. It was a firm with an awesome ability to gather and interpret statistics and at the same time operate in a decentralized fashion that spurred innovation and creativity. On the other hand, Henry Ford had proudly announced in 1922 that "The Ford factories and enterprises have no organization, no specific duties attaching to any position, no line of succession or of authority, very few titles, and no conferences." He should have added that Ford was also losing its grip upon industry leadership. In 1924, '25 an '26, Model T sales fell and whereas in 1921 Ford controlled 55.7 percent of the market, a decade later its share was 24.9 percent. General Motors, over the same time, moved its new car sales from 12.7 percent to 43.9 percent. In 1925 General Motors introduced the six cylinder Pontiac and in its annual report informed stockholders that "The Corporation has established the fundamental policy of building a car for every purse and purpose." This meant that at the lower end of the market would be found a Chevrolet that was extremely competitive to what Ford had to offer; was capable of instilling in owners a high degree of loyalty and, for those individuals experiencing upward mobility, create satisfied car buyers who would cheerfully seek out a Pontiac or Oldsmobile dealer when their dreams of affluence became reality. It all paid off extremely handsomely. In 1928 General Motors reported a profit of $296,256,223, truly a milestone of American industrial development. In January of that year the four millionth Chevrolet was completed and before the year ended the fifth millionth, an AB Coach was manufactured.

Sandwiched as it was between the arrival of the 1928 Ford Model A and the new six cylinder Chevrolet the following year, it's been easy for automotive history to ignore that last (that is until 1962) of the Chevrolet Fours. This has been unfortunate. Not only did it help (with sales of 769,9927) GM make that just mentioned mountain of money, but it was also a very fine automobile. Chevrolet which already had the new engine on tap and ready to go was still able to report in 1928 that "this great new car is everywhere hailed as an amazing revelation in automotive value." With its larger 107 inch wheelbase (which represented a four inch increase from 1927) and tasteful restyling it was, said Chevrolet, an automobile of "arresting new beauty." Perhaps a bit overstated, Chevrolet. The 1928 model still looked a little top heavy but a new grille shape and a winged wheel embellishment for the bow tie overseeing the front end were nice touches and, like other American automobiles, the Chevrolet's lines were beginning to soften into the more pleasing shapes that were waiting for the 1930's to arrive.

Chevrolet also spoke of the "thrilling new acceleration" of its 171 cid engine which with a higher, 4.5:1 compression ratio was capable of producing 35 horsepower. With a weight of 2,435 pounds the Chevrolet was in reality a modest performer but with new, four-wheel mechanical brakes it was for 1928 a well balanced family car, that Chevrolet appropriately proclaimed, "The first choice the nation for 1928."

With its additional four inches of wheelbase positioned in the hood section, the 1928 National Series Chevrolet was obviously paving the way for 1928 and that little four-cylinder engine seemed out of place under its spacious hood. But let's give credit where it's due. The 1928 model was indeed "the bigger and better Chevrolet"; an automobile that maintained Chevrolet's reputation as an outstanding value. Neither extreme nor flashy, it none-the-less was an automobile like millions of Chevrolets that followed. Reliable beyond reproach and constructed with integrity it was very much "the world's most luxurious low-priced automobile."

1928 "National" 2dr "BA" Coach

1928 Imperial Landau

1928 Coupe

Mastering the Marketplace

'31 Chevy Was Smart Car For Smart Buyers

By John Gunnell

For 1931, Chevrolet offered a line of larger cars with all-new body styling and many technical refinements at prices $15-40 lower than the year before. These Chevys were more modern and richer looking than ever, but provided better value at the same time. This was part of a concentrated effort to keep cars rolling from the factory while the depression deepened — no doubt a reason why General Motors was able to weather the declining economy without going into the red.

Advertising for '31 placed great emphasis on the technical advantages of Fisher body construction. In addition, the handsome styling and fine appointments used in fashioning Chevrolets was highlighted, too.

In one advertisement Chevrolet stressed important price reductions on Fisher body parts. "Now there is no longer any dollar-and-cents reason why any body repair shop should not use genuine Fisher body parts for Chevrolet service work," claimed one ad layout showing an "X-ray" of the Chevy sedan and offering, free of charge, a copy of the *Chevrolet Master Parts* list.

"Fisher styling and craftsmanship bring new smartness and distinction to the Chevrolet Six!" announced another ad. It described how GM artists and designers had added more smartness, grace and luxury to the '31 models.

In addition to smart new lines and attractive new colors, Chevys featured roomier, more comfortable interiors; mohair or broadcloth upholstery; a deeper windshield; wider windows; wider, deeply cushioned seats and sturdier hardwood and steel construction.

Mechanical improvements for this Independence Series AE lineup included changes to the frame, clutch, transmission, steering and front axle. The six-cylinder powerplant had a more efficient harmonic balancer, more rigid camshaft, redesigned flywheel and strengthening ribs cast into the block.

The 2-pass. five-window Independence coupe had a list price of $545 and weighted 2,490 lbs. Beginning serial numbers for this body style were 8AE1000 and up. The prefix "8" identified the five-window coupe and was not used on other models, which had their own prefix followed by the same unit production code range. On closed cars, this number was located on the right body sill, under the floor mat.

Each Chevrolet motor also carried an identification number, which was found on the right side of the motor block in back of the distributor. The prefix on this number denoted the assembly plant according to the following legend: "1" — Flint, Mich.; "2" — Tarrytown, N.Y.; "3" — St. Louis, Mo.; "5" — Kansas City, Mo.; "6" — Oakland, Calif.; "8" — Atlanta, Ga.; "9" — Norwood, Ohio; "12" — Buffalo, N.Y. and "21" — Janesville, Wis.

Passengers inside the five-window coupe sat on a single, 39 in. wide bench seat, which had a 3½" maximum adjustment for driver comfort. Styling was typical of the

1931 Coupe

general theme of this era, but the radiator shell was particularly handsome being tall and slim with the Chevy "bow-tie" at top center. An extra-cost radiator screen added greatly to appearances. Chrome-rimmed headlamps were affixed to a gracefully curved tie bar. The "Neva-Lost" Chevrolet radiator cap, cast by Welker-Hoops Mfg. Co., perched atop the shell. The hood had 22 louvers punched into a panel on eithr side. A Fisher V.V. (Vision & Ventilation) type windshield was used. Front diagonal body pillars measured 2¾" thick. The top of the roof was of slat type construction with an overall height of 69". From the interior side of the firewall to the rear of the body the car was 41-9/16" long.

Chevrolet standard equipment included Ternstedt interior hardware; AC speedometer and gasoline gauge; Trico vacuum wipers and Guide stop and taillamps. Extra-cost items included a clock; cigar lighter; shatterproof glass; heater; front and rear bumpers; backing light and power tire pump.

Under the hood was the improved Chevrolet six-cylinder motor with an inline cylinder layout and overhead valve train. Bore and stroke was 3-5/16 x 3- compression of 116 lbs.-ft. at 1,800 r.p.m. The overall gear ratio was 4.1:1.

An AC fuel pump, driven off the camshaft, pulled gas from an 11-gal. tank to the Carter Model RJH08 one-inch venturi carb. There was a 2-in. O.D. exhaust system and a 3-gal. Harrison radiator to handle cooling chores.

Chevrolet's improved transmission was a 3-speed manual type geared 3.32:1 in low; 1.77:1 in second and 4.10:1 in high (4.20:1 reverse). It drove through a clutch with molded type facing and 6¼" in I.D.; 9" O.D. the driveshaft used a Spicer universal at front and was enclosed in a torque tube at the rear.

Wheelbase for all '31 Chevys measured 109" with treads of 56¾" front, 57-9/16" rear. The all new frame was manufactured by A.O. Smith Co., of composite material, and had a 5" depth, 9/64" thickness and 2¼" flange width. The front axle, fashioned of chrome vanadium, was of I-beam design and mounted to semi-elliptic springs. At the rear were 54" long Eaton semi-elliptic leafs. Allemite chassis lubrication was used. Steering was of Chevrolet's own worm-and-sector design with 2.6 turns lock-to-lock and a 21¼ ft. turning diameter. Four-wheel mechanical brakes, Lovejoy hydraulic shock absorbers and 4.75 x 19" six-ply tires were mounted on Kelsey-Hayes wire spoke wheels.

The five-window, 2-passenger coupe was a new model for 1931 and proved to be the seventh most popular of twelve Chevrolet body styles. It accounted for a total of 28,379 assemblies between November 1930 and December 1931.

Twenty-three color choice were available for '31 Chevrolets.

1931 2dr Sedan

1931 Chevrolet with Goodyear Air Wheels

1932 RS Coupe

The Great American Value for 1932

By Peter J. Winnewisser

1932 Touring

For this country as a whole, and the automobile industry in particular, 1932 was the cruelest year of the depression.

The cold statistics reflect five to six billion dollars in business losses, daily bank closings, about 25% of the work force jobless (12-17 million), national income cut in half to about $300 per capita, and a family of four with a yearly income only 50% of what it earned in 1929.

The human realities were an army of drifters and homeless people, breadlines, panhandlers and Hoovervilles. In addition, millions tasted the bitter inadequacy of fruitless job hunting and the inability to make ends meet.

The automobile industry led the downward spiral. 1932 production of new cars and trucks in the U.S. totaled 1,431,000, the poorest since 1918 and a 75% decline from 1929. This translated into a deficit of $122,000,000 and one customer for every four at the end of the twenties.

Yet, for Chevrolet, 1932 was a paradox. On the one hand, a near 50% cut in output to 323,100 units meant that Chevy shared in the dramatic production drop off. On the other hand, Chevrolet was the only car division within General Motors to show a profit that year.

1932 was also, for many enthusiasts, the year in which Chevrolet came out with its finest styled auto of the classic tradition. A car which, in the opinion of noted auto historian Menno Duerksen, "was and is the most beautiful Chevrolet ever produced."

Faced with the deepening depression and the awesome prospect of a low-priced Ford V-8 for the 1932 model year, Chevrolet, under Knudsen, opted to forego radical changes and instead concentrate on engine and styling improvements, economy, and a liberal owner's service policy. As a result, numerous styling changes and 117 improvements were incorporated in the new Chevrolet Six Confederate Series.

As an added appeal, Chevrolet backed up its cars with a service policy that promised free inspection and adjustment at 500 miles, regular free inspection every 1000 miles, and replacement with no charge for parts or labor specified items.

Scrambling to sell cars, the company initiated a sale's campaign in newspapers, magazines and on the radio. These ads, such as the one in the April 9, 1932 issue of *The Literary Digest,* stressed that the Chevrolet Six, "The Great American Value," set the pace for motoring economy. With the triple appeal of low cost, economy of operation and upkeep, and classic styling, Chevrolet sought to attract both the traditional low-priced market and those who would normally purchase expensive cars, but now were unable or unwilling to buy at that level.

As an additional sales gimmick, unique style packets were mailed from Detroit to prospects across the country. Each packet contained fourteen 7½x4" colored cutouts of the 1932 models plus explanatory information and an announcement of the new price scale effective April 1st. Here again, the appeal was to styling (the cut-outs) plus economy and low-priced value. ". . . the big 60 horsepower engine answers every motoring need, and at less cost than any other car. More than six cylinders would mean a sacrifice of Chevrolet's famous economy. Less than six cylinders would sacrifice Chevrolet's smoothness and inherent balance."

The style packet left no stone unturned. It even contained a small six-page appeal to civic pride and responsibility. Titled, "71 Days of Work," this short pamphlet stressed that by buying a new Chevrolet the purchaser supplied a total of 71 days of employment and, therefore, "is placed among those sensible, sober people who are actually contributing to the restoration of normal conditions."

All 1932 Chevrolets were produced in the Confederate Series BA, a total of 12 models and 20 different combinations plus a sedan delivery. The models were: Standard Five-Window Coupe, Sport Coupe, Standard Coupe, Five Passenger Coupe, Phaeton, Convertible Landau Phaeton, Convertible Cabriolet, Sport Roadster, Roadster, Coach, Special Sedan and Standard Sedan.

Effective April 1932, price tags on all models were cut in order to make them competitive with the long-awaited Ford V-8.

Prices ranged from a low $445 for the roadster ($15 less than the Ford) to $625 for the Landau Phaeton. This price cut took the economy argument away from Ford. It was, says E.D. Kennedy in *The Automobile Industry,* "a historic reduction . . . the first time since the early days of the automobile industry that a major producer with a volume comparable to Ford's had marked a car down to the Ford price."

One of the chief reasons for the popularity of the Confederate Series lay under the hood, in the 194 cubic inch six cylinder valve-in-head engine. This featured a 20% horsepower boost to 60 to 3000 r.p.m. due to many improvements including a down draft carburetor, new intake manifold, counter-balanced crankshaft, rubber insulated mountings, and changes in the valve timing. Top speed was advertised as "65 to 70 miles per hour without effort," and acceleration "from a dead stop to 35 miles per hour in less than seven seconds."

Other new engineering developments included pressure lubrication, stabilized front end, and syncro-mesh transmission which brought easier shifting at all speeds.

Another widely advertised 1932 item was a simplified vesion of "Free Wheeling." (Simplified because it has only three moving parts instead of the customary twenty or more.) This is activated by pushing in a half dollar size button on the dash thereby permitting the car to coast freely and quietly with the engine turning at idling speed, although the transmission is in gear and the clutch engaged.

Also found in other cars of the era, "Free Wheeling" was acclaimed because it decreased engine wear and saved fuel. Unfortunately, it also created an additional driving hazard because it placed extra strain on the four wheel mechanical brakes, since the full braking power of the engine was not available. It was an innovation that vanished from Chevrolet and other models rather quickly.

Improvements in the engine and new engineering developments are only part of the 1932 Chevrolet story. The Confederate Series BA is also recognized as a superb example of "classic" car design patterned on the Cadillac of the era and sometimes dubbed the "Baby Cadillac."

Beauty highlights of these models included 18 inch wire wheels, four vertical ventilating doors or hood parts instead of the old style louvers (chrome plated on deluxe models or special order standards), and a restyled front appearance. The entirely new front-end ensemble featured an elliptical radiator, built-in grille, arched double tie-bar, trumpet-type horn and bullet-type headlamps — all plated with gleaming chromium. In addition, the external visor was eliminated, the windshield raised for greater visibility and the area above it gracefully covered.

For the convenience of both driver and passengers, a number of innovations were also available on some or all models. These included an internal sunvisor, cowl ventilator, a driver's seat that could be adjusted while sitting on it (in closed cars), one or two ash trays, roll down back window, non-glare windshield, rear window curtain, arm rests, vanity case, robe rail and a front window that raised straight up about 1½ inches.

Basic body colors for the model year remained the same. There were changes in the stripping and/or wire wheels and new colors added. In the style packet Chevrolet announced that it was the first to bring the new Opalascent Duco Colors to the low-priced market. This satiny finish was available on several body styles at a slight additional cost.

According to *Generator and Distributor,* the publication of the Vintage Chevrolet Club of America, there were three Opalascent Duco colors: Bronze Glow Pearl Essence, Moon Glow Pearl Essence, and Sky Glow Pearl Essence. These were used on the hood, cowl and lower body. The upper body and fenders were finished with regular Duco.

The 1974 issue of *The Chevrolet Story* states that the 1932 Coupe models are considered by many to be among the most outstanding Chevrolets ever made. These coupes were made in seven standard and deluxe models and totaled about 25% of the production for the year.

In the compeition between Ford and Chevrolet, the 1930's were a different story than the teens and 20's. Chevrolet out-produced Ford eight out of ten years during that decade, failing only in 1930 to the Model "A" and, briefly, in 1935 to the "V-8." The 1932 Chevrolet certainly played an important role in that 80% success ratio.

Although not an official "classic" as that word is interpreted in automotive circles, the 1932 Chevrolet is valued because it was and is a class car, a product both of the ingenuity of Chevrolet's engineering staff and the artistry of Chevrolet and Fisher Body craftsmen.

"Knee Action" — Less Jounce to the Ounce

By A. Stanley Kramer

The 1934 Chevrolet was the first year for the new Dubonnet "knee-action" suspension.

Almost from day one in the automobile business, a smooth ride was an important selling feature. Yet in 1933, all General Motors cars — as well as most others — were still cart-spring. They had solid front axles connecting the wheels and leaf springs.

Then, in March of that year, Chevrolet's chief executive, William S. Knudsen, along with the managers of four other GM divisions, witnessed a demonstration of independent front suspension. The unconnected front wheels practically stepped over the bumps, disturbing the car less than ever before. The managers were all enthusiastic and wanted to introduce this new, easier-riding development on their '34 models.

Knudsen made it plain that even though Chevrolet was the lowest priced, it was not going to be left out. O.E. Hunt, his chief engineer, tried to dissuade him. As a practical matter, he insisted, there simply were not enough centerless grinding machines available in the entire United States to grind sufficient wire for the coil springs for Chevrolet alone.

"Bunky" took the bit in his teeth. The machine tool industry, he said, had been in a bad way for years. Well, now they were going to be darned busy for the next year at least.

"Knee-action" (the authorship of the phrase has been variously claimed) made its debut in the 1934 Chevrolet. The system, developed in France by Andre Dubonnet, was soft riding, but for many it was too soft, making the car unstable on the turns.

So, in 1935 Chevrolet took a step backward and offered again a model with a solid front axle, the "Master without knees." The option was offered through 1940.

Meanwhile, development had gone on, and in 1939 a stiffer coil and wishbone front suspension replaced the weak knees. It combined easy riding with firmer cornering, and the solid axle option was soon dropped.

The Most Popular Chevy for 1935

By Gerald Perschbacher

1935 Chevrolet Standard

Entering the market at $485, the most popular Chevrolet of 1935 was the Standard Coach, a two-door-sedan variety. More than 226,000 were produced, holding a substantial lead over the second-best-loved Chevrolet for that year, the Master DeLuxe Coach which registered almost 103,000 units.

What did the Standard Coach have going for it that placed it firmly atop the line-up of 11 different Chevrolet body styles for that year? Looks was one big point. For the conservative buyer, the car was not as streamlined as the Master DeLuxe series which was introduced in'34 but took on a streamlined flare in '35. Two-door versions leaned toward the sporty in looks, and length and openness were accentuated by long side windows. The coach struck a nerve with its looks, and sales proved it.

Its price didn't hurt either, since it was the cheapest closed sedan in the Chevrolet playpen that year. At $550, the Standard Sedan four-door was $65 higher; and at $580, the Master DeLuxe Coach reached past the Standard Coach by $95 more. Those were in the days when a dollar carried a considerable amount of buying power and when houses could be purchased at around $2,000.

The Standard Coach weighed 2,625 pounds and was tailored in mohair upholstery. Colors tended to be on the dark side. While the Master DeLuxe series boasted a 113-inch wheelbase, the Standard Series retained the older 107-inch wheelbase. There were no side mounts available in '35 for Chevrolet, so buyers had to be content with other options to dress up their new car.

Engine-wise, the Cast Iron Wonder six put out 74 hp.

With its new turret-top, a GM innovation for 1935, the Master DeLuxe Series Chevrolet cured the problem of leaky roofs which still plagued the Standard Coach. But in spite of its weak points, the Coach carried the Chevrolet crown in sales for '35.

'42 Convertible

By Tim Howley

In the summer of '42, when the closest to Laramie I'd ever been was Lake Minnetonka, 12 miles west of Minneapolis, I had my first encounter with a convertible. It was a nearly new 1942 Chevrolet, painted a rich maroon and elegantly upholstered to match. The seat tops were a deep red leather. The door panels were a soft red leatherette. The car was not a blackout model, but was chromed. So it must have been built before Jan. 1, 1942. As a small child then, I had no idea how rare the car was or how collectible it would become. I only knew it was a red convertible, my "someday" car.

The owner was a young lady who later married my cousin, Tommy. She took me on many long rides along the near deserted boulevards and parkways around the Minneapolis lakes. Remember, those were the darkest days of World War II. Not only was gas rationed, but it just wasn't patriotic to go Sunday driving, especially in a convertible. Long before the war was over Janet sold the car, and I have absolutely no idea what happened to it. I know now that Chevrolet produced only 1,782 convertibles for the short model year which ended abruptly on Feb. 9. Allegedly only one exists today, and the odds are 1,781 to one it isn't Janet's.

Actually, all pre WWII Chevrolet convertibles are quite

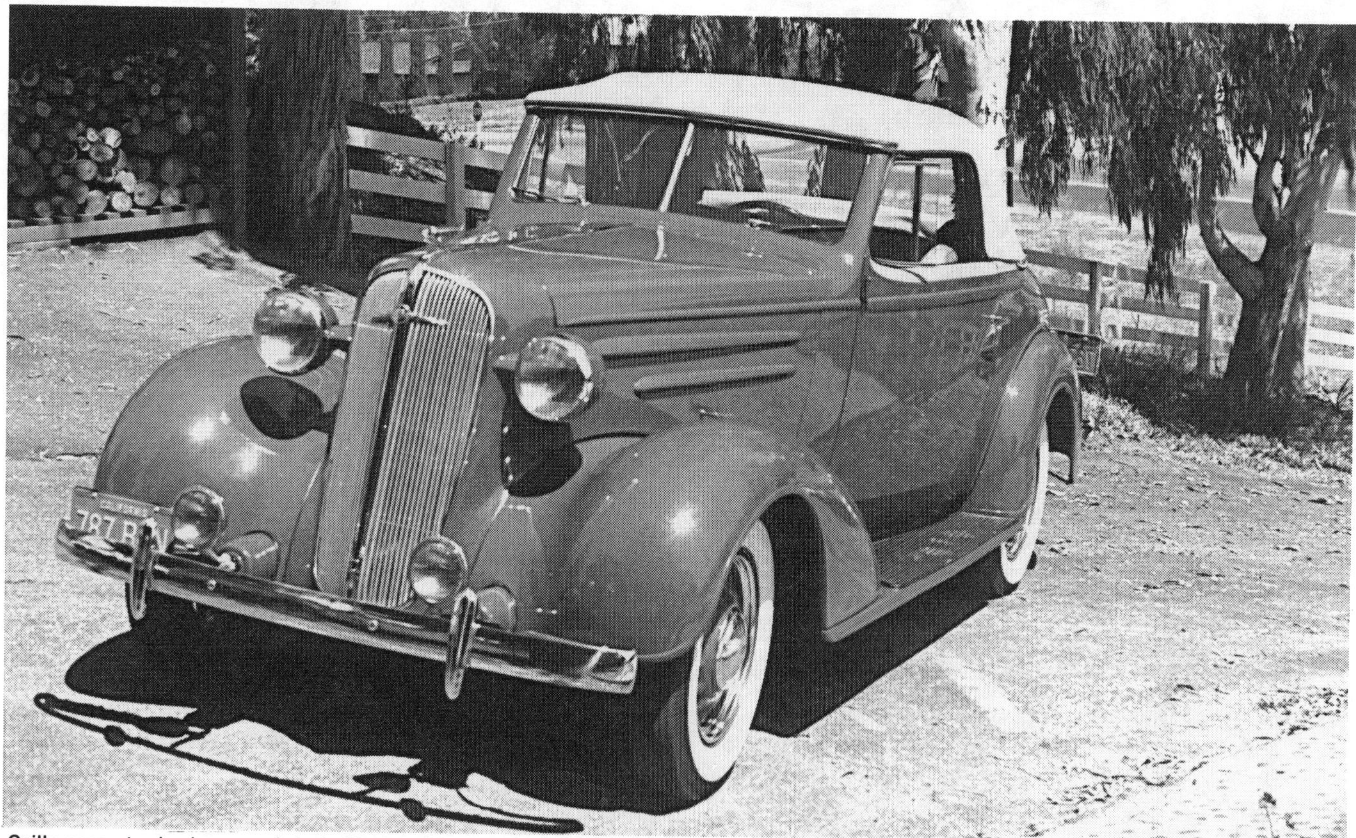

Grille was steel, chrome plated. Chromed center strip and stainless steel outer trim.

rare, especially compared to Fords. This was a time when Ford nearly owned the low priced open car market. Ford had the speedy V-8 and the sleek open car look which captured the imagination of open car lovers. Chevrolet's success was built primarily on "sedanny" types of cars which appealed to just about everybody by offending almost nobody. Chevrolet gave only token attention to the open cars, especially after 1934. It is this era we are dealing with, specifically 1935-1942.

During this period, and even before, Ford and Chevrolet together produced half the cars sold in this country. From 1928 thru 1942 Chevrolet held the number one position for nine model years and Ford held it for six. For all its beauty, the 1932 Chevrolet lost out to Ford, which introduced the V-8 that year. For 1933, Chevrolet came out with completely redesigned models and returned to the number one position. But even the introduction of Knee-Action independent suspension plus a newly redesigned engine couldn't keep Ford from overtaking Chevy for 1934. Ford remained number one is 1935, aided by the introduction of their new Ford model 48 and a devastating Chevrolet strike at Flint.

Chevrolet moved back up to number one for 1936. Ford nearly beat Chevy in 1937, but not quite. From 1938 thru 1941 Chevrolet continued to increase its margin of victory over Ford with each succeeding model year. Chevrolet had hydraulic brakes in 1936, Ford not until 1939. Chevrolet continued to offer Knee-Action on its high end models, and in 1941 made it standard on all models. Chevrolet rear springing was semi elliptic. Ford stayed with its horse and buggy front and rear springing thru 1948. Chevrolet had a vacuum column gearshift in 1939. Ford not until 1940.

Ford had the superior performing V-8, but Chevrolet had the features which most buyers wanted in the sober, somber late Thirties and early Forties. Ford would not unseat Chevrolet for the number one position again until the 1957 and 1959 model years.

The 1935 Chevrolet was offered in two models. The 1934 model on its 107" wheelbase was continued over as the 1935 Standard Series, and was offered only with a solid front axle. An entirely new 1935 Master DeLuxe Series was offered on a 113" wheelbase. There had been some resistance to Knee-Action, so in addition to this EA Series there was an ED Sub-Series with the I-beam axle. The 1935 Master DeLuxe's biggest feature that year was the new one-piece "Turret Top" made possible through the development of larger presses and dies. So much did Chevrolet stress closed car comfort and safety at this time that they dropped the cabriolet altogether, and offered the phaeton and the roadster in the Standard Series only.

For 1936, the Standard went to a 109" wheelbase and carried a redesigned body which resembled the Master's. Though few body parts were interchangeable. The Master DeLuxe came in the FA Series with Knee-Action and the FB Sub-Series with I-beam. All Standards still had I-beams. The cabriolet returned, but only in the Standard Series, Chevrolet still built roadsters and phaetons in South American and Holden produced Chevrolet phaeton bodies in Australia. But the Division continues to downplay open cars in this country. Ford, that year, offered six different open models.

Only 3,629 cabriolets were produced for the 1936 model year. All were rumble seat models. Since they were only Standards, they had only one taillight, one sun visor, one windshield wiper, and painted headlight housing instead of chrome, Yet, the top bows were chromed and high grade leatherette was used on the front seat and rumble seat.

Our feature car once belonged to MGM, and had only 29,000 miles at the time they disposed of it. The first buyer resold it to Dave Peterson of Escondido, Ca., who spent three years restoring it. Peterson sold the car to Dave Gilbert, San Diego, a Thirties Chevrolet Authority.

In the restoration, Peterson added a few authentic extras such as a radio, glove box lid with clock and ash tray, and whitewall tires. He says the car does not have quite as strong a body as the 1936 Ford cabriolet or roadster. Ford was then using nearly all steel in it's bodies, but Chevrolet was still using a lot of wood. The Chevrolet also lacks the Ford's punch, but, in its own way nearly makes up the difference in the smoothness and quietness of its mechanical operation and overall smoother ride, says Peterson.

For 1937, Chevrolets were again all new, and now both series were offered on the same 112 1/4" wheelbase. Gone were the confusing sub series designations. The Standard Series, now called the Master Series, had an I-beam front axle. The higher priced Master DeLuxe Series came only with Knee-Action. Chevrolet continued to de-emphasize open models offering them only in the Master DeLuxe trim. Only cabriolets were produced, and only 1,724 were built. However, the roadster and phaeton, the latter now called the tourer, were continued in Australia.

Our second feature car, while not another cabriolet, is, indeed, a rare model. It is a "trunkless" four door sedan with rear mounted spare tire. Actually, there was a small trunk via pulling up the rear sent back. After 1935, the four door sedan and its companion, the coach, fast gave way in popularity to the sports sedan and town sedan

1937 Chevrolet convertible

which had outside trunks. The four door sedan and coach, together, found only about 12,000 buyers in 1937, less than half that numer in 1938, and were dropped early in 1939 after only 1,652 were built. The 1939 Master DeLuxe became one of Chevrolet's all time low production models with only 68 built. Out feature car is a 1937 Master four door sedan, of which 2,755 were built. It is owned by Frank Conklin of San Diego.

1938 Chevrolets got a new horizontal grille, plus many mechanical improvements which are often overlooked. 1937-1938 differences would actually be subject for an article in themselves, so we won't dwell on them here. The only open Chevrolet for 1938 continued to be the cabriolet, of which 2,787 were produced. All were in the Master Series with Master DeLuxe trim, Enough other Master DeLuxe features and accessories could be added so that the car could easily be made into a Master DeLuxe in all but name and the most important feature of all, Knee-Action. Roadsters and tourers were still produced in Australia that year.

1939 was a major facelift, so much so that few if any body panels are interchangeable with earlier years. 1939 was a sad year for open Chevrolets. Not a single one was produced in this country. Roadsters, but not tourers, were produced in Australia, but this was their last year to be offered there. However, Chevrolet did begin offering wooden bodied stations in both series for 1939. These had also been offered in extremely limited numbers in 1937, but on a commercial chassis. One additional 1939 model was the Master 85, a new "mid-series" Chevrolet.

1940 saw all new styling on a new 113" chassis. For the first time Chevrolet had a front opening hood. The open Chevrolet returned now with a special X-member frame and vacuum operated power top. The rumble seat was eliminated and a rear seat was added. At long last the open Chevrolet moved up to the top-of-the line Special DeLuxe Series with Knee-Action and all the other goodies. It was the correct move for 11,820 Chevrolet convertibles for 1940 were produced.

The 1941 Chevrolet was restyled again. The chassis grew three inches longer and front seat passengers gained three inches more width. Doors now flared over the runningboards.

All body panels had smoother, rounder contours than the 1940 model. 1941 Chevrolets are considered by many to be the best looking Chevrolets of the 1935-1942 era. They are respectable performers too, with horsepower from 85 to 90. The Master 85 Series was dropped. Now there was just the DeLuxe and Special DeLuxe, and Knee-Action was standard on both models.

1941 Chevrolet convertible production rose to 15,296. The model retained its vacuum operated power top. 1941 Ford convertible buyers now had the luxury of an electrically operated power top. 1941 Chevrolet buyers, however, could opt for a shortwave radio. 1941 Ford buyers could choose between a V-8 or a six. Both makes had a lot to offer the public that year. Ford production was slightly over 600,000. Chevrolet production nearly one million. Of four million cars built in the U.S. in that last year of peace, nearly one quarter of them were Chevrolets.

The 1942 Chevrolet is a facelifted '41. The hood was lengthened to the door edge and the front fenders were carried back into the front doors. For 1942 Chevrolet produced a Fleetline Aerosedan fastback, another rare car now. By the summer of 1942 any remaining cars had been spirited away to Federal warehouses, and it literally took an Act of Congress to get one. Chevrolet convertibles would return with the 1946 model, and during the Fifties the open Chevrolet would grow tremendously in popularity. Eventually, I did get my "someday" red covertible. It was a bright red 1952 Chevrolet Bel Air, and was followed by a brand new 1955 Bel Air hardtop. I did not come back to Fords untl 1959, and have always had a special fondness for the open Chevrolets.

All 1936-1938 Chevrolet cabriolets had rumble seats.

1939: Chevy's Missing Convertible

By Tom LaMarre

Forget the glamorous ads. Convertibles were always launched with apprehension and generated sales charts that were as unpredictable as a Dizzy Dean curveball. No manufacturer had a more ambivalent attitude toward the ragtop than Chevrolet.

Although Chevy had offered a convertible as early as 1928, sedans were the Division's bread-and-butter models. Production of the phaeton and Master sports roadster ended in 1935 and cabriolet production was also suspended, probably because of the Depression and the emphasis on the new Fisher Turret Top bodies. For the first time, larger presses and dies could produce an entire sedan top in one stamping. The new, improved sedans were perfectly suited to Chevy's emphasis on business and family transportation.

When the cabriolet did return in 1936 it had joined the cheaper Standard series. Then came two years in the economical Master series, a sure sign that the ragtop had fallen from favor. Chevrolet general manager Marvin E. Coyle and sales manager W.E. Holler specialized in selling deluxe-grade Chevys; the cabriolet was not an important part of their plans.

Chevy built 2,787 cabriolets in 1938, and the spartan list of standard equipment included only a few dress-up items, such as bumper guards, runningboard moldings, decorative door-sill plates, and medallions on the window moldings. The rumble seat was upholstered in pyroxylin-coated moleskin fabric.

In 1939, when *Fortune* magazine called Chevrolet "the greatest common denominator of what the American public thinks a good car should be," the ragtop was again missing from the line. That is, it was absent from the U.S. line. Some convertible sedans were made, but not for domestic sale.

Old Cars Weekly reader R.G. Fellenstein writes: "While stationed in Tokyo, Japan in 1946, I passed one on the Ginza. I immediately turned around and tried to run it down, but lost it in traffic. Curious about this oddity, I wrote my father about this convertible that 'didn't exist.' He was with Chevrolet Division at that time.

"He then contacted someone in Detroit and found out that 50 or 60 convertible sedans were produced for export to Mexico. How one found its way to Japan is anyone's guess."

The export-only convertible sedans weren't the only Chevy ragtops built in 1939. The roadster, long discontinued in the United States, was still being built in Australia as part of the Standard series. However, lack of buyers killed it before the end of the model year.

On the domestic front, Chevrolet built its 15-millionth vehicle in 1939. Chevy's most popular car was the town (two-door) sedan, and a new station wagon, with body built by Mid-States Body Corp., made its debut. As if to compensate for the deletion of the convertible, Chevy

1939 Chevrolet

boasted that larger windshields and narrow corner posts gave its 1939 models "observaton car" visibility.

Why did Chevrolet drop the convertible? One reason was the desire of almost all car buyers for an integral trunk. The rumble seat was a thing of the past, and even Ford would discontinue that body style after 1939. Meanwhile, Chevrolet eliminated the last of its trunkless models in mid-model year.

Another explanation for the disappearance of the convertible was that Chevy was anticipating that introduction of its first power top, a feature already offered by Plymouth. A vacuum operated top was one of many advances that distinguished the revived 1940 cabriolet from its predecessors.

The 1940 Chevy catalog said of the cabriolet: "This newly added body model differs from former cabriolets in that all passengers ride within a single compartment, under cover when the top is up. In place of the rumble seat is a large space for luggage. The cabriolet is virtually a two-door phaeton, accommodating four to six passengers."

Available only in the top-of-the-line Special DeLuxe series, the cabriolet had steel body sills instead of wood, a choice of top colors (all 1930-'38 tops had been tan), and a full, albeit somewhat narrow, rear seat.

The improvements, and Chevy's "Royal Clipper" styling, brought the cabriolet into the modern era and gave it new prestige. Priced at $898, it was second in cost only to the station wagon, yet production jumped to 11,820.

Convertibles would continue to grow in popularity during the 1940s, though at the 40th National Automobile Show in October 1940, the most popular body style was still the four-door, six-passenger sedan, followed by the two-door sedan.

Not until 1976 would the convertible again disappear from the Chevrolet line.

Would I Ever Own Another Chevy?

By Ed Robinson

I should like to depart from my usual litany of complaints and talk about Chevys which I have enjoyed. (This is not to suggest that there haven't been a few that I was sorry I bought, glad I sold, etc.) In describing Chevys which I have enjoyed while I owned them is not so much a matter of whether to but which one.

I could start chronologically and recall fond memories of a 1927 coupe which I used to haul my fifteen year old girl friend to the movies when we were both young enough to get in for a dime. I could describe oiling the felt pads which covered the valve train rocker arms or trying to stop with two wheel brakes. I could describe climbing in the window after cranking the engine. I climbed into the window because the wooden door posts had rotted as they always did on Fisher bodies and the driver side door fell off if you opened it. To use that one and describe associated pleasures and enjoyment would involve more talking about girls than cars and this publication is Old Cars Weekly not young girls daily (or whenever the chance presented itself.)

I could describe the 1924 Chevy four ninety touring car that I once traded for two sports coats and ten dollars. I knew the sports coats wouldn't quite fit but I also knew that the Chevy's new owner was going to have a hard time finding any more used rear axles in any of the surrounding junk yards.

Then there was the 1937 coupe that we hack sawed and cold chiseled into a pick up truck in order to haul fire wood — but you don't admit to such wanton waste when you are writing for collectors and enthusiasts. Thirty seven was not a particularly good year for me; my father's Sunday car which I wrecked after the senior prom when I graduated from high school was also a 1937 Chevy.

I could write a several page dissertation about which is uglier, a 1937 Ford or a 1940 Chevy. Such an ugly car contest would probably be declared a draw. I only feel that the chief designers for those two models should have been fired immediately. I managed to sell the 1937 Ford, but the 1940 Chevy was the only car that I ever flat out gave away just to get it out of my sight.

I could write several books about the 1957 Continental Kit Mounted Chevy Convertible which I bought for my wife. Should I attempt to write such books I am sure that I could say nothing new. In my opinion, the 1955-56-57 Chevys have been discussed in print Ad Nauseum. The same thing would be true of almost anything I could relate concerning the 1956 Corvette which I once owned. OCW readers have already read everything good that could possibly be written about a Vette of any vintage.

I had one Chevy which stands out in my memory as a truly unique experience. it was different on two counts. First, in my entire car watching career I've only seen one other model like it; second, the thing was damned near indestructible. I'm referring to a 1936 straight axle, floor shift, rumble seat, roll up windows Chevrolet Convertible Coupe.

I bought the bright red, black-topped Convert from Roy Campbells Pontiac Garage in Richmond, Indiana in 1939. (Pontiac Garage was what you called the factory authorized dealership in those days.) I paid two hundred and eighty five dollars for it. This was my first car at over fifty dollars and my first introduction to installment payments. I was seventeen years old, making twelve dollars a week pushing sodas in a drug store. From the moment I saw the Chevy sitting in the show room, I ignored the new Pontiacs on display. From that moment until I could scrounge up the down payment, I did not enjoy food, I had trouble sleeping, I even fantasized about wheels instead of girls. My love affair lasted slightly over two years. In a moment of weakness I traded it, in 1941 for a 1935 Lafayette Coupe. They both were exceedingly rare in our part of the country. During my entire two year stint I never saw or

1936 Convertible Coupe

met anyone else who had seen another '36 Chevy Convertible. It's been almost forty years since I owned one and last year, for the first time, I saw another. It was at Hershey and it was not in the Flea Market area. I know that I could probably query OCW and find out how many were made that year. I think I prefer to keep my illusion that I had one of the only two ever created. Thank God the one at Hershey was not painted bright red.

Shortly after I got home with my new dream machine I discovered that the block was cracked. The crack was external, about seven inches long, in the water jacket, on the right side. The same day, I discovered the crack I learned the meaning of the phrase "as is" on a purchase contract. Mr. Campbell has been dead now for several years. I never forgot, I never forgave — several times before he finally went out of business, we made other trades. I got even. Richmond, at that time had several miracle workers in residence. One of them was Sam the Welder. That was his name, never Sam, never The Welder, but always the full title, Sam the Welder. In the intervening years I've learned a good bit about both gas and arc welding but I still don't know how Sam the Welder managed to weld that crack with the engine still in the chassis. I remember he kept the car four days and he charged me eighteen dollars.

Absolute top speed on the Chevy was seventy three miles per hour. That was also the constant cruising speed, on straight roads, on crooked roads, out in the country, around town, in the daylight, and after dark. You started the motor, shifted into low, floored the gas pedal and took off. Double clutching or other refinements were ignored. You let her roar a while in low and then you jammed her into second still holding the accelerator firmly depressed as far as possible. When it stopped going faster in second you yanked it back into high and simply stood on the gas.

The old long stroke six never complained. The gear box stayed together. The clutch didn't wear out. I never had to change a "U" joint.

Of course, this heavy-handed, lead-footed driving style occasionally ended up in confrontations and conflicts. The 36 and I made unplanned contacts with several objects both stationary and moving. Once we ricocheted off a street car, against a brick building, and finally kissed a parked Hupmobile. We both were slightly bruised and considerably battered but we continued on our customary seventy three miles per hour way. Once I inadvertently tried to breed the Chevy to a 35 Buick Roadmaster.

It wasn't that I was reckless. (I also was not Wreckless.) It was just that I had more enthusiasm than my 550 x 17 tires had coefficient of friction. The Chevy would sit right up straight and slide either sideways or forward. The only problem was that on occasion she would slide just a little farther than we had planned. Once, one of our regularly practiced broad side drifts around a well known gravel curve ended in contact between my left rear fender and left front fender of an innocent oncomer. My mother had difficulty understanding how I could have been at fault when it was the rear of my car and the front of the other car which were damaged. My father unfortunately understood about four wheel drifts on two lane gravel roads. He even knew about spin outs.

In the brief two year period during which the Chevy and I roared together, we knocked the front axle out once on a stone pillar, the rear end and springs were knocked loose on a hidden stump. We gently lay over on one side in a dirt ditch. We chewed up several front bumpers and grilles. I finally removed the running boards permanently. In those days, fenders, both front and rear, bolted on. I gave up on straightening mine and simply gathered up a supply of spares from the wrecking yards. I even painted them red in advance.

I don't know what prompted me to trade off the old Convert. I am reasonably certain that had I not done so I would not be here to write this article. I'm convinced that in 1936 General Motors made a Chevy convertible that was tougher than I. I was indestructible.

Yes, I have owned a Chevy or two in my day. I have even given a few to my children. My oldest daughter still hasn't decided whether she is more sentimental about her 1963 Corvair Convert, or her 1959 "348" Impala. I have no such problem. My sentimental nostalgia says 1936 when you say Chevy.

New Mid-Year Baby For Chevrolet:

The 1941 Fleetline Sedan

By Gerald Perschbacher

Call it the baby of the bunch, but with more styling bounce than any of its older brothers or sisters. Chevrolet's 1941 updated styling over the previous year was nicely applied and attractively proportioned. Minor touches included headlights which were truly an integral part of the front fenders; a broader, lower grille; and a host of slight trim changes, The previous Master Eighty-Five series was no more.

For 1941, the Master DeLuxe Series covered the lower-priced models, while the Special DeLuxe Series covered the top range of Chevrolets. But mid-year, Chevrolet introduced what amounted to a new series or at least a new sub-series with its new styling on the Fleetline sedan in the Special DeLuxe Series. Of the three four-door sedans offered by Chevrolet in '41, the Fleetline baby was the least in production with only 34,162 bounding out of the factories. At $877 it also was the most expensive four-door sedan in the Chevrolet playpen that year.

There was little baby fat on this newborn. There was no ephemeral rear quarter window to lengthen the roof line and cut down on the tapered look. Without diapers it weighed 3,130 pounds and raced along on all fours, stretching low across its 116-inch wheelbase.

When this baby wanted to go, it shook the six rattles in its Victory engine or 216 cubic inches and quietly scooted along with 90 horsepower at 3300 r.p.m. This Fleetline was pinned together with welded all-steel construction. Chevrolet's famous Knee-Action was standard up front on the entire '41 line.

With the Fleetline Sedan leading the passenger car pack, Chevrolet could boost in its ads. "Again — Chevrolet's the leader. Here's the biggest car ever built by the leader. . .the biggest sizeful, the biggest eye full, and the biggest money's worth. . .in fact, the biggest package of value, anyway you care to look at it.

"It measures several inches longer than the great Chevrolet which last year earned the title 'longest of all lowest-priced cars.' It has a longer, larger, wider Fisher Body, bringing it ever more closely into the class of high-priced cars," said the ads. "Even three couples aren't a crowd in this big, roomy, wide-seated Chevrolet for 1941! All sedans are sized for six, widened out to give 'three-couple roominess."

Even for parents who wished to adopt, there was no way of totally knowing what they were getting with a newborn. But when it came to the Fleetline Sedan '41, buyers who wanted to visit any new car adoption agency could try out the luxurious advantage promoted in print: "It pays to pick the leader. . .Chevrolet. . .Better EYE IT, TRY IT, BUY IT — today!"

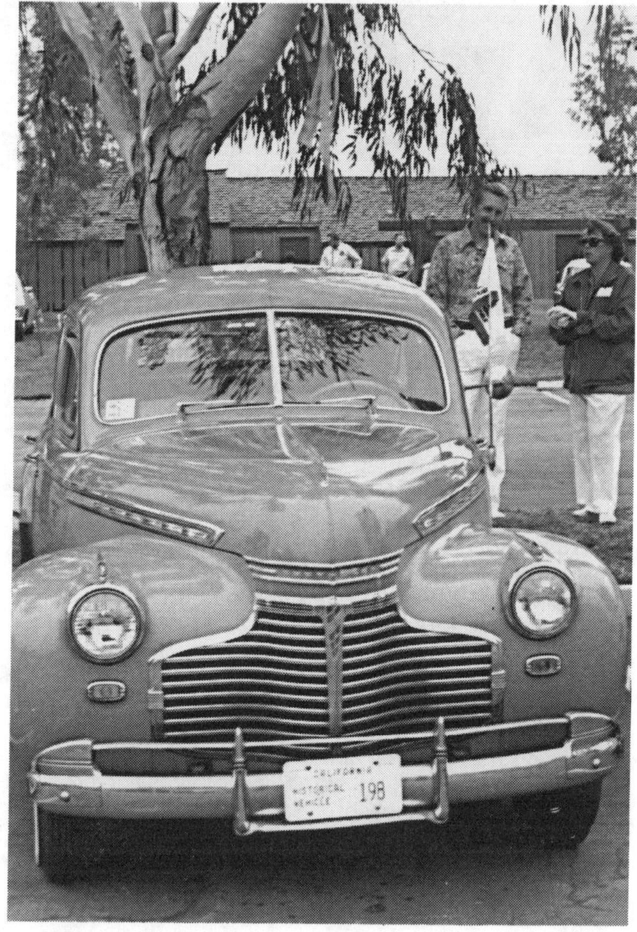

1941 Chevrolet Special DeLuxe 4-dr sedan

'41 Chevrolet Redesigned for Second Year in a Row

Bill & Mary Mason

The 1941 Chevrolet Special DeLuxe coupe was a popular model with salesman preferring a luxurious business type car. (Bill Mason photo)

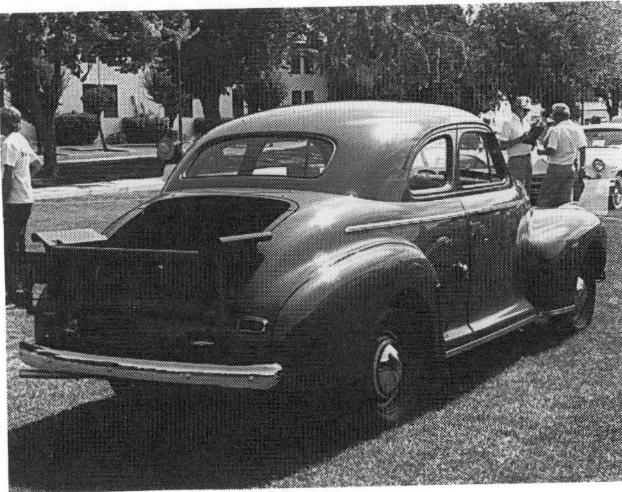
1941 Master DeLuxe Coupe Pickup

The 1941 Chevrolet line of cars was completely restyled for the second season in a row. Although the company had been the top-selling American brand in 1940 — the year the 25th million Chevy was assembled — it did not seem wise to take the number one position for granted.

New bodies were the most apparent of numerous changes for 1941. They had all-welded construction, concealed runningboards, flush mounted headlamps and parking lights and three inch wider front seats.

There were mechanical improvements for 1941, too. An increase in horsepower was brought about through the use of new pistons, smaller combustion chambers and a general reworking of valve train components. New 10mm spark plugs were used. Chevy said they warmed up quicker, but ran cooler in hot engines. They were said to perform better at high speeds.

Other 1941 Chevrolet characteristics included a three inch longer wheelbase, longer, wider, lower body and concealed hinges on all doors and the trunk lid. The slope of the windshield, rear windows and upper body sides was increased for a more streamlined look. Knee-Action suspension was made standard on all Chevrolets.

There were two different series. Both utilized the same drive train and chassis. The Master DeLuxe was the bread and butter line and included four closed models priced between $712 and $795. Special DeLuxe was the top series with six body styles selling between $769 and $995.

Our feature car is a five-passenger club coupe from the fancier, pricier line. Current owners Loretta and Charles Carroll, of Chico, Calif., purchased the car about two years ago.

According to the Carrolls, the car was originally ordered by Minnie Poessnecker of Atkinson, Neb., who used it sparingly until it was obtained by a Southern California "Classic" car dealer. He sold it to Dr. David Underwood, of West Covina. The Carrolls obtained it from him and have driven it less than 300 miles since taking possession.

The coupe has all of the distinctive new 1941 styling features including more massive fenders, a larger and deeper hood and an attractive, die-cast radiator grille.

The car's serial number — stamped in a plate located on the right side of the floor pan, ahead of the front seat — is 5AH0756003. The first number "5" indicates that it was built at the Chevrolet factory in Kansas City, Mo. The "AH" represents the Special DeLuxe series code. The remaining numbers identify its production sequence on the factory assembly line.

Options on the coupe include grille mounted fog lamps, fender skirts, wheel discs with chrome trim rings, white sidewall tires, OSRV mirror, radio, antenna, front fender stainless steel trim moldings, bumper guards and an accessory hood mascot. In case you're wondering, that's about 300 prewar dollars worth of genuine factory extras.

1941 Chevrolet Six Specifications

Model	Special DeLuxe 2-door coupe
Price	$800.00
Wheelbase	116 in.
Weight	3050 lbs.
Engine	Inline, ohv six
BxS	3½ x 3¾ in.
Disp.	216.5 cu. in.
BHP	90 @ 3300 rpm
Net HP	29.4
Carb.	Carter 1 Bbl
Top Speed	85 mph (approx.)
Fuel Mileage	18-20 mpg (approx.)
Tires	16x6.00
No. 1 Value	$5,800 (approx.)

Stylish Stovebolts

Chevy's Postwar Woodie Wagons

By John Gunnell

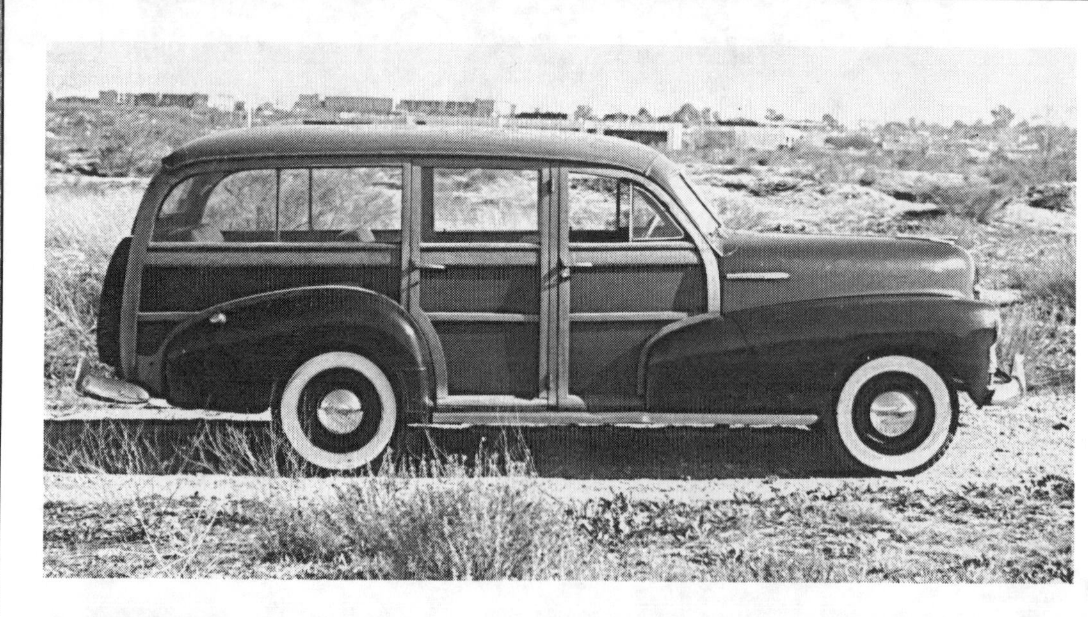

Postwar Chevrolets with wood framed or wood grain trimmed bodies are not exactly rare vehicles, since whatever Chevy built was made in relatively high numbers. On the other hand, using an individual model basis, there were fewer years of Chevrolet "woodies" (or semi-woodies) than there was for the major competition — Ford.

Chevy's most interesting postwar woodies came, undoubtedly, in the years immediately following the end of the fighting overseas. From 1946 to 1948 there were station wagons, suburban Carryalls, school buses and even Aerosedans, put together with real wood body framing or appliques. Some were products of the Chevrolet factories, while others were constructed by body building firms such as Campbell or Cantrell. All of these vehicles hold special interest to collectors today and will be the main focus of this article. We will, however, talk about some later woodie collectibles, too.

For the 1946 season, the Chevrolet station wagon was a late year addition to the line, since it took time to get assemblies rolling after the war's duration. The wagon, quite obviously, did not have top priority in production schedules. When it finally appeared, it was part of the 116 inch wheelbase Fleetmaster line in the Model DK series.

The station wagon was rated an 8-passenger model (3 seats) and was priced $1,712, which worked out to just under fifty-cents per pound. Power was supplied by the tried-and-true 3-1/2 x 3-3/4 inch bore and stroke Chevrolet six, with 216.5 cubic inches of displacement and 90 horsepower to 3,300 R.P.M. Only 804 examples were built.

Similar to station wagons in general styling were a number of privately built wood wagons or Carryalls constructed on the Model DP, 115 inch wheelbase half-ton commerical chassis or the Model DR, 124-1/2 inch wheelbase three-quarter ton chassis. Both of these chassis were available in two forms called "chassis-cowl" or "chassis-cowl-windshield". The names aptly describe what you got for your money, which was $744 and $764 respectively for the lighter model and $833 and $853 respectively for the heaviest.

We have no documentation that any of these type vehicles were built in 1946, though there have been several letters from readers indicating this was so. Hopefully some deeper research will surface eventually. It is definitely recorded (in the Crestline book *Sixty Years of Chevrolet*) that truck-based wood wagons were built in Bombay, India during 1946. Some came with masonite panels, teakwood framing and with righthand steering. Another book, *Great American Wagons & Woodies*, indicates the half ton edition had white ash framing with mahogany panels and that these wooden components were supplied by Cantrell, a Long Island, N.Y. body firm. Therefore, it would not be surprising if some of these truck/station wagons were also made for the domestic market.

1947

Except for price, there was no great change in the Chevrolet wood-bodied station wagon for 1947. It was continued with the same specifications as the previous year, but now cost $1,893. Both series and model designations were slightly revised, making the wagon part of the Chevy Model EK, or Series 2100 line. The model number was 2109. The wooden sections of the bodies came from the Ionia body Co. of Michigan, or from Cantrell, in New York. For 1947 Chevrolet had a bolder grille with horizontal bars extending into the front fenders. Production amounted to 4,912 station wagons.

There is little doubt that wood-bodied commercial vehicles were built on the 1947 Chevrolet truck chassis, too. Again, there is very little documentation for these models, though Cantrell appears to have been the big supplier in this field. One interesting rig, seen recently at New England car shows, is a restored woodbodied Chevrolet school bus constructed on the large 1½ ton chassis. The body on this particular bus — with a 1947 serial number — was made by a New England firm named Campbell. The bus has had an excellent owner restoration and is quite a sight to see.

Of even greater interest to collectors was the appearance of several 1947 fastback Aerosedans with so-called "Country Club" wood trim. These cars had white ash framing and mahogany paneling placed over the sheetmetal on the front doors and rear body quarters. This made the Chevrolet the same look as the Chrysler Town & Country or the Ford/Mercury Sportsman models. By 1948, some convertibles got this treatment, too.

There is some bit of controversy over the source of the wood trim. It was first thought to be a factory feature made by either Chevrolet or Fisher body. However, the Country Club edition does not appear in any Chevrolet literature or parts manuals. It seems that the wood trim was produced as an aftermarket kit by Engineered Enterprises

of Detroit and may have been installed on some cars by authorized Chevrolet dealers.

1948

Featuring the 1948 Chevrolet station wagon was another price increase, a slight reduction in weight and a better looking grille. General specifications stayed about the same, with the wagon now part of the Series 2100 FK Fleetmaster line. It had an overall length of 207½ inches and tipped the scales at 3,430 pounds with a $2,103 basic price tag. As in the two previous years, 6.00 x 16 size tires were used. Production climbed to 10,171 units as the postwar wagon boom began to get into gear.

Seen again this year were Cantrell built Chevy Carryalls with wood bodies and a variety of other custom made woodies, as well as Country Club kits for dealer installation on Aerosedans and convertibles. All these are now highly desirable collector cars (and trucks), although there is still considerable historical research needed in this area.

1949

The 1949 model year was marked by new postwar styling, replacing the basically prewar look carried over in 1946-48. The new model lineup included two sleekly streamlined wagons, though only one was a true woodie. It was the model 2109 version and proved to be a milestone of Chevrolet history . . . the last wood-bodied wagon ever made.

This car no longer had a fabric covered slat roof like earlier station wagons, but instead featured an all-steel top, complete with headliner. One distinction was wood framed body construction at the rear quarter area. The 3,485 pound car could seat 8-passengers on its three vinyl covered seats and sold for $2,267. A 216.5 cubic inch engine was carried over as the powerplant with no big changes. New specifications included a 115 inch wheelbase; 198 inch overall length and 15 x 6.70 tires.

The wood wagon was considered a part of the Styleline DeLuxe model range or the 2100 GK series and production began in January, 1949. The more modern look dictated inside storage of the spare tire (a new feature) and a number of other touches that made it more passenger car like. No longer did the Chevy wagon look like a relative of the company's trucks and Carryalls.

In terms of sales figures, the wood wagon was not a popular model this year. There was a marked buyer preference for the all-steel Model 2119 station wagon, which seemed a lot more durable machine. This car had all the good features of the woodie edition — including simulated wood graining — and was only $10 costlier. As a consequence, sales of the all-steel, 3,485 pound wagon hit 6,006 units.

Also seen in 1949 was the Cantrell-bodied Suburban Carryall, still being made in the body builder's Huntington, Long Island factory. This remained a custom built station wagon type vehicle constructed — in most cases — on the Chevrolet 1/2-ton truck chassis. The body was 218 inches long.; 63 inches wide and 60 inches high with a load space that measured 86 inches. This truck/wagon carried the GP Series designation and had a 116-inch wheelbase and a 216.5 cubic inch truck engine. It was

1947 Fleetline 2dr with wood kit.

undoubtedly built on the commercial range chassis-cowl-windshield offering, which Cantrell purchased for about $900 and then the wood body was added to it. The cost of the finished product is not known, but was likely in the $1,800 range. The use of the Chevy cowl and windshield meant that the front windows rolled up and down. The remainder of the body sections had sliding glass. The Cantrell Carryall Suburban was produced through the 1955 model year.

1950

For the 1950 model year Chevrolet's station wagon production jumped to 37,100 units or 24.5 percent of U.S. wagon production. It was a big increase and was reflective of the all-steel model's popularity. There was only one wagon available, as body style number 50-1062. This made the car part of the Styleline DeLuxe 2100 HK series, with a 115 inch wheelbase and 198¼ inch overall length.

As usual, the wagon came with a standard three-speed manual transmission and a 216.5 cubic inch displacement six as standard equipment. However, the engine was now rated 92 horsepower at 5,400 R.P.M., which represented a slight increase. A bigger change in the powerplant department was the optional combination of Powerglide automatic transmission with a new 235.5 cubic inch displacement six. This motor had a 6.70:1 compression ratio and developed 105 horsepower. In a surprise move, the price of the station wagon dropped by $25 (to $1,994), while the weight jumped to 3,460 pounds.

In reality, the all-steel body and lower price were just two factors that boosted wagon sales. There were some additional considerations, such as Powerglide automatic transmission becoming available and the fact that Ford's only offering for the year was a two-door station wagon with somewhat less utilitarian appeal than the four-door Chevy.

1951

There are several different sources for production totals of 1951 Chevrolet wagons. *The Production Figure Book for U.S. Cars* says that 23,586 were made, while the 1952 edition of *Ward's Automotive Yearbook* estimates Chevy's wagon output at 38,000 units and 19.7 percent of industry. In any case, there was just one all-steel edition sold. It carried body style number 51-1062, in the Styleline DeLuxe 2100 HK series and was priced $2,191 with a 3,450 pound weight. Overall length was down to 197-7/8 inches and detail changes to the grille, parking lamps, side spear trim and hood ornament were seen. Otherwise, the car was very much like the 1950 product with simulated wood trim, standard fender skirts and a two-piece tailgate.

1952

Chevrolet's station wagon line included just one model again in 1952. This was essentially the same car as the year before with a toothier grille and some small trim revi-

The Custom Country Club Coupe . . . Beautiful wood panelling adds the smart effect of long lines to the cozy intimacy of this popular close-coupled Custom Country Club Coupe.

1948 Coupe with optional wood trim.

sions. Power choices remained unchanged as well. According to *Ward's* Chevy made 25,000 wagons this season, although other sources give a figure of just 12,756 units. A footnote in the *Ward's 1954 Automotive Yearbook* seems to indicate their figures include station wagons mounted on truck chassis. This is interesting, since the suggestion would then be that some 12,000 Carryall station wagons make up the difference in totals. That's about the closest we've ever come to Carryall production figures. This might be of interest to truck buffs. (All of the Carryalls did not have wood bodies).

1953

In 1953, Chevrolet began the practice of building station wagons in more than one series. The lineup now included two 2100 B Deluxe "210" station wagons and the lower priced 1500 A Special "150". The first used body style number 53-1062 and was called the Two-Ten Townsman; the second was style number 53-1062F or Two-Ten Handyman; the third was the 53-1262F One-Fifty Handyman. The main difference between the wagons was in trim level. Only the Two-Ten Townsman featured wood grain trim.

This DeLuxe wagon was a handsome rendition of Chevy's new for 1953 sheetmetal. It used the old 115 inch wheelbase and had a 198-7/8 inch overall length, but came with a 235.5 cubic inch displacement engine, regardless of transmission. When linked to the conventional three-speed, the motor used solid lifters and had a 7.1:1 compression ratio with horsepower rating of 108 at 3,600 R.P.M. The Powerglide version was 7.5:1 compressioned, with hydraulic lifters and 115 horsepower at 3,600 R.P.M.

The wood grain trimmed Townsman was priced $2,123 and tipped the scales at 3,495. It had a fold-down third seat to provide accommodations for 8-9 passengers. For those who needed cargo space, the center seat could be removed. Thus, with the rear seat folded into the down postion, a large amount of carrying space was produced. In the floor behind the rear set was a hidden compartment for storage of the spare tire and tools.

An interesting note about all 1949-54 station wagons was the fact that the wood graining was added with a decal or transfer. Repair kits included a bonding agent a top coat; one-quarter pint cans of solid or highlight Di-Noc and two Squee Gees.

In addition to wood grain trim, the Townsman was distinquished by the use of sliding rear quarter windows. Production of the fanciest Chevrolet wagon went no higher than 7,988 units this year. This was considerably lower than Two-Ten Handyman (18,258 units) and One-Fifty Handyman (22,408 units) production totals.

1954

In an attempt to pump-up sales of the more luxurious station wagon, the Townsman edition was made a part of the topline Bel-Air series for 1954. Using body style number 54-1062D, the car had a steeper $2,283 factory base price and weighed in, with 3,540 pounds, as the heaviest model of the year. Only a small band of simulated wood grain trim was seen. The nine passenger car turned out to be a slow seller, with production of only 8,156 units.

1947 Station Wagon

1947 Station Wagon

The 1954 wagon was about the same as the 1953 model, except for the addition of Bel Air contrast trim, full wheel covers, fender skirts and revised treatments for the bumpers, grille, lights and hood ornament. The engine was of the same capacity, but got a number of internal improvements to compression ratio and lubrication. The standard motor was a 7.5:1 compression, 115 horsepower version of the 235 cubic inch mill. Optional, with Powerglide, was a 8.0:1 compression edition with 125 horsepower . . . the most powerful engine any Chevrolet had known.

It was not in engineering, however, that the 1954 Townsman wagon stood historically significant. Of greater interest was the fact that it became the last wood grain trimmed Chevrolet to appear until 1966! In an unusual move, the company went a full 12 years before returning to the use of wood-type appliques for station wagons.

Three of a Kind for '48

By Gerald Perschbacher

The Chevrolet Fleetmaster cabriolet or convertible ran smooth and quiet on an in-line six at 90 hp. The convertible was the second most expensive Chevrolet in '48.

1948 Chevrolet Club Coupe

Eleven gunboats were launched from the Chevrolet factory at the onset of the new model run for 1948. And three of them were forceful weapons against the hungry postwar competition.

Boasting in advertisements that "Chevrolet — and only Chevrolet — is first! First in production, first in sales, first in registrations," the GM Division was out to prove that it was tops in the hearts of Americans throughout the 17-year period from 1931 to 1948.

With a bang, the new 1948 Chevrolet Fleetmaster (FK) was launched from its mooring and steamed boldly, with a total of 20,471 units, against the convertible class in the low-price range. Designated Model 2134, base price listed $1,750 for a 3,340-pound beauty. A gussied-up '47 with a new mechanical improvement in precision-type main bearings for the engine, the convertible made the young-at-heart its main target and looked well-dressed in accessory front and rear bumper wing guards, chrome-plated gravel shields, deluxe push-button radio, cowl spot light, fog light and white-wall tires.

Likes its brothers (excluding station wagons), the Fleetmaster convertible ran a 116-inch wheel base with an overall length of just under 198 inches. The power block boasted 216.5 cubic inches in six formations, pouring out 90 hp at 3,300 rpm. Also called the cabriolet, the convertible was the second most expensive Chevrolet in '48, following behind the station wagon at $2,013.

Chevrolet spaced its armada into three navies: The Fleetmaster (of which the convertible was one of five models) covered the price range around $1,400 to $2,000. The Stylemaster counted four in its pack and was at the lower range in price, from $1,244 to nearly $1,400. The Club Coupe was one of the gunboats.

Slicing down the pavement with its trim but stable shipping weight of 3,020 pounds, the club coupe (also called sport coupe) carried a crew of five passengers midship. Factory price was hoisted to $1,323, a noticeable increase over the '47 counterpart which sold at $1,202.

Certainly not fancy with its less-trimmed sides and plainer accompaniment (especially inside), the Stylemaster Club Coupe was fourth from the bottom in Chevrolet production for '48.

The flagship of the Chevrolet fleet was the Fleetline two-door Aero sedan for five passengers, a two-door beauty with fast-back styling that was great on looks but hard for looking — when the driver at the helm wanted to look back at oncoming barges. At 211,861 units the two-door Aero Fleetline rode the Chevrolet crest of consumer popularity for '48 and took its battleship of the Division's total production of nearly 716,00 cars for the model year.

Three of a kind — and three different kinds of economical transportation — highlighted Chevrolet's battle-worthy line up for '48.

'48 Fleetmaster Wagon

Chevy's High and Low

By Gerald Perschbacher

It was a true "woody wagon." Weighing 3,405 pounds, the body structurally was made of wood, ash framing to be exact, with true mahogany panels. Owners knew the car was one of the last true "woodies" because of its tendency to creak, pop, moan and groan, depending on the weather and condition of the road.

But there was something about the '48 Chevrolet station wagon which made it more than visually attractive. It offered wide spaces in the back, space for carrying or playing, riding or sleeping. On the outside the car carried a dash of class with a fresh smell of country air. More than a few drivers considered themselves country squires — even if they weren't country boys — because the car was so handsomely rugged and rustic.

The '48 Fleemaster versions was Chevrolet's high and

low. Record production for the model reached 10,171 units, the highest model year production for the style with true structural wood construction.

The '48 Fleetmaster wagon marked a low for the General Motors Division, since it was the scarcest model among the 11 offered that year. However, as would be expected, it was the heaviest model and most expensive, too.

The '48 wagon was a combination of contrasts bringing mixed blessing to Chevrolet throughout the car's sales life. In 1950, when the Division produced its all-steel-construction station wagon, sales skyrocketed to almost 167,000 units. But the autumn drives through country scenes complete with brisk fall breezes and the changing colors never would be quite the same.

1949-'52 Chevrolet

America's Faithful Friend

By Robert C. Ackerson

1951 DeLuxe 2dr

In an early 1949 ad Chevrolet described its "bow tie" logo as the "greatest trade-mark in automobiles. This trade-mark symbolized a reputation for quality and dependability that increases in value and prestige as the years roll by." There was an awful lot of truth in what Chevrolet said. By 1949 Chevrolet had put together an eleven year winning streak in its production contest with Ford and as the world's most popular automobile it obviously did enjoy a reputation quite unlike any other automobile in production. But when a Chevrolet was closely examined, there were virtually no areas where it stood out as exceptional in design or performance. On the other hand it also possessed no serious vices or flaws. It did what its owners expected it to do without fuss or bother and with just a bit of style thrown in for good measure. When the 1949 model first debuted, at least one observer noted it had the appearance of "a small Cadillac without fins". Whatever the reporter's intentions, this connection was one of Chevrolet's great sales attributes. Rubbing elbows with the upper crust had its benefits and in Chevrolet's case it was hobnobbing with an automobile Americans admired most.

Like the other new postwar model's from General Motors, the 1949 Chevrolet's styling was extremely well executed. The retention of a rear fender line accentuated by brightwork surrounding its outer form eliminated the slab-look common to some other post-war automobiles. It also kept the Chevrolet's appearance in tune with tradition, modern but not extreme and attractive but not gaudy. A two-piece windshield was retained, but unlike the 1949 Plymouth and Ford, Chevrolet could boast of curved glass as well as 30 percent more glass area than its 1948 model. The general reaction to the Chevrolet's new look was favorable. Tom McCahill who regarded Ford's changes for 1949 as representing a greater change from the previous model than did Chevrolet's wrote, (*Mechanix Illustrated,* May 1949). "The new 1949 Chevrolet has been sexed up quite a bit. It's not dazzling enough, though, to cause the boys at the firehouse to fall off their chairs in a swoon everytime one passes their door..."

Across the Atlantic, *The Motor* (April 13, 1949) found the Chevrolet to its liking, reporting that "well-balanced lines unspoilt by excessive ornamentation make the latest Chevrolet a truly handsome car."

Chevrolet felt it appropriate to launch its new automobiles with new model series designations. Thus instead of Fleetmaster and Stylemaster Chevrolets, we had DeLuxe and Special models. Somehow the older titles had more class and style to them. No one would deny they were more original. However, the Fleetline label was retained for use on Chevrolet's two and four door fastback models which like the notchback models (available as Business Coupe, Sport Coupe and four door sedans) were offered in either DeLuxe or Special versions. The distinction between these Chevrolets was very apparent. The more expensive DeLuxe models had chrome side trim and rear fender shields plus bright accents around the front windshield and rear window. The more proletarian Special had none of these features and had to struggle through life with a rubber shield providing rear fender protection. Interior distinctions were also obvious. DeLuxe models had two-spoke steering wheels with horn rings (the Special's was a three-spoke version with no horn ring) and all dash knobs on the DeLuxe models had stainless steel inserts.

Chevrolet began the model year offering a wooden bodied, six-passenger station wagon as well as an all-steel, eight passenger version. However, before the year was ended the old-fashioned Woody was discontinued.

Mechanically all Chevrolets were identical. The 215.6 cid, 90 hp ohv six was unchanged and while the new Chevrolets looked considerably longer than the older version they were at 197 inches, actually 0.75 inches shorter. The respective wheelbases of the 1948 and 1949 models were 116 and 115 inches.

Chevrolet described its powerplant as the "World's Champion Valve-In-Head Engine." Exactly what it was champion of wasn't revealed but even the Stovebolt's critics conceded one of its strong points was reliability. That is, if you didn't have a taste for sustained, high-speed driving. Tom McCahill (*Mechanix Illustrated,* May 1949) quoted an "old engine man from way back" as claiming, "Drive them all day long at 68 miles per hour and they'll last forever. But just get to 69 and keep it there and you can make book on whether you'll burn out a bearing, throw a rod or lost a timing gear. It will be one of the

Chevrolet was all new for 1949 and outsold its competition handily.

three." Less graphic but still in the same ballpark was *Consumer Union's* comment of 1951 that Chevrolet was the best buy "for the driver who generally stays below 60 mph."

Actually, most Chevrolet owners did just that and given the Chevrolet's primary function as a low-priced family automobile, its performance was quite surprising. Tom McCahill attained a zero to 60 mph of 16.8 seconds but it's likely in the light of post 1949 road test results that this was an extra-quick Chevrolet. Some critics must have suspected McCahill had been out in the West Coast smog too long when he wrote that in the hills surrounding Los Angeles "the Chevrolet held those tough curves like an English MG.."

However, after testing a 1950 model, *The Motor* (January 31, 1951) reported "the car corners easily and steadily, under complete and precise control, at quite brisk speeds..." And after experience with a 1951 model. *The Autocar*, August 31, 1951 concluded "The car corners well both on fast bends and on tight corners, although a certain amount of tire squeal is noticeable at

1951 DeLuxe 2dr

high speed." Finally, from the viewpoint of *Motor Trend* (September 1950); "they handle well in corners and have good maneuverability."

As expected, a review of the Chevrolet's suspension, brakes and steering reveals no surprises. Everything was strictly conventional. But it was well constructed and well designed. Front suspension was by coil springs with unequal length transverse arms and telescopic shock absorbers positioned within the springs. A big plus for the Chevrolet's road manners was the large front stabilizer bar. By inclining the king pins at 5° the Chevrolet's suspension engineers gave it "center-point steering" which translated into a high degree of straight line stability. At the rear were strictly conventional, 49 inch long semielliptic leaf springs.

1951 DeLuxe Station Wagon

1951 DeLuxe 2dr

Chevrolet's claim that its 1950 models possessed "smarter style, new Luxuries and improved Performance" was in general, substantiated with solid fact. The Chevy's styling wasn't of course all new but it was tidied up around the edges for the better. Its grille was simpler in format thanks to the removal of most of the vertical bars used in 1949. Due to a more prominent hood ornament and the removal of the built-in license plate frame in the bumper it was difficult to confuse a 1950 Chevrolet with a year old model. At the rear the Chevrolet's taillights were just beginning to assume an identity of their own. They were still mounted inboard of the rear fenders but with a nubbin-like shape they held the promise of maturing into a key Chevrolet styling feature. The combining of the trunk handle and rear deck ornamentation into a single entity also was an easily identified change for 1950.

But the big styling news for 1950 from Chevrolet was the Bel Air two-door hardtop. Ford and Plymouth were clearly outmaneuvered by Chevrolet on this point although Ford's Crestliner was a clever and by no means unattractive response. But it was still a two-door sedan and once again Chevrolet's conservative reputation had belied the fact that its shakers and movers knew exactly what they were doing. Hardtops were associated with more expensive automobiles and it never hurt Chevrolet a bit by trading on its image as the Cadillac's little cousin.

Similarly, Chevrolet scored another touchdown against the opposition by being first among the "Low Priced Three" with a fully automatic transmission. Said *The Motor* (January 11, 1950), "the 1950 Chevrolet makes motoring history by being the first producers in the low price market to standardize a fully hydraulic system." A year later after road testing the Powerglide Chevrolet, *The Motor* was still impressed concluding, "such an appli-

1950 DeLuxe 4dr

cation of the latest engineering practices to popular motoring is an event of outstanding significance." Chevrolet, which offered Powerglide only on its DeLuxe models wasted no time in exploiting its competitive edge telling its prospective customers, "Get ready to enjoy the simplest, smoothest driving in the low priced field...all you do is set the lever in 'Drive' position, press on the accelerator—and go! There is not clutch pedal..no gear shifting to bother you."

Powerglide was in design a torque converter not dissimilar to Buick's Dynaflow and although somewhat leisurely in acceleration, was so smooth in operation the *The Motor* found the experience of driving a Powerglide Chevrolet "altogether delightful."

To cope with the Powerglide's relative inefficiency, Chevrolet adopted a modified version of its truck engine, which of course powered the early Corvettes, and was rather interesting. Its 3-9/16 inch bore and 3-15/16 inch stroke were respectively 1/16 and 3/16 inches larger than the standard Chevrolet engines and provided 235.5 cubic inches of displacement. Among its other features

1950 DeLuxe Coupe

were larger intake and exhaust valves, a higher lift cam, stronger cylinder block and improved lubrication. "All in all" said Tom McCahill, "this engine is a honey." With a 6.7:1 compression ratio it was rated at 105 hp at 3600 rpm and 189 lb-ft at 1200 rpm. Both the Powerglide engine and the 215.6 cid version (which now was rated at 92 hp at 3400 rpm) used a new Rochester carburetor for 1950.

Using both Low and Drive ranges, Tom McCahill reported a 0 to 60 mph time of 15.2 seconds with a Powerglide Chevrolet but this just doesn't jive with other contemporary test reports nor for that matter with this writer's experience some years back with a stick-shift 1952 Chevrolet. That car was no jackrabbit in acceleration and surely couldn't run to 60 mph in 15 seconds. However, it never ever was beaten by a pre-1952 Powerglide Chevrolet. Its strong point incidentally was its third gear performance. More than once it proved to its owner's satisfaction that John Bond was right on the money when he wrote (*Road & Track,* February 1955) that "it is strange that so few owners know that since 1937 a Chevrolet will out-perform its competitors, year for year, in high gear acceleration from 10 to 60 mph." A Powerglide Chevrolet, on the other hand was lucky to run from zero to 60 mph in less than 24 seconds in Drive range. With luck a couple of seconds could be lopped off this time by starting in Low and shifting to Drive at approximately 45 mph.

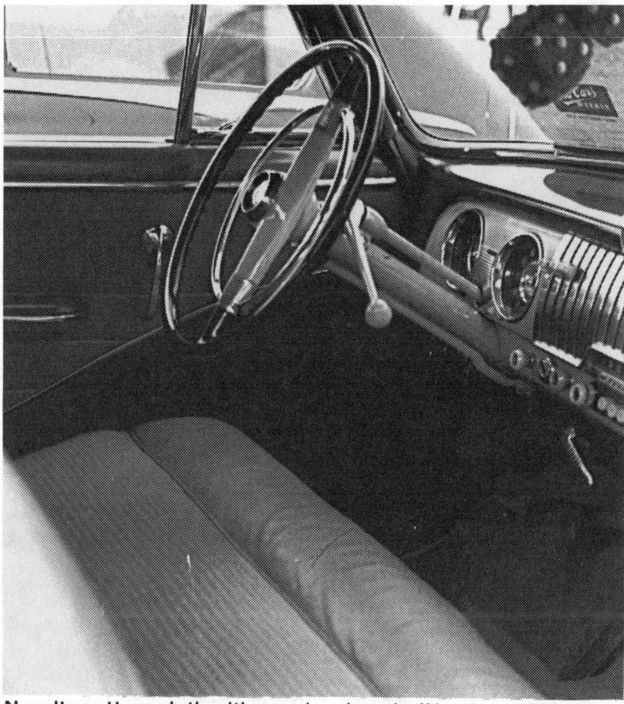

Novelty pattern cloth with genuine deep-buff leather in Bel Airs.

But no matter. The world of real Turbo-fire V-8 performance was still far in the future. What counted in 1950 was Chevrolet's ability to give the customer what he wanted at a price he could afford. This was very much a time when Chevrolet did go hand in hand with baseball, hot dogs and apple pie. One advertisement even put Chevrolet's role as an integral part of American lifestyle into poetry:

"Wherever you are...wherever you go
In a sleepy little hamlet.
On a bustling city's street
On the highways—on the byways,
You'll find a familiar friend—Chevrolet."

This was as everyone knew, no idle boast. For example Floyd Clymer's Owner's Report on the 1951 Chevrolet (*Popular Mechanics*, June 1951) revealed that 26% of drivers of 1951 Chevrolets had owned five or more Chevrolets! It's also interesting to note that 38% said they would prefer an eight cylinder engine in their next car.

For the most part, changes for 1951 were cosmetic. A new, more angular grille, reshaped side trim for the DeLuxe models and rear fenders fitted with small chrome spears and incorporating the taillights were the most obvious exterior changes. There were also slightly larger, "Jumbo Drum" brakes. But by and large the 1951 model was more of the same and that was by no means bad for either Chevrolet or General Motors. *The Autocar* still liked the Chevrolet very much, reporting in its August 31, 1951 issue, "it is evidently good value for money and unlike a car that has been built down to a price." And over at *Road & Track* John Bond traded his 1949 Ford in for a 1951 Chevrolet.

If a Chevrolet owner was so inclined he could reduce his car's zero to 60 mph by some three seconds by purchasing a hop-up kit offered by Rajo Automotive Research.

There's no denying that in comparison to the 1951 Ford's the 1952 Chevrolet's appearance was dated. Its two-piece windshield was old fashioned, its fastback model had been big news back in 1942 but a decade later didn't get anyone excited and, whereas Ford had a peppy new ohv six to brag about, Chevrolet just offered up the same old stovebolt! So what happened? Chevrolet still sold more cars than Ford! For the record Chevrolet did bend its chrome side trim into a new shape and fiddle around with its front grille shape. In addition a new,three-point (instead of five) engine mount system was introduced on the 1952 Chevrolet that did improve its handling and ride. But more Chevrolets were sold than Fords not because of this innovation or for that matter its altered appearance. Chevrolets sold because as *Speed Age* (August 1952) observed it was "a conservative, durable automobile, offering effective performance and reliability in the highest degree."

But the times were changing and while Chevrolet was still trading handsomely off this reputation, there was a big event being planned behind closed doors in Detroit. But if Chevrolet's new V-8 in 1955 gave it a whole new personality, then the 1949-1952 models had kept the faith, helping to bridge the gap between the Chevrolets whose roots were pre-war and those automobiles that rewrote the book of high performance.

Introducing...

The '53 Chevrolet

By Gerald Perschbacher

It used to be that dealers went all-out to promote a new car back in the '50s. Much of that spirit no longer exists today.

January 1953 was dealer introduction time for Chevrolet's new offering which was placed as a sacrifice to public opinion through dealerships everywhere. The main theme that year was "Mister Chevrolet," a top-hatted, tuxedoed image of a well-to-do man-about-town whose good taste brought him to Chevrolet.

The Humphrey Chevrolet Co. in Milwaukee, Wis., attired their salesmen—more than a dozen—in tuxes while two beautiful damsels added an extra touch of class in the show room. It was a red-carpet treatment par excellence. Humphrey Chevrolet Inc., in Evanston, Ill., wanted Mr. Carbuyer to meet Mr. Chevrolet in person, bringing the image of the car and its name into personal, high-classed atmosphere.

Jack Kennedy Chevrolet Co., St. Louis, Mo., went all-out with a carnival atmosphere including a full orchestra, a merry-go-round and even a Ferris wheel. The carnival atmosphere "really pulled them in," said owner Kennedy. He claimed that sales had doubled over the introduction time of previous years.

In Detroit, Grand River Chevrolet claimed that more than 30,000 people had attended their grand unveiling of the new '53 models, and orders had been received for almost a million dollars worth of new Chevrolets. The dealership emphasized fashion shows to add glamour. Mr. Chevrolet appeared in Zanesville, Ohio, at the White Chevrolet Co. It was reported that the dealership commissioned two young gentlemen, in tuxedos, to wear a sandwich board which said, "All new 1953 Chevrolet—Jan. 9, White's." A local undertaker got into the act, and the dealership borrowed an ambulance every morning during the week preceding the showing to haul them to a different busy spot in town where they unloaded them on ambulance stretchers. The men then walked through the busy sections of town throughout the day." The commotion gained quite a bit of attention!

A $500,000 jewel collection flashed by fashion models and television stars in mink and ermine wraps also was used at a dealership. A local TV star had her program telecast from the dealer's showroom floor. The publicity was priceless.

Service activities were emphasized by dealers, too, and graphic displays showing how the Blue Flame Six, 115 hp engine operated, along with the improved Powerglide and the new power steering unit.

Where are those days? Where are the red carpets, the brass bands, the tuxedos, the flair and finesse of new-car introduction for Chevrolet?

Those days may exist in an isolated corner of some forgotten spot. But mainly, those days of razz-ma-tazz salesmanship live on as cherished memories of the past.

1953 210 4dr Hardtop

1953 Bel Air Convertible

1953 210 Station Wagon

Bel Air

An American Success Story

By Terry Boyce

Postwar car buyers were ready for a car like the Bel Air, Chevrolet's new-for-1950 hardtop Sport Coupe.

Offering the style and approaching the openness of a convertible, but without the leak and noise problems inherent in that body type, the hardtop was also the most modern design of the moment. Less than a year before, General Motors had released a trio of upper-bracket special hardtop models - the Buick Roadmaster Riviera, Cadillac Coupe deVille and Olds 98 Holiday. Expensive and in short supply, these beautiful luxury cars attracted a lot of attention. Now, for 1950, Chevrolet brought this sensational styling to the low-priced bracket.

The first Bel Air was, not surprisingly, a success. Sales were strong and would get stronger. The basic body was face-lifted for 1951, then continued into 1952 with only minimal additional changes. Often, these six cylinder Sports Coupes left the show rooms of Main Street America laden with many of the accessory goodies offered by Chevrolet. Sun shades, front and rear bumper end guards, wheel discs, a radio and a heater were among the popular items.

A stop at the local auto supply store could result in the addition of blue dot taillights, a spot light or two and, no doubt, a lucite "necker knob" for the steering wheel.

By 1953, Chevrolet felt the Bel Air name would carry the Chevrolet top series well, so it was expanded to a more complete series of body styles, including a convertible, and two- and four-door sedans in addition to the Sport Coupe. Every Bel Air had a contrasting paint band on the rear fender, with the series script mounted there; adding a roof of the same color made a handsome "two-tone" at minimal cost. Bel Air trim levels were top notch, too, with quality fabrics and brightly colored vinyl or leather for the Sport Coupe and convertible.

Working with the same basic body as 1953, Chevrolet stylists came up with a really pleasing 1954 Bel Air lineup. A new grille and front bumper ensemble gave the car a more substantial, richer appearance. There was a new model, too, the Beauville four-door station wagon: the first Chevrolet wagon offered with Bel Air interior and exterior decor. This interesting model featured vestigal wood body side panels, the last sliver of the warmly toned age of the woodie wagons.

The 1954 Bel Airs were quiet, nicely appointed and retained Chevrolet's traditional durability. They were a fitting summation of the GM Division's six-cylinder era.

But, car buyers were looking for more than traditional values in cars by 1954. They were demanding and getting performance and excitement. Chevrolet responded in 1955 with a single master stroke that almost overnight revolutionized the meaning of the name Chevrolet - yet without losing the following that had so long made the marque America's number one best selling car-line.

About the only thing that wasn't new for 1955 were the series designations. The Bel Air script was still affixed to top line Chevrolet models, with their new low and crisp styling, high-revving optional V-8s and wrap-around windshields. America loved this new Chevrolet right from the first, so it was not surprising that the 1956 models were more of the same, but with a new, more up-level front appearance, slightly sleeker lines and even more horsepower.

For 1957, a third version appeared, a handsome restyle that had more than a little Cadillac influence. By now the V-8's reputation was made; its legend had begun. Topping the engine charts this year were Rochester fuel-injected engines offering as much as one horsepower per cubic inch.

There were new body styles during this classic era. During mid-1955 yet another station wagon appeared.

This was a two-door job with hardtop style door windows and one of the prettiest roof lines ever to grace a

1951 Bel Air

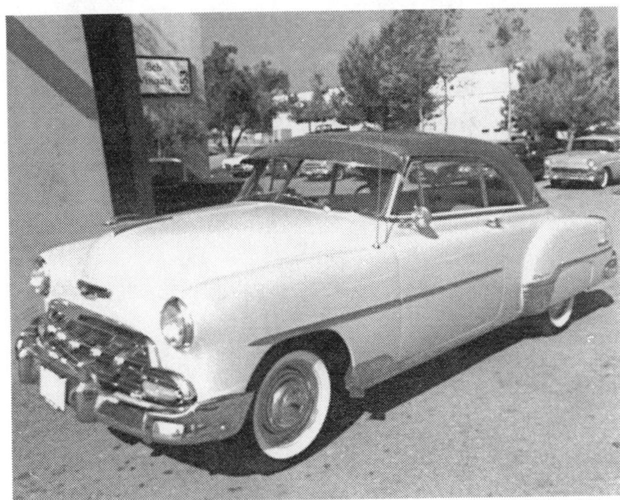
1952 Bel Air 2dr Hardtop

1954 Bel Air 4dr Sedan

car of this body type. It said Nomad on the tailgate, but the Bel Air script appeared on the rear fenders. New for 1956 was the Sport Sedan, an effort to expand the popular "hardtop" concept to a four-door body style. Though never as popular as the Bel Air two-door hardtop, the Sport Sedan found favor with families who liked a sporting-style car.

The 1955-57 Chevrolets with their tightly packaged yet eye-pleasing styling, perky power teams and exceptional

Dream car of a generation - a '57 Bel Air hardtop "factory fuelie."

durability were held dear by many owners who found the Chevrolets that followed not nearly as appealing. As late as 1963, Chevrolet marketing managers were still trying to figure a way to pry the '55-'57 models away from their original owners. It was no coincidence that the 1964 Chevelle was very comparable to these cars in size and equipment.

But, by this time, there was a whole new market for 1955-57 Bel Airs. The baby boom was going to high school and the cars of choice in mid-sixties school parking lots were - you know it - '55-'57 Chevys An impromptu poll at any 20th or 25th anniversary reunion is sure to turn up a surprising percentage of former Bel Air hardtop owners. And, there will likely be a few lucky persons who still have one.

But two decades ago, as the 1958 models were being styled, it appeared that lower, wider and heavier were the ways to go. And, to go along with this theme of more of everything, it seemed that new models were in order to top the Chevrolet line. Thus, greeting 1958 car shoppers were a pair of Impalas, a Sport Coupe and convertible. For this one year - although no one but historians remember - these were technically "Bel Air Impalas," special models topping the Bel Air line, which was still trimmed inside and out in top-level finery throughout its series lineup.

For 1959, however, the Impala expanded to become Chevrolet's top series and the Bel Air was relegated to the mid-line slot. There wasn't even a Bel Air Sport Coupe this year (although, strangely, there was a Bel Air Sport Sedan). The 1960 Bel Air lineup did include the Sport Coupe once again, but with its truly mundane interior it attracted only a fraction of the sales scored by the colorful Impala.

Capping a sensational line of 1955 Bel Air models was the beautiful Nomad wagon.

Eclipsed by the new Bel Air Impala Sport Coupe pictured here, the 1958 Bel Air two-door hardtop, though brightly trimmed and plushly upholstered, was still down-line.

More Than a Million Chevrolets For 1953

By Tom LaMarre

Chevrolet was still advertising its 1953 models as late as November of that year, saying "...this year the preference for Chevrolet is greater than ever. Latest available figures for 1953 show that over 200,000 more people have bought Chevrolets than the second-choice car!" When model year production did come to an end, more than 1,300,000 Chevys had rolled off the line.

More good news was that over 400,000 of the '53 Chevys were ordered with Powerglide automatic transmissions, an option in the 210 and Bel Air series only. With the automatic transmission came a special version of the new Blue-Flame six-cylinder engine. This powerplant had a compression ratio of 7.5 to 1 and produced 115 hp at 3600 rpm. For comparison, the standard 235.5 cubic inch Blue-Flame engine had a 7 to 1 compression ratio and a horsepower rating of 108.

The big styling news for 1953 was Chevy's adoption of a wrap-around windhsield. In addition, all cars except the economy-priced 150 Special models featured a wrap-around rear window as well.

Setting the top-of-the-line Bel Air apart from its less expensive brethren visually was its spear type rear fender trim. The panel of color within the trim lent a sporty appearance to Chevy's style leader. Like all of the regular '53s, the Bel Air had a 115 inch wheelbase and overall length of 195.5 inches. Somehow, though, its fender skirts made the car look massive.

Station wagons were an important part of the Chevy line for 1953, and a four-door Handyman model was included in both the 150 and 210 series. But it was the 210 Townsman wagon that was the most expensive model in Chevy's regular line. Priced at $2,273, only 7,988 were made.

The most scarce of all '53 Chevys is the 210 convertible; 5,617 were built. Apparently most buyers preferred to spend a little bit more for the Bel Air version, which had a production run of 24,047.

It all added up to a great year for Chevrolet. Faster and sleeker Chevys would follow, but many collectors still regard the '53 as one of the best-looking models made.

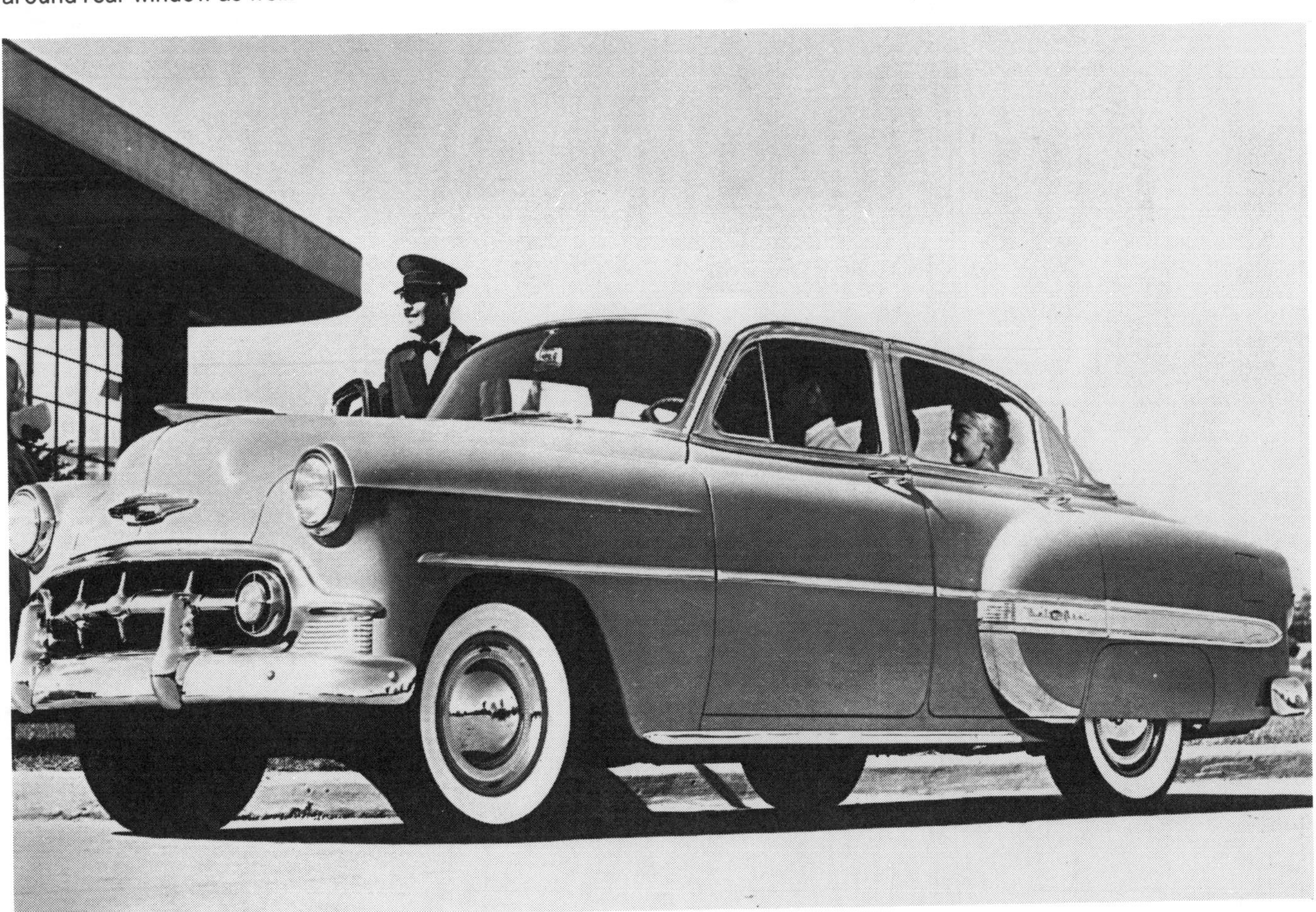

A 1953 Chevy Bel Air four-door sedan.

Mid-Century Masterpieces

The High Performance Cars From Chevrolet

by Robert C. Ackerson

1955 was a pivotal year in Chevrolet history. Prior to that time Chevrolet had more or less accepted a second best postion when it came to performance to its great rival, Ford. This really wasn't as self defeating as it sounds because since 1936 Chevrolet had let its arch rival in sales and that after all was said and done, was really what the automobile business was all about.

Without downgrading the profound impact of Henry Ford and the Model T and Model A Fords upon the automobile industry and indeed virtually every facet of our lives, it's equally important to recognize Chevrolet's role in the same frame of reference.

In the years following William C. Durants' second and final exodus from the leadership of General Motors, his successor, Alfred P. Sloan served as the chief architect of the design of a new corporate philosophy which was to prove fabulously successful. In part his policy was to design automobiles in each price bracket of the market that offered just a bit more to the customer than their competitors. This "bit more" was a composite of factors such as riding comfort, styling innovations and interior appointments that in total conveyed an impression to the customer that he was getting more value for his dollar when he purchased a General Motors product. Thus reasoned Sloan, he would have little objection to paying a slightly higher price.

Chev's new, little V-8 for 1955 carried 162 horsepower.

As General Motors' entry in the low price field, Chevrolet was perhaps the prime example of just how successful Sloan's strategy was.

It took time for Sloan to fully implement this plan but by the late 20s Chevrolet was openly referring to its cars as "Bigger and Better . . . " offering "an order of elegance never before thought possible in a low priced car." When the decade had begun, Ford was of course clearly in a position of superiority but as the years passed the Model T's sales margin over the Chevrolet steadily dwindled. In terms of meeting the desires of the buying public as compared to meeting the transportation needs of the nation, the Model T was clearly in a state of decline. In 1924 Model T sales reached a figure of 1,870,000 but dropped the following year to 1,675,000. In the same time span Chevrolet moved from 280,000 sales to an impressive 470,000. The following year (1926) price reductions failed to stem the tide and Ford sales dropped nearly 400,000 while Chevrolet, under General Manager William S. Knudsen, saw its sales continue upward to reach 732,000.

After its peak year in 1923 when 2,091,000 were produced, the Model T had by 1927 clearly reached the end of the road.

Chevrolet moved ahead of Ford (which had to shut down for six months to prepare for the manufacture of the Model A) in 1927 and maintained this lead into 1928 when 786,670 Chevrolets were produced compared to Ford's total of 713,528. The following year Ford made a great comeback producing 1,715,100 cars which was virtually double the comparable Chevrolet figure.

Yet in spite of this trouncing, Chevrolet sales in 1929 stood at an all time high and the fact that its 1929 models were powered by a new 194cid overhead valve engine must be seen as a major step forward in the design of the modern low priced car in America. Furthermore under Knudsen, Chevrolet had managed to make the change over to the six cylinder engine in record time. Certainly this application of the "Bigger and Better" philosophy was a prime mover in pushing Henry Ford toward production of a V8 in 1932 and Walter Chrysler's concurrent act of offering hydraulic brakes on his Plymouth, and in 1933 a six cylinder engine as well.

During the middle thirties, the number one position in automobile producers swung back and forth between Ford and Chevrolet but in 1936 Chevrolet established a lead of nearly 180,000 cars over Ford and for the next 22 years was the nation's top automobile producer.

Yet Ford remained the nation's sweetheart when it came to performance. In reality however, by the early fifties Ford's right to this amorous relationship with the public was based more on fancy than fact. Granted that Chevrolet's trusty old six was getting a bit long in the tooth (it had been introduced in 1929 and had received a major redesign in 1936), Ford's flathead V-8 was also in need of replacement.

A comparison of the performance of the 1952 Ford and Chevrolet reveals just how similar their relative performance had become:

	Ford V-8 (110bhp)	Ford Six (101bhp)	Chevy Six (92bhp)
0-60mph	20.47 sec	19.45 sec	20.46 sec
10-60 in high gear	26.93 sec	24.40 sec	23.83 sec
30-60 in high gear	17 sec	15.34 sec	15.68 sec
Top speed	86.70 mph	86.28 mph	80.93 mph

Furthermore in the last Mexican Road Race of 1954 C.D. Evans drove a 1954 Chevrolet to a class victory. As set up for this race Evan's Chevrolet had a top speed of approximately 104mph.

The impact of this racing success upon Chevrolet sales was probably minimal but both behind the scenes and in public Chevrolet was gradually shedding its conservative image. The visual segment of this transformation was of course the Corvette, the hidden element centered around the arrival of Ed Cole at Chevrolet as its new Chief Engineer in May, 1952. Cole, who had earlier worked on the design of the Cadillac ohv V-8 of 1948, was, if any one individual is to be singled out, the man who "made" the 1955 Chevrolet.

1955 was a great year for the Big Three (and a corresponding disaster fo what remained of the independents). With the exception of Lincoln and the senior GM cars (Buick, Oldsmobile and Cadillac); Ford, General Motors and Chrysler offered cars with all-new styling, and major engineering advances.

Even as the new cars were making their debut amidst the holiday mood which prevailed at new car announcement time back in those days it was clear that the new Chevrolet was the fairest of them all.

From every angle the 1955 models represented a major watershed in Chevrolet's long history. For once the adage "All New" was justified as a description of the Chevrolet. For example, the 1955 Chevrolet contained some 4,500 different parts of which 3,825 were changed from their 1954 model counterparts. And that styling. Seldom has there been an American car that bore such a styling change from its predecessors and yet managed somewhat to resemble them. It doesn't seem at all improper to refer to the 1955 Chevrolet's front end as a classic design. Nothing was overdone, there were no extremes. Even today that simple yet elegant egg crate grille still remains as one of the best ever to appear on an American production car. A close look at the Chevy's head and parking lights illustrates GM's unmatched attention to detail. The headlights had just the slightest suggestion of what was called in those days an eyebrow. Not over done to excess, it was a far more graceful application of this styling point than that which appeared on the 1955 Fords and Mercurys (and even worse, on 1955 Packards). Similarly, the front parking lights were a simple teardrop shape, hard to criticize from any point of view. One of the amazing things about the styling of the '55 Chevy was that in spite of it being an all new body style that broke with the past it still managed to look like a Chevrolet. Furthermore, there were some individuals who unabashedly expressed the view that it looked like a "little Cadillac." Apparently this similarity didn't hurt because Chevrolet set a new production record of 1,830,028 passenger cars.

A total of 14 different body styles in three lines (One-Fifty, Two-Ten and Bel Air) were offered, each sharing the notched fender line which Harley Earl was so fond of. The mid-fifties saw the use of two and three tone color schemes reach a pretty ridiculous extreme but Chevrolet, while offering 21 different two-tone color combinations by and large didn't fall into this category.

Beneath the Chevrolet's finely proportioned body was a new chassis that was 5 stiffer and 18% lighter than the one it replaced. Both front and rear suspension were major steps forward from their 1954 counterparts. In the front a ball joint suspension with tilted coil springs and new control arm geometry combined with outrigger positioned rear springs (9" longer than in 1954) to give the new Chevrolet vastly improved handling.

Walt Woron (*Motor Trend,* December, 1954) summed up his impression of the quality of the new Chevy's handling by going out on a limb and writing: "I wouldn't be afraid to stack it up against many of the so-called sports cars." *Road & Track* was a bit less enthusiastic about the Chevrolet's prowess in this area, noting in its February, 1955 issue that there was "plenty of room for improvement in this department."

The new Chevrolets were first shown to the press at GM's Proving Ground on October 12, 1954. The Chevy's new styling, exciting as it was, took a back seat to its new 265cid V-8. Much has been written about this engine and deservedly so. In terms of durability, versatility, production costs (Roger Huntington once estimated that Chevrolet could build this V-8 for just a little more than what it cost Ford and Plymouth to build their V-8s), and sheer ability to produce gobs of power it stands as one of the finest American engines ever produced.

In both its wedge-type combustion chamber shape and its over-square design (3¾" bore and 3" stroke) the Chevrolet V-8 was similar to the earlier Oldsmobile and Cadillac V-8s. Although its displacement was at 265 cubic inches relatively modest, the Chevrolet V-8s fairly generous 3¾" bore allowed large, 1¾" intake and exhaust valves to be used. Likewise the exhaust ports were for an engine of this size, huge.

Anyone having their first look at Chevy's "Turbo-Fire" V-8 was impressed by its incredibly compact dimensions. Its block measured only 22" in length and total engine width a mere 26½."

Most Chevy V-8s destined for use in family sedans and wagons carried a single 2-barrel carburetor and were rated at 162bhp gross (137bhp, net). If a standard transmission was ordered the V-8 was equipped with solid valve lifters whereas Powerglide V-8 used hydraulic tappets. In both cases the horsepower rating remained unchanged.

Eager to avoid a problem similar to that which Ford experienced in 1954 with the camshafts of their new ohv V-8, Chevrolet went to great lengths to make certain that their new engine was as trouble free as possible. A step in this direction was the electronical balancing of each engine after its assembly. Furthermore, the new V-8 passed the usual tests for durability with flying colors. In one such trial a V-8 ran for 35 hours at 5,500 rpm without

The 50 millionth General Motors car — a 1955 Chevrolet Bel Air Sport Coupe. Built and introduced on November 23, 1954, it marked the first time any auto manufacturer had reached this milestone. The '55 Chev can easily be counted as one of the most attractive post-war cars.

This'57 Two-Ten Sport Sedan is a natural progression from the "all new" '55s and pretty '56s.

failure.

Right from their initial press preview the evidence was overwhelming that the Chevrolet had become, virtually overnight, one of the world's best performing sedans. Mixed in among the various production models at GMs Proving Ground for th October 12, 1954 Press Day was "Ed Cole's Baby," a four door Bel Air equipped with what was to become part of the jargon used by automobile minded America, the "power-pack." The official title for this performance option was the "Plus Power Package" but this term never caught on. Whatever you wanted to call it, A Chevy duly equipped was a car to be reckoned with. For $55 the buyer received a 4-barrel carburetor, an intake maniforld with larger ports, and dual exhausts. Horsepower went up to 180 (160 net). In this form the V-8 weighed just 469 pounds dry.

What a great car a '55 Chevy with power pack was. For well under $2,500 you could get a nicely appointed Two-Ten coupe with the 180bhp engine and three-speed overdrive transmission that could hustle you from zero to 60mph in 9.7 seconds. Mounted on a 115" wheelbase and weighing just under 3,400 pounds the Chevy was a lithe little machine with only 18.9 pounds for each horsepower to tote around.

Furthermore it was a fairly economical car. *Road & Track* (February, 1955) reported obtaining an average 24.4mpg for some 300 miles of driving around which included "cruising at 80 . . . occasionally hitting 90 . . . getting 100mph (in second gear overdrive) and making lots of use of the kickdown.

As would be expected, Chevrolets were in abundance at the 1955 Daytona Speed Week. While not the fastest cars on the sand the power-pack Chevys were near the top. In the flying mile competition the fastest Chevy was clocked at 112.877mph. The only faster were the Chrysler 300 (127.580mph), Cadillac (120.478mph), Buick Century (116.345mph) and a Chrysler New Yorker (114.631mph). In acceleration over a one mile distance from a standing start the Chevrolet's power and light weight (almost 200 pounds less than a comparable Ford) put it very near the top of the pile. Only Cadillac with a speed of 80.428mph proved superior to the Chevrolet's best run of

This is the 1957 Bel Air convertible. It is quickly becoming one of the most desirable collector cars in America; with or without speed equipment.

placement of 283 cubic inches was to be a familiar figure in a couple of years. Numerous Chevrolets with this larger bore plus a longer ¼" stroke allowing a 306cid prowled not only the nation's dragstrips but its highways as that grand old American tradition known as street racing took on a new and far more interesting form.

Chevrolet's slogan for 1956, "The Hot One's Even Hotter" indicated that it had no intention of relinquishing its position as one of America's great high performance automobiles. Things got off to a fast start on September 9,1955 when Zora Arkus-Duntov drove a pseudo-disguised '56 Chevrolet to set a new stock car record up the 12.42 mile run (which also included 170 sharp turns) to the summit of Pikes Peak, 14,110 feet above sea level.

Duntov's time of 17 minutes, 24.05 seconds shattered Cannonball Baker's old mark of 19 minutes, 25.7 seconds which had stood for 21 years. Both Baker and NASCAR President Bill France were interested on-lookers to Duntov's achievement. After the run was completed, officials from NASCAR, which sanctioned the run, tore the car down and certified it as a stock car. Eventually Chevrolet also made it available for press use, the only change made being the replacement of its heavy duty clutch with a standard unit.

Bel Air Beauville Station Wagon

The 1955-1957 wagons haven't escaped the loving eye of collectors. The car came in both two and four-door models.

78.158mph. For the record, some comparative speeds were: Chrysler 300 (77.436mph), Ford (73.428mph) and Plymouth (72.072mph).

It's also worth noting that given the greater rolling resistance the sand at Daytona offered to tires of a car passing over it, it's fair to say that a 180bhp Chevy was a good deal quicker and faster than its Daytona speeds would indicate.

In June, shortly after the 1955 Indianapolis "500" at which a red and white Chevrolet Bel Air convertible served as the Pace Car the 195bhp hotter cammed V-8 which had been an option in the Corvette became available for all Chevrolets.

At this point Chevrolet became *The Car* at National Hot Rod Association drag strips from coast to coast. A similar situation existed in NASCAR stock car competition where Chevrolet won 13 of 25 short track events in 1955. In addition, Chevrolets finished second 11 times, and third 12 times. Its closest competitor, Dodge won only five races.

During the 1955 racing season some hot rodders jumped the gun on Chevrolet and took it upon themselves to increase its internal dimensions. Frank McGurk of Inglewood, California produced pistons for Chevrolet engines that were bored out an additional ⅛". The resulting dis-

The 1956 Chevrolets underwent a fairly substantial sheet metal change that was, as face lifts go, quite successful. 19 models were available including nine passenger sedan and the then current hot styling idea from Detroit, the four door hardtop.

1956 Chevrolets also offered seat belts and shoulder harnesses as options. Like Ford and virtually all American producers, Chevrolet found customer interest in these features rather limited.

The 1955 Chevrolet's suspension was carried over into 1956 with only minor changes, the most notable being a slight tilting of the front control arm which reduced nose dive in extreme braking situations by 45%. At the rear 1" wider rear spring hangers which helped fight spring compression resulting from the axle's side-thrusts under acceleration were small but worthwhile changes.

The initial high performance offering for 1956, the Super Turbo-Fire V-8 was rated at 205bhp with a 9.25:1 compression ratio. This engine used the same cam as the 170bhp V-8 which was available only with Powerglide.

Anyone who loved the sounds emitting from the twin

pipes of a '55 Power-pack Chevy was bound to be a little disappointed after his first audio experience with its 1956 counterpart for the 205bhp engine used longer mufflers and shorter exhaust pipes which made them somewhat quieter than the '55s.

The 205bhp V-8s, when hitched to a three speed transmission used a high capacity clutch of coil spring design in place of the diaphragm spring unit used on less powerful Chevrolets.

Like all Chevy V-8s the 205bhp version had a remarkably flat torque curve which was a major explanation of its phenomenal performance. At 3000rpm, torque was a respectable 268 ft.-lbs. and even at 4,600rpm where its peak horsepower of 205 was reached, stood at an impressive 234 ft.-lbs.

This gave a 205bhp Chevrolet a pretty snappy performance, especially when it was teamed up with a three speed/overdrive transmission. 60mph came up from a standing start in just 8.5 or nine seconds flat and top speed with a 3.70 rear axle was a nifty 111mph. Naturally Chevrolets that were tuned to within an inch of their lives could substantially improve on these figures.

Just before the 1956 Daytona Speed Weeks, Chevrolet made the Corvette 225bhp V-8 with dual-four barrel carburetors, 8.25:1 compression ratio and solid valve lifters optional in any model.

The 1956 version of Daytona's annual orgy of speed was marked by a high level of factory participation that followed at times a no-holds-barred format. This kept NASCAR officials charged with insuring that the cars running were bonafide production models hopping.

Quite a few Chevys at Daytona developed a strange tendency towards losing their fan belts during speed runs which had the effect of increasing their top end potential by several miles per hour. Nearly as quickly as they finished their runs however a NASCAR official was on hand to disqualify them. One such Chevrolet made one run through the flying mile at 136.62mph before receiving its pink slip from NASCAR.

Eventually the fastest "legal" Chevrolet recorded a new class record of 121.335mph for the flying mile with a second Chevy reaching 81.335mph for the standing start mile run. In this event Chevrolet could not quite equal the winning speed of a Dodge D-500 of 81.78mph. It's also worth noting that prior to the Daytona Speed Week a 240bhp Plymouth Fury had been clocked at 82.52mph for the standing start mile. Overall at the 1956 Daytona Speed Week, Ford with 584 points to Chevrolet's 566 was awarded the Pure Oil Manufacturers Trophy.

The last year for the Chevrolet body introduced in 1955 was the 1957 model run. To many Chevrolet fans 1957 is the year as far as they are concerned. Whether or not the styling of the '57 is superior to that of the '55 and '56 models is obviously a matter of personal choice, but judging from the current *Old Cars Price Guide* the '57s seem to have the edge.

Both Ford and Plymouth broke with the normal three year cycle of new body designs and emerged with new bodies and in Plymouth's case a fairly sophisticated torsion bar suspension for 1957. It's definitely a tribute to the quality of the 1955 Chevrolet's styling that it could be sufficiently updated to enable Chevrolet to finish in a virtual deadheat with Ford in the 1957 production race. According to Ray Miller's *Chevrolet-U.S.A.-1*, Ford produced 1,522,408 1957 model cars to Chevrolet's 1,522,549.

It's hard to determine which was the greater catalyst to sales, Chevrolet's styling or its ability to perform. In both cases Chevrolet was loaded for bear. Although my personal preferences leans to the '55s as the best looking Chevrolet of the 1955-57 era, the current and apparently timeless greater appeal of the '57 as a collector's car seems to put me in the minority.

"Sweet, Smooth and Sassy" was how Chevrolet described its 1957 models with that last adjective obviously intended as a succinct description of its performance capability. Even if the '57s had been visually unchanged the availability of the "Ramjet" fuel injection system on any Chevrolet would have assured Chevy of a good deal of favorable publicity.

With the introduction of this system Chevrolet became the first American car to offer fuel injection on its passenger cars. More over its top form, the "Super Turbo-Fire 283," with 283bhp at 6,200 rpm became a member of the elite "one horsepower per cubic inch club" which had always had a distinctly European character to it.

It's no wonder that with this engine to back its ad claims up, that Chevrolet could print advertisements with copy that read: "Chevy Comes to the Line *Loaded* for '57! That's the big scoop this season — for Chevrolet has more goodies under that bold hood that you'll find this side of Stuttgart!"

Built by GM's Rochester Products Division, which provided them to Chevrolet completely adjusted and ready for installation. Chevrolet's fuel injection system was a continuous flow unit in which a fuel pump supplied fuel to a fuel bowl where a high pressure gear pump, driven by a cable stemming from the distributor housing sent it on to the fuel control valve. This pump was capable of providing up to 200 pounds pressure. At the fuel control valve a spill plunger, controlled by the pressure inside the valve chamber determined, along with diaphragms by both airflow through an air meter and past a throttle valve, the volume of gas going to the injector nozzles. At the nozzles air was mixed with the gas with the combination then sprayed into each intake port.

In a fuel injected Chevrolet there was no acceleration lag as was the case occasionally with Chevys equipped with dual four barrel carbs, although some early F.I. Chevrolets did experience problems that caused a fuel cut-off during acceleration. A second problem, rough idling which occurred when the fuel nozzles got warm was solved by slightly increasing their length which extended them into the airstream. Furthermore the fuel injection system was unaffected by altitude and the position of the car. Thus there was no fuel starvation in hard cornering.

Chevrolet V-8s for 1957 were offered both in 265 and 283 cubic inch versions. The 265cid, 162bhp V-8 was available only when linked either to a three speed or overdrive equipped Chevrolet.

The larger V-8 derived its extra cubic inches from a growth in bore to 3.875" from 3.75" and came in 185, 220, 245, 250, 270 and 283 horsepower rating. All V-8s of 220 and more horsepower using manual transmissions had semi-centrifugal clutches which Chevrolet claimed produced greater force on the pressure plate.

The 270hp V-8 with two four-barrel carburetors used the famous Duntov cam and solid valve lifters of the 283hp fuel injected engine.

This seemed destined to end the flow of high performance cars from Chevrolet or any other manufacturer for that matter. But the American competitive spirit and the half-century old love affair Americans had enjoyed with their automobiles were twin forces too powerful for any scrap of paper to stifle and for Chevrolet and its compatriot competitors. The best was yet to come.

Identification

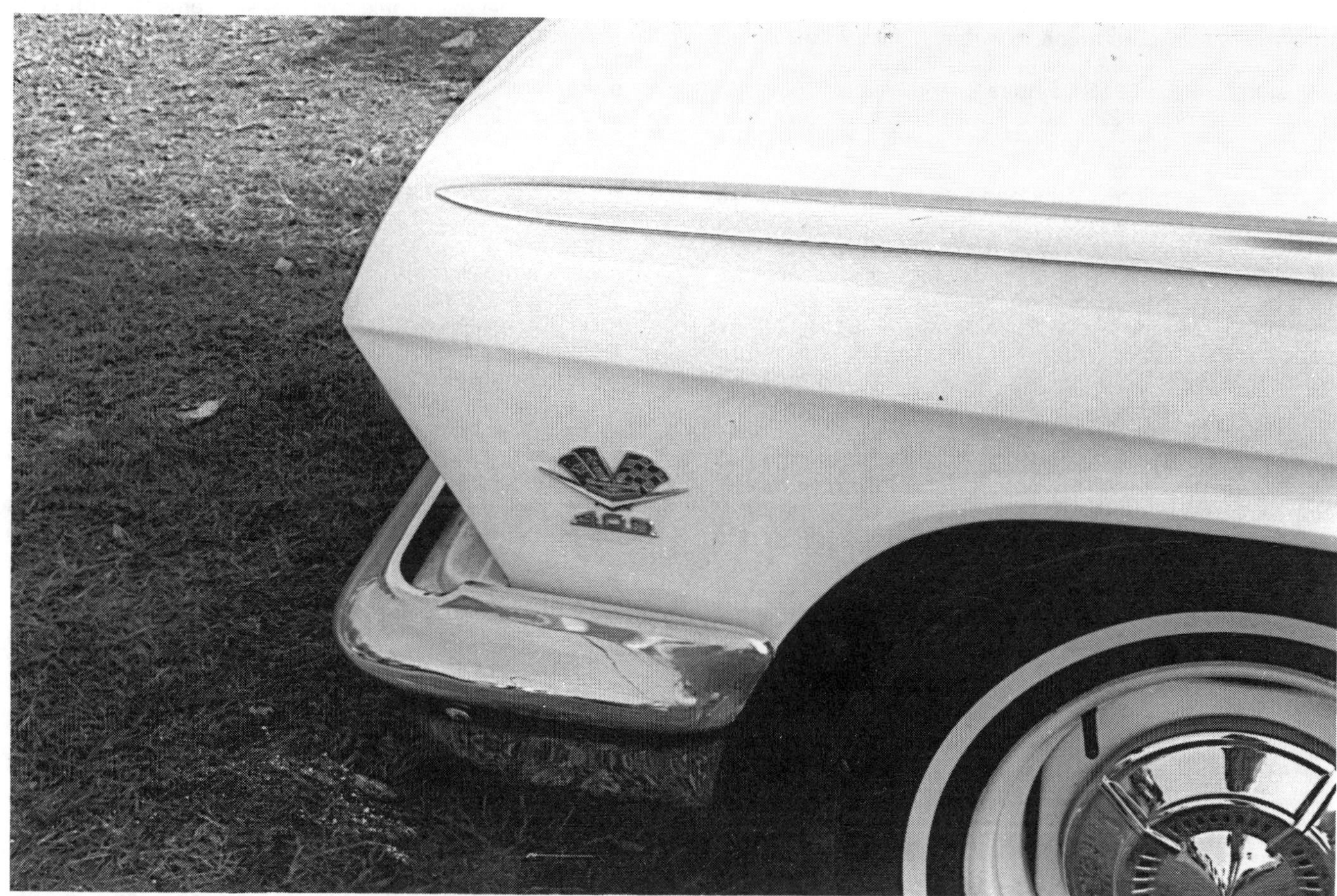

If you were a young lad growing up in the late 40's or early 50's, there came a time in your life when great changes began to occur. You suddenly began taking notice of things you had never paid attention to before. It seemed to be an affliction common to most seventh or eighth grade boys; and by the time you reached high school, it was hopeless.

The symptoms usually began with the identification of different makes of automobiles. It progressed through this initial phase to a more complex one — the specifications of each different model. It cumulated, in certain critical patients, with the identification of different makes of cars — entirely by the sound they made.

You found yourself stopping at automobile showrooms on the way home from school; and lengthy discussions as to which car was the best, often preceded most of the homework assignments. Everyone had a favorite car - an ideal car. Maybe, if you were like many of those youngsters, your favorite was the hot Olds Rocket 88 — "The fastest thing on wheels" — they said. If you couldn't have an Olds, you thought you might settle for a Ford V8. True it wasn't a modern overhead valve engine, but it was a V8, and nobody else in the low price field offered one.

Chevrolet, like Plymouth, was known to most young people, as the old folks car. It was the kind of car your

by Bob Hovorka

older aunt and uncle owned. You know the ones; they always came over on Saturday nights and spent hours talking about the depression, the war, and how much better things were back then. You never could understand why they wanted to talk about all that "old stuff."

Well, one Saturday morning, your mom received a phone call from them, saying they would be over early with a big surprise. Time passed slowly, hindered by anticipation; and when they finally did arrive, everyone in the family crowded around the front bay window, peering through the folds in the pulled back, lace curtains. Your sister was the first one out the door; you following close behind. Yes, they had a new car, and any new car was sure worth a hard run down the driveway to see. The whole family was out by the time the car had pulled up to the door. Your uncle shut off the brand new 1950 Chevrolet, and walked around to open the hood, so your dad could see the engine. It might have been new, but the Fleetline 4 door, with its fastback styling, looked old fashioned. The Styleline, with its notched roof, looked more modern — but that was just like your uncle!

Soon the whole family was piling in for a ride. "Yes sir," exclaimed your uncle — "No need to shift anymore; it's all automatic."

Your mother seemed fascinated by the Powerglide. "Why anyone could drive this car!"

But you could count on dad. "No, I like to shift for myself, you've got no control over this thing." Little did dad know, that a few short years later, he too would be putting the gear shift lever into drive, instead of first.

As the car pulled into the street, you understood what all the fellas at school were talking about. The engine sounded like it was flying, but the car, now loaded with four adults and two children, moved slowly ahead. "Takes a little getting used to," smiled your uncle. "But once you get the hang of it, there's nothing like it. Really easy to drive." You listened patiently, as your dad and uncle talked about the new car. Economical, easy to drive, easy to work on — were the words you heard — and you hoped your father wouldn't buy one!

But years pass quickly at that age. And soon your generation was passing out of school and haunting used car lots for a vehicle of their own. You dreamed of that brand new two seater Thunderbird, or maybe a new Chevy - now a V8 with power pack. Yet, you knew it was not to be. So, as you walked down the "automobile row" of your town, your eyes glanced past the first two rows of cars, almost wishing they weren't there. You had to look further back. The third or fourth row, or maybe that old Chevy convertible parked along side the garage in back. You walked over the crushed stone parking lot to the old wooden garage. A small addition that looked like a front porch formed the office. The car didn't look too bad, and it was a '49, so at least it couldn't have Powerglide. As you walked around the car, the door of the office opened, and a large heavy set man, carrying a half eaten sandwich, walked over. He wiped his mouth with his hand. "How 'about it son — it's a good car — just took it in this morning — haven't had a chance to have my mechanic go over it yet, but I'm sure it'll run out just fine — You interested? — Here's my card — just call me Sam — Yes sir, Sam, the GOOD used car man — bring your father and you can take it out." Of course, you never got a chance to utter a word; so you nodded, put the card in your pocket, and left.

Getting dad to look at the car wasn't the easiest thing you've ever done. But finally, after a day or two of prodding, with your mind emersed in the constant fear that the car would be sold; dad agreed to go. After some haggling, which even dad seemed to really enjoy, the car was yours; and even dad said 250 bucks wasn't a bad price.

Upon driving you "new" car for a while it was discovered that a valve job was in order. Now the words of your uncle, "easy to work on," were really appreciated. A valve job on stovebolt was a nice Saturday afternoon project - your first experience at working on your own car. Most times it didn't even entail new valves, just a tube of "Prussian Blue" and a hand grinding tool; which looked like a stick with a rubber suction cup on one end. For $2.44, you bought a new head gasket; 52¢ more added a manifold gasket set, and for another 50¢ you bought a rocker arm cover gasket. It was a great father and son project; for the old stovebolt was very lenient as far as any critical tolerances were concerned. After doing the valve job, which of course you bragged about to all your buddies, you thought of yourself as a skilled mechanic. And even though it was a 6 cylinder - it was a convertible.

Soon you made other improvements. A bullnose strip set you back about $2; while what you really wanted - a split manifold and dual intake manifold with twin carburetors — would have to remain a dream. After all, the cheapest split exhaust manifold kit was about $22, while the dual intake manifold was $39. The carbs were about another $17 apiece, and that added up to nearly one half the price of the car.

It wasn't fast or flashy, but the old stovebolt was reliable. Many times it carried more people than the law legally allowed in any car. And, through all the years you owned it — it never failed to start, or get you wherever you were going. It probably had more coats of Blue Coral lovingly applied to its somewhat less than new exterior, than most brand new cars would receive in their lifetime. Its tires were replaced with some obscure brand, and even they seemed to give reliable service when installed on the old stovebolt. It was that kind of car. Though it acquired a set of lowering blocks along the way, it never did get the dual carburetors — and the closest thing to dual exhausts, was a glass pack muffler with a set of flexible pipe extensions, that branched back from the single exhaust pipe. As the years passed, it burned a little oil, but still remained dependable — probably the most dependable car you've ever owned — and maybe ever will!

But there was a new wave coming. A second generation. These auto adolescents (the time boys first begin to notice cars) came of age just as the small block Chevy came of age. Their dreams were of those hot performers. They didn't want to settle for a seven year old Chevy — one three or four years old, was old enough — they wanted those 55's through 57's.

They grew up with the ads that proclaimed Chevy's new V8 was actually lighter than the 6 it replaced. They thrived on the pictures that showed how Chevy engineers had cut the weight of the frame with a U-shaped cowl and stamped underbody, that fastened to it for added strength. They didn't want that high, "old folks" car - when used car lots were showing those low, lightweight Chevys that looked fast even sitting still beneath the glare of the open faced light bulbs.

Every boy knew that the new body, coupled to the 162 hp, stock in 1955, or the 270 hp power pack in 1957, made Chevy the top performance car available. Oh, they dreamed of the 283 hp fuel injected Chevy, but few ever saw one on the street. And even if they bought a lower H.P. series, all the hop up accessories were available to make it a top performer.

The look of the school parking lots changed drastically; from either no student cars, or very few old ones — to practically all brand new cars by the end of the decade.

And there came a further split. The custom look, versus the strict performer. Though the convertible or hardtop was ideal for cruising through the neighborhood drive-in, the stripped down two door suddenly became the king of the hill.People soon found out that the long time status symbol — the convertible — though flashy, gave away too much of a weight advantage to the cheaper two door sedan. And many can still remember the night it happened.

Mighty fine — 1949

A '56 sedan with power pack — "The Sleeper"

The quiet summer air hung heavy over the small drive-in, as a young man and his girl sat munching fries and sipping malts. The convertible occupied the front row, paint glistening and top carefully stowed beneath its vinyl cover. It looked long and lethal, as it crouched down on its lowered rear springs. The accessory continental kit nearly touched the ground, and the twin pipes hinted of the mighty power packed V8, that nestled snugly beneath its highly polished hood. The multi-colored fluorescent lights, which hung beneath the overhang of the drive-in, reflected rainbow hues across its deeply wrapped windshield; and the combination of sparkling lights and sparkling chrome, lent an aura of magic to the vehicle. While not new, its engine had been worked on several times, and the twin quads, though thirsty, kept it more than able to do battle with some of the newer, bigger and heavier cars.

Suddenly there was a loud rumble as a two door, 150 sedan — which looked like someone had borrowed it from their grandfather, and sounded like they had blown out the muffler — waddled through the drive-in. It of course was parked next to the convertible, and the owner blipped the engine slightly, several times before shutting it off. He looked like trouble — tight faded Levis, worn low — and a white T-shirt, with a pack of cigarettes forming a rectangular bulge in one of the rolled up sleeves. He got his malt, climbed back into the car with a scowl, and everyone knew the convertible would have to prove its mettle.

The arrangements were made, and on a scheduled road, the race was on. But it only took a short while. The two cars left the line together, each small block screaming a series of rapidly ascending notes - holding the final high note, till it sounded like a wailing siren about to burst its mountings. A shift came at a time far beyond the wildest expectations and once more the obstreperous shriek began to rise. There was a further shift — but by that time it was all over. The heavy bodied convertible was finished. The ex-champ still had "Class" — but that night, the humble looking two door sedan, became king of the hill.

He retained his throne for quite some time; mocking the 348 Chevy — too heavy! He now occupied the front row of the drive-in. Although he had no top to put down, he could still roll down the windows and enjoy the soft summer breeze that caressed his shiny, unadorned exterior. A breeze that carried with it, the sweet scent of chocolate malts, and the pungent tang of salty fries - and a new sound that had begun floating across the country - a surfing sound. And there were more new sounds coming!

Through 1959 and 60, Chevy was big for bigs sake. It had lost is lean, lethal look. In 1961, although within inches of the 1960 size, it looked more unified - more taunt, than it had in years. And, there were rumors of a new engine; an engine that would once again put a new Chevy on the top of the hill.

By mid '61, there were several testers who claimed to have driven this new engined car. The magic 0 to 60 times smacked of seven seconds - stock! But very, "very" few '61's ever saw that new engine. However, in 1962, it began to be seen around the country. It created the same sort of sensation, nurtured the same sort of mystical following, the first small block had done. The sounds of the Beach Boys, and their popular car songs filled the air. But one song, more then all the rest put together, told it all. Just three numbers — three big numbers — 4-0-9. In 1962, the acceleration times were blinding. Chevy had finally dethroned the old monarch. Even with a single quad, it reached the magic 60 mph, from rest, in about seven seconds. With two quads, a 4 speed, and a breathed engine - well, let's just put it this way — 409 was the new undisputed king — and his praises were sung throughout the land.

But his reign was a short one. By mid '63, Ford's new 427 was the big gun. Though the 409 was still offered through the start of 1965, everyone knew it was all over. Chevy's new Turbo-Jet 396, would have to do battle.

However, big cars of all makes were having troubles by '65. In 1966, Chevy offered the 427. But the GTO had begun to rumble. Chevy countered with 396 Chevelles — and the end of the big super cars was in sight. The battle of the little giants had begun!

The new mid-size cars, using the same big engines simply beat the pants off the big guys. The new kings of the hill were reverting to the original sizes, that started it all. Chevy for 1955, was mounted on a 115 inch wheelbase, as 195.6 inches long, and 74 inches wide. Chevelle for 1966, was mounted on a 115 inch wheelbase, was 197 inches long, and 75 inches wide. The big difference was the engine. The '55, had 265 cubic inches, the '66, had 396! It may not have handled as well with that heavy engine — but go? — It sure did!

The 396 grew to 427 in the big cars. Then, with pollution controls becoming more and more stringent, and robbing more and more power, it mustered in at 402 and finally 454. Pollution controls, and a while later high gasoline prices, wrote "fini" to an era. An era in which America's lowest priced cars, offered more straight line performance than any other mass produced cars — in the entire world! There were faster, better handling cars being built in Europe; but they cost nearly six or seven times as much.

So, if you have one of those hi-performance miracles — of America's engineering and production know how — keep it, treasure it, and be proud of it. For on a dollar for dollar basis, there "is" nothing in the whole world, that can touch it!

Mighty fine — 409 — 1962 Bel Air Style

Sometimes Dreams Come True

By David Reed

Ever since I was a kid I've been interested in cars. I remember that when the 1955 Chevy was introduced, I thought that it was the nicest looking car I'd ever seen and when the 1956 Chevy came out, I thought it was an improvement over the '55 because it looked more dignified, but when the 1957 Chevy was introduced, it was love at first sight. Without a doubt, it was the most beautiful car that had ever been made.

I still remember seeing my first '57 Chevy convertible. It was mounted on a turntable, sitting in the middle of the showroom floor. I first saw the gold grille and massive chrome bumper and bumper guards. As the car slowly turned, I saw the little gold louvers on the front fenders, then the chrome strip going all the way down the side and

A 1957 Bel Air convertible, one man's dream.

dividing into two pieces with a large chrome insert between the other two pieces of chrome. Finally, I saw the back of the car. The thing that immediately caught my eye was the continental kit with its stainless steel ring and the bumper forming a little fence around the bottom of it. The car was painted Sierra Gold. The combination of chrome, gold paint and beautiful styling were forever etched into my mind.

By the time I graduated from high school in 1959, I had learned a lot about the mechanics of an automobile and I was more than ever convinced that the '57 Chevy was the car for me. The 283 V8 was easy to work on and a good performer.

By the fall of 1960 I had a steady job and enough money saved for a down-payment on a car. My father told me he would lend me the rest of the money to buy the car and my search began. Within a month I had located a Sierra Gold '57 Chevy convertible on the front row of a used car lot. The following Saturday my father and I went to take a look at it. After giving the Chevy a close inspection, it was obvious that it had had a hard life. Setting next to the Chevy was a brown and yellow '57 Ford two-door hardtop equipped with a continental. After having a short one-sided discussion with my father, at which time it was pointed out that it would be cold in the winter and that somebody would probably cut the convertible top, we decided that I should buy the Ford. I should have known that my father would like the Ford better than the Chevy. I had heard him tell the story many times about the Model A he drove all through the Second World War and up until 1950 when he bought a new Ford, not to mention the '59 Ford he was driving at the time.

I will always remember as I drove off the car lot with the '57 Ford. I looked back through the rear-view mirror and saw the Chevy and knew I had made the first big mistake of my adult life. I consoled myself with the fact that the Ford had a continental and the Chevy didn't.

As time goes by, things like '57 Chevy convertibles are pushed to the back of one's mind. I got married, bought a house and acquired my fair share of bills.

In 1971 I decided to restore an old car. I spent six months looking for a good restorable '57 Chevy convertible but living on the East coast, all the '57's I found were eaten up with rust and were not the car of my dreams.

I purchased a 1928 Chevy Landau Coupe in good restorable condition and spent the next three years restoring it. The following year I took it to a lot of car shows and won some trophys and had a great time, but there was still something missing, namely the fact that I wanted a gold '57 Chevy convertible. I decided to sell my '28 and renew my search for the car of my dreams. After giving it careful consideration, I decided that I would check out any unrestored original '57 Chevy convertibles that I could find listed for sale within a thousand miles of my home. I spent a lot of money on gas and phone bills over the next few months. It started to seem like the more '57's I looked at, the farther my dream car got from me and I totally gave up my search for about a year.

I may not have had the car but at least I had the dream. I had decided many years before that if I ever did get the car, that I would chrome-plate everything under the hood that should be chrome-plated, install wire wheel covers like the ones used on a '64 Chevy Super Sport and, of course, a complete set of gauges under the dash.

One Friday evening while talking to my wife about starting another search for a '57, she said that I should let the seller come to me instead of me chasing all over the country. I said it sounded good but how do I do it. She stated that I should run an ad in my local Sunday paper, to which I said that I had lived in this area all my life and I knew of every '57 Chevy within a hundred miles. She rebuffed me with: "nobody knows where all of anything is." If they did, nobody would ever find a buried treasure or a lost Rembrandt. To keep from having a long discussion with her on the pros and cons of her idea, I told her I would place the ad. The ad read: "wanted: '57 Chevy convertible; will pay your price for the right car."

On Sunday I got three phone calls about cars I had previously looked at. The ad only ran in the Sunday paper, so I didn't expect any more calls. On the following Tuesday evening I got a call from a man who said he had a '57 Chevy he would like to sell. When he gave me his address, I knew it was a car I hadn't previously known of since it was located only about four miles away. I made an appointment to see the car the next day, but after hanging up the phone I realized that the man hadn't stated whether or not the car was a convertible. I further realized that it may not be a '57 or even a Chevrolet. By the next morning I had decided that looking at the car would be a total waste of time but I didn't have anything else to do so I went to take a look.

When the man opened the garage door I couldn't believe my eyes; there sat a Sierra Gold '57 Chevy Bel Air convertible. As I walked along the side of the car, I noticed that the paint was faded but the body was not rusted out. When I neared the back of the car I saw the stainless steel ring. Yes, there it was, a factory continental. I turned and asked the man how much he wanted for the car. He informed me that he would not dicker and that I would have to pay his price. I agreed not to dicker. He then said the price was $800, take it or leave it. I said I'll take it. I left and went to the bank and returned within 20 minutes. As I handed him the money he said he had changed his mind. He stated that the tires on the '57 had better tread on them than the tires on his regular car and that he now wanted $850. I handed him the extra $50 and he gave me a bill of sale and said he would have to look for the title. He also said that the car hadn't been started in about 15 years and that he figured the motor was frozen. It was at that time I realized that I hadn't checked to see if the car even had a motor. I returned the next morning with a car trailer to retrieve my prize. When I opened the car door I was amazed at the condition of the upholstery. There were no tears or stains. As my eyes wandered, I saw a Wonderbar radio, automatic transmission and an odometer reading 51,788 miles. Once I had pushed the car outside, I opened the hood to discover a 283 V8 with a four barrel carb and attached to the back of the generator was a power steering unit. When I stepped back to admire the car, I saw that it had 1965 California tags on it.

When the previous owner handed me the title he indicated that he had only owned the car for three weeks. The story he related to me was that his brother was a career man in the Navy and that he had bought the car new in Los Angeles. In 1965, he was transferred to Norfolk, Va. and had driven the car east. After being there a couple of months he was transferred to Japan and at the time he stored the car in the garage. He expected to return in about a year but when the year was up, he decided to spend the rest of his Navy career in the far East. As the years went by he lost interest in the '57 Chevy and gave it to his brother but the brother didn't want the car so he sold it to me.

After getting the '57 Chevy home I decided it would be safer to rebuild the motor than to try and start it. While rebuilding the motor, I had most of the parts under the hood chrome-plated. I installed a new top, four new white wall tires, and rebuilt the complete brake system. I then gave it a fresh coat of Sierra Gold paint, added wire wheel covers and gauges under the dash.

Now that I have restored the '57 Chevy exactly the way I always wanted, I realize that if you want something bad enough and long enough that sometimes dreams do come true.

Country

Cruisin'

By Paul Holt

In the spring of 1954 I'd just graduated from high school. Getting a job, looking at college, trying to impress the opposite sex, living at home and making some effort to be mobile can all be very demanding. At times the priorities get shuffled.

In my particular case, finding a job was put at the top of the list. After all, without money hardly any of the other goals could be reached. With a little help from my relatives I was able to locate a position with a company that would keep me in my homestate for ten years. I would grow mentally, physically and financially during this time. But it's the first four years that hold a special affection for me.

The Midwest is a good place to live and grow up in. My cousins lived on farms — big ones — 500 to 1,000 acres of grain and livestock. I ran around with them and spent many hours and days on these farms. The small towns, long flat highways and dusty roads were all part of growing up in rural America. So were grain elevators, hay rides, tractors, corn fields, cattle, and outhouses.

My brother, 16 months younger than me, and I were close. At the age of 18 we began to drift apart. He stayed with the family business and I decided to strike out on my own. We still lived at home, slept in the same room and discussed our awkward adolescence. I supposed I could be referred to as the maverick in the family. Hell raising came easy and one escape was to vent my feelings on the farm with my cousins.

Getting the job fresh out of high school was a natural. After all, I worked every night and weekends during high school. Riding my bicycle and walking home from work during these school days gave me an opportunity to stop and visit one of the local drive-ins. A quick fried tenderloin, a soda and some jukebox music and maybe a game of pinball was often required before going home for supper.

After high school, walking to work on my first job was proving to be a little too much. So, as most young men my age, I began looking at the great American automobile. At my time and location in life, there was only one make of car if you were to be considered one of the "in" persons. This car, FORD, had it all over competitors for style, speed and hotrodding, not to mention affordability.

However, rumors were out that something big was happening at General Motors. Something that would be the start of the horsepower race. Something that would challenge Ford, be a great step forward for GM and, to this day, be *the* answer for young Americans wanting a power car.

My dad told me if I were to get a job and become able to afford a car, he would help with the financing. It would be my responsibility to make the payments and keep the maintenance up. With this support, I began looking at the new offerings.

After a hard, cold winter with the frost coming out of the ground, spring couldn't be far away. My mind began to wander. One car fascinated me. The style, the flowing lines and the color combinations were all just too much to imagine. I was young and impressive. It was a whole new beginning, both for me and the car. I took a chance. With a new job and the necessity of impressing the ladies on the line, I did it! The order was placed and it would take four to six weeks for delivery. After three weeks, I couldn't wait anymore. I accepted one from the sales floor. The only difference was that it had an automatic transmission instead of a standard shift. It was even more beautiful to touch and sit in than expected. That first new car means something special.

One of the most impressive things was the engine performance. It had power and speed to spare. A real experience to drive. What else could you expect from *Chevrolet in 1955*. Yes, it was the Bel Air two-door hardtop, Gypsy Red and Shoreline Beige, V8 and powerpack. Purchased from Manning Chevrolet, Des Moines, Iowa.

I won't go into all the differences of this particular car vs. the competition. The engine and the new body style were two of the important reasons I bought the Chevrolet; the most important reason is that it was best for me.

I literally drove the wheels off this car. Many trips to Minnesota, even New York City and back, all in the first seven months. I was in New York when I heard the sad news that James Dean, my movie idol, had died. His movies and lifestyle had made an impression on me. Mixed up kids, fast cars and parents who seemed not to understand. At one time I guess we all were "A Rebel Without A Cause."

The Chevy was washed and waxed weekly. Daily trips to the local drive-in were required. Jukeboxes, hamburgers, tenderloins and frosty mugs of root beer and cute car hops were all part of the lifestyle. Cruisin' the downtown streets, looking for a one-to-two block drag, just to impress those who might be watching. Golden Tone Glass Pack mufflers were the rage — fuzzy dice and an occasional set of lowering blocks were too.

I remember a very satisfying drag I had with an early '56 Ford convertible. With me in my '55 Chevy, it started from a dead start and ended with me passing him at 97 miles per hour on the two-lane highway and topping out at 107 miles an hour. The passengers in my car were witnesses and couldn't stop talking about it for weeks.

But this was only the beginning of what would turn out to be one heck of a year for a young man and his first new car.

Another time on the way home, some 11 miles out of town in the early evening, I slammed down on the accelerator. The rear end settled down as the automatic downshifted in passing gear. The Golden Tone mufflers screamed as they came alive. The car lurched forward and fishtailed a little. I straightened it out and away we went. 40-50-60 then 80 miles an hour. Still the speedometer climbed. Close to 100 and still climbing. Ahead was five miles of flat Iowa highway. Almost immediately another car came in behind me and started to pursue. For the next four miles I tried to outrun him. He flashed his high beams at me. What did this mean? Was it an unmarked highway patrol car? Was it one of the local police cars from the small farming communities patrolling this section of the road? Knowing the back country roads was to my advantage, I made a hard right turn onto the dirt road and, sure enough, he followed me. The chase was hopeless. My car, the only one of its type and style in these small farming towns, was well known. I didn't have a chance. I pulled over and got out. To my great surprise, pulled in behind me was a man getting out of a 1955 Packard. He had heard of the power in these '55 Chevys and just wanted to see what it would do. He was disappointed that the Packard couldn't catch and pass me. I sighed of relief and drove slowly and carefully the rest of the way home.

Nineteen fifty-five gave way to 1956 and, sure enough, Chevy outdid itself again. In less than 12 months I put over 25,000 miles on the '55 odometer. That was a lot of miles in those days, with no superhighways.

In March of '56 there was an early thaw and the grass was turning green. A young man was happy to see winter pass and his fancy again turned to cruisin'.

One Sunday, my brother, cousin, a close friend and I started downtown cruisin'. We picked up two female riders and decided to show them what a '55 Chevy would do. Six of us, sitting shoulder to shoulder, headed for the country roads. A lot of small talk, the radio was playing Elvis and other rock 'n' roll. Not too much to worry about. Gravel rocks from the road were being thrown into the fenders, the car began to swerve a little, soft sand in the middle of the road created a handling problem. Suddenly over a rise we went, then down a hill and then a sharp 90 degree turn to the right. I began to realize that I wasn't going to make the turn. I looked to the right and saw a big ravine covered with large boulders. That wasn't the way to go. I pumped the brakes a couple of times, then my mistake. I locked them up. We began to skid sideways, I looked up and saw passengers where the roof was supposed to be. I realized that we were rolling over. The sound was deafening. The car left the road, skidded 265 feet, then went into a ditch, taking about 35 feet of fence, before coming to a stop upside down. All was quiet; the only noise was the wheels turning. Slowly I began to get up. I noticed that my door was open and I was half outside of the car. I began to call out the names of the other riders. All answered but one. My cousin "Goat," why had he not answered? The top was crushed down to the seats. It took a few minutes to recognize the broken mass of metal. Five of us were out without even a scratch.

"Goat's" arm was pinned under the door post. A large gash in his forehead gave us reason for concern. The girls asked to sit by the side of the road. Confusion reigned everywhere. Suddenly "Goat" began to moan, we rushed to his side. He complained about his feet hurting. We freed his arm and told him not to move.

The weather was cold, the wind blew off the open March fields. We all were shivering and the girls were crying. A noise came from the top of the hill, telling us that a farmer was on his way with a tractor. He heard the crash and knew what to expect. (We were not the first to leave the road in this particular spot.) He gave us assistance and called the highway patrol.

The ambulance had to come some 35 miles from town to get us. We waited over an hour. Some of the passengers were going into shock and the cold wind wasn't helping any. When the ambulance arrived, "Goat" was carefully loaded onto the stretcher and we began the long ride back into town. He was complaining about his feet hurting all the way.

My brother went to tell the bad news to the parents of the other passengers. The girls were left off downtown where we picked them up. The patrolman knew my family, followed me to the hospital and cautioned me to stay there. There was the matter of the ticket. Since his superiors were with him, the charges were going to be tough. "Reckless driving."

Now, just prior to this Sunday drive, I had talked "Goat" out of taking his car. It seems I had more money for gas. It may have been a good thing. You see, "Goat's" car was a

I'll always remember Country Cruisin'. It started with a '55 Bel Air two-door hardtop with a 265 V8 and Powerglide.

I settled down a bit in '57 but my Bel Air was plenty "cool."

'55 Chevy convertible. Goodness knows what could have happened to us.

The feeling one has after such an ordeal is hard to explain. This should be a lesson; the sound of the crash is terrible but the silence that follows will stay with you forever.

At the hospital, after many hours and seeing some very excited parents, we learned of "Goat's" condition. He had a minor fractured forehead and one very badly broken back. It came so close to paralyzing him that he couldn't stand the weight of his pants on his legs. That was the reason for his feet hurting. Here I was unhurt but due to my poor judgement, I could have put my best friend in a wheelchair for life.

"Goat" did not have surgery but an eight month cast completely enclosing his body from neck to abdomen helped make us all appreciate life and slow down some.

Since the '55 was now junk, what was I to do for wheels? The answer was a black 1956 Chevrolet convertible, powerpack-stick shift. Just once I wanted to be first off the line in a drag race. The old automatic had staying power, but the stick shift beat everyone out of the hole. But where I was raised you needed more than a good start. Racing normally meant three to four miles or more of just out and out running.

The '56 convertible was used in 4th of July parades and used to carry homecoming queens to the football games. The '56 received the same tender-loving care as the '55. When you are one of the fastest, the challenges for racing don't come as often.

As time progressed, I became wiser. The street drags were becoming old stuff and I decided to slow up, hopefully for good.

In the spring of '57, my brother came home with a new Chevy that topped them all. A Bel Air two-door hardtop with fuel-injection. It really could blow the doors off anything. He showed me what it would do and I couldn't believe it. Ninety-five miles per hour in second gear and it topped out at over 120. The time had come for me to hang it up. This was just too fast for an old man of 21.

I traded the '56 for a '57 Bel Air hardtop, regular V8, and left the racing to the younger kids. The record books would be written that year around fuelies and for the rest of the year, all around the country, Chevy would be out in front.

Nothing spectacular happened with the '57. I just needed a new one to feel part of the "in" crowd. Good solid transportation, reliable, dependable and good lookin'. I had my fun but '58 was coming and so were the Impalas.

The '58 Impalas were too much to pass up. The horsepower wars continued and again Chevy had another hot one. The 348 engine was just more than I could resist. This time it was a two-door hardtop Impala with Turboglide. The car had real power and could easily cruise all day at 80 miles per hour. I took some long trips with it and highway cruisin' was a dream. I might add that it was one of the first cars that drank gas with a vengeance. But at 26 cents per gallon, who cared?

The Impala served me well but like many cars before it, it got away and is lost in the past.

Time, business and circumstance would relocate me to Florida. But my roots are still in the Midwest, where those long rolling two-lane country highways are probably still being used for racing.

On one of my return trips to Iowa a few years ago, I retraced many of those roads and reminisced about the days in the '50's. Things have changed, Interstate highways now cross many of the old hangouts and the drive-ins have given way to the fast food houses.

During the '50's, the hamburger was just another sandwich. It was the giant tenderloin that was king. And for 25 cents, too.

A lot of the past now seems like a dream — some good and some bad. There are too many memories of yesterday to put into words. They will eventually get a little foggy and probably fade away.

For now, my fondness for these four cars held a special place in the corner of my heart. I longed to someday replace those hot Chevys. Twenty-six years after buying the first '55, the long search began to come true. The prices are considerably higher but so is everything else. But I'm finding these treasures now in the Midwest. Could they be the same cars I owned way back when? I don't know but I love them.

The old adage that "you can take the boy out of the country but you can't take the country out of the boy" still holds true. I'll always remember Country Cruisin'.

P.S.: "Goat" fully recovered and today is working on a farm. My brother is still with the family business. He wrecked the '57 by running it into a lake in Northern Iowa on his way home from visiting his girlfriend. My other cousin still owns a farm. He recovered from a bad accident with his car. The two girls were only seen once more walking downtown. They completely ignored us. As for me, I can look back and at times laugh and at times cry.

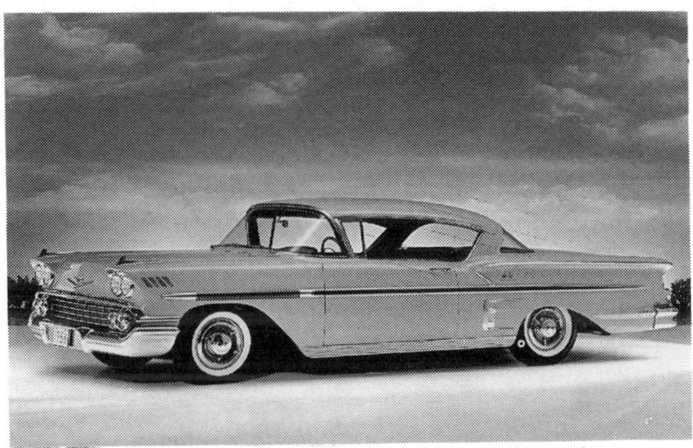
When the '58 Impala was introduced, I just couldn't resist.

Nostalgia

By Bob Hovorka

I think it was the rain — the rhythmic patter of silver droplets that broke against the driveway like shattered crystal — the tinkling water that created an abstract symphony as it orchestrated across the shingled roof and down the galvanized gutters. It was the rain that splashed against the overhang, never reaching the open windows, but making its presence known nonetheless.

I leaned back in the office chair, staring into the translucent veil that distorted familiar shapes as it thickened in the distance — watching and listening, as it shut out the sights and sounds of today — creating misty glimpses of a time long past. Years ago, we called it daydreaming — today, we call it nostalgia.

But just what is nostalgia? Webster coldly defines it as: "A longing to return to a past time or irrecoverable circumstances." Yet, auto buffs know it's much more than that. They can see it; they can feel it. To them, it's the sparkle of an early teens, brass bound Model T . . . or the sound of an overhead cam Stutz, of the '20's . . . or the elegance of a 1930's front drive Cord . . . or even the shattered remnants of Preston Tucker's post war dream.

It may not be stock — but this is what many '57's looked like during the '60's — and what many look like today.

For some, it's the throaty rumble of a '32 Ford flathead . . . for others, it's the crisp style of a '41 Cadillac, Series 60 . . . for still others, it's the agile performance of a '55 through '57 Chevy. That's what's so great about automotive nostalgia. It has different meanings for different people — *and* — it's continually changing!

Back in the late '40's, who would have dreamed that pre-war Packards and orphaned Duesenbergs would command the prices they bring today? Even closer; who in the '60's, could predict the large sums of money that would change hands whenever a '55 Nomad, or '57 Chevy convertible changed garages.

Those '55 through '57 Chevys have become far more meaningful than their designers ever dreamed possible — they've become a breed unto themselves. They were born in the post Korean war economy along with many others — they matured more gracefully than most. They carried the gospel of automotive enjoyment to several generations of automobile enthusiasts — and they're not through yet! They introduced an engine that was so inherently right, that decades later, the ability and availability of off the shelf components, still make it viable for everything from home-built hot-rods, to full fledged race cars.

During the 1960's, the Beach Boys began singing the praises of the mystical 409, and young Chevy owners began equating with the surfing sounds. But even saving their pennies and their dimes; few could afford to buy a brand new 409. However, fives, sixes and sevens were plentiful. They were simple cars to work on; repair parts were readily available — and most important — so were bolt on, hop-up items.

Few '55 through '57 Chevys passed through their entire lives without some touch of their owner's personality — be it custom hub-caps and fender skirts, or '59 Caddy tail light lenses. Fewer still turned their speedometers much past 55,000 miles, without some type of engine modification; be it cam, carb or a simple set of headers. They were loved and fussed over then, and they're loved and fussed over now!

And if you don't believe how much universal charisma they have, all you have to do is take one ride. There is an aura about them that will convince the staunchest disbeliever. He still may not personally like them, but he will have to admit they cause quite a stir. You can't go down any street, or stop at any gas station, without hearing; "My dad owned one of those — my uncle had one just like it, only it was a four door — I owned one in college." Yes, it seems that nearly everyone owned one at some time during the last 30 years.

And, possibly because of the advertising blitz that touted fuel injection and one horsepower per cubic inch (even though most people never saw a fuel injected Chevy in 1957) the '57 seems to stand out. Today, a '57 Chevy is still considered (right or wrong) one of America's fastest cars. It has a mystic quality that is second to none. Even now, thirty-three years after the fact, people still say; "There's nothing built today that can touch that baby!" — True? — False? — It doesn't seem to really matter. People want to believe it! Whatever it had, it still has. Its deeply hooded headlights, and wide mouthed grille, resemble a 1950's jet fighter. Its fins, while not upswept like the '57 Plymouth, or canted like the '57 Ford, are still a focal point for many people. Comments like; "If Chevy would build 'em like that today, they'd sell millions," are quite common.

But back in 1957, things weren't quite so rosy. Ford introduced a completely new car that year, calling it; "A new kind of car, so big, so new, so daringly styled, you'll hardly believe it's a Ford."

Plymouth too, offered a totally new car for 1957, advertising it as; "So far ahead in engineering that it will take the other low-price cars three years to equal it!" They added, "When you drive a PLYMOUTH, suddenly it's

1960."

Chevrolet was stuck in the last year of a three year cycle. Chevy ads spoke of "sparkling new advances." — "You can *see* that a block away, in Chevy's brand new bumper-and-grille front, in the bold flare of its rear fenders, the clean-lined simplicity of its integrated taillight assembly."

That all sounded good on paper, but the leading car magazines looked upon the '57 Chevys as a rehash of 1955 and '56. Even with Chevy's new optional 283, its engines, both standard and optional, were smaller than either Ford or Plymouth. So the big feature articles that year revolved around the all new Fords and Plymouths. Of the '57 Chevy, *Motor Life* quipped; "The car has been extensively restyled to bring it up to date, but it's still short of the 'new look.'"

Why then, is it so popular today? Why do '57 Chevys sell for nearly twice the price of similar model '57 Fords and Plymouths? What magic does it possess? Better yet, is there any way to determine which 1960's or '70's Chevy *might* become the "'57 Chevy" of the '90's?

First of all, there is no way of guaranteeing what car buffs of the '90s will be looking for. The rule that governed the collectibility of the great Classics — that of high quality and limited production — has gone out the window; as witnessed by the popularity of not only '55 through '57 Chevys, but Henry's Model T's, A's and flatheads. Even the new wave of burgeoning '60's muscle cars, while not reaching the production figures of standard bread and butter lines, are certainly far beyond the production numbers of any of the Classics of the '30's. So while it's nice to talk of rare, limited production cars — and those few will always be more valuable than their standard, high volume cousins — there is still a need for some kind of high volume collectible.

One of the biggest factors for extending a car's popularity has been parts availability and after market hop-up accessories. Everyone wants his car to be a little better than his neighbors. It *was* an important factor in the popularity of Ford's Model T's and flathead V8's — it certainly *is* a factor in the popularity of Chevy's small block.

The other thing that helped extend the popularity of the '55 through '57 Chevys, was the drag strip. That magical quarter mile, and its many different classes, kept the 5, 6 and 7 body style (no matter what engine rested betwen its frame rails) a familiar shape to many people who were too young to remember those cars when they were new. And while there are dozens of other factors, these two might be a good clue to the next high volume collectible.

Based on the number of raised rear end and mag wheeled Novas on street and strip, that once lowly compact has some strong points in its favor. While beginning life as a "go for groceries" four or six cylinder, it was quickly recognized as a potential screamer. It wasn't long before Bill Thomas put a 360 HP, 327 fuel injected Corvette engine into a Chevy II. Ray Brock put together an in-depth article for a 1962 issue of *Hot Rod* that quoted 0 to 60 times of "5.2 seconds." Chevy later made over the counter V8 conversion kits available. For 1964, Chevy offered a factory installed 283, as an option. In 1965, the little Chevy could be ordered with a 327, sporting 300 horsepower. For '66, Chevy II was reskinned, and offered a 350 HP, 327. But for 1967, Chevy introduced the Camaro. It wouldn't look good to have Mustang's competition upstaged by Chevy's lowest priced line, so the Chevy II's 327, was dropped to 275 horsepower. For '68, Chevy II was new from stem to stern. That year the Chevy II/Nova sold over 200,000 vehicles. The body style would last, with one major metal reskinning in 1975, until 1979 — when it was unceremoniously given a set of rectangular headlights, and then phased out in a short production year that ended in January of '79.

Nova — could it be the "'57 Chevy" of the '90's?

Through all those years, the Chevy II/Novas were good reliable transportation. They had their hot moments however, with some high horsepower 327's, 350's and even some 396 big blocks. Of course, hop-up accessories are still readily available for both big and small blocks; although the small blocks might prove a little more popular with today's high gasoline prices.

The earlier 1962 through '67 series, are already popular as late model Chevy collector cars. The '68 and up Chevy II/Novas are still quite common — so much so that they're usually not even noticed as they go about their daily business of carrying moms and pops for groceries. But here and there, some young car buff finds a clean, rust free body. Of course, if it has a Super Sport option, so much the better. But Chevy Novas have clean, uncluttered lines, and even the plain jane models take well to a few dress up tricks. A V8 with four speed would also be ideal, but it can be inserted in any model without too much trouble. However, with the high prices of gasoline, there even seems to be an acceptability for nicely detailed sixes.

In parking lots, you see them intermingled with other Novas — but they always look a trifle different. They sit a little higher in the rear haunches, and the mag wheels usually carry some pretty wide tires. If you could look beneath the highly polished hood, you would probably see the small block Chevy, complete with special manifold, cam carburetor and headers, that awaits its master's return. A turn of the key, and Chevy's universal V8 spins to life. A few stabs at the accelerator pedal slows the idle, but it never quite comes down to the familiar smoothness that standard American V8's were so well known for.

Several people look up, and you wonder if it's the meticulously applied candy apple paint, or the bark of its turbo mufflers. Not quite stock! — But neither were 80% of those '55 through '57 Chevys when they were ten or twelve years old. The youthful driver carefully slips the Hurst shifter into first, lets off the clutch, and even the wide tires chirp lightly as he leaves the parking lot. As the clean-lined coupe rounds the corner, and its small block revs a little higher than normal before shifting; you wonder if you might just be watching the "'57 Chevy" of the '90's.

Jim Wangers

Helped Make The Hot One Even Hotter

By Paul Zazarine

To Detroit insiders and post-war performance enthusiasts, the name Jim Wangers is most often associated with Pontiac in general and the GTO in particular. In the past, mention of his name usually ends there. What is little known about this marketing genius is his eary background in high performance, particularly his days with Chevrolet's Campbell Ewald ad agency.

Jim Wangers started his career in the industry early in 1952, joining the W.H. Weintraub and Co., who had just taken over the faltering Kaiser-Frazer account as an account management trainee. After six weeks his knowledge of automobiles so impressed management that he was transferred from New York to Detroit. There he trained under Burt Durkee, who in the past had managed accounts for such automobile companies as Ford and Packard before being wooed to Kaiser-Frazer.

Jim Wangers (on right) is Father of the GTO

Kaiser-Frazer was working under a great disadvantage in the early fifties. While most of the industry was firmly committed to the V-8 engine, KF lacked sufficient capital to develop their own V-8 to be competitive. In a last ditch attempt to bring their cars up to snuff in the marketplace, KF worked with McCullough Paxton to develop a supercharger for the ancient Continental six.

Wangers, realizing that super-chargers create their own atmospheric pressure, saw a way to promote the supercharged six by campaigning it in some type of timed hillclimb. Inquiries to AAA, forerunner of USAC proved fruitful: the Pike's Peak hillclimb record was held by a 1932 Ford V-8. "It was so slow," says Wangers, "it could be broken going up hill backwards."

He put a campaign together, using a supercharged Manhattan to assault the Peak at a projected cost of $150,000 for advertising. Wangers submitted it to management, but the program was turned down as entirely too costly. During his interim with KF, Wangers could see the handwriting on the wall that KF wasn't going to survive in the automobile business, and left Weintraub in the spring of 1953.

He signed on with Campbell-Ewald. It was, as Wangers put it, "like moving from the bottom to the top." Development work was already on the 1955 Chevrolet, and he was assigned to advance planning and sales promotion. There he worked with Ed Cole, developer of the incredible new 265 cubic inch Chevy V-8. Wangers understood the enormous peformance potential of the engine with it's light weight block and drive train. The problem was that Chevy was not yet geared to packaging a performance concept with this engine. Up until that time Chevy had not had the hardware nor the image. Now they had the hardware, but lacked direction.

So when the new "Motoramic Chevrolet" was introduced in the fall of 1954, new styling, paint and trim were stressed, but the new "Turbo-Fire V-8" was only briefly mentioned. Wangers was disappointed that Chevrolet wouldn't focus on the performance aspect of the new V-8, especially in light of it's superiority over Ford's V-8. When he voiced his frustration to higher ups, he got nowhere. A catalyst would be necessary to turn things around, and he found it in the Power Pack.

Initially, released as a police car option, the package consisted primarily of a 4bbl carb and dual exhausts, pumping out 180 hp. In the spring of 1955 it became available as a regular production option. Wangers wrote a memo to management suggesting that Chevy take it's new Power Pack to Daytona Beach and participate in the

Speed Week activities. He argued that Chevrolet would truly come into it's own competing against Chrysler, Ford and Plymouth. His memo was filed away as just another junior executive whim.

Speed Week at Daytona was a rather informal event in the early days. It was NASCAR at it's grassroots. All one needed to do was register, pay a small fee, and one could run on the beach. Enthusiasts flocked to Daytona for Speed Week, culminating in the Daytona 500 stock car race. There was no high speed banked oval as today. Instead, cars ran on the hardpacked sand of the beach and onto a two lane blacktop road that ran parallel to the beach. When brakes got too hot, it was not unusual to run into the edge of the water to cool them down. Chrysler was there to compete with their new 300, as was Ford and Plymouth, along with a few privately sponsored Power Pack and Police Package Chevrolets.

Wangers was proved right. 1955 Chevrolets did well at Daytona, falling short only to the potent Chrysler 300s. Even so, Chevrolet set records in acceleration, in the standing quarter mile and the flying mile events, and was clocked 11 miles per hour faster than Ford and 17 mph faster than the fastest Plymouth. Duran County Police Chief Harold Tapscott had the fastest Chevy at Daytona. His 210 2 door Police Package was clocked at 112.95 mph.

The extraordinary success of Chevrolet during Speed Week was carefully observed by Jim Wangers. He had taken a week's vacation to attend Speed Week to watch his predictions come true. As he returned to Detroit, he composed another memo outlining the phenomenal successes of Chevrolet at Daytona, detailing how much impact Chevy could still have by promoting it's victories.

Also observing Chevy's success were the wire services, whose articles were picked up by the sports pages of newspapers all over the country extolling the remarkable sweep by Chevrolet at Daytona. Two weeks after Speed Week, the public, reading Chevy's great press, began flocking to Chevrolet showrooms, wanting to find out more about the Chevy that had set so many new records at Daytona Beach.

Very few salesmen or dealers knew what the big flap was about, so they called their zone offices, who didn't know either. The zone offices were calling the Chevy Central Office, but were drawing a blank there as well. Management was at a loss to understand what the big hulabaloo was about, although engineering and product planning knew, as they had supplied parts to make sure the Chevys at Daytona were runners!

Management assigned Campbell-Ewald to find out why suddenly there was so much interest in Chevrolet performance. Wanger's memo resurfaced, and suddenly the "whim" of a junior executive was rushed to sales and advertising, and then reprinted and distributed to dealers and salesmen.

To call it a new era for Chevrolet would be an understatement. Chevrolet revised their advertising posture, and in weeks the entire approach was changed. The concept of the "Hot One" was conceived, and Chevy's commitment to performance had begun.

Jim Wangers was now an integral cog in Chevy's performance marketing machine. He was put in charge of approving each piece of advertising, sales promotion and merchandising copy that was relative to Chevrolet performance. He helped to prepare a racing program, recommending how to help stock car teams in preparing Chevrolets for victory.

In the summer of 1955 planning for the 1956 advertising campaign was in full swing. Since the "Hot One" would be even "Hotter," Chevrolet wanted an event to emphasize the car's increased performance. Refinements had been made in styling, and engineering had improved intake manifolds and camshaft design. It didn't take Wangers long to dig up the old Pike's Peak hillclimb proposal that he had presented to Kaiser-Frazer only two years before. He dusted it off, updated it, and found out that no one had made a run at the record since KF had turned it down.

Wangers presented it to management, and they approved it enthusiastically, with a total budget of two million dollars. It was a tremendous campaign, using print as well as radio. Burl Ives, a popular country western singer, was commissioned to write a song about how man and machine had conquered the mountain. "The Ballad of Pike's Peak" was the result, getting much radio airtime. Magazine ads were prepared, one in particular highlighting the assault with artwork of a '56 Chevy Bel Air Sport Sedan "on the Pike's Peak road where Chevrolet broke the record." Other more mundane ads mentioned the hillclimb record prominently in the copy. The message was clearly stated: "The Hot One's Even Hotter."

Chevrolet was now riding the first crest of what would become a tidal wave of performance oriented cars. Jim Wangers was now recognized as one of the most visionary performance packaging men in Detroit, was written up in most of the industry journals, but he was leaving Campbell-Ewald to join Dodge Division to promote their stock car racing program as Assistant Sales Promotion Manager. Wangers worked with Carl Kiekaefer in promoting Chrysler's racing program, using Chrysler 300s on the large stock car tracks and Dodge D-500s on the smaller ovals. Wangers wanted to promote the successes of team drivers like Tim Flock, Lee Petty and Buck Baker to merchandise and sell Chrysler Products.

From there, Jim Wangers left to join McManus, John and Adams, Pontiac's advertising agency. Again he contributed his knowledge and enthusiasm for packaging and selling performace cars, working with men like Bunkie

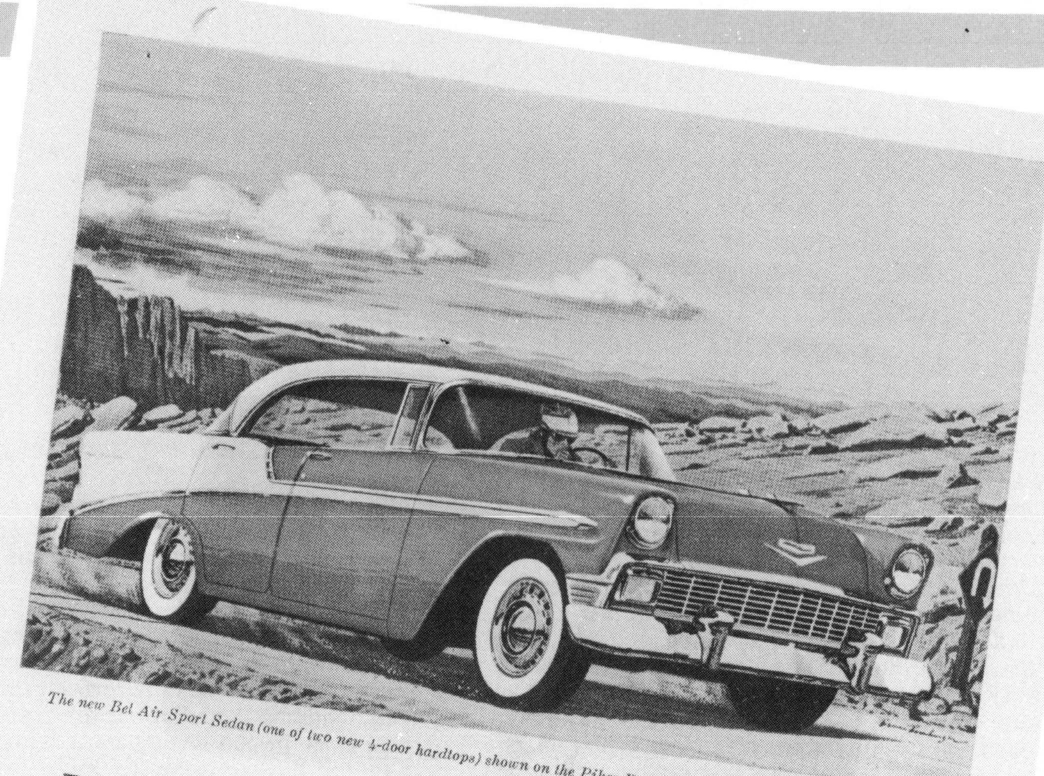

The new Bel Air Sport Sedan (one of two new 4-door hardtops) shown on the Pikes Peak road where Chevrolet broke the record.

Nothing without wings climbs like a '56 Chevrolet!

Aim this new Chevrolet up a steep grade—and you'll see why it's the Pikes Peak record breaker.

Ever level off a mountain with your foot? Just point this new '56 Chevy uphill and ease down on the gas.

In the merest fraction of a second you sense that big bore V8 lengthening out its stride. And up you go with a silken rush of power that makes a mountain seem as flat as a roadmap!

For nothing without wings climbs like a '56 Chevrolet! This is the car, you know, that broke the Pikes Peak record. The car that proved its fired-up performance, cat-sure cornering ability and nailed-down stability on the rugged, twisting Pikes Peak road. And *all* these qualities mean more driving safety and pleasure for you.

You'll see that when you *drive* the new Chevrolet. You've 19 frisky new models to choose from, with new higher horsepower—ranging up to a top of 205!

Borrow the key to one at your Chevrolet dealer's. . . . Chevrolet Division of General Motors, Detroit 2, Michigan.

CHEVROLET
Highway-test it—
it's a beautiful
thing to handle!

THE HOT ONE'S EVEN HOTTER

Knudsen, Pete Estes and John DeLorean.

His days at Pontiac are how he is most remembered. He is credited with the Royal Bobcat and the GTO, and was part of a team that conceived the GTO Judge and the original Trans Am. Today he is again working with Dodge, his latest success being the Charger 2.2, developed from the Dodge Omni. It is a spirited little performance sedan, sort of a musclecar for the 80's, and is selling quite respectfully.

For thirty years Jim Wangers has been a driving force behind the scenes in Detroit, conceiving, packaging and selling performance cars. His marketing genius has gone mostly unrecognized outside of Detroit, save for the automotive press and Pontiac enthusiasts, and that's a shame, because his hand has touched many successes, including the Hot One from Chevrolet.

Spiffy Styling, Hot New V-8 Engine Made 1955 a Banner Year for Chevy

By R. Perry Zavitz

1955 Chevrolet styling was a radical departure from their conservative postwar styling progress. Ferrari-inspired grille, neat head and taillight treatment, restrained use of chrome made the car a hit in the showroom and on the road.

Most expensive model in the 1955 Chevrolet line was the Nomad wagon. It's avidly collected and restored today and the design still looks fresh after 35 years.

"Baseball and hot-dogs, apple pie and Chevrolet" are America's favorites, so the commercial jingle states. Since this is neither a sports nor a gourmet publication, all we have left to discuss is Chevrolet. "Now that makes sense, yeah that makes sense" the jingle continues.

Specific models aside, the most desirable Chevrolets among current collectors seems to be the 1955, 1956, 1957 models. So let's zero in on those little gems.

The 1955 model year was one of the most outstanding postwar years. Especially in terms of styling. Except for Lincoln, every major American car got new styling. (Kaiser and Willys might technically be called exceptions, but they did not survive into the new year for more than a few weeks.) New styling, as always excited the Madison Ave. crews to extol the virtues of "all new" cars, when under the surface little had been changed.

Chevrolet's 1955 models were about as all new as any car ever becomes in one model change, though. In addition to the styling, exterior and interior, a new V-8 engine could be had under the hood. The V-8 was optional; the old faithful six was still standard equipment. It had been bumped 7 per cent in power to 123 hp., however.

Chevrolet's position was not unique. Plymouth also debuted a new V-8 and body for 1955, which also proved quite successful.

The 1955 body was the first Chevrolet passenger car to use a wrap-around windshield. (Corvette had used one since 1953, but it was a sports model, of course.) An automobile's grille is regarded by many stylists as the most identifiable part of a car. The 1955 Chevy had a brilliantly simple horizontal rectangle grille. Thin chrome bars created an egg crate pattern within the opening. The grille's Ferrari look was probably no more coincidental than the tail lights resemblance to Cadillac's famous illuminated fins. The instrument panel obviously got its inspiration from the early Corvette.

The three Chevrolet model series from 1954 were continued in 1955 unchanged in name. The lowest-priced 150 series included a 2-dr. sedan, sedan, 2-dr. Utility and a 2-dr. wagon, the Handyman.

Traditional coupes had disappeared by this time. The hardtops had replaced the club coupes, and there was little demand for business coupes. Yet, there was some need for them by traveling salesmen with their samples. To fill that need, the Utility was concocted. It was simply a 2-dr. sedan without a rear seat. It also served as the jumping point in price competition. Chevrolet prices could be advertised as starting at $1,593, but that was $92 less than the lowest priced 6-passenger 1955 Chevy.

The mid-priced line of Chevrolet's was called 210. Why such unimaginative names like 150 and 210 were used is a mystery. These numbers were related to factory designations but few people know, much less care about, the factory model number of the car they buy.

The 210 was a bit more deluxe than the 150. The 150 had no side chrome except for the "Chevrolet" script on the front fender. In addition to this, the 210 had chrome on the belt line, and another strip splitting the fender about mid-way up. Another piece of chrome ran diagonally forward, from the dip in the belt line, to the lower strip. On the 210 wagons, this diagonal piece was reduced to a much shorter wing tip raised, from the fender chrome. The belt line on the wagons was straight. The 210 interiors were finished in better and more attractive materials than the 150.

There were seven models in the 210 series. These were the 2-dr. sedan, 4-dr. sedan, Delray club coupe, 2-dr. hardtop, 2-dr, Handyman station wagon, and 4-dr. Townsman station wagon.

The Delray was a 2-dr. sedan with a two-tone vinyl interior. At $1,835, it sold for $60 more than the other 210 2-dr. sedan, but was $124 less than the 210 hardtop.

Though different, its interior was supposed to rival the luxury and attractiveness of the hardtop.

The top series was called Bel Air — a name which was originally given just to the hardtop Chevy. The Bel Air was, of course, more deluxe and more costly than the 210, model for model. It was identifiable by more side chrome. There was a strip running from near the headlight, back onto the door. It was slightly higher than the rear chrome. The rear horizontal strip had a painted groove in it, usually white. There was chrome trim above the side windows. Instead of the script on the front fenders, the Bel Air name along with a gold anodized Chevy bow-tie were located in the angle formed by the chrome strips ahead and above the rear wheel. The Bel Air interiors were upholstered in luxurious materials, color-keyed to the exterior finish.

Chevrolet generally had an unusual feature color and for 1955 it was coral orange with a metallic grey roof.

There were six models in the Bel Air line. The lowest priced was the 2-door sedan at $1,888. Others were the 4-dr., 2-dr. hardtop, 2-dr. convertible, 4-dr. Beauville station wagon, and the Nomad station wagon.

The Nomad, recognized by the Milestone Car Society, was, and still remains, a unique approach to station wagon styling. It was derived from a Corvette experimental show car.

Three quite different versions of the Corvette were displayed in GM's 1954 Motorama. One of them was a slope-back mini-station wagon named the Nomad. Like many other GM idea cars, many of the Nomad's features were soon to be translated into production.

The 1955 Nomad came out in January, 1955. It had just about the same angle of rear slope as the Corvette Motorama job. The tailgate sported seven vertical chrome strips. The rear side window glass curved around the rear corners to meet the back window. Running across the roof above were nine grooves in the sheet metal. The door window and the side windows were separated by a comparatively wide pillar, not too unlike the pillars on some GM cars today. However, on the Nomad it leaned forward at about the angle of the rear slope. The rear fender panels were devoid of chrome except for the Bel Air script and Chevy gold emblems. The Nomad used an opened-up wheel cutout unlike any other Chevy at the rear wheel opening. From the cowl forward the Nomad shared standard 1955 sheet metal, but had special trim strips and pot metal "eyebrows" over the head lamps. Standard passenger car taillights were used.

At a base list price of $2472, the Nomad was the most expensive 1955 Chevrolet passenger car. It cost $210 more than the Bel Air Beauville wagon.

The new V-8, with overhead valves, over-square dimensions and high-compression heads on its 265 cu. in. block was the most exciting mechanical feature of the 1955 Chevy. It was a $99 option that actually weighed less than the standard six by 40 pounds.

The V-8 had a 3 3/4-inch bore and 3-inch stroke that gave the displacement of 265 cubic inches. In its basic form, with 8:1 compression and dual throat carburetor, this motor was rated at 162 hp. A $95 power package was available, which consisted of a 4-barrel carburetor and dual exhausts. It delivered 180 hp. at 4,600 rpm. (In the Corvette, the 265 was rated at 195 hp. at 5,000 rpm.) This engine was the first to use stamped steel rocker arms, which permitted higher rpm's.

Chevrolet made the V-8 available in any model, and those so equipped had small chrome "V" decorations below the taillights. Nearly 45% of the '55 Chevys were V-8 powered.

Also available in all Chevrolet passenger cars were three transmissions: three-speed manual, three-speed manual with overdrive at $108 extra, or Powerglide automatic transmission for $178 extra. Either the six or the V-8 were available with any of the three transmissions. With Powerglide, the 6 was rated 136 hp.

1955 saw the introduction of one of the most famous and successful V-8s ever built, the tough and tuneable small-block Chevy.

Other factory options included electric windshield wipers, tinted glass, electric power windows, and power steering. On the 210 and Bel Air models, electric-power front seat adjustment was offered. Air conditioning was available in all V-8 equipped models, except the convertible. It was the most expensive option, costing $565. For the first time, tubeless tires were standard on all models.

The 1955 Chevrolet had a new frame, which was claimed to be 50 percent more rigid than before. The 115-inch wheelbase was retained.

Overall length of the 1955 Chevrolet was 195.6 inches. That seemed about average for a full-size car at that time. Ten years later, the mid-size Chevelle was 196.6 inches long. Now the compact Nova stretches out to 196.7 inches for 1975. The trend seemed pretty well established over the two decades after the 1955 came out. But, now the sudden turn to smaller cars may once again magnify the 1955 Chevy into a larger car.

New car registrations for calendar 1955 showed a total of 1,640,681 new Chevrolets. That was up 15.8 percent over 1954. However, the industry as a whole had posted a 29 percent gain. The Plymouth, Chevy's never-too-close competitor had made a spectacular gain of 69.8 percent in 1955.

During the following two years Chevrolet built on the foundation laid with the 1955 models.

Coral & Grey

'55 Chevrolet

By Tim Howley

On Sept. 3, we attended the '55-'57 Chevrolet Owners Regional Convention at the Holiday Inn on Harbor Drive here in San Diego. I suppose a lot of our readers would reel at the American Graffiti atmosphere of this four-day conclave, sponsored by the San Diego Region of the Classic Chevy Club International. For it was hard to find a single authentic Chevy among the mild California customs and wild west coast hot rods. I don't particularly like to see some of my favorite cars with fat mag wheels, hairy racing engines and far out paint jobs. Nor do I like seeing them separated from earlier and later years. But I'm sure it's all a part of the distinct appeal of these three particular years. And if you don't understand it, then you probably don't understand what these cars were all about from year one.

With the 1955 model, Chevrolet zoomed overnight from country road transportation to the newest dust kicker on the tracks. The car was built to appeal as much to stockers as to your maiden aunt Tillie from Davenport. And if Tillie liked, she could have her non-descript green 210 sedan equipped with an overdrive, V-8 and power pack. From 1955 on, it's been a whole new ball game back in Detroit, and anybody who thinks of a '55 Chevy in terms of pure stock should probably come over and try out my front porch swing.

The phenomena of the '55-'57 Chevrolet is unlike anything else in the hobby. Collectors, customizers and street rodders alike have called these cars classics for nearly a quarter of a century, with absolutely no apologies to the CCCA. Although the price guides would indicate that the true faith lies somewhere very close to originality, the emotional appeal goes all the way out to a 25th Century version of the Nomad called "Darth Vader." We have talked to Bob Wingate in San Dimas, Calif. He's sold over 2,000 vintage cars, most of them Fifties Chevrolets. 90% of his cars go somewhere east of Omaha, and at prices that are beginning to make early Ford V-8 collectors gasp like my old man's '37 on the bumpy road to Martin Lake. The secret of the prices he gets, says Wingate, is "Originality, originality, originality." If it's what he calls a "Graffiti Car" then it must be done in "Super Taste."

I wouldn't argue with the rodders and customizers today any more than I'd laugh at the guy who just put a $50,000 price tag on his non fuel-injected '57 Bel Air convertible. I'll just sit up here in my simulated ivory old car tower, and quietly kick myself for the day I traded in my coral and grey '55 Chevrolet Bel Air hardtop. I bought that slick little buggy new from Hubert Hennen Chevrolet in Forest Lake, Minn. in the summer of '55. I owned it for three years, and the only trouble I ever had with it had to do with college coeds. For all I know, it's still bouncing along the Minnesota back roads, right behind my '46 Ford club coupe. The universal appeal of '55-'57 Chevrolets is something you can't really describe. It's something you just feel. How would you analyze the appeal of an Elvis Presley, a James Dean or a Marilyn Monroe? Could you separate any one of them from the whole mystique of the Fifties? There were certain products of the decade that were purely fads. You would not wear a Davy Crockett cap or go to a drive-in to see a Kim Novak movie today. But you could still pull up to the swankiest country club in town in a '55 Chevrolet Bel Air. For there is a little piece of that point in time which will probably outlast the century.

The '55 Chevy was Ed Cole's baby. (He became Chevrolet chief engineer in '52, Division General Manager in '56, and GM President in '67. His credits include the '49 Cadillac ohv V-8, the '55 Chevy, the Corvair, and some eighteen major inventions prior to his untimely death in a plane crash.) Never before or since has Chevrolet offered the American public so much, so new, all at once. Like the Jordan Playboy of another day and age, the '55 Chevrolet stole many of its best ideas from all of the right places. The ball joint front suspension was copied from Ford and their road race Lincolns. The classic egg crate grille was taken from the Ferrari. The rear suspension came from the Corvette; so did the basic styling of the instrument panel. The basic body shape was scaled down from the bigger GM cars of 1954. The cut down doors were inspired by the Buick Skylark. The eyelids over the headlights came from Cadillac, and the taillights hinted of Cadillac fins. Happily, the new Chevrolet resisted over use of chrome, bloated body panels and unnecessarily large size. It was super compact, super swift, and super handling. It was the first low priced American family car which had successfully incorporated sports car styling of the time. It was easy on gas, without sacrificing power. But if you were inclined in that direction, it was a machine just itching to be hopped up.

What it didn't copy was the big Cadillac ohv V-8. This engine would have been far too expensive to scale down. So Ed Cole and Harry Barr designed it from scratch, and it turned out to be 40 pounds lighter than the Chevrolet Six. One of its major breakthroughs was a new casting process using a green-sand core which allowed them to do pecision casting down to 5/32 jacket walls. Stamped rocker arms and hollow pushrods (features shared with Pontiac) were other breakthroughs. Chevy's upper cylinder lube system, unlike Ford's, did not depend on the uncertainties of oil passages through the cylinder heads. This wonderful little 265 CID. V-8 was designed to be built up, but only to

1. The fun-loving Bel Air Convertible 2. The versatile "Two-Ten" Handyman 3. The glamorous Bel Air Sport Coupe

about 302 CID. The big 350 and 400 inch sizes have come about only through much later technological developments. The original engineers never dreamed their low cost, high production ohv V-8 would outlast two decades.

Original horsepower was rated at 162 at 4,400 rpm. With power pack, horsepower was raised to 180. This consisted of a four-barrel carburetor, bigger intake manifold ports and dual exhausts. Later in the year a 195 hp engine was offered. Zero to 60 time for the 162 hp job was 12.5 seconds, with Powerglide. Shave it to 9.6 seconds with a standard transmission and powerpack.

Yet, with all its engineering innovation, sharp design,

1956 Chevrolet 210 2-dr sedan.

1957 Bel Air with continental kit.

and superb handling, the '55 Chev was far from a perfect car. It had almost, but not quite as many problems as the revolutionary '49 Ford. The most serious problems were oiling. Some of them had to do with the rings, but the hollow push rods had a tendency to pump too much oil up into the valve chambers. They had a lot of trouble with water leaks at the bottom edges of the new wraparound windshields. Dust got into the trunk, and in the four door sedans, dust came in under the back doors. The new 12-volt electrical system proved to be a small nightmare. Most of these problems were not really solved until 1956.

The '56 was a better car all around, although not better styled. The distinctive Ferrari grille was exchanged for a conventional Detroit fence. Restrained use of side trim gave away to typical Detroit zig-zags. But the rather spartan, and not terribly durable, '55 Bel Air interiors were replaced with much better looking and much longer lasting interiors for 1956.

In 1955, Chevrolet offered 14 models, including the distinctive Nomad station wagons at the top of the line. The Nomad was continued for both '56 and '57. A new model addition for 1956 was the 4-dr. hardtop in both the Bel Air and 210 series. The 210 series 2-dr hardtops were available for all three model years. Interestingly enough, the Bel Air was always offered in a 2-dr sedan, a model usually associated with the 210 series. And there was a special 210 model, 1955 only, called the Del Ray. It had a special custom all vinyl interior. No wonder there is now so much confusion about Chevrolet models for these years. And here's another rub. The 1956 Bel Air 4-dr. hardtop is a striking car, but collectors value it so little today that it will bring about half the price of a Bel Air 2-dr in comparable condition.

As might be expected, the V-8 was greatly improved for 1956. The standard horsepower rating was 170. Special performance packages boosted it up to either 205 or 225 hp. Other improvements included steering geometry, springing and optional safety features.

1957 Chevrolet

1955 Chevrolet Nomad.

For 1957, Chevrolet had a major facelift including the adaptation of a heavy integrated grille and front bumper that was originally rejected for the 1955 model. The '57 models have new interiors too. They're quite rich in the Bel Air series. The instrument panel was greatly influenced by the Cadillac. To a certain extent, so was the whole car.

The standard V-8 was now 185 hp. There were optional engines rated at 220, 245, 250, 270 and finally 283 with a fuel injection system developed for the Corvette by GM's Rochester Division.

Chevrolet became quite a different car with the 1958 models, and the previous three years began enjoying new popularity on used car lots. That popularity has never diminished. A '55-'57 Chevrolet cult was already growing in '58 and '59, and over the years the cars have slowly evolved into collectibles. Nomad-mania has finally peaked out, and today all '55-'57 Chevrolets have found their place in the sun. Some still like to customize them; others prefer hopping them up; another group, not here on the west coast, prefers keeping them stock, or mostly stock. All still admire them for what they still are. Just a lot of automobile styling, engineering and value in a sensible mid-size that for a long time Detroit almost forgot.

We didn't quite find our coral and grey hardtop at the San Diego meet, but we came close. One participant from Burbank brought down a near mint coral and grey Bel Air 2-dr sedan. The 2-drs are extremely rare. They sold for $60 more than the Del Ray, $60 less than the Bel Air hardtop, and found very few buyers. This car was a ground-up restoration, done so well you might easily mistake it for an all orginal car. But when you look inside you'll see a '58 Impala steering wheel, and when you lift the hood you'll discover a 1970 Chevy 350. Even after all these years it's still hard to leave a good thing alone. But, then, that was the whole point of the hot little Bel Air.

Facelifted '56 Chevys Offered More Models And A Hotter V-8

By R. Perry Zavitz

Following the thoroughly changed 1955 Chevrolet, the 1956 models had comparatively minor differences. However, the styling face-lift was apparent from all sides, even to a novice.

The 1956 Chevy grille was redesigned and made lower and broader. It engulfed the larger, rectangular, parking lights. Some chrome spilled around the corners to the front wheels. The grillework was altered so that the criss-cross pattern emphasized the horizontal effect.

New bumper guards were straighter than in 1955, and tilted slightly forward. The top of the front fenders was straighter, and the head light hoods were more pronounced than before.

Chrome side trim was substantially altered for '56. Even the bottom line One-Fifty series got some trim. A chrome strip ran from near the head light, straight back two-thirds of the length of the car. Another piece of chrome, with simulated vent slots, went from the dip in the belt line downward and forward to meet the first piece.

On the Two-Ten, the horizontal chrome was extended all the way to the rear. As it widened slightly, it curved very gently down to the top corner of the rear bumper.

Side trim on the Bel Air was different but related to the Two-Ten trim. Two chrome strips were used. On the front fender, they were joined together in a very sharp point near the head light. The upper piece went straight back about two-thirds the length of the car, then suddenly turned up, in a steep climb, to the belt line dip. The lower chrome piece was much the same as the full length strip on the Two-Ten.

The space between these two chrome pieces was often painted a contrasting color. Of course, this area also included the whole rear deck. Ten solid and fourteen two-tone combinations were offered. Chevy's most striking two-tone finish for '56 was probably the light, almost purplish, blue with metallic grey.

The side trim on the station wagons duplicated that on the other cars, for each series. However, the Nomad used a slightly different version of the Bel Air trim. The change was in the angle of the chrome dropping from the belt line. It went toward the rear instead of the front. This put it in line with the center pillar.

At the rear of the 1956 Chevrolets, new tail lights were quite evident. Within a frame slightly taller and narrower than for 1955, there was an entirely new design. Near the top was a small round red lens, not unlike a truck clearance light. Below this, and almost lost in the chrome, was a small square backup light. Then at the bottom there was a tiny red reflector button. The left tail light assembly folded down to reveal the gasoline filler cap, like early 1950's Cadillacs.

Overall length of the '56 Chevrolets increased almost an inch to 197.5. Wagons were 200.5 inches long. Wheelbase, of course, remained the same 115 inches. Token changes were made to the interiors of each series.

The Blue-Flame 6-cylinder motor was standard, of course. Its compression ratio was raised to 8.0:1 and the power rating increased to 140 hp. This year all sixes were the same horsepower regardless of transmission choice.

The $99 optional 265 cu. in. Turbo-Fire V-8 was still rated at 162 hp/ (170 hp. with automatic) in its basic form with a two-barrel carburetor. The hotter Super Turbo-Fire had 9.25:1 compression and used a four-barrel carb and dual-exhaust to develop 205 hp. That was up 25 over the year before. A 225 hp. version was only obtainable in the Corvette.

V-8 powered Chevrolets sported a wide angle "V" just below the marque medallion on both the hood and rear deck. Over 57% of the Chevrolets had V-8's in '56, so the sixes had become a minority.

Three transmission choices remained for '56. They were the 3-speed manual, overdrive for $108 more, and

1956 Bel Air 4-dr

Powerglide automatic costing $189 extra.

As already inferred, the 1956 Chevrolet was offered in the same three model series as in 1955. The bargain basement One-Fifty was available in 2-door sedan, 4-door sedan, 2-door Utility (no rear seat), and the 2-door Handyman station wagon.

Basic list prices ranged from $1,734 for the Utility to $2,174 for the Handyman — up $141 from the previous year. In '56 about one Chevrolet in ten was from the One-Fifty line.

The mid-range Two-Ten series included no less than eight body types — two more than before. Available was a 2-door sedan, 4-door sedan, 1-door Delray Club Coupe, 2-door Sport Coupe hardtop, 4-door Sport Sedan hardtop, 2-door Handyman station wagon, 4 door Townsman station wagon, and 4-door Beauville 9-passenger station wagon.

Prices ranged from the 2-door sedan at $1,912 to the Beauville listing for $2,348. On comparable models, the '56 prices increased $136 or $137 on the Two-Tens. This series accounted for almost 47% of production.

Bel Air was just about as popular at 43%, and offered seven body styles — one more than in 1955. The Bel Air buyer could choose from a 2-door sedan, 4-door sedan, 2-door Sport Coupe hardtop, 4-door Sport Sedan hardtop, 2-door convertible, 4-door Beauville 9-passenger station wagon, and 2-door Nomad (6-passenger) station wagon.

1956 Bel Air Sport Sedan

1956 Bel Air Station Wagon

With the same price increases as the Two-Ten, Bel Air models listed from $2,025 for the 2-door sedan to $2,608 for the Nomad. There were 8,103 of the Milestone recognized Nomads built during the 1956 model year.

If you kept track, you will know that there were 19 Chevrolet models in the 1956 stable. There were no deletions from 1955. The three new models were the Two-Ten Beauville, and the 4-door hardtop in both Two-Ten and Bel Air form.

Four-door hardtops were made in small quantities by Kaiser-Frazer as early as 1949. In 1955 Buick and Oldsmobile were the first to put that body type into mass production. Chevrolet and almost all other U.S. car makers were producing and peddling 4-door hardtops in 1956.

Two major options on the '56 Chevys, other than engines and transmission, were power steering and air-conditioning. The price of power steering held at $92, but the cost of air-conditioning (available only with V-8's, and not on convertibles) was cut by $134 to $431. So in effect, despite the basic price increase of the cars, the Two-Ten and Bel Air models with a/c were just about the same price in 1956 as they had been in 1955.

Other options included power brakes, power front seat, and power windows on all but the One-Fifty.

While Ford was making much ado about its safety features in 1956, Chevrolet was quietly moving in the same direction. Direction signals, formerly optional, were made standard. Safer door latches were used. Seat belts and shoulder harnesses were available optionally. The strength of the webbing, buckles and attachments, it was claimed, exceeded minimum standards laid down by the Civil Aeronautics Authority.

The auto industry experienced a year of record high production in 1955. Two consecutive record high years are rather unlikely, and 1956 confirmed that fact. U.S. car production in the calendar year was 5,806,756 which was equal to only 73% of 1955 production.

Chevrolet production was down to 1,621,018 cars, in 1956 but that was about 88.5% of its 1955 total. In other words, Chevrolet increased its share of production. Its share of the total number of cars built in calendar 1956 was almost 28%. That was a climb from 23% in 1955.

During 1956, Chevrolet produced just about as many cars as the whole Ford Motor Company.

A Collector Favorite Today, the '57 Chevrolets Nearly Lost First Place to Ford

By R. Perry Zavitz

Model year changes were quite evident from all angles on the '57 Chevrolet. A new bumper and bigger, full width grille accomplished a new look at the front. The very fine criss-cross grillework was available with a gold anodized finish — an option receiving much publicity at the time.

Redesigned head light assemblies combined air intakes for the car's interior. Side trim again distinguished each of the three series.

The One-Fifty had some trim on the rear quarters very similar to the '55 Bel Air trim. The '57 Two-Ten had a single chrome strip which ran horizontally almost the whole length of the car, from near the head light all the way back to the rear bumper. It was much like the side piece on the '56 Two-Ten. This strip was also on the '57 Bel Air. In addition, the Bel Air had another piece of chrome below the rear fender top, running forward from the end of the car. Where it was about to join the other chrome strip, it curved downward to meet it. In the triangle thus formed, there was a big sheet of bright metal, with many horizontal grooves or ribs. Actually some Two-Tens had this triangle, but without the bright siding. Instead, the triangle was often painted a contrasting color, perhaps matching the roof.

The rear fenders had very prominent horizontal fins. These were level with the belt line, but protruded rearward at the top, and slanted inward at the bottom. Just above the new rear bumper was a not too large half-moon tail light. The back edge of these fins was treated with a generous coating of chrome. The fuel filler cap was hidden behind a door in that chrome on the left fin. These fins were probably intended to emulate Cadillac, but somehow the overall effect came off looking more like the '56 Plymouth fins.

Overall length of the '57 Chevrolet was 202.8 inches — a growth of about five inches over the previous year, despite the same 115-inch wheelbase. Tires were changed to 7.50 x 14 from the earlier 6.70 x 15 size.

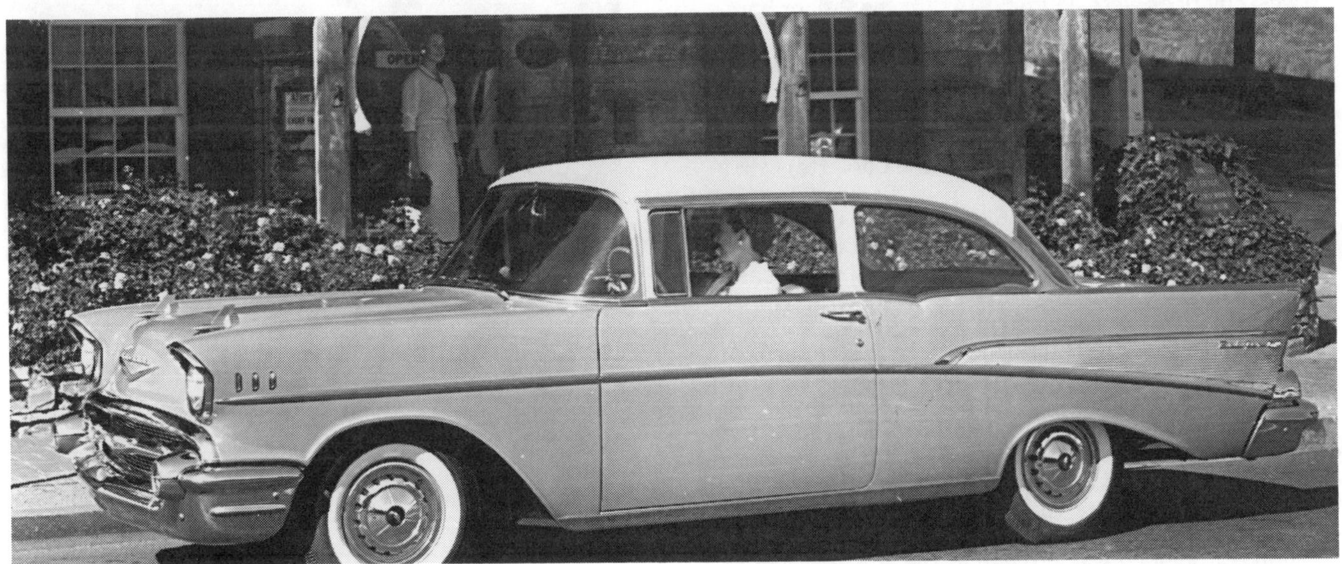

1957 Chevrolet Bel Air 2-dr

Chevrolet came in the usual three series in '57, the One-Fifty, the Two-Ten, and the Bel Air. There was no change in the availability of the models, or their names, in the One-Fifty or Two-Ten series, as we listed in the last issue. Only a slight change occurred in the Bel Air line. In '56 there was a Bel Air Beauville station wagon, but this was replaced by a Townsman for '57.

For those not too familiar with Chevy nomenclature of that period, what it simply means is this. There was just a 6-passenger 4-door wagon offered in the Bel Air line, whereas in '56 there was a 9-passenger wagon instead. The 9-passenger Beauville was still available in the Two-Ten line.

The Milestone Nomad wagon was continued for its last season. The Nomad name was subsequently used on the top model wagons, but the vehicle itself was routine in design.

An excellent array of engines was offered to the '57 Chevy buyer. The 140 hp. 6-cylinder motor was still there, and it was standard. The 265 cid. 162 hp. V-8 was the lowest cost optional power. The other V-8's were larger. A 1/8 inch greater bore brought the displacement up to 283 cubes. This excellent engine was to remain in service for eleven model years.

In its basic tune of 8.5:1 compression, and a single 2-barrel carburetor, the 283 developed 185 hp. Next up the option ladder was a 9.5:1 compression, single 4-barrel carb version. It turned out 220 hp. With the same compression, but two 4-barrel carburetors, the rating was 245 hp.

Chevrolet's most exciting news for 1957 was its fuel injection engines. Utilizing the same 283 block, fuel injection was available in two strengths. The tamer version with 9.5:1 compression was rated at 250 hp. A wilder edition used 10.5:1 compression and boasted 283 hp. These engines were offered in any Chevrolet model from the One-Fifty Utility to the Corvette, according to the catalog.

According to the Corvette catalog, the 283 hp. fuel injection engine made world history. It stated in headline form "For the first time in automobile history — ONE hp. for every cubic inch."

But back to the 1957 Chevrolets. Prices rose on the '57 models, but not in a very predictable manner. Increases for the One-Fifty models varied from $136 to $179. The Utility base price was $1,885, and the 4-door sedan was up to $2,048.

Two-Ten prices were up from $141 for the 2-door hardtop, to $219 for the 4-door sedan. The lowest priced Two-Ten was $2,122 for the 2-door sedan and the highest price was the Beauville wagon at $2,563.

The Bel Airs rose from $123 to $222, with prices ranging from the $2,290 4-door sedan to the Nomad, which again topped the price list (except for the Corvette) with a tag reading $2,757.

Those are base prices. Over 63% of the '57 Chevys had V-8 engines. These came at various extra prices. The 265 cid. V-8 was $100 more than that standard six. The basic 283 V-8 was $143 above the six. And so it went right on up to well over $400 for fuel injection.

There were four transmissions offered. Standard, of course, was the 3-speed stick shift. Overdrive added $108 to the cost. Powerglide automatic cost $188 extra.

New for '57 was an improved automatic called Turbo glide. It was a $231 extra, which gave smoother and more efficient operation. It used a combination of three turbines and two planetary gear sets. An additional feature was the Hill Retarder. With the quadrant lever in "HR" position, turbulence was created in the transmission to aid in downhill braking.

Chevrolet was at some disadvantage in 1957 by not having a brand new body to offer. Other GM divisions, except Pontiac, had new styling. But more important to Chevrolet, Ford and Plymouth had completely new bodies for '57.

During calendar 1957, the U.S. auto industry as a whole experienced a 5.4% production gain over '56. Plymouth chalked up a whopping 44.6% increase, and Ford scored a good 10.8% gain. Meanwhile Chevrolet sustained a 6.1% drop in production. With a total of 1,522,549 cars, Chevrolet still outproduced Ford — but by a mere 141 cars.

That was a close call for Chevrolet, but it happened 33 years ago. Today, there is a noticeable stronger demand for Chevrolets than Fords among the normal passenger car models of the '57 vintage.

By R. Perry Zavitz

1957 Chevrolet 150 2-dr

1957 Chevrolet 210 2-dr

57 CHEVY

The 1957 Bel Air Convertible: Chevrolet's Greatest?

The 1957 Chevrolet Bel Air convertible.

By Robert C. Ackerson

The 1957 production race between Ford and Chevrolet was one of the closest on record. For the calendar year, Chevrolet finished just ahead of Ford with an output of 1,522,549 to Ford's final tally of 1,522,408.

In terms of actual 1957 model production however, the winner was Ford which assembled 1,655,406 cars to Chevrolet's 1,515,177 final tally. Thus Ford became the nation's number one automobile. But even in defeat it seems as if Chevrolet has the final word since a check of the *Old Cars Price Guide* reveals that a 1957 Chevrolet convertible in no. 1 condition has a value that is roughly twice that of a Ford Sunliner convertible.

The Bel Air soft top was rare even when new since only 47,562 were produced. To put this in perspective, output of the Bel Air four-door sedan was 254,331 units. With the base 235-cubic inch 140 h.p. Blue Flame six, the convertible's price was $2,511, which was exceeded by the Nomad ($2,757) and the four-door station wagon ($2,580).

As was the case with all Bel Air models, the convertible had many exterior trim details that set it apart from the less expensive 210 and 150 series. On V8 powered models the Bel Air's hood V was gold colored rather than chromed as on the other Chevrolets. Whereas the Bel Air's grille insert was constructed of anodized gold aluminum, that of the less expensive versions was silver anodized aluminum. Also unique to the Bel Airs were the three simulated air scoops on the front fenders fitted with gold bars. This infatuation with America's favorite precious metal was carried over to the convertible's rear fenders where a gold-colored Bel Air script and a Chevrolet emblem were positioned.

Yet another feature found on the Bel Airs were extended chrome stripes along the top of the rear fender fins. Two options limited to installation on the Bel Airs were a lower body sill molding plus a ribbed silver aluminum panel insert for the rear fender chrome trim.

Although the convertible, with a weight of 3,414 pounds, was at a slight disadvantage when compared to the 3,237-pound Bel Air two-door sedan, the availability of seven optional V8 engines really made this a matter of concern only to the intense drag racing competitor. The original 265 c.i.d. V8, rated at 162 h.p., was available only with a three-speed manual or overdrive transmission. By increasing this engine's bore by an eighth of an inch to 3.875 inches (stroke remained the same at three inches), the first 283-cubic inch Chevrolet V8 was developed.

For 1957 it was available in six different power levels of 185, 220, 245, 250, 270 and 283 h.p. Attracting the most attention were the two fuel injected engines with their 250 and 283 h.p. ratings. The latter engine shared the Duntov cam with the dual four-barrel carbureted 270 h.p. engine. Its compression ratio was a heady 10.5:1.

Also new for 1957 was a new automatic transmission from Chevrolet, Turboglide, which was available only with the 283 c.i.d. V8s. Its primary features included three turbines, a variable pitch stator and two planetary gearsets. The result was an automatic with only a single forward speed and a Hill Retarder quadrant position.

V8 linked to the two-speed Powerglide automatic could propel a Bel Air from zero to 60 m.p.h. in just 11 seconds. With the 270 and 283 h.p. versions, the same speed could be reached in eight seconds or less. At the 1957 Daytona Speed Week, a batch of fuel injected Chevrolets were on hand and one, driven by Paul Goldsmith, was the winner of the flying mile runs for stock production cars with a speed of 131 m.p.h.

Of course, we can't really declare the 1957 Bel Air convertible the greatest Chevrolet of all time. Instead, let's be content to regard it as one of the best packages that Chevrolet put together in the fifties.

Specifications
1957 Chevrolet Bel Air convertible

Original price: $2,511
Wheelbase: 115 inches
Overall length: 202.8 inches
Height: 59.1 inches
Width: 73.9 inches
Tires: 7.50 x 14, tubeless
Weight: 3,414 pounds
Rear axle rations: 3.55:1 (standard transmission), 3.36:1, (Powerglide and Turboglide), 4.11:1, (overdrive)
Major options: power steering, power brakes, power front seat, E-Z Eye glass, padded instrument panel, air conditioning, electric wipers, white sidewall tires.
Number one condition value: $52,000

Classic Chevy International staff

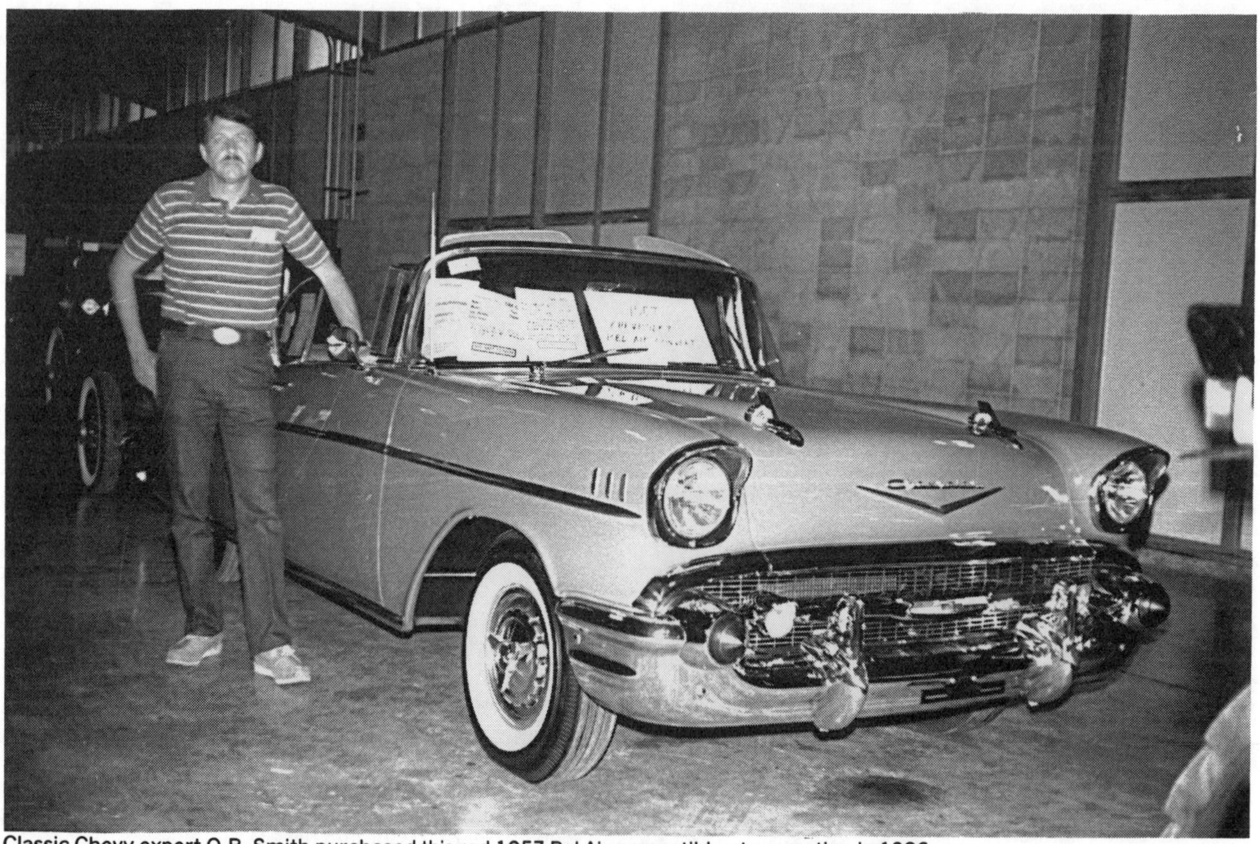
Classic Chevy expert O.B. Smith purchased this red 1957 Bel Air convertible at an auction in 1986.

Late-Great Legacy

William L. Mitchell — Proponent Of "Good Automotive Design"

Probably no individual in the past half century has had so great an impact on international design trends as has William L. Mitchell.

Although his name may not be familiar to everyone, his work certainly is.

Mitchell served as Vice President of Design for General Motors Corporation from 1958 until his retirement in July, 1977. In that capacity, Mitchell was responsible for the appearance of the wide variety of products produced by GM's domestic divisions and foreign subsidiaries. Chief among those products, which ranged from small appliances to massive earthmoving equipment, were the cars and trucks of GM's automotive division.

In the nineteen years Mitchell held that position, he was responsible for the design of more than 100,000,000 individual Chevrolet, Pontiac, Oldsmobile, Buick, Cadillac, and G.M.C. car and truck models. His innovative approach to design resulted in exciting, trend setting vehicles that firmly established GM as the automotive style leader while setting design standards for the entire industry.

Many of the designs conceived by Mitchell were immediately acclaimed as "classics" and proved to be among the best selling automobiles in history. The 1938 Cadillac 60 Special, The Chevrolet Corvette Sting Ray, the Buick Riviera, the Chevrolet Camaro, the Oldsmobile Toronado, the Cadillac Eldorado, and the last two Cadillac Seville models, including the 1980, are among them. These vehicles had a profound effect on the taste levels and lifestyles of every American as well as millions more people around the world.

Mitchell joined GM as a member of the Cadillac design staff at twenty-three years of age. A year later, in 1936, he became Chief Designer for Cadillac. His first production car, the 1938 Cadillac 60 Special, has been described as the vehicle that ushered in the "modern era" of automotive design. It was certainly a departure from any car produced up to that time. It had a much lower profile, no running boards, a tremendously increased amount of window area, and the slenderest possible roof supports which gave it an appearance similar to the hardtop designs Mitchell would later introduce.

Under Mitchell's design stewardship, Cadillac became the most prestigious, most wanted car in America, and the name itself became a synonym for excellence.

1963 Corvette

William L. Mitchell (Right)

The Impala Look

Chevy In The Late Fifties

By Wick Humble

Ed Cole's Chevrolet Division was smarting. For the first time in over 20 years, archrival Ford had edged them in new-car registrations. Even though calendar-year production figures later tilted their way (by a paltry 130 units), Chevy knew they had a tough row to hoe in 1957. Ford had only used its 1955 body one additional year, facelifting it slightly for '56, and then had popped for a new, lower, longer wider model in '57, while GM's biggest division, along with Pontiac, had to soldier along with just another facelift. Plus, traditional bridesmaid Plymouth had Exner's "Forward Look" that year — well, we can well imagine that Cole didn't need his legendary crystal ball to know that a three-year styling cycle was just too long that time around.

Sure, other things sold cars in the late 'Fifties era, but for the most part, performance and price were to all appearances very nearly equal between the "Low Priced Three" in that pre-compact, pre-personal luxury, pre-model proliferation era. *Styling*, that could make or break a line-up among the status-seekers of suburbia back then. Americans had mostly gotten used to the idea of only keeping a car three or four years, and trading for a newer, more contemporary looking one. (And a fat new payment book!) GM Design, still under the administration of the late Harley Earl, did have very "new looking" cars readied for the 1958 model introduction — cars that would have four headlights across the board, and low, wide stances, and plenty of chrome and stainless steel. Chevrolet's all-new Impala line, originally only offered as a two-door hard top and convertible, would triumphantly lead the line to its first thirty-percent market penetration, and outsell Ford by over 250,000 units. (The fact that Ford styling may have shot itself in the leg, trying to adapt the '57 body to quad lights and the new T-bird look, may have

1960 Impala Sport Sedan

been a factor in these figures!)

But Chevy stylists, under studio chief Clare MacKichan, got the unexpected advantage of a further new body for the succeeding year, due to a corporate shift of the gears that lumped all the divisions together with one basic body, whereas before they had shared two, one for Chevy/Pontiac, and another for Olds/Buick. Cadillac had perennially gotten pretty much whatever body and roof treatments that would sell big, garish luxury cars — and then passed its gimmicks down to the junior divisions who thought they could use them. So there was, one could well guess, plenty of pressure on division stylists to come up with something that would really one-up the competition for good, and another fresh body and roof unit to hang their best — or was it worst — work in! Remember the comparatively conservative '58 line was in the works while Chevy was still enjoying fat times, selling record numbers of tightly styled, conservatively trimmed 1955 and '56 models. Yes, back in the dim recesses of the old design area there were some very overdecorated and obnoxious clays that had been proffered to the men who made the styling decisions, but the resultant '58 cars were nearly the embodiment of restraint and taste as they emerged. Of course, no Detroit automaker could have shaved off enough trim and appliques to satisfy the hard-core neo-street-rodder of that era, but MacKichan and Co. had at least gotten them out with homogeneous lines and pretty fair taste.

To look *big* was to look good in those days. (Wonder how many of us today secretly still feel that way!?) That the '58 Chevys didn't last but one model year was only a fluke of timing — many designers were disappointed to see them go in favor of the new B-Body, but glimpses we've gotten at facelifts proposed for '59 on the A-Body leave '58 fans grateful that they were stillborn! However, that unrealized styling cycle was to be the last under Earl, supplanted as he was by his handpicked successor, William "Bill" Mitchell, and the last for the custodians to clean up at the old quarters in Detroit, as the new Design Center in Warren, Michigan was now open.

A certain amount of design schizophrenia seems to have set in at this point. Even though the Impala and the '58s were being well received at the dealerships, what with the pressure from the previous year and the upheaval at their place of work, the designers seemed to have suffered a certain lack of direction in their studies. Perhaps their primary driving force at that time was just to *never* be upstaged by Ford or Plymouth again in the public's eyes — and it's pretty safe to say that for the next two-year styling cycle, they weren't! Where the '58 had achieved a dramatic rear-end treatment with its "gull-wing" trunk lines and scooped-out rear fenders, the 1959 cars went all out for the tail-fin look. The "seagull" rear treatment featured horizontal fins, instead of the usual vertical empennage, and almond shaped tail-lights, features that made the '59 cars readily identifiable from the rear both day and night. (Perhaps the '59s mother was frightened by a Beechcraft Bonanza . . . ?) At the front, a number of very diverse themes were mocked up, including one dilly that featured two small quad-type headlights in normal fender positions, and a central pod — Edsel style — that contained the other two! Clare MacKichan was quoted as saying that "It was mocked up and ready to go; fortunately they did not come out with it." Probably because, thank goodness, Chevy would have had to convince every state in the country to change its headlight laws to accommodate it — something many were hesitant to do just to allow quad lights in the first place.

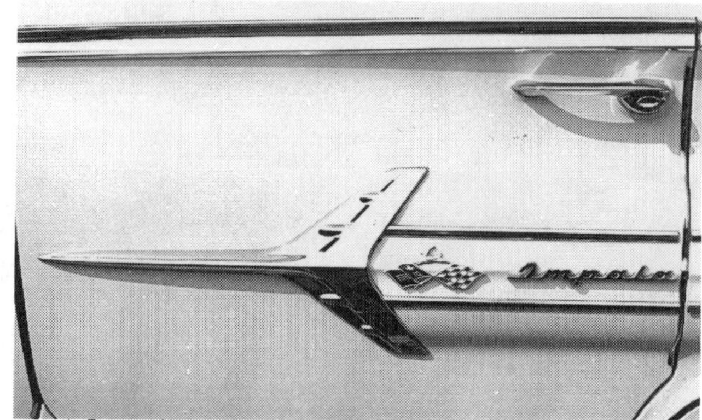

Side Trim on 1960 Impala Sport Sedan

What did come down for the '59s front end was conventional headlights, supporting a toothy 'Vette-like grille and surmounted by two hood-edge scoops that one contemporary customer commented looked like ". . . someone had stood too close to it with a body grinder!" He, of course, would be happy to fill them with lead, if you felt the same. Somehow, though, the front and rear elements of that year never seemed to integrate on the car, almost as if two different groups had designed them, and handed them to a third to make sense out of the themes. This situation was largely rectified for the next year, however.

The B-Body allowed the four divisions to share underpinnings, which probably allowed many economies as Fisher Body, while permitting fairly radical outer panel divergence in appearance, for essential product identification. The roof lines, however were almost identical. Except for Buicks' borrowing of a Cadillac roof on the Electra 225 four-doors, the divisions shared three basic roof types: a.) the Sport coupe or two-door hardtop with a sharply-angled tumblehome/rear glass, b.) the two and four-door sedans "imitation" of this line, and c.) the so-called "flying-wing" style for the Sports Sedan or four-door hardtop, with its flattened roofline, the wrap around backlight. These were continued through the next season also.

The 1960 Chevys were being finalized in mid-1958, as far as the Design Center was concerned, and to all appearances it seems that someone had noticed that the '59, for all its newness, was a bit of a hodgepodge. Much of what remains of those clay proposals shows both an effort to better integrate the design elements, and to reinstill more brand-identification. The high rear deck edges were retained — the general shape was pretty well dialed-in by then, since the body was shared with other divisions, all making larger models, but the '58 Impalas triple tail light treatment was revived from the earliest studies. These were to continue until 1965, incidentally. The horizontal fins were somewhat muted in effect, and ran forward along the beltline to intercept the grille. One of the '59s better features, the clean, bland-like bumpers were retained, although lots of alternatives were tried and abandoned. A number of grille treatments were toyed with, including one that looks like the aftermarket chrome-tube units offered in the '60s, several that resemble other GM divisions or even early '60s Dodge 440's, and one simple, blacked out cavity with floating crossed flags and tri-color that looks uncannily like the early Chevelle SS treatment!

1959 Bel Air 4dr hardtop

1958 Impala

1958 Bel Air 4dr hardtop

The fluted rear-fender side scoop was unique to the '60, and the "airplane" trim fronting it was originally to be a simple "pitchfork" molding, reminiscent of the '58 Impalas. The second year of the B-Body design picked up rather more chrome detail encrustation, as Detroit styles tend to do as they age. Despite the fact that the facelifted '60s seem more homogeneous, stylistically, they tend to pale before the flamboyance of the '59s, which in turn look outlandish in comparison to the relatively conventional lines of the 1958s. All three were large cars, the latter growing 9 inches in length and almost 4 inch width over the 150+ pounds lighter 1957. And the 1959-60 cars had 4 inches more wheelbase while being 4.5 inches lower than the '57. "Unquestionably (the Impala) marked the advent of larger, heavier Chevys that were the Division's 'standard cars' right on through 1976 . . ." says Chevrolet historian Pat Chapell in *The Hot One*. And while she doesn't say so, I imagine she and most fans of the so-called "Classic" and older series Chevrolets consider the Impala-era cars to be ever-so-slightly decadent in size and shape!

Now, some dissention exists among authorities as to whether Chevrolet was outsold by rival Ford in 1959, or whether it is just in how the numbers can be read — whatever the answer, we had a close race that year, and a very bland Ford lineup battled the radical Chevrolets tooth and nail. The story goes that both camps were startled at what the opposition fielded, and at least Ford *did* enlist Designer Alex Tremulus to revamp its 1960 models with a steeply-sloped new roof/backlight, and notably, long horizontal fins! By the time 1960 was over, though, Chevrolet had again gained a comfortable lead, and one that it has never relinquished. Impala style had really caught hold of the buying public by the end of the 'Fifites era!

The 1959 and 1960 Impalas, and other models too, are becoming more popular to collectors today — partially because of the pressure from the "Classic" 1955-7 series, of course, but also because of their own intrinsic values: both as practical, easy to restore drivers' cars, and as nostalgia trips for those who owned (or merely longed to own) one 'way back when. The three years were tremendously popular with the younger set in those long gone days, and the same lines that their designers hoped would sell cars to their "conspicuous-consumer" parents fairly shouted for attention on the cruisin' scene, especially when appropriately lowered, dechromed, striped and/or scalloped and fitted with loud glasspacks! A goodly number of the early Impalas one sees nowadays are the modified variety, either in the neo-Fifites' guise, or as "Low Riders!"

Whatever the designers had in mind, the late '50s Chevys are a remnant of an age of outlandish cars that will never come again. What actually was produced, wild and crazy as they were, really don't compare with what was *considered*, back in 1957 and '58. Mostly of clay, styling models or handbuilt fiberglass pre-production mock-ups they are all courtesy of GM Photographic, through the good offices of GM Design Staff.

1958 Chevrolet Impala On Its Way to Fame

By Pat Chappell

1958 Impala convertible.

IMPALA. Webster defines it as "a gracefull fast-running antelope from the African plains." But for GM's Chevrolet Division in 1958 it was the beginning of a new image. The first Impala is now becoming one of Chevy's more collectible entries.

In 1958 Chevrolet introduced the Impala, which in time expanded to an incredibly successful model line. Additionally, 1958 was a unique one-year-only body design. The original Impala was limited to the highly collectible two-door hardtop coupe and convertible body styles, exclusive not only in trim but in sheet metal which differed from the cowl back. The name Impala had originated for a 1956 GM show car, and 1958 production styling bore a definite relationship to both the 1955 Biscayne and the 1956 Corvette Impala Motorama entries.

The first Impala was introduced by Chevrolet Division on Oct. 31, 1957, weighing in at 3,650 pounds on a 117.5 inch wheelbase, 209 inches long, 77 inches wide and 56 inches high.

For 1958 Chevrolet regained the title of "U.S.A. Number 1," capturing the sales lead it had lost to Ford the year before. Coming back with a brand new design, more powerful engines (the 348 cid V8 Turbo Thrust made its debut), a new Cadillac-inspired X-member frame, all coil-spring suspension, and an "upper" Bel Air series of fleet-footed Impalas, the Division handily outsold Ford by a

1958 Impala Trim

quarter million units. It also gleaned 30 percent of the passenger car market for the first time in history while Ford dropped to 22.3 percent and Plymouth to 9.6 percent.

Chevrolet for 1958 was completely different from the Division's entries of 1955-57 and those to follow in 1959. A one-year offering was quite unusual for any division.

Clare MacKichan, head of the Chevrolet Design Studio during that era, said '58 styling was axed after one year because "in 1959 we went to a shared body shell with Pontiac, Oldsmobile and Buick. This was an effort to save money in the corporation. The idea was to make the outer surfaces different so that nobody would know they were shared, but the things underneath that cost the major amount of money would be shared."

The 1958 Chevy Impala — limited to 125,480 two-door hardtops and 55,989 convertibles — represented 15 percent of total production of 1,217,047 for the model year. It was an attractive model in many ways, but particularly pleasing to the eye were the sheet metal variations.

The Impala sport coupe had its own distinctive roof which wore a chrome-edged, rear facing dummy air scoop in the curved contour crease molded into the back of its roof. Other sheet metal special to the Impala involved the lower body from the "A" piller back: different dimensions in doors, rear compartment lid, and rear fender panel extensions. Understandably, these sheet metal changes dictated special glass. Though the Impala was the same size and weight as the Bel Air sport coupe, the rear deck was longer, resulting in a shorter interior compartment.

The two-tone paint treatment was handled differently for the Impala with the secondary color application limited to the roof of the sport coupe and the fabric top of the convertible. Distinctive wheel covers, stainless steel rocker panel trim, and a large, dummy chrome plated air scoop directly in front of the rear wheel well were all variations on the basic 1958 theme. From the rear, the Impala was particularly identifiable: The triple taillamp arrangement graced the right and left of the automobile.

1958 Impala with Continental Kit

1958 Impala 2dr Hardtop

The Impala's interior, designed by Ed Donaldson, had many hallmarks identifying it. The competition style two-spoke deep hub steering wheel was trimmed with an Impala medallion. The door trim panels had brushed anodized aluminum inserts which were color coordinated to match the horizontally striped seat upholstery which blended with the exterior paint.

Collector interest in the 1958 Chevy Impala, unlike its older brothers, 1955-57 Chevys, has been slow to develop. Hidden in the shadow of these highly popular cars for the last decade, the Impala is just recently emerging into popularity among automotive enthusiasts.

The Impala attracts young, middle-aged and older automotive hobbyists and collectors alike. It lends itself comfortably to both stock and modified restorations. Strictly stock ones often wear numerous factory accessories like continental kit, dual rear-mounted antennae, simulated exhaust ports on the rear quarter, and wonder-bar radios mounted in the dashboard.

With the growing interest in 1958 Chevys in general, it was inevitable they would be accepted in the hobby club structure. Welcomed by VCCA, and more recently by AACA, as well as VMCCA and CHVA, it was actually the National Impala Association and The Late Great Chevrolet Association (1958-1964 Chevrolets) that started helping members with technical information and parts availability.

Editorial Director Bob Snowden, of the Late Great Chevys, said that presently more parts are available for 1958 Chevys than the other years within the club, and even more are on the way.

Impala owners are faced with the same problem that 1955-1957 Chevy Nomad owners used to have: finding trim parts and sheet metal particular to the model. But Impala owners, unlike Nomad owners, have *numbers* on their side. Consider the following. From 1955-1957 only 23,000 Nomads were produced. For 1958, 181,000 Impalas were built — eight times as many. Even if only one-eighth of the Impalas survive (and it's estimated about one-fourth do), the number of 1958 Impalas which remain would be equal to the *original* production of Chevy Nomads, i.e. 23,000 — a considerable and ripe market for reproduction manufacturers.

Even though 1958 Chevy Impalas, like 1955-1957 Nomads, had numerous rust problems involving the headlight area, lower front fenders, rocker panels, rear wheel well, lower rear quarters and floors, we've seen a good many Nomads develop — via N.O.S. and repro parts — from virtual rust buckets to sound restorations during the last decade.

And, like the Nomad, from the "A" pillar forward, the first Impala was basically the same as any other Chevy that year, and 1,217,000 1958 Chevys were manufactured, so many parts and sheet metal are still available.

A small town nocturnal auto adventure

By Terry J. Berkson

I saw a red and white '58 Chevy Impala at a car show last week. It reminded me of when I was in high school, away from home in Brooklyn, NY, living with my Uncle William in Richfield Springs, NY. There, one new friend drove a '51 Mercury, another a '56 Ford. Every so often these guys would change cars like hermit crabs change shells, to take on a new look.

My friend Gerard was the one who owned the '58 Chevy. He lived on a farm just outside of town and had quit school the year before. He had sold a cow in order to buy this second-hand car of his dreams. Sometimes he'd cruise past the house at night and signal for me to come out and ride with him.

Uncle William was a thin, gray-haired old man who seemed to view everything through clouded eyes. He didn't change cars like the guys in town, having owned his '46 Packard for more than a decade. I was sure he'd forgotten what it was like to be 16 years old. He was very strict and wouldn't allow me out on school nights. It was depressing to be in that old house with its large, cold rooms and faded wallpaper. There wasn't even a television. So I'd fake being tired and go up to my room, drop some shoes on the floor and climb out the window.

One night, hefty Walter Burdock was waiting with Gerard.

"Let's get some beer," Walter said when I got in the car. He was always thirsty or hungry, but never had any money.

"I've got half-a-buck," Gerard said, smiling, his broken nose pulling to one side.

"Me, too," I said.

We drove to Sam Morris' grocery and bought some Topper beer at three quarts for $1. Old Sam never checked out IDs and always said the same thing: "Topper beer gives you vitamin P."

Then we cruised around the lake, sometimes speeding, sliding around Deadman's Corner, the beer spilling and making Gerard upset about stains on the Chevy's seats. There wasn't very much to do at night in this small town, especially in late autumn. When Gerard downshifted and hit the gas, the three two-barrel carburetors on that 348 engine would kick in and throw us back against the seats as the tires barked like dogs and the glass-packed mufflers "burrrappped" like machine guns. There was no car that could beat Gerard's '58 Chevy.

We circled the lake in good time and headed back to town, except when we got to the 30 mph sign, Gerard was doing 70, which we knew would alarm Tank Patterson, the town policeman. Sure enough, a pair of headlights went on in Tank's favorite hiding place behind the Agway barn at the edge of town. We were all laughing in the car as Gerard slowed down to a teasing 40 and Tank was gaining rapidly.

"Hit it!" Walter yelled. "Let's get the heck out of here!"

"Take it easy," Gerard said.

"What do cops here do to guys from Brooklyn?" I asked.

"You don't want to know," Walter said.

When Tank was almost on our bumper, Gerard made a left turn onto James Street and accelerated. The cop faded behind until his car straightened out, then he was gaining on us again. The patrol car had a siren but I think the ex-stone crusher was ashamed of the commotion it made, so he didn't use it.

Tank had a handicap. He had lost his left arm in an accident in a stone quarry in the nearby town of Jordanville. So when he had to turn a corner and downshift at the same time, his hand had to let go of the specially fitted steering knob, making the wheel spin back out of control.

The town had supplied the officer with a '57 Ford that had a suicide knob on the steering wheel and a three-speed shift stick on the column.

We rode around town at a leisurely pace, taking extra time at the stop signs, Walter Burdock looking back and laughing as Tank's headlights grew brighter in the rear view mirror and the whine of his overworked six-cylinder grew louder. There were no cars or people on the streets.

Then we shot to the edge of town and entered the park. Gerard shut off his headlights so Tank wouldn't spot us, and drove by the moonlight up the rocky mountain road to where it was high and we could see the whole lake and the town.

We spotted a single car winding and darting through the maze of streets below.

"That's gotta be him." Gerard said. "He's trying to catch up with us!"

After waiting for Tank to give up, we finally headed back down the hill, with our lights still off, the stones thumping beneath the Chevy's tires. Once we were back in town, Gerard dropped me at the house, where I shinnied up the leader line and climbed through the window.

I remember when Gerard finally traded in that '58 Chevy for a 409 convertible. Though he loved that car, he acted as if he'd forgotten all the good times it had given him. The motor had been run so hard that he had to put 90-weight oil in the crankcase to quiet the bearings. It was one of the few times the used car salesman got the oily end of the dipstick. There wasn't one thing on the car that was right anymore.

Later, we heard the dealer fixed it up with a smaller engine and a new drivetrain and said that it had belonged to a toe dancer. If Gerard had babied that beautiful car, today it would be worth something. But, like most people, my friend wasn't sentimental about this old love affair. It was behind him now. Like a hermit crab, he just moved into something new.

Middle-Weight Wagon —

'58 Brookwood

By Gerald Perschbacher

The Brookwood Biscayne was one of five station wagons available from Chevrolet in 1958. It was a middle-weight, the middle-priced model aimed at the buyer who wanted a fancier station wagon than the run-of-the-mill but could not justify buying a Nomad.

Factory price for the Brookwood when it was introduced in October 1957 was $2,571 in six-cylinder form. The wagon came in four-door, six- or nine-passenger form. And it weighed a hefty 3,748 pounds. The Brookwood carried Biscayne trim.

Total station wagon production for four-door versions was 170,473 in '58.

In six-cylinder version, the 235½-cubic-inch block was rated at 145 hp at 4200 rpm, with an increased compression ratio of 8.25:1. Many Brookwoods came with the large V insignia front and back, designating the car as a V-8 with a 283-cubic inch block with 185 hp at 4600 rpm. Compession ratio was standard at 8.5:1 or was boosted to 11.0:1 with 315 hp at 5600 rpm in the fuel-injected maximum performance package (although that would seem out of place on a station wagon of this caliber).

Extras included power steering at $70, power brakes at $38, power windows at $102, power front seat at $43, oil filter at $9, and oil bath air cleaner at $5, dual exhaust at $16, and deluxe heater at $77. Four-ply whitewall tires (7.50 x 14 inches) cost $32 more. Tinted glass cost the buyer an extra $38, electric wipers ran $7, and special padding for the dash was $16 more. A push button radio could be had for $84, air conditioning ran $468, and the bane of 1958 — the evasive, leaking air suspension — cost $124 more. A Positraction rear axle, for the forgotten man who had to drive on many bad surfaces, cost $48 with a 3.36 or 3.55 ratio.

Long and impressive, the Brookwood for '58 was a little brother to the Chevrolet Nomad.

Chevy for '59

All New . . . Again

1959 Bel Air four-door sedan

By Pat Chappell

Imagine, if you will, a little girl fleeing in fear from the family garage screaming, "Mommy, mommy! Something's eating my bicycle!" That was the essence of a Ford-inspired cartoon reacting to Chevrolet's gull-winged entry for 1959. Tom McCahill wrote for *True Automobile Yearbook:* "Chevrolet will go down as the 1959 car with the wildest styling, barring none. With a double decked manta ray stern the new Chevrolets are calculated to bounce the eyeballs right out of the average low-priced field buyer. The Impala is long, low and sexy, and with enough glass area to start an orchid factory if the engine poops out . ." Carl Renner, of the Styling Section of Chevrolet in the Fifties, recalled the 1959's horizontal rear fins in an interview some 20 years later as resembling a "butter-fly tail" or a "seagull." In a piece for *Special Interest Autos*, Wick Humble designated these wings "empennage" and former *Old Cars Weekly* editor, Tony Hossain, more kindly noted these fins gave the rear of the car "a rather wild bow tie look."

We'd like to hop on that bandwagon, because the entry for 1959 was one of the wildest styled Chevys that had ever come off the design boards. It was an automobile which you either loved or hated, and when the public sees one on the road today, they sit up straight and stare in utter disbelief. We know . . . we've had one since the fall of 1960. But it never in all those years of careful garaging and shelter has eaten a single bicycle! Oil, yes! Gas, yes! Wheel bearings, yes . . . it chewed them up like pretzels . . . but never either of my daughters' many bicycles. Perhaps it's because we keep it backed in, with the venetian blinds at the windows in the back of the garage tightly drawn, so its frontal horizontal air scoops, fancy grille and awfuly low double headlights aren't quite as frightful a scene upon entering as the gull-winged rear end is. Ours is particularly fun to own for it's a Gothic Gold Impala convertible which we've often thought would make a super parade car in a couple of decades or so. Talk about culture shock!

As early as August, 1959, *Motor Trend* reported ways in which customizers tried to improve the breed. Such appendages as floating grille bars, dummy teardrop spots and frenched taillights grew from the front. The rear could be further enhanced by replacing Chevy's cat eyes with 1957 DeSoto station wagon taillights, frenched and extended five inches into the original Chevy light panels. If that didn't do the trick, how about plastic lenses which transmitted light into frosted plastic teeth in a frenched taillight housing with eyelids extended four inches? The "wild one" became wilder!

How many of these 1959 Chevys were made, and who really cares about them today, anyway? It was an interesting year in the history of the Division for a number of reasons. Ford claimed to have taken the lead from Chevy in 1959 calendar year production: 1,528,592 to Chevy's 1,428,980 total. But in model year production Chevy led — 1,481,071 to Ford's 1,394,684, so it depended on which figures you quoted. It is important, today, to realize that not only was the 1958 Chevrolet a complete departure from the much revered 1955-1957 series, but for 1959, as advertised, the Division's entry was "All New All Over Again." This was mandated by a GM decree which was explained to us by Clare MacKichan, formerly of the Styling Section of Chevrolet, in an interview in 1976: "In 1959, we went to a shared body shell with Pontiac, Oldsmobile and Buick. This was an effort to save money in the Corporation. The idea was to make the outer surfaces different so that nobody would know they were shared, but the things underneath that cost the major amount of money *would* be shared." Asked what direction Chevrolet styling might have taken had this decision not been made, MacKichan said, "I suppose there were facelifts made, but I don't know where they are or what they were. I think the idea of going to a new body shell came very early, so we did not do much on a facelift."

The newly introduced Impala convertible and two door hardtop of 1958 grew into an entire series of four models for 1959, with the addition of a four door sedan and a four door hardtop, all this replacing the top-of-the-line Bel Air series. The middle Biscayne series was redesignated Bel Air, and the bottom-of-the-line Delray was replaced by the Biscayne series. More Impalas than Bel Airs were sold with 473,000 built, compared to the middle Bel Air series produced in quantities of 447,100.

The people who care about these Chevys today are first of all dyed-in-the-wool Chevrolet enthusiasts who probably had one once, and still want a Chevy of the Fifties, but less pricey than the ever-popular 1955-1957 models. They can join up with all the Vintage Chevrolet Club of America members, or The National Impala Association, or The Late Great Chevrolet Association. And the source for parts and technical information is excellent — those individuals involved in reproduction of original 1955-1957 parts have just extended their wares into 1958 and 1959 and the Sixties. We remarked three years ago how few 1958 and 1959 models we were seeing at local or national shows, and our manufacturing, dealing and vending friends assured us they *were* being restored because of the constant demand for parts. Today, we're seeing more and more 1958 and 1959 models competing at multi-make shows and in car shows sponsored by clubs which have since been formed. And for the most part, they're looking good . . . if not better than new!

How that 1959 Chevrolet grew! It dwarfs our 1956 Nomad garaged next to it in all dimensions except height. The wheelbase stretched from 115 inches to 119 inches; overall length increased from 200 to 211 inches; the width spread from 73 to 80 inches, and weight from 3342 to 3650 pounds. Only height shrunk — from 60.7 to 54 inches.

Many of the engineering features new for 1958 were carried over in 1959. The 235.5 cubic inch Six Cylinder engine which developed 135 horsepower at 4000 rpm was installed in 38 percent of the 1959 Chevys, which seems amazing. The 283 cid V-8 engine developed 185 horsepower at 460 rpm, and many optional power plants were available including the 348 cid engine which developed 250 horsepower at 440 rpm and could be stretched to a top horsepower of 315 with special goodies under the hood.

Some of those 1959 Chevys could really blow the doors

1959 Impala 4dr Hardtop

off some of the competition and *Motor Trend* paid special attention to the 1959 Chevrolet Police Pursuit Biscayne in an issue toward the end of 1958. This hot Chevy used the regular 348-cubic inch engine, with bore and stroke the same, but the compression ratio was upped from 9.5 to 11 to 1. Solid lifters, a special high-performance camshaft (not unlike the famous Duntov cam available for the Corvette), heavy-duty main and connecting-rod bearings, special high compression pistons with clearance for valve overlap, and a larger-capacity manifold completed the heavy-duty touches. In a car which weighed in at 3900 pounds carrying two passengers, top speed of 135.5 mph was reached with a 3.36 axle. By 1960 a 1959 Chevy hardtop driven by Junior Johnson won the Daytona "500."

Our 1959 convertible never came anywhere near reaching the top speedometer reading of 120 mph while we have owned it, but it is fun to recall some of the experiences we have had with it since we bought it as a "used car" in the fall of 1960. Sitting on the lot of the local Wilmington, Delaware Olds dealership, it was a cream puff with 18,000 careful miles and a reasonable buy at $1500. Resting there in its Gothic Gold paint with a black top and wide white walls — it was an impressive sight. (In 1960 no one dreamed the industry would ever stop production of assembly line convertibles within the next decade).

Our convertible was never referred to as "the Impala" — instead it was fondly called "The Turkey" — one imagines it was because it was brown and bought near Thanksgiving, not that it gobbled. Though we do remember on its round trip across the United States in 1965 from Wilmington to El Paso, Texas and back again — for an Army Reserve summer camp, it did gobble up three wheel bearings and one fuel pump. Gas mileage was pretty fair, though that wasn't a major consideration with reasonable mid-Sixties prices. The car was a behemoth, one of the heaviest of the line, outweighed only by station wagons. The trunk was and still is cavernous, and that summer its contents defied all sorts of gendarmes, hauling 42 quarts of assorted liquor from Juarez, Mexico back across many, many state lines. Four or five passengers could be seated comfortably, though the guy in the middle of the back seat had the radio speaker decorated with that fleeting Impala and crossed flags emblem engraved in his back long after the trip ended. Contrary to popular belief which still abounds (we were reminded of it recently via the loud speaker at a local auto show as an Impala sport sedan drove through "Victory Lane" for a trophy), these 1959s never really became airborne on the highways at high speed. Their concave sculpture fins and considerable body weight held them to the road like the tires were embedded in tracks.

We drove the kindergarten car pool for a number of years, and the five year olds were delighted on bright, sunny days when we had the top down and the game was to see how far their coloring papers would fly once released from their tiny hands. Six little folks plus the harried driver left lots of room for papers, jackets, sit-upons, and show-and-tell items, too.

And it has been a great "tour" car for regional Vintage Chevrolet Club outings. We remember particularly a tour of Philadelphia with the Liberty Bell Region of VCCA where sightseeing of famous skyscrapers, Independence Hall and "Billy" Penn's statue were all quite visible with the top down.

We especially recall what a wonderfully heavy and solid-riding car that 1959 convertible was as the daily-driver for over twelve years (before we started "saving it" so it could live to be a "Vintage Chevy.") Steering was a chore even prior to the onset of our arthritis — a power steering unit would have been a much appreciated option. All in all, it was a heck of a good buy at $1500, and now, three tops and numerous back windows later, the odometer reads 75,810.6 as it sits in the garage growing older and perhaps a little uglier, but never mouthing little girl's bicycles.

What was once advertised as "dramatic styling" by Campbell-Ewald seems today more unusual and weird than "dramatic." In fact this particular Impala for 1959 is something of a pre-historic animal judging by the standard set by Impalas of the Sixties and Seventies.

But we still love it, else why would we have kept it longer than any of our other Chevys . . . the 1948, the three 1951s, the 1955, 1956 and 1957 . . . over 30 years for heaven's sake. That's a long time to hold on to a "turkey."

1959 Impala Convertible

'59 Impala

Chevrolet's "Gull-Winged" Beauty

By John Lee

Destined to be the industry's best-selling car model during much of the 1960's, the Impala began its reign as a Chevrolet series in 1959.

Bestowing a new name on a series after introducing it on a sport model was a Chevrolet pattern. The automaker's first two-door hardtop, in 1950, was called Bel Air; by 1953 Bel Air designated the top-trim series.

In 1958 a pair of dolled-up sports models, a convertible and a hardtop coupe, with tops and rear quarter treatments distinctly different from the rest or the line, were introduced. The two were named Impala and were a subseries of the Bel Air.

The following year Impala was Chevy's top series, embracing not only the hardtop coupe and convertible, but a four-door sedan and four-door sport (hardtop) sedan.

Styling was totally new, the second complete change in as many years. In that time it went from the vertical emphasis of the 1957 through the 1958 transition models to 1959's aerospace style featuring horizontal lines. Tailfins were nearly horizontal, dipping in the middle to resemble a gull's wings, and they shaded horizontal, "cat's eye" taillights.

The double-rail side trim spear, usually with a contrasting color stripe, and a simulated air scoop above the back window of the two-door hardtop and four-door sedan and hardtop were identifying touches carried over from 1958. The frontal aspect also stressed horizontal lines, with the quad headlights lowered to line up with the grille and narrow air scoops above echoing the shape of the taillights.

Eight engine options were available for the Impala and all 1959 Chevys. They ranged from a 135 hp six through four versions of the 283-cubic-inch V8 and three of the 348-inch V8. A 283 with 10.5:1 compression ratio and Ramjet fuel injection was rated at 290 hp, while the top 348, with 11.25:1 compression and three two-barrel carburetors, churned out 335 hp. Performance buffs often chose the floor-mounted four-speed transmission, while three-speed manual, overdrive and Powerglide and Turboglide automatics were also available.

The flamboyant styling would be toned down considerably the following year, but for 1959 Chevrolet was a stunning machine, and the Impala series was launched on a successful career.

The Three Lives of the El Camino

By Robert C. Ackerson

Most everyone knows that Ford beat Chevrolet by two full model years when it entered the personal pickup field in 1957 with the first Ranchero. On the other hand, Chevrolet's response, the El Camino, remained in production after the last of the Rancheros had been built.

We want to examine the evolution of the El Camino through its three basic design stages and perhaps uncover a point or two about it that will prompt a restoration or two to begin on what are very appealing vehicles that deserve a place in the old car world.

When Chevrolet introduced the El Camino on Oct. 16, 1958 it described it as, "More than a car — more than a truck." The El Camino was a dual purpose vehicle that would be suitable for personal transportation and the carrying of loads of up to 1,150 pounds. As far as the latter was concerned, the El Camino offered a pickup box with a capacity of 33⅞ cubic feet with double walls and a steel floor with built-in skid plates on top of a sub-floor that was supported by four steel cross members. The tailgate which Chevrolet perferred to call an "endgate" was also double walled and when lowered to its horizontal position helped provide a level load space of 91 inches. The only real shortcomings of the El Camino's design that would reduce its appeal as a light-duty pickup were its lack of protection for the back of the cab if the load should shift and move forward with much force, and the narrow distance between the endgate and the road when it was lowered.

Since the mechanical base of the El Camino was essentially a two-door Chevrolet station wagon, it was fitted with an "X" type frame, front and rear coil springs as well as a rear anti-sway bar. The last feature was an obvious plus for the El Camino, but in spite of it and a surprisingly good weight distribution of approximately 53 percent front and 47 percent rear, the El Camino was no sports car in the turns. The springs were too soft and the steering too slow to allow for any vigorous cornering in the El Camino. Furthermore, with a width of nearly 80 inches, the El Camino had a distinctly ungraceful appearance as it leaned over in the turns.

Despite the El Camino's attractive exterior, the interior was somber. There was no problem in seating three adults in comfort, but the seats and side panels were available in only a drab gray plastic covering. In addition, such items as a right side sunvisor, arm rests, foam seats, padded dash and cigarette lighter were optional.

But this really wasn't a major sales impediment, at least as far as the El Camino's appeal to a select group of potential customers who studied its engine option list was concerned. They weren't excited about its standard six-cylinder engine with its 235 cubic inches and 135 horsepower. Enthusiasm rose considerably over the various versions of the 283 cid V-8 which ranged in power from 185 to the fuel injected model's 290 horsepower. Joining these engines were four versions of the 348 cid Chevrolet V-8, the most powerful of which had triple Rochester carburetors, a special cam, to the land of the living in 1964, it was considerably smaller in its overall dimensions than it had been back in 1959-60. Instead of a 119-inch wheelbase, it rode on the new Chevelle's 115-inch wheelbase chassis and its overall length was down from 210.9 inches to a more manageable 198.9 inches. Furthermore, its width had also been shrunk from 79.9 inches to 74.6 inches. The 1964 El Camino was obviously a fresh, new package but it maintained a link with the older model with its good looks and sparkling performance. As Chevrolet

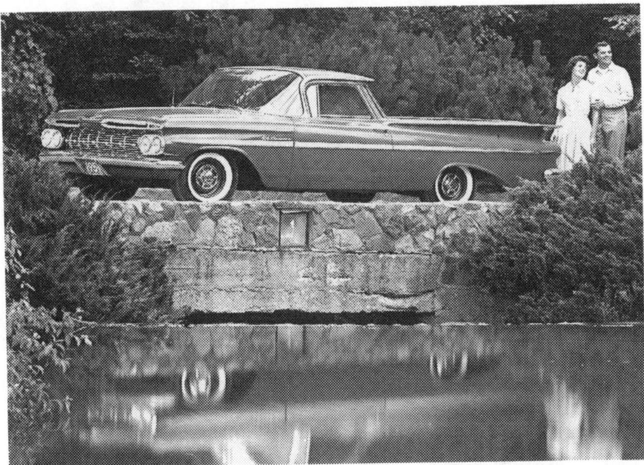

A 1959 El Camino.

suggested, the 1964 El Camino was "equally at home at the country club or the loading dock." It was available with several versions of Chevrolet's 327 cid V-8.

When the 1964 model year began, the El Camino was offered only with two six-cylinder engines (194 cid, 120 hp or 230 cid, 155 hp) or the 283 cid V-8 with either 195 or 220 horsepower. However this situation was soon improved when the 327 cid V-8 became an El Camino option. The only restriction was that Chevrolet wouldn't install the fuel injected version with 375 hp in an El Camino.

By 1966, with the supercar era well underway, the El Camino was offered with RPO 135 which represented an SS396 El Camino with a 325 hp, 396 cid V-8. Also available for the El Camino was the 350 hp version of the 396 engine.

Since the El Camino was in a sense a captive of the design boundaries of the Chevelle, it tended to follow the trends that dominated the mid-sized car field. Thus as the supercar era faded away, so did the super quick El Caminos. As the Chevelle was periodically restyled, so was the El Camino. But it had a few distinctions of its own.

There were, in addition to the SS models, El Caminos known as Classic, Royal Knight and Conquista versions. These were essentially trim options, but their availability enabled a customer to order an El Camino that was tailored to suit his or her personality.

The re-sizing of the Chevelle in 1978 brought with it the third and, at least up to the present, the final form of the El Camino. But this time around the El Camino received its own special floor plan with a 117.1 inch wheelbase. Although this was longer than the previous year's 116 inch wheelbase, the new model was, at 201.6 inches, shorter by 11.7 more, the 1978 model's pickup box was 78.6 inches in length which was an increase of seven inches from that of the 1977 model. At the same time, the new El Camino's curb weight was 3,165 pounds, which represented a reduction of 599 pounds as compared to that of the 1977 model.

The El Camino's standard engine was a 3.3 liter, V-6 (California models had a 3.8 liter V-6), but also available were two 5.0 liter V-8s, one of which was the LMI version with a single Rochester four-barrel carburetor that developed 170 hp at 3800 rpm. This provided, with Turbo Hydramatic, a respectable zero to sixty mph time of approximately nine seconds.

The Fabulous Impala Super Sport

By Tony Hossain

The number one success car of the 1960s was the Chevrolet Impala. Millions were sold, but the ones we cherish most today are all labeled Super Sport.

Since its introduction in 1958, the Chevy Impala had a strong performance image, enhanced by the respected 283 V-8 and the multi-carbureted 348. The '61 Impala was smaller, lighter, and prettier than its predecessors. It was also an excellent starting point for a truly memorable performance machine, the 1961 Impala SS that was introduced mid-season.

The '61 Impala SS package was created to showcase another late entry, the 409-cid engine. The 409, basically a bored-out 348, was designed for drag and stock-car racing, but production problems stopped '61 output after only 142 engines had been installed. Not all SS cars were 409-equipped, but the factory "kit" required at least a 348 and four-speed. Other components for the '61 Super Sport package included "SS" exterior identification, wheel cover spinners, padded instrument panel, power brakes and steering, heavy-duty suspension, metallic

1961 Impala Convertible

brake linings, 7000-rpm tachometer and 8.00 x 14 narrow-band whitewall tires.

The '61 SS was as interesting for what it wasn't as for what it was. Bucket seats, which would soon become the primary identifying feature of any Super Sport, weren't available. In theory, one could offer SS equipment in any '61 body style, including two-door hardtop, convertible, two-door sedan, four-door hardtop, and even the four-door sedan. Total production of the first, and largely unknown, Super Sport amounted to just 453 units.

If the '61 was an unknown, the 1962 Impala Super Sport was quite the opposite. A pleasing facelift gave the '62 SS a slightly heavier, more formal appearance. And there was exciting news under the hood, too. The 235.5 cid six and the 283 V8 were carryover entries, but a pair of new 327-cid V8s replaced the 348 as middleweight performance options. Rated at 250- and 300-hp, these small-blocks were far more potent than any 352- or 390-powered Ford. The ultimate weapon in the Chevy arsenal, though, was a new edition of the 409. This time Chevy did

1961 Impala wheel cover

1961 Chevrolet 283 CID V-8 Engine

1961 Impala Interior

1961 Impala Convertible

1962 Impala SS 2dr Hardtop

1963 Impala SS Convertible

1964 Impala SS Convertible

1963 Impala SS 2dr Hardtop

1965 Impala SS Convertible

1965 Impala SS Sport Coupe

1966 Impala SS Convertible

Chrome Super Sport signature appeared on front fenders of SS models in 1966.

it right, and full production went ahead on schedule with 380- and 409-hp versions on tap.

Super Sport content changed dramatically for '62. This year's car (still an option package) was available only in two-door hardtop or convertible form. Equipment included all-vinyl upholstery with front bucket seats, instrument panel grab bar, locking center console, swirl-pattern aluminum trim inside and out, and exterior SS identification. A '62 SS could be ordered with any full-size Chevy engine (even the six but few were built that way). Three-speed and four-speed manual transmissions came with floor-mounted shift levers but the optional Powerglide automatic still featured a column-mounted shift. For 1962, over 99,000 Impalas were equipped with the SS option. The Super Sport was off to a fast start.

A crisp facelift marked the 1963 Chevrolets. The Impala SS received a plusher interior with a pleasing new instrument panel, and a host of new color combinations. Popular new options included a seven-position tilt steering wheel, a vinyl top for the Sport Coupe, and a "street" version of the 409, developing 340 hp. Two other 409s were available, a single four-barrel version rated at 400 hp and a dual-quad 425 hp heavyweight. The Impala SS buyer could also choose from a new 230 cid six, a 195 hp version of the venerable 283, or the pair of increasingly popular 327s. Super Sport production topped 153,000 for the model year.

Tony Hossain is standing by his 1965 Impala SS convertible

1967 Impala SS Trim Details

In recognition of its astounding sales success, the Impala Super Sport became a full-fledged series for 1964. Styling was crisp and formal and the plush, all-vinyl interior took on new elegance. Model year production topped 185,000.

The all-new 1965 Chevrolet was enthusiastically received. As usual, but for the last time, the Impala SS was the top-of-the-line Chevy. Styling was clean, dechromed and the Sport Coupe's fastback roofline was a real departure from the 1962-64 "fake-convertible" look. The interior was as handsome as ever and full instrumentation was standard for the first time. Production topped the 237,000 mark, making the '65 the best-selling Super Sport ever.

There were really two model years in '65. Until February, one could still order an Impala with the 409 (340 hp or 400 hp versions only). Then, the 396 replaced the 409 as Chevy's top performance option. Other mid-year shuffles included the introduction of the three-speed Turbo Hydra-Matic (available with the 325-h.p. 396 only) and the Caprice option for the Impala Sport Sedan. The Caprice eclipsed the SS as Chevy's most exclusive offering and was expanded into a complete series for '66.

Most Chevy enthusiasts found the 1966 full-size line a mixed bag of good and bad. Good was the new 427-c.i.d. engine, available in 390-h.p. and 425-h.p. form. More good news was the elegant Caprice Coupe with its luxurious optional bucket-seat interior and lengthy list of custom features. The bad news was the obvious downgrading of the Impala SS. The bucket seat interior was still standard but it was clearly an offshoot of the standard Impala seating and no match for Caprice upholstery. Those popular '65 wheelcovers were continued, but body side moldings and a blunter rear view gave the SS a more sedate, conventional appearance. Sales were down sharply, to under 120,000 units. With the Caprice stealing luxury-car buyers and the SS396 Chevelle and Pontiac GTO taking away the all-out performance customers, the Impala SS was fast becoming a car without a reason.

Chevy shuffled its full-size SS offerings for '67, possibly in reaction to disappointing '66 sales. The results were some rather ordinary and some rather fascinating Impalas. SS Impalas were broken into two groups; the conventional Super Sport Coupe and convertible continued as before, and a new SS427 coupe and convertible was introduced.

The traditional Impala Super Sport retained the usual styling touches and the bucket-seat interior. Engine choices again ranged from the six nobody ordered to the 396 and 427 powerhouses.

The SS427 variant was available with the top 385-h.p. 427 only. Features of this car included a specially-domed hood with fake center air inlets, bold SS427 ornamentation, and oversize tires.

Perhaps it was the bulkier styling. Or the dominance of the mid-size supercars. But Impala SS sales declined again for 1967, and the SS427 is an especially rare, desirable car today.

Another indignity was heaped upon the Impala SS for 1968. It was downgraded to its 1962-63 status, an option package for the Impala convertible, Sport Coupe, and the new formal-roofed Custom Coupe. The interesting SS427 package continued, and it too was available in all three body styles. Super Sport production totalled 38,210 for the '68 model year, including just 1,778 SS427s.

For 1969, the full-size Chevrolet grew bigger. Elegance, not performance, was the operating word. The new Impala Custom Coupe was very attractive, but an awkward Sport Coupe unsuccessfully tried to bridge the gap between "formal" and "sport." There probably weren't many who noticed back then, but the "regular" Impala Super Sport was no more. You *could* still approximate a Super Sport by ordering an Impala coupe or convertible with bucket seats and console (the first time a non-SS big Chevy could be so equipped). Curiously, while the garden-variety Impala SS was no more, the SS427 did continue to the end of the '69 model year. And it would be Chevy's last full-size super car.

The SS427 was once again available in convertible, Sport Coupe, or Custom Coupe form. In addition to the mighty 390-h.p. 427, equipment included 15-inch rally wheels, a sport suspension, SS identification, and a black-accented grille. The standard Impala all-vinyl bench seat was base fare but a console and front buckets were available at extra cost. Only 2,455 were built for '69, and then Chevy's full-size sports car became history.

A child of the '60s, the Impala Super Sport faded away with the decade that created it. The Super Sport name would continue to identify some of Chevy's most exciting cars, but there would never again be an automobile quite like the original Impala SS. From 409 to 427, it was quite a trip.

1967 Impala SS Convertible

1968 Impala SS Convertible

Stylish but affordable 1962 Impala

By Robert C. Ackerson

Although the Chevy II attracted the lion's share of public attention when the 1962 models were introduced, it was the Impala that most Chevrolet dealers eagerly awaited. They knew that once perspective customers entered a Chevrolet showroom, only the most inept salesman could keep them from gravitating toward a fancy Impala hardtop or convertible. No matter that they had come in determined to purchase nothing fancier than a simple Biscayne or middle-of-the-line Bel Air, one glance at an Impala was all that was needed to banish such dull ambitions from their mind.

Chevrolet had worked hard to endow the Impala with the proper combination of distinctive identification features and appointments that suggested to relatively impecunious buyers that here was a car at a reasonable price that gave them virtually all the luxury features one reserved for only America's most costly automobiles. In the eyes of most Chevolet drivers that meant only one car — Cadillac — and it was no mere happen-stance that more often than not Impala's lines were suggestive of Cadillac's.

Chevrolet followed up its all-new and somewhat downsized 1961 models with 1962 versions that carried all new exterior body sheetmetal. There wasn't anything even vaguely suggestive of radical design thinking to be found in the new Chevrolet's lines. Instead, Chevrolet remained faithful to past practice — keeping the looks of its products up-to-date but not stepping too far away from the mainstream.

Here, too, Chevrolet was not unlike Cadillac. Both marques were willing, when they sensed the time was ripe for a new design to take hold in America, to move out in front of their competition. But more often than not, their new model followed each other in a wonderfully predictable, evolutionary fashion. Cast in this mold, the 1962 Chevrolet Impala wasn't a styling landmark. But neither was it a styling disaster. Indeed, nary a critical word about its appearance was printed in contempory motoring journals. One, *Motor Trend,* in July 1962, saw fit to observe that "the Impala's hardtop styling brought general approval.

1962 Impala Sport Sedan

1962 Impala Convertible

1962 Bel Air 409 with factory optional tach.

1962 Impala Wheel Cover

Simple and to the point, it is one of the cleaner, best thought-out designs to come along." Since the hardtops roof line was patterned after that of the Impala convertible, there's no doubt that *Motor Trend* also held an equally positive opinion of the soft top's looks.

Even though it probably mattered little to most new Chevrolet buyers, there were some very exciting performance options just waiting to be installed beneath the new Chevrolet's handsome lines. The most awesome of these was a 409 cid V8 engine, that when fitted with dual four-barrel carburetors developed 409 hp. Only slightly less potent was the single four-barrel version rated at 380 hp. Both examples had 11.0:1 compression ratios.

The 409 engines, some of which had been produced in 1961, were derived from the 348 cid V8 that Chevrolet had introduced in 1958. Similarly, Chevrolet's new 327 cid V8 was a derivative of the 283, which in turn had grown out of the original 265 cid V8 of 1955. Two versions of the 327 engine were offered, both with four-barrel carburetors. One with 250 hp used a Carter carburetor with 1.4375 inch barrel diameters. When a larger Carter carburetor with 1.5625 inch primaries and 1.6875 inch secondaries was installed, peak horsepower rose to 300.

In contrast to the lofty power levels of the 409 and 327 engines, the standard Chevrolet V8, with 283 cid, a mild 8.5:1 compression ratio and a small two-barrel carburetor developed a modest 170 hp. Yet the performance of this engine in combination with the two-speed Powerglide transmission was acceptable for the average motorist. Zero to 60 mph required approximately 12.5 seconds and the quarter-mile was completed in 20.3 seconds at 73.5 mph — neither mind-boggling nor neck-snapping, but surely satisfactory.

Eventually the Impala name lost its top-of-the-line status to the Caprice, which originated in 1965 as Chevrolet's response to Ford's LTD. But in its prime, Impala stood for a lot of Chevrolet at a reasonable price.

Chevy II's 'Super-Thrift' 4

By Robert C. Ackerson

1962 Chevy II 300 4dr Sedan (Center)

Everyone knows how terrible the Detroit auto industry treats the poor, gullible, misguided consumer. Remember all those nasty high performance cars of the sixties that were stuffed down our unwilling throats? Recall all those scenes of thousands of young people being brainwashed by crafty ad copy writers into purchasing those undesirable Road Runners, Chargers, 427 Super Sport Chevys, Mach I Mustangs and of course that absolutely outrageous GTO?

That's the way many self ordained critics of the automobile industry would like automotive history to be written. The only problem is that it wasn't that way at all and it still isn't. We bought what we bought back then because we wanted to; it's as simple as that. If you were hooked on foreign-econo cars you drove a VW Bug. If power was your game a Road Runner with a 440-Six pack was tucked away in your garage. Freedom was the name of the game. You shopped around, took a lot of test drives, tried your hand at haggling and then found it hard to wait till the day you took delivery.

Mort Sahl once said that "If the government made a car in America I guess it would be a two-door gray Valiant." Now don't get me wrong, I've nothing against two-door gray Valiants but the idea that someone else is going to decide what's best for me doesn't square very well with Jefferson's belief that we *all* possess the right to pursue happiness without some super-sized government getting into the act.

A far better way of deciding what kind of automobiles are to be built is to let the buyer decide which are best suited to his needs and economic positions. In other words let him pick the car that will make him happy. It's a pretty simple idea and furthermore it works!

After all that's been said and written about the Edsel the reason for its demise was simple, that not many people wanted it; in other words ownership of an Edsel didn't make many people happy.

Almost at the same time the Edsel bit the dust, Chevrolet was choking on some airborne dirt kicked up by the sales success of the Ford Falcon. Ed Cole had high hopes for the Corvair but in sales it was no match for the Falcon. The old marketplace sent a loud and clear message back to Chevrolet. American economy car buyers (apparently) liked their economy cars straight forward and practical. No fancy rear-engine and swing-axle jive for them. Within months Chevrolet responded with its "Car H" project. Its goal was to develop an automobile of "maximum functionalism with thrift . . . to provide good basic transportation for the average American family and at the most reasonable cost. This includes not only the original purchase price but also more economical operating and maintenance expenses."

The end result of the Car H project was of course the Chevy II which debuted in 1962 and which as the Nova was in production until 1979 when the Citation was introduced. Although it was extremely orthodox in design, the Chevy II did possess several interesting technical features, the most interesting being its single leaf rear spring which was subjected to laboratory testing that duplicated 1,500,000 miles of highway driving.

But, to anyone who has looked under the hood of a Chevrolet Citation, the Chevy II's most interesting feature was its four cylinder engine for the X-cars gutsy little four-banger is really nothing more than that Chevy II engine brought up to date.

When Chevrolet put the Chevy II into production most journalists were more interested, after taking a few measurements, in reporting that a 327 cid V8 would fit under its hood rather than detailing the features of the Chevy II's four-cylinder engine. Such bias was understandable since this was the early spring of the great age of American performance cars and in that environment a U.S.-built four-banger was nothing more than a white crow.

As a result, sales of Chevy II's with the 153 cid-four never amounted to anything. For example they were installed in only 2% of all 1963 Chevy II's. Yet at the same time some 12% of the Chevy II's assembled were equipped with the Super Sport trim package that carried a $161.40 price tag . . . *Car Life* magazine (December 1963) thus concluded "This luxury-oriented market of today just isn't interested in 4 cyl. engines . . . The slightly improved gas mileage and lower first cost, as compared to a six, doesn't mean a thing. This is one area where GM market forecasters guessed wrong." Yet Chevy continued the four through 1970 after which it remained dormant until resurfacing as Pontiac's Iron Duke in 1977.

One reason why Chevrolet persisted so long with the four was the low cost of keeping it in production. A new automated assembly line was used for both the four and six cylinder engine and since both shared many parts with the 283 V8 (such as pistons, rods and some valve-train components) they were not expensive to produce. At the same time the little four was one tough engine. Along with the 194 cid six, it had chalked up nearly one million miles of pre-production testing and its simple but rugged design along with five bearing crankshaft and high-chrome cast iron cylinder head, gave it an excellent record of reliability at the hands of its owner.

Compared to the 194 six and 283 V8 the four was a lightweight engine, tipping the scales at just 360 pounds; comparative weights for the other engines were 455 and 596 pounds respectively. When compared to the four-cylinder engine Pontiac used for its early Tempest, the Chevy II four was 21% smaller in displacement but weighed 35% less! With fairly good breathing characteristics the little four developed 90 hp at 4400 rpm and 152 lb. ft. of torque at 2400 rpm. This latter output equalled just about one lb. ft. per cubic inch. In late 1961 Chevrolet published a power curve for the 153 cid four that placed its net horsepower and torque output at 75 and 144 respectively.

Obviously a Chevy II with this engine was not a performance car. With Powerglide its zero to 60 mph time was 20 seconds. A three speed stick model didn't do too bad though, reaching 60 mph in 17 seconds. This wasn't "Chevy Two Much" performance but remember that with just 360 pounds of engine weight on its front wheels a four cylinder model was the best handling Chevy II and both metallic brake linings and genuine, knock-off wirewheels were available. A 2-door Chevy II in the lowest priced "100" series had a base price of $1827 and with the aforementioned options would have made for a neat, sporty and economical car in the early sixties. Today it would make for a neat, sporty, economical and *different* car to share a collector's garage with a Nova 396SS.

Late Sixties 4-cylinder Chevy II's were available with Torque-Drive, a semi-automatic transmission priced at approximately $65. That price is significant because for just $59 Chevy II customers could opt for the larger six cylinder engine.

Thus there were no tears shed when the four-cylinder Chevy engine was phased out. Lots of cars and engines have been described as being before their time but somehow, such pompous declarations don't seem to be appropriate for what was really just a simple no-nonsense economy engine. But what the heck, with gas prices creeping up to the $1.50 per gallon mark somebody might just speak out and say, "hey, remember that little 4-cylinder Chevy II that came out back in '62? Now that *was* a better idea!"

1963 Chevrolet Impala Sport Sedan

Chevy for 1963

1963 Chevrolet Impala Sport Sedan

By Robert C. Ackerson

Although the year was just 21 days old when all GM automotives divisions were ordered to wind down their racing activities, the 1963 Chevrolets were off and running with barrel-fulls of performance goodies available for anyone who was familiar with their RPO numbers. Along with the sales momentum provided by its "Hot Car" image, Chevrolet was also enjoying a growing reputation for engineering expertise. In 1962 *Car Life*, in giving its annual award for engineering excellence to the Chevy II described it as an automobile that "represents an important development in the American automotive field . . . a return to sensibility in terms of basic transportation." The Chevy II didn't overhaul the top selling Falcon or Rambler during the 1962 model run but its total production of over 326,000 had little negative impact upon Corvair sales which increased due primarily to the popularity of the Monza series.

While the Chevy II was positioned in one of the industry's most competitive zones, the Corvette enjoyed unique status as the only volume-produced American sports car. In its dramatic new form the 1963 Corvette made it two-in-a-row for Chevrolet as *Car Life*, citing the Corvette as "tomorrow's car, on the streets today" selected it as the recipient of its 1963 engineering excellence award.

Although laurels of this type weren't bestowed upon the full-sized Chevrolets, they had little difficulty in maintaining both their top position as America's best selling automobile and, thanks to a very young engine lineup, a high visibility among the supercar class of 1963. While it was by no means a performance unit, Chevrolet's new 230 cid six-cylinder engine was noteworthy since it replaced the long-lived, 235.5 cid six that had remained basically unchanged since 1937. In a clever mix of the 3.875 inch bore used in the Chevy II four-cylinder engine and the 3.25 inch stroke of the six-cylinder version, Chevrolet was able to create a seven main bearing six displacing 230 cubic inches. This engine, weighing approximately 100 pounds less than its predecessor developed 140/hp at 4400/rpm and 220 lb.-ft. of torque at a low 1600/rpm. Its acceleration potential didn't suck the socks out of anyone's shoes but a zero to 60 mph time of 17 seconds was acceptable for a full-sized Chevrolet equipped with Powerglide.

Only one version of Chevrolet's 283 cid V-8, which had been in production since 1957 was offered but it entered 1963 as one of the most popular engines in the world. Although it was rated at a relatively modest 195/hp, this engine when linked to a 3-speed manual transmission was a surprisingly strong performer. *Car Life* (January, 1963) tested a 3500 pound Biscayne two-door sedan with this engine/transmission combination and reported a zero to 60 mph time of 10.7 seconds. Priced at under $2,500, such a car, with its 119 inch wheel providing plenty of space for passengers and their luggage, was capable of out-accelerating many far more expensive foreign sports cars. In the hands of the *Car Life* testers it also averaged 17 mpg. But such plain vanilla Chevrolets weren't particularly hot sellers in the early sixties. Chevrolet had struck a very popular chord with new car buyers back in 1961 when it had introduced the first Super Sport option for the Impala 2-door hardtop and convertible and during 1963, 31% of all Impalas produced were Super Sports. Although SS Impalas for 1963 were available with any engine Chevrolet offered, the more interesting versions were powered by V-8s whose cubic inches totalled 327, 409 or 427 cubic inches. Chevrolet had first introduced the 327 in 1962 and for 1963 it was available for installation in full-sized Chevrolets with either 250 or 300/hp. Although both engines' 10.5:1 compression ratio made the use of premium fuel mandatory, they represented a popular mix of performances and untemperamental behavior. Zero to sixty mph times with Powerglide (a $199.10 option) ran in the second range for the 250/hp version. The more powerful 327 turned the same trick in approximately nine seconds.

Both in 1961 and 1962, Chevrolet's 409 cid V-8 had been a strong drag strip performer as demonstrated by its Stock Eliminator championship at the NHRA summer nationals. As a means to further exploit its legendary status among American engines, Chevrolet offered a "detuned" version for 1963 that for the first time enabled 409 engines to be linked to Powerglide. The temptation was strong to downplay this 409 as simply a lazy, big engine designed for easy but listless traveling along the interstates. After all, the combination of Powerglide, a modest cam and hydraulic lifters seemed to suit such motoring conditions perfectly. This analysis was only partially correct. Compared to the RPO L80 409 engine which for 1963 was rated at 425/hp, the RPO L33 engine's 340/hp output seemed relatively modest. However whereas the L80 developed 425 lb.-ft. of torque at 4200/rpm, the L33's maximum torque was a nearly identical 420 lb.-ft. which was available at 3200/rpm. Furthermore its torque curve was very flat from 1200/rpm

1963 Chevrolet Impala 4dr Hardtop

1963 Chevrolet Impala 2-dr Hardtop

1963 Chevrolet Impala 2dr Hardtop

to 4400/rpm. Over that rpm range a minimum of 360 lb.-ft. was available and from 2400/rpm to 3600 rpm it was well above the 400 lb.-ft. level. It's also worth noting that Powerglide's overall starting ratio of 12.4:1 gave plenty of standing start punch. Thus *Car Life* (March, 1963) described its 340/hp/Powerglide Impala Super Sport test car as "big and strong, with a smooth transmission and plenty of muscular draft horses up front, it begins to approach the ultimate in U.S. performance cars." Even though equipped with only a 3.36:1 rear axle the *Car Life* test car turned in some startling acceleration times. From zero to 30/mph it required only 2.6 seconds. The zero to 60/mph run was completed in 6.6 seconds and the Impala reached 100/mph from rest in just 19.6 seconds. *Motor Trend* (March, 1963) tested an identical Chevrolet and reported slightly slower zero to 30/mph and 60/mph

Brand new for '63 was the Corvette Sting Ray coupe.

1963 Impala SS Interior

times of 3.0 seconds and 7.7 seconds.

Positioned between the 340/hp 409 and the RPO L80 version with its twin 4-barrel carburetors was a third 409, the RPO L31. With the same mechanical lifters, cam and 11.0:1 compression ratio of the 425 hp/409 but with a single 4-barrel carb, it was rated at 400 horsepower. Yet another Chevrolet performance engine, RPO Z-11 was available but only in very limited numbers since as Chevrolet explained; "Buyers require approval from the Central Sales Office before the order can be filled." This option, priced at $1,237.40 included a 4-speed, all-synchromesh transmission, heavy-duty suspension, dual exhausts, 4.11:1 positraction rear axle, metallic brake linings, 6.7x15 tires mounted on 15 inch rims and a tachometer. Since the primary purpose of the Z-11 was drag racing, its body was fitted with an aluminum hood, front fenders and bumper. By using a larger 4.406 inch bore, Chevrolet managed to expand the 409 V-8 to 427 cubic inches for use in the Z-11. Also unique to the Z-11 was its 12.5:1 compression ratio, revamped heads with high-velocity ports and improved high-riser intake manifold. In light of these changes plus its ability to reach 120 mph in the quarter mile its official rating of 430/hp, five more than the L80-409, was downright silly.

Although the full impact of its ability wasn't fully experienced until the mid-sixties, Chevrolet's Mark II, 427 V-8 made a brief but glorious appearance during 1963. Of totally different design than the 409 derived Z-11, the 427 engine with its "porcupine" valves and light weight (only about 50 pounds more than a fuel injected, 327 cid Corvette V-8) was capable of a maximum horsepower output above 570 at 6000 rpm. At the five-mile General Motors track at Mesa, Arizona it propelled a full-size Chevrolet to a 500 mile average of over 172 mph. A top speed of 180 mph was rumored and an acceleration time of just 18 seconds from 90 mph to 150 mph was also reported. Although the best placed 427 Chevrolet in the 1963 Daytona 500 finished ninth, its record shattering performance in the qualifying runs left little doubt that after a few shake down races, the 427 Chevrolet could have been a NASCAR Grand National champion. On the first day of qualifying runs, Junior Johnson set a new, two-lap Daytona average of 163.681 mph. This mark was later broken by Johnny Rutherford whose Smokey Yunick prepared Chevrolet lapped Daytona at 165.183 mph.

The Chevy II Nova Sport Coupe was available only with the 120 hp six-cylinder engine. Series 100 and 300 sedans could be ordered with a 153 cubic inch four-cylinder engine.

Production versions of this engine, initially in 396 cid form appeared in 1965 but their absence from the 1963 Chevrolet lineup had minimal impact upon Chevrolet's popularity. Supporting the strong and varied Chevrolet engine lineup was effective staying with new lower body panels and nicely reshaped front and rear sheet metal. The most notable change was the replacement of the "wrapped-over" compound curved windshield and its contorted, "dog-leg" corner posts with a less complex unit. This change which brought the era of the wrap-around windshield to a close also eliminated, at least until Americans took up jogging, the prime source of sore knees.

1963 Corvair Monza Spyder Convertible

Among the more practical changes Chevrolet incorporated into the construction of its 1963 models were their "wash and dry" rocker panels. This scheme which was used earlier on the 1962 Chevy II models allowed air and rain water to circulate through the panels and thus flush out rust-causing concentrations of road dirt. Also debuting on the 1963 Chevrolet was a new aluminized muffler and exhaust system plus a Delcotron alternator. In a move towards modern, long-interval service schedules Chevrolet announced that the use of special chassis

1963 Corvair Greenbrier Sports Wagon

grease and Teflon bearing surfaces enabled lubrication intervals to be extended (along with oil and filter changes) to 6000 miles or six months.

It's doubtful that these developments or Chevrolet's new 24,000 mile-24 month warranty were of greater importance in convincing people to buy new Chevrolets than the RPO Z03 Super Sport option. As we earlier mentioned, close to ⅓ of the nearly 400,000 Impala Sport Coupes and convertibles produced during 1963 carried this $161 option. As has been demonstrated time after time in automotive history, Americans have little interest in stripped models offering basic transportation. The key features of the Super Sport package included vinyl upholstery, front bucket seats, a unique Super Sport steering wheel emblem and instrument panel insert. If the M20 manual four-speed was ordered an electric tach was standard as was a floor mounted shifter. A similar arrangement was provided for the Powerglide shifter. Also included with either of these transmissions was a center console complete with an SS emblem, plus a lighted and lockable storage area. External body identification of a Super Sport wasn't difficult. The rear fenders carried circled SS letters, special triple spinner wheel covers were installed, and the lower body trim carried anodized aluminum inserts. Non Super Sport Impalas had this narrow trim strip painted white and on the Bel Air models narrower chrome bar was used. Incidentally, no Bel Air hardtops were offered for 1963. Instead, only 2 and 4-door sedans plus a 9-passenger station wagon were available. The bottom of the rung, Biscayne models were offered in the same three body styles.

Since the Chevy II had been an all-new design in 1962, changes for 1963 were very minor. Most apparent was a new grille with wider spaced horizontal bars plus revamped side trim for the up-market 300 and 400 series. Both the middle line 300 and the rather basic 100 models were available with the 153 cid, 90/hp four cylinder engine or for an additional $59 the larger 194 cid, 120/hp six. This latter engine was standard in the top ranked Nova 400 model. Mechanical changes in the 1963 Chevy II were also minor. Three of the seven steering points were now permanently sealed and Teflon was used on the upper ball joint surfaces. Although there were no performance engines available, the SS option was a popular first year option for Nova hardtops and convertibles. Its $161 price included special nameplates, exterior and interior trim, 14-inch wheels with Impala SS wheelcovers, bucket seats and an all-vinyl interior. A nice touch was an SS instrument package which provided gauges for oil pressure, battery change rate and engine temperature. The Super Sport's engine didn't make it a memorable accelerator but with Powerglide it provided an adequate zero to 60 mph time of 16 seconds and a 91 mph top speed. Nonetheless the SS package sold well; over 42,000 Nova coupes and convertibles of a total output of 87,415 were so equipped.

As in 1962 Chevrolet did provide a dealer installed conversion for the Chevy II that swapped the 120/hp six for the 327 cid V-8. But at $1,555 plus installation charges this was a costly proposition. Behind the scenes Chevrolet was working on special versions of the Chevy II with fastback styling and 360/hp, fuel injected Corvette V-8 engines. Although three vehicles were built the project apparently was axed due to General Motors' anti-racing policy. Nonetheless a Chevy II entered by Canadian Chevrolet dealers without factory support was the overall winner of the 1963 Shell 4000 Trans-Canada Rally. This was no easy feat since Falcon Sprints (which finished second and third) with their 164/hp/260 cid V-8s were tough competitors.

In a fashion similar to the Chevy II, the Corvair entered 1963 with only minor styling and mechanical changes. However with the RPO 690 Spyder package (priced at $317.45) and the very successful Monza series the Corvair's popularity for 1963 was assured. Unlike the Chevy II however, advanced engineering and styling examples of the Corvair received considerable publicity during 1963. These were the Monza GT coupe and its running mate the Monza SS roadster. Although a virtually stock Corvair engine was eventually installed, the 91 inch wheelbased Monza GT first appeared with a 178 cid modified version developing a reported 200 hp. It's more than idle conjecture to speculate about the impact such a car would have had upon the Porsche and Corvette if it had been placed in production.

But if these dream versions of the Corvair were destined to remain might-have-beens, the 1963 Corvette Sting Ray proved to be a very fine dream come true. Its form had, thanks to Bill Mitchell's racing version of 1959-60, become familiar to most American sports car enthusiasts, but it remained nothing less than a sensation for a production automobile. Some criticism was levied against the non-functional vents and ornamentation that did detract from the Sting Ray's basic form, yet as a total package the 150 mph Corvette was a giant step forward for Chevrolet.

On only rare moments had a single manufacturer offered automobiles with such broad appeal as did Chevrolet in 1963. Its full-sized models combined pleasing styling with performance and the Chevy II models fulfilled Chevrolet's traditional role as a provider of low-priced transportation. In the Corvair Spyder and Corvette, Chevrolet had two very exciting automobiles that essentially covered two key areas of the sports car field. Chevrolet regarded its 1963 lineup as offering a "one-stop showcase of value" and judging from their popularity this wasn't an understatement.

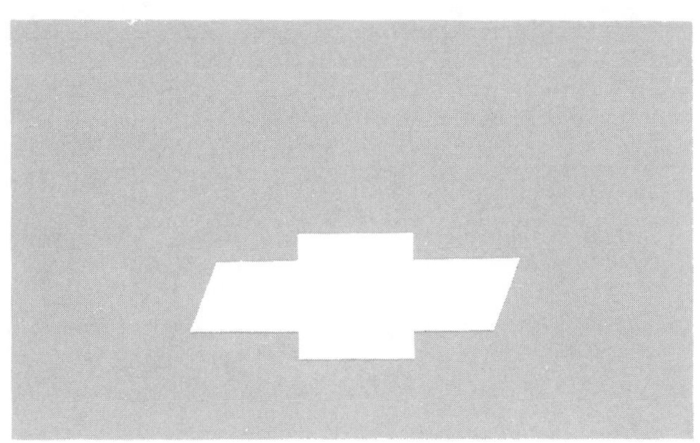

The Long and Short of It

THE *Chevelle* STORY

In 1964, Chevrolet introduced a full line of mid-size cars under the name Chevelle.

Chevelles were 11 inches longer than Chevy IIs and 16 inches shorter than Chevrolets. Many buyers thought it was the ideal size car.

It could be tailored to one's needs. Chevelle buyers had their choice of 14 different engine/transmission combinations. The Borg-Warner T-10 gear box was replaced by a new GM built Muncie four-speed. Three-speed manual (with or without overdrive) and Powerglide transmissions were carried over from 1963.

The Chevelle was offered in 13 models, beginning with the base 300 series. Next came a sport coupe and convertible, plus a sedan and two station wagons. Top models were the Malibu Super Sports. A fourth series was the reborn El Camino.

Like full-size Super Sports, Chevelle SS models came standard with bucket seats, vinyl upholstery and a console with Powerglide or four-speed.

SS insignia inside and out also distinguished Super Sport models. Exterior trim on Malibu Super Sports differed from conventional Malibus. Among Chevelle's seven interior colors, two were available only in Super Sports. Chevelle came in 15 exterior colors, with Golden-wood Yellow exclusive to Super Sports. Super Sports cost $162 more than comparable non-SS models, so that the $2,695 Chevelle Malibu V-8 Convertible Coupe cost $2,857 when ordered with SS equipment.

Styling was neutral, since Chevrolet was aiming for volume, rather than the enthusiast market. Over 338,000 Chevelles were produced during the 1964 model year. They competed with Buick-Olds-Pontiac intermediates and clashed head on with the Ford Fairlane, Mercury Comet and Dodge Dart.

Chevelle engines began with the 120 hp 194 cid six and added a 155 hp 230 cid six, plus 195 and 220 hp versions of the 283 cid V-8. The 327 cid V-8 option was approved by management in mid-'64. It came in 250 and 300 hp versions.

For 1965, Chevelle was lengthened by 2.7 inches and lowered about an inch. There were minor chassis refinements, but Malibu SS models were the most noticeably changed. Revised moldings, insignia and a partly blacked-out grille distinguished '65 Chevelle Super Sports.

An hydraulic lifter version of Corvette's 350 hp 327 cid V-8 was offered in Malibu and Malibu SS models in mid-'65. For the dragstrip, a few 365 hp versions of the 327 were also built.

Chevrolet's new 396 cid V-8, intended for '66 models, went into 201 of the '65 Super Sports.

For 1966, Chevelle Super Sports came with a 396 having 325 standard or 360 optional horsepower.

The big-block 396 engine was not available in other Chevelle models, except the El Camino Custom, which could also be optioned with SS equipment minus emblems. Super Sports were distinguished from everyday Malibus by SS-396 emblems, a black-accent grille, SS lettering on the quarters, wheel house moldings, distinct bodysill moldings, color-keyed body stripes and simulated hood air intakes.

Super Sports cost $285 more than regular Malibus in '67 and came standard with Firestone Wide Oval F70 x 14 tires on six-inch rims. These tires were a $64.10 option for the '67 El Camino.

Super Sports and Chevelles shared hubcaps, which could be replaced with four wheel cover options. Rally-style covers were part of a $79 front-disc brake option.

Bucket seats ($113) remained optional in 1967, even in SS cars. The tach-and-gauges ($79) option was carried over from 1966.

The 325 hp 396 V-8 was standard in Super Sports and a $182.95 option in El Caminos. A 350 hp 396 cid V-8 was

1965 Chevelle Malibu SS Convertible

optional in SS ($105.35) or El Camino ($290.55) models. Optional in Chevelle Super Sports was a 375 hp ($476) version of the 396.

Motor Trend (July 1967) compared 325 and 375 hp Chevelle SS-396 models and found the hotter SS-396 about a second faster both from 0-60 and in the quarter-mile. The 325 hp had Powerglide, the 375 a close-ratio four-speed. The 325 hp went from 0-60 mph in 7.5 seconds versus the quicker six seconds of the hotter car.

Chevelle was redesigned for 1968 and rode on a new 112 inch wheelbase. Exceptions were four-door and wagon models, which had a 116 inch wheelbase. Though sharing body and chassis with the standard Malibu, the SS 396 Chevelle was elevated to a distinct model in 1968. A new luxury four-door wagon, the Concours, was added to the Chevelle line.

Fender lines on the new '68 Chevelles were sleeker and less boxy than prior years. The hardtops had new fastback roofs. New hidden windshield wipers came standard on SS 396 and Concours models. All '68 Chevrolets had new side-marker lights in the fenders. Rally wheels became optional for all Chevelles and wheel options were expanded to include wire and two mag styles.

Super Sports had blacked out grilles, new rear panels and taillights, black lower-body paint, quarter-panel chrome, Firestone Wide Oval tires and optional bodyside striping that was made standard on SS-396 Chevelles at mid-year. SS-396 grille insignia, SS emblems front and rear and 396 fender emblems were continued in '68.

SS-396 Chevelles came standard with the 325 hp engine with optional 350 hp (hotter cam) and 375 hp versions available.

Chevelles still came standard with drum brakes, but, in 1968, got finned front drums to aid cooling. Sintered metallic linings were optional, as were front discs. Chevrolet sold over 400,000 Chevelles in 1968, leading *Motor*

1967 Malibu Six Sport Coupe

1967 Malibu Six Sport Coupe

Trend to call it, "America's biggest-selling super car."

Power front disc brakes became standard on 1969 Chevelles. This same year, GM discontinued butterfly windows, which gave all models a cleaner look. Super Sports were no longer a distinct model, but an option package available on any coupe or convertible. An anti-theft, self-locking steering wheel became standard on all GM cars in 1969.

Engines and transmissions were unchanged from '68, except Powerglide was dropped in 1969 in favor of the three-speed Hydra-Matic gearbox.

Car and Driver (Jan. 1969) compared an automatic 325 hp Chevelle SS-396 with the Ford Cobra, Mercury Cyclone GJ, Pontiac GTO Judge, Dodge Super Bee and Plymouth Hemi Road Runner. If based solely on ride quality and quietness, they said, Chevelle would have been the overall winner.

The Chevelle had a 14.41 second quarter-mile time, versus the first-place Hemi Road Runner's 13.54 seconds. Chevelle went from 0-60 in 5.8 seconds versus Road Runner's 5.1 seconds.

In 1970, the Chevelle reached its peak as the SS-454. Its optional ($321) engine was a 450 hp 454 cid V-8 derived from the Corvette's 427 block. The 454 was shared with Monte Carlo in 1970 and had either 10.25:1 or 11.25:1 compression. Both had a solid-lifter cam and the Corvette's large exhaust valves and Holley four-barrel.

Though options mandatory with the 450 hp engine boosted the SS-454 Chevelle's price to $4000, its performance, by any era's standards, was awesome. Quarter-mile times were in the 13 second range and close to the 427 Corvette's.

1971 Malibu SS-454

1969 Chevelle SS-396 2dr Hardtop

1973 Chevelle Laguna 2dr

The SS-396 Chevelle came standard with 350 hp or optional with 375 hp. Chevrolet bored some 396 blocks to 402 cid, but horsepower ratings were 350 and 375, just as in the 396.

Two four-speeds and Hydra-Matic transmissions were available with these engines. The SS option consisted of blacked-out grille with SS emblems, domed hood with hood pins, wheel house moldings, rear-bumper SS identification, chromed exhaust outlets, SS-396 or SS-454 fender emblems, Firestone Wide Oval tires and interior SS insignia.

Only sport coupes and convertibles could be SS optioned, as could the El Camino, which could also be 454-equipped. Super Sports had distinct instrument panels and a new hood-and-deck stripe option that came standard with the $147.65 extra cowl-induction hood. Built-into-the-windshield radio antennas were first offered in 1970, too. Vinyl roof covers were still offered, as were 15 exterior and seven two-tone colors.

Government-mandated emission controls and insurance surcharges forced compression ratios down in 1971. The hottest Chevelle SS-454 now delivered 425 hp. Chevelle was slightly restyled for '71, but the SS option was essentially unchanged from 1970. New magstyle sport wheels, white-letter tires, power front disc brakes, and remote-control outside rearview mirrors were included in the SS option at $357.

For 1971, Chevelle and Chevelle SS cosmetics were essentially carried over from 1970. Vinyl roof covers were now available in black, brown, navy, green and white. Power tops became standard on convertibles.

A blacked-out grille, Rally wheels, special body striping and decal identification went into a new "Heavy Chevy" model added to the Chevelle line. It was essentially a Malibu sport coupe with decals on it. Heavy Chevy could be optioned with 307 and 400 cid V-8's.

There were few changes for 1972, the year the last Chevelle convertible was built. SS equipment was still optional only with convertibles and sport coupes, but now any Chevelle V-8 could be ordered with these SS models. A 270 hp 454 (which came standard with M-22 four-speed) was an option exclusive to SS cars. A three-speed manual gear box came standard with 305 or 307 cid V-8's. A heavy-duty three-speed was standard for the 402 cid V-8.

An all-new Chevelle was unveiled in 1973, riding on a 113 inch wheelbase. Both the Malibu sport coupe and station wagon could be optioned with SS equipment. A 165 or 205 nhp 350 or 245 nhp 454 were available.

The SS option was dropped from the Chevelle line (except the El Camino) at the end of 1973, but a new luxury Laguna model was introduced. Laguna borrowed the SS theme and used 350, 400, and 454 cid engines until 1976, when the 454 was discontinued.

Chevelle was down-sized and completely re-engineered for 1978. Its full-frame construction and rear drive layout were clearly dated by late-70s standards. In fact, in 1977 the Chevelle (which wasn't officially retired until 1984) passed the mid-sized family car mantle onto Chevrolet's front-drive A-car, the Celebrity. Though El Caminos continued to be offered with optional Super Sport trim, in 1985 the intermediate-sized personal-luxury Monte Carlo resurrected the SS package in its '83 Monte Carlo SS.

Since Monte Carlo was the only Chevrolet on NASCAR's eligibility list, it was a natural for Chevy to introduce a distinct SS model. A 175 hp 305 cid V-8, with four-barrel and 9.5:1 compression, came standard. The Monte Carlo SS came standard with Chevy's F-41 sport-suspension, front and rear stabilizer bars and wide Goodyear Eagle GT tires on styled-steel wheels. It sold for $10,249.

A Legacy of Muscle Kept Growing Through Chevelle's Short Life

By R. Perry Zavitz

The beginning of the 1978 models unfortunately brought an end to the Chevelle. With the drastic change in dimensions and design of the intermediate Chevrolet, it perhaps seemed an opportune time to break with the past and drop the Chevelle name. Over its 14 year life-span, some 5,000,000 units of that popular model were built and sold.

While demand for compact cars remained too strong to ignore, and the standard size models grew with abandon during the early-mid 60s, a chasm developed between the two. For 1962 Ford fielded a redesigned Fairlane to fit into the obvious gap. By 1965 Plymouth evolved a Belvedere for middleweight class.

The only new car when the 1964 models first appeared was the Chevelle, Chevrolet's entry in the in-between size. Overall length was 193.9 inches for all models but the station wagon. That made the Chevelle 16 inches shorter than the full-size Chevrolets, but 11 inches longer than the Chevy II. It was comparable in length and wheel-base to the contemporary Fairlane. Incidently, the first Chevelle had the same wheelbase and was 1.1 inch shorter overall than the Chevrolet of one decade before.

That Chevrolet had a choice of just one engine — two if you consider the higher output standard with Powerglide. By contrast, the Chevelle was introduced with seven engine choices. They ranged from the small 194 cid, 120 hp. six, and the larger 230 cid. 155 hp. six, through the 283 cid. V-8 with 195 or 220 hp.

Four different transmissions were available — the standard three-speed manual, Powerglide automatic, overdrive, and four-speed manual. Only with the 283 V-8's could any of these four transmissions be ordered. Transmission options were limited on the other engines, nevertheless, a total of 20 engine/transmission combinations were obtainable.

Chevelle came in 11 models in three series. The 300 series (no relation to the Chrysler 300) offered two and four-door sedans, and two and four-door station wagons. The Malibu, the name still used in 1978, offered a four-door sedan, two-door hardtop, convertible, six-pass. wagon, and nine-pass. wagon. The top series Malibu Super Sport had a two-door hardtop and a convertible. Prices spread from $2,231 for the 300 two-door to $3,240 for the Malibu four-door station wagon.

Oh yes, there was one more related model. The El Camino returned after a three year hiatus, utilizing the 115 inch Chevelle wheelbase, and front end styling.

Styling for the Chevelle could be described as contemporary conservative, but pleasant. Nothing about the styling would excite anyone, but by the same token nothing would upset anyone — a wise way to introduce a new car.

Production took place in Baltimore, Md. Kansas City, Mo. and a new plant at Fremont, Calif. A total of 338,286 Chevelles were built in its first model year. A very substantial sum indeed for a new model, and it accounted for 4.3% of the industry's production for the model year. Of all '64 Chevrolets, 14.5% were Chevelles. Sales of the Chevelle during calendar 1964 were a success, and lead Fairlane by a five to four margin.

The 1965 Chevelle got a redesigned grille, but otherwise its styling remained much the same as before. Yet the car managed to grow about three inches longer. The 300 series had a two-door wagon instead of a four-door wagon. A new 300 DeLuxe series had a four-door wagon, as well as two and four-door sedans. The Malibu line remained as before, but with nine pass. wagon discontinued. The Malibu Super Sport offered a two-door hardtop and convertible again.

Engine availabilities were changed to include the 327 cid V-8 in Chevelle's second year. The rating of the larger six and the most potent V-8 were raised to 140 and 350 h.p. respectively. There was no 220 h.p. V-8 for '65.

Probably the rarest of all Chevelle models was the SS 396, of which only 201 were built.

The special batch of super Chevelles was assembled at the Kansas City assembly plant early in 1965. The special RPO Z-16 package built around the new 375 hp. engine was designed to effectively showcase it. The cost for the option package was $1501.05, shoving the price of a Chevelle SS hardtop so equipped to more than $4500.

Besides the very heavy duty engine, the buyer got a four-speed, special exterior and interior trim, vinyl top, fake Chevy mag wheels, Goodyear gold line tires, bumper guards and even Delco's new AM-FM Multiplex stereo system. On the dash a 160 mph speedometer and a tach red lining at 5800 rpm reminded the driver that he was not chauffeuring just a jazzed up car with no real guts.

Chevrolet had to do considerable beefing underneath the Chevelle to provide for the punishment of the 375 h.p. 396. Convertible frames, with bracing, were used, although all 201 units were apparently hardtops. The

1970 Chevelle SS-454

driveline was strengthened in many areas. Sometimes the modifications, as in the case of the brakes, involved the mere substitution of units from the big Chevs of the same year. The engine itself was the same as the 425 h.p. Corvette 396 introduced concurrently, except that it used hydraulic lifters instead of the 'Vette's solids.

Motor Trend tested one of the very few '65 SS 396s to reach California late in 1965. They called it, "...the hottest and finest car of its type ever made."

The Chevy 396, which emerged from the famous 1963 Chevrolet racing engine, would appear in many subsequent Chevelles. But none could ever match the power or scarcity of the first 201 '65 SS 396s, just as *Motor Trend* inadvertently predicted.

Prices were reduced on 1964's comparable models. They started at $2,109 for the 300 two-door — the lowest basic list price of any Chevelle. The most expensive was the Malibu Super Sport convertible at $2,690. Production of the '65 model increased modestly to 343,894.

Entirely new styling appeared on the 1966 Chevelles. Still a bit conservative, perhaps the most unusual styling feature was found on the two-door hardtops. The flat rear window was on a steeper slope than the rear quarter roof panels. The result was a flying buttress shape. This was fashionable in the mid 60's, but was originated by John Fitch on his Sprint conversions of the first generation Corvairs.

Wheelbase was stretched an inch to 116 inches, but overall length remained approximately the same. Although 12 models were offered as before, there was an omission and an addition. The 300 two-door wagon was gone, but in the Malibu lineup Chevelle's first four-door hardtop appeared. The Super Sport also became known as the SS 396.

1969 Malibu Convertible

1969 Malibu Convertible Interior

The standard engine for the SS 396 was rated at 325 h.p. but 360 h.p. was optional. The extra muscle came from a four-bbl carburetor, special camshaft, and dual exhausts. Neither of these 396 engines could be ordered for any other series. They were for the Super Sports only.

There were changes in the optional V-8s for Chevelle, although the standard 283 cid, 195 h.p., V-8 remained. The 220 h.p. 283 V-8 was back after skipping the '65 models. Only one of the 327 cid. V-8s could be had. It was the 275 h.p. version.

A new model year production record was set again, when 412,155 Chevelles were built. That sum pushed the total number of Chevelles over the 1,000,000 mark.

With only minor styling alterations, the 1967 Chevelle did not sell as well as the '66. Model year production amounted to 369,133. Yet that was the car's second best year. Overall production of the '67 models was down. Chevelle still carved out for itself a 4.8% slice of the production pie, like it had done the year before. The Fairlane was not faring quite as well.

The same models were made available in the '67 lineup, with one addition. A luxurious four-door six-pass. station wagon was introduced. Called Concours, it was separate from all other series. It was easily identifiable because of the woodgrain trim along the sides and across the lower part of the tailgate.

Some changes occurred in the engine compartment for '67. The 194 cid. six was dropped. The 230 cid. six became standard. The 250 cid. 155 h.p. six of the full-size Chevrolets was available optionally for the first time in the Chevelle. What was referred to as the standard V-8, the 195 h.p. motor, was the only 283 cid. V-8 available. The optional 327 V-8 could be had in either 275 h.p. or 325 h.p. potencies. The 396 V-8 was still only available in the Super Sport models. The advertised horsepower of the high-output version was reduced to 350 h.p.

No fewer than six transmission choices were offered. In addition to the previous four, a new special three-speed floor mounted stick shift was available with any engine. It was standard in the SS 396. An option in those models, but not in the other lines was GM's Turbo Hydra-Matic.

A new body appeared on the 1968 Chevelle. The sedans and wagons kept their 116 inch wheelbase, while growing to 201 inches overall. The coupes and convertibles were four inches shorter in both wheelbase and overall length. In this case the term coupe was used in the literal sense. It comes from the French word for "cut". These models were in effect cut shorter than the sedans.

The 14 models offered again represented a few changes. The four-door sedan was no longer offered in the 300, but a four-door wagon was. New to the 300 DeLuxe line was a two-door hardtop. There were four Chevelle wagons and all were four-door six-pass., models. The 300 version was called Nomad, and the 300 DeLuxe was the Nomad Custom. What a disappointment to the lovers of Chevrolet's most prestigious station wagon of '55 to '57 to find that name relegated to the marque's most austere wagons. It was probably the deliberate strategy of the sales and advertising people to cash in on the renowned image of the original Nomad. The Malibu wagon had no special name, and the Concours was no longer called a station wagon, but Estate wagon — a title borrowed from Buick.

There seems to be no evidence that the name manipulation caused difficulties. Production of the '68 Chevelle set a new record of 422,893. A production record was set in June when 49,792 Chevelles were made. To our knowledge that monthly total has not been exceeded even though model year totals have since surpassed that of '68.

Again a few changes in engine availabilities were made. The faithful old 283 V-8 was retired in'67. For 1968, the standard V-8 for Chevelle was a 307 cid motor, which developed an even 200 h.p. and was offered in addition to the 275 and 325 h.p. editions.

Chevelle had been on a two year cycle of complete restyling. The 1969 model was the off year, which often means a slight easing of a car's acceptance. Such was not the case for Chevelle, however. An increase raised the model year's production to 439,611, which was a record. That figure also represents another peak. It was 5.2% of all '69 model cars produced. That was Chevelle's greatest proportion. Also, during the '69 model run, the 2,000,000th Chevelle was built.

Series changes were made for '69. The 300 line was abandoned. The bottom line then became the 300 DeLuxe, which consisted of coupe, sedan, and hardtop. Malibu offered the same body types as before, except the station wagon. All the wagons were in a separate series of their own. The Nomad was again at the cheap end of the range (although at $2,668 its base price was $196 more than the first Nomad). Next up the wagon ladder were the Greenbriers. One was a two-seat wagon and the other a three-seat model.

(Does the name Greenbrier sound vaguely familiar? The larger Corvair station wagon of '61 to '64 — the van styled model — was called Greenbrier. But going even further into the past, there was a Nash Rambler station wagon called Greenbrier in 1953).

The Concours also came in two and three-seat models. That is a total of five wagons, but with V-8 power two more were offered. The Concours Estate — those with woodgrain side trim — were available in two and three-seat editions. Dual-action tailgate was standard on the three-seat Greenbrier and all Concours and Concours Estate wagons. This tailgate, which also doubled as a door if you wished, was optional on the other two Chevelle wagons.

There was a Concours Sport Sedan, but it was a special exterior and interior trim option on the Malibu Sport Sedan, the four-door hardtop. Alas, the SS 396 also became an option. Offered on any coupe or the convertible for an extra $348, it meant the same as before — a 396 cid V-8 of 325 h.p. or 350 h.p. Chevelle. SS 396 insignia announced this option on virtually all sides of the car.

Another engine was retired. A 350 cid. V-8 of 255 h.p. or 300 h.p. replaced the three versions of the former 327 cid. V-8. Transmission availabilities remained the same, except for the deletion of overdrive. It is surprising to some that overdrive was offered on Chevrolets for so many years. Many people associate overdrive with Studebaker, Nash and Ford, but seldom with Chevrolet. Yet Chevrolet offered it sometimes when it was

1970 Chevelle Malibu (Non-SS) Convertible

1970 Chevelle SS-396 Sport Coupe

unavailable on some of those other cars.

Right on schedule, the 1970 Chevelle received a new body. The two wheelbases continued, but overall length grew an inch, although station wagons were an inch shorter than previously.

The 300 DeLuxe name was eliminated but not replaced. A coupe and sedan were in the unnamed series. Malibu offered the same body types as before. Among the wagons, six-cylinder engines were restricted to the two-seat models of Nomad, Greenbrier, and Concours. But V-8 power could be had in all these as well as the three-seat versions of the Greenbrier, Concours, and both Concours Estate models.

SS was an option on the Malibu two-door hardtop and convertible. The cost of this package was raised to $446, and included a special hood, black accented grille, and wide oval white lettered tires. Standard SS power became the 396 cid, 350 h.p. V-8, which had been the optional version. A new option was the whopping 454 cid. V-8 rated

1971 Malibu SS-454

at 360 h.p.

Other engine availability changes included a re-rating of the less potent 350 cid, V-8 to 250 h.p., down five. Another new optional engine was a 400 cid. V-8, which developed 350 h.p. (Actually this engine had a displacement of 402.3 cubic inches. It had the same stroke but 1/32 inch greater bore than the 396 cid motor).

One more transmission option disappeared. Just one three-speed manual shift was available. It could be had only with the six and the two least powerful V-8's.

Production for the '70 models was down about 10%. But so was total production for the model year, so Chevelle held onto its record share of 5.2% of total U.S.

production.

Styling changes for 1971 were minor, as might be expected. The main difference was the change to single headlights. All previous Chevelles used the dual headlight system. But at the rear, dual round taillights were inserted in the bumper.

The model range for '71 was unchanged from the year before. However, the six-cylinder engine was no longer obtainable in a growing number of body types. The Malibu four-door hardtop and convertible, as well as all wagons except the Nomad had V-8 power only.

Washington was moving into Motown, and one of the evidences of this was beginning to show up in the engine horsepower ratings. Indirectly because of exhaust emission regulations, output was reduced in many cases. The six was reduced to 145 h.p. The standard 307 V-8 remained at 200 h.p. but the optional 350's developed 245 and 270 h.p. — down five and 30 h.p. respectively. The 400 (402) V-8 was down 10% to 300 h.p. Contrary to

1972 Chevelle Malibu Sport Coupe

the trend was the 454 V-8. Its output was raised five to 365 h.p. Interestingly, an optional version producing 425 h.p. was available.

The SS package was made available on the Malibu two-door hardtop and convertible with any optional V-8 engine. The 454 V-8 was only available with the SS package, though. A hardtop with the 425 h.p. engine had a ratio of just under eight pounds per horsepower. That compared with about seven and a half pounds per h.p. for a '71 Corvette with the same engine. Pricewise the 425 h.p. SS Chevelle was about 40% less than the similar powered Corvette.

Production of the 1971 model Chevelle was down to 327,157 for its lowest total thus far. Some consolation was gained when the 3,000,000th Chevelle was built.

Several serious external influences were beginning to be felt in Detroit. The car market was behaving in an erratic manner. Certain models would be hot selling items for a few months, then interest would suddenly shift to an entirely different type of car. Perhaps such uncertainties were a factor for the 1972 Chevelle retaining for a third year its old body style. The pattern had been to change every second year without fail. Minor grillework alterations were the greatest external changes for the '72 models.

Even the model choices were static for '72. A new option package called Heavy Chevy was offered on the basic Sport Coupe hardtop. In this package, the standard engine was the 307 cid. V-8, but any other V-8, except the 454, could be ordered. Adding to the performance image, the Heavy Chevy had a special domed hood with lock pins, black grille, special side striping just below the belt line, and Heavy Chevy decals. Rally style wheels with center caps and bright big nuts also appealed to performance oriented youth. To state it simply, the Heavy Chevy was an economical SS. The SS continued as a Malibu hardtop coupe and convertible option. Any optional V-8 was available, but the 454 V-8 was exclusive with the SS.

Engine output had to be rated as net horsepower, proclaimed Washington. Actually it was a realistic move, because so much power robbing pollution paraphernalia had to be a permanent part of the engines that gross horsepower figures were meaningless exaggerations. The net ratings for '72 Chevelle engines were 110 h.p. for the six; 130 h.p. for the 307 V-8; 165 h.p. and 175 h.p. for the 350 V-8; 240 h.p. for the 400 V-8; and 270 h.p. for the 454 cid. V-8. The high-output 454 V-8 was not available.

With stifled engines, and market vagaries, the Chevelle did not sell as well in '72 as '71. However, production of 357,820 exceeded the previous year's model year total. This contradiction was probably a result of the spasmodic market.

The 1973 Chevelle donned brand new styling. On its established wheelbases, the new models were five inches, and wagons seven inches longer than before. Part of the reason for extra length was the new front bumper, which absorbed minor impacts without damage.

A record number of 17 basic models were fielded by Chevelle. The bottom line finally received a name, DeLuxe. It included a two-door coupe and four-door sedan. So did the Malibu. A new top line called Laguna also offered a coupe and sedan.

The convertible was missing in the '73 range. Equally significant, though less noticed perhaps, was the fact that the hardtop had also become extinct as far as Chevelle was concerned. The coupes and sedans were called Colonade hardtops by Chevrolet, but these models did not have a cut-off B-pillar and could not be opened above it. So, at least in our definition of the term, the Chevelle hardtop was defunct.

No fewer than 11 Chevelle station wagons were offered. Imagine nearly twice as many wagons as all other Chevelle body types combined! The Nomad name was replaced by DeLuxe. The lowest priced DeLuxe wagon had a six-cylinder motor — the only such powered Chevelle wagon.

The V-8 wagon list included a two-seat and a three-seat model in each of five series or sub-series. There were DeLuxe, Malibu, Malibu Estate, Laguna, and Laguna Estate lines. The Malibu Estate and Laguna Estate wagons each had woodgrain exterior trim. The Concours name was laid aside, then picked up later by Nova.

Incidently, all Laguna models had front end styling totally unlike the DeLuxe and Malibu. A distinctive one-piece urethane panel covered the whole front end, except for the headlights and grille of course. It served as the the bumper. Painted body color, it was dent resistant, and mounted to the new energy absorbing bumper system.

Further engine tinkering reduced net horsepower ratings still more. The six was only 100 h.p. (It was 21 years since the standard Chevrolet engine output was that low, but a comparison of gross and net horsepower is perhaps unfair.) The 307 V-8 yielded a modest 115 h.p. The lesser 350 V-8 was 145 h.p. but the other version still developed 175 h.p. net. The 400 V-8 was not available. The giant 454 was choked off at just 245 h.p. Transmission choices were dwindling too. Powerglide was no longer offered.

Standard engine for the Laguna series was the 145 h.p. 350 V-8. The Heavy Chevy was lifted from the option list, but the SS continued. It was offered on the Malibu coupe, and surprisingly on the Malibu station wagons. Power for the SS was either of the 360 V-8 versions, or the 454 V-8.

1973 model Chevelle production dropped to 328,533.

Minor appearance changes for the 1974 Chevelles were not unexpected. An extra wide Mercedes style grille embellished the front of the Malibu and Malibu Classic models. These were the new names for the lower and middle priced series. Coupe and sedan body types were offered in each line. In addition, the Malibu Classic offered a Landau coupe. It came with a vinyl covered roof, and a few other trim goodies like pin-striping, and dual mirrors.

With an unpredictable market and a serious energy crisis to face, it is understandable that the assortment of station wagons was reduced. All had V-8 power, which in retrospect turned out to be the wrong move at that time. There were two and three-seat wagons in the Malibu, Malibu Classic and Malibu Classic Estate series.

There were no Laguna wagons for '74. In fact, the Laguna line was limited to just a coupe. It was officially renamed the Laguna Type S-3.

No SS package was available for'74. Therefore the 454 engine was available on any V-8 model. Engine choices and net horsepower ratings were otherwise unchanged.

For the first time, model year production fell below 300,000 but a highlight of the year was the 4,000,000th Chevelle.

We have traced the Chevelle beyond the point where it can hardly be considered an old car, so we had better draw this review to a quick conclusion before we get kicked out of this newspaper. It should be pointed out, however, that for its remaining three model years Chevelle used the same body styling begun with the '73 models.

In 14 model years the Chevelle had grown in overall length from 193.9 inches to 209.7 (215.4 for the wagons). It was literally just one silly centimeter shorter than the '64 Impala, when the Chevelle was first introduced.

More regulations from Capital Hill have set strict minimum fuel consumption standards. To meet them the car makers, among other approaches, have been reducing size to reduce weight. No more heavy Chevys. That is why the 1978 Malibu shrunk. Coincidently the Chevelle name was left off. The Chevelle has ended, but the Malibu lingers on.

'66 Impala SS: Super Safe?

By Tom LaMarre

"Somehow Impala doesn't seem destined to be big with secret agents. Imagine nobody noticing you in a car that looks like this."

The 1966 Impala SS ad, inspired by James Bond and *The Man from U.N.C.L.E.*, said: "from the distinctive front styling to the smart new wraparound taillights, the Impala SS demands attention. Not a line's wasted."

The Impala SS was available in coupe and convertible

1966 Impala SS Convertible

versions and featured Stratobucket seats and an interior with bright metal and brushed aluminum accents. Engine options ranged from a 250-cubic-inch six to a 425-horsepower Mark IV 427 V-8.

Midway through the '66 model year, rear seat belts became standard on all new domestic models, reflecting increased concern about safety. In 1966 Congress passed the Highway Safety Act and the National Traffic and Motor Vechicle Safety Act, and the Department of Transportation was formed. A safety package was standard on all 1966 models. Ads for the Impala SS mentioned eight safety features, including padded instrument panel and sun visors.

But was a 425-horsepower engine compatible with a safety campaign? Many people didn't think so. A cartoon in the *Chicago Sun Times* showed a dealer painting a banner above a flashy new model: "You'll never get hit in the rear when driving the 1966 Screaming Panther. Ferocious Turbo-Flash Jet-Flame V-8 with Power-Blast boost." The salesman explained to a bystander, "It's part of our society campaign."

Although more than 237,000 SS Impalas were built in 1965, production in 1966 declined to 119,000. Auto sales in general decreased in 1966. Some people blamed the safety scare. However, many other factors also affected auto sales. Tighter credit restrictions made it more difficult to obtain financing. The return of the federal excise tax made cars more expensive. And the Vietnam War took thousands of potential buyers into the military service.

Chevy's Hot 427 Caprice

By Linda Clark

Chevrolet tapped the high-performance luxury market in 1966 with its hot 427 Caprice.

Nowhere is imitation a more sincere form of flattery than in Detroit, and in 1965 Ford's mass-market luxury car received homage from its toughest competitor. Just months after Ford's LTD premiered, Chevrolet had its Caprice on the market.

A year later, Ford and Chevrolet added yet another variation to the mass-market luxury theme: the mass-market performance car. Operating on the premise that LTD and Caprice sales could expand to include buyers looking for high-performance, both companies introduced hotted-up versions of these cars in 1966.

Ford changed the name to Seven-Litre while Chevrolet stuck with Caprice, but the tactic was the same in both camps: keep all the luxury inside while wedging the biggest engine available under the hood.

Ford bored and stroked its faithful 390-cubic-inch workhorse for the job, boosting displacement to 428 cubic inches. (This should not be confused with Ford's hot 427 engine, which was the company's outright performance engine. The two blocks were different and there was only a superficial resemblance between them.) The Seven-Litre was rated at 345 horsepower, though a 360 h.p. version was available in a police interceptor package.

Chevrolet turned to its new 396 for duty in the Caprice. The engine was bored out to 427 cubic inches and in its detuned form developed 390 h.p. at 5200 r.p.m. While both Caprice and Seven-Litre were aimed at the same market, Ford touted its sporting flavor with louvered wheel covers and pinstripping along the beltline. (Eventually, Chevy would imitate this too.) But in 1966, the Caprice was subdued, without any hint beyond fender emblems that it was anything out of the ordinary.

Inside, Ford combined Mustang GT trimwork with Thunderbird gadgetry, plus thin-shell bucket seats. The Caprice was unadulterated Cadillac, with dark vinyls, rich fabrics and deep-grained veneers. The overall effect was quiet luxury. Optional "Strato-Back" buckets offered adjustable headrests.

Both cars offered a choice of transmissions, but Ford's three-speed Cruise-O-Matic and Chevy's three-speed Hydra-Matic were the most frequently optioned in these big, sumptuous grand touring machines. The Seven-Litre came with front disc brakes, while Caprice used conventional drums. In Jan. 1966, *Car and Driver* got an automatic 427 Caprice to 60 m.p.h. in 7.6 seconds, and knocked off a 90 m.p.h. quarter-mile in 15.7 seconds. A bit slower, an automatic Seven-Litre had an 8.1-second 0-60 time and best quarter-mile of 83 m.p.h. at 16.5 seconds.

Car and Driver found Caprice the better overall performer, but Ford a better handler, due to the Seven-Litre's standard heavy-duty suspension package. Not mentioned was Chevy's $31.37 suspension option of stiffer springs and shocks, plus a rear stablizer bar.

Expensive for their day, both cars were in the $4500 price bracket, around $1500 more than the bread-and-butter Impala and Galaxie. The mere fact that so-called low-priced Ford and Chevy entered this market was an indication of the American economy's vitality. Despite jokes about their size — both cars had a 119-inch wheelbase and weighed around 4500 pounds — they were outstanding value for the money.

Of course, premium fuel was recommended for these engines. Even so, you could cruise at 80 m.p.h. in five-passenger comfort for some 400 miles on a single tank of gas. Despite their front weight bias, these machines were relatively agile and safe, offered excellent visability, were mechanically indestructible, and could be pressed into stock car racing or dragstrip duty besides.

More than 800 pounds were shaved off the Caprice in GM's 1977 downsizing program. Ford trimmed its LTD down to a 114-inch wheelbase in 1979. Both nameplate survived over two decades and became synonymous with the big American car. By 1980, Caprice retained the front-engine rear-wheel drive format. It came with a 305-cubic inch V-8. The LTD also retained the front-engine rear-drive setup and came with a 302-cubic inch V-8 which put the price at around $9600.

By 1980, both cars had been trimmed to around 3600 pounds and achieved an amazing 20 m.p.g. economy — a laudable feat amid the gas-conscious '80s. Wheelbase was now 116 inches for Caprice and 114.3 inches for the LTD. In Feb.1980 *Motor Trend* compared these cars, equipped with three-speed automatics, and got 0-60 m.p.h. of 12.5 seconds for the LTD and 10.9 seconds for Caprice.

In 1983, Caprice was still wooing buyers with a combination of room, ride, comfort, safety, and surprising 30 m.p.g. fuel economy. *Car and Driver* rated Caprice among its "Ten Best" that year and said that, "At $9277, it is a hard-to-beat value." Caprice still rode on a 116-inch wheelbase but Ford reduced LTD to 105.5 inches, derived from the defunct Granada (an overgrowth of the Fairmont) platform.

1966 Caprice 2-dr Hardtop

Ford minimized the fuel-efficiency penalty with a standard four-speed overdrive automatic transmission coupled to a 4.9-litre V-8 with fuel-injection in its 1986 LTD, now called LTD Crown Victoria. Still riding on a 114.3-inch wheelbase, the LTD Crown Victoria remained a front-engine rear-driven family sedan.

Caprice may have been the best big sedan GM ever built. By 1986, it had taken everything Detroit learned from 70-odd years of building conventional rear-drive sedans and combined it with the latest technology in low-calorie design. It remained Detroit's expression of the American car, and still ranked among the top ten best-selling domestic models.

SPECIFICATIONS 1966 CAPRICE 427

Wheelbase	119 inches
Length	213.2 inches
Width	79.6 inches
Height	54.4 inches
Weight	4553 pounds
Brakes	11-inch drums
Tires	8.25 x 14
Engine	427 cu. in.
Bore x stroke	4.25 x 3.76
Compression	10.25:1
Carburetion	One 4-bbl.
Power	390 b.h.p. @ 5200 r.p.m.
Torque	460 lbs-ft. @ 3600 r.p.m.
Fuel capacity	20 gallons

1968 Caprice

Chevrolet Luxury

By John Lee

Chevrolet's big news for the 1968 model year was totally new styling for the Corvette. The racy, low-slung design that replaced the beautiful Sting Ray after its successful five-year run really grabbed the fancy of the motor press. The new 'Vette showed up on several magazine covers and got lots more ink inside them.

Meanwhile the Camaro, introduced in 1967, was giving Ford's Mustang a run for its money, and the Chevelle SS 396 had some new competition in the form of the econo-performer, Road Runner from Plymouth, among others.

With the performance explosion of the mid- to late-1960s, we sometimes forget that the auto-makers' main business was building family transportation. In that regard, Chevrolet was still the leader, and Caprice was the model the leader offered as proof.

Similar to the pattern established with the Bel Air and the Impala, Chevy introduced the Caprice name in 1965 as an option, RPO Z-18, for the Impala four-door hardtop. It was principally a luxurious trim package with rich interior fabrics, body sill moldings, color-keyed striping on the sides of the body, black accents in the grille and rear panel; but a stiffer frame and different suspension components were also included.

Again following past practice, Chevrolet made the Caprice a full series in 1966 with a hardtop coupe, hardtop sedan and six- and nine-passenger station wagons. Now, instead of moving up from a Bel Air to an Impala, the upwardly mobile had another step, from the Impala to the Caprice.

And 181,000 of them did in 1966, not counting those who bought the top-of-the-line wagons. The line-up of body styles in the series would remain unchanged for the next several years. The novelty of the Caprice wore off somewhat, dropping the hardtop coupe and sedan production totals to 124,500 for 1967 and 115,500 for 1968, then rebounding to nearly 167,000 for 1969.

For the 1968 model run the Caprice was most easily distinguished from the more mundane Impala by its hideaway headlights. When closed, the headlight doors continued the rectangular pattern of the stamped grille out to the forward-thrusting fender tips. The slender bumper bar horizontally bisected the grillework and ended with vertical tips on the fenders. The Caprice and other full-sized Chevys hid the windshield wipers away behind the aft lip of the hood for '68.

A new rear bumper appeared to float between the deck and a smooth lower valance, and taillights that had been inching downward the last few years were set into the bumper. Caprices and Impalas had three lenses on a side, with the center one a back-up lamp, while Bel Air and Biscayne models had only two per side.

Instead of the Impala's combination of a rub strip midway down the bodyside and rocker panel trim, the Caprice had a wide trim band just above the lower character line on the body. The example shown here also has a protective rub strip added in the same location as the Impala's.

Chevys for '68 showed up with a number of new safety features required by federal legislation. Armrests that shielded the inside door handles from being tripped accidentally, padded windshield pillars, energy-absorbing front seat backs, front and rear seat belts and side marker lights were among them.

Other standard Caprice equipment included full wheel covers, courtesy and ashtray lamps, an electric clock and an armrest in the center of the front seat. The four-door hardtop with basic equipment listed for $3,271, a premium of $408 over the equivalent model in the Impala series.

Unlike other full-sized Chevys, the Caprice was not available with a six-cylinder engine, but there was a full-range of V-8s. The one in our feature car is the familiar small-block Chevy V-8 with the stroke increased from the three inches of 283 form to 3¼ inches to create a new base power plant of 307 cid. With the Rochester two-barrel carburetor, it churned out 200 horsepower at 4,600 rpm. Various versions of the 327 cid small-block and 396 and 427 cid big-block engines were common in Caprices. Along with a Turbo-Hydramatic 350 transmission, this car is fitted with air conditioning, power steering and power brakes.

Not everyone owned, or even aspired to own, a performance car in 1968. Most families were completely satisfied with the reliable, comfortable and roomy sedans of the day. And for those for whom basic wasn't good enough, Chevrolet offered Caprice.

SPECIFICATIONS:

Make/Model	1968 Chevrolet Caprice
Body Style	four-door hardtop sedan
Wheelbase	119 inches
Weight	3,754 lbs.
Bore & Stroke	3.875 x 3.25 in.
Displacement	307 cu. in.
Compression Ratio	10.0:1
BHP	200 @ 4,600 rpm
Carburetion	Rochester two-barrel
Transmission	350 Turbo-Hydramatic
Production	115,500 (Caprice two-door and four-door hardtop figures combined)
Factory price	$3,271
No.1 value	$3,800

1968 Caprice two-dr hardtop

'68 Caprice: The Grand Chevrolet

By Tom LaMarre

"Park it next to an expensive limousine — it comes off looking great," said ads for the 1968 Caprice.

There was a time when family cars were boring people-movers. Not in 1968. The top-of-the-line Chevrolet Caprice had styling that proved full-size practical cars could be exciting, too.

The concept of a dolled-up Impala, a super Chevy, materialized in 1965. By 1968 its sales credentials made it a well-established and respected member of the Chevy family.

A fold-down center arm rest, extra sound insulation, and "the look of hand-rubbed walnut" were luxury features that the Caprice buyer expected. A 200 hp 307-cubic-inch V8 was standard, compared to the Impala's standard inline six-cylinder powerplant.

But to be successful, the Caprice had to have a visual identity that set it apart from its less costly brethren. All Caprices had distinctive side moldings and full wheel covers with black centers and the "Caprice" script. In addition, retractable headlights were an exclusive Caprice option.

However, the trim frills were only the frosting on the cake. The big Chevrolets had new body side lines and a restyled rear end with taillights recessed in the bumper. An upswept hood accommodated concealed windshield wipers. For the coupe, there was a new roof and ventless windows.

As with all 1968 cars, there were also 20 new safety items required by law, including a dual-cylinder brake system, windshield washers and defogger, safe door latches, and an impact-absorbing steering column. Shoulder harnesses were required on all cars manufactured after Jan. 1, 1968. And all '68 models had to have side marker lights and pollution control devices.

The trend in 1968 was toward longer option lists, and the Caprice was no exception. There were 327, 396 and 427 cubic-inch engines, wire wheels or mag-style 14-inch wheels, a stereo tape system . . . and more. Gold seems to have been the most popular color.

The only thing missing was a convertible, which had never figured into plans for the Caprice line. After all, the model was intended to be practical as well as luxurious, which explains why six- and nine-passenger station wagons were included in the Caprice range.

Specifications:
1968 Chevrolet Caprice four-door sedan
Series 166
Factory Price — $3,271
Weight — 3,754 lbs
Wheelbase — 119 inches
Overall Length — 214.7 inches
Overall Width — 79.6 inches
Track — 62.5/62.4 front, rear
Engine — 307-cubic-inch V8
BHP — 200 @ 4600 rpm
CR — 10:1

1968 Nova SS

By Tom LaMarre

The 1968 Nova SS, one of the most collectible versions built during the model's long production run.

Forget the joke about "Nova" meaning "no go" in Spanish. The durable Nova was a good car in its day and its long production run yielded collectible versions that are sleepers in the current market. Perhaps the best example is the scarce 1968 Nova SS.

Chevy advertised the first Nova as "The Not-Too-Small Car." Technically, it was the Chevy II Nova, but it more closely resembled a scaled-down version of the Chevelle than the original Chevy II. The 1968 Novas are easily distinguished from later models by the "Chevy II" lettering along the top border of the grille.

The totally redesigned compact drew rave reviews. "It's a smart-looking car featuring more than a dash of sporting flavor," automotive editor Bill Kilpatrick wrote in the October 1967 issue of *Popular Mechanics*. "Available as the Nova coupe, a four-door and the Nova SS, the car is six inches longer than the '67s, boasts many styling features reminiscent of far more expensive cars.

"Power choices are many and transmissions include fully synchronized three- and four-speed manuals and an automatic. The Nova SS, with the 350 cid, 295 hp V-8, is a dazzling performer. This model, by the way, comes with a lot of special performance-oriented trim. Bucket seats are available in the coupe only."

The SS option package (RPO L48) cost $210 and included a black-out grille with SS emblem, lower body trim with black center section and raised "Super Sport" lettering, twin louvered hood panels, sport steering wheel, 350 Turbo-Fire engine and red stripe tires mounted on six-inch wheels.

Although the Chevrolet Division's press release pictured a Nova SS with plain wheel covers, optional rally wheels greatly improved the car's appearance. Fake mag wheel covers were also available.

The effects of the new safety law were evident in the Nova's side maker lights and shoulder harnesses, which were required on all cars sold after Jan. 1, 1968.

Other items in the standard safety package were windshield washer and defogger, a dual-cylinder brake system and impact-absorbing steering column.

The Nova appealed to a wide market because of its many engine choices. A 153 cid, four-cylinder power plant was standard. The optional engines were a 230 cid six, a 307 V-8, plus 327 and 350 cid four-barrel carburetor V-8s.

The Nova SS engine was derived from Chevrolet's original 265 cid V-8 of 1955, instead of the up-to-the minute 396 cid. Increasing the 327 cid engine to 350 cid was primarily a matter of stroking, using a crankshaft with longer throws. Chevy built almost 201,000 Novas in the 1968 model year, including an unspecified quantity equipped with the SS package.

Specifications

Year	1968
Series	Nova
Model	11427
Body Style	2-dr. sedan
Option Package	RPO L48
Original Price	$2,577
Wheelbase	111 in.
Overall Length	187.7 in.
Overall Width	70.5 in.
Track f/r	59.0/58.9 in.
Engine	V-8
BxS	4.00 x 3.48
Disp.	350 cu. in.
BHP	295
Carb	4-bbl.

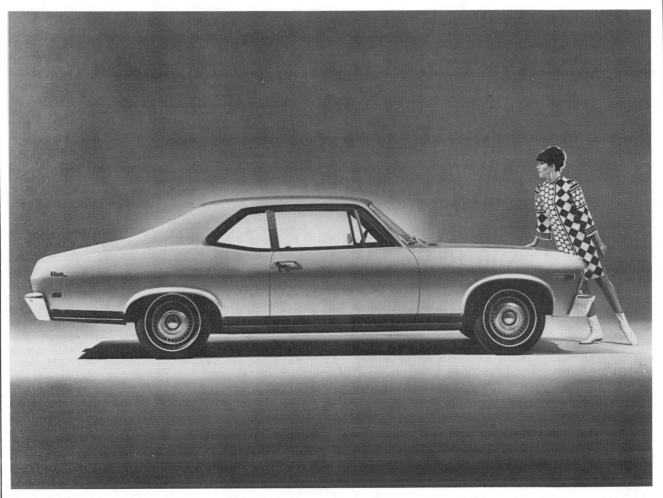

Completely redone for 1968, the Chevy II Nova was a pleasingly designed, smaller car that displayed styling features reminiscent of more expensive cars and offered a broad range of power train options.

With its compact size and large engine availabilty, the new Nova became competitive in drag racing. Here, Bill "Grumpy" Jenkins puts a 396-cid, 375-hp version through its paces.

The Monte Carlo Was an Immediate Hit

By Terry Boyce

The first Monte Carlo, appearing in September 1969 as a 1970 model, was a stylish "personal" car with a six-foot long hood, simulated burl grain walnut instrument fascia and thoroughly conventional Chevrolet chassis and powertrain. Elitist automotive publications were disdainful, but the new car was a hit with the more than two million 1970 announcement day visitors to Chevrolet showrooms.

Ford had first recognized the personal car market, targeting it with the original Thunderbird and its four-passenger progeny. General Motors had responded with the Buick Riviera of 1963, followed by Olds in 1966 with Toronado, Cadillac in 1967 with the revised front-wheel drive, and the Pontiac with the reborn Grand Prix of 1969.

Like its GM cousins, Chevrolet's personal car was available only in Sports Coupe form (though a convertible and even a four-door hardtop were subject of Monte Carlo styling studies). Styling was cleanly elegant, with the long hood/short deck hallmark of such cars preserved. There was more than a hint of the 1963 Riviera in Monte Carlo's body lines.

Wheelbase was 116 inches, but the considerable front overhang made the car appear even longer—a styling touch that would almost become a cliche by the end of the '70s. Monte Carlo was actually based on the intermediate Chevelle, using the same basic body shell with distinctive sheet metal and a four-inch chassis extension ahead of the cowl. Assembly took place on the same lines as Chevelles and other GM A-body cars. The Monte Carlo had additional sound-deadening, upgraded suspension and more luxurious trim than Chevelle, of course.

Though smaller than the contemporary Caprice, Monte Carlo carried a prestige price tag within the Chevrolet lineup. Base price for the 1970 Sport Coupe was $3,123,

1970 Monte Carlo Sport Coupe

compared to $3,474 for a similar Caprice. A 350 cubic-inch high-compression V8 was standard; transmission choices were optional automatic or four-speed (and very few of these were chosen).

In the Chevrolet tradition, Monte Carlos could be custom-equipped by the buyer from a long and comprehensive option list. Adding fender skirts, a vinyl top and plenty of power amenities created a boulevard cruiser of the first rank. Leaving the wheel wells open and specifying 15-inch Rally wheels gave a totally different look.

There was one performance package offered for Monte Carlo in 1970: RPO Z20, the SS 454. This coupled a 360-h.p. version of Chevrolet's monster motor with a Turbo-Hydramatic and highway gearing that produced exceptional high-speed cruise capability if not astounding quarter mile acceleration—a loaded SS 454 might not break 90 m.p.h. at the drag strip, but it would run all day at that speed without straining. Huge dual exhausts terminated in rectangular chromed outlets beneath the SS 454's rear bumper. Otherwise, this Super Sport was identified only by small SS 454 badges on the front fender extensions of the lower body side moldings. Only 3,823 of these brute force Monte Carlos were sold in 1970.

All Monte Carlo buyers could add typical performance items to their cars, including power front disc brakes, bucket seats in cloth or vinyl, special instrumentation including tachometer and gauges and a floor console to house the transmission shift lever.

Add a choice of exterior color combinations to the listing of options, and it is evident there were few identical cars among the 130,657 Monte Carlos built during the first year of production.

The annual model change concept was beginning to fade by the time Monte Carlo appeared. Hence, the hot-

1972 Monte Carlo Coupe

1973 Monte Carlo

1981 Monte Carlo 2-dr

1973 Monte Carlo

selling 1970 was changed very little for the 1971 sales year. The grille was refined, while bumper-mounted parking lamps were now rectangular instead of round as in 1970. The hood ornament was of the stand-up, spring-loaded safety type for this one year only.

The SS 454 was back, with a bit more exterior identification courtesy of a black rear panel with SS badge to the right just above the rear bumper. Some 1971 SS 454s had an unusual black rubber bumper rub strip, too. Special suspension components, large tires and automatic level control on the rear continued as part of the RPO. Inside, the SS instrument panel now had European-style soft knobs; a new four-spoke Sport steering wheel was optional.

Although compression had been cut, the 454 cubic inch V-8 that was the heart of RPO Z20 was rated five horsepower higher, at 365 h.p. for 1971. Still, Monte Carlo SS 454 production dropped to about half the 1970 level, stopping at 1,919 units.

Surprisingly, total Monte Carlo production for 1971 also declined—although minimally—to 128,600 units.

Originally, there was a new body slated for Monte Carlo in 1972, but the demands placed on GM and other automakers to develop new safety and emissions systems created a delay in new styling programs. Thus, the original body was released for yet a third year.

Once again, styling changes were minimal. Departing from the normal practice of adding more trim to an aging design, Monte Carlo's stylists created a restrained new grille that contributed to the original elegance inherent in the overall concept. The grille itself was a bright egg-crate design similar to some Cadillacs. Flanking this plated high-impact plastic were new vertical turn signal housings with clear lenses. The front bumper was now devoid of any lighting devices.

At the rear, there was a new satin-finished anodized trim strip crossing the rear of the body just above the bumper—a touch that looked so good one wondered why it took so long to appear.

Though the 454 V-8 was still available—now with considerably less horsepower, there was no SS 454 package for 1972. Most of the SS features were still available, though, as separate options. A new ride and handling package, the Monte Carlo Custom, could be combined with the performance goodies to make a really strong road car out of Monte Carlo.

Preparing for the 1972 model introduction, Chevrolet told dealers what had been learned about buyers of Chevrolet's personal car. Perhaps it was no surprise that 85 percent selected Monte Carlo on the basis of style; an equal percentage of buyers were male. Young, with a median age of 38.4, they tended to be well educated and relatively affluent.

Monte Carlo buyers loved to option their cars liberally; many cars were loaded with comfort and convenience items.

The third time turned out to be a charm for the original Monte Carlo. Sales figures for 1972 wound up at 180,819 —making the final version by far the best-selling of the first generation.

During years of subsequent use, these original design Monte Carlos proved to be extremely satisfying cars for many owners.

A complete restyle appeared in 1973; it would last, with modifications, through 1977. Then Monte Carlo was down-sized, going a separate way from Chevelle/Malibu. An interesting historical footnote is the success of the reintroduced Monte Carlo SS. Appearing in mid-1983 with a breathed-on 305 and the heartiest exhaust rumble heard in a production car for many a year, the new SS soon accounted for a large share of Monte Carlo sales, continuing to be a strong seller right into 1986.

1985 Monte Carlo

1986½ Monte Carlo Aero Coupe

1970-'72 Monte Carlo: A Chevelle in a Dinner Suit

By Linda Clark

1970 Monte Carlo 2dr Hardtop

1971 Monte Carlo

"Why would Chevrolet put a Chevelle in a dinner suit?" asked *Car and Driver* in the fall of 1969. The car in question was not Chevelle, but Chevrolet's new Monte Carlo, which premiered in September 1969 along with Chevy's other (except Corvette and Camaro) 1970 models.

Under its skin, the Monte Carlo was indeed a Chevelle (the two-door hardtop's wheelbase lengthened four inches to 116) and its "dinner suit" was in the "personal luxury" mold of its Pontiac counterpart, the Grand Prix. Then Chevrolet chief stylist Dave Holls was responsible for the Monte Carlo's slab sides and stiff, traditional lines. Holls had been inspired by such Classics as Packards, Duesenbergs, Continentals and especially Bentleys and Rolls-Royce.

For economic reasons, Monte Carlo was built on the Chevelle five-passenger coupe platform. In addition to the lengthened wheelbase, the Monte Carlo got four extra inches of front overhang. Even though the Chevelle sedan had a 116-inch wheelbase, that frame couldn't be used for Monte Carlo because its extra length was under the passenger compartment. Windshield, upper roof panel and rear glass were identical on both cars, even though Monte Carlo's wide C-pillars tended to disguise these similarities.

Mechanically, the cars weren't much different either. Then Chevrolet engineering director Alec Mair was the wizard behind the subtle changes. While the Monte Carlo's front wheels had been moved ahead, the engine remained in the same place so that Chevelle's linkages and drive-shaft could be used. Only minor suspension refinements and a more absorbent sound package contributed to the Monte Carlo's slightly smoother ride.

It mattered little to Chevrolet marketing that there was a Chevelle under the skin since Monte Carlo was intended to sell primarily on looks. And if aesthetics didn't lure Pontiac "personal luxury" buyers to the Chevy fold, it was hoped the Monte Carlo's $862 lower price would. In fact, Chevrolet's Monte Carlo outsold rival Pontiac Grand Prix 130,657 to 65,750 in 1970.

By and large, Monte Carlo was considered both conservative and elegant. A mesh die cast grille, single headlamps, integrated side marker lights, lower body-length chrome panel and its long hood/short deck proportions all served to distinguish Monte Carlo from other Chevrolets of the period. Fender skirts ($31.60), color-keyed

1972 Monte Carlo

wheel covers ($15.80) and vinyl roof ($126.15) were optional. Monte Carlo, however, shared the Chevelle's trunk lid.

Inside, the Monte Carlo got nylon fabric upholstery and a fiberglass instrument panel. The simulated wood dash fascia was a plastic reproduction of the genuine burled wood used in Bentleys and Rolls-Royce. Unlike these English cars' high gloss finish, the Monte Carlo's "pseudo-wood" was dull. To reinforce this elegant image, the Chevrolet nameplate appeared only once, in small print under the right rear corner of the deck lid. For some $218 more than a comparably equipped Chevelle two-door hardtop, Monte Carlo was clearly selling prestige.

Contemporary road testers often linked the Monte Carlo's lines to Oldsmobile and its ride to Buick. Equipped with the standard 350 cubic-inch V-8, Monte Carlo delivered a moderate 250-h.p. Optional was a 265-h.p. 400 cubic-inch V-8 (a bored and stroked version of the small-block 265 cubic-inch introduced in 1955), and a high-performance 360-h.p. 454 cubic-inch V-8 that was part of a $420.25 Super Sport package. In addition to the four-barrel 454 engine, SS equipment included such items as dual exhausts, automatic level control, special suspension, larger 15x7 wheels, wide oval tires and "SS" identification trim.

Even in SS trim, (3,823 SS454 models were sold in 1970), Monte Carlo came standard with automatic transmission, bench seats and power front disc/rear drum brakes. Front bucket seats ($121.15) and console ($53.75), including console-mounted shifter, were optional. So were a three-speed automatic ($221.80) and two four-speed manual transmissions.

Other popular options for Monte Carlo were air-conditioning ($376), tinted glass ($42.15), power steering ($105.35), appearance guard group ($50.65), whitewall tires ($46.95), AM/FM stereo radio ($133.80), deluxe seat belts ($12.15), power door locks and four-wheel disc brakes.

For 1971, Monte Carlo was facelifted with a smaller-mesh grille, spring-loaded hood emblem, rectangular parking lamps (as opposed to the prior round ones), minor interior changes and an expanded option list. Due to the combined forces of 1970's Clean Air Act and the swelling ranks of horsepower critics—added to pressure already put on the industry by the 1966 Highway Traffic Safety Act—Detroit adopted SAE net (rather than gross) horsepower figures for 1971. In political lip service to the advantages of low-lead gas, General Motors also lowered the compression ratio of most of its high performance engines from 11.0:1 to 8.5:1. (Some Corvettes, Camaro Z/28 and Pontiac Trans-Am were exceptions.)

For 1971, the Monte Carlo's 454 V-8 was thus rated at 285-h.p. (or 365 gross), up five horsepower from the prior years, despite the lower compression ratio. Tighter springs, heftier front and rear stabilizer bars and heavier-duty shocks were part of 1971 refinements to the Monte Carlo's chassis.

Monte Carlo was little changed for 1972 and was restyled for 1973 with a higher $3,561 base price and a new top line landau coupe that sold for $3,805 before options. Sales of all Monte Carlos reached 290,695 in 1973. Prior to its current incarnation as a bona fide NASCAR racer in 1985 SS trim, Monte Carlo grew increasingly luxurious during the seventies, often being likened to a Cadillac rather than a Chevelle. But the original 1970-1972 models, known for their strong 245-h.p. 350 cubic-inch V-8 and good handling, remain the favorites of collectors. And for enthusiasts who want to pass everything but a gas station, the 1970-1972 Monte Carlo SS454 big-blocks are the only way to go.

SPECIFICATIONS
1970-72 MONTE CARLO

Base Price:$3123 (1970), $3416 (1971) $3362 (1972).
Wheelbase: 116 inches.
Length: 205.8 inches.
Width: 75.6 inches.
Height: 52.6 inches.
Curb Weight: 3,818 pounds.
Brakes: front 11-in. discs/rear 9.5 in. drums.
Tires: G78-15 (optional G70-15).
Wheels: 15x6 (optional 15x7).
Suspension: Front: independent, unequal-length A arms, coil springs, tubular shocks, stabilizer bar. Rear: rigid axle, four-link trailing links, coil springs, tubular shocks, stabilizer bar, self-leveler.
Frame: perimeter with cross members.
Fuel capacity: 18-20 gallons.

Camaro: Chevy's Sporty Car

By Phil Hall

1967 Camaro SS 2-dr Hardtop

1969 Camaro RS Convertible

1973 Camaro LT

The accomplishment of the Camaro staying on course can't be considered lightly, for it came through a period of drastic changes in the domestic industry, many 180 degrees opposed to its defined direction.

With the falling off of the muscle car market in the early 1970s, the insurance onslaught against young buyers at the same time, the deluge in federal safety and emission standards, and the so-called energy crisis of 1973-74 all taking dead aim at the Camaro's market, competitors fell by the wayside en masse.

Some died and others changed direction, retaining the name, but abandoning the original concept.

Of course, the Camaro was not the only sporty compact to survive and thrive; its sister under the skin, the Pontiac Firebird, started life as a 1967½ model based on the Camaro body and chassis and paralleled each of Camaro's steps as they are built on the same production lines. Like Camaro, Pontiac Firebird created its own legend, but that's another story.

While Camaro may have soldiered on through some mighty rough times, it was by no means a pioneer in its field. That honor clearly belongs to the Ford Mustang, which turned out to be a bold and successful move into the sporty compact market on April 17, 1964.

The Mustang was based on a chassis design and driveline from the compact Ford Falcon. The long hood, short deck body, clean lines, low initial price and long option list made the Mustang a runaway best seller.

Mustang's intro coincided with the explosion of the youth market of the 1960s, and its variety of equipment, body styles and effective marketing turned out to be a success beyond Ford's wildest dreams.

For once, mighty General Motors was caught by surprise and Ford had close to 2½ model years to itself without direct competition from GM.

Chevy brass hoped its all new rear engine 1965 Corvair would counter the attack but didn't foresee the problems that nameplate ran into shortly after introduction.

When the answer to the Mustang did come out, it was anything but spectacular. The Camaro was nicely styled, followed the Mustang basics with low priced leaders, many options and performance packages, but looking at the competition, the Camaro had its work cut out.

Camaros came in two-door hardtop and convertible form. Mustang started with those styles, but added a 2+2 kind of fastback in the fall of 1964. Also, the 1967 Mustangs were restyled and came with an optional big block 390 V-8 under the hood in a muscle-conscious time frame.

Starting the 1967 model year, Camaros had a new 350 inch version of Chevy's small block V-8 as the top option. A 396 big block came on stream mid-season.

Model year 1967 wouldn't just be a Mustang-Camaro battle. Mercury was given a stretched version of the Mustang hardtop, the Cougar. Over at Plymouth, the Barracuda, which was around as long as the Mustang, became more than a glass-backed version of the Valiant. It got a new body and like the Mustang, came in three versions.

Throw the Firebird into the ring and you had a dogfight for the young buyer's attention.

Camaro may have started slow, but it had a lot going for it. It had the Rally Sport option, SS option and combinations thereof.

Mid-year, a lasting Camaro tradition started when the Z28 option was announced. In order to legalize cars for competition in the Sports Car Club of America's Trans-American Sedan racing series, a special run of hardtops was made with 302 cubic inch V-8s, heavy duty suspensions and trick options. You could literally build a race car from the parts from Chevrolet.

When the 1967 model year statistics were in, Camaro rolled up a respectible production run of 220,917, but that was pale compared to Mustang's 472,121.

For 1968, minor styling and mechanical changes were made by Camaro and its competition. American Motors joined the field with its Javelin and later a shorter two-passenger version of it, the AMX.

Camaro production advanced a bit for 1968 to 235,151, but Mustang, hurt by a Ford strike, fell to 317,404.

Three-year styling cycles were common in the 1960s and the third and final season for the first generation Camaro was the facelifted 1969 models, which featured more sculptured lines. Production continued into late 1969 as there were problems bringing the all-new 1970 models to the ready stage. Some late 1969s were titled as 1970s.

The extended run raised the Camaro total for 1969 models to 243,095, a record, but still short of Mustang's 299,824 for the restyled 1969 models.

Designed in the heat of early success, replacements for the sporty compacts began life as 1970 models. Chrysler Corp. redid its Plymouth Barracuda and added the Dodge Challenger for that year with enough room under the hood for everything up to and including the famed Hemi V-8.

Introduced early in 1970 as a 1970½ model, the second generation Camaro and Firebirds showed sleek three-window styling on a fastback body. Gone were the convertibles; preserved was Camaro's image as a personal sporty/performance machine.

Back were all of the good guys, the Rally Sport, SS and Z28, now with 350 V-8 power instead of the 302.

Mustang still offered three body styles and there still were competitors from every major domestic company.

While the products reflected a continuum of the muscle-crazed 1960's, the market for new performance cars had slacked off considerably with insurance problems and changes in consumer tastes to more luxury being factors. That was clearly reflected in the Mustang's drop to 190,727 cars produced. Camaro, only getting in a partial model run for 1970, fell to 124,889.

The situation worsened for 1971. Mustang and Cougar went the bigger is better route with their new 1971 models, with the size creeping up toward that of the intermediates.

Production for all the sporty compacts fell as the months of the 1970s passed. Since manufacturers like to sell cars where the volume is, departures were being planned for the once populous sporty car field.

After the end of the 1973 run, Ford put the Mustang nameplate on a product based on the subcompact Ford Pinto. The Mustang II never did rival its predecessors in performance or image.

The Cougar nameplate went on to a loaded version of the Montego intermediate for 1974, leaving the sporty field entirely. Introductions were made of the 1974 Javelin, Barracuda, and Challenger, but the start of the energy thing at the same time wiped out what little was left of the market. Barracuda and Challenger never made it to the end of the model year and Javelin did, but no further.

The Camaro and Firebird were also to bite the dust, but an 11th hour executive decision saved them and they continued to be made. However, the Z28 option was deleted from the Camaro list after the 1974 finale.

Styling for the timeless Camaro design was far from dated and the sales dive had bottomed out with 151,008 1975 models being made, up from 1973's 96,756. Firebird sales were also holding, and in mid-1975, Chevy brought out a graphic Rally Sport option that hadn't been offered since the 1973 models. As the 1970s progressed, so did the situation improve for the now unique Camaro and Firebird. The Z28 returned to the option list in the spring of 1977. Production increased every year. A new rubberized front end on the 1978 models blended in well with the still fresh-looking 1970 body.

1979 Camaro Z-28 Coupe

Ford revived the straight Mustang name for its all-new 1979 models, which now were sized somewhere between the little II and bigger originals. Ford would gradually return performance engines to the Mustang arsenal in the coming years.

Probably Chevrolet could have gone on selling the Camaro styling for several more years, but new technology and demand for higher mileage ratings by the federal government dictated that a new Camaro be made ready. The 1981 models were the last for the old style, which served well for nearly a dozen model years.

The all-new 1982 Camaro retained the clean lines, sleek nose and wraparound taillights of the earlier models, but incorporated a rear hatchback, coil rear suspension in place of the leaf springs and a new front suspension utilizing modified Mac-Pherson struts. Wheelbase fell from 108 to 101 inches, length from 197.6 to 187.8 inches, and width from 74.5 to 70.6 inches. Weight also tumbled several hundred pounds.

However, unlike most of the newly introduced cars of the 1980s, the Camaro retained its rear wheel drive and option of V-8 power. Actually the package size of the 1982 Camaro was fairly close to the original 1967 model.

The third generation Camaros retained the Z28 option and added a new twist with the IROC-Z version being added when the 1985 models came out. IROC means International Race of Champions, which has used Camaros for many years and features top racing drivers from several segments of the sport.

Classic Styling Sets Camaro Apart

By Linda Clark

What will set the Camaro apart is its *style*—that linear mastery of sheetmetal that stands out from the automotive landscape and compels a second look. Not the '67-'69 Camaros, although these *were* sporty and youthful, and at that time the brightest meteor in Chevy's sky. These first-generation Camaros did follow GM's "fluid" design theme of that era—and under the excellent direction of then GM Design Vice-President Bill Mitchell—but they were designed by committee, and plagued by its resulting compromises. Notably, the height of the cowl, and the length of the dash to front-axle span, which it shared with the Nova in 1968.

The high-style Camaro was the second-generation 1970½. Even Bill Mitchell, who oversaw this version also, called it "a designer's design." It was an all-new body (which it shared with the Firebird, of course) minus any compromises. Its long hood-short deck, single side window, pointing fenders, and tapered quarters were admittedly inspired by Pininfarina's Ferrari Short Wheelbase Berlinetta. It's been called "the most tightly controlled body to come out of Detroit," and in *Contemporary Classics*, author Rich Taylor considers the svelte '70-'73 coupe "one of the most attractive American cars ever designed."

Even after two decades of habituation, the 70½ Camaro skin still shows plenty of old-fashioned head-turning power. Its sleek, sexy shape looks good enough to have been designed in Italy, and had it been produced in limited quantities, we'd no doubt be singing its styling praises even louder. The growing number of Camaros being "collected" by hobbyists only serves to underscore the rightness of a shape that seems to get more attractive as the rest of the automotive world gets boxier.

Thankfully, Chevy engineers chose to distinguish the Camaro from its stablemates with better than average handling. Not extraordinary, but commendable for a balance between ride and handling so rarely found in American sport GT's. Considering even the high-performance Z/28's humble solid-axle and thick front and rear sway-bars, handling is second only to the Trans-Am, with which it shares steering linkage and suspension geometrics. Ironically, many Z/28 owners in particular want to give up a little handling, a little steering response, and a little braking to avoid what they consider the Trans-Am's grotesque graphics.

Camaros are notorious, of course, for being "tail happy" and lack of suspension travel is another perennial shortcoming, but none of that matters. Camaros are first and foremost *road* cars. They were designed, according to Chevy's chief Z/28 suspension engineer Jack Turner, Jr., for day-long stretches. Its smooth and soothingly quiet Interstate cocoon refuses to get ruffled, even when you're throttling along as quickly as you can get away with before the authorities confiscate your radar detector. Comfort is right up there, too. Handsome upholstery, optional full-instrumentation, a 4-spoke steering wheel you can really get a grip on, and enough goodies on the option list to entertain, inform and comfort you and your heart's (or checkbook's) desire. Of course, the rear seat is traditional peanut gallery, and the trunk will only hold a toothbrush and a six-pack. But that's not important, either.

What *is* important is the aura of race-bred excitement that permeates the Camaro. Even owners who didn't want a go fast car did want a look fast car. The Camaro

1972 Camaro Sport Coupe

1973 Camaro

1974 Camaro

1977 Camaro

1978 Camaro 2-dr

qualified, of course, on both counts. "Camaros won 18 out of 25 Trans-Am races in 1968-69 and took the SCCA championship both years," according to Michael Lamm in *The Great Camaro.* Sponsors Roger Penske and Smokey Yunick, and driver Mark Donahue are perhaps three of the most famous from the racing fraternity who assisted Chevy's Research and Development by transferring the lessons they learned with the Camaro on the track to the showroom floor where enthusiasts could benefit.

If one model alone deserves credit for the Camaros performance legend, it's the Z/28, which was the brainchild of Chevy engineer Vince Piggins. Of the 220,917 Camaros produced in 1967, 602 were Z's. Compared to the base Camaro coupe's 140 hp 230 CID inline Six, the Z's standard powerplant was a 302 CID V-8 delivering 290 horses. While hood and deck stripes were standard equipment on Z's, the rear spoiler was not. It was an option, as was Rally Sport equipment. Powerplants, including the "semi-hemi" 396 and big-block 454 came and went during the reign of the anti-musclecar zealots in Washington that followed.

The Z/28, however, remained admirably noble throughout its declining compression ratios,(first reduced in '71 so it could burn unleaded) lowered hp ratings, change from solid lifters to hydraulic cam in '73 and—as if that wasn't enough—due to '73's addition of "exhaust gas recirculation," the high-rise aluminum intake manifold surrendered to a conventional cast-iron one, necessitating the highperf. Holley carb to succumb to a Rochester Quadrajet.

Diluted, the pavement-pounding Z retrenched during 1975-76 model years, only to come back in 1977 as a polished, low-profile machine with impeccable road manners. Mechanically muted, and softened by a massive facelift, the Z enviably retained the Ferrari snout and dive-plane tail Camaro lovers had faithfully lusted for since 1970½. Anyone tempted to relegate even the 1981—and last—Z/28 to the gas-guzzling gorillas barely able to get out of their own way, would be wrong. That's the tragedy. For all its excesses, the Z/28 still does 0-60 in under 9 seconds—one of the few under-$9000 cars that does—and corners with more dignity than all but the most properly-optioned Corvette.

The '67 and '69 Indy 500 Pace Car replicas are second only to the Z in popularity with Camaro collectors, and finding a low-mileage original is an absolute joy. Although the Pace Cars were RS/SS396 Turbo Hydra-matic convertibles, the replicas were—in most cases—SS350 Powerglides.

Although enormously desired by collectors, few of the 50 factory-installed aluminum-block 425 hp 427 CID V-8's (with triple 2bbl carbs) that went into '69 Camaro coupes to qualify for NHRA drag racing are likely to show up in the local classifieds. However, Dana Chevrolet (Los Angeles) and Nickey Chevrolet (Chicago) installed 427's are not uncommon at Camaro events. In fact, when one drives on the field, the news spreads FAST.

In declining order of popularity are RS and SS Convertibles, RS and SS coupes, V-8 convertibles and coupes and —as with most performance oriented collectibles—the bigger the engine the better. The Camaro's heavy breathing through the gas pedal guaranteed time lost in gas lines, but getting there was always fun. For an old car now, the Camaro will hold its own.

Mid-'75 Rally Sport.

'73-'79 Camaros

Cooler But Still "Cool"

In the fall of 1972, the super-high-performance era ended. Government regulations and rising insurance rates were two factors. Another was the required switch to lower compression engines that could run on low-lead fuels.

Chevrolet began to change its thinking, moving from brute horsepower to variety. There were new model names and new model options to take up the slack. The Camaro's future was a bit cloudy and enthusiasts were wondering if Chevy could keep its cooled-down ponies "cool" enough to survive.

As we know, they succeeded. After coming near death during the Lordstown strike of 1972, the Camaro got a new lease on life. Little by little, between 1973 and the end of the decade, the situation improved. Today's car collectors are starting to take a much closer look at the "cool" Camaros of these years. Who says there were no collectible cars made in the 1970s?

New for 1973, was the Camaro LT (luxury touring) model. An hydraulic lifter 350 cu. in. engine was the new Z-28 power plant. It had 10 less horsepower, but a new open-element air cleaner that produced a nice growl. Fifteen new colors were introduced, along with seven shades of vinyl roofs. There was a soft-rim four-spoke steering wheel, extra rear seat padding and an optional Space-Saver spare. Air conditioning was available on Z-28s for the first time. Styling updates seemed to be mostly in minor grille changes.

Camaros had a new, shovel-nose front end in model year 1974. It was made of soft urethane and fitted with an eggcrate grille. More massive one-piece aluminum bumpers and recessed headlights were used and the old, round

Cars like this '76 Camaro can still be purchased low, but experts expect values to start climbing soon.

1973 Camaro Z-28.

taillights gave way to horizontal wraparound lenses. The RS appearance package was dropped, as was the 307 cu. in. V-8. The base "350" engine was unchanged, but now featured lower 160 and 185 h.p. ratings. All models were up seven inches in overall length.

General Motor's "Efficiency System," including a catalytic converter and High-Energy Ignition (HEI) was used on all 1975 Chevrolet products. A sporty looking, wraparound backlight was new for Camaros. There was no longer a Z-28. The base edition two-door hardtop came as either a six or V-8. The Type LT coupe used a V-8 as standard equipment. Engines employed were the 250 cu. in./105 h.p. inline ohv six or the "350" with 145 and 155 h.p. options. Even though a new Sport Decor package was marketed, overall production dropped some 5,000 units.

Bob Lund was promoted to Chevrolet General Manager in 1976. He came aboard a little too late to make any drastic model year changes. The Camaro looked like a carbon copy of last season's. But, returning in mid-year was the optional Rally Sport package featuring Rally spoke wheels, dual sport mirrors and two-toning on the roof, hood and front fenders. Engines were the unchanged six, 305 cu. in. V-8 with 140 h.p. or the 350 cu. in./165 h.p. V-8 job. Camaro sales climbed almost 37,000 units.

In its fourth year without a major restyling, the 1977 Camaro debuted in sport coupe and Type LT models. Engine choices were carried-over, but given the year's five extra horsepower. Then, at the International Race of Champions (IROC) finale at Daytona Beach, Chevy announced a new Z-28 as a mid-year addition to the line. It came with only one power plant—the hydraulic lifter

350 cu. in. V-8 with four-barrel—which churned out 170 h.p. at 3800 rpm. Z-28 features also included a NASA hood scoop, rear deck lid spoiler, Borg-Warner four-speed transmission, stiff suspension, GR70-15 tires and "open" exhaust system with dual resonators in place of mufflers. Distinctive Z-28 graphics appeared in the grille and on the hood and bodysides.

Performance recorded for the Z-28 included an 8.15 second zero-to-sixty time and a 15.4 second quarter-mile with 90.05 m.p.h. terminal speed.

The 1974 Camaro LT coupe, not really a performance car, but definitely collectible.

A new, body-color soft nose section, a urethane-steel rear bumper and wedge-shaped wraparound taillights characterized 1978 Camaros. New Rally Sport coupes and LT Rally Sport coupes sported contrasting paint schemes, while the Z-28 had front fender louvers, a scooped hood and rear deck lid spoiler. There were new Rally wheels finished in body colors and chassis and suspension improvements. Power plant changes included a new aluminum manifold for the base six-cylinder engine, plus a 185 horsepower Z-28 option. Otherwise, engines were unchanged.

Dealer sales of Camaros in model year 1979, through August, totaled 233,802 units compared to 247,437 for the same period in 1978. The drop came despite the launch of a new Berlinetta which sported exterior pin striping, a bright-finished grille and black lower body perimeter finish. All Camaros had a restyled instrument panel, new steering column lock and expanded sound system options. The Z-28 came with front wheel-house flares and a three-piece front air dam for better aerodynamics. Also available were the Sport coupe and the Rally Sport coupe. The 4.1-litre six was the base engine, while the 5.0-litre V-8 came on all, but the Z-28. A 185 h.p. version of the 5.7-litre V-8 was considered standard equipment for the high-performance Camaro, while other models could be had with the same power plant at additional cost.

A little more H.P. in 1977.

During the 1980s, the Camaro would continue its revival as the "cool" Chevrolet for enthusiast drivers to own. In fact, it got even "cooler" when the third-generation types appeared, in mid 1982, reintroducing the American high-performance automobile and bringing four-wheel excitement back to the domestic industry.

However, it was the models of 1973-'79 that laid the foundation upon which the second coming of the American musclecar was built. These Camaros are still available, at reasonable prices, today. They represent one of the best investments, for the money, that you'll ever find in the collector market right now.

1978 brought new grille.

Vega With Muscles

By Tony Hossain

It never was Chevy's brightest star on the sales charts, appearing only briefly on the automotive scene. Introduced in mid-1975 and discontinued at the end of the 1976 model year, only 3,508 Cosworth Vegas were built, a bitter disappointment to Chevrolet.

Like the Nomads, "fuelie" Corvettes and Turbocharged Corvairs that preceded it, the exotically engineered CosVeg went largely unappreciated by the new car buying public.

To fully understand the Cosworth Vega story, one should have some knowledge of the 1971-'77 Chevrolet Vega and that car's position in the small car marketplace.

As the first '71 Vegas appeared in dealers' show rooms, the car was already in deep trouble. Not only had Ford undercut the Vega by $200 when it tagged its new Pinto at $1,919, but Vega production was almost immediately stopped by a long UAW strike.

Adding to the Vega's problems was continued employee discontent at the Lordstown, Ohio plant where the Vega was built. The national news media quickly pounced on the Lordstown story, and the Vega's reputation was badly tarnished.

If all this wasn't enough, the Vega soon developed a reputation as the disposable car. Total engine failures and severe rusting problems were making the car a symbol of what was wrong with American technology in the early '70s. It must be noted that Chevrolet went beyond its normal warranty obligations in helping owners who experienced problems with their Vegas.

For all that was wrong with the Vega, there was a lot that was right with it as well. The little Chevy's distinctive style and innovative engineering features appealed to enthusiasts who wouldn't give the Pinto or any number of other American cars a second look.

1976 Cosworth Vega

1977 Chevrolet marked beginning of a revolution

By Robert C. Ackerson

Growing up in the forties and fifties may have had its disadvantages (one is that it puts you into the middle age bracket in the eighties!). But for many middle-class Americans whose automotive loyalty leaned toward General Motors, it usually meant that a late model Chevrolet sedan resided in your family's garage and just about every three years it was replaced by a new model. There was something solid and sure about that process since each new resident of that garage had attributes that you could predict with uncanny accuracy. Sure enough there were changes; Powerglide and the Bel Air 2-door hardtop came along in 1950 and of course everyone learned about performance in a hurry in 1955. But Chevrolet still retained its trim size and small town simplicity in spite of having become one of America's greatest performers. Gradually however, the Chevrolet's wheelbase, width and overall length expanded outward and before long that faithful old garage just couldn't cope with a '59 Chevy's 79.9 inch width and 210.9 inch length. There was a reprieve of sorts from this process in 1961 but before long we found ourselves going downtown for a loaf of bread behind the wheel of a 1976 Impala whose 222.9 inch length easily exceeded that of a 1964 Park Avenue Cadillac.

We're not however, subscribing to the premise that GM was forcing us against our will to drive those big Chevrolets. When gas was selling for 30¢ a gallon fuel economy ranked low on the list of priorities for most American car buyers. General Motors had traditionally been the proponent of providing a car for every segment of the market and that, virtually by definition meant it would become the industry's most proficient producer of big automobiles. Furthermore Chevrolet had less than a happy experience with its smaller and lighter 1961 models and as a result some last minute styling changes were made on the 1962's in order to make them appear larger.

The enlargement of the full-sized Chevrolet was of course accompanied by the development of the Chevy II and Chevelle that were considerably more compact but nonetheless it became increasingly more difficult to accept the standard Chevrolet's bulk as necessary or logical. However, it's also important to point out that neither Chevrolet nor the consumer was totally to blame for the 4300 pound weight of a 1976 Impala coupe since government regulations were responsible for at least 500 pounds of that bulk. The logic behind the ownership of a large American automobile was put under great stress several years earlier during the great gas shortage of 1974. If it didn't make much sense to drive a two-door Chevrolet a couple of miles to the shopping center it made even less to queue up in one to wait your turn at the gas pumps. But in those unhappy times, Chevrolet was developing a replacement for its full-sized models that history will undoubtedly regard as one of the most significant Chevrolets of the post war years.

But preceding the actual beginning of Project 77 which would lead to GM's new line of B-bodies for all five of its automotive divisions a study had been completed which outlined the means by which the weight of GM's current full-size cars could be reduced by 400 pounds without impacting upon their overall physical dimensions. This would obviously improve their fuel economy but with the federal government and the industry moving toward fuel economy goals for 1977 that were beyond the capability of these automobiles, GM committed some $600 million to prepare automobiles which in their Chevrolet form would represent the greatest single-year change in the division's history. Instead of a 400 pound reduction, the 1977 Chevrolet's would weigh in 611 pounds (in coupe form) less than a 1976 model. The sedan differential would be 637 pounds and the wagon's, 871 pounds. In terms of overall dimensions the Chevrolets would have a 116 inch wheelbase (down 5.5 inches from 1976), 2.3

inches and 2.8 inches less front and rear overhang and a width reduced 4 inches from the 79.6 inches of its older counterpart.

Perhaps not since 1948 when Cadillac's then revolutionary tail fins debut had a GM automotive division taken such a risk with a new product. Chevrolet wasn't alone of course, since Pontiac, Oldsmobile, Buick and Cadillac were also in the same B-body boat. But Chevrolet was GM's standard bearer, and its great opponent Ford, whose president was none other than Lee Iacocca, was gambling that a fair number of disgruntled Chevrolet-types would come on over to a Ford showroom and ride off in a 121 inch wheelbase LTD which the Ford salesman would quickly point out was a far larger automobile than the comparatively priced Chevrolet Impala/Caprice. If this tactic didn't bring the desired results Ford gave its sales staff a second shot with the LTD II. This was the old Torino series masquerading as an all-new Ford. It really didn't compare in terms of space efficiency with the new Chevrolets but with wheelbases of 114 inches for the 2-door models and 118 inches for wagons and 4-door sedans, the LTD II conveyed (Ford hoped) the impression of being a similarly downsized automobile that was priced several hundred dollars less than the Chevrolet Impala.

First of the "downsized" cars, the '77 Caprice Classic was chosen as Motor Trend's Car of the Year. It also outsold all other cars, big or small, that year.

This challenge wasn't to be easily discounted. Ford had demonstrated plenty of savvy about consumer preferences since the Edsel's failure and its gamble that the American car buyer would perceive the 1977 Fords as better values than the Chevrolets was also buoyed by customary buying habits that had resurfaced in the form of a resurgence of customer interest in full-size autos.

1959 Impala Convertible

Everyone at GM was of course aware of the possibility of a negative response to its new car. GM Chairman Thomas Murphy noted (*Fortune*, July 1976) that "we think our cars are going to be successful. The miserable part of it is, until we put them on sale we don't know what's going to happen. It's a risky business and always has been."

However, the reports from preview clinics conducted by Chevrolet indicated that this risk was well worth taking. Although no leading questions or promises were made, participants (who were not told they were viewing the

1977 Chevrolet) liked what they saw very much. Tom Zimmer, the chief engineer for the 1977 Chevrolet recalled that "People talked about being surrounded by a generous amount of useable space. About its 'feeling big without looking big.' About its functional look. They spoke of the relationships between the big car they were driving and this 'new size' new car. Some wondered about the ride and handling of the car, though they had never even driven it. In short, it was one of the most positive clinics we have conducted."

This reaction, while pleasing to Chevrolet really wasn't a revelation. Early in the new Chevrolet's development major objectives were established that maintained a link with previous Chevrolets without diminishing in any way GM's commitment to new standards of fuel economy and design philosophy. As Zimmer detailed, the most important factor was to "maintain the sense of value which people had come to expect from the traditional-size Chevrolet." Also ranking high among Chevrolet's priorities were improved structural integrity, the reduction of "needless exterior size and weight" and a "more efficient use of people-oriented space." Fuel economy was of course to be improved but without any reduction in what Zimmer described as Chevrolet's "historic road performance."

1961 Impala Convertible

1960 Impala Convertible

The key to achieving these goals was the use of modern technology from the earliest stages of the new Chevrolet's development. Most of these concepts such as finite element analysis, 3/8 scale modeling and aerodynamics testing, were not new and Zimmer readily admitted they had been used in the past. "But usually," he explained, "they were used to solve isolated problems with specific components. In the 1977 Chevrolet, these tools were put to work in the design stages—at the very beginning of the program. In a very real sense, we used these tools, not to fix problems, but to prevent them in the first place..." Thus, Chevrolet's claim that the new Impala/Caprice had been created from the most advanced technology in the history of the industry was much more than an empty boast.

Furthermore, the dynamics of Chevrolet's engineering was matched by the creativity of its design staff. Late in

1972 work began in Chevrolet's Advanced Studio on the new styling format that would bring to an end the longer, lower and wider philosophy that had dominated the American industry for some two decades. In its place, explained Chuck Jordan, who then served as Chevrolet's design executive, was "a new lean, efficient look of crispness, elegance and simplicity."

The designers of the 1977 Chevrolet worked outward from a mandate that called for a passenger compartment that was not only roomier and more comfortable than the 1976 Chevrolet's but also provided improved ease of entrance and exit. Key elements for their success in achieving these objectives included higher front and rear seats, plus a new thin silhouette shell seat. Basic body changes included a reduction of body curvature both above and below the beltline.

Perhaps the ultimate compliment for the new full-sized GM cars came from Henry Ford II who after giving them the once-over said they were "Very nice...very good to sit in." But of all the forms the B-body took in 1977 it seemed

1971 Caprice

that the Chevrolet version was the most successful. Its trim lines were in tune with the times and somehow its designers had maintained a link with the marque's basic personality while offering a fresh, crisp new appearance just a bit more successfully than their counterparts elsewhere at GM.

The ability of the Chevrolet's designers and engineers to create a car that offered both more overall interior passenger space plus increased luggage room within a trimmer and lighter package also enabled a major shakeup of Chevrolet's engine line-up to take place. In 1976 the standard Impala/Caprice engine was the 145 hp, 350 cid V-8 with a 2-barrel carburetor. Available as options were a 165 hp, 4-barrel version plus a 400 cid, 175 hp V-8 as well as the super-sized 454 cid - 225 hp V-8. For 1977 there were just three choices. The standard engine (in coupe and sedans) was Chevrolet's 250 cid six cylinder which, with standard Turbo Hydra-Matic, provided a respectable zero to 60 mph time of 15.1 seconds. Also available was the 145 hp - 305 cid V-8 and, for an additional $210, the 4-barrel, 350 cid V-8 rated at 170 hp. Chevrolet's comparison of the acceleration capability of 1977 Chevrolets

1977 Chevrolet Impala

powered by these engines to their 1976 counterparts provided dramatic evidence of what Tom Zimmer was talking about when he said that "weight and size reductions are circular in nature. This means that weight reduction in one area often opens the way for weight saving in another location. By reducing the total load that will be moved about, we can reduce the size of the powerplant needed to do the job." Whereas the standard 350 cid V-8 engine used in 1976 provided a zero to 60 mph time of 12.9 seconds, the 1977 Chevrolet with the 145 hp, 305 cid V-8 came through the same run in just 11.4 seconds. While the big 4-barrel carburetor, 400 cid V-8 of 1976 edged out the 1977's 350 cid V-8 time of 10.8 seconds from zero to 60 mph it was only by 0.1 seconds. On the flip side of the performance coin, economy, the 1977 models had a decided edge since Chevrolet reported owners "can reasonably expect to get about three more mpg than last year's purchasers."

It wasn't long before the new Chevrolet's sales reports confirmed the accuracy of GM President E.M. "Pete" Estes' view that its introduction marked the end of an old era and the start of a new one. Whereas the 1976 Impala/Caprice had been the third best selling American automobile, its successor moved into the number one spot. Although they had expressed some initial apprehension about its saleability, Chevrolet dealers were soon declaring the new model as one of the best Chevrolets of all time. A similar sentiment was expressed by *Car and Driver* (October 1976) which told its readers that "the most jaded car critics are in fact tripping over each other trying to be the first to anoint this sedan the best full-sized Chevrolet ever made." *Car and Driver* also had kind words about the virtues of Chevrolet's F41 suspension option. For a mere $36 this feature which included the Monte Carlo's GR70-15 tires and seven inch wheels will, said *Car and Driver,* "make you think your Chevy came from the Black Forest instead of Detroit."

Not surprisingly *Motor Trend* declared the Caprice its Car of the Year in 1977 which was in a sense just another confirmation of Tom Zimmer's belief that "In the short run, we think the new Chevrolet design will prove to be one of the most remarkable successes in our history."

The 1977 Chevrolet doesn't of course yet qualify as an old car by any stretch of the imagination. But thanks to its innovative design and excellent styling, its place in Chevrolet's history is already worthy of recognition.

1974 Caprice Convertible

Corvette 1987–1990

A news leak that would shed significant light on the Corvette's future came during Chevrolet's 75th anniversary year. Unrelated to the nearly unchanged 1987 models, the statement made by chief engineer Dave McLellan revealed to the Detroit Auto Writers' Group that Corvettes would soon be available in two different levels of performance: basic and ultra-high. McLellan was, of course, hinting about cars that would carry the Corvette to startling new heights and set the collector car world off in new directions. Among them: the Calloway Twin Turbo, the Corvette Indy concept car and the limited-production ZR-1.

But, the 1987 factory lineup was far from revolutionary. Two Corvettes — a targa coupe and a convertible — were listed. They shared a single 5.7 liter Tuned-Port-Injected (TPI) V-8 good for 240 hp at 4000 rpm. This engine did have some improvements in the area of anti-friction enhancements, due to its use of roller type hydraulic valve lifters.

Both Corvettes looked the same as 1986 models. Several new options included a Bosch four-wheel ABS brake system and a Z-52 Sport Handling package with Bilstein shocks, quick steering and 9.5 inch wheels (for coupes). Also new was a six-way power passenger seat, a computerized lateral-G sensor for improved braking while cornering, a low tire pressure indicating system and a lighted driver's visor.

Corvette gear boxes were carried over from 1986. Buyers could choose a four-speed overdrive automatic or a Doug-Nash 4-Plus-3 manual transmission, which *Motor Trend* described as "mulish." Regardless of such minor criticisms, *Road & Track* and *Car and Driver* both selected the 1987 Corvette for their "10 Best Cars" lists. Chevrolet General Manager Bob Burger mentioned this in a unique satellite television broadcast to his employees.

Several historic developments took place during 1987 in Corvette-land. One was the appearance of the Corvette Indy, then exhibited as a non-running prototype. It showcased such advances as total wheel control, an "active" suspension and a powerful dohc V-8 intended for future use in the CART/INDY racing cars.

The Calloway Twin Turbo option (RPO B2K for the coupe) was also in the news during 1987. It was a semi-aftermarket package, which 40 Chevrolet dealers handled. Calloway Engineering, of Old Lyme, Conn., did the conversion of assembly line cars, swapping the factory engine for a blue-printed one with four-bolt mains, a forged crank and other goodies, plus twin turbochargers. Cars so-equipped were good for 178 mph at top end and zero-to-sixty in 4.6 seconds. The option cost $19,995 ($2,999 more with an appearance upgrade) and 200-250 were expected to be sold.

In the special interest area, the late Rick Carroll (a well-known collector) displayed his restoration of the rear-engined XP-819 Corvette prototype at a car show in Port St. Lucie, Fla. The unique experimental vehicle had been completely refurbished by Carroll.

With prices starting at $27,999, the 1987 Corvette proved a bit harder to sell than the previous model. Retail sales declined from 33,027 in 1986 to 25,437.

The 1988 Corvettes had front and rear suspension refinements, available 9.5 x 17 wheels and new R-rated Goodyear Eagle tires. Power door locks, cruise control and an AM/FM cassette radio were made standard. New colors were released, too. Bodies and drivelines stayed about the same, with horsepwoer boosted to 245 at 4000 rpm.

Of special interest to marque collectors was a 35th anniversary edition Corvette featuring special badging and the build sequence number on its console. This $36,000 coupe came only with a white exterior, black roof bow and white leather seats. Plans to produce 2,000 copies were made, but sales moved slowly. To most enthusiasts the convertible, priced at $34,820, seemed a better buy.

Back for 1988 was Reeves Calloway's Twin turbo Corvette. It offered 365 hp at 4000 rpm and 440 lbs./ft. of torque. Top speed was over 170 mph, though it met all emissions standards. The Calloway-equipped Corvette did the quarter-mile in 13.2 seconds at 109.1 mph.

More big news for 1988 was the Corvette Challenge Race Series in which 50 identically-equipped new Corvettes competed. The cars cost $15,000 extra and were sold only to racers. They had special performance and safety features. Stu Hayner, of Kalamazoo, Mich., took the championship and $145,000 in prize money. By December, Challenge Series race cars were being advertised in *Autoweek*, as collector items, with $45,000 price tags.

GM released a profile of the typical 1988 Corvette owner: a 40-year-old, married male with a college degree and $43,000 income. In September, the company reached tentative agreement to sell its St. Louis assembly complex. All Corvettes had been built there from 1953 to July 31, 1981.

After two years on the show circuit, the Corvette Indy prototype was turned into a functional experimental vehicle in 1988. Another "experiment," — this one intended for the showroom — was the LT-5 engine being developed jointly in England by Chevrolet and Lotus. Earmarked for the upcoming ZR-1 model, this dohc, four-value, all-aluminum motor was to be built by Mercury Marine Corp. in Oklahoma. *Automotive News* highlighted the power plant as "one of the year's most significant engineering developments."

Corvette retail sales for calendar 1988 fell again, dropping to a total of 23,281 units.

The ZR-1 continued to generate press in 1989, although its planned release during the year was pushed back several times. When it ultimately came to market, it was labeled a 1990 model. This made a Chevrolet-issued poster depicting the 1989 ZR-1 an instant collectible.

Standard engine for the 1989 Corvette was the L-98, a 5.7 liter power plant which provided 240 hp at 4000 rpm and topped out at *only* 140 mph. A new ZF six-speed manual transmission was welcome news for the performance-minded. The four-speed automatic also remained available. New options included an FX-3 Selective Ride Control system. In March, the first removable Corvette hardtop seen in 10 years was added to the factory options list.

During 1989, collectors watched with interest as GM waged court battles to halt the sale, at auction, of two early CERV concept cars. An injunction had stopped the sale of CERV I at Rick Cole's 1988 Monterey auction. However, by January, the case was dismissed and the CERV I and CERV II were offered at the Barrett-Jackson sale. Later in the year, at a Rick Cole auction in Detroit, the 1963 CERV II went to $525,000 for a no-sale.

An interesting 1989 aftermarket release was the aerodynamically enhanced Kaminari Corvette, designed and built by Pete Brock. But no one had to add kit components to a Corvette to make it exciting or expensive. The standard models qualified as America's fastest production cars and carried price tags of $32,479 to $37,764.

The Corvette Challenge Racing Series continued in its second and final year, with more races and larger purses for 1989. Fifty new Corvettes again received competition improvements. Some later wound up in collectors' hands.

Creating more Corvette mania in 1989, was a contest sponsored by VH-1, a new all-music video television network. The grand prize was one Corvette from every year of production 1953-1989. When it was over, Dennis Amodeo, of Huntington, NY, had 36 sports cars and no place to keep them. He later sold the entire collection to pop-art genius Peter Max.

The 1990 Corvette had the first major interior changes since 1984. They included an aircraft-inspired instrument panel and a console with analog and digital gauges. The L-98 engine was now good for 245 hp at 4000 rpm with sport mufflers. Other improvements included an enhanced ABS braking system, new Polo green paint and 17-inch cast aluminum wheels.

Finally available, with a $59,175 sticker price, was the ZR-1. "It's been a while since General Motors deliberately set out to be the best at anything," said *Automobile* magazine. "So, the ZR-1 comes as an especially welcome piece of automotive news. It's a truly great automobile."

With attributes like a 4.3 second zero-to-sixty time and 13.1 second quarter-mile at 110 mph, prices for the "King of the Hill" Corvette immediately shot up towards $100,000 in the collector market. *Playboy* named it "the best car to buy and tuck away".

During the first two days of March 1990, Corvettes broke three world speed records and set nine other international class marks during a Stockton, Texas endurance run. Two Corvettes — one LT-5 and one L-98 — were used. Among the records eclipsed was a 24-hour speed mark that Ab Jenkins set in July 1940 behind the wheel of the Mormon Meteor Duesenberg. The 1990 Corvette averaged 175.885 mph for 24 hours.

Three months later, on June 1, 1990, chief engineer Dave McLellan was promoted to platform engineering director for the Corvette Group. It was a fitting honor for the man who had mapped the development of late-model Corvette history.

Chevrolet Corvette

Detroit, Mich. — The popular Chevrolet Corvette spans a history of over 35 years. During that period some of the most exciting automotive names have been associated with the vehicle.

Harley Earl, Edward N. Cole, Maurice Olley, Zora Arkus-Duntov, William Mitchell and Larry Shinoda, to name a few.

Robert D. Lund, Chevrolet General Manager and a vice president of General Motors, has called the Corvette mystique a key to Chevrolet's overall product image, particularly among young people and automobile enthusiasts throughout the world.

The Corvette received its first public exposure in 1953 when it appeared as a dream car in General Motors' famous Motorama auto show at New York City's Waldorf Astoria Hotel. It was an immediate hit. The Corvette name came from the sleek, fast submarine chaser and convoy escort vessel of World War II.

The original open roadster was done by a design team under the direction of Earl, then vice president in charge of GM's Styling Staff. He brought it to the attention of Cole, then chief engineer of Chevrolet Motor Division and later president of GM. Cole assigned Olley, a brilliant British engineer, to design a special chassis for the vehicle. The standard Chevrolet 115-horsepower, six-cylinder engine of the time was transformed into a 150-horsepower version for this new fiberglass-bodied sports car.

Although the public liked the original Corvette design, the car received only a lukewarm reception from sports car enthusiasts.

A Belgian-born and Berlin-educated engineer, Arkus-Duntov — along with Cole and Earl — set out to remedy the situation. During the next four years they totally transformed the Corvette. They incorporated several new features and, most importantly, dropped Cole's new Chevrolet V8 under the hood. In fuel-injected form it produced 283 horsepower — nearly double the 1953 output of the original L6 engine. Reception for both the 1956 and 1957 Corvettes by sports car enthusiasts and the general public was outstanding.

Cole, Mitchell, Arkus-Duntov and Chevrolet sales executive Joe Pike were members of a team that developed the next Corvette milestone car — the famous 1963 Corvette Sting Ray.

The Sting Ray still stands as one of the outstanding sports car creations in American history, and is one of the most sought-after collector cars in the world. The vehicle brought to sports car lovers a closed coupe with teardrop-shaped roof, and, for the first time, a split rear window. The vehicle also featured hidden headlights and an ingenious independent rear suspension by Arkus-Duntov.

It was an instant sales success with some 20,000 units built in the 1963 model year — a production record.

The peak of the muscle-car era, 1965, saw four-wheel disc brakes added to Corvette along with a 396-CID V8 optional engine.

Then, just five years after the debut of the '63 Sting Ray, another major revamping of the 'Vette occurred in 1968. Mitchell's chief stylist, Shinoda, is generally credited with the styling concepts for both cars.

Other Shinoda creations include the Mako Shark I and II, the Cerv I and II, the Corvair Super Spyder, Monza GT and SS, the Astro I and the mid-engined Astro II.

A major Corvette milestone occurred March 15, 1977, when the 500,000 'Vette came off the line at the St. Louis plant. The following year — the 25th anniversary year for Corvette — saw it named Pace Car of the 62nd annual Indianapolis 500 automobile race.

Because of lack of adequate expansion space at the St. Louis facility, plans were drawn to transfer Corvette production to a plant in Bowling Green, Kentucky. Twice the size of the St. Louis facility, the Bowling Green operation was designed to be one of the most modern and highly computerized automobile assembly plants in the world.

On July 31, 1981, the last Corvette was produced at the St. Louis plant. It was the 695,124th Corvette assembled since the first one was completed 28 years earlier.

General Motors' investment in this newer, more modern Corvette facility is clear evidence of Chevrolet's confidence that Corvette's future remains bright.

Zora Arkus Duntov

1953 Corvette

Corvette History

1953–1962

By Sam Folz

1953 Corvette

When Design Chief Harley Earl's kids wanted a go-to-school roadster, he noted that General Motors had not made that style of body since Chevrolet had stopped producing one with the end of the 1935 models. Mr. Earl is reported to have had the simple, yet elegant 1932 roadster in mind when he first requested his styling staff to toy with the idea and to come up with some sketches for an inexpensive, sporty vehicle. The year was 1952, and what they came up with after the usual evolution of a design, followed by a shorter than normal gestation period, was a sexy roadster to be shown as Chevrolet's project at the Motorama to be held at New York City's Waldorf Astoria Hotel in January, 1953.

The car, just coincidentally had the same 102" wheelbase as then current Jaguar roadsters, with which it also shared common width and approximate weight. Known internally as "Project Opel" (to adopt the German subsidiary's name for code purposes) the new unit had a special frame designed by Maurice Olley, and a basic layout arranged by a promising young engineer named Bob McLean. McLean moved the old, heavy, (and only one available) six-cylinder mill back on the frame as far as he

could and still maintain tolerable driveline angles to the differential.

In those days, the Woodill Wildfire was available in kit form with glass fibre body to go with the chassis of your choice, as was the Alembic I. The latter happened to be on display for a time in the lobby of the GM Building on Detroit's Grand Boulevard. This car had caught the attention of Mr. Earl and it seemed to him that this would be a good time and the opportunity to fabricate the new show-car-to-be in that material.

The first prototype cars (there were actually three made), were built up in-house by a special group of skilled tradesmen, some of whom had prior boat hull building experience. One of the leaders of that crew was Steve Koss, now retired and living in Florida—an active National Corvette Restorers Society and Florida Chapter member. The first components were all of the hand-lay and/or bag molding process, and it was truly a learn-by-doing experience.

The Corvette that evolved just made it to the Waldorf show in the nick of time. In fact, it was completed on the display stand because GM attorneys had advised Styling that their prototype nose emblem could not be used. The prototype design emblem contained the familiar black and white checkered flag, and with crossed staff, there appeared an American flag. As it is not acceptable to incorporate Old Glory in a product design, new prototype emblems were rushed to New York, and the now familiar red Chevrolet flag was now used in place of the Stars and Stripes. That's been the Corvette's emblem ever since.

The name "Corvette," submitted by GM employee Myron Scott, was selected from many submitted for the project, and it fit the parameters of "C" names, as well as having panache and euphony.

The obvious practical limitations dictated both by time to engineer and low cost are obvious, and manifest themselves throughout the chassis. Starting at the front, the cross-member with spring towers, upper and lower control arms and bushings, spindles, axles, brake drums, all existed on other Chevrolet products. The third arm was unique to Corvette, as was the steering gear. The trusty overhead valve six had been opened up to 235 CID for Powerglide-equipped cars and also the trucks, so being available, it was employed. It is noted here, however, that both horsepower and torque curves were seriously adjusted upward by use of a compression ratio increase from 7.5 to 8.0, an altered cramshaft with higher lift and more overlap, solid valve lifters, split exhaust manifold, and a new cast aluminum intake manifold, balanced to accept three Carter-type YH side-draft carburetors. These carburetors allowed the necessary very low hood line, as well as providing a very free-breathing intake. The upper tank was removed from the radiator, again due to low hood clearance, and relocated alongside the cylinder head. The only manual transmission available to the design team was adjudged inadequate to handle the output of the reworked engine, so the newly modified and rugged 2-speed Powerglide automatic was drafted as standard with no other transmission options available. This presented one other problem in Engineering, however, as the typical column-mounted transmission control shaft could not be used due to interference with the rear carburetor which lies just above the steering column. The fix proved easy and Styling loved it—a floor-mounted control lever. The hole in the instrument cluster where the transmission control shaft would have gone made a nice place for the emergency-brake warning flasher.

The power from the Powerglide unit, which was stripped of external oil cooling deemed unnecessary, was taken via Hotchkiss (open propellor shaft) to a 3.55 rear axle. Adopting what was a torque-tube application in the Chevrolet passenger car to Hotchkiss was facilitated by the availability of an output adapter assembly created for the Pontiac Division so that Pontiac, which had Hotchkiss drive, could use Chevrolet Powerglide units following the 1952 fire that destroyed the Hydra-Matic Plant at Willow Run, Michigan. Today, though very scarce, these old 1953 Pontiacs with Powerglide provide the necessary components to faithfully restore an old Corvette that had been altered from stock drive-line configuration.

The body was pure Harley Earl, with smooth bulges and curves that play well with highlights and shadows and included the then "in" windshield, low, severely raked, and also sharply bent around the corners, all framed in heavy chrome. The folding top was to be simple and neatly stowed, out of sight in its own closed compartment, a la 1936 Cord, and this feature was to later nearly spell the end of the project, as customers found it cumbersome to erect, hard to collapse and stow, and more important, it provided less than tight weather-proofing.

A couple of other neat Earl touches were the enclosed, recessed license plate at the rear to be viewed through a contoured clear acrylic lens, and to take advantage of the plastic body, a piece of common window screen was built into the trunk lid to serve as the radio antenna, a job it does very well.

Another Earl touch, reflecting his then current passion for things aeronautical, were the rocket-like tail lamp pods projecting rearward at the top of the fender line, as well as the recessed, contoured headlamp buckets with a formed stainless wire grid.

The body beautiful and its short, rugged chassis sat on standard Chevrolet Bel Air wheels and 6.70-15 whitewalls. A special wheel cover was created for the Corvette to include an integral two-bar spinner.

The Motorama car was a huge and instant success. Interest was intense and GM management not only planned for production at the earliest possible time, but felt that selling 10,000 units per year would be an easy matter.

The first car off the line rolled June 30, 1953, to be followed by 299 additional Corvettes to be produced at the old Customer Delivery Building at Flint, on a line only six-chassis long. These cars were very unique. They are probably the closest thing in both appearance and features to a Motorama special display vehicle ever made before or since, and have established themselves as prime pieces for serious Corvette or sportscar collectors. In 1963, GM's slick magazine *Corvette News*, offered a sterling silver custom dash plaque to all owners of 1953 Corvettes who would forward a vehicle identification number plate tracing to the magazine. Over 150 responses attest to a remarkable survival rate for these rugged machines. One presumed reason for high survival goes back to GM's marketing strategy for the car. You had to be "somebody" or know "someone" to be able to buy one. All 300 cars were "placed" by Chevrolet's Sales Management into the hands of well-known entertainment stars such as Dinah Shore and John Wayne, ranking military officers, and prominent business leaders. This writer's own 1953 Corvette was sold and delivered to a man who owned a manufacturing plant that shipped parts to Chevrolet and availability was promised verbally by Tom Keating, then Chevrolet's General Manager.

When the few 1953 Corvettes did hit the road, two basic problems surfaced. The body and top were not sealed effectively enough to preclude water entry at the doors and windshield, and stories abound regarding standing water on the floor and also of door-mounted ashtrays full of rainwater. The other; the triple side-draft Carter carburetors were a new sight to the factory trained mechanics at the corner Chevy dealer, and new techniques had to be acquired to balance them. Ironically, what appeared so involved in 1953 seems so mundane today, as there is nothing about these vehicles that is particularly hard to fix or once fixed, to keep it that way, as compared to more modern units.

It is to be noted that under the hood panel there were many changes from Motorama to production. As the Show Car revolved on its turntable, hydraulics cycled the hood panel open and shut, as well as the deck lid. Typical of show cars, much of the hardware that was chrome plated was to be finished in cadmium or paint on production units. But for simple side trim changes, the 1953 Corvettes bear an almost exact resemblance to the Star of the 1953 Motorama.

By mid-December, 1953 the production facility for Corvette was completed at St. Louis, Missouri, and fifteen early 1954 Corvettes were assembled that month, serving as production prototypes for the expected 10,000 to come from St. Louis in that model year.

Aside, it should be noted that the fiberglass body came near to being abandoned at this point, and only a great, concentrated effort by Bob Morrison and his Molded Fiber Glass Body Company of Ashtabula, Ohio, kept the body in its intended material.

The Corvette, like most new products, and particularly those that are rushed to production, saw many running specification changes. In the 1953 models, early bodies reveal many of the 46 components formed in glass cloth by the hand-lay or bag method. As the serial numbers ascend, panels become much smoother, being preformed from matte, and final-formed in matched metal molds.

The first 1954 Corvettes were evolved from late 1953 specifications with the usual running changes that were later to challenge the serious restorer and the technical people of the National Corvette Restorers Society. Soft tops for 1954 were changed from Black to Tan. No other choices. In addition to the now familiar Polo White body with Sportsman Red interior used on 100% of 1953 production, Pennant Blue with Dark Beige interior, Sportsman Red with Red interior, and a very few Black cars were shipped carrying Red interiors. Road wheels with all body colors were Sportsman Red.

One of the more obvious changes during the 1954 run was a new air-cleaner system. The 1953 and early 1954 engines were equipped with three chromed inlet caps known as "bullets." These caps have three side vents covered with window screen and no other element. Now that's fine for stopping rocks and butterflies, but not effective at all against dirt. So a "twin-pot" system was used which placed two conventional oil-wetted metal gauze elements in surrounds atop a metal duct that coupled to the three-carb inlets. Interestingly, the reason for change listed on the official Engineering Change Authorization was shown as "to eliminate hiss and roar." The writer's opinion is that the change was to provide not only dust protection for the engine, but also importantly to provide fire protection, as side draft carbs drip when flooded and too many of us have seen or experienced this hazard.

The 1954 cars came to include many other less obvious changes, such as carburetor couplings, wiring harness, soft-top irons, and exhaust extensions, plus others. Some subtle, some not so subtle, but a would-be counterfeiter who would retrofit a faked 1953 VIN plate to a 1954 car would surely be foiled in such effort for so nearly impossible would be the task to alter all of the known differences between these seemingly identical cars.

1954, which had seemed like the "make" year for Corvette came near to being the "break" year instead. December, 1954 saw more than 1,000 unsold Corvettes in factory and dealer stock, and when you realize that this was about one-third of the 3,640 such models produced, and such a far cry from the 10,000-unit sales forecast, it's not hard to imagine the "beancounters" having the last word over the sales types.

A couple of things helped save the project from oblivion. Ford began 1955 Thunderbird production late in 1954 and Chevrolet was not to avoid that battle. Also, the now legendary Zora Arkus-Duntov had joined the Corvette engineering group and had a lot to offer by way of performance and handling improvements.

So 1955 production was authorized, with no budget for restyling, but the big news was the availability of the new 265 CID V-8 with its 195 horsepower rating. This engine appears similar to a 1955 Chevrolet with power-pak, except a revised cam, higher compression, and solid lifters allowed 10 HP more than the passenger version. Visibly, the Corvette used a shallow chrome air cleaner, and Corvette could not use the then optional oil filter of the Bel Air due to the low hood clearance, the filter having been bracketed to the thermostat housing. The standard Corvette frame was indented at the front to give clearance to the fuel pump, and the inner right hand fender skirt was re-contoured to accept the larger 12-volt battery. The cockpit appears essentially identical to 6-cylinder cars, except that the manual choke space is blank on the panel, the four-barrel carb containing an automatic choke. Inside rearview mirrors on all but the earliest 1955 jobs now had a thumb-screw adjustment to allow vertical travel so as to allow better rearward scan. The colors for 1955 began as 1954 carryover, but by March, Pennant Blue had been dropped; Gypsy Red, Harvest Gold, and Corvette Copper being added to the line. Note that both the Red and Gold were passenger car hues. Aside from color, the only way to identify a V-8 powered 1955 model at a glance is the larger, gold-colored "V" overlay used with the chrome "Chevrolet" script on the front fender-side.

The mystery cars of 1955 were the very few 6-cylinder jobs actually produced, possibly eight or ten, and the almost as rare 3-speed stick shifts, possibly 25 or so, which served as the 1956 pre-production manual-shift prototypes. Both of these versions are much sought after today.

The minor changes for 1955 were not enough to turn the project around and the model year saw only 700 units produced. Something really had to change for 1956 if there was to be a Corvette in the model lineup. And change there was, for Styling had come up with the roll-up window, lift-off hardtop version for the 1954 Motorama, which with its higher windshield helped solve the weather and wind problems of the first-type bodies. The top hardware was completely redesigned for smoother operation and a power-option offered. The power-train was reissued per late 1955 with the 3-speed getting the majority of sales in 1956—and Zora Arkus-Duntov's chassis "tweaking" paid off in much more secure handling. The tail light pods were scrapped and a recessed chrome bezel held a simple round lens. Headlamps were raised and corner chrome was simplified. The recessed rear license gave way to a standard exterior mounting. The significant styling detail was to be the side scoop or cove behind the front wheel cut back through most of the door. This area lent itself well to two-toning, a new factory option. Ironically, similated fresh-air scoops which had been seen on the 1953 Motorama car and located atop the front fenders near the windshield were added to the 1956 version, even though they had been deleted for 1953-1955 production. They remained non-functional and the original, working top-cowl fresh air ventilator was retained. The standard, stainless steel wheel covers were restyled and received a new heavier two-bar spinner hub that was to remain through 1952 models.

The interior of the 1956 car was freshened up with a beautiful new three-spoke steering wheel, racing style with a stamped stainless steel spider. Seating lost the snazzy saddle-stitching of the earlier cars, but saw the advent of the now famous "waffle" patterned vinyl, first used on the 1954 Motorama Corvette and in production 1955 Chevy Nomad wagons. While the earliest 1956 units retained the large recirculating-type heater of earlier cars, most of production saw the installation of more modern fresh-air heaters. Outside air was ducted via flexible inlet tubing from just behind the grille, and this system solved one of the earlier cars' most serious complaints.

Engine choice was the base 265 CID V-8 at 210 HP with single 4-bbl. carburetor, or optionally 2-4 bbl. carburetors yielding 225 or 240 BHP.

These cars were cornerstone models for Corvette with production back up to 3,467 and much more interest being expressed by "true" sportscar people and those interested in putting the car into competition.

1957 was more of 1956, only better. The 265 engine was opened up to 283 CID with more than slight added performance. The two cars looked the same, but watch out! The now famous Rochester fuel injection was added to the option list and helped turn the car into a screamer, yielding one full horsepower per cubic inch displacement in full tune with Duntov cam and solid lifters. The oft-repeated figure of 240 FI cars produced for 1957 has been found by NCRS to be entirely incorrect. Actually, 1,040 or more FI 1957 models were sold in the several forms in which it was offered, and when one considers that the price was a then hefty $450, fuel injection was a smashing success. That's over 16% of the 6,339 units produced for that model year.

The 1957 cars got other notable changes. Midway through the run, the 4-speed stick was offered as a transmission option and wider based wheels and metallic brakes, along with off-road exhaust let the serious competition buy or assemble a car that would begin to tear up the race tracks.

The top of the 1957 line included the very rare, much sought after, "air-box" cars. This option, RPO 579E, included a revised induction air inlet such that cold air came in through the left front fender skirt to the FI unit. The option included higher compression, altered cam, and of course, mechanical lifters. In the cockpit, the center-mounted dashboard tachometer was omitted with its large hole to be plugged with an extra front Corvette emblem. An 8,000 RPM cable-driven tachometer was clamped to the steering column in a Plain Jane case with its drive cable passing through the dash, using what had been the brake flasher lamp mounting hole. Vented metallic brakes, wide base (5½K) wheels and the other performance options were to be ordered with this "EN" engine package.

Colors for 1957 remained as for 1956 with the exception of Inca Silver being added. This one color was supplied in the then brand new acrylic-type lacquer which GM placed into 100% of all passenger—and Corvette—production in the 1958 model year.

1958 was a unique year for Corvette and for the industry. Chrome and the "heavy look" were "in." Corvette received new front fenders to contain the quad headlamp system, new grille surround with lateral front "scoops," new hood-panel with its unique similated louver or "washboard," and two heavy chrome bars down the deck lid. The louvers and bars were to be one model year gimmicks only, helping to assure the uniqueness of 1958 models.

In the cockpit, the dashboard received a complete rework, with all gauges except the clock now mounted in front of the driver. The steering wheel and shift console of 1956-1957 were retained as they were to essentially remain through the 1962 models.

Mechanically, the 1958 cars were virtually re-bodied 1957 units with engine options and power ratings up slightly.

Sales were up slightly to 9,168 in what was a poor auto sales year, helped in part by the new style and new and unique colors. Black was not available now, having been replaced by the unique "Charcoal," and the bright red, known as Signet Red was also to be used in 1958 only. Some believe that Black was made available as an option prior to the 1959 models, where it again appeared and was to remain.

1959 models featured carry-over horsepower ratings on the 283, revised competition suspension, altered color choices, and for identification, the bodies were cleaned up, having been stripped of the fake hood louvers and the die cast deck lid strips. Also the unique embossment pattern in the vinyl interior of the 1958 model was replaced with a more subtle grain. Production was on the increase as the country recovered from the economic dip, with 9,670 units produced. As before, single and double four-barrel options were available, as well as the now refined FI units in several stages of tune, both with hydraulic and with mechanical lifters.

1960 saw production go above 10,000 units for the first time to 10,261, as the successful 1959 model saw such minor change that only dedicated Corvette types can spot the differences. The two most easily checked 1960 identifying marks are the addition of red and blue horizontal bars added to the aluminum trim panel in the recess ahead of the passenger, and the hot-stamped seams in the vinyl seat cushions were run fore and aft, instead of across. These seams on early 1960 production were often defective, splitting out early, causing GM to make replacements or adjustments to many owners for some time. Horsepower ratings were again increased and minor changes were made in rear end stabilization. These cars were exhibiting a high degree of fit, finish and performance and were indicative of a car that had "arrived," being able to acquit itself well in concours, street, strip, as well as gymkhana, and oval racing.

1961 saw 10,939 units produced. By now the yet to come Sting Ray was well along in design. Bill Mitchell had assumed charge of Styling, and the Sting Ray rear treatment, affectionately known as "duck butt" was used for 1961 as a slight preview of things to come. Also, for the first time Corvette lost its "teeth" as the remaining nine of the original 13 vertical grille bars from the Motorama car were no more. The grille surround now contained a slightly convex anodized aluminum die casting with a horizontal slot motif. The 1961 car was the last year for the 283 CID engine and the last year to use "wide" whitewalls when that option was specified. Fuel injection remained popular, and the 4-speed was now "the" transmission, although the 3-speed manual and 2-speed Powerglide were to remain available. For 1961 *Corvette News* included with one issue as a supplement, a 7" 33⅓ RPM phonograph record with Chevrolet Sales Manager K.E. Staley and Zora Arkus-Duntov chatting about this car prior to Duntov's taking the car for a few laps around the GM oval, and letting the microphones pick up all those nice 4-speed, fuel injected, high RPM noises. That record, "Sounds of Corvette," is rare and sought after today.

1962 was a fine year. The last of this breed of straight axle Corvettes. The first of the 327 CID Corvettes. The first and only bodies to retain the popular side cove, but without two-tone option and without the bright metal surround. These cars were the cleanest and fastest yet produced with the top FI 327 rated at 360 HP.

Styling remained similar to 1961 with the bright grille insert now flat black, except for a few cars where a gold anodized finish appeared for some yet-to-be-fully-explained reason. As the bright trim around the cove was removed, a wide, ribbed, bright rocker panel molding was added, both tending to make the car appear lower. The rib inserts on some of these moldings carried black paint; some did not, again, without obvious correlation. Tires, for the first time were "white stripe" when ordered optionally, as 90% did, and in those cases, cars with standard 5K wheels received black painted wheels with carryover 1959 and later wheel covers. As before, cars with optional 5½K wheels were equipped with small, Chevy passenger size hub caps and body-colored wheels.

As in 1961, the exhaust was no longer brought out through the body or bumpers, as tailpipes exited at either side behind the rear wheels. 1962 cars, as the finale to the straight axle produced a high degree of refinement in the tenth year of the series, represent a sort of high-water mark among connoisseurs and collectors, and while any pre-Sting Ray Corvette may be considered collectible, these 1962 cars hold a special place.

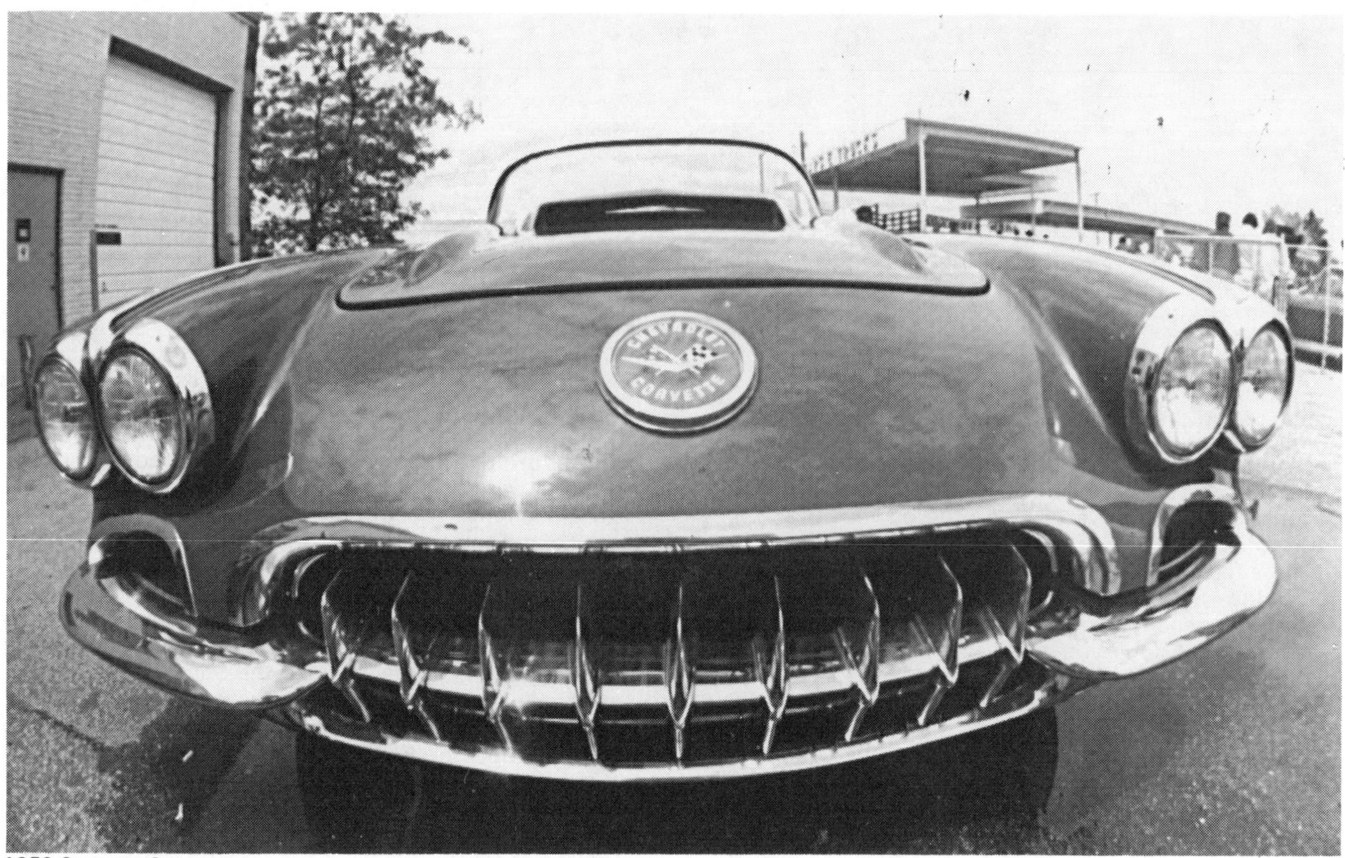

1959 Corvette Convertible

Corvette Was Always Different

By Rich Taylor

One of the things that fascinates me most about big corporations is how they have to actually be an assemblage of small companies in order to function. Each little company is relatively autonomous in the great scheme of things, each under the dictatorial control of one or two men. It has to be that way. If any one person tried to keep tabs on everything going on in a giant corporation, there would be absolute chaos all the time. Witness Ford Motor Company in the late Thirties, if you don't believe me.

On the other hand, look at General Motors. Everything is so diversified that nobody knows which end is up. The various divisions spend half their time cutting each other's throats, developing nearly identical engines and transmissions, literally competing for both share of the market and patent office receipts. Only one man truly cuts across the traditional GM spheres of power with impunity, and he's the Director of Styling. Whether that's what Alfred P. Sloan intended when he set up GM Art and Color for Harley Earl in 1926, that's what's happened ever since. And that's still what happens today. Taken in that context, Harley Earl, and his successor Bill Mitchell, have been just about the most powerful men in General Motors history.

Now most GM cars come from the divisions to the stylists. In other words, somebody in the field says, "Hey, we oughta have one of *them* things to sell," and the division agrees and does a lot of market research to prove that 43 percent of the housewives in St. Clair would buy one, and engineering whips up a chassis and then, finally, Styling gets to bend a body over the thing. That's how you end up with monstrosities like the Monte Carlo, for example, a self-serving instance of GM Styling giving the market just what it deserves, corporate tongue planted firmly in cheek all the while.

But one GM car is different. Always has been, from the very beginning. And that's the Corvette. The Corvette originated in Styling, and it has always stayed as the combined pet of Styling and Engineering. GM Corporate was ready to scuttle the Vette many times, and Sales certainly didn't make any money off it. In fact, for the first five years of production, the Corvette ran deeply in the red. But always, there were enough enthusiasts at GM in positions of power to keep the Corvette assembly line slowly moving.

The first of these powerhouses was Harley Earl himself. Every year in the early Fifties, Styling had to come up with a centerpiece for the GM Motorama, a dramatic and futuristic "dream car" to be shown in a dozen major market centers across the country. In 1951 and '52, Earl presented the LeSabre and XP-300 showcars, which introduced tailfins, wrap-around windshields and "Dagmar" bumpers. The outlandish LeSabre, in fact, was probably the most influential styling study ever built anywhere.

But for the '53 Motorama — which he was already thinking about in late 1951 — Harley Earl thought he'd try and tie into the latest sports car rage. U.S. Rubber had installed its Alembic I roadster in the auditorium, where Earl had to pass it twice a day to reach his office. The Alembic I was really Bill Tritt's original Glasspar fiberglass roadster that later went into production as the Woodill Wildfire, but in the fall of '51, it was still a one-off special, just about the first good-looking fiberglass car anywhere.

Harley Earl was intrigued. Which of course, was exactly what the Naugatuck division of U.S. Rubber was hoping for. At the same time, Earl's son Jerry was pestering for a new sports car to take to college. Everything came together in Earl's mind as easy as falling off a log. What he'd build for the Motorama was a fiberglass sports car. What could be easier?

Harley Earl was no dummy. So to draw up the preliminary showcar presentation, he got a young stylist named Bob McLean to help him. McLean was from Cal Tech, and had degrees in both engineering and industrial design. And even better, he had been exposed to the Kalifornia Kar Kulture long enough to get a good dose of sports car fever. All he was given in the way of direction was a target price of under $2000, so this hypothetical sports car could compete with the MG-TD. The GM sports car, in other words, should cost no more than a mundane Chevrolet.

Rather than draw out an oversize chassis such as Earl used for the LeSabre and put a "sporty" body on it, McLean decided to get as close to a real sports car as he could. Still using stock GM parts as much as possible, of course. Which made the engine part easy. If the car was to retail for under two grand, it had to use Chevrolet parts. And the Stovebolt, the famous Blue Flame Six, was the only engine Chevrolet had.

The legend at GM Styling is that McLean started drawing a full-scale profile plan on the wall of his studio, beginning with the rear wheel. Then he drew the seats as close as he could manage to the rear tire, and then snuggled the long Blue Flame Six as close to the firewall as he dared. When he drew in the front wheels, he found he had a wheelbase of 102 inches. Innocent as it seemed, McLean's decision to work with a super-short wheelbase was *the* crucial moment in the whole history of the Corvette. When Harley Earl accepted McLean's proposal, it meant that unlike any of the previous showcars, the Corvette would have to be built on an all-new frame. It also meant that while the finished car would have excellent weight distribution and classic longhood, shortdeck sports car proportions, it could never compete with the inexpensive MG. An all-new frame meant the Corvette would have to retail for more like Jaguar prices.

In May of 1952, Harley Earl formally presented a full-size plaster model of McLean's proposed Motorama showcar to Ed Cole — the new chief of Chevrolet Engineering — and Harlow Curtice, president of GM. Another GM executive who was also there later told Karl Ludvigsen that Ed Cole "literally jumped up and down" when he saw the new car. Red Curtice would have given Cole the moon if he'd asked for it, so bright was Cole's star at GM. Curtice not only told them they could have the Motorama car, but that Cole could start making production plans if the public response at the Motoramas seemed enthusiastic.

Cole and Earl were ecstatic. Maurice Olley — probably the best chassis development engineer in the U.S. — was put in charge of turning McLean's idea into a working automobile. In less than a year — lightning fast for General Motors — Olley managed to boost the old Six from 115 to 150 and engineer the new — albeit deadly conventional — chassis that the 102 inch wheelbase necessitated.

By January 1953, not only was the Motorama car finished and on display at the Waldorf Astoria, but the GM test track was littered with similar engineering prototypes. For the Motorama, too, the car finally picked up a name. Corvair was the earlier choice, but for the Motorama it was changed to Corvette. Said the official press release, "It is named after the trim, fleet naval vessel that performed heroic escort and patrol duties in World War II."

As hoped, the Motorama car was a stunning success. Curtice ordered the Corvette into limited production in June 1953. Right up until the last minute, there was talk of

1956 Corvette

1957 Corvette

1959-'60 Corvette

1953 Corvette Assembly Line

1960 Corvette

building the production car from steel, formed over disposable Kirksite dies. The novelty value of fiberglass was still so great, however, that it had become a major selling point. And no one knew what the eventual market might be. Kirksite dies were only good for ten to twenty thousand cars, and Ed Cole later figured it would have cost nearly $4-5 million to tool up for volume production in steel. In plastic, it cost only $400,000.

Chevrolet built 300 cars beginning in June, but it was December before they really got production going in St. Louis. The bodies were supplied by Bob Morrison's Molded Fiber Glass of Ashtabula, Ohio who had ironically underbid U.S. Rubber for the initial $4-million body order. Morrison literally had to invent a new way of fiberglass molding in order to supply the bodies Chevrolet wanted. And that took time. Chevrolet was no quicker, and production crawled through the first two years.

Chevrolet built less than 4,000 Corvettes in 1953 and '54. And incredibly, they only sold 2,863. The remaining 1,076 were still sitting on loading docks in January 1955. For 1955, the total was a whopping 700 cars, and the whole marque nearly went away completely. The problem was two-fold. The price was right up there with Jaguar's at $3,490. So the Corvette was too expensive for the American mass market. At the same time though, the string-back gloves types wouldn't be caught dead in a Corvette. It had, horror of horrors, a two-speed Powerglide transmission. Even in America, everyone knew that sports cars didn't have automatic transmissions. Aargh.

Happily, just like in the movies, a hero rode up out of nowhere and saved the heroine's honor. This was Zora-Arkus-Duntov, expatriate Russian, Allard engineer, designer of the famous Ardun conversion for flathead Ford V-8s and parttime racing driver. Zora Duntov helped Ed Cole stuff his new 265 cubic inch V-8 into late 1955 Corvettes. Thanks to Duntov's timely assistance, the Corvette was given enough of a respite for Ford Motor Company to introduce its Thunderbird. And the T-bird saved the Corvette. For GM was now forced to continue Chevrolet's competing model.

By 1956, the car was beautifully restyled into a surprisingly clean package. Bigger than it needed to be, but handsome as all get out. John Fitch and Walt Hansgen finished ninth at Sebring in a factory car, and Zora Duntov himself drove a prototype V-8 with his famous "Duntov cam" over 150 mph at Daytona Beach. Dr. Dick Thompson, the Washington D.C., dentist who literally owned Corvette racing for years, won SCCAC-production in 1956. He owned the car, too, but it went back to Duntov for rebuilds after every race.

Once Zora Duntov and Ed Cole had gotten the Vette sorted out, they left it pretty much alone. Except for quad headlights in 1958 and a high-lift tail added by Bill Mitchell's crew for 1961, the Corvette stayed substantially the same from 1956 through 1962. However, there were two important changes in 1957. John Dolza and Duntov designed a fuel-injection unit for the bored-out 283 V-8 that allowed Campbell-Ewald Chevrolet's ad agency to advertise "one horsepower for every cubic inch." According to Harry Barr, chief engineer at Chevy at that time, the average fuelie V-8 was actually good for 291 hp on the dyno, but the agency was more intrigued by 283 hp from 283 cubic inches. So that's the way they called it.

In 1957, too, the famous Borg-Warner T-10, — the Muncie 4-speed — was made an option. With the 283 V-8, a good Vette would now run the quarter-mile in under 15 seconds at over 95 mph — that's with a 4.11 differential — and *still* go over 130 mph. *Sports Cars Illustrated* said a $3,600 fuel-injection Corvette "is the fastest-accelerating genuine production car *SCI* has ever tested. In fact, up to 80 mph, it's not so far from the data posted by the Mercedes 300SLR coupe, which is generally regarded as the world's fastest road car."

The 4-speed made all the difference for road racing. Dick Thompson and Gaston Andrey won the GT class at Sebring, Thompson won B-production and hundreds of private owners won everything from NHRA drag races to SCCA road races. Even the factory got into the act before the AMA ban on racing went into effect. At Sebring, John Fitch lasted 23 laps in the weirdly styled, overly sophisticated Corvette SS. Despite the factory ban and sad SS, standard Corvettes simply owned A and B-production until the Cobras came out to play in 1964.

The highpoint of early Corvette racing was LeMans in 1960. John Fitch and Bob Grossman got into eighth overall in one of three standard Corvette coupes entered by Briggs Cunningham. It was a perfect indicator of the far-reaching influence the Corvette had on the sports car market. And how far it had come in a decade. In 1960, Cunningham took true production Vettes to LeMans. He just went out and *bought* them. In 1950 when he wanted to race there, he'd had to *build* his own cars first.

Still, the Corvette grew slowly. It was 1960 before Chevrolet built more than 10,000 Vettes in a year, and it's a fact that the Corvette program lost money until after 1958. Part of the reason, paradoxically enough, was the low price. What had started out as a $2,000 sports car ended up around $4,000 for most of its first decade. But because this was still less than half of what comparable sports cars like the 300SL, Aston Martin and Ferrari 250 GT cost, the Corvette was never taken very seriously by the hardcore sports car fraternity. If the Vette had sold for twice the price, it would have been heralded as one of the greatest cars ever built. At $4,000, it was just "American iron."

Corvette Interior

Fuel Injection Set-Up

Corvette - America's Sports Car

By Tony Hossain

For many years Chevrolet advertised its Corvette as America's only sports car. For some of those years it has been and for some of those years it has not. But the fiberglass-bodied Chevrolet Corvette has always been the premier American sports car and one that competitors have always aimed for.

Upon its introduction in July, 1953, the Corvette was looked at with disdain by connoisseurs of European sporting machinery. It was, after all, little more than a rebodied Chevrolet Six. In a marketing blunder that Chevy would need years to overcome, a 2-speed Powerglide automatic was the only transmission available. But changes were quick in coming as Chevrolet was determined to stay in the sports car business.

Nineteen fifty-five saw the welcome addition of a 265 cubic inch V8 engine but the 1956-57 models were the real salvation for the marque. New body styling was adopted with more than a few Mercedes overtones, roll up windows were standard and powertrain options were expanded. Most Corvette buyers in '56 chose the three-speed manual and a power-packed version of the 265 V8. Although cosmetic changes were insignificant, 1957 is remembered as the year of the classic Corvette. A four-speed manual was offered for the first time but the big news was fuel-injection. The Chevy V8 was bored out of 283 cubic inches and, with the optional fuel injection unit, horsepower was rated at an impressive 283. No longer was the Corvette being ignored by the purists. The Corvette could out-accelerate, out-handle most of the respected European cars and the price was very competitive. Corvette, in 1956 and 1957, was offering top sports car value for $3,500.

Corvette enthusiasts generally consider the 1958-60 models to be somewhat less desirable than the lithe 1956-57 cars. Nineteen fifty-eight was not a year of restraint for Detroit's stylists and the '58 Corvette made its debut lacking the clean lines of the '57. Dual headlights were adopted, the body was wider and heavier and there was a rather liberal application of exterior trim. But the general public seemed to approve as production shot upwards. The Corvette was becoming an economically viable product for General Motors. The 1959-60 models

1956-1957 Corvettes

were cleaned up a bit but that's about it. Performance remained impressive and Corvette sales went over the 10,000 mark for the first time in 1960.

Corvette for 1961 was a preview of things to come. Around back the lines of the 1959 show car, the Sting Ray, were adopted. Industry observers speculated that the handsome Sting Ray would soon be in production. They were correct but the Sting Ray would appear in '63, not '62 as was commonly believed.

There was a lot to like about the 1962 Corvette, the last of the first generation cars. The Corvette had lost much of its excess chrome by that time and, under the hood was a rather potent version of the famous small block Chevy V8. Displacing 327 cubic inches, this new engine made the '62 Corvette one of the fastest ever in fuel-injected form. But everyone was still waiting for the new Corvette. It arrived in 1963.

The 1963 Corvette Sting Ray was an enthusiast's dream. With the addition of a coupe body style, the Corvette could now be considered a true GT automobile. The roadster, still available, was a nod towards tradition and it remained a popular choice. Four-wheel independent suspension greatly improved handling and the 327 V8 gave the slightly lighter car plenty of go. But "America's Only True Sports Car" was gradually evolving into something that European enthusiasts didn't understand in the early Sixties. Boulevarders were making up a growing part of the Corvette's market in the mid-1960s and Chevrolet responded with a car that was gradually evolving to reach a new group of buyers. Air conditioning and AM/FM radios were first offered on the 1963 models. Many buyers were choosing the docile 250 and 300 hp version of the 327 V8, often hooked up to...Powerglide! Leather interiors were first available in 1963 but it was a leather rather like the Cadillac's, not the Jaguar's.

A very few Grand Sport Corvette Sting Rays were prepared by Chevrolet for the sports car racing circuit in 1963. The cars were dramatically lightened and extensively modified Sting Rays, bearing little relation to the production cars. Chevy never did get the bugs out of the cars and the program was dropped in 1963. Initially high hopes were placed on the Sting Ray's chances in organized com-

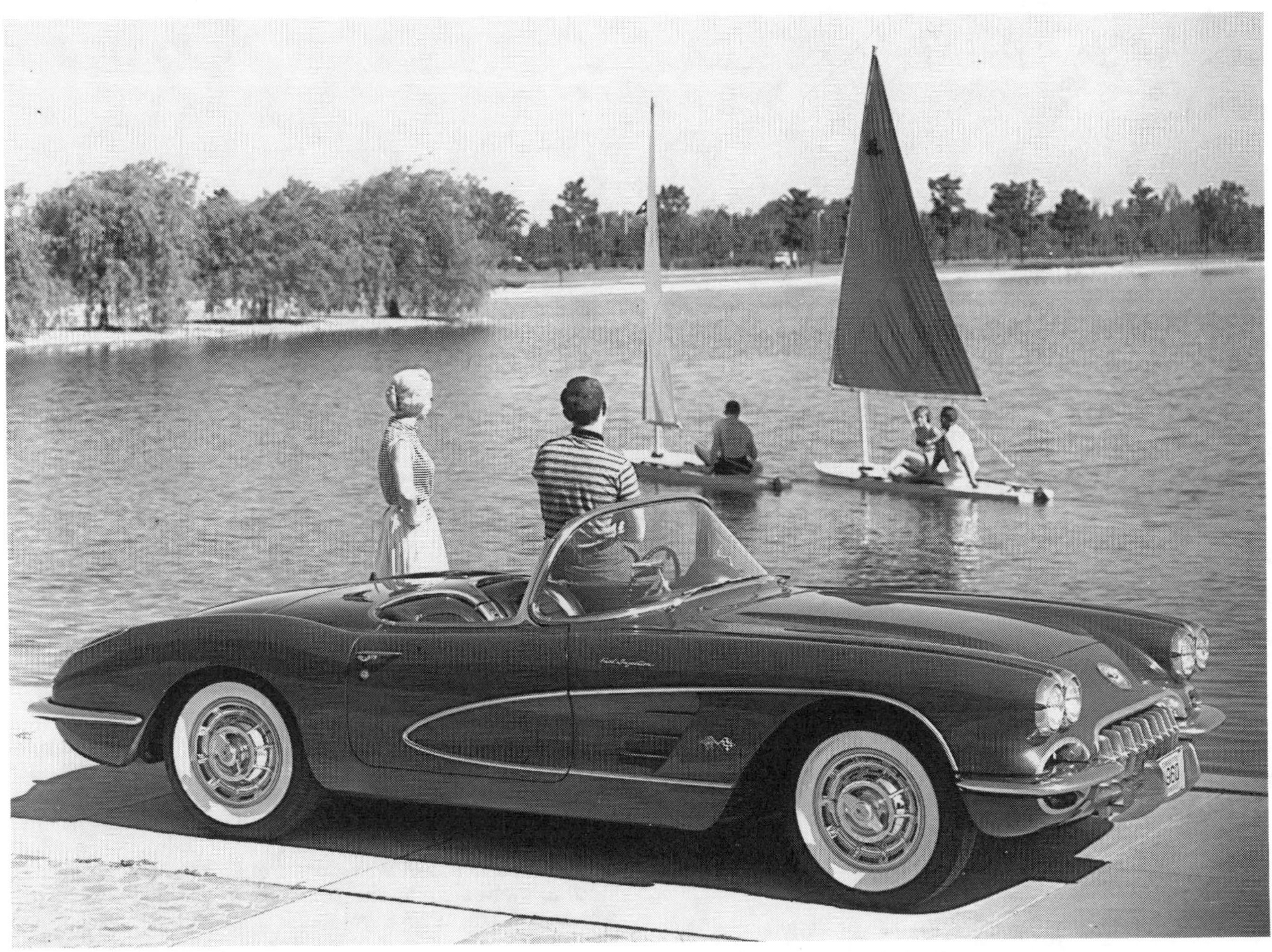

1960 Corvette

petitive events. But Carroll Shelby would quickly dash those hopes with his fire-breathing Ford-powered Shelby Cobra. Too much weight and not enough brakes made the Corvette more for show than go. But on the street it was still king.

Nineteen sixty-four saw little change in the Corvette. Most noticeable was the one-piece rear window which improved visibility to the rear and made the 1963 split-window coupe of special interest to collectors. Corvette owners had long complained that the car's brakes were not up to the job and their pleas for better brakes were finally answered in 1965. The Corvette featured a four-wheel disc brake system that was the equal of the best European braking systems.

With the high-output fuelie 327 V8 and the disc brakes, the 1965 Corvette is recognized as one of the best all around sports cars ever built. It was capable of tremendous speed, it was well-balanced on the road course or on the highway and the brakes were fade resistant and reliable. And that fuel injected 327 was extremely fuel efficient for the amount of power it developed. Big block

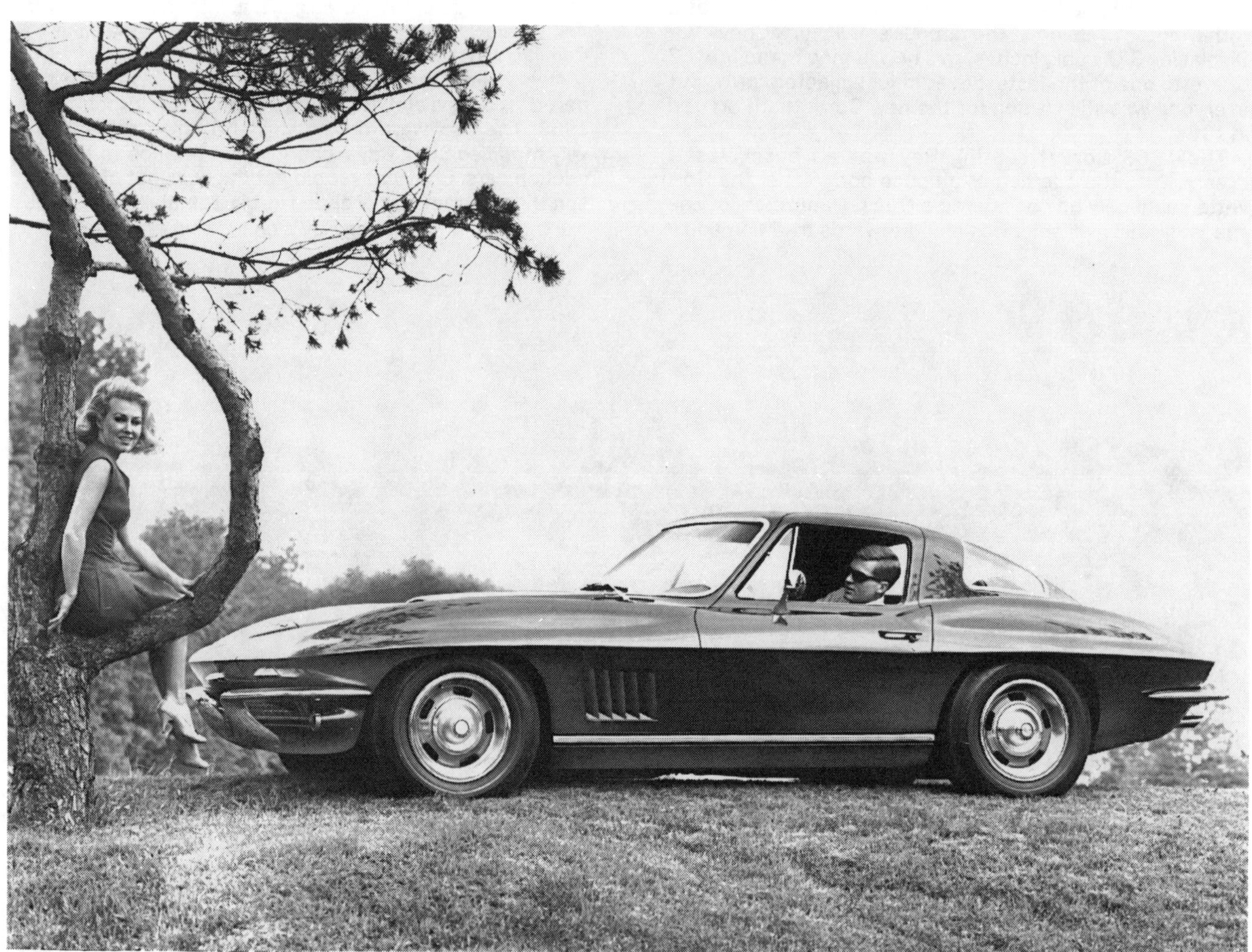

1967 Corvette Stingray Sport Coupe

power, though, in 396 cubic inch form, arrived in mid-1965 and it meant the end of the fuel injected Corvette engine. So the 1965 Corvette remains a collector's dream: the last of the fuelies and the first of the disc braked Vettes.

For '66 the 396 was bored out to an awesome 427 cubic inches while the rest of the car underwent few changes. The 1967 Sting Ray is a favorite of many. It was superbly refined and it was the cleanest Sting Ray yet. Some pretty hairy engine options made properly equipped '67s the fastest Corvettes ever. Yet they remained docile, competent sports cars for American drivers and American roads. But the public was ready for a new Corvette. Sales were down for the first time since 1955.

The 1968 Corvette (Chevrolet still called it a Stingray but nobody else did) was the heaviest, most luxurious fiberglass car Chevrolet ever built. Inspired by the 1965 Mako Shark show car, the purists hated it and the public loved it. The shape, with its bulging fenders and T-Top roof, was as radical in 1968 as the Sting Ray had been five years earlier. But quality on the '68 Vettes was not up to traditional standards and there were plenty of complaints. It was not until 1969 that Chevy really got its quality together with the new Corvette.

Nineteen-seventy was the last year of a real supercar in a Corvette body. The 454 V8 had an incredible 460 hp rating, the 350 was available in a high strung LT-1 version and there was a tremendous selection of powertrain combinations. In 1971 compression ratios got the ax, the LT-1 disappeared in '73 and the 454 was gone in 1975.

1969 Corvette Coupe

1954 Corvette

Corvette Was Chevy's Big Bid For Fifties Sports Car Market

By R. Perry Zavitz

"An American sports car, made of plastic, by Chevrolet? They've got to be kidding." So thought skeptical spectators at GM's 1953 Motorama.

Americans were showing signs of interest in sports cars by the early 1950s. Chevrolet sensed this trend, so took aim at that segment of the market with the Corvette. The experimental prototype was displayed at the '53 Motorama show, which toured the country.

In the following year, many new sporty models were introduced by Detroit firms. The Chevrolet Corvette went into production June 30, 1953 in Flint, Mich., almost concurrently with the Kaiser-Darrin fiberglass sports car in nearby Jackson.

Corvette production was soon transferred to St. Louis, Mo., where it has remained. The Jackson operation was only a trial production run, though the cars were not prototypes.

The Corvette was a two-passenger car on a 102-inch wheelbase. Although its styling was totally unlike the completely restyled '53 Chevrolet passenger models, the Corvette used many common mechanical components. The engine was the reliable old 235 cid, "stove bolt six," though much modified.

Compression ratio was raised to 8.0:1. Mechanical valve lifters were used, along with a different camshaft and valve timing. Three sidedraft Carter carburetors and dual exhausts aided breathing. The result was an output of 150 hp.—up 35 from normal. Early publicity claims of 160 hp. were over optimistic.

Price of the Corvette was $3,513, available in any color the buyer wanted, as long as it was white. Likewise, the buyer had a transmission choice of Powerglide—period. An automatic transmission as standard in a sports car turned off the purists.

Production of the 1953 Corvette amounted to only 300 units. Of those, only 61 percent had found buyers by the end of '53. The Corvette obviously got off to a very slow start—slow enough to kill a lesser make of car.

No changes were made to the Corvette for 1954, but production was stepped up to 3,640 cars for the model year. Black and blue were added to the color choices, but no compromise was made in the Powerglide-only transmission policy.

Chevrolet's Maurice Olley justified this stand in an October 1953 S.A.E. meeting, when he said: "As the sports car appeals to a wider and wider section of the public, the center of gravity of this theoretical individual is shifting from the austerity of pioneer towards the luxury of modern ideas." That was the truth, but not the whole truth. Potential buyers, who were determined to shift for themselves, were being discriminated against. By the end of 1954, only 83 percent of all Corvettes had been sold.

Few changes were made to Corvette's 1955 model, though some facelifting had been contemplated. Nine colors were made available, and the 6-cylinder engine output was increased to 155 hp. by some camshaft changes.

Chevrolet's new V-8 was optional in the Corvette. This engine, of 265 cid, came in three versions for the passenger models, but only the most potent was used in the Corvette. It produced 195 hp., compared to 162 in basic form.

Beginning in 1955, Corvette faced some native competition from Ford's Thunderbird. Although Ford very carefully avoided any reference to the T-bird as being a sports car, it was directly competitive with the Corvette. The Thunderbird came with only a V-8 motor rated about the same horsepower as the Corvette's, but the T-bird buyer had a three-way transmission choice: 3-speed manual, 3-speed manual with overdrive, and automatic. Base price for the Thunderbird was $2,944.

To combat the 'Bird, Corvette dropped its price to $2,934 for the V-8 equipped model. The 6 was $135 less. It is reported that very late in the season a 3-speed stick shift was made available, but only 25 were so equipped.

1956 Corvette

Corvette production was cut substantially—to just 700 for '55. By the end of that year, Corvette sales were catching up to a more acceptable percentage of production. The Thunderbird, on the other hand, was a runaway success. There were 16,155 produced for 1955. Not until the Corvette had four years under its belt did total production reach that volume.

So, for 1956, the Corvette underwent some needed changes. In its first styling facelift, the headlights were brought out of their screened hollows to a prominent position on the fender fronts. Bumperettes were revised and parking lights relocated. Longitudinal bulges appeared on either side of the hood.

On the sides, interest was added by a concave section outlined with chrome trim. Tail lights were changed, and the 1952 Ford style gave way to '49 Buick inspired signals. Newly designed wheel covers replaced the former ones, and remained through 1962. Eight colors were offered on the '56 Corvettes.

The 6-cylinder engine was replaced by the V-8, in two versions. Compression was raised to 9.25:1. With a single 4-bbl. carb, it developed 210 hp. Dual 4-bbl. carbs were optional, giving 225 hp.

Although the base price was raised to $3,149, two bucks less than the '56 T-bird, more options were available than before. The dual carb engine was $172.20. Thunderbird's detachable roof no doubt caused Corvette to offer one of its own, at a price of $218.50. A power operated mechanism for the cloth top was a $107.60 option which even raised and lowered the tonneau cover. Roll-up windows were standard for the first full model year.

Corvette production was up sharply to 3,467 in 1956, still a long way from the Thunderbird level.

Corvette continued its list of options for 1957 models. A 4-speed fully synchronized manual transmission was a $188 option made available in the spring of '57. The 3-speed manual and Powerglide automatic continued to be offered.

No less that five engine options dazzled the buyer. The basic block was bored ⅛-inch larger, yielding 283 cid.

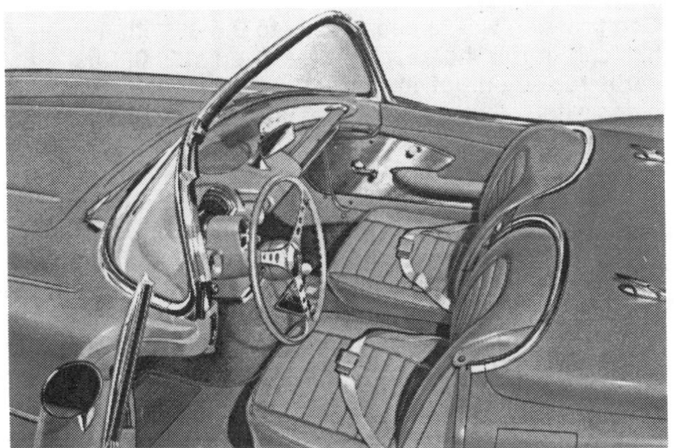

Cockpit of 1959 or 1960 Corvette. Powerglide transmission was standard, operated by a stick-like lever.

6,339 for '57, the highest up until then. Even so, it was much below Thunderbird production.

Road & Track tested Corvettes frequently. A glance at the car's performance over the years, compared with its contemporaries, is interesting.

The 6-cylinder Corvette of '54 produced times for 0-60 and ¼ mile accelerations of 11.0 and 18.0 seconds, respectively. A top speed of 106.4 mph. was reached. In 1953, Road & Track tested a Jaguar XK 120M. Its acceleration was 8.5 seconds for 0-60 and 16.7 for the ¼ mile standing start. Top speed was 120.8 mph. The Jaguar was clearly better, but Corvette was still very respectable for a neophyte.

The 1956 Corvettes were tested again by Road & Track, and some differences were noted. From 0 to 60 took 8.9 seconds. The ¼ mile remained at 16.5, but top speed jumped to 121.3 mph. with the 225 hp. engine and Powerglide. Quite a revelation was the test of another Corvette with 3-speed manual transmission, which went from 0 to 60 in just 7.3 seconds; the ¼ mile speed was up to 129.1 mph.

1958 Corvette

Compression was upped slightly to 9.5:1. With a single 4-bbl. carburetor, horsepower was rated at 220. Dual 4-bbl. carbs raised output to 245 hp. A special camshaft combined with the two carburetors shoved horsepower up to 270 in another version.

The Corvette's coup de grace for '57, however, was fuel injection. Two f.i. versions of the 283 V-8 were offered, rated at 250 and 283 hp, the latter with 10.5:1 compression. Chevrolet claimed this was the first time in automobile history that an engine developed one horsepower from each cubic inch of displacement.

Only 240 Corvettes were equipped with fuel injection during the '57 model run. Perhaps the $481 premium price explains part of the reason why more were not snapped up.

Very little styling change marked the 1957 Corvettes. The headlight rims were chrome, not painted as in '56. Six, two-toned color combinations were optional. Using the side hollows for the secondary color was a natural. Solid choices were down to six.

The base Corvette price for 1957 was $3,465, down two dollars from the year before. The T-bird price was down to $3,408. Corvette production was increased to

The 283 hp. fuel injected Corvette of 1957 was subjected to Road & Track's scrutiny with fantastic results. Zero to 60 time was 5.7 seconds, but the ¼ mile time was chopped to 14.3 seconds. Top speed was 132 mph. Those three respective figures compare closely to what Road & Track found that year in the Ferrari TRC, the Jaguar XK-SS, and the Lotus Mark XI, all of which were considerably more expensive than the fuel injected Corvette.

The Chevrolet Corvette was now established, with little reservation, as an American sports car. It had a disappointingly slow beginning. Some errors in policy were made at the start, though these were much clearer in retrospect than they were at the time. The Thunderbird hit the market target much better than the Corvette, but it helped the Corvette get on the right track.

In 1958, the best thing that happened to the Corvette was the four seater Thunderbird. Ford opted out of the sports car class, which they had never admitted they were in, and left Corvette to enjoy that field all to itself. Corvette, once on the right track, has pretty well stayed on course.

Corvette - A Break From Tradition

By Gerald Perschbacher

To look at it, it was thoroughly impractical. It could seat only two people, was available only as a convertible, and looked too European for the tastes of most American automobile buyers. Besides, it had a fiberglass body, and nobody knew what that really meant! Would it shatter? Could it be repaired? And with three carburetors, was it an economy car?

Back in 1953, these and other thoughts were racing through the minds of nearly everyone who owned or wanted to buy a Chevrolet. It was the Corvette that caused this soul-searching for it marked a break from tradition that has been a blessing for Chevrolet and General Motors to the present day.

Until the early 1950s, the Chevrolet was a good family car, a shopping companion and not a flashy chariot. Customizers tried to give a healthy transfusion of new ideas in styling and trim to old Chevrolets, and the young-at-heart buyer was intrigued with new ideas to spruce up Chevrolet's standard business suit.

So in 1953, the Corvette was born. It was a planned birth, dating back to the early years of the decade. The post-war market was tightening as buyers were few and products became bland. A new wave was needed, and in the Corvette Chevrolet moved in the direction of splashy styling and racy road power.

There probably have been as many books and articles printed on the subject of Corvettes as there have been units made. Why does the car continue to command a faithful following and grow in esteem? It all goes back to that break from tradition.

1961 Corvette

The standard Chevrolet passenger car of 1953 rode nicely, handled well, was more luxurious than past Chevrolets and was an all-around good vehicle for the money, which ranged from $1,524 for a three-passenger business coupe to $2,273 for an eight-passenger station wagon. But the Corvette was different.

It was for the dreamer, the driver who dared to be unconventional, who wanted to be set aside from the crowd, who laughed in the face of danger.

Or at least that's what many buyers thought—and nearly everyone from salesmen to corporate executives working for Chevrolet encouraged that type of thinking.

The Corvette broke one tradition and established another. First based on a 102-inch wheelbase in 1953 and carrying a 235 cubic inch engine, the car performed but was bigger on looks than on fire power. Only 300 were produced in that year in Flint, Michigan.

By 1954, production shifted to St. Louis, Mo., and the car received only minor improvements. About 80 per cent of those 1954 Corvettes were white, but that trend would change in succeeding years. A total of 3,640 1954 Corvettes were produced. That was good, especially for a two-year-old car that was a new concept aimed at a new market. But 1957 would prove to be the first really big year for the new venture.

The 1957 Corvette tore up the road with its 283 cubic inch engine, the biggest ever placed in a Corvette up to that time. Only about 43 of the total 6,339 Corvettes produced for 1957 had the special RPO 579 E fuel-injected engine which moved the snappy car from a stop to 60 miles per hour in 5.7 seconds and pushed the car up to the top speed of 132 miles per hour. From then on, all 168 inches of the car's length was viewed as pure power, a challenger that had become a champ.

Colors abounded for 1957 as Corvettes offered a two-tone exterior finish as a $19 accessory. Small luxuries were available, including radio, electric windows, hydraulic power-top, detachable hardtop, courtesy lights and parking brake alarm. That list of accessories would increase as Chevy made the Corvette its prize leader and crown prince.

Styling took a jump on the 1958 version, and refinements of that design continued up through the early 1960s.

For 1961, Corvettes came in seven exterior colors with two-tone paint available at $16.15. For the long-range driver, a 24-gallon fuel tank was available as an option. By 1961, just under 52 percent of all Corvettes came with a detachable accessory hardtop, and slightly over 64 percent had a four-speed manual transmission. Also 1961 was the last year that wide whitewall tires were offered on Corvettes. Another break with tradition!

With its fiberglass body and still riding on a 102-inch wheelbase, the 1961 version carried the 283 cubic inch power plant and was still a performer, although the emphasis for 1961 was more on looks. By then the factory price on the vehicle had reached $3,934, a modest increase over the original price in 1953 of $3,498.

Real American Sports Car Emerged In'53

By Wally Wyss

Mesh stone guards over headlights, triple side-draft Carter carburetors and Powerglides are only a few memorable features of early Corvettes.

The early 1950's were years of discovery for the naive American auto industry. Detroit's executives knew that, in far off lands, there were strange cars called "sports cars" but they weren't sure whether Detroit should, or could, build them.

So they compromised. Detroit started building sporty-*looking* cars to try and capture some of the hairy-chested devil-may-care image which somehow attached itself to drivers of cars like the MG-TC roadster from England.

The first results were cars like the Buick Skylark and Packard Caribbean. They were still two-ton, four-seater beasts, but Detroit claimed they were sports cars because they had wire wheels.

But the makings of a real sports car did emerge in 1953—the first Corvette. It was a two-seater built on a standard five-seater Chevy passenger car frame.

Originally, Chevrolet planned to manufacture their own bodies for the Corvette in a factory at Flint, Mich., but after producing 300 cars which came out rough-surfaced, they gave up and went to a boat-building firm in Ohio with more experience in fiberglass, Molded Fiber Glass Co.

The first Corvettes were quite plushy for a sports car; at least if you compare them to, say, an MG. The automatic transmission was standard, along with white-wall tires, a clock and a cigarette lighter. But, like the MG-TC owner, the Corvette owner had work ahead of him if he wanted to put up a side window. Because there were no roll-up windows, the car driver had to install plexiglass "side curtains" which were held in place by the convertible top.

The performance of the 1953 Corvette was not nearly as exciting as its styling would lead you to believe. The road testers of that era reported reaching 106 mph with a redline of 5500 rpm.

It always seems collectors are eager to buy the first or the last of a particular series, whether you're talking coins, stamps or cars. But the first Corvettes were literally thrown together in Flint and were not tight, well put together cars. The 1954 models, of which 3,640 were produced, came from the St. Louis plant and were better cars. The same body style was carried into 1955 with improvements like an optional stick shift and 265-cubic inch V8. But only 700 were sold that year. Why the drop in '55? Because arch-rival Ford had introduced the Thunderbird, a sleek two-seater with more plush conveniences even though it fit the definition of a sports car even less than did the Corvette.

What is it like to drive a 1953 Corvette? You open the door and slide inside on to a bench seat trimmed to look like two bucket seats. The gearshift lever is on the floor, small and out of the way. It looks like the decision to put it on the floor was an afterthought.The speedometer is large but the other gauges are almost minuscule by comparison and you must squint to read them.

Part of the Corvette's handling problem is it was set up to "understeer," which is a sports car driver's term for "unresponsive." Some foreign cars "oversteer" meaning, when you turn the steering just a bit, the car over-reacts. In most American cars, it is the opposite. You have to turn the wheel a lot to make the car change direction a little.

A 1953 Chevy ad claimed the 2800-lb. Corvette "whistled through curves as though it were running on rails." This was no small exaggeration. It wasn't until 1960—using the same basic chassis—that Chevrolet Engineering actually began to offer some anti-roll bars and springs that would make the Corvette a car with "sports car handling."

It was in 1956, when Zora Arkus—Duntov, an engineer who had actually raced at LeMans, joined GM, that the Corvette started to become a sports car. Duntov set to work on its suspension and engine. Within a year, Corvettes were beating Mercedes 300SL's and Jaguars in the U.S.

1954 Corvette vs.Bel Air sedan: family feud?

By Robert C. Ackerson

Although Chevrolet introduced the Corvette in mid-1953, it wasn't until 1954 that they were available in any significant numbers. Even then, the possibility of seeing a Corvette on the road was remote, for only 3,640 were assembled during 1954.

No doubt there were plenty of new car buyers who, after imagining just how much fun it would be to own a car that could knock the neighbor's socks off, came back down to earth and did what about a million other Americans did each year—purchased a new Chevrolet sedan.

But there almost always was a time, perhaps when the salesman was busy drawing up the sales contract, when the customer took one final, longing look at that polo white Corvette positioned among the mundane Chevrolet sedans and wagons, and wished that *it* was the car he was going to make payments on for the next three years.

In reality there weren't many new car buyers who seriously contemplated choosing between a Chevrolet sedan and a Corvette. But with comparison tests all the rage nowadays, the possibility that a customer might have engaged in this sort of activity is intriguing. To begin with, the sedan would score a win over the Corvette in terms of price. The top-of-the-line Bel Air listed for $1,884. At $3,523, the Corvette's starting price was nearly twice as much.

Both cars used the same basic engine that had served Chevrolet since 1937. At that time, the original Chevrolet six-cylinder (of 1929) was redesigned via a four main bearing crankshaft and a new bore and stroke. John Bond, writing in *Road & Track* for June 1954 wasn't exactly telling the world much that it didn't already know, when he noted that this engine "though not exciting or dramatic has stood the test of time."

When used in most 1954 Chevrolet passenger cars, the engine was offered in two forms. One with 115 hp was intended for cars with manual transmissions. The second version, with 125 hp, was used in conjunction with Powerglide. But the Corvette's version was different. The use of three Carter one-barrel carburetors and a boost in the compresion ratio from 7.5:1 to 8.00:1 raised the horsepower to 150. The only available transmission for the Corvette was Powerglide.

1954 Chevrolet Two-Ten two-door

1954 Corvette

By virtue of its 2,850 pound curb weight, Corvette enjoyed a significant weight advantage over the Bel Air, which weighed nearly 3,500 pounds. Translated into power-to-weight ratios, this gave the Corvette a respectable 19:1 rating. By comparison each of the Bel Air's 125 horsepower had to haul 28 pounds. This gave the Corvette a performance edge over the full-sized Chevrolets.

No contemporary road test of a manual transmission Bel Air was published, but a reasonable rule of thumb was that a 115 hp stick shift Chevrolet would beat a Powerglide rival from zero to 60 mph by about 2 seconds. This didn't make it one of America's hot cars by a long shot, but it's worth keeping in mind that a Chevrolet finished first in the small stock car class in the 1953 Carrera Panamericana road race. Furthermore, older models were driven by the likes of Juan Fangio to numerous victories in the rough and tumble world of South American road racing.

Contrary to what many cynics hoped, the Corvette possessed excellent handling characteristics. For example, *Road & Track*, which was seldom inclined to deal kindly with American automobiles, noted in its June 1954 road test that the Corvette demonstrated a "really good combination of riding and handling qualities." Since Corvette used many of the sedan's suspension components, it was no surprise that Griff Borgeson reported in his road test of a new Bel Air (*Motor Life*, April 1954) that "the car behaved very properly in cornering tests and was well suited to the broad limits of 'transportation' motoring.

In terms of appearance the Corvette obviously was the winner. In its first report on the new Corvette (June 5, 1953) *The Autocar* noted: "Contrasted with the normal Chevrolet saloon, the new Corvette has an engaging appearance." But the 1954 Chevrolet, if admittedly just a tad staid looking, was well proportioned and certainly not an unattractive automobile.

Incidentally, the press photo used by *The Autocar* displayed a pre-producton Corvette alongside a stock 1953 Bel Air sedan. Later, for a very early Corvette sales folder, the same photo was retouched to depict a 1954 sedan and a production Corvette.

If the sedan came off second best in most wheel to wheel comparisons with the Corvette, it came away the winner in two categories. The first was trivial—there was only a single Corvette model available in just a single body color (polo white) and interior (sportsman red), the full-sized Chevrolet was available in 161 different combinations of colors and body styles. More importantly, total Corvette output was only 3,640 while 1954 model year Chevrolet passenger car sales amounted to 1,151,486. That was a ratio of over 316:1 in favor of the standard Chevrolet, a pretty good performance by any measure.

Elusive Encore: The 1955 Corvette

1953-'54 Corvette

By Robert C. Ackerson

When it was a new vehicle, the 1955 Corvette was somewhat of an embarrassment to Chevrolet. This wasn't because it was a bad automobile. It was because Chevrolet wasn't accustomed to losing, and when the sales were tallied up for 1955, the Corvette was a BIG loser to the Thunderbird in their highly publicized production race.

The results showed 16,155 Thunderbirds produced compared to just 700 Corvettes. This was a humiliation of the first degree for Chevrolet, and for many years it also cast a shadow over the 1955 Corvette. The awareness, a few years back, that the supply of 1955 Corvettes was extremely limited drove their prices sky high. That phenomenon in turn made it even more difficult to evaluate those Corvettes strictly on their merits as sports cars of the mid-fifties.

Viewed from that perspective, the Corvette was a curious mixture of design features that illustrated both Chevrolet's naive view of what it was that sports car buyers were looking for and its ability to learn very quickly.

The greatest single error Chevrolet had made in the design of the 1953-54 Corvette had been the decision to make Powerglide the only transmission available. Actually, the performance of the two-speed automobile wasn't that bad, but for a new generation of Americans who were eager for the precise control and the subtle social status a stick shift provided, the Powerglide Corvette was out of the action. Chevrolet made the first, hesitant step in their direction in 1955 by offering the Corvette with an optional three-speed manual transmission. Less objectional, and not to be remedied until 1956, was the Corvette's indifferent weather protection.

Ironically, the area where the Corvette really wasn't terribly outclassed was where it was most dramatically improved for 1955. This was due of course to the offering of Chevrolet's sensational new V-8 engine as a Corvette option for a reasonable $135. At the same time, the Corvette's standard Blue Flame six was boosted to 155 hp at 4200 rpm, but this modest increase generated little interest for obvious reasons. The 265 cid V-8 was rated at 195 horsepower at 4600 rpm and 260 lb./ft. of torque at 2800 rpm. This substantial power advantage over the six-cylinder engine didn't bring with it any weight penalty. Instead, the V-8 actually weighed about 40 pounds less than the six.

The net result was a Corvette that had to be ranked among the fastest accelerating production cars then available. Contemporary test results indicated that a Powerglide Corvette could reach 60 mph from rest in the 8.5 to 9.1 second range.

The Corvette's major weaknesses that were still to be found in the 1955 model that prevented it from being a full fledged competitor in sports car racing were its slow 3¾ turn's lock to lock steering, weak brakes (for racing use) and lack of a four-speed gear box. On the plus side (besides its V-8 engine) were its excellent handling, reliability and high speed stability.

Within a year, the pieces would be in place to put these assets to good use. Top ranked drivers such as Dick Thompson would be driving Corvettes to major victories, a factory team would perform with honor at the 12-hour Sebring race, and slowly but surely, Corvette sales would start on the upswing.

But playing an important role as a bridge to those successes was the 1955 Corvette. If the original Corvette was the "first of the dream cars to come true," then the 1955 Corvette was the first of the Corvettes whose performance really attracted the attention of the sports car world.

SPECIFICATIONS: 1955 Corvette

List price	$2,934
Wheelbase	102 inches
Tread	57 inches (front), 59 inches (rear)
Tires	6.70-15
Length	167 inches
Weight	2,705 pounds
Engine	six-cylinder, overhead valves
BxS	3.56 inches x 3.93 inches
Displacement	235.5 cubic inches
Compression ratio	8.0:1
Horsepower	155 @4200 rpm
Optional engine	eight-cylinder, overhead valves manual optional
Number One Value	$45,000 (six-cylinder) $50,000 (V-8)

'57 Vettes
Are The Ones To Have

By Wally Wyss

1957 Corvette

Somehow the year 1957 is a magic one to the American car enthusiasts. That was the year Ford put tailfins on the T-bird. That was the year Cadillac put the stainless steel roof on the Brougham. And it was the last year of single headlights across the board, for already Detroit was girding its loins for that Technological Marvel, quad headlamps.

Maybe that's what makes the 1957 Corvette worth a bunch more than the '58 through '62 models which followed it. Then, too, the '57 was the first Corvette to feature fuel injection.

The '56, which had the identical styling, hadn't exactly been a slouch. It had a 265-cubic inch engine, with a four barrel as standard equipment, rated at 210 hp at 5200 rpm. If you were a "hot shoe", you ordered the Power Pack which gave you a different manifold carrying twin Carter four barrels ("twin pots" or "dual quads" in 50's slang) and a rating of 225 bhp at 5,200 rpm. Unfortunately, in '56, you could only order a two speed "slushbox" (50's slang for the Powerglide) or the 3-speed manual shift. It wasn't until 1957 that a true four speed transmission was available for the Corvette and it made a world of difference. Ford countered by offering overdrive on their T-Bird as an option, but it just didn't have the same magic as "four on the floor."

The styling of the 1956 and 1957 Corvettes was considerably slicked up from the earlier 1953-'55 Corvettes but still a bit space-age and Buck Rogerish, especially around the rocket-style exhausts and with the phony scoops atop the fenders. The dashboard was a half-hearted attempt at a real racing car layout but the gauges were only the size of half-dollars and designed to reflect the sun in your eyes.

There weren't as many Corvette options back then, but if you were bucks-up, you ordered the power-operated fabric top, and then laid out another $215 for the lift-off fiberglass hardtop.

The '57 Corvette's fuel injection was the brainchild of a Russian engineer named Zora Arkus-Duntov who, just after WW II, had invented the Ardun head for flathead Fords—a device which greatly added to the engine's power without compromising reliability. Dr. Dick Thompson, a Washington D.C. dentist, and noted amateur race driver, was hired to run the development tests of the "fuelie" Vette in the winter of 1956. The goal was to make a package that had instant response with no bogging down in the corners.

The unit was somewhat delayed in getting into production but when it made it to market in the new 283-cubic inch version, there were two fuel-injected options to choose from. The first was on a hydraulic-liftered engine with a mild 9.5:1 compression ratio which was rated at 250 bhp at 5,000 rpm. The second was on a solid-liftered engine with a higher 10.5:1 compression ratio and a high-lift "Duntov" cam. That was rated at 283 hp at 6,200 rpm. The ads made much of the "one horsepower per cubic inch" figure. Back in those days, Detroit auto-makers advertised horsepower with undisguised glee. Ford retaliated by building a limited edition of Thunderbirds with Paxton-McCullough superchargers but the blown Birds were stuck with an Achilles heel—brakes that couldn't stop the 135-mph beast once it got going full tilt.

Chevrolet had been working on the handling of the Corvette since '56, when they discovered that, according to Dr. Thompson "the only way to make this car handle is to make the springs so stiff it slides like a go-kart." Chevy made a racing suspension and cerametallic brakes available to racers and private owners which soon put the T—Birds on the trailers. Ford was more than happy to abandon the 2-seater T-Bird in '58—it was obvious Chevy had built a sports car that did a better job on the racetrack.

The value of the '56 and '57 Corvettes have risen as collectors have realized how relatively rare they are. There were just 3,467 Corvettes built for '56 and only 6,339 units built for '57. That's an aggregate total of under 10,000. The fuel injected Corvette is the prize.

The '58 and later Corvettes offered more power out of the fuel injection than the '57 unit, but few more luxury options. The handling was even improved, so that by 1962, the last of the solid-axled Corvettes (the '63 Stingrays pioneered independent rear suspension on the Corvette) handled very well for a car that had started out unpretentiously in 1953 as an overstyled and underpowered American answer to the European sports car.

But nostalgia fans aren't all that interested in technical improvements. To them the year 1957 is one to remember—the first year they saw a fuel injected Corvette blow the doors off the fastest car in town. Who cares what they came out with later?

283-cu. in. Fuel Injection Engine

Whatever Became of

Route 66

By Alan Mende

At the outset let me say that I am not a Corvette owner. But like any normal American male who grew up during the Fifties and Sixties, I have always wanted one. However, when it comes to basic transportation, a Corvette just does not fit into the picture. So I have always had to settle for looking and longing.

I guess my first real exposure to the Corvette came from watching "Route 66" on television. Oh sure, I saw Vettes on the road, but in 1960, spotting one of those fiberglass dreams tooling down the asphalt was, at best, a sometimes thing. Once a week, though, I could tune in CBS and watch Buzz Murdock and Todd Stiles as they drove across the U.S.A. stopping only long enough in the one horse towns to solve everyone's problems. With no visible means of support other than being employed for sixty minutes (I guess they worked during commercials) at the feed mill or lumber yard, Buzz and Todd always managed to have a new Corvette at the start of the Fall TV season. I watched "Route 66" religiously and at night in my dreams I would be the hero in the crimson two-seater putting things right while the Nelson Riddle theme music filled my ears.

My father watched "Route 66" also and once, in passing, he mentioned that he'd like to own a Corvette. My heart bounded into my throat. Maybe someday he'd spring for one of those sleek beauties and my dreams would come true. In 1963 my father changed jobs and figured that parking his 1950 Chevy in the executive parking lot would cause adverse comment. So he went shopping for a new car, with the entire family coming along to "help" him. First stop was the Chevrolet dealer where I hoped I could steer him to the new Sting Ray that I'd heard about but had not yet seen. There it was sitting in the center of the showroom floor. The radical styling changes were almost too much for my adolescent heart. After years of watching "Route 66"'s protagonists drive virtually unchanged Vettes, it seemed to me that the Sting Ray had compromised the Corvette ideal. But the September season premier found Buzz and Todd driving a Sting Ray, and soon, in my dreams, I was driving one, too. My ever practical father, however, bought a new Pontiac sedan. After all, a family of six can't find adventure along Route 66 in a two-seat Vette.

"Route 66" did not spark my father's fantasies, but it certainly did mine. It also taught me a few things: owning a red convertible Corvette spontaneously imparted deep wisdom and boundless eloquence. Along with that went the solemn responsibilities of rehabilitating the disabled Vietnam advisor (remember them?) and saving a beautiful Iowa farm girl from whatever the script writers could image. Owning that Corvette made you a knight errant and obliged you to bask in the adoration of the yokels (who were driving Edsels and clapped out DeSotos). Sometime later I learned that Hollywood and the real world were two very different places.

The real world was populated with people like my rich college buddy, Ed, who in 1971 and '72, commuted to classes in a turquoise '57 Vette with factory installed fuel injection. He gave me a ride in it once. It was during a long break between afternoon classes. We put the Corvette on. You don't sit in a car like this; like a fine suit of clothes, you wear a '57 Corvette. That turquoise jewel was the reality that spawned my childhood dreams. From the moment I took my place in the righthand seat, the theme music of "Route 66" welled from the very depths of my memory, violins stroking out the melody while the piano played the counterpoint. For a few short moments I was Todd Stiles. As I turned myself into the low rumble of the brute under the hood, Ed complained of how the hardtop leaked when it rained. The cold wind of reality easily blew away the mists of my reverie. But he talked of selling the car because he was restoring a '54 Vette at home and he had just bought a '71 coupe. Of course, the dream of ownership was to remain just out of my reach. I could put myself through college or own a Corvette. Sometimes I still wonder if I made the right decision.

A few years later while working at my first real job, I met up with another Corvette owner. His name was Dave, but everyone called him Mad Dog. He too, had a 1971 coupe. I don't know what it had under the hood, but it was FAST. Every day at five he would leave the parking lot in, literally, a blaze of glory, engine roaring, tires screaming and smoking up a storm. This was not a car from a Route 66 dream, but the product of a nightmare, a black-blooded

1961 Corvette

fiend devouring everything in its path.

A few times a week when my wife's lunch break coincided with my own, I'd walk uptown to meet her. One particular lunch hour will always remain etched in my mind, the day Mad Dog offered to drive me to my rendezvous. It was four traffic-congested blocks along Main Street and normally I could reach my destination faster on foot. But for me, a ride in a Corvette is not to be turned down. Once inside this fiberglass artillery shell, Mad Dog switched on the ignition and the radio blared to life. Acid rock. Nothing Nelson Riddle about this machine. Half a second after he fired up the beast, we rocketed away from the curb. I swear we pulled 3 G's of acceleration. If we didn't, the passenger seat had to have been upholstered with silly putty. It wasn't the acceleration that got to me, although my stomach did remain glued to my spine for a few hours afterward. What got to me was sitting with my rear end about three inches off the pavement and weaving through midday Main Street traffic at what must have been 90 miles an hour. That's what turned my legs to jelly and boggled my mind. Buzz would never have done that to Todd. Rolling out of the snorting Vette, I thanked Mad Dog but I couldn't remember for what. As I wobbled into my wife's office, she looked at the clock (it showed 12:01) and said, "What did you do, fly?"

It has been years since CBS, or any other network for that matter, broadcast reruns of "Route 66." Whatever became of those two eloquent men who piloted their Corvette across America from one adventure to another? Buzz changed his name and got a job driving a Los Angeles police car for NBC. He started talking like Jack Webb. Todd just dropped out of sight. He's probably married with a family, a cat, a dog, and a mortgage. He probably drives a four door sedan. He may even write for *Old Cars Weekly* under an assumed name. But late at night when he dreams, it's 1960 and he's a hero once more in a crimson Corvette.

1962 Corvette

The End Of The Beginning

By Robert C. Ackerson

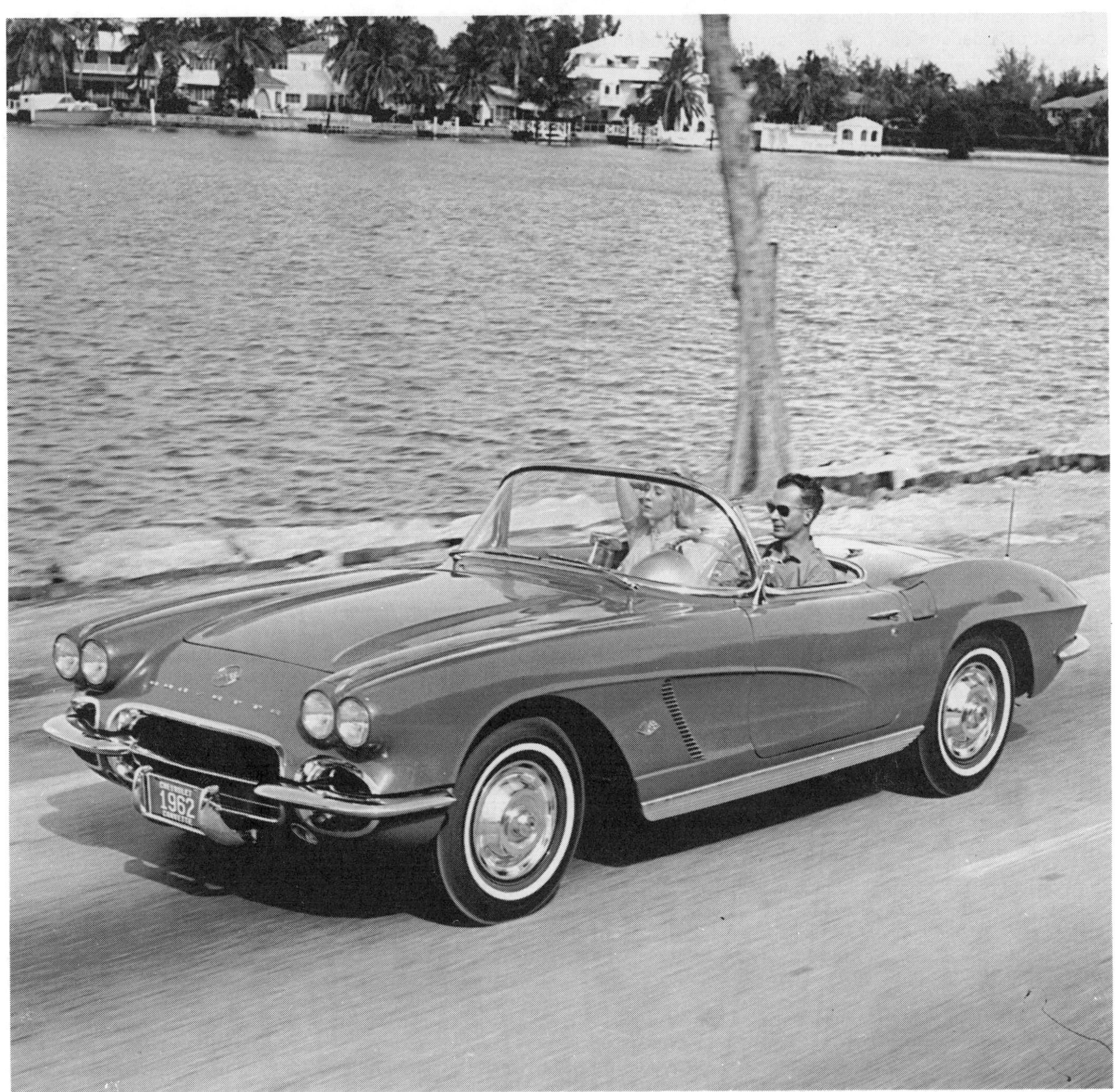

1962 Corvette.

The introduction of the 1962 Corvette marked the conclusion of a decade of Corvette history whose beginning had been all but forgotten in the frenzy of explosive V-8 power, seductive styling and a string of SCCA National Championships.

All told, Corvette production from 1953 through 1961 totaled 54,484. An impressive number, perhaps, by European standards, but only the equivilent of two weeks output of full-size Chevrolets. But numbers were a poor measurement of the Corvette's status among American automobiles.

After it shook off the dead hand of the past manifested by the old Chevrolet six-cylinder engine and the two-speed Powerglide automatic transmission, the Corvette blossomed into a sensationally performing sports car, capable of defeating the Jaguar XK140 and Mercedes-Benz 300SL models.

But if the Corvette earned respect from sports car fans who had previously considered the products from Coventry and Stuttgart as all-conquering, it was still regarded as an American primitive whenever suspension systems were discussed.

The Corvette, in terms of performance, was something of a paradox. It possessed a first-rate powertrain but its undercarriage, with Hotchkiss drive, was based upon the design introduced on the 1949 Chevrolet. No wonder then that in 1962 Zora-Arkus Duntov remarked that the Corvette would not be receiving a more powerful engine until it adopted an up-to-date chassis/suspension.

From this perspective, influenced by the revolutionary 1963 Sting Ray, the 1962 Corvette might be seen as some sort of automotive dinosaur on the verge of extinction. But this view was sadly out of focus.

While the Corvette's solid rear axle wasn't exactly world-class in either design or concept, it was only under extreme conditions that its rather prosaic heritage became obvious. Also remember that the vast majority of foreign sports cars similarly used solid rear axles and other components from mass-produced sedans.

A more accurate perspective of the last of the first generation Corvettes is of an automobile whose performance exceeded the sum total of its parts; a vehicle that, if of humble origin, had evolved into a sports car, both potent and handsome, that on any performance scale was outranked by only the world's most expensive automobiles.

Although styling changes were modest, it was easy, even at first glance, to spot a 1962 Corvette. Viewed from the front, its identity was confirmed by a black-painted grille, which replaced the bright-finished version used in 1961. Not as obvious was a revised crossed flag emblem positioned on the hood and side fender cove. In profile, new-for-1962 styling elements included a wide chrome rocker panel, the removal of the chrome fender cove outline and the use of a finely textured fender grille.

But the most significant development was the use of a larger 327 cubic inch V-8. Although based on the 283 cubic inch V-8 adopted in 1957, only the connecting rods were interchangeable between the two engines. Coinciding with the use of this engine was a revamping of the Corvette's engine lineup, which now consisted of four rather than five choices as in 1961. No longer offered was an engine combining the Rochester fuel injection system with a mild street cam. Also a casualty of progress was the dual four-barrel option for the Corvette. The elimination of this induction system ended a string of such Corvette engines that extended back to 1956.

The standard transmission for the Corvette continued to be a three-speed manual unit. Two sets of gear ratios were offered for the optional Warner four-speed transmission. Corvettes with either the 250 hp or 300 hp engines used a wide-ratio set up with a 2.54:1 low gear. This was the same gearing as used on the full-sized Chevrolets. The standard rear axle ratio for Corvettes with this engine/transmission combination was 3.36:1. But for excellent acceleration Chevrolet recommended a 3.08:1 ratio which was offered as RPO 203.

The two top power-rated engines continued to be offered with the close ratio gearbox with a 2.20:1 first gear. However, Chevrolet did offer all four engines with either four-speed transmission on special order. Only Corvettes powered by the base engine or the 300 hp engine were available with the two-speed Powerglide automatic transmission.

Most car buffs of this age were attracted to the 360 hp Corvette due to its stirring performance. After all, it was capable of zero to 60 mph runs in less than six seconds in conjunction with standing-start quarter-mile runs of 14.2 seconds at nearly 103 mph. But the mild mannered 250 hp Powerglide Corvette was no slouch either, moving from zero to 60 mph in 8.8 seconds and attaining quarter-mile times of 16.8 seconds.

The 1962 Corvette's attributes seemed to suit its fans who saw to it that a new Corvette production mark of 14,531 was established. The arrival of the first Sting Ray inaugurated a new era of Corvette history, highlighted by independent rear suspension, four wheel disc brakes and engines as large as 454-cubic inches.

Unfortunately, the growing sophistication of the Corvette, which continues today, was paralleled by a steady rise of Corvette prices that gradually moved it beyond the reach of many of its earliest fans and owners.

Corvette Introduces the

Sting Ray

By R. Perry Zavitz

Convincing enthusiasts that the 1953 Corvette was a serious attempt to break into the sports car field was begun rather feebly by Chevrolet.

This plastic car came with a sluggish transmission connected to Chevy's old stove-bolt six (albeit souped up to near Jaguar power levels). The $3,513 price was two-thirds more than the popular MG. Just 300 Corvettes were made, which also cast the manufacturer's seriousness in doubt.

It returned for 1954, but with no noticeable changes. At

1963 Corvette Convertible

that time, how could the largest division of the world's biggest carmaker dare offer a 1954 model looking like a '53? Even the 1955 models appeared virtually unchanged, with one significant exception. Chevrolet now had a V-8 engine available in any of its models. The most potent 195 hp version was offered in the Corvette. That provided better performance, but the slushy Powerglide transmission was still mandatory.

Slowly, the idea that Chevrolet had something worthy of a little consideration for the sports car enthusiast was beginning to sink in. By 1956, a three-speed manual transmission was available. That cleared the way for more enthusiasts to think of the Corvette as a border-line sports car. Also, the six-cylinder engine was discarded and very powerful V-8 options were made available.

By 1958, whether or not they liked the Corvette, sports car purists had to recognize it as a home-grown sports car. But that was half a decade after its introduction. It may not have achieved its due recognition that soon if the Ford had continued doing what so many people wanted—the continuation of the two-seat Thunderbird. The four-seat Thunderbird was the best thing that ever happened to the Corvette in its early years.

Now that the Corvette had no domestic competition in its class, it was able to comfortably make many changes that were hardly viable before. Minor styling changes

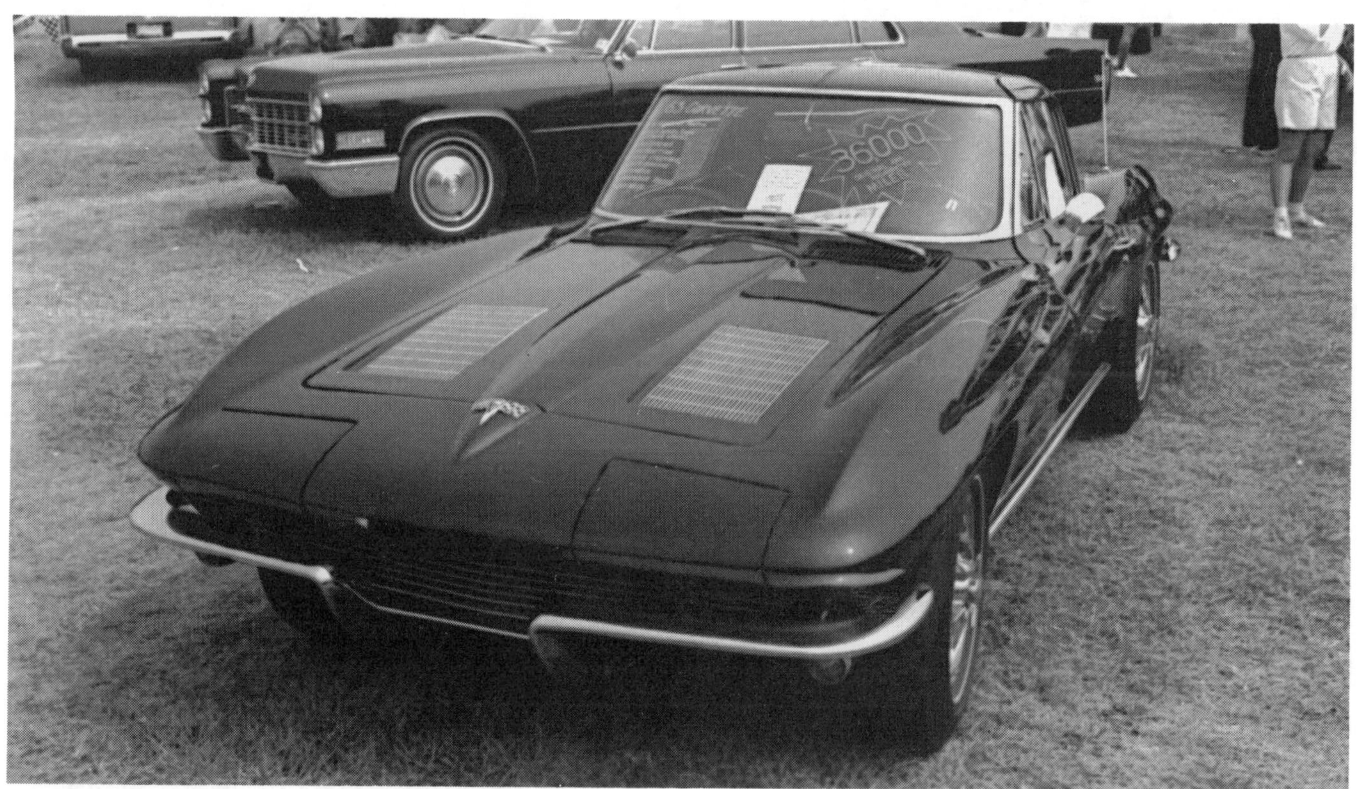

were made each model year, yet the original 1953 shape remained evident. It lasted for 10 model years, which must have set some sort of American record for the post-Model T era.

More and higher powered engine-options were offered in the Corvette. Most were the same as available in Chevrolet passenger cars, but some with the greatest horsepower were obtainable only under the fiberglass hood of the Corvette.

The 10th anniversary Corvette was introduced with a totally new body—well, 97 percent new. The lower edge of the rear was a carry-over from the 1961-'62 Corvettes. But the rest was new. Styling was largely based on a one-off Corvette experimental car of the late 1950s called the Sting Ray. The 1963 Corvette, also called Sting Ray, offered two body styles for the first time. Instead of just a roadster or convertible, a coupe was available as well. There was an auxiliary ($237) hardtop available for it. It was the coupe that caught the attention of many people.

New as the body was, it revived some extinct styling features. The long sloping back had been popular from the late 1930s to the early 1950s. The Corvette resurrected that shape, which became known as the fastback, and it has remained more or less over the last quarter century.

An odd feature the Corvette revived was hidden headlights. The only cars that used them before were the 1936-'37 Cord and the 1942 DeSoto. Since the Corvette adopted hidden headlights in 1963, they have also made scattered appearances to the present time. But the Corvette added two new twists to this idea. They were power operated. They were also the first dual headlights to be hidden.

The 1963 Corvette body had one more characteristic that had appeared earler. The trunk, or stowage area, had no exterior access. In other words, no trunk lid. This was a feature of some early slope-backed cars in the mid-1930s. The last example was probably the 1951 Henry J.

The mention of these previous features is not intended to degrade the 1963 Corvette at all. The coupe was a stunning car, and carried all these features exremely well. It was both individualistic and up-to-date looking.

The fast-back coupe, with its split window, is usually what we first think of when the 1963 Corvette is mentioned. There were 10,594 of them made. Actually, it was slightly out-produced by the 10,919 convertibles. Seldom thought of, outside the ranks of Corvette owners, is the convertible with the option hardtop in place. Its notchback appearance is a bit unusual for a Corvette of this time.

Power for the 1963 Corvette came from a choice of four 327 cid engines. The standard motor was rated at 250 hp. Optional were 300 and 340 hp editions, costing $54 and $108 extra, respectively. All these had four-barrel carburetion. Most powerful, for $431 extra, was a 360 hp fuel-injected engine.

Three-speed manual transmission was standard regardless of engine. A four-speed was optional with any engine. Powerglide was available only with the two least potent power plants.

By now, sports car devotees were more inclined to accept some luxury that previously was considered sacrilege in a sports car. Chevrolet, ever eager to meet those demands, if not aggressively encourage their installation, offered power brakes ($43), power steering ($75), power windows ($59), tinted windows ($16), AM-FM radio ($174), and even air conditioning ($422). But the purist was more interested in the heater/defroster deletion ($100 credit), Posi-Traction rear axle ($43), sintered metallic brakes ($38), four-speed transmission ($188), cast aluminum knock-off wheels ($323), and even the 36-gallon fuel tank ($202).

While production was increasing to meet the ever growing Corvette demand, 1963 model production shattered all previous records. There were 21,513 coupes and convertibles built—a jump of nearly 50 percent over 1962.

This second generation Corvette lasted only four model years, in contrast to the first generation's 10. Yet in those four years, over 95,000 Corvettes were built—an increase of 38 percent over the first 10 years. The Corvette's shaky beginning was a thing of the past. No longer were people wondering if its history would be measured in months. It was now judged in generations. Is there any other car in American automotive history that has survived 37 years of economic boom and bust, yet remained faithful to its original concept as closely as Corvette?

1963 Corvette Sting Ray Specifications

Engine type	V-8
Bore	4.00 in.
Stroke	3.25 in.
Displacement	327 cu. in.
Compression	10.5:1
Horsepower @R.P.M.	250 @ 4400
Horsepower per cu. in.	0.77
Torque (ft/lbs) @ rpm	350 @ 2800
Rear axle ratio	3.36:1
Overall length	175.3 in.
Overall width	69.6 in.
Overall height (coupe/conv)	49.8 in.
Overall height (conv/hdtp)	49.3 in.
Wheelbase	98 in.
Tread	56.3 in. (front)
	57.0 (rear)
Weight	2859 lbs. (coupe)
	2881 lbs. (conv)
Tire Size	6.70 X 15
Original base price	$4,037 (conv.)
	$4,252 (coupe)
Current No. 1 Value	$47,000 (conv.)
	$42,000 (coupe)

1963 Corvette "Splits"

Corvette for '65 Offered The Best of Everything

By Tony Hossain

The 1965 Corvette Sting Ray fastback was beautiful refinement of impressive '63 design. Highlight was addition of four-wheel disc brakes and big-block V8.

Traditional roadster outsold coupe in '65. This was the last year Corvette buyer could check off Ramjet Fuel-Injection on the order form. The injected 327 was good for 375 horsepower.

There are many who consider the 1963-1967 Sting Rays the best of the Corvettes. They have the sophisticated suspension design that the earlier Corvettes lack and they aren't burdened with the excess weight of the post-1967 Shark-inspired design. The Sting Rays are, in a word, classic.

If the Sting Rays are the best of the Corvettes, quite possibly the 1965 model is the best of the Sting Rays. It is, most assuredly, a memorable Corvette.

Refinement was the key word again in 1965. The '64 Vette offered as improvements a higher horsepower fuelie engine option, smoother ride and better insulation. But the best was saved for 1965. The big news in '65 was the addition of four-wheel disc brakes as standard equipment. The small-block 'Vettes could always go. Now they could stop!

Styling changes were held to a minimum although Corvette enthusiasts would immediately spot a new one by the functional front fender louvers, new wheel covers and a restyled grille. With no depressions or trim, the 1965 hood was not interchangeable with the 1963 or '64 unit. The model range again included a choice of convertible or sleek fastback coupe. Sales reached a record 23,562, including 15,376 converts.

Corvette continued as Chevy's prestige leader and the inside story was a decidedly plush one in '65. Newly styled bucket seats were offered and genuine leather seating surfaces were optional. Options few European sports cars could match included power steering, power brakes, power windows, air conditioning, AM-FM radio, telescopic steering column and a wood-rimmed steering wheel.

But the performance enthusiast was usually drawn first to the engine/powertrain spec sheet. Standard equipment, and meant for the boulevardiers, was Chevy's tried and true 250 horsepower 327 cubic inch Turbo-Fire V8. Next step up was a 300 hp version of the 327 and new for '65 was the precursor to the famous LT-1. This 327 developed an impressive 350 horsepower, combining "sizzle with calm, cool behavior." Up next was the most powerful carbureted 327, putting out 365 advertised horsepower.

A legend since 1957, Ramjet Fuel-Injection made its final appearance in 1965. At $538, fuel injection was a very expensive option but it made the 327 V8 a 375 hp world class stormer. It was the ultimate small-block.

The introduction, in April 1965, of the 396 cubic inch big block V8 marked the beginning of a new era for the Corvette. The 396 was introduced concurrently in the full-size Chevrolet, in the Corvette and in the Chevelle. Rated at 425 hp and priced at only $292.70, the 396 made the FI Corvette seem superfluous in those days of cheap, high octane gasoline. Three ninety-six Corvettes could be immediately identified by the "power bulge" on the hood. Introduced at the same time as the 396 were new side-mounted exhausts, a $134.50 option.

Although the FI Corvette remained available through the end of the 1965 model year, it was not widely available and was quietly dropped when the '66s made their appearance. Interestingly, 1965 was also the only year of the 396 'Vette. In '66 that engine was bored out to 427 awesome cubic inches.

Nineteen sixty-five was a vintage, memorable year for Corvette. It was the only year you could buy a fuel-injected, disc-braked Sting Ray. It was the first year for the big block and side-mounted exhausts.

And with prices starting at $4,106, the 1965 Corvette Sting Ray was quite a bargain.

Billy Mitchell's Stylish Sting Ray

By Rich Taylor

When Bill Mitchell took over GM Styling from Harley Earl in December of 1958, he wanted to put his own stamp on things, naturally enough. But on the other hand, he didn't want to move *too* quickly and antagonize GM corporate or any of Earl's legion of supporters within the company, many of whom would love to have seen Mitchell fall on his butt. Harley Earl, though, was a clever old coach and he hadn't picked Mitchell as a successor for nothing. Mitchell flat outsmarted his detractors, just as Earl knew he would. He called an end run around GM corporate that left his critics panting far behind, and the field wide open for a game-winning score. Mitchell's play was called the Sting Ray, and it's one of the great, all time maneuvers.

Bill Mitchell personally "bought" the chassis of the Corvette Sebring SS practice car. This "mule" was basically identical to the ill-fated SS that raced a handful of iaps at Sebring in 1957 before expiring from terminal ineptitude. Mitchell's brilliant young assistant, Larry Shinoda, helped him design an all-new fiberglass body for the tired SS chassis, one that had a completely unique look about it. It borrowed nothing from the Sebring SS, nor even from the wild one-off SR-2 racer that Mitchell had styled for himself in 1956. No, the Sting Ray, as they called it, was totally new. It had an extremely high belt line from nose to tail, with wide protruding fenders, a small headrest and a full-width grille. Shinoda's concept was that of an airfoil upside down, theoretically for better roadholding. It was dramatic, different and somehow, unlike the SS, extremely modern without being silly.

Mitchell got John Fitch and later Dick Thompson to race the Sting Ray for him. It was ostensibly a private racing team, though it *was* maintained by Ed Zalucki and Dean

1956 SR2

1967 Corvette

Bedford from Corvette Engineering and Ken Eschelbach from Mitchell's own design staff. Zora Duntov, the doyen of Corvette racing, thought the whole project was beneath ridicule, and pointedly avoided doing much at all on Mitchell's new toy. But no matter. Once they managed to sort out Duntov's complicated SS chassis, Thompson was able to fairly fly with it. He was SCCA C-modified national champion in 1960, despite having brakes that never worked right and handling that was more than a little twitchy.

Meanwhile, back at engineering, Zora Duntov was putting together *his* little project, code name XP-720. XP-720 was an all-new chassis for the Corvette, prepared with Ed Cole's blessing. Cole had been running Chevrolet for less than a year when Mitchell took over Styling. So naturally, he wanted to come up with something new that would put his name up in lights, too. And Zora Duntov was equally ambitious. So while Mitchell was flamboyantly parading his revolutionary styling ideas around the race tracks, Duntov was quietly working in the back room to develop an equally innovative chassis.

He reduced the Corvette wheelbase to 98 inches. He used passenger car front suspension pieces and drum brakes in order to cut costs, and then spent what he'd saved to engineer a whole new independent suspension for the rear. It was hung over a transverse leaf spring and located by huge, stamped steel radius rods. The previous car was front heavy, the XP-720 had 53 percent of its weight on the rear wheels. After careful cost accounting, Duntov figured they could manufacture his new chassis for just about the same as the old one. His improvements were all free, in other words.

Cole was aiming at 1963 with the XP-720. Mitchell was aiming at anything he could get with the Sting Ray. He cleaned it up after the 1960 championship and exhibited it in major auto shows on the Styling turntable. He revamped it a bit more, and drove it to work on sunny days. Every time Ed Cole turned around,there was that metallic silver Sting Ray again, just kind of sittin' there, lookin' mean. He got the hint. When Mitchell finally got the okay to put a body on XP-720 for production, Larry Shinoda was the one who drew it up.

From the beltline down, the production body was nearly identical to the Sting Ray racer, except that it was marginally smaller. The first prototype also had the familiar split window fastback top, and the high-prowed nose of the original Sting Ray. Which was a problem. The racer was virtually unmanageable at high speeds, because Shinoda's "inverted wing" idea was a bummer. Instead, the Sting Ray nose acted like a sail, and the whole car wanted to lift off and fly away. Mitchell knew it, Shinoda knew it, Dr. Dick Thompson knew it better than anyone. But still, they left the flaring nose, purely for style.

Mitchell, in fact, seems to have had something of a fetish about this high nose. The original Sting Ray ran in C-modified. Which meant it could get by with vestigial headlights, just tiny bulbs that met the letter, if not the spirit of the rules. To keep the same shape on a street machine, the only way was retractable headlights and they cost a bundle. But Mitchell wanted them, and such was his clout, that he got 'em.

It's interesting that Duntov could have his independent rear suspension—which was a genuine improvement—only by cutting costs elsewhere. Mitchell's headlights cost a fortune to engineer—they went through *five* complete redesigns—were expensive to manufacture and created dangerous aerodynamic lift. And yet there was never any question whether the production Sting Ray would have retractable headlights for 1963. Even more ironic, after wind-tunnel testing, the new "aerodynamic" shape was found to have just as much drag as the old one. The Sting Ray was an aesthetic, not functional, tour de force.

But everyone was proven right in the end. Duntov's chassis was vastly superior to the old one. And Mitchell's body was breathtakingly beautiful. Corvette sales bounced from 14,000 in 1962 to 21,000 in 1963. So GM corporate was happy, which made Ed Cole happy, too. Cole's star had risen so fast, in fact, that he had already moved up the corporate ladder by the time the '63s appeared. Bunkie Knudsen was head of Chevrolet for the five years that the Sting Ray shape survived.

As much as anything, the Sting Ray succeeded because it was cheap. Base price was just a little over $4000, and for another $600 you could have a 4-speed and 360 hp, fuel-injected. Rough road handling wasn't very good with the stiff suspension, quality control was poor and the brakes weren't great. But even *Motor*, the most chauvinistically British of all British auto magazines, called the Corvette "the equal of any GT car to be found on either side of the Atlantic." Curiously enough, like every other road tester, the scribe from *Motor* hated the split rear window, which was Shinoda's favorite motif, and one that he and Mitchell had to fight to get past Zora Duntov. It's the one feature, too, that distinguishes the '63 coupes from later Vettes. But it was deleted by popular demand for 1964.

For most car magazines, the fuel-injected Sting Ray was the fastest, quickest street car they'd ever tested. *Sports Car Graphic* got zero to 60 in 5.6, 0-100 in 14 seconds and the quarter-mile in 14.2 at 102 mph. Top speed was 151. In other words without even thinking much about it at all, a lead-foot Corvette driver could suck the doors off Aston Martins, Ferraris, Maseratis and all sorts of street exotica that cost three times as much. For the price, the Sting Ray was so good that most buyers assumed the magazines were just blathering on. But they weren't. The car really *was* that good, and if the price tag had been 15-million lira instead of $5,000, it would have been acclaimed the best car in the world, bar none. Over the five years of Sting Ray production, it got better. Variable rate springs, less chrome trim, the one-piece rear window and 375 hp from the fuel-injection engine were the big changes for 1964. And in '65, Delco four-wheel disc brakes became standard. The big-block, 396 cubic inch, 425 hp V-8 appeared at mid-year, for folks who wanted to go *really* fast. The last thing the Vette needed was more weight on the front end, though, and the fuel injection small block continued to be the most balanced set-up through 1965.

By 1966, Detroit was no longer content with simple high performance. A car was judged on its "Performance Image." The Corvette got a tacked-on hood bulge that wrecked Shinoda's streamlined styling, and some funny optional paint treatments. The 396 had become a 427, however, and while the result wasn't pleasant as the '65 Fuelie, it was pretty damn fast. For 1967, the 427 got three two-barrel carbs, which *Car and Driver* admitted were "as smooth and responsive as fuel injection."

The 427 was hardly the top of the line, however. The big 427 Cobras were blowing the doors off Sting Rays in those days, and Duntov was frantic to come up with something that would keep his baby competitive. His answer was the L88, a full-race, 427 cubic inch V-8 that put out somewhere around 560 hp at 6500 rpm. At 3200 lbs, though the Vette was just too heavy to compete against the Cobra no matter how much power Duntov pumped into it. And for the street, the L88 was sheer madness. Glorious, but mad.

As far as I'm concerned, *the* Sting Ray to own is a silver metallic with black interior, 1965, 375 hp fuel-injection coupe. This gives you the clean Shinoda body before it got mucked about, but also disc brakes and the best fuelie engine. The factory knock-off mags are the ultimate touch on one of these, if you can find them.

Corvette for 1968

427-equipped Corvettes (shown) and 327 models had different hoods.

By Linda Clark

By the mid-1960s no American sports car loomed larger over the automotive world than Chevrolet's fiberglass Corvette. Since an estimated four million persons first viewed "that white Chevy roadster" at its Motorama appearances throughout the U.S. in 1953, the two-seater Corvette had become flashier and faster, internationally recognized and, for Chevrolet at least, profitable.

It was in the wake of this success, and despite some internal conflicts, that efforts toward the restyled 1968 Corvette began to evolve in the fall of 1965. Originally intended to debut as a 1967 model, Chevrolet postponed production of the Corvette's all-new body for twelve months while problems with the new shape were being worked out. For 1967, meanwhile, the existing body was refurbished.

When Elliott "Pete" Estes became Chevrolet General Manager in 1965 (following Bunkie Knudsen) the Corvette was facing competition from cars within its own division. Notably, the Corvair which, having potential for development to even higher levels of performance and handling, offered a cheaper alternative to Chevy's two-seater. The Camaro Z/28, furthermore, posed an even greater threat for, if it were to fail in the marketplace, Chevrolet stood to lose much more than if it were to cut into Corvette sales. "If a decision had to be made between the cars," opined Karl Ludvigsen, "there was little doubt which way it would go."

Two factions within Chevrolet's Engineering Center, meanwhile, had ideas about originating the design for the new Corvette. One was Frank Winchell's Research and Development Group which, in 1965, designed a rear-engined two-seater with the engine mounted behind the rear axle under a coupe body resembling the Mako Shark II, which had been the personal "dream car" project of Bill Mitchell earlier that year. Such a design, reasoned Winchell, would achieve handling with 70 percent of the car's weight on the rear wheels by using markedly wider tires at the rear. Both cooling and handling problems, though, ultimately ruled out this design for production.

Simultaneously, Zora Duntov's engineering group was working on a mid-engined design based on a 99-inch wheelbase with the engine placed ahead of the rear wheels and the radiator in the rear, behind the engine. The high costs of producing the required transaxle for such a mid-engined design ultimately ruled out this proposal, as well.

The needed alternative came in the form of a second "theme" model which had been styled just prior to the

Mako Shark II model in Larry Shinoda's studio. While it had been styled along the lines of the Mako II, it was, more importantly, aimed at possible production on the Corvette's existing front- engined chassis. Chief Chevrolet stylist David Holls was given the assignment to transform this Shinoda/Mitchell model into the new body design for the then-anticipated 1967 Corvette.

The styling model for this new Corvette, from which a body would be molded for the first engineering test car, resembled Mako Shark II in fender, side and nose treatment. A car with this new shape was tested at the Milford Proving Grounds in the fall of 1965. With no big chassis changes forseen, the engineers were primarily interested in how the car would perform with the aerodynamics of the new body. Using the 1965 Corvette as a base for their tests,they encountered several shortcomings. The new body, for one, had a tendency to lift at both ends with increased speeds. The increase in front end lifting forces, for another, brought with it additional side drag. Then, the rear spoiler and roof design limited rear vision, and the new body's high fenders partially blocked the forward view.

At this point Duntov alerted Estes of the need to postpone production of the new body until 1968 when, it was hoped, these problems would be corrected. The new body, then, went back to stylists Shinoda and Henry Haga for revisions, which included trimming the fenders, the rear spoiler and the roofline for improved vision. The grille was also moved forward and an aerodynamic dam built into the underside. The vent louvers in the sides of the fenders were also enlarged for better cooling.

Evaluation of these changes in the wind tunnel with the first prototype of the actual car revealed that there were still some structural challenges to be overcome. Chassis and body flexing had proved the one-piece lift-off roof panel to be noisy and unreliable. Addition of a central strut to join the windshield and rear roll-bar together, plus dividing the roof panel into two pieces, solved the problem, but at the cost of delaying production of the now-1968 coupe.

Special engineering and test work was required of Chevrolet's body men for the Corvette's new interior features, as well. Among these were the new seat design, fresh-air inlets in the rear deck and a fiber optic system—borrowed from the Mako Shark II—which informed the driver that his running lights were working. Concealed windshield wipers, also Mako-inspired, and swing-up headlights were new, too. When illness sidelined Zora Duntov for two months, during which Chevy's engineering staff underwent rearrangement, shortcomings in the new design's cooling system were left unresolved.

It wasn't until July 1967 when Duntov, upon his return, realized that the Mark IV-engined prototype coupe, scheduled for press preview that month, still had inadequate cooling provisions. Although Duntov personally performed last-minute revisions to the prototype's air inlet and spoiler to improve cooling ability, there was no time for a shakedown run to test these changes. Testing would have to be left in the hands of the motoring press itself.

The prototype's aluminum-head L88 Mark IV V-8 engine had been coupled with the new-for-1968 (in the Corvette) Turbo-Hydra-matic transmission. Despite a full day's testing by the press in warm weather, the prototype successfully ran at normal operating temperature and Duntov's refinements were later incorporated into production models. Buyers of Mark IV-engined Corvettes, nevertheless, were informed of these engines' marginal cooling abilities and with the L88 option in particular, a special hood which drew cool air at the base of the windshield was supplied.

Duntov was to incorporate still more changes to the chassis of the 1968 model, which, when coupled with that model's new wider wheel rims and low-profile F70x15 tires, increased the Corvette's stability. The new body had upped the Corvette's weight by nearly 100 pounds, but with its wider track and reduced height, the visual effect was exactly as David Holls and his styling staff had wanted it to be.

Both a funky and a formal wheel disc were available for 1968, one being a straightforward cap and trim ring and the other an elaborately-ribbed disc. Interior and trunk space had been sacrificed to the new body's sleekness and the dash lacked a glove compartment but included, instead, a lockable storage bin. As it had since 1963, the spare tire remained suspended under the rear of the chassis. The fuel tank likewise remained at the far rear of the Corvette's frame.

Reviews of the new Corvette by the European motoring press, where the car had been shown at the motor shows in the fall of 1967, were rewarding, but not so in the U.S. where *Car and Driver* panned the new model's "design flaws, mechanical failures, and shocking lack of quality control." Later, similar complaints from Corvette owners indicated that the panning was not so far off the mark. Chevrolet had tried to integrate its "only true sports car" into the regular engineering program but learned that its most expensive car (the '68 Corvette coupe at $4,636 surpassed even the top-of-the-line Caprice which was in the $3,500 range) would be best restored to its separate place within the Engineering Center. And so it was, with Duntov resuming his authority over every aspect of the Corvette, as well.

Later in 1968, although *Road & Track* still opined the "improved" Corvette to fall short of European counterparts, *Car and Driver* called the car "an almost irresistible temptation to buy American." The Sting Ray name was no longer carried on in these models although it was to return as a single word "Stingray," in 1969.

The Corvette's new shape still inspired racers, though the results on the track were mixed. At the Daytona 24 Hour Race in February 1968, the new Corvettes were bested by a 1967 model. Later at Sebring, though, Corvettes placed 6th overall in the 12-hour race, and 1st in the GT category. The new long-nosed Corvettes also captured two divisional championships in SCCA's Class A Production during the 1968 season. The Corvette's 1968 design was also the basis for the "Astro-Vette" show car, a pseudo-aerodynamic white roadster so massive in appearance as to be nicknamed "Moby Dick." Having emerged from the Styling Studio in the spring of 1968, it encompassed fully-enclosed rear wheels, a long tapered tail, a low plexiglass windscreen around the cockpit and an extended nose.

The production model in 1968 sold nearly 6,000 units more than the prior year's Sting Ray, but the Corvette's production peak was yet to come. . .

Being the First of its Body Style May Make the 1968 Corvette A Collector Car While it's Young

By Wally Wyss

You've heard it a million times: "Why, if I woulda thought of it, I'd a-bought up a coupla those cars when they were cheap. . ."

Spotting future classics or collector's cars in advance isn't easy. However, the 1968 Corvette qualifies on several counts as a soon-to-be collector model. First, because it represents the first example of the sixth major body changes in the Corvette style since 1953, when the first Corvettes rolled out of GM's Flint, Michigan pilot plant (later, Corvette production was switched to St. Louis).

The '68 Corvette, as GM would like us to believe, owes its styling to a Mako shark that GM styling VP Bill Mitchell caught off Bimini lo these many years ago. He immortalized the shark's features in a show car called the Mako Shark II which metamorphized into the '68 Stingray.

The new Stingray had some novel features, like a "Kamm effect" tail end. Dr. Kamm, for whom it is named, was a European aerodynamycist who believed that chopping the tail on a car induced turbulence just aft of the car which then created downforce to aid rear wheel traction. Much more subtle was a small undertray spoiler up front to prevent front end lift.

On the side of the car were functional air grates to exhaust hot air from under the hood. The wheels for 1968 were an inch wider than the year before, at 7" wide and 15" tall.

The '68 had several suspension changes, which accomplished a lowering of the rear roll center some 2½" for flatter cornering. The front springs and front anti-roll bar were stiffened. GM engineers had as their goal the keeping of the inside rear wheel on the ground in tight cornering. The result was a car that would corner at 0.85 g, or slightly better than a 1977 Firebird Trans-Am.

1968 Corvette

The hot engine options for 1968 included a 350 hp 327 cubic inch mill designated L79, along with five healthy 427 cubic inch versions, the mildest of which was the L36 option with a 4 barrel carburetor giving 390 hp. A similarly prepared block with three two-barrel carburetors was offered as option L68 at 400 hp at 5400 rpm, and could move you from 0 to 60 mph in under seven seconds with fair regularity. Either of these options would move your '68 to a top end of 140+ mph with the 3.08:1 rear axle option. For the real performance minded drivers option L71 provided a 427 cubic inch block featuring four bolt main bearing caps, a high lift camshaft, mechanical lifters and an 11.0:1 compression ratio fed by three two-barrel carburetors. The same engine was offered to the weight conscious competitor with aluminum cylinder heads as option L89. For the track only, Chevrolet continued the L88 engine option which could be had only with all the other racing options for 1968 including positraction and the M22 "Rock Crusher" heavy duty close ratio four speed transmission. The L88 design features included a single Holley 850 CFM carburetor on a specially designed hi-rise intake manifold, a 12.5:1 compression ratio, a specially designed camshaft and mechanical lifters. At the bottom of this wide spectrum of engine options was the base 300 hp 327 cubic inch standard Corvette V-8.

One of the interesting options in the 1968 Corvette was the availability of the Turbo-Hydra-matic three-speed transmission, the heavier duty 400 model. The trans could be downshifted, but the way it would react was interesting—it would wait until the revs dropped sufficiently so that the downshift wouldn't over-rev the engine. For instance, if you were at 6000 rpm and downshifted from Drive to two (for second gear), the downshift wouldn't take place until the revs dropped to, say, 4000 rpm, so when the tach needle did jump back up, it was still below redline.

The 1968 Corvette, being the first of a new body style, was not without its flaws. For instance, one of the vacuum operated hidden headlights would invariably stick, giving your car a one-eyed look. The vacuum operated door covering the windshield wipers could catch your hand like a beartrap. The new lift-off roof panels squeaked and leaked, and if you put them in the cargo space without stuffing them in their little baggies, then they would toss around and scratch the paint off each other. Editor Steve Smith of *Car and Driver* wrote in his December, 1967 issue "With less than 2,000 miles on it, the Corvette was falling apart." After a trip from New York City to Watkins Glen and back, Smith judged the car "unfit for a road test." But not all '68's are plagued by these quality control problems and conscientious owners have managed to de-bug many of them.

Motion Performance Vette

There's been a re-emergence of special musclecars that have been termed "street rats." Some of these are Chevrolet products equipped with Motion Performance Co., performance equipment packages. There are very few Motion Performance modified cars in existence, especially Corvettes.

What is the magnetic force these cars hold over man? Nostalgia! Speed! Investment! Individuality! They are machines that can't be duplicated.

Our feature car is a 1969 Corvette Stingray with "motionized" high performance equipment and body modifications.

This particular Corvette has 30,000 original miles on its factory speedometer and all-numbers-match 427 cid tri-power big-block engine. This four-speed car nearly flies when fueled by high octane racing gas.

The factory color, Lemans blue, is as deep in color as the waters of the Caribbean, with a wide white racing stripe for distinction. An SS-427 emblem sits proudly on the Motion Performance designed hood scoop. The optional headers, side pipes, special racing mirrors, gas cap and S-200 prototype wheels also make this car unique.

Its other desirable features include original factory window and gas tank stickers, an original owner's manual and the original keys. It is for sale, with marketing aspects being handled by Morry Leahy of Moline, Ill.

Other Motion Performance modified cars included Novas, Camaros, Chevelles and Monte Carlos. After 20 years, recognition is taking hold and their contribution to the history of the musclecar movement is gaining exposure.

The key characteristic of cars with the Motion Performance treatment was street racing and winning. They were built with serious quarter-mile running in mind and had enough power to make any challenger take notice. The thrill that came with controlling more power than any other local driver dwelt within such vehicles.

'To own the fastest car in town' was the goal of Motion Performance customers and the "motionized" cars delivered great potential to win such a reputation. They earned an unequalled reputation for car and driver alike.

With musclecars coming back into the full attention of the public, there's an interesting note. To many of the younger generation, cars such as this Vette appear to be little more than customized. This is not so and more and more fans are getting educated as to the contribution these modified "street rats" made in the late '60's.

Corvettes such as this one were styled similarly to that of popular Baldwin-Motion cars of the same era. The cars first became famous on the East Coast.

Changes were made in accordance with an individual owner's desires and price range. There were no standard catalog specs and no dealer invoices...only plenty of action and attention.

Today, these rare finds bring back the old days with a growing admiration. This blue car, for instance, has always turned heads with its awesome exterior and flawless interior. The visuals are accompanied by a really tough sound that's backed by a raw horse power. It brings reality to the dreams of many a street race car lover and gives new meaning to the term "Poetry in Motion."

After 21 years, this car still has all its draw, plus a collector's value that is climbing. It is now re-emerging as a most desirable "street rat."

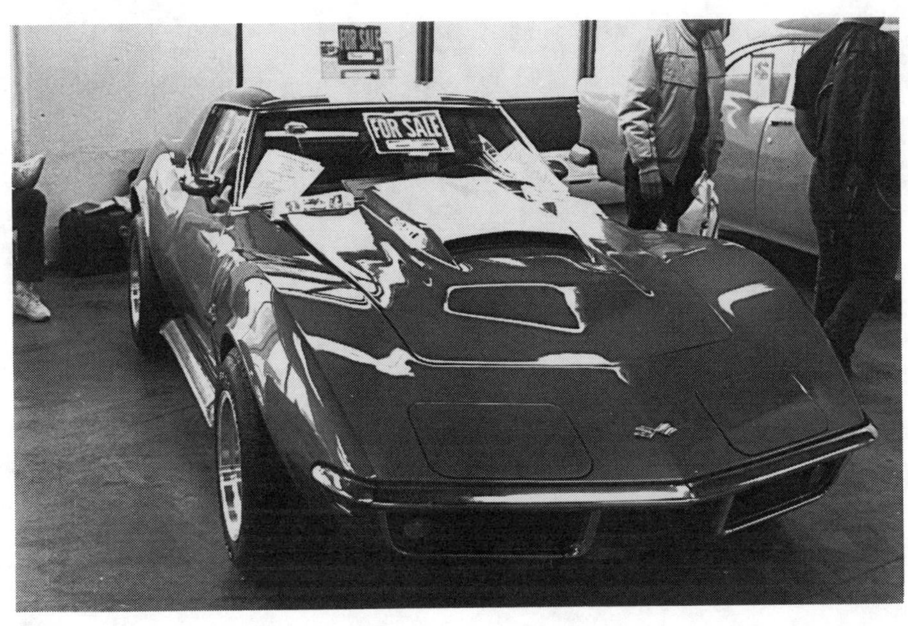

ZR-1 Corvette destined to become a collectible

Could it be that Chevrolet Motors Division has decided to launch an effort to compete in the space race? The 1990 Corvette ZR-1 is a rocket ship that might give that impression. Another impression the ZR-1 is sure to impart is this built-for-speed "bowtie" creation will become an instant collectible car.

The collectibility status of the 1990 ZR-1 goes beyond initial demand for the car, which has far outpaced supply. Subtle styling changes that set it apart from the '90 Corvette coupe and low production numbers in its debut year mark the ZR-1 as a car collector's target. Recently revised estimates from Chevrolet have only 2,000 ZR-1 Corvettes being produced for 1990.

The ZR-1, at first glance, looks similar to the Corvette coupe. The ZR-1 has been stretched one inch and it is three inches wider to accommodate increased rear tread width. The most telltale difference between the cousin Corvettes is the revised rectangular taillamps of the ZR-1.

What really puts the stamp of uniqueness on the ZR-1 is found in the car's drivetrain. The ZR-1's all aluminum 350 cid V-8 LT5 engine produces enough thrust to launch the Corvette from 0 to 60 mph in 4.3 seconds according to

This 1990 Corvette ZR-1 was number 114 off the production line and the first to be delivered to a dealership. The car was purchased by Glenn Ross of Ross Technologies Inc., of Marietta, Ga. Ross is offering this "piece of history" for sale for around $100,000.

Chevrolet. The LT5 engine is rated at 375 hp, and is constructed by boat engine specialists Mercury Marine.

A ZF six-speed manual transmission has been mated to the ZR-1's LT-5 powerplant. This transmission was offered as optional equipment on '89 Corvette coupes. The ZR-1 does not have an automatic transmission option.

The first 1990 Corvette ZR-1 to orbit public roads was purchased by Glenn Ross of Marietta, Ga. Ross' car was the 114th ZR-1 produced and the first delivered to a dealership.

"The ZR-1 is head and shoulders above the Ferraris and Lamborghinis," Ross said. "It drives like it's on silk." He added that he placed the order for his ZR-1 14 months prior to its arrival in September 1989. "Ninety-five percent of the cars were preordered by March 1988."

The factory list price of a ZR-1, as shipped with both the automatic climate control and one-piece removable top options, is $62,675. This is compared to the 1990 Corvette coupe's asking price of $37,990. But, because of the great demand for ZR-1s, dealers have been asking—and getting—prices that are out of this world.

The 1990 ZR-1 Corvette is powered by a 11:1 compression, 32-valve, dual overhead cam V-8 350 cid engine.

Corvair

A Cool Chevy For the Hot Sixties

It tried to be everything to everybody. From a sedate sedan for Aunt Matilda and a station wagon for the family, to a van for the business man and a sports car for the auto buff. Its entire life span was a mere nine years, during which it rose from GM's unpopular "cousin" to one of its most popular cars — before agonizingly settling into oblivion.

The dispute as to whether Ralph Nader's book actually sounded its death knell, like so many other auto-related controversies, will never be satisfactorily settled. However, more significant than Nader's book, was the fact that 1962 brought the first flexings of the muscle cars. Dodge's 413 suddenly set fire to the drag strips. For '63, Dodge ads read, "If you want to tear up the strips, just say so. You can lay it on hotter'n a charcoal bed with the new 426 Ram Charger that'll burn rubber as long as you let it." Pontiac stuffed a 326 cubic inch V8 in their little Tempest. And in 1964, what is considered to be the grand daddy of all muscle cars made its debut. The Pontiac GTO.

It became a power race. Cubic inches and 0 to 60 times were the standards by which cars were judged. And while vehicles like the GTO were reaching 60 mph in 6½ to 7 seconds, Corvair's air-cooled six — even with an optional turbocharger — took nearly 11 seconds. With cheap gas prices and carefree living, those were days when the fastest car from the stoplight was the car with the "mostest" sales — and Corvair was not a street dragster. Its small six couldn't compete in the stoplight grand prix's, and it was left to suffer an ignominious death. It certainly deserved better!

When it was first introduced in late 1959, it bristled with innovations. Chevrolet called it the "First *specific* design for an American compact car." While Rambler's American, Studebaker's Lark, Ford's Falcon, and Plymouth's Valiant all followed the tried and true, water-cooled engine in the front, driving the rear wheels; Chevrolet breached the norm. It crossed into areas where few major American automobile manufacturers had dared to tread — and where no American manufacturer had ever completely succeeded.

Chevy's clean-lined compact rested on a 108 inch wheelbase and stood a mere 51½ inches high. It had all four wheels suspended independently, giving Corvair "a new kind of ride for the compact car — in every way the kind of ride expected in an American car."

A three-speed transmission with floor-mounted shift lever was standard, but Chevrolet offered a fully automatic transmission as one of its options.

However, its most unique feature was its engine. The 140 cubic inch, 80 HP six, was the first American air-cooled engine since the air-cooled Franklin ceased production in 1934. Air cooling, and its rear engine placement, immediately targeted the car for controversy. The fact that it looked like no other car, coupled with the problems that arose on some of the early cars, added fuel to the fire. The most talked about problem was the habit of the blower drive belt popping off its idler pulley. To be fair to Corvair, the problem was quickly remedied. Yet, the story of belts coming off persisted for years. Carburetor icing was also a problem on some of the early cars; again quickly remedied.

Stories of its distinctive handling properties began with the first road tests. Testers either praised its "sports car-like handling," or decried it for being "too touchy!" Rumors were circulating that the car was prone to overheating — or that it had no heat! Rumors and stories, and facts and fiction soon became jumbled together. So, although it was the most interesting mass-produced American car in several decades, Corvair found itself lagging in sales. In fact, Ford's Falcon outsold Corvair right from the start.

Initially offered only in a four-door configuration, the

1963 Monza Convertible.

1964 Monza convertible.

Corvair 700 4-door sedan for 1960.

first announcements stressed the thorough testing that had gone into this *family* car. "In all, more than half a million miles were logged by the test cars." It continued, "When Chevrolet engineers say that the Corvair is 'specifically designed as a compact car should be,' it carries a ring of authority. This car was nine years in the planning and experimental stages. It was carefully developed to provide the ideal answer to America's need for six-passenger compact car transportation.

The four-door sedan was soon joined by a two-door coupe. A short time after that, the two-door Monza 900 coupe was introduced. In addition to the Corvair's standard features, Monza offered a set of bucket seats, an optional 95 HP engine and a 4-speed transmission. Suddenly, Corvair found itself with a winner!

For 1961, Chevrolet increased the bore slightly, expanding the engine to 145 cubic inches. The Monza line was extended to include a sporty four-door sedan. Sales began to climb, and it was not the low priced economy versions that brought the increase. By the end of '61, the Monza coupe accounted for nearly 34% of total Corvair sales.

Accessory manufacturers began flooding the market with ram induction systems, quick steering kits (which it really needed), camber compensators. Its distinctive exhaust rap echoed throughout America. The only disheartening sign was, while Monza sales had increased dramatically, total Corvair sales were about the same as 1961.

For '62, the sporty Monza line was expanded to include a station wagon and convertible. The 80 HP, 145 cubic inch six was still the standard engine, but Monzas with automatic transmissions acquired 84 HP. A sportier version that developed 102 HP was offered, although it required premium fuel.

In late spring of 1962, Corvair dropped another bombshell. It offered a new Monza called the Spyder. The Spyder package was available in either coupe or convertible form, and carried special identification and an instrument panel that included manifold pressure, cylinder head temperature, and tachometer, in addition to the regular gauges. However, its most important feature was a "Turbo-Supercharger" that pushed 150 HP from the 145 cubic inch six. People were clamoring for performance, and this was Corvair's answer.

To handle the extra power, the Spyder package also included a 3.55 axle, heavy-duty suspension and sintered metallic brake linings. While the early Corvair had been compared to the air-cooled Volkswagen, the Spyders found themselves being compared to Porsches.

Sales for '62 rang with Monza's success. The coupes now accounted for about 46% of total sales, while the complete Monza line accounted for 66%. With a distinctive belt line that encircled the entire car, Corvair joined the ranks of the very few American cars to influence European designers. Over the years, many Corvair imitators dotted the European shows, a tribute to the men who styled Chevy's compact.

Corvair remained basically unchanged for '63. But at the stoplight drags, things were changing. The younger buyers who had purchased Monzas as a hot sporty car were being beaten. The older folks who bought them for economy were being disappointed. Sales began dropping.

For 1964, the engine displacement was increased to 164 cubic inches. Horsepower climbed to 95 and 110 for the non-turbo engines. Handling was improved by making an anti-roll bar standard in the front, and by adding a single leaf spring traversely across the rear. Sales fell sharply. Ford's new Mustang took direct aim at the sporty market Monza had enjoyed; and Mustang offered a V8!

Corvair had to do something. Rumors alluded to a fire-breathing flat eight that would blister the Mustangs and GTOs.

When Corvair bowed for '65, it was in fact new — excitingly new! Its body grew curvaceous, and like its predecessor, it was beautiful. Again, Chevy's stylists had worked wonders. It was clean and sleek, stunning from every angle.

From an engineering standpoint, it offered a completely new suspension system. Double jointed driveshafts eliminated the earlier swing axles. No longer did the rear wheels tuck under during extremely hard cornering. No longer did it change sharply from an understeer to an oversteer condition without plenty of warning. No longer did it have to apologetically explain that it had been sired by an economy sedan. It was a real road car. And with the new top of the line Corsa, Corvair could deservedly be labeled an American sports machine.

But one thing hadn't changed: the 164 cubic inch six. Though now offering an optional 140 HP, four carburetor engine — or a 180 HP turbocharged version, it couldn't compete at the stoplight drags. For 1965, Mustang's horsepower climbed to 271. Pontiac's GTO offered 335 HP.

By 1966, even Chevy was stuffing 396's into its intermediates. (Although it actually built about 200 Chevelles with 396's in '65, they were not available to the general public.) Plymouth offered a scorching 426 cubic inch, 425 HP Hemi in its Belvedere. Corvair sales plummeted to less than half of 1965.

But there were people who believed strongly in its capabilities. People like John Fitch, who had built and sold his own modified versions called Sprints, since the early series. Tastefully reworked, the Sprint was truly a grand touring machine. When the new Corvair was introduced for '65, Fitch offered yet another Sprint. Based on the Corsa, the breathed-on carburetored engine developed 155 HP. Special Sprint suspension and steering made the car a joy to drive. Stylewise, a unique new buttress type roof line was grafted to the top, making the Sprint look different from all other Corvairs.

And on the race tracks of America, Corvairs like Don Yenko's, a Chevrolet dealer from Pennsylvania, were doing very well. Yenko's modified Corvairs were called Stingers — and stingers they were! In 1966, Yenko's Stinger won six SCCA national grade races in a row. In '67, a Yenko Stinger became the SCCA's "D" Production sports car national champion. In addition to the road racers, Yenko produced several street versions. The bright yellow Yenko Stingers were popular cars wherever they appeared.

But Corvair was learning what Hudson had learned in the 50's. Wins on race tracks do not guarantee wins (sales) in the showrooms. Chevrolet iced it in 1967 with the Camaro. If people wanted sporty cars with V8's, GM would supply them.

Corvair sales were less than 30,000 for 1967. Many people predicted that there would never be a '68, but there was. With no new developments taking place, except to meet safety and emission standards, the end was in sight.

For 1968, Corvair's entire lineup consisted of the 500 coupe, the Monza coupe, and the Monza convertible. (The Corsa models having been phased out at the end of '66.) Sales dropped to about 15,000. It was really all over.

Yet, for some strange reason, GM persisted. When the new 1969 cars were introduced — there was Corvair. But it was the same old car. Complete lack of development and sales promotion were its rewards. Production was discontinued in the spring of 1969, after about 6,000 cars had been produced.

Throughout the years, many automobiles have tried and failed. Most died fighting! None had ever been left to die so ungraciously!

Compact with Enthusiast Appeal

by Linda Clark

Chevrolet's small, rear-engined Corvair was unveiled in showrooms on Oct. 2, 1959. Although it lived for only a decade, it had a lasting impact on American life.

The popularity of small imports and domestic compacts from Rambler and Studebaker in the late '50s prompted Chevrolet to build the Corvair. Chevy also foresaw an increasing number of two-car families in need of a smaller car.

Chevrolet's Research and Development arm had been working on a smaller car — then known as the Cadet — as early as 1946. However, it wasn't until a decade later, in 1957, that GM and then Chevrolet General Manager Ed Cole decided to build the first Corvair prototype.

Radical for its day, the rear-engined Corvair was air-cooled and had swing-axle suspension. This four-wheel independent suspension was primitive by today's standards, but nowhere near the ill-handler its detractors said it was. Chevrolet recommended tire pressures of 15 psi in front and 26 psi in the rear which, according to the November 1959 *Road & Track*, "gives the Corvair positive understeer and makes it inherently stable at all times."

The beloved Tom McCahill also liked the new Corvair. Reporting his driving impressions in the November 1959 *Mechanix Illustrated*, he said, "This is the best-handling rear-engine car I've ever driven."

Its aluminum flat six engine used cast-iron cylinders instead of aluminum (as originally planned) to meet production schedules, thus weighing 338 pounds, som 100 more than intended. This, too, was said to adversely affect Corvair handling.

The engine developed 80 or 95 hp and, even given the rarity of flat sixes, was a complete design having two cylinder heads (the bore was 3.375 inches, the stroke 2.60 inches) and divided crankcase. Displacement was 140 cubic inches.

Initially, Chevrolet offered the base 500 Corvair, the fancier 700 model, and, at mid-year, the sporty 900 Monza. Corvair rode on a 108-inch wheelbase, weighed around 2,300 pounds and started at $1,984 for the 500 model.

Sales were impressive, with 250,007 Corvairs leaving showrooms in 1960. But it was quickly noted that Ford's Falcon and the Plymouth Valiant that premiered that year were more than serious rivals for Chevy's compact. Falcon soon had the compact-car sales lead, and Corvair owners began registering assorted minor complaints when viewing their cars against the more economical Falcon.

Ultimately, it was the Monza coupe that rescued Corvair. It was an "image" car in the best sense of the word. It came with bucket seats, chrome trim, special wheelcovers, rocker panel moldings, and simulated air vents on the rear deck. Monza also had standard sun visors, ashtrays, courtesy lights, and a folding rear seat, all of which were extra-cost options on other models.

In 1961, Chevy offered an optional four-speed gearbox and Monza sales took off.Chevy sold 143,690 Monza models alone in 1961.

The Corvair line itself expanded for '61. The 500 and 700 coupe and sedan were joined by 500 and 700 Lakewood station wagons. The flat six Turbo-Air engine was also increased to displace 145 cubic inches, developing 80 or 98 hp. Total Corvair sales climbed to 329,632.

New interiors and performance options (heavy-duty suspension, sintered metallic brakes, and Positraction rear axle) were added in 1962. The biggest news was the March '62 introduction of the turbocharged Monza Spyder, available in coupe or convertible.

Turbocharging is commonplace today, and even though it dates back to at least 1910, it was a revolutionary idea back in 1962. Gas was plentiful then, and if you wanted more horsepower you increased displacement, carburetion, or compression. Maybe all three.

Getting a small engine to perform like a big one by turbocharging — essentially providing the engine with a pressurized charge of air/fuel mixture — was innovative, like the Corvair itself.

The exhaust-driven turbocharged Spyder model has a 105 mph top speed. The Spyder option went for $421.95 and included the 150 hp turbo engine, four-speed gearbox, special instrument cluster, identification emblems, heavy-duty suspension, sintered metallic brakes, and 3.55:1 "performance" axle gears.

The engine also had a number of beefed-up parts to withstand the extra heat and pressure of the turbocharger; compression was 8.0:1. With Monza models still leading the way, Corvair sales totaled 328,500 in 1962.

For 1962, the Lakewood nameplate was dropped, but wagons were still offered in both 700 and Monza series.

Subtle trim and interior changes distinguished 1963 Corvairs from '62 models. The station wagon disappeared, usurped by the Chevy II wagon. Corvair sales declined in 1963, due in part to competition from the

Chevy II, a front-engine rear driver that no doubt appealed to traditional Chevy buyers who found the Corvair too radical.

In 1964, horsepower was raised to 95 and 110 in the Turbo-Air and Super Turbo-Air engine by increasing displacement to 164 cubic inches. The turbo engine remained 150 hp, but torque, to improve low-end performance, was increased in all three engines.

The 1964 Corvairs enjoyed suspension improvements: A transverse leaf spring was added at the rear, and a front anti-roll bar was made standard. The model lineup was the same except that the 700 coupe had been dropped, and the Spyder coupe and convertible were now a separate series rather than a Monza option.

In the spring of 1964, Ford's phenomenal Mustang arrived on the scene and would give the Corvair a challenge as formidable as the lawsuits that now plagued GM. As early as 1962, however, Ed Cole has targeted 1965 as the year to initiate the redesigned second-generation Corvair. A series of sleek show cars provided the inspiration. The angular lines of the 1960-'64 Corvairs were smoothed and elongated on the dramatically restyled 1965 Corvair, which had a pillarless, flowing roofline that looks contemporary even today.

The Corvair's striking new design is credited to Bill Mitchell, then chief of GM Styling. Underneath its new skin, the '65 Corvair offered fully independent suspension, differing from the Corvette's in that it had coil springs instead of transverse leaf springs.

Other mechanical changes included raising the horsepower to 140 in one of the engines, and boosting the turbocharged engine to 180 hp, mainly through a new four-carb intake system. Quicker steering and improved brakes also brought 1965 Corvairs on part with sophisticated European imports.

The new Corsa series was the star of the Corvair lineup. Available as a sport coupe ($2,519) or convertible ($2,665), it came with full instrumentation, distinct trim, deluxe interior, and the 140 hp four-carb engine. The $158 optional turbo engine was available on the Corsa only.

The Spyder name was dropped, but earliest Corsa turbos reportedly had Spyder script on their fenders. The new Corvairs in 1965 were also three inches longer and two inches wider than 1960-'64 cars. Wheelbase remained 108 inches, but colors, interiors, and instrumentation had all been revamped.

Corsa premiered with the beautifully restyled 1966 Corvair, which was as striking as the original had been five years earlier.

and Corsa had buckets. New extra-cost options for 1965 included AM/FM radio, offered also in stereo, a telescopic steering wheel, and remote-control outside rearview mirror.

The '66 Corvairs were refined even further. Models still included two 500s, three Monzas, and two Corsas.

History records that GM had decided in the spring of 1965 to end development work on the Corvair, but it was still a harsh blow when Corvair sales plummeted to 103,743 in 1966. The Corsa couldn't better Ford's peppier Mustang, but even once-heralded Monza sales were declining.

Corsa was dropped in 1967, leaving only two 500s and three Monzas in the Corvair stable. Initially, just the 95 and 110 hp engines were offered, but the 140 hp engine was reinstated shortly after the '67 model year began. You could still option a Corvair with plenty — sport suspension and an array of comfort and convenience features.The 1967 Corvair also carried GM's first five-year engine and drivetrain warranty. However, only 30,637 Corvairs sold in 1967.

Minor cosmetic changes appeared on the 1968 cars. The quickest way to distinguish a '68 from a '67 was by the side-marker lights on all fenders. Sedans were discontinued throughout the line, and in 1968 there were only a 500 coupe and a Monza coupe and convertible.

Car Life praised the 1968 Monza coupe and said, "It's too much car to kill." Nevertheless, it was obvious the Corvair had only a few monthsto live. Even those unaware of GM's own sentencing of the car were aware of the rising tie of consumerism, and the adverse Corvair publicity in the wake of Ralph Nader's 1965 book, *Unsafe at Any Speed*. Even some Chevrolet dealers refused to handle Corvairs.

On May 14, 1969, the last Corvair — an Olympic Gold Monza — rolled off the assmebly line. The '69 models had amber front side-marker lights, unlike the white lenses used on '68 cars. Front shoulder belts were standard on all 1969 models, except the convertible. There were no changes in engine and transmission from 1968, and heavy-duty suspension could still be had.

Chevrolet sold 6,000 Corvairs in 1969, and this great little car that was years ahead of its time died an undeserved death. In today's context, the Corvair seems ideal. So maybe the times, after all, finally caught up with the innovative Corvair.

Buyers complained in 1960 that the basic Corvair was just too basic. This is the four-door sedan.

1960-'64 Corvairs

The First Generation

by Tony Hossain

There are more expensive collector cars. There are larger, more powerful, and more luxurious collector cars. But few cars are as loved by their owners as the sporty Chevrolet Corvair. And few cars have been subject to such rigorous scrutiny by people who have never even driven one as the Chevrolet Corvair. Its safety and its engineering integrity have been attacked from the day it was introduced, and before, but the Corvair has been vindicated in test after test.

The Corvair was designed to be a driver's car and it still is. Therein lies its charm.

Corvair owners divide the cars into two basic groups, the 1960-64 "first generation" cars and the 1965-69 "second series" cars. We'll examine the early cars in this article.

Chevrolet introduced the Corvair in the fall of 1959 (as a 1960 model) in response to the growing inroads foreign small cars were making in the American marketplace. The Volkswagen, in particular, was catering to buyers that Detroit had ignored as its cars became larger, thirstier, and finnier. And the foreign automakers weren't the only ones having sales success with compact cars. Rambler had its best year ever in 1958 and the smaller 1959 Lark gave Studebaker a new lease on life. The time was ripe for

1961 Corvair 700 coupe

new small cars from the Big Three and Chevrolet would not be alone.

Also introduced as 1960 models were the Falcon from Ford Motor Company and the Valiant from Chrysler. There was a tremendous amount of interest in these new cars but it was the Corvair that was scrutinized most carefully. Because it was different. The Corvair was the first American production car to combine such features as an air-cooled aluminum engine *mounted in the rear*, four-wheel independent suspension, and unit body construction. Coming from General Motors, this was radical engineering.

Almost immediately there were questions about the Corvair's handling qualities. Ford Motor Company added fuel to the fire by mentioning that the Falcon's engine was "up front, where it belonged." But magazine road testers found nothing unsafe about the Corvair's behavior on the test track. *Motor Trend* named it their Car Of The Year and staid *Consumer Reports* labeled it a competent handler. Even so, the public didn't seem to want anything as exotic as the Corvair. While model year sales of the utterly conventional Ford Falcon reached 435,000, the Corvair found only 250,007 buyers in its first year. Something was wrong at Chevrolet Motor Division.

Chevrolet's initial marketing strategy to pitch the Corvair as an economy compact fell on deaf public ears. The Ford Falcon and the American Motors' Rambler were simply more logical family sedans. They had better interior accommodations, more trunk space, and seemed to offer more real value for the money. And the Corvair seemed to be a rather unknown quantity. Adding to the Corvair's troubles was the cost problem. Ed Cole, the chief engineer on the project, was in love with the concept and didn't let costs get in the way as he designed the package. As the car neared production, it became clear that it wouldn't be competitive with other small cars unless the manufacturing cost was brought down. The critical decision to cheapen the interior trim level was made. Combined with the fact that only one body style was available at the start of production, the Corvair represented a rather bleak package. So sales suffered.

The 1960 Corvair was offered as a Series 500 four-door sedan or a Series 700 sedan. Interiors on the 500 were taxi-cab plain. Although ten exterior colors were available, only gray was offered as an interior hue. Black rubber floor mats completed this depressing picture. The price was $1,869 and did not include armrests, heater, or even a right-hand sun visor. For $51 more, the Series 700 sedan offered a choice of gray, green, or blue pattern cloth bench seats, anodized-aluminum glovebox door applique and color-keyed rubber floor mats.

Things brightened up considerably for Corvair enthusiasts in January 1960 with the introduction of the good-looking coupes, in both 500 and 700 form. With the optional floor-mounted 4-speed transmission, performance rear axle ratio, and a power-packed version of the 140 cubic inch six, the Corvair was attracting a whole new group of admirers. But Chevrolet found the real market for its floundering Corvair almost by accident.

In May 1960, Chevrolet announced the Monza Club Coupe. On the outside, the trim was upgraded. Inside, luxurious bucket seats highlighted a very plush interior. Standard equipment included a folding rear seat, back-up lights, wheel covers, and a glove box light. Although it was only in production about three months before changeover to '61 models, 11,926 Monzas were manufactured and sold to an eager public. With the Monza, the Corvair finally found its niche, as a gutsy sportster...for the Pepsi Generation.

When the 1961 Corvairs were being planned, it was not known that the Monza Club Coupe would be the salvation of the line. At first it was though that making the Corvair a full range of small cars would make it competitive with the Ford Falcon. So, for 1961, new Corvair models included Series 500 and Series 700 Lakewood station wagons and a line of Greenbrier vans, Corvan 95 trucks, and pickups. A lot like the VW Bus in appearance, these vans are highly sought after by Corvair collectors today, especially in

Chevrolet introduced the Greenbrier and the Corvan forward-control Corvair trucks in 1961. Enthusiasts, to this day, prefer these vehicles to more utilitarian Ford and Chevrolet vans.

their unusual forms. These unusual forms include Rampside pickups and DeLuxe three-seat Greenbrier Sportswagons.

Although Chevrolet had high hopes for the 1961 Lakewood wagons, they never caught on with the public. Only 5,591 Series 500 and 20,451 Series 700 wagons were sold in their maiden year. It was giving Chevrolet production planners fits but while the Corvair wagons and sedans were being ignored, demand was skyrocketing for the bucket seat Monza. Production couldn't keep up with the orders in '61 and Monza Club Coupe sales went over the 100,000 mark. Early in 1961, a Monza four-door sedan was introduced with the same base price as the coupe — $2,201. The bucket seats were becoming a Monza trademark but they were a $54 option in the sedan.

Other changes for 1961 were of an evolutionary nature. Trim was changed slightly and handsome full wheel covers were standard on the Monza, an $11 option on other models. The engine was bored out to 145 cubic inches and a forced air heater replaced the gas unit of 1960. Listening to dealer complaints, interior decor on 500 and 700 Series cars was upgraded considerably. To increase trunk space, the spare tire was moved back to a position atop the engine. Model year production reached 329,632, a high point in the history of the Corvair.

By 1962, Corvair advertising was finally recognizing the car's sporting nature. Wagons and sedans were virtually ignored while the Monza Club Coupe was promoted as "the car that started the bucket seat brigade." Retreating from the family sedan market with the Corvair, a Falcon-clone called the Chevy II was rushed to market to do battle in the econo-sedan class. Corvair wagon fans, and there were a few, praised the introduction of the luxurious Monza wagon but few others noticed. The big news for '62 was the spring arrival of the Monza convertible and the Spyder turbocharged engine option on Monza coupes and ragtops. Interest in these new sporting Corvairs was intense but few noticed that the Corvair wagons were dropped at that time.

The Monza Spyder's turbocharged engine was rated at an impressive 150 advertised horsepower. Other Spyder features included full instrumentation, four-speed transmission, heavy-duty suspension, 3.55:1 rear axle, and sintered metal brakes. In its first outing, the Spyder accounted for 9,468sales, including 2,574 convertibles.

Things were pretty quiet on the Corvair front for 1963. Spyders and convertibles enjoyed their first full year on the market and Corvair wagons were no longer seen in Chevrolet showrooms. Prices remained remarkably stable. The 700 sedan that listed at $2,103 in 1960 was now only $2,110. But it was the first year that demand really fell for the Corvair. Sales amounted to only 281,539, compared with 328,500 in 1962. Basically unchanged since 1960, the Corvair was getting a little old hat in an industry that "facelifted" cars every year. Over 80% of total Corvair production this year was in the Monza series. Four-door Monzas now had bucket seats as standard equipment, in a choice of seven colors. The turbocharged Spyder was continued into 1963, a $327 option on Monza coupes and convertibles.

The 1964 Corvair was the last of the "first generation" cars. Many also consider it to be the best. Handling was improved with the addition of a transverse rear leaf spring and an anti-sway bar up front. Ralph Nader would later maintain in his book, *Unsafe At Any Speed*, that these changes were made because the 1960-63 cars were dangerous. Not so, according to a report released by the U.S. government in 1972. Of course, by that time the Corvair had already been sacrificed.

Another improvement worth noting is the increased power available in 1964. Engine displacement was increased to 164 cubic inches and the standard engine was now rated at 95 horsepower, up 15 from the four previous seasons. The optional engine was rated at 110 horsepower, but advertised power for the Monza Spyder remained at 150. As in years past, Spyders could be had with a three or four-speed manual transmission only.

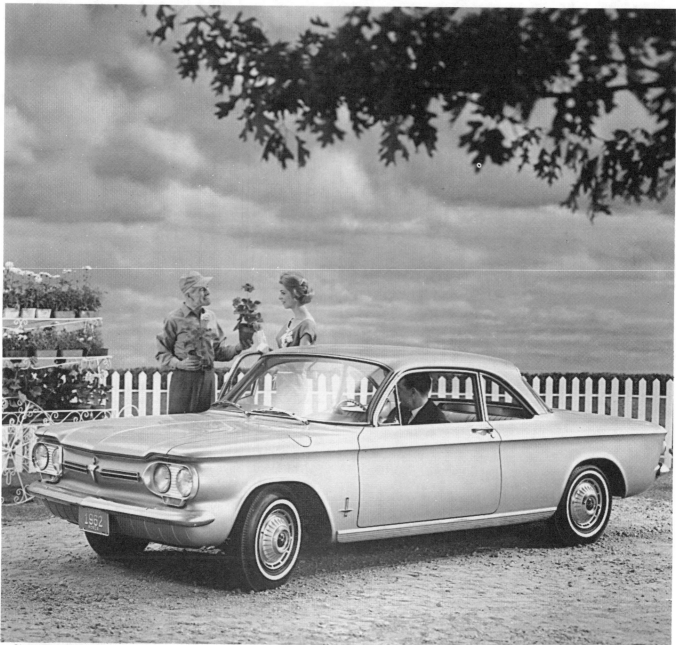

Changes were minor for '62. By far the most popular Corvair of all time was the Monza Club Coupe pictured here. With its gutsy air-cooled six and plush front bucket seats, the Monza was almost an institution in suburban America.

In its first full year on the market, the Corvair convertible did well. Production reached 44,165 units in 1963. Never again would so many Monza ragtops be sold in one year.

would not be enough to overcome Ford's claim that Mustangers had more fun. In any event, by 1964, the story of the "first generation" Corvair had reached its conclusion.

One cannot really mention the early Corvairs without coming to terms with the accusations by Mr. Nader about "one car accidents" caused by faulty Corvairs and the "unconscionable efforts" of General Motors to sell such a dangerous machine. The fact is that the Corvair was proven to have cornering abilities superior to any other early Sixties production car, save the Chevrolet Corvette.

The Corvair was involved, proportionately, in more accidents than Ford Falcons or Plymouth Valiants of similar vintage. But Corvairs tended to be driven by younger, more inexperienced, more exhuberant drivers. As are Pontiac Firebirds and Mazda RX-7's today. Handling improvements in 1964 only made the Corvair that much superior a road machine to the competition. The modifications were not made to belatedly "fix" a defective product, only to make a remarkable machine so mcuh more so.

So, the 1960-64 Corvairs are now vindicated. They remain timeless in concept, in design, and in execution.

Model choice was again limited in 1964 as the 500 and 700 Series cars became less important in the Corvair scheme of things. The 500 was available only as a coupe and the 700 was offered only as a sedan while Monzas came as coupes, sedans, convertibles, and the Monza Spyder became a separate series unto itself.

Greenbrier, Corvan, and Rampside production totals declined again in 1964 as that model was neglected by Chevrolet as it prepared to introduce its conventional front-engine Chevy Van. Although it was barely recognized by Chevrolet, the Greenbrier would continue in limited production into the beginning of the 1965 model year.

The beginning of the end for the Corvair came in April 1964 when Ford introduced the Mustang. It was all that the Corvair Monza was, without controversial engineering and with a V8 engine. Chevrolet would release a new Corvair in 1965 with continental styling and more power but it Fun was the theme and Corvair offered plenty of it. As one Monza ad, dated 1963, put it: "It growls for the men and purrs for the ladies." That's the beauty of an early Corvair.

1964 Corvair Monza coupe

That Sporty Corvair Wagon

By Tony Hossain

When the Chevrolet Corvair was introduced in the fall of 1959 as a 1960 model, it was available as a four-door sedan only. The two trim levels were both rather austere although the base 500 series was particularly devoid of any superfluous trim. In spite of its rear engine and radical engineering features, sales were slow right from the start. At the same time, the conventionally engineered but better appointed Ford Falcon was setting first year sales records.

Chevrolet decided that an expansion of the model lineup would improve the Corvair's competitive position. The first step was the introduction of a sporty coupe to complement the four door cars.Then, almost as an afterthought, they upgraded the interior, threw in some bucket seats and called it a Monza. But the transformation of the Corvair into a full line of compact family cars came in 1961.

The 1961 Corvairs were available in three series, the 500, the 700 and the bucket seat Monza. In addition, a full range of Corvair based trucks were unveiled. They included panel trucks, pickups and window vans. The trucks were called Corvans while the passenger vans were called Greenbriers. But Chevy's highest hopes for increasing Corvair sales volume rested with its new Corvair station wagons. Named the Lakewoods, they were available in 500 or 700 series trim. The Lakewood name corresponded to the full size Chevy Parkwood and Brookwood wagons. Portions of the body design were shared with the new-for-1961 Pontiac Tempest, Olds F-85 and Buick Special wagons but there was much that was different. Most importantly, as in other Corvair models, the engine was located in the rear. Although this cut into rear load space, Chevy was quick to point out that the design offered the advantage of a lockable front trunk.

Things didn't turn out as Chevrolet product planners would have guessed in 1961. Buyers flocked to the conservative, sensible Ford Falcon station wagons while they virtually ignored the Corvair wagons. Falcon wagons found over 120,000 buyers in '61 while less than 26,000 Lakewoods left Chevy showrooms that year. Of these, only 5,591 were of the stripped 500 series wagon.

But it was that mid-1960 afterthought, the Monza Club Coupe, that saved the Corvair in 1961. Exactly 109,945 Monza Club Coupes were sold, making the little bucket seat sportster one of the sales successes of 1961. The Corvair had found its niche in the marketplace, not as an economical family car but as a four-on-the-floor, bucket seat machine for enthusiasts. It should have been apparent right from the beginning that Chevrolet was trying to sell a car to the Consumers Reports crowd that was really much more attuned to the *Road & Track* reader. The Monza was in short supply all year long while Lakewood wagons and 500 series sedans languished on dealers' back lots.

By the beginning of the 1962 model year, Chevrolet was finally getting a handle on the Corvair market. Advertising now concentrated on the Monza and its sporty car virtues while other models, the wagons in particular, were ignored. But based on the dismal track record of the 1961 wagons, some realignments were made. The Lakewood name was discontinued and the slow-selling 500 wagon was dropped. Wagons were now either 700's or the new for '62 Monza. The Monza wagon was very plush and offered a choice of a fabric bench seat or vinyl buckets. But several factors were working against the 1962 Corvair station wagons. One of the most important was the introduction of conventionally engineered 1962 Chevy II family of cars. Those few Corvair buyers who were still interested in its virtues as a family sedan were now being steered into Chevy II's by the Chevrolet sales force. The Chevy II station wagon was an immediate sales success while the Corvair wagon was now little more than a curiosity. But Monza sales were booming. Over 200,000 were sold in the 1962 model year, surpassing all expectations. Only 2,362 of those Monzas were wagons, though. Another 3,716 wagons were sold in 700 trim.

Adding more sparkle to the Corvair sales picture was the mid-1962 introduction of the Monza convertible and the turbocharged Monza Spyder. To make room for these new models on the assembly line and also to increase production capacity for the Chevy II, Corvair station wagon production ceased in April, 1962.

The 1961 Corvair Lakewood 700 station wagon.

In its short 1.5 years on the market, the Corvair wagon never really made an impact on anyone. Wagon buyers preferred the conservative nature of the Falcon and other front engine compacts while sporty car buyers were buying their Corvairs in Monza Club Coupe form. But that Corvair wagon makes plenty of sense to enthusiasts of the marque today. It remains a very attractive station wagon and its low production assures it collector status.

Caviar Corvair

By Gerald Perschbacher

Many connoisseurs of Corvairs savor the Corvair Monza Spyder as much as connoisseurs crave caviar.

When the '64 version was launched on Dec. 26, 1963, the world was walking to a faster pace as the decade of the '60s unfolded. "Don't lose your head to gain a minute — you need your head, your brains are in it," said the Burma-Shave signs that appeared along the roads in '63. The wisdom of the saying seemed aimed at the typical Corvair buyer who had a streak of speeding in his veins but still was sensible enough not to let it get the best of him.

The Monza Spyder convertibles, along with the coupe, came as a two-door. It brandished a crossed-flag design just below the rear-engine deck lid and whispered its Spyder heritage with a special signature below the Monza badges on the lower portion of the front fender. The turbo-charged engine had 20 extra cubic inches but still was rated at 150 hp. The convertible in '64 cost $2,811 and weighed 2,580 pounds — heaviest in the Corvair lineup that year. Production for the Spyder convertible was lowest for Corvair that year, also, with only 4,761 units pounding the pavement.

But the 164 cubic-inch engine — complete with aluminum block and horizontally opposed six-cylinders, was a good power house. New gaskets and redesigned hardware proved to be a better deterent to oil leakage from the rocker arm covers — a common problem on older models. Rear brakes were improved this year, and a transverse leaf spring added extra stability to the rear suspension. Many people rated the new '64 Corvairs — including the Spyder — significantly improved versions of a good-selling product.

Some extras like heater or radio came on nearly all Corvairs for 1964, while the automatic transmission was ordered only on 47 percent, air-conditioning on a little over three percent, and bucket seats were just short of 80 percent of Corvairs.

On its 108-inch wheel base, the Spyder stretched out to 180 inches. 6.50x14-inch tires were standard on all models, and 75 percent of total Corvair production flashed whitewall tires.

With top down, the Spyder for '64 proved to be an economy car that ran several hundred dollars more expensive than your standard Corvair. It may not have been a Corvette, but the Spyder still had its share of fun in the sun.

Popular in red and other bright colors, the '64 Spyder was a cute little package with a mean little bite.

1965-69 Corvair Against All Odds

by Tony Hossain

After five years of basically unchanged styling, Chevrolet introduced a spectacularly new Corvair in 1965. It still looked like a Corvair, the air-cooled engine was mounted in the rear, but the design was decidedly European in character. The Corvair no longer made any pretenses to being a family sedan. It was strictly an automobile for enthusiasts.

The 1965 Corvair, and the all-new '65 full-size Chevys, followed curvaceous new styling themes introduced two years earlier on the Buick Riviera. Body lines were flowing, the fender line was curvaceous, and the side windows were curved inwards. Bill Mitchell, GM's design chief at the time, called it "as new as a new car has ever been". The press immediately took a liking to this new car. *Car and Driver* said: "Chevy's all-new Corvair, we love it!"

The Corvair model lineup was revised in '65. The only models available were a two-door hardtop, a four-door hardtop, and a convertible. The Corvair had never before been offered in hardtop form. Gone were the four-door sedans and the coupes. Also disappearing was the 700 series, which had been around since 1960. The 500 series remained the Corvair price leaders, now available as a two-door hardtop and a four-door hardtop. The popular Monza was available in those models and also as a convertible. Replacing the Monza Spyder as the top-of-the-line sports model was the Corsa, available in two-door hardtop and convertible form. Addition of the Corsa nameplate was a very last-minute decision and it has been reported that a few Corvairs with Monza *Spyder* nameplates were produced very early in the 1965 model year.

Underneath the handsome new styling was a new suspension that corrected any deficiencies that might have existed in the original swing-axle design. Based on the design used by the 1963 Corvette Sting Ray, the Corvair retained the advantages of a fully independent suspension but rear-wheel "tuck-under" and drastic camber changes were now eliminated. Next to the Corvette, the Corvair was now one of the best handling cars made anywhere in the world.

There were some important changes in the engine compartment as well for 1965. Displacement of the "Turbo-Air" horizontally opposed six cylinder engine had been increased to 164 cubic inches in '64 but Chevy "hot-rodded" the engine even more for '65. The base engine, rated at 95 horsepower and standard in 500 and Monza models, was unchanged as was the high compression 110

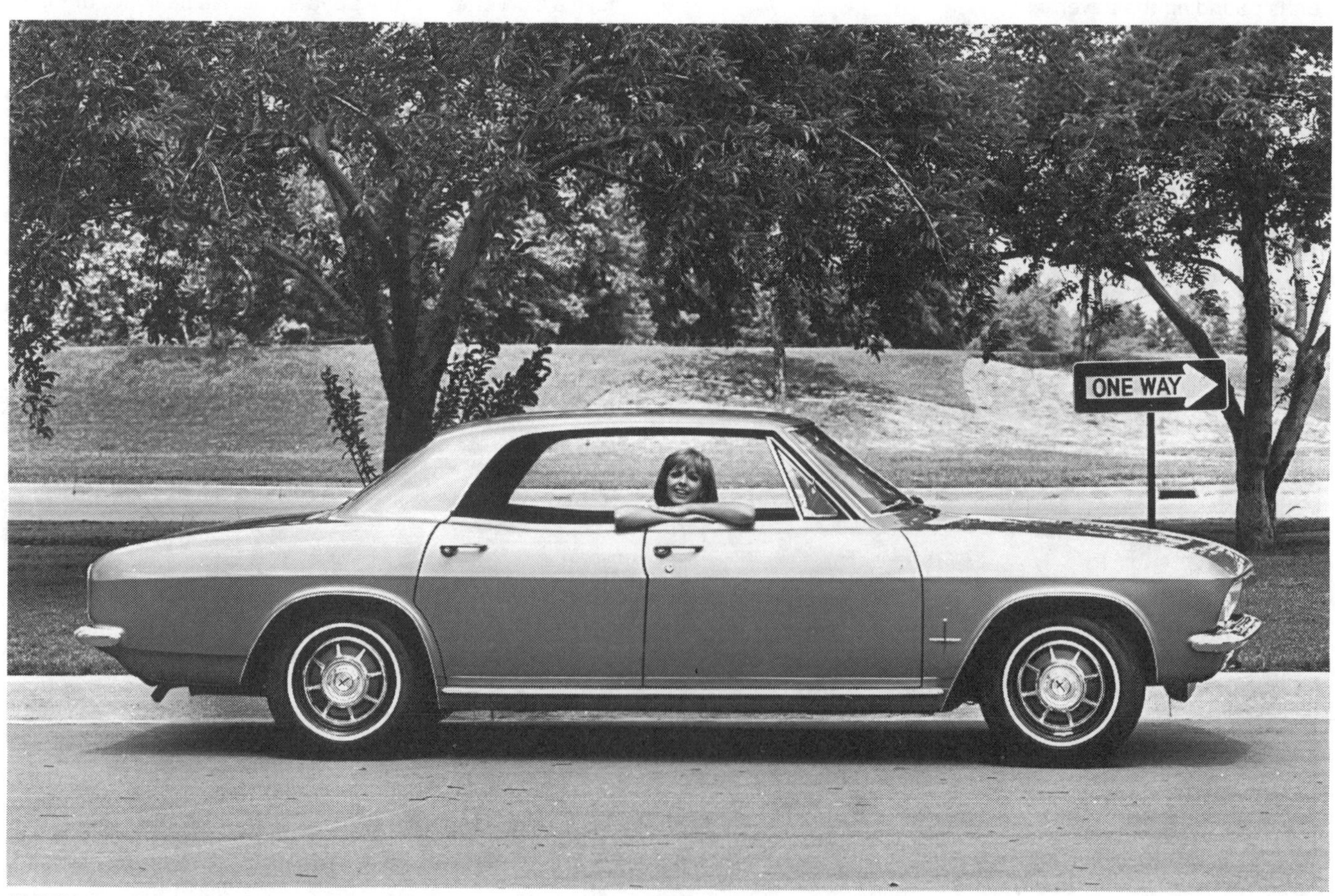

1967 Monza Sport Sedan.

hp version. An alternator replaced the generator, though. Big news was the addition of a four single-barrel carb engine option that was rated at 140 hp. This was the highest horsepower rating ever claimed for a carbureted Corvair. The 140 was an option in the 500 and Monza and was standard in the Corsa series. Replacing the turbocharged 150 hp engine of the 1962-64 Monza Spyders was a 180 hp turbocharged engine optional only in the Corsa.

The standard transmission in all Corvairs was a three-speed manual unit, floor-mounted. A four-speed was optional on all models and the automatic Powerglide was available on 500 and Monza cars only.

Sales of the Corvair in 1965 were up to 235,528 cars plus 1,528 Greenbriers. Yes, Greenbriers. It's not common knowledge but Chevrolet continued Greenbrier production into the 1965 model year on a limited basis. However, by January 1965, the conventional front-engine Chevy Van had replaced the Greenbrier as Chevrolet's entry in the compact van market. Even though sales were up in '65, the model year was something of a disappointment. Only in 1964 had Chevrolet sold fewer Corvairs and the immensely popular Ford Mustang was stealing away many former Corvair Monza buyers. The most popular Monza was, by far, the most popular Corvair. Chevy spared little to make the 1965 version appear well-equipped and it was every bit as plush as the new Mustang. Standard equipment included well placed exterior chrome highlights, Monza identification, full wheel covers, and chrome roof drip mouldings. The inside story was where the Monza really came into its own. All-vinyl bucket seats were offered in fawn, red, blue, saddle, black, slate, and white. The white bucket seat interior featured a choice of aqua or black carpeting and accents. Monza models also featured a standard fold-down rear seat, silver finish dash panel, and a distinct steering wheel emblem.

All in all, 1965 was a successful year for the all-new Corvair. There was pressure, to be sure, from Ford and lawsuits over accidents involving 1960-63 Corvairs were gaining national attention. Chevrolet decided in mid-1965 that the Corvair was not sufficient competition for the V8 Mustang and proceeded with development of a conventional sporty car. It would be called Camaro. In April 1965, despite the relative success of the '65 car, Chevrolet made a decision to stop all further developmental work on the Corvair. Production was intended to stop at the end of

1965 Monza Hardtop with aftermarket side molding.

Corvair, again in 1965, was the Monza coupe. It found 88,894 buyers. The rarest is also, now, the most desirable...the Corsa convertible. Only 8,353 were sold. In addition to the Corvairs built in the United States, another 10,036 were built in Canada. It's not known how many of these cars were shipped to the United States and elsewhere in the world.

The austere Corvair 500 was the only series to feature a front bench seat instead of buckets. Interior color choices were limited to fawn, aqua, or red and rubber mats covered the floor. Standard equipment included dual sun visors, front seat belts, cigarette lighter, lockable glove box, dome light, and heater-defroster.

As Chevrolet fully expected, the luxurious, bucket seat

The 1969 Monza interior featured vinyl bucket seats, a Monza trademark since 1960.

the 1966 model year when the Camaro was to be introduced.

Ralph Nader put a monkey wrench in Chevrolet's plans in November 1965 with the publication of *Unsafe at Any Speed* which devoted its first chapter to a sharp indictment of General Motors and the Corvair. The book's ascent to the best-seller list coincided with Chevy's introduction of the 1966 model Corvair. Because General Motors thought that the end of Corvair production might appear to be a suggestion that the automobile was indeed dangerous, it was decided to keep the car in production as long as there was any demand at all. Nader destroyed the reputation of one of America's finest automobiles in the mind of the general public and was instrumental in the plummeting sales totals of 1966 but he did not hasten the car's demise. Ironically, the car survived through the 1967, 1968, and 1969 model year precisely because of Ralph Nader and his well-publicized book.

Many Corvair lovers consider the 1966 model to be the very best Corvair ever built. The model lineup was unchanged. The four-door hardtop, available in 500 Series and Monza form, remained one of the prettiest four-doors ever built. It's easy to tell a 1965 and a 1966 Corvair apart because of the different wheel covers and minor trim changes made but it's almost impossible to differentiate a '66 model from a later one because very few changes were made after that.

Changes for 1966 included the new wheel covers, standard on Corsas and Monzas, thinner chrome trim around the wheel openings, a Corvair script relocated on the front left panel, new tail lamps, and a one piece engine air exhaust grille. The chrome band at the front was also changed, something that had been done in every year since 1960...but would not be done again. Corsas no longer used a body side pinstripe.

New mechanical features included larger tires, a spoiler under the front bumper, fully synchronized three-speed manual transmission, and an improved carburetor linkage on the 140-horse four-carb engine.

Because of the rapidly brewing safety storm in Washington, last-minute additions to the standard equipment list on all Corvairs included front and rear seat belts, padded dashboard, two-speed windshield wipers, outside rear view mirror and padded sun visors. A raft of new colors, both inside and out, were offered. Three colors, Marina Blue, Lemonwood Yellow, and Chateau Slate, were available exclusively on Monza and Corsa models.

1966 Corvair Monza

The only outside change for 1968 were the side marker lights that can be seen in these photos. On January 1, 1968, front shoulder belts became standard on all Corvairs. This is the Monza Sport Coupe.

There were newly styled bucket seats in the Monza and Corsa series and the 500 featured an upgraded vinyl interior.

Engine choices remained unchanged and the Corsa was still available with the 180 hp turbocharged engine, unique in the American auto industry.

For all the revisions and subtle improvements on a car already considered terrific by the "buffs," things were not going well in the sales department. Nader's attack was having its effect. Sales declined rapidly to 103,743 cars, making this Corvair's worst year ever. Of these, only 7,330 Corsa coupes and 3,142 Corsa convertibles were built. Many collectors consider these models to be the most desirable Corvairs of them all. Another 6,137 (including 839 Corsas) were built in Canada.

New options for 1966 included headrests, four-way flashers, shoulder belts, mag-type wheel covers, and the F41 performance suspension. Only 2.2% of the '66 Corvair customers specified the telescoping steering column. Sixty-eight percent chose whitewalls and 26.7% of the cars were equipped with the optional four-speed manual transmission.

Chevrolet didn't want too much in-house competition for its new Camaro so the already crippled Corvair was stripped of the performance Corsa series in 1967. Also removed from the option list was the 140 hp four-carb engine which was previously standard in Corsas and optional on the 500 and Monza cars. But Corvair lovers were surprisingly vocal on this point. After receiving many complaints from dealers and customers, the 140 engine was reinstated in mid-1967 as a *limited production option*.

The only other changes of any significance in 1967 were safety-related. An energy-absorbing steering column was added as was a dual master brake cylinder system. A new, stronger three-spoke steering wheel and thin-shell bucket seats on Monzas were the most noticeable interior revisions. "Energy-absorbing" knobs and added dashboard padding were also introduced in '67. Shoulder belt anchorage points were standard and the belts became a regular production option. The optional wire wheel covers lost the pointed spinner in the name of pedestrian safety. New options in 1967 included a stereo tape system and an emergency road kit. A five-year warranty was introduced in 1967 and it would be standard on all 1967, '68, and '69 Corvairs. Popular new exterior colors included Bolero Red, Butternut Yellow, Granada Gold, and Royal Plum. Traditional favorites included Ermine White, Tuxedo Black, and Madeira Maroon. Interior color choices were trimmed to black, blue, and fawn in the 500's and gold, bright blue, and black in the Monzas.

Production plummeted from already disastrous 1966 levels for '67. The final tally showed that only 27,253 Corvairs left the Willow Run, Mich., assembly plant and production was stopped entirely in Canada. The rarest model was the Monza convertible. Only 2,109 were built. There was no logical reason to let the Corvair live past '67 without any ad support but General Motors had to save face. The Corvair was almost totally ignored by the factory and Chevrolet dealers but it was announced in the summer of 1967 that, yes, there would be a 1968 Corvair.

When the 1968 Corvair was announced, it was immediately realized that the axe had fallen once more. The handsome four-door Corvairs were no more. The Corvair lineup in the early Sixties had consisted of forward control trucks, station wagons, coupes, sedans in a multitude of trim levels but now only the Monza coupe and convertible and the 500 coupe survived.

But there was a bit of good news. The 140-horse version of the 164 cubic inch Turbo-Air six was back as a regular production option. Transmission choices again included the three and four-speed manuals and the automatic Powerglide.

Outside revisions for '68 were limited to side marker lights while added padding and newly textured bucket seats on Monzas identified the new models. Interior color choices were limited to black, blue or gold on both series.

All 1968 Corvairs featured, thanks to the air quality of Los Angeles County, an air injector anti-pollution system. Because of this system, air conditioning was no longer available on Corvairs. Popular new exterior colors in '68 included Ash Gold, Teal Blue, and Palomino Ivory. Corvair production for the model year was down to 15,399, and they were being assembled at almost a hand-built pace.

The announcement of the 1969 Corvair astounded even the most loyal of its promoters. It was practically unchanged from the '68 models. The 140 hp engine was still around as was the Monza convertible. It seemed, though, that not many were interested anymore. Only 6,000 Corvairs were built in the final model run. And it was a shame. The last Corvair assembled at Willow Run was an Olympic Gold Monza coupe. Carrying serial number 105379W706000, it left the plant at 1:30 p.m. on May 14, 1969. After it was loaded onto a rail car, nobody knows where it went. There are reports that General Motors still owns this car.

There were many eulogies and great sadness in the automotive press at the time of the death of the Corvair. But the fact remains that the car had few buyers in 1969 and GM couldn't justify further production of the car. Besides, its replacement in the compact segment of the market, the Vega, would be in production in just over a year. There was much speculation as to what the Corvair could have been if GM would have tried a little in the last years of its life. Now as we look back, from the perspective of the Nineties, it's clear that the Corvair owners among us are some pretty lucky people indeed. The early models, especially the Monza Club Coupes, have that "just right" look and the 1965-69 models have all the appearance of contemporary Italian customs...at a fraction of the cost.

Now, if I can just find that '66 Corsa convert...

This is Corvair, 1969. As indicated in this factory photo, the car is practically unchanged from the model introduced in the fall of 1964 with great fanfare. The last Corvair, an Olympic Gold Monza Sport Coupe, was built on May 14, 1969.

The Real Corvair Story

by Bill Artzberger

1961 Corvair 4 Dr

Is the Corvair dead? As Mark Twain once stated, "The report of my demise has been grossly exaggerated!"

The sporty little Corvair is indeed very much alive and well as can be attested to by nearly 7,000 CORSA (Corvair Society of America) members. Between the fall of 1959 and the spring of 1969, 1,786,243 Corvairs were manufactured. At the last count, nearly 300,000 are registered and running — a very respectable survival rate of 17 percent. Most automobiles of similar vintage can expect a longevity rate of only five to seven percent.

But are they safe? Most everyone is aware of the history of the Corvair and the young lawyer and consumer advocate, Ralph Nader. The Corvair automobile and Nader became synonymous and still are. However, as the facts unwind, it's clear that he wasn't a major factor in the decision to stop building the Corvair.

Ed Cole was the father of the Corvair. Some of his credentials as a General Motors engineer were his work with World War II army tanks at the GM Cadillac Plant, the '49 Cadillac high-compression engine, his development of the famous small-block V-8 Chevrolet, and his early rise to General Manager of Chevrolet Division of GM in 1956. (Cole eventually became President of GM in 1967 at the age of 58.)

The Corvair was the product of Cole's creative imagination. Rear-engined foreign cars were readily being accepted by American car buyers. The German Volkswagens were selling as rapidly as they could be unloaded from a ship. Renaults were, too. And the Porsches were being snapped up faster than any sports car of the period.

It would be speculative to say that GM had in mind developing a "poor man's Porsche," but Cole tested his new Corvair engine in a Porsche body and was elated. This was the stepping-stone needed to further develop the new Corvair.

The original engine plan was to have a flat six-cylinder, air-cooled engine cast from aluminum in two halves. The cylinders and head and intake manifold were to be cast en bloc. The first of these engines experienced excessive cylinder wall wear due to poor aluminum alloys. The Reynolds Aluminum Co. claimed they could correct this problem using a silicone aluminum alloy. This was never developed further after it was discovered to be too hard to be machined economically.

The accepted plan was to use separate cast iron cylinders and two separate cylinder heads. Because of the 11 engine castings necessitated, as opposed to the original plan of two, the engine grew proportionately expensive. A compromise was then made and the go-ahead given to produce the new Corvair. The costs were cut elsewhere, but not in the engine. These cost cuts would eventually come back to haunt GM as a charge was made in one of their lawsuits that the lack of a front sway bar (to save money) caused the car to be unsafe. (This was disproved, but nevertheless remained indelible.)

The Corvair reached the showrooms in the fall of 1959. An old adage states: "First impressions are best." The Corvair missed on its first shot. Rubber floor mats and gray upholstery were not what car buyers were searching for. The performance of the 80-hp, 140-cid engine, especially with the two-speed Powerglide transmission, was feeble. Sales were less than expected for a Chevrolet.

Even before the first Corvairs were shown, Cole and his crew of automotive engineers and designers no doubt had planned the Monza 900 model. Zora Arkus-Duntov (the Corvette expert) was corralled to add some spirit to the car, and he did. Whatever the initial 500 and 700 models lacked, the Monza 900 did not. It was nearly a total new car! With bucket seats, stainless steel, and anodized aluminum trim, it was the automobile that set the styling aesthetics for cars to come. In the luxury sports car field, it was the epitome! The Monza 900 sold more than any

1962 Monza 900 Club Coupe

1962 Monza 900 Club Coupe

1963 Corvair Monza convertible

other Corvair model until its end in 1964.

It was quickly recognized that car buyers wanted more high performance. A new, larger, and consequently heavier engine would be necessary, but impossible. In a clever effort to boost horsepower, the Chevrolet engineers came up with a turbocharger. (The first one appeared in 1962.) This model was named the "Spyder."

By the time 1964 rolled around, the engine was stroked to 164 cid and a rear sway bar was added. (This was in addition to the front sway bar that was added in 1961.) Improvements were made to brakes and the original 1960 austere, low-priced compact car was transformed into a very respectable automobile that was fun to drive. Although Corvair sales didn't match the more conventional Ford Falcon, Rambler, or Valiant sales, they were hefty enough to make a small profit and the Corvair temporarily filled a void in the GM lineup of auto offerings.

The 1965 (through 1969) Corvair was a completely new automotive milestone. Both the body styling and the controversial suspension were exhaustively changed. There was a new high-compression engine with four progressively linked carburetors offered at 140 hp. The Monza nameplate was continued while the Spyder was dropped in favor of "Corsa." The 140-hp turbocharged engine was upped to 180 hp. The rear suspension was no longer swing-arm. It was now a trailing-arm nearly identical to the Corvette, but with two coil springs instead of a transverse spring.

1963 Greenbrier Van

1965 Corvair convertible

It was trumpeted as one of the best automobiles ever to be run off any American assembly line. Writers and engineers alike couldn't praise the car enough. Photographers conceded the new body style had no bad angles for picture taking. Some still think it's one of Detroit's best looking cars. Performance-wise, it won races on road courses and was (and still is) a favorite for parking lot slalom racing.

And that is the first half of the Corvair story. The second half really began early on while the first half was taking place.

Sometime in early 1961, a son of a California malpractice attorney was killed in a Corvair. In July of 1961, the attorney's law partner, Mr. Harney, filed a suit against GM claiming the Corvair had a defective design. Ads were placed in several lawyer-oriented magazines in an attempt to organize a group of attorneys interested in furnishing information that could be used against GM and the Corvair. The American Trial Lawyers Association and Nader entered into the picture. The A.T.L.A. is a group of attorneys who act for the plaintiff in product liability cases. While Nader wasn't involved in a court case against GM up to that point, he gained recognition with an article he had written titled, "The Safe Car You Can't Buy." He was becoming a self-appointed consumer advocate.

Soon, Harney had 30 cases on his docket. All were against GM and the Corvair. In June of 1964, the first of these, the Pierini case, was brought to trial. Mrs. Pierini claimed that her Corvair suddenly, and for no apparent reason, went off the road. While trying to return from the soft shoulder onto the road, her Corvair, at 30-35 mph, wildly and uncontrollably crossed the highway. It struck an embankment and rolled over, severing her arm.

The case went on for three days before GM's attorneys decided they were ill-prepared and would ask to settle the $300,000 lawsuit out of court. Harney agreed and the case was settled for $70,000.

The media latched onto the decision and in headlines interpreted it to say that GM lost and conceded to building faulty Corvairs. (A court settlement isn't an admission of guilt. The media chose to ignore this fact.) Americans were given the choice to believe that GM, a company that had been building automobiles for some 60 years, was deliberately negligent in choosing the Corvair design;

knew the Corvair was unsafe; cut costs to gain profits; and was willfully and intentionally building an automobile that would kill customers!

Some Americans believed this, and some didn't as they continued to buy Corvairs. They were in the minority, of course, but they remained undaunted.

The outcome of the Pierini case caused other cases against GM to be filed as fast as paper could be wound into a typewriter. To be precise, the number of cases grew to 294.

Little attention was given to the cases that GM won. Ten cases were tried and eight verdicts were for GM. The two cases against GM were appealed. One resulted in favor of GM. The other was a comparative negligence verdict and GM was held responsible for only 12 percent of the damages.

Back at the factory, it was business as usual. The first series and body styles were phased out in favor of the new '65 models. By the time these cars hit the showrooms, they were completely overshadowed by the '64½ Ford Mustang. The Mustang was introduced with the largest advertising campaign ever known to the auto industry. The '65 Corvair, the marvel of innovation, was on the road to the orphanage. The order from the top was to begin winding down the Corvair. It was obvious that it couldn't be developed to compete with the upsurging muscle car era.

No other automobile ever had as much notoriety as the Corvair had to this point. But the most damaging was yet to come. The United States Government would enter into a conflict that would last until March of 1973, four years after the last Corvair came off the assembly line!

Abraham Ribicoff, a senator from Connecticut, was assigned to a subcommittee to investigate something — anything — that seemed important and timely. He took aim at automobile safety. Nader was immediately selected as his primary consultant. He was the perfect choice. There was no one who was more interested or more concerned about auto safety. And the timing couldn't have been better. GM had just settled a lawsuit involving a stuck accelerator on a '60 Chevrolet. Nader was listed as the defense council in a successful appeal brief.

It's difficult to imagine that the giant of industry that GM was, a top auto manufacturer in the world, could be so void of wisdom. After the Pierini case was settled for $70,000 because they were ill-prepared, it would have been logical for GM high-level executives to work to avoid bad press in any other confrontations.

Not so.

In November of 1965, *Unsafe at Any Speed* reached the book stores. Now, Nader had become their target. Who was he? What did he want? What was he trying to prove? They handed the job of investigating Nader to Aloysious F. Power, GM's chief counsel. Power hired a private investigator, William F. O'Neil, to look into Nader's past.

He checked out Nader's hometown of Winsted, Conn. He checked his school, his Sunday school, his employment as a newspaper boy, his family, and his family's business. His years at the Harvard Law School were checked. If anything was against Nader, it was his backward, colorless lifestyle that was dull by comparison to the standards of youth. He was untarnished.

GM, not satisfied, decided to go further. (This was during the period that the Ribicoff hearing was in full swing.) They went to their own Eileen Murphy, the GM law librarian. It was she who became insistent that something less than perfection could be discovered about Nader.

It's not against the law to investigate a person's private life. However, it's against the law to harass a person. Nader accepted the prank phone calls in the middle of the night. He accepted the gumshoes who secretly watched his every move from doorways. Then, in the course of events, on two different occasions, Nader was approached by very attractive young ladies. This upset Nader — it was the final straw. He was certain that someone was trying to discredit him and he let it be known. Newspaper headlines read: "Nader Claims He Was Trailed and Harassed."

GM's President James Roche was summoned to Ribicoff's subcommittee floor for an explanation. While denying any harassment, Roche admitted to an investigation into Nader's life. In an attempt to placate all parties, Roche publically apologized. His statement was a public admission that GM had indeed investigated Nader. Power and his investigators were cross-examined and emphatically denied any activities other than questions and some surveillance. For reasons unknown, Murphy was never questioned. The hearing lasted one day. The memory of the meeting lasted much longer.

The Ribicoff hearings on auto safety continued with '60-'63 Corvairs fingered as the center of controversy. GM, once again ill-prepared, had to shift into high gear to strengthen their case. First, they had to educate their own attorneys as to the fine points of automotive engineering. Then, they had to educate everyone involved who'd have a bearing on any decisions of the committee. The testimony of race drivers including Stirling Moss, Juan Fangio, Carroll Shelby, and Phil Hill was used. GM wanted nothing left to be questioned. They did their homework.

The hearings cost both the taxpayers and GM millions of dollars. In the final analysis, it was proven that GM wasn't negligent and the Corvair wasn't unsafe. A statement was issued in July 1972 by the U.S. Department of Transportation and it read: "The handling and stability performance of the 1960-1963 Corvair does not result in an abnormal potential for loss of control or rollover, and it is at least as good as the performance of most contemporary vehicles, both foreign and domestic."

The very innocent Corvair, while proven not guilty of any wrongdoing, was guilty — guilty of being too far ahead for public acceptance; guilty of being too sophisticated and stylish; and guilty of causing the onslaught of safety regulations that were to begin and continue to this day.

While the Corvair hasn't yet gained an overwhelming popularity with collectors because of its misunderstood reputation, it shouldn't be overlooked. It's one of today's most unique and affordable collectible automobiles.

Chevrolet Corvair — Proven Safe in Obscure Gov't Report

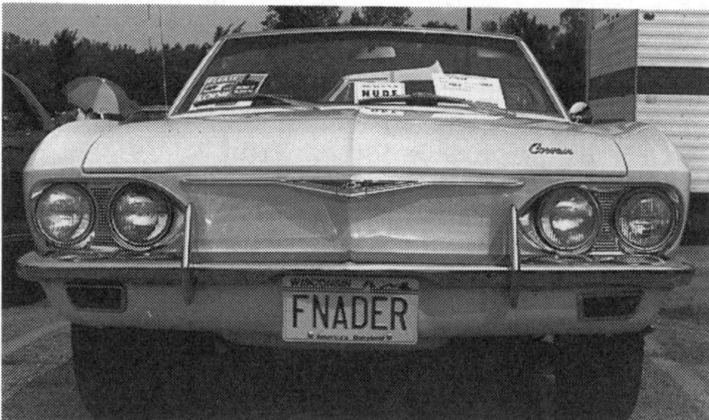

The early Corvairs, with their swing-axle suspension, did have a tendency towards oversteering in high-speed cornering. But with the all-new 1965 Corvair, a sophisticated rear suspension inspired by the Corvette Sting Ray was adopted. The new Corvair handled like a sports car and was priced like a Falcon. But the damage had been done and the Corvair was allowed to wither away. Car pictured is a 1965 Corvair Corsa convertible. (photo courtesy Chevrolet Motor Division)

This innocent little car was the subject of a storm of controversy in the mid-1960's. Critics said that the 1960-63 Corvairs were unstable and, in fact, "unsafe at any speed." The U.S. Department of Transportation refuted this contention in the early 1970's but by then nobody was listening. Car pictured is a 1961 Corvair 700 four-door sedan. (photo courtesy Chevrolet Motor Division)

Editor's note: Since its introduction in the fall of 1959, and especially since Ralph Nader's rise to prominence in the mid-1960's, the sporty Chevrolet Corvair has been the subject of controversy. There were some who said that it was a dangerous, unstable car which should have been taken off the American road. The attacks were too much for the little car and it was taken off the market in 1969.

But Corvair owners loved their cars. Back in the early sixties, Corvair clubs counted thousands among their members and Sunday rallying was part of the fun. The Corvair was an enthusiast's car, and to this day thousands remain enthusiastic.

Unfortunately, the vast majority of Americans and many Corvair drivers heard the cries of "consumer groups" and their shrill attacks on the "unsafe at any speed car" but never were informed of the Corvair's vindication. Yes, its vindication.

At the insistence of those who wanted to run the Corvair off the road, the U.S. Department of Transportation undertook an investigation of the Corvair's handling characteristics and found the car "at least as good as the performance of some other contemporary vehicles both foreign and domestic." They found that the car had no safety-related defect. This report, released in the early 1970's, unfortunately, never received the same publicity as the original attacks. And it came too late, several years after the Corvair had been forced off the market.

But for those of you who want to know a little bit more about the Corvair and how it compared to the competition, the Department of Transportation's conclusions, which were sent to concerned Corvair owners in a letter, are reprinted here:

Dear Corvair Owner:

This letter is being sent to you by the Department of Transportation's National Highway Traffic Safety Administration (NHTSA) to inform you of the results of our comprehensive investigation of the handling and stability characteristics of the 1960-63 model year Corvairs. We believe you have a right, and a need, to know the results of our efforts because of the controversy concerning this vehicle and the extensive publicity associated with it. We have concluded that the handling and stability of the 1960-63 Corvair does not result in an abnormal potential loss for control or rollover and that the handling and stability performance is at least as good as the performance of some other contemporary vehicles both foreign and domestic.

This investigation began in September 1970. It commenced with the gathering, review and analysis of all documents, films and test data in the possession of General Motors relevant to the handling and stability question. This included the review of certain test films alleged by Mr. Ralph Nader to prove that the Corvair rolled over. Also included in the investigation was our analysis of a Ford Falcon-Corvair comparison test film made by the Ford Motor Company also alleged by Mr. Nader to prove the Corvair defective. In addition, we analyzed available accident data to determine whether the Corvair rolled over more frequently than other comparable vehicles.

After completion of our review and analysis of all available documents, test reports and test data, and statistical information, it was determined that NHTSA would undertake to objectively define the handling and stability-characteristics of the Corvair through tests of its own. A concentrated program of Government testing of the Corvair and contemporary vehicles commenced during the Spring and Summer of 1971. The vehicles compared were the 1962 Falcon, 1962 Volkswagen, 1963 Corvair, 1963 Renault, 1960 Valiant, and a 1967 Corvair. The tests were designed to incorporate steering and braking maneuvers under increasingly severe conditions, including those conditions most likely to precipitate a rollover.

To evalutate the objectivity of NHTSA testing and analysis, a three man advisory panel of recognized and independent professional engineers was retained: Ray W. Caldwell, B.S., M.B.A., President of Autodynamics Corporation; Edwin Resler, Jr., B.S., Ph.D., Director of Graduate School of Aerospace Engineering, Cornell University; Paul H. Wright, B.S., M.S., Ph.D., Associate Professor of Civil Engineering, Georgia Institute of Technology. The panel was requested to review the scope and competence of the NHTSA investigation and specifically to identify any additional vehicle testing believed to be necessary.

From an evaluation of the extensive data obtained from General Motors and from other sources, from an analysis of the NHTSA comparative vehicle testing, and from the recommendations of the advisory panel, the following findings are called to your attention:

1. The available accident data indicates that the rollover rate of the 1960-63 Corvair is comparable to other light domestic cars.

2. The Corvair handling and stability compared favorably with the other contemporary vehicles used in the NHTSA testing programs. Vehicle rollover did not occur in any of the comparative tests for the Corvair, Falcon or Valiant. The Volkswagen and the Renault did rollover in some of the comparative tests.

3. The GM test films which Mr. Nader alleged showed Corvairs being rolled over at speeds from 28 to 30 mph in fact showed that these vehicles were being deliberately rolled over by experienced test drivers for experimental purposes, and that they were developmental tests not representative of the practical driving environment. Such drivers could turn over other cars under similar developmental testing.

4. The Ford Falcon-Corvair comparison is not an authentic evaluation of the Corvair's handling and stability characteristics and is repudiated by other Ford evidence as well as the evaluation undertaken by the NHTSA.

5. The 1960-63 Corvair will transition from understeer to oversteer at high levels of lateral acceleration, between 0.4g to 0.5g.

(The term understeer is illustrated by imagining someone driving rapidly around a curve to the right. If speed is increased and it is necessary to turn the wheel toward the right in order to stay in the lane, then the vehicle is understeering. If the steering requires no additional input, the vehicle is then in neutral steer. If the steering requires the driver to straighten the steering wheel of turn it toward the left, then the vehicle is oversteering. The 1960-63 Corvair will transition from understeer, through neutral steer, to moderate oversteer. Most drivers will not voluntarily operate their cars so as to encounter this transition because it occurs only during a turning or skidding movement which the normal driver would find very uncomfortable. This condition is technically known as high lateral (side) acceleration, and is expressed in g's, or gravity forces.)

6. The advisory panel concluded that the NHTSA investigation was adequate in scope and depth, basically sound in design, and professional in its performance. It also concluded that the 1960-63 Corvairs quantitatively meet or exceed the standards set by contemporary cars in stability tests, cornering tests, and rollover tests. The panel concluded that the Corvair is not more unstable or more likely to rollover than contemporary automobiles. Although the panel agreed with the NHTSA engineers that the characteristic transition from understeer to oversteer occurs at lateral accelerations seldom encountered by average drivers, it was concerned about driver response to the transition in emergency situations of high lateral accleration. The panel recommended, therefore, that Corvair owners be advised that, in its opinion, in emergency situations of hard cornering, such as when the vehicle is not being operated normally and prudently and is exceeding safe speed limits on a curve or expressway exit ramp, it may exhibit unusual handling characteristics. The panel also recommended that Corvair owners be advised to maintain the tire pressures recommended by the vehicle's manufacturer.

The NHTSA engineers concluded that many vehicles may exhibit unusual handling characteristics in emergency situations. The typical conventional passenger car is basically an understeering vehicle. However, under various load, speed, and tire pressure conditions, some vehicles, both foreign and domestic, also transition from understeer to oversteer. In the extreme emergency situation, the typical driver makes a brake application, resulting in wheel lock up. In this situation both understeering and oversteering vehicles are uncontrollable. The NHTSA engineers also noted that in extreme emergency situations when wheel lock up does not occur, only a MODERATE AMOUNT of steering movement in the 1960-63 Corvair is required. Drivers will normally correct the steering wheel angle to follow driving direction without any awareness of having made the correction.

Thus, Corvair drivers should realize that hard braking in a turn or skid:

(a) can lock the wheels and eliminate steering, and

(b) aggravates oversteer.

While not enough can be said about being alert and avoiding conditions that can cause skidding movements, if these conditions are encountered Corvair drivers should remember:

(a) that **moderate** steering motions will normally be sufficient for corrective action, and

(b) that rapid jabbing applications of the foot brake is superior to a hard constant application that will lock the wheels.

Accordingly, drivers are encouraged to avoid the pitfall of wheel lock up and be advised to follow their natural reactions to the steering wheel angle, even in emergency situations. Finally, NHTSA engineers are of the opinion that the transition from understeer to oversteer in the Corvair does not result in an unusual risk of loss of vehicle control.

CONCLUSIONS:

A. The NHTSA concluded that the handling and stability performance of the 1960-63 Corvair does not result in an abnormal potential for the loss of control or rollover, and that its handling and stability performance is at least as good as the performance of some contemporary vehicles both foreign and domestic.

B. Based upon its analysis of all available data, its own comparative vehicle testing, and the recommendations of its advisory panel, the NHTSA concluded that no safety-related defect exists with respect to the handling and stability characteristics of the 1960-63 Corvair.

FUMES:

In addition to the foregoing, we would like to again remind those of you who have 1961-63 Corvairs of another matter. This agency has previously concluded that the Corvair direct air heater system in these models does create an unreasonable risk of accident and injury to persons in that engine fumes are transferred from the engine compartment into the passenger compartment, and such engine fumes do in some cases contain carbon monoxide in sufficient concentrations to harm or endanger the occupants of the vehicle. If you have not already responded to the instructions of General Motors in the two letters previously sent requesting that you have your vehicle exhaust-heater inspected, we strongly urge you to (a) follow the instructions in those letters (if you suspect fume intrusion problems leave your windows open) and (b) have the inspection undertaken as soon as possible.

Speaking Of Chevys

By Pat Chappell

Women as Car Buffs

by Pat Chappell

Speaking of Chevys, I read recently in *The News-Journal* (Wilmington, Del.) a headline saying, "Chevrolet focuses attention on women buyers in auto market."

Well, I had to read beyond that, particularly because the "Pat" part of my name is short for Patricia.

I'm not a women's libber nor does the hair on the back of my neck bristle every time I get a letter addressed to *Mr.* Pat Chappell. I find most male auto writers, whom I meet through the Society of Automotive Historians, show nothing but respect. But I seriously doubt that predecessor Terry Boyce ever received mail addressed to *Ms.* Terry Boyce.

There's an assumption that women write about "other" things like cooking, fashion, and decorating. The whole situation reminds me of our married son who is a systems engineer and the "spouse" of a lawyer. He's going to a lawyer's convention with his wife and is concerned that seminars for spouses will include a fashion show, crafts, and basket-weaving!

Speaking of Chevys again, the piece in the paper went on to say that Chevrolet is inaugurating the most comprehensive women's marketing effort in its history. The reason is obvious: females are buying 50 percent of all Novas and Spectrums sold and more than 40 percent of Chevettes and Cavalier hatchbacks. Indeed, Robert D. Burger, Chevrolet General Manager and GM Vice President, says he expects to see the percentages rise in coming years.

With this knowledge, I glanced at a couple of auto magazines currently on the newsstand and, sure enough, I found that women are coming back into Chevrolet advertising.

Not all *Old Cars Weekly* readers will remember advertising in the 1920s, but most of us have seen the vintage ads: the Duesenberg artwork where you saw the person who bought the car — the lady overlooking her staff of gardeners or the man in his stuffy club — but not the car.

The granddaddy of automotive advertising, Ned Jordan, used a romantic appeal to attract "a golden girl from somewhere...going to the place where dreams come true." The woman and her "sassy" pony were in the foreground. The Jordan cabriolet was parked at the crest of the hill in the background. Ned Jordan's female representative was Eve, "who never cared about mechanical things, but knew values far better than Adam, because his feet got tired before he even began shopping." So much for that, Jordan's Eve would be in her eighties and I'd expect, by today, *her* feet would be tired, too.

But I was speaking of Chevrolet. Jordan's woman, "who loved the range of the open road," has been transformed, according to Chevy's marketing department, into someone who is looking for: (1) a helpful and knowledgeable sales person, (2) a car equipped with safety features with a reputation of quality behind it, and (3) attractive credit/financing.

Chevrolet Motor Division's Womens Marketing Committee is offering two-day "Strategies for Success" career conferences in 10 cities, increasing to 20 in 1987 and 1988, with presentations by luminaries such as Sally Ride and Barbara Walters. Additonally, a "Women in Motion" article has been sponsored by Chevrolet as an eight-page insert on health and fitness in *Cosmopolitan* and *Women's Sport and Fitness* magazines.

Speaking of Chevys: Convertibles

by Pat Chappell

Speaking of Chevys, it's convertible weather here in Delaware. We're reminded of our first convertible, a used blue 1951 Styleline DeLuxe which we bought, on a whim, in the spring of 1955, and enjoyed that summer sightseeing in Washington, D.C. We sold it in the fall, mainly because we had no garage. But we had a chance to experience top-down motoring and learned how to enjoy and care for a convertible. We wish we still had it.

Much can be said about the magic of having a convertible. Harry Atkins of *The Philadelphia Inquirer* captured its essence: "Once, in a happier America, hair blowing in the wind, we toured the highways and byways of the nation with the top down; we dreamed and parked high in the hills with the stars blinking above and the city lights below. And we were Jimmy Stewart and June Allyson, or were we Clark Gable and Carole Lombard! Romance was alive in the land."

The convertible died in 1976, but car buffs, romantics, and others were responsible for bringing it back in the eighties.

There are reasons the soft-top left the market. They prompted *Time* magazine to comment, "Once a symbol of status and romance, the convertible is well on its way to joining tailfins on the scrap heap." *Newsweek* said, "Now that the United States has developed freeways that invite breathtaking speed remember, no 55 m.p.h. limit, air that chokes with carbon monoxide and a growing concern for safety that does not mesh with roofless automobiles, the once-coveted convertible appears headed for the great junkyard of nostalgia."

To sort out reasons convertible output declined, we refer to a 1976 comment by Mike Knepper, editor of *Motor Trend*: "I have owned a convertible. But I don't own one now. I am part of the reason the convertible is passing. We quit buying them, so Detroit quit building them."

The reason for a product no longer being made is lack of demand. This caused AMC to drop convertibles after 1968, Chrysler after 1971, and Ford after 1973. Convertible sales peaked in 1963, at 490,000 or almost seven percent of the market. By 1975, production was 20,000. This represented one-half of one percent!

Several factors contributed to lack of demand. One was hardtop styling, which had been growing rapidly since 1955. Little wonder: It looked good in that it was sporty like the convertible, and it provided the winter comfort of a closed car. Maintenance was low, compared to convertibles. By 1956, over five million two-door and one-half million four-door hardtops had been manufactured.

Another problem with convertibles was noise and pollution with the top down versus a sporty hardtop/vinyl top car with air conditioning. Even 15 years ago, air was installed in 60 percent of all new cars and vinyl roofs were on 43 percent.

By the early seventies, the romantic appeal of convertibles waned. Noted one scribe: "The post-pubescent crop of young romantics hasn't found a rag top part of its image building program. Many people have turned to vans (some luxuriously outfitted), pickup trucks or anything else that would carry them from point A to point B."

Sun roofs on U.S. autos, in the seventies, also hurt sales. The installation of sun roofs on new cars, by 1972, had more than tripled the total of 1971.

Frankly, one has to be willing to live with a convertible in order to own one long. Not that present day convertibles are unsafe or only good for bugs in one's teeth. We're delighted there are enthusiasts and buyers around in quantities sufficient to support the decision to, once again, produce them.

There's much to be said for the desire of wanting something no longer available. We wish we could buy a Chevy convertible, brand new, and save it 25 years, or find unlimited garage space to house some special soft-top Chevys from the past: Corvair, Camaro, Corvette, to join our 1959 Impala convertible.

Nostalgia is a pleasant experience we're entitled to practice in small doses. "Nostalgia removes the rocks and whirlpools from the flow of time," James Burnham once wrote, "and soothes the pscyhe with a gentler music and lingering perfume. We return to wondrous days when things were covered with a magical glow."

And, we can add, when convertibles never leaked or rattled; when it never rained when the top was down; when winding country roads were abundant and when original convertible tops had lifetime guarantees!

Speaking of Chevys: Florida Models

by Pat Chappell

We've just come back from two weeks on the west coast of Florida, staying at Siesta Key on the Gulf of Mexico, near Sarasota.

Sound exotic? It was and we loved it, though several times we were reminded of our *first* love: Chevrolets.

A maroon four-door Cavalier, rented at Tampa Airport, transported us to Siesta Key. It was a typical rental in that the odometer showed little over 19,000 miles, yet the Cavalier already had lost much of its gallant splendor through a multitude of drivers. Suffice it to say, we were duly impressed with its fuel economy, maneuverability, spacious trunk, and reliability. We were again reminded of Chevrolet that evening, while reading the *Sarasota Herald-Tribune.* First on the list of ultimate gifts for the holiday season was a one-of-a-kind contemporary "fantasy" desk produced by Allison Forge Corp. of Brookline, Mass. We quote: "For the car buff (we have) a 60-by-45 inch Bel Air desk with a single drawer on the occupants's side and a replica of a '57 Chevy Bel Air dashboard on the other. A great conversation piece, it is priced at about $19,800." Imagine! For that price one could get the whole '57 Chevy. As we read on in the classifieds, we found a "beautifully restored" 1957 Corvette being offered for $18,000, which seemed a much better buy than the desk!

Interest in America's only sports car is high in the Florida area. Little wonder. The Sunshine State provides a perfect setting. During our vacation, a Corvette meet was held on Sarasota's bayfront. Sponsored by Corvettes of Sarasota, 30 fiberglass beauties were on display.

Sarasota is the home of Bellm's Cars & Music of Yesterday Museum. We felt right at home, entering the museum's gift shop, where the latest *Old Cars Price Guide* was for sale. The museum houses over 170 vintage automobiles, including several interesting Chevrolets ranging from a 1923 Superior touring to a 1972 Corvette. There is a heavy emphasis on Corvettes and Corvairs. The Corvairs reminded us of our friend and fellow Chevrolet historian, Tony Fiore, who makes his home in Sarasota.

We had a chance to chat with Tony about Corvairs, and we discovered that his well-researched and popular book, *The Corvair Decade*, is just about sold out, so we're hopeful this history will be reprinted in the near future.

Tony served as editor of *Corsa Quarterly*, the national club magazine, for eight years. Presently he is active in the Gulf Coast Corvair Club, serving as newsletter editor and treasurer. The address of this club is Corvair Society of America Inc., P.O. Box 550, Midlothian, IL 60445-0550.

Sarasota is also home of George Dammann, who is well-known in the hobby as owner and founder of Crestline Publishing Co., which has produced 17 illustrated automotive histories. While talking to George, we found out that *60 Years of Chevrolet* is being expanded and retitled to include "75 Years of Chevrolet." We're especially looking forward to an updated edition of this book, which has become the standard in its field with 50,000 copies published since 1972.

All in all, our vacation in Florida not only gave us a chance to flee from Delaware's first snowfall of the season, but also reinforced our belief that a very strong interest in Chevrolets still prevails in Florida, particularly in the Gulf Coast area.

Speaking of Chevys: 1955 Bel Air

by Pat Chappell

Speaking of Chevys, I was pleased to read in the February/March issue of *American Heritage* that Brock Yates had honored the 1955 Bel Air as one of the 10 greatest American cars.

I recalled the list published in *Life* magazine some time ago where the 1955 Chevy was also included.

Once again, I saw a Chevy sharing the limelight with such classics of the thirties as Cord, Cadillac, Duesenberg, Lincoln, Marmon, Packard, Pierce-Arrow, and Stutz. The Ford Model T (1908-1927) also was honored, for it is long remembered as being "the automobile that put America on wheels." This reasonably priced car for the masses, built in quantities of millions, had a very important economic and social impact during its years of manufacture.

Recently, *Old Cars Weekly* subscribers were asked to cast individual ballots for the top 10. This will no doubt generate many responses. We're certain it will bring forth some questions about the 1955 Chevy Bel Air being included in such prestigious company. It is, in fact, one of the greatest American cars manufactured from the teens to the eighties. And if so, why?

More than 30 years ago, the 1955 Chevrolet, specifically a golden Bel Air sport coupe, rolled off the assembly line celebrating GM's 50 millionth production car. The date was Nov. 23, 1954. The place was Flint, Mich. In Chevy's hometown of Flint, 100,000 people attended a colossal parade and open house, and an all-out corporate celebration was held across the country.

The fact that this 50 millionth car manufactured by GM was the all-new Chevrolet Bel Air sport coupe was fitting. The division had made up nearly 60 percent of the first 50 million GM vehicles. Indeed, the 1955 Chevy experienced a rather historical birth, wearing gold paint and gold-plated trim. It was the beginning of a golden age for Chevrolet, and an historically important life was to follow in the next 30 years.

Chevrolet, for 1955, was a tremendous change from 1954's entry. Entirely new styling was accompanied by a brand new light and efficient 162 h.p. valve-in-head "Turbo Fire" V-8 that would become legendary. The "classic" styling prompted Chevrolet's advertising agency to illustrate the Bel Air convertible in the foreground of a Pebble Beach concourse...brand new! The light, efficient V-8 engine prompted the agency to show a 1955 Chevy in motion, capturing one NASCAR race after another. A 1955 Bel Air convertible was chosen to pace the Indy 500 that May, an appropriate honor for a "don't argue with this baby!" type car, which was taking competition "to the cleaners."

And yes, there were honors from the contemporary press that year. *Motor Trend* awarded its "best handling and most roadable car" award to Chevy (in a tie with Mercury).

All this background, by itself, would be enough to impress a prominent automotive scribe to consider the 1955 Chevy Bel Air as one of the 10 greatest American cars, but there was more. What developed from 1955 to 1986 was a tremendous following from a segment of Chevrolet history (1955-57). Enthusiasts restore, drive, and show examples of this era. From the early sixties and into the mid-eighties, the 1955 Chevrolet has emerged as possibly the most collectible Chevy passenger car.

We feel Brock Yates' list of 10 is a well-balanced one. Dealing with classics, he had picked eight truly deserving and prestigious automobiles, although they were out of reach for the majority of people. However, he also chose two very historic production automobiles: the Ford Model T and the 1955 Chevrolet. Both were manufactured in great quantities and were affordable for the average buyer.

The Model T brought the masses out of the horse-and-buggy era. A generation later, Chevrolet put a very stylish, reliable, hotly performing car within the reach of nearly everyone, thus exemplifying the growing sophistication of the automotive industry.

Recently, one writer described the 1955 Chevy as a "car for the enthusiast, in an enthusiastic era." That writer, by the way, was Terry Boyce, former contributor to this column.

We couldn't agree more.

Speaking of Chevys: 30 Years of '56 Chevys

by Pat Chappell

Speaking of Chevys, our 1956 Nomad is sitting in the garage, resting after 2,130 miles to St. Ignace, Mich. and back. It ran well and did not overheat in a 2½-hour parade. My spouse had one word for its performance: "Awesome!"

In 1986, we celebrated the 30th anniversary of 1956 automobiles and 100th anniversary of the first automobile. The difference between an 1886 Benz patent motorcar and a 1956 Chevrolet Bel Air Nomad is considerable. So, we pause and wonder how, many years down the road, our 1956 Chevy will stack up against, say, a 2056 "Futuremobile."

It's to the credit of car collectors, libraries, museums, and the hobbyist that we have the pleasure of looking at and reading about historically important automobiles that celebrated their centennial anniversary in 1986. Think of those that will follow next year...and the years after.

But, getting back to the 1956 Chevrolet, a Chevy club member wrote a letter that pointed out the inappropriateness of the style used when talking and writing about mid-fifties Chevrolets. It affects the 1956 enthusiast in particular.

The writer said he had wearied of reading about '55-'57 Chevys or '55/'57 Chevys. He pointed out that his 1956 Chevy was not a (-) or a (/). Or for that matter a (thru) or a (through)!

We couldn't help but feel empathy for him and, at the same time, feel guilty for being one of the automotive writers who writes about "1955-1957" Chevys, meaning, of course, all three years.

Some time ago, the 1956 Chevy was written about in *Special Interest Autos*, and the title of the piece was "1956 Chevrolet V-8: Caught in the Middle." Sort of like saying the 1958 Chevy Impala was "The Forgotten Hot One" or calling all 1958 (-), (/), (thru), (through) 1964 Chevys "Late Greats."

We've been proponents of 1956 Chevys for years. We had the good fortune of driving a new hot one off the showroom floor in February 1956. It was our first brand-new car, a Bel Air Sport sedan (read that four-door hardtop), which was a new model added to the lineup in 1956. It was painted Dusk plum and India ivory, just like the one featured in the sales brochure that year. We felt, at the time, it was a stunning example of mid-fifties styling complete with wide whitewalls and handsome black and white interior. And like the first boyfriend (or girlfriend), it was the one we'd never forget.

A decade later, we sold it to an acquaintance; its odometer showed 57,961 miles. But we couldn't forget it. So, exactly a year later, we bought a "used" 1956 Bel Air Nomad and fixed it. It filled the gap in that it incorporated all the goodness of our original 1956 Sport sedan, plus the good-looking Nomad body, which was just becoming collectible in the late sixties. We've been close to 1956 Chevys ever since and were especially close this past June, driving through Pennsylvania and Ohio to Michigan and coming home through Ontario, New York, and Pennsylvania. We watched the odometer as it clocked off the miles from 20,480 to 22,618 without missing a beat.

"The Hot One's Even Hotter" was Chevy's slogan for 1956. And that was no idle boast. Zora Arkus-Duntov's ascent of Pikes Peak in September 1955 set the new American stock sedan record, and other records were slashed by Jerry Unser and Smokey Yunick. No question about it: "The Hot One" was even hotter.

Chevy's performance for 1956 was better due to improvements, refinements, and capacity increases based on its successful 1955 V-8 engine. The "Turbo-Fire" V-8, with cubic inch displacement at 265, still developed 162 h.p. with standard or overdrive transmission, as in 1955. But Powerglide models were equipped with a new higher-lift cam that increased power to 170 h.p. at 4,400 r.p.m. (compared to 162 h.p. in '55). A "Power-Pak" was an option that delivered 205 h.p. at 4,600 r.p.m. (compared to 180 h.p. in '55). An even more lusty unit equipped with Corvette goodies had increased horsepower to 225 at 5,200 r.p.m.

Awards were many for the new '56 Chevy. *Motor Trend*'s "best handling" and "best performance per dollar" honors established a high-water mark of acclamation from the press. The sporty Nomad station wagon was judged "the most beautiful version" of its particular body style. But more important, General Motors' Chevrolet Division increased its share of the automotive market from 23.04 percent in 1955 to 27.94 percent in 1956. This was a notable accomplishment considering that total auto production had suffered a 27 percent drop — from 7,942,131 in 1955 to 5,801,864 in 1956. Chevy led Ford by only 65,000 untis for the entire year in 1955. In 1956 Chevy beat out Ford *monthly* by 20,000 units.

Automotive journalism has changed over the past 30 years, as have the cars. But allow us one of our favorite quotes about 1956 Chevys from automotive journalist Tom McCahill writing for *Mechanix Illustrated*: "It would whiz by a Duesenberg like Halley's Comet, and the vacuum as it went by would suck the stork off a Hispano-Suiza."

Now, we've never passed a "Duesy" or a "Hisso" on the highway, but we like to look up the road ahead, hoping wistfully that one day we will have the chance to prove Uncle Tom's prediction. Here's to the stepsister, the middle child, the automobile seemingly carried along in a grouping, somewhere between the '55 and the '57, holding its own, over 30 years later!

Speaking of Chevys: Cruising 1986

by Pat Chappell

Speaking of Chevys...

We've been getting ours ready for the season. Suddenly, it's time for cruisin' 1986. After dusting off our "Cruisin' 1956" cassette tape, it sounds better than ever playing Chuck Berry's "Roll Over Beethoven," "The Great Pretender" by the Platters, and "Tutti Frutti" by Little Richard.

On the East Coast — at least in the mid-Atlantic area — the tradition of cruisin' continues. We celebrate it at a local drive-in restaurant, south of Wilmington, Del., called The Porch.

The second Saturday night of each month, the local 1955-'57 Chevy Club and the Delaware Street Rodders join to eat pizza, sip Cherry coke and have homemade ice cream (served by waitresses on roller skates). We kick tires, enjoy ourselves, and watch the low-riders go up and down. In short, we become "part" of the cruisin' scene. One journalist describes this as "a pilgrimage of sorts, where the faithful show their devotion in a parade of heavy metal."

Cruisin' or going to the drive-in or the local fast-food joint, in some vintage metal — be it light or heavy — is an ongoing tradition tied up with the nostalgic desire to return to the past. That's when the songs were "grooviest," the "chicks" the cutest, and the cars the "toughest."

Cruisin' had its origin in the late forties, in California, the shrine of the car culture. Californians remember those beginnings, near the Piccadilly Drive-In, on the outskirts of Los Angeles, on Sepulveda Boulevard. The custom grew up in the fifties and matured in the sixties, with contemporary music providing the background to the "varoom-varoom" of engines.

In the classic portrayal of a California town in 1962, the movie "American Graffiti" gave us the chance to meet, again, with the howling, prowling "Wolfman Jack," and hear super music from the mid-fifties and early sixties. We got to see gals in poodle skirts and hear some hairy cars breathing. And all of this was set against the background of Mel's Drive-In.

One contemporary film reviewer noted: "classics are born when all ingredients blend to a near perfect state...'East of Eden' was such a film. So is 'American Graffiti.'" Not only were the film's California surfing tunes important. In addition, the Beach Boys' "Little Deuce Coupe" and "409," as well as Jan and Dean's "Dead Man's Curve" and "Bucket T," all exemplified the car-crazy culture which existed.

One of the biggest cruise nights we've witnessed is held during the end of June, in the state which built most the these automobiles: Michigan. Set in the upper peninsula of Michigan, the town of St. Ignace's Car Show and Collector Car Festival is an experience most every enthusiast would enjoy. After the Friday night parade, the road fills with cars on their way to the Big Boys restaurant for the granddaddy of them all. With Dick Biondi, of Chicago's WJMK-101, headlining a performance by Dr. Ernie Fever & Cruising Tunes, the scene will literally knock off your bobbysox.

We've been watching the cruisin' segment of the car hobby grow for some time now. It's where enthusiasts of both stock and modified automobiles come together, in harmony, for an evening filled with fun. And we're encouraged to see several drive-in restaurants cooperating and promoting. They enjoy having car clubs meet for cruise nights and many also supply a place for regular club meetings.

According to some sources, a few of the national fast-food chains are inviting clubs to bring out their cars, on certain nights, and giving the clubs a percentage of the extra profits generated by the people-pulling cruisers. This sure exemplifies good will. Gone are the days when getting covered with grease while working on an old car under the nearest shade tree was something undesirable. Restoring, collecting, and driving some of the treasures of the American automotive past is now a very acceptable hobby.

We'd be interesting in hearing from readers how your Chevy clubs have been involved with local merchants, drive-ins, mall shows, and similar activities. It's a considerable plus getting our automobiles out there for the public to see and encouraging the public to join us in our interest in the automotive past.

Note: For those interested in tunes of the '50s and '60s, Krause Publications produces *Goldmine* magazine. The *Goldmine* magazine is the premier publication for vintage music fans and record collectors. A one-year subscription to the bi-monthly newsmagazine is $35 or contact: Goldmine, 700 E. State St., Iola, WI 54990 for a $2.25 sample copy.

Speaking of Chevys

by Pat Chappell

Speaking of Chevys and writing about them is something we enjoy. When we received a phone call from *Old Cars Weekly* the other day, asking if we would like to take over this monthly column, we accepted gladly. We have something in common with former columnist Terry Boyce: We've both authored postwar histories on Chevys, his about Super Sports, ours about 1955-'57 Chevys.

Our interest in Chevys really started with a 1949 Styleline DeLuxe four-door sedan which was the family's transportation for many years. The next Chevy we owned was a 1951 two-door sedan. We drove a number of Chevys over the years, most of them used: a 1941, a 1948, two more 1951s, a 1956 Bel Air Sport sedan (our only new Chevy), a 1957 Nomad and a 1959 Impala convertible. All of these Chevys are long gone now, except for the 1959 convertible. We've had it since 1960; a quarter century. Though we've also bought, and still have, a 1955 sport coupe, 1956 Nomad and 1976 Malibu four-door sedan, the '59 holds the longevity honor. So it seems appropriate to continue with the column's original logo, the rear end of a 1959.

We're looking forward to writing "Speaking of Chevys" (now on a monthly basis starting in 1986), and we hope to include history of this marque, which is the biggest Division of General Motors. We want to focus on the men who were responsible for the development of Chevrolet and, also, include some personal profiles of people who have been and are presently invovled with collecting and restoring prize Chevys. Perhaps we will get into some of the functions of Chevrolet clubs throughout the country and report on particular meets and shows. But most of all, this column will feature things the enthusiast wants to read.

On occasion, we'll touch on Chevrolet-oriented publications and report on new reproduction materials and the general direction of the automotive hobby as it pertains to Chevrolet.

We're looking at 1986 as a year which brings the reader over a dozen columns about Chevy, and that really isn't very much copy about an automobile which has been produced in quantities of millions from its humble beginnings as a car called the Little. Ironic, that nomenclature. Chevrolet was to become anything but "Little" in accom-

Speaking Of Chevys

By Terry Boyce

plishments, sales and general history.

We'd enjoy hearing from our readers if there is anything in particular in the history of Chevrolet which might be researched. We're mostly familiar with postwar Chevys, but the background of this marque is of particular importance — something not to be forgotten. Let's hear from you!

Speaking of Chevys

By Terry Boyce

Can you imagine An American without a Chevrolet experience somewhere in his or her memory? We can't. Those millions of cars and trucks carrying the bow-tie logo since 1912 are part of our shared national and cultural history. We are presenting this column as a way to share some of those memories, recall Chevrolet trivia, look at Chevy memorabilia and in general have a good time talking about the great old Chevys as they were — and are.

We will be meandering through the Chevrolet story, stopping here and there at random. We'll see how Chevrolets were sold, how they were used and how they were — and are — part of their owners' lives. Please feel welcome to join us with your own Chevrolet memories, anecdotes and adventures. And hey, speaking of Chevys . . .

No one would really want to return to the depression days of the 1930s, but still, wouldn't it be nice to kick a tin can down the byways of the past? We'd kick it back to Marysville, Calif., 1935 and see Clyde Williams' used car lot. We can't be there, of course, but we do have a nice photo of Clyde's lot that was taken that year and shows us how it was. By intention, or otherwise, Williams pitted the Chevys against the Fords. On the left are the Chevys. We have a '31 sport coupe up front, with a '34 next in line and a '32 panel truck visible behind it. Across the lot, representing the opposition, is a '34 Deluxe Ford V-8 sedan and a pair of Model A Fords. Two trucks that we don't recognize stand at the back of the lot — one has rare accessory Woodlites; a strange addition to a truck. The Chevrolet factory-style signs are in the best Art Deco fashion, and it's interesting to see that, even in 1935, Chevrolet used cars were "Guaranteed OK." Williams' lot used wooden curb ramps for ingress and egress — a driveway would come in more prosperous times.

When your columnist was nearly a teenager, the older boy next door bought a new, black '61 Impala Sport Coupe. Even then, we knew the crossed flags on the deck ornament meant it was a "348." Man, how we coveted that car! The arrival of the "409," and subsequent performance developments in the sixties, has sort of dimmed the '61 Impala's impact, but we still think it's a great car. Checking our reference files, we find that 177,969 of those pleasingly styled '61 sport coupes were built, but not all were Impalas. Some — a small percentage — were Bel Air models. Much lighter in appearance (about 50 pounds lighter in fact), the fleet-looking '61 was a real tiger with the top-rated 350-h.p. 348 V-8. Did you remember that there were *five* different 348s for 1961? There were two 9.5:1 compression 4-barrel versions, rated at 250 and 305-h.p. Then, there was the 11.5:1 compression, 340-h.p. engine, again with 4-barrel. Two additional 348s came with triple two-barrel carburetion and the high compression. One, with mild hydraulic cam, was rated at 280-h.p.; the other was the 350-h.p. solid lifter screamer.

Just to further complicate the 1961 picture, we have to add that Chevrolet released the 409 late that year. It was based on the 348, of course, and rated at 360-h.p. Only 142 were built, all with single 4-barrel carbs. A sharp '61 Impala or Bel Air Sport Coupe with any engine is a treat today, but those with the "stump-pulling" 348s are among the scarcest, even though Chevrolet reported 66,929 were built in 1961.

We like to look for pictures of old Chevys in all sorts of printed materials — and we're often surprised at what we find. One old Automobile Manufacturers Association bulletin, for instance, shows a "rolling drug-store" that worked the streets of suburban Los Angeles neighborhoods just after World War II. Hitched to the pharmacist's trailer is a white 1940 business coupe, already six years old when it was drafted into pulling the "Traveling Pharmacy" around. New cars were still scarce in the early days of peacetime 1946, but we trust the ol' '40 got the break it so deserved not too long after the photo was taken.

Chevrolet, the super-start division of General Motors, seems to get the preference when it comes to vehicles commemorating corporate milestones. A silver 1940 Special DeLuxe 2-door sedan, built on January 11, 1940 at the Flint assembly plant, was the 25 millionth GM vehicle built after the corporation was founded in September, 1908. A gold 1955 Bel Air hardtop — what a prize — was the 50 millionth GM car. It left the Flint assembly line on November 23, 1954. A Pontiac had a chance at the glory for the 75 millionth celebration; a new 1962 Bonneville convertible held the honor, being built at Pontiac, Mich. on March 14, 1962. Just five years and five weeks later the 100 millionth car was produced. Chevrolet was given the assignment and assembled a 1967 Caprice custom coupe for the ceremony. This car was built April 21, 1967 at the Chevrolet-Fisher Body Assembly Plant in Janesville, Wis.

Derham, the Rosemont, Penna., builder of custom-bodied classics for kings, presidents and the very rich, turned out at least one Chevrolet. It was a very pretty 1949 DeLuxe sport coupe. A custom padded top was apparently the extent of Derham's custom work, but that was enough to entitle the little coupe to wear the prestigious Derham badge on its hood sides. Derham was one of the few coachbuilders to survive the depression and World War II, but the tradition-steeped firm was near the end by 1949. Where is their little jewel of a '49 Chevy today?

One of the more unusual Chevys of the sixties was the "409" of 1965. Chevrolet had a new look for 1965 — and a new chassis underneath. Everyone presumed that the long-awaited production version of the "Daytona Mystery Engine" would appear under the hood. But, the venerable 409, which had been in volume production since 1962, was still the big-inch engine option for 1965. Chevrolet even advertised the 409 rather heavily in the winter months of that year — it turned out to be a close-out promotion, though. The Mark IV "Mystery Engine" finally made it, as a 396 cu. in. V-8, in mid-February 1965. The 409 was dropped for good at that time. Just 2,828 of the 409s had been installed in 1965 passenger cars, of which 2,086 were 340-h.p. hydraulic cam engines — often teamed with Powerglide transmissions. The remaining 742 were the solid lifter 400-h.p. high performance engines. Both 409s had single 4-barrel carbs. You might still find a '65 edition by watching for the fender insignia numerals designating this engine. The 409 was available in any full-size 1965 Chevy (except the Caprice, which came out after it was dropped). The 340-h.p. engines were very useful for towing boat and travel trailers and quite a few found their way into station wagons. Florida 409 collector Floyd Garrett said recently that he has noticed 1965 versions, long among the *least* valuable of their type, beginning to appreciate. He says collectors are becoming more aware of their scarcity.

The Louisiana Library Commission created that state's first bookmobile in 1930, using a new Chevrolet sedan delivery to carry the tomes from town to town. This commercial body style is a rare item today.

Speaking of Chevys

By Terry Boyce

A surprising number of luxury car owners were visiting Chevrolet showrooms in the early 1930s. The great General Motors stylist Harley Earl was responsible. He had directed the design of Chevrolets, beginning in 1929, that were pocket editions of General Motor's finest cars — the family resemblance was unmistakable. Many a monied father added a new Chevrolet to the carriage house collection. Nimble and easy to drive, the six-cylinder Chevrolets were perfect commuting cars for younger family members, for the maid's shopping, or for those early-morning trips to the golf course when the heavy steering of the "big car" was especially noticeable.

By 1932, with the Depression cutting off much of Chevrolet's mass market, the marque was openly promoted as a finely-crafted, compact version of GM's top-line cars. With lavish chrome, a chain-mesh grille guard and wire wheels, the handsome 1932 Deluxe Chevrolet was very much a "baby Cadillac."

Chevrolet even advertised their new Landau phaeton in the prestigious *Fortune* magazine in 1932. (*Fortune*'s subscription price was $12 for 12 issues that year — when the lowest priced Chevrolet listed for $445.)

"A genuine pleasure for you to drive," intoned the ad's headline, beneath the illustration of the Landau phaeton fancifully placed into an old English coaching/hunting scene.

"With a Chevrolet in your garage, it doesn't matter which vehicle you use — the big automobile or the personal car — you keep on enjoying yourself just the same. You keep on being comfortable," the ad promised.

That it was not accidental that the new car resembled the Classic Cadillac of 1932 was shown by the ad's concluding sentence: ". . . Chevrolet comes closer to looking like your big custom car — both inside and out — than does any other automobile of lowest price."

A 1932 Chevrolet Landau phaeton would still be a nice car to come home to.

Speaking of Chevys: Powerglides

by Terry Boyce

Remember coming up behind a '50-'52 Chevy, with Powerglide deck badge, at a stop sign? You knew you weren't going anywhere fast for a while. Those early Powerglides gave new meaning to the term *slow*. The prime reason for their unhurried demeanor, of course, was their inherent slippage. Designed to start from a standing stop in Drive range, the first Powerglides rivaled the original Buick Dynaflow in smoothness and inefficiency.

Chevrolet actually designed a new power train for the 1950 Powerglide option. Cars with automatic transmission also had a larger, more powerful engine. It was a 235-cid six, replacing the standard, time-honored 216. Horsepower was 105 at 3600 rpm, or 13 more than the manual gearbox cars. Rear axle ratio for the Powerglide was 3.55:1, instead of the 4.11:1 gears in standard Chevrolets. The numerically lower rear axle ratio decreased acceleration capability in the automatic-equipped Chevy, but increased highway mileage — a trade-off to balance out the relatively poorer town driving economy.

Motor Trend compared the 1950 Powerglide with a manual transmission-equipped car, finding the Powerglide-equipped Bel Air hardtop used for the tests took 25.8 seconds to reach the quarter mile's end, while their manual gearbox sedan reached it in 21.64 seconds. Reaching 60 mph took 27.5 seconds, compared to 19.84 for the manual gearbox car! Interestingly, in light traffic, the Powerglide gave 20.5 mpg compared to 18.67 mpg for the standard car and at any speed was within two miles per gallon of the standard car's fuel consumption. *MT*'s test drivers must not have been in a hurry, though. Young and impatient drivers found their average varied considerably — downward — if they tried to prod the early glides along too vigorously.

Chevy began to find acceptance with the majority of drivers.

The Great American Race Chevys

by Terry Boyce

Not all surviving Chevrolet "stovebolt" sixes are taking it easy in the '80s. While most of the sturdy prewar cars are enjoying retirement in comfortable garages, venturing forth only on sunny days to a local tour or show, there are exceptions. Several "stovebolts" were in the starting line-up of this year's Great American Race — and there was even one four-cylinder Chevy in competition.

This year's edition of the Great Race was the most grueling test of vintage machinery yet. Starting from Hollywood, Calif. on June 26, the field of nearly 100 pre-1937 vehicles crossed the United States in eight days. The finish this year was in New York City, where the event concluded in the midst of that city's gala Fourth of July parade.

A 1914 Dodge entered by Californian Jack Cassan claimed the $100,000 first prize. None of the Chevrolets entered placed in the top 10 this year, but the "bow tie contingent" was very much in competition. Their vehicles were spectator favorites with those who delighted in seeing a vintage Chevrolet "just like Grandpa had" flash by in the midst of the impressive array of motor vehicles making up the race's entry list.

Through the courtesy of LeRoi Smith, publicity director for Great Race Ltd., we are able to present here scenes of Chevrolets in action during the 1985 Great American Race.

Once in a while, being wrong isn't so bad. Such is the case with our recent column on GM's world-wide auto industry (*Old Cars Weekly*, July 25). In that column, we spoke of cars being shipped "CKD", which we have explained in print as meaning "crated, knocked-down." It turns out the CKD has a significantly different meaning, as we learned from a pleasant and informative letter sent by reader John Jackson of San Jose, Calif.

Jackson is one of those great sources who knows of what he speaks because he was there. "Having worked in Central Stores at the Pontiac Motorcar Division from July 1944 to August 1946, (your column) brought back many memories," he writes.

"Part of these memories had to do with those periods in which I was responsible for ordering both domestic and overseas shipping material for the Division. There were four types of Pontiacs then, including the 6 and 8, and shipping material was different for each," Jackson says.

"Now this brings us to CKD — and the SUP. I must take exception to your definition of CKD. Actually, we referred to CKD as 'completely knocked down' as opposed to SUP or 'single unit pack.' The SUP was also crated — but one car to a crate.

"The Division had a team constantly working to reduce the cubage displacement of both the CKD and SUP as the shipping companies charged by the space occupied. On the CKD, even frames were knocked down to be assembled at their overseas assembly plant destination. As I remember, 12 axles, rears, and 'knee action' assemblies were in one crate. The engines, transmissions, etc. were in a second and the frame pieces, fenders, panels, etc. were in a third."

Jackson recalls using Canadian white shop pine to construct the shipping crates. Other materials used included tar, roofing paper, tongue and groove lumber, tie down brackets, corner braces and banding iron. "It was a full-time job fo the receiving clerk, the saw mill, carpenters and myself," he says.

About five percent of Pontiac's production went to export markets during the years John Jackson worked on the program. Though technically not really "Speaking of Chevys," Jackson's comments illuminate a little known bit of General Motors history, and we appreciate his sharing them with us.

Speaking of Chevys

By Terry Boyce

A neighbor, knowing of your columnist's automotive interests, gave us a small key-shaped pocket tool kit several years ago. Cast into the case is the Chevrolet bow-tie and the words, "The Key to Chevrolet Performance." Sandwiched between the bronzed-end plates are 11 thin tools, including a two-inch ruler, carburetor float gauge and feeler gauges for adjusting intake and exhaust valves, spark plugs and breaker points.

About the size and weight of a fully-equipped Victornox Swiss Army knife, the Chevrolet key fits nicely into my pocket (we carry it to Chevy events occasionally).

We've sometimes looked at our key tool kit and wondered about the how and why of its existence. Recently, sorting through the files of a long-closed dealership, we found the answers in a grimy manila folder. It contained a sheaf of "New Tool Bulletins" sent to Chevrolet service managers by the Kent-Moore Organization of Detroit. K-M made all those special tools and equipment that you see referenced in your shop manuals (". . . use tool J-301 to loosen shaft"). They also made our Chevrolet key.

Bulletin C-7 shows the key, calling it "A complete tune-up kit in one tool." KMO stock number 1043, it was available for $1.50.

Kent-Moore called the key, "The handiest and most useful device ever created for the Chevrolet mechanic."

Dating the sheet is the listing of an .040 spark plug gap gauge for the 1937 Chevrolets, to be added to earlier key tools. Our key doesn't have the 1937 gauge, so it must date from 1936 or earlier. We don't know how many versions of the key were produced by Kent-Moore, nor the number of years it was available. But we do know that we're glad our neighbor thought of us when she spotted the key in a box of "trash" headed for the dump as her family cleaned out an estate.

Speaking of Chevys

By Terry Boyce

Chevrolet speed equipment. If you grew up in postwar America, you probably bolted some onto your stovebolt six or small block V-8. But, if you're old enough to remember Herbert Hoover's presidency, you may have purchased Chevrolet speed equipment for your Ford. *Ford?* That's correct. Among the largest suppliers of speed equipment for the Model T Ford were the Chevrolet brothers, Louis and Arthur.

Louis had gone back to his real love — racing machines — after leaving General Motors in the time of Billy Durant. During the '20s, he and Arthur formed the Chevrolet Bros. Manufacturing Co. to produce racing cars and equipment under the Frontenac trade name. A reorganization, in 1929, put the speed parts under the banner of the Arthur Chevrolet Aviation Motors Corp.

A reprint of the 1929 Chevrolet racer's catalog reveals that complete, ready-to-race "Fronty Fords" were still available. Heart of the racer was the all-out version of the Frontenac head-equipped Ford four-banger, with 16 overhead valves operated by dual overhead cams. Top rpm was reached at 5600. Single overhead cam and pushrod-actuated overhead valve heads were also cataloged for the Model T block.

Though the Chevrolet/Frontenac equipment was best known for its Ford applications, there were Chevrolet four-speed items cataloged as well. A street performance kit, including a special head with aluminum cover, 1½ inch racing carburetor, and performance inlet and exhaust pipes, could be had for $100. This was said to put the little four-cylinder Chevy into the 75-mph top speed range (we remember the brakes of the time and wince). A serious racer's edition included single or dual carburetors and promised 100 mph performance from the tiny engine.

Dream Cars

Dream Cars

The term, "Dream Car" is believed to have been penned in connection with the General Motors Motorama car shows of the early and mid-Fifties. Harley Earl, then head of General Motors Styling, used the Motorama shows to bring to the public the stylists' ideas of future automobiles.

All too often the inspired design of a stylist was hacked at and watered down by all the different committees his design passed through on its way to production. Earl used the Motorama to wake up corporate management as to what could be done given a clean slate and few restraints. The result brought forth dozens of inspired (and not-so-inspired) car designs that influenced future production more than anyone ever imagined.

Practically every auto company jumped onto the "Dream Car" bandwagon. Chrysler's Virgil Exner began an association with Ghia that lasted for over a decade. Ford's early show cars began their second 50 years with new excitement and flair. But it was GM that really pushed the idea to the fullest. Earl's brilliant Le Sabre and Charles Chayne's Buick XP-300 had the automotive world buzzing with excitement. The public was still "starved" for anything new. World War II was still a recent memory and Europe, particularly Germany and Italy, were still in a huge rebuilding program. "Dream Cars" caught the public's fancy and millions of people thronged to auto shows all across the nation.

Among the many examples of Harley Earl's Advanced Styling Studio products, Chevrolets were abundant. The following photographs show some of the extreme styling ideas where a "no-holds-barred" approach was encouraged. Not only did some of yesterday's dreams become tomorrow's realities, but today, in the Nineties, collectors are unearthing some of these Motorama cars, and restoring them.

1953 Corvette. The Corvette was shown at the New York Auto Show in January of 1953. It was supposedly strictly a show car but public reaction was so great that Chevrolet rushed the car into production. And, on July 1, 1953, the first Corvette rolled off the line at Flint, Mich.

1958 Corvette XP 700. What began as a personal car for William Mitchell, head of GM styling, became a test bed for future Corvettes. The car started out as a stock '58 Corvette. The rear end treatment found its way to the '61 Corvette. By 1959 the XP 700 was elevated to "show car" status.
(Applegate & Applegate photo)

1960 Cerv I. The Chevrolet Engineering Research Vehicle (CERV) was used mainly for testing of suspension and steering componets.

1963 Corvette Mako Shark I XP-755. Here Mitchell has taken the 1958 XP-700 closer to the production Corvette of 1968. The engine is a supercharged version of the new 409 cubic inch powerplant. Note the functional external competition exhausts. The plastic roof is both tinted and treated inside with vaporized aluminum to deflect sunlight. The Shark door handles were flush type, with opening handles that flipped out when an integral button was pressed. (GM photo)

1962 Corvair Monza GT Coupe. William Mitchell went all out with this version of the Corvair. He named it, like the '61 Sebring Spyder, after a famous sportscar racing track — Monza, Italy. Retaining the Corvair rear engine, the fiberglass body had several unusual styling features. Entry to the car was gained when the entire forward part of the passenger compartment hinged forward in one piece. The extreme slant of the windshield was possible when the two seats were moved close together, thus allowing the rakish slant.

1964 Corvette Coupe Rondine. Built by Pininfarina in Italy, this one-of-a-kind features a reverse-slant roofline and much smoother, less aggressive front end treatment. (Applegate & Applegate photo)

1963 Corvair Super Spyder. Bill Mitchell carried the Sebring Spyder of 1962 a little farther into the "Dream Car" zone with the Super Spyder. Note the external exhaust at the rear. The front end received more aggressive styling also. This car, along with the Corvair Monza GT and Monza roadster, made its public debut at various sports car racing facilities across the country.

1965 Corvette Mako Shark II. With modification, the style set forth by the Mako II Corvette "Dream Car," became the production 'Vette for 1967.' There were no less than 17 electric motors to run such things as headlights, wipers that retracted under the hood, adjustable head-rests suspended from the roof, movable venetian blind rear window shades, adjustable clutch, brake and steering wheel (all electrically adjustable), adjustable rear spoiler, remote controlled gas filler, and a retractable rear license plate (none of the above made the production version except the headlights)! (Applegate & Applegate photo)

1963 Corvair Testudo. Built by the Italian coachmaker, Bertone, this Corvair-based show car was designed by Giorgia Giugiaro, who gave the world dozens of wild and not-so-wild automobiles. To enter, the entire cockpit cap swung forward (similar to the Corvair Monza FT).

67 Astro II XP-880. Frank Winchell and Larry Nies of Chevrolet set about to design the new mid-engined Corvette for the '70s. The Astro II is the result. It had a spot-welded steel backbone frame. The radiator was mounted in the rear so that hot radiator hoses wouldn't have to pass through the passenger compartment. Engine used was the Mk IV 390 h.p. unit with power passing through a two-speed torque converter of a 1963 Pontiac Tempest transaxle. (GM photo)

1973 XP-987 GT Corvette 2-Rotor, GM was heavily into the development of the radical Wankel rotary engine in the early '70s. Two famous show cars developed during this time and this is the first one. Originally not called a Corvette, this snappy two-passenger sportscar was also considered a replacement for the German GM division's little "mini-Corvette," the Opel GT. Horsepower from the 2-rotor was about 180. The front end treatment saw production on the Chevy Monza 2-plus-2 in 1975. (Applegate & Applegate photo)

1967 Corvair Astro I. A bored-out Corvair flat six cylinder engine, displacing 176 cubic inches, powered this far out GT coupe. Unlike the earlier 1963 Monza GT, the entire pod over the passenger compartment swung up and backwards for entry (the GT's pod swung forward). The Astro was built on an 88-inch chassis and the engine put out 240 h.p. (GM photo)

1969 Astro III. The Astro III is a two-passenger show car that features a tricycle-type wheel arrangement. It was designed with turbine-power in mind. Closed-circuit television provides rear vision. (Chevrolet photo)

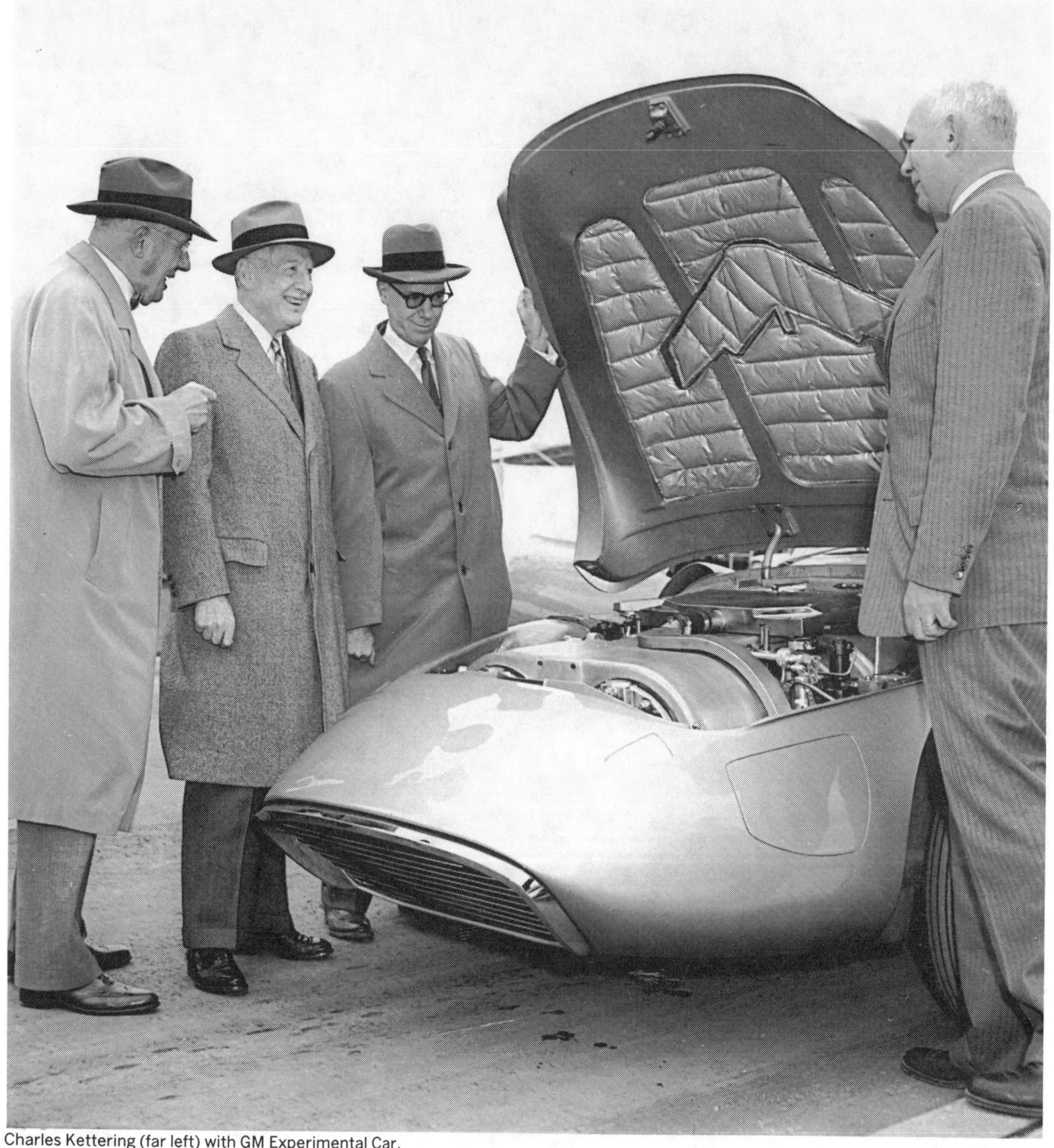

Charles Kettering (far left) with GM Experimental Car.

GM's Fabulous Motorama Cars

by Pat Chappell

As General Motors Corporation celebrates its 75th Anniversary we can't help thinking about all the fabulous show cars and experimental models which came from the advanced styling studios of GM. The highlight in the opinion of many was the era of GM's extravagant road shows, the Motoramas. Held eight times from 1949 to 1961, these showcases of styling and engineering were a natural outgrowth of Alfred P. Sloan's yearly industrialists' luncheons which had been held in New York City in January since 1931. Over the years, Motorama played to an audience of 10.5 million people in a total of eight major cities. They were something from the golden age of postwar styling of which dreams are made. They were the grandfather of all automobile shows, before and after — the creme de la creme. What is most important, they were the first public viewing of what was to come.

Some of these show cars would go into limited production with varying degrees of change from the original. These included the Chevrolet Corvette and Nomad, Buick Skylark, Oldsmobile Fiesta, and Cadillac Eldorado Brougham. Many innovations appearing in Motoramas came on the market within a year or two of their preview. Eventually many production vehicles carried names which originated at the shows: Biscayne, Bonneville, Corvair, Cutlass, Firebird, Impala, Le Mans, Le Sabre, and Wildcat.

Newsweek called the show "a moving mountain of logistical problems." Reporters referred to the crowds at the 1955 Boston showing as "something like the equivalent of nine consecutive holiday double-headers at Fenway Park." *Collier's* saw the Motorama as "show business on wheels...GM's top salesman, its best prognosticator and barometer of business." Harley Earl, head of GM's Styling Section during those years, saw his experimental cars as "small opinion laboratories." William Mitchell, director of styling under Earl, spoke of these show cars as "the dessert in our regular meals." William F. Hufstader to whose budget Motorama was charged as vice-president of distribution for GM stated: "automobiles can't be sold out of catalogues. You have to see them to appreciate them. Motorama gives us the opportunity to display our wares in the best possible setting."

These successful shows were the responsibility of Spencer D. Hopkins, who headed GM's sales section. He was assisted by T.H. Roberts, show manager and a 34-year GM veteran. Leroy E. Kiefer was director of product and exhibit designs, and Harold B. Stubbs was the display man. The first event in 1949 was called "Transportation Unlimited" (not Motorama), and over half a million people attended the New York and Boston showings. Attendance dropped off the following year to 320,000 with a single show at the Waldorf. In 1951 and 1952 no show was held due to involvement in the Korean War and necessary military commitments.

But it was full steam ahead for 1953. That year the term "Motorama" was applied to the GM traveling exhibits which were to become memorable. Perhaps you were there at the Waldorf in 1953 and may remember ... seeing a Chevrolet Corvette for the first time (it would be in production by five months); rubbing elbows with other enthusiasts like yourself, which totalled almost one and a half million by the time the Motorama toured Miami, Los Angeles, San Francisco, Dallas, and Kansas City. Or was it the fiberglass Buick Wildcat you remember, gleaming black with vivid green upholstery about which a fan-of-the-times was heard to remark: "that's the special, the super duper, the non-stop car..." Oldsmobile's entry was a fiberglass Starfire; Cadillac's Le Mans, Eldorado and Orleans graced the ballroom floor; and Pontiac fielded its Landau.

No one seemed to know how much this extravaganza cost. One reliable magazine reported the show cost GM one and a half million dollars, while a second source estimated over four million. Spencer D. Hopkins, director, was quoted by a third publication as saying: "the Motorama costs about three times as much as most people think it does."

It was a big bucks production. It was an important time for the movers and shakers of the auto industry to combine the trip east with the inauguration of President Eisenhower in Washington that January. They flocked in from Michigan, with the "Detroiter," a crack train that ran between Detroit and NYC, carrying two extra sections the

"Corvair" was first used as a GM name for this 1954 Motorama fastback entry.

week before the show. Five hundred GM people, plus officials from other auto manufacturers, fled en masse as Motown moved to Manhattan. Meanwhile, over the road, the gigantic parade of GM trucks and vans had been enroute carrying cars, scenery, props, and a troupe of entertainers. The show was attended by 700 reporters, publishers, company officials, and celebrities and was kicked off with a high-level press party headed by Paul Garrett, GM's public relations vice-president. The next day at noon 500 auto manufacturers and banking executives met with the Company's top brass for luncheon on the Waldorf's Starlight Roof, followed by a private viewing of the show cars in the Grand Ballroom. Some have referred to the 1953 Motorama as the birthplace of the American sports car — not only was it the first glimpse of the Corvette, but four of the five divisions showed sports type experimental cars created with fiberglass bodies. These plastic beauties literally stole the show!

After the Motorama of 1953, one imagines those in charge may have commented: "That's a tough act to follow." But follow they did with a return to Waldorf-Astoria, revisiting Miami, Los Angeles and San Francisco. Dallas and Kansas City were replaced by Chicago, which at the time promised a better drawing. Attendance was excellent for 1954, with almost two million people visiting the multimillion dollar show. By then, the contemporary press had given up on exact cost figures. Overall, GM had retooled for 25 new production models and 11 experimental cars, and was coming off a 3.5 million car year with 45.6 percent of the market. Expansion was the name of the game with a one billion dollar program under way for 1954 and 1955.

We were to see new design features from previous show cars on actual production Buicks, Oldsmobiles, and Cadillacs for 1954: wrap-around windshields, cut-down doors via beltline dips, an overall lower and longer look. The show cars were breathtaking: one can hardly forget Buick's Wildcat II. This fiberglass convertible, only 48 inches high on a 100-inch wheelbase powered by a 220 hp V-8 engine, featured clam-shell fenders which resembled Stutz-Bearcat. The experimental "Corvette Nomad" made its debut that January. It made a great impact on the attending public. So much so that Harley Earl phoned Clare MacKichan, head of Chevrolet Design Studio, back in Detroit. The message: "When I get back in two days I want to see that whole car (the Nomad) and how you would do it on a 1955 Chevrolet." We *were* to see the end product a year later at the 1955 Motorama.

With the unwritten law that each show must be a little more spectacular than the last, Harley Earl and his advanced styling studio, and Spencer Hopkins and his staff started planning for 1955's Motorama shortly after the '54 show was put to bed. It debuted at the Waldorf in January 1955, then toured Miami, Los Angeles, and San Francisco. Chicago, which had a good dealer show of its own, was replaced by Boston because of pressure from New England dealers. Turned out to be a good move, with Boston topping the other four cities with almost 600,000 attendees in nine days. Over two million attended the '55 Motorama during its five city tour. *Business Week* reported the extravaganza cost GM two million dollars. GM reported that the show sold $1.2 million worth of cars in the NYC stand alone, with 50 people a minute swarming the show at the Waldorf. Over a hundred exhibits displayed GM's huge line of products ranging from household appliances to earth movers. But the dream cars were the stars.

In many ways, the dream cars were different in 1955 from the previous years when they were almost all flashy sports models. Many noted that they looked as if they might be next year's production models. Indeed, the Chevrolet Nomad, which had been ordered by Harley Earl from the "Corvette Nomad" in 1954's Motorama would be available to buyers shortly, as would its kissing cousin, Pontiac's Safari wagon. Cadillac's Eldorado Brougham, a four passenger, four-door hardtop would be available in limited quantities by 1957. Oldsmobile's Delta "88", Chevy's Biscayne, and Buick's Wildcat III never made it to the dealer's showroom, but their names did and so did many of their features. GMC's delivery truck entry, called Expedier or L'Universelle, certainly predicted the tremendous popularity of vans in years to come.

The Impala, Chevrolet's 1956 Motorama entry, suggested lines for 1958 production cars.

The traveling Motorama road show was something of a legend in its own time, and looking back some 30 years later, we can't help but be amazed at the logistics of the undertaking. Spencer Hopkins once remarked: "Moving the Motorama around is like moving to a new house. The carpet is the last thing you take from the old house and the first thing you put in the new one." Carpets? For 1955's show GM had five trucks for carpets...plus seven trucks for the dismantled 72-ton steel stage with five giant hydraulic arms. The entire caravan consisted of 99 red, white and blue trailers and trucks with over 1000 crates. Three hundred fifty people worked full time to run the Motorama, including 115 truck drivers, 125 in the show troupe, 115 men participating from GM's 33 divisions who oversaw the setting up and staging of their own exhibits. Additionally, part-time help was hired in each city in the form of guards, porters, local musicians, and college girls to hand out souvenirs. *Newsweek* described the phenomenon which was the Motorama show: "the cars burst onstage through a cloud of smoke, whirling on turntables on the ends of the stage's arms over a 900-square foot pool of water while the orchestra thumped from a bandshell suspended overhead..." Wow!

Suddenly it was 1956, and the gigantic show was on the road again, with repeat visits to New York in January, Miami in February, Los Angeles and San Francisco in March, and Boston in April. The Motorama continued to be a lavish display of all of GM's products which whet the appetite of the buying public and predicted what might be available in the future. The GM caravan grew even larger with 125 trucks and trailers insured for a cool five million. The props weren't cheap either, with 26 cutaway models costing between $90,000 and $100,000 each. The dream cars had cost from $200,000 to $250,000 each to produce. Remember, this was in 1956 dollars! Over two million attended the '56 viewing, and along with production models a show car was exhibited from each division. Setting the theme for the show was the titanium bodied Firebird II which combined the thinking of all five divisions. Its predecessor, Firebird I, shown at the 1954 Motorama, was a single-seat, jet-shaped gas turbined rear-engined car which reportedly was unfit for highways due to its torrid exhaust. Firebird II, a continuation of GM's gas turbine development, was a much safer model because its power plant was placed forward. Its clear plastic top, hinged in the center, opened in gullwing fashion. We were, in time, to see a Firebird go into production from GM's Pontiac Division. However, it was to be a much milder version than its namesake.

Chevrolet's Impala predicted some of the things to come for that division in 1958, especially the name which has by now become ubiquitous. The Impala show car was eight inches lower than the regular production 1956 Chevys, and its fiberglass body was trimmed with stainless steel. Driver safety had been considered with a padded bar across the instrument panel and a steering wheel with padded center strut contoured to the chest of the driver. Pontiac's entry, Club de Mer, "strictly for use in straightaway time trials" as one auto magazine noted, was powered by a 300-horsepower V8. Oldsmobile's Golden Rocket was an extrmely aerodynamic looking two-passenger sports car. Buick's Centurion was another fiberglass beauty, four inches shorter than regular production Specials. Cadillac's town car, though it resembled the Eldorado Brougham, was designed to be chauffeur driven, aimed at the "youthful wealthy." All in all, it was a beautiful field of cars, as it was a fabulously exciting era of dream machines.

No Motorama was held in 1957, due to the rebirth of the National Automobile Show held at New York's Coliseum December 8-16, 1956, and sponsored by the Automobile Manufacturers Association. This was the first postwar National Automobile Show, a tradition which had begun at Madison Square Garden in 1900 and continued through 1940, when the threat of World War II intervened, causing the cancellation of the 1941 show. Postwar readjustments, the Korean War, and a lack of suitable show facilities were some of the reasons for the long hiatus.

The newly constructed $35 million Coliseum exhibition hall had three floors devoted to the show. Five automobile

The Corvette Nomad, show car from 1954 Motorama, was the birth of the 1955-1957 production Nomad.

manufacturers displayed 124 1957 passenger cars, and 11 truck manufacturers brought 66 trucks and busses. GM's Chevrolet Division showed its 36th millionth Chevrolet, Cadillac's $12,500 Eldorado Brougham was present, as was Pontiac's Bonneville Special convertible. The theme was "America on the Move," and it was a united effort to promote automobile sales. It gave the viewing public an opportunity to compare style against style, price against price, and quality against quality with all makes and models under the same roof.

The GM Motorama was absent from the scene in 1958, but returned for 1959, playing to a total of 600,000 in New York City and Boston. The next and final Motorama was held in 1961 in New York, San Francisco, and Los Angeles with a healthy turnout of over one million attending.

All good things come to an end, as did the fabulous GM Motoramas. Reasons for its demise were varied. Certainly the revival of the National Auto Show was one; the fact that television was drawing larger and larger audiences in the home setting was another. The tremendous annual expense was a factor, and the fear that competition was ripping off GM's brilliant styling ideas was pretty evident. Some even felt the 1964 World's Fair offered a good bit of competition.

Show cars and experimental models were still built by the advanced styling studios, and from time to time they were shown and on display in major auto shows. But the annual gala event which had brought so much excitement and pleasure to the 10.5 million lucky attendees was gone...forever.

Rumors abound about the whereabouts of all those Motorama vehicles. Were they all destroyed? Are they secretly squirreled away in the inner sanctum of GM's property? Are they in the hands of GM designers of private collectors? Have marque club enthusiasts reconstructed any according to specifications?

As General Motors prepared for its 75th Anniversary Auto Expo to be held September 24 at the Technical Center in Warren, Michigan, we had been wondering how many of these famous Motorama cars would suddenly make another appearance. Wouldn't it be exciting to see them, after all these years, alongside the production models they influenced?

The experimental fastback appeared at the 1954 Motorama with the Corvette Nomad Station Wagon and two pre-production type Corvettes.

Chevrolet

Show Cars

1959 Stingray Show Car

Imagine the family sedan of the 21st century. Chevy thinks it may resemble the "Express," a slippery-shaped concept car with a cruising speed of 150 m.p.h. and economy of a 4-cylinder compact.

It is the latest in a line of Chevy concept cars and drew rave reviews at shows across the country during Chevy's 75th anniversary celebration.

The roadster made an encore appearance at the 1954 Motorama with a companion car, the Corvette Nomad. This radically-shaped display vehicle revolutionized the whole station wagon concept by mating practicality with sporty appeal.

Public reaction was so enthusiastic that a version of the Nomad, this time based on an all-new full-size Chevrolet, was in production by early 1955.

For '55 shows, Chevy tested two concepts — Biscayne and Impala. Both became legendary Chevy nameplates.

The Biscayne was a splashy sport sedan, while the Impala was a Corvette-inspired hardtop. The Biscayne previewed the 1956 Bel Air four-door hardtop, while the Impala served as inspiration for the racy '58 Impala Sport Coupe.

1962 Corvair Monza GT taken at Temple University Music Fair, Amber, Pa. in 1972. (Photo courtesy Marc Kemp, Paulsboro, N.J.

Chevy unveiled two special competition cars in 1957, the Corvette SS and the SR2. These engineering test-beds featured fuel injected engines with aluminum cylinder heads, inboard center-plane brakes and magnesium-alloy body construction.

The '50s ended on a spectacular note, with the debut of the Sting Ray racing machine. Although this Corvette-based two-seater was briefly campaigned on the nation's road courses, futuristic styling was its noteworthy feature. The acclaimed 1963 Corvette Sting Ray was an offshoot.

CERV meant Chevrolet Engineering Research Vehicle. This '60s concept car offered such exotica as an all-aluminum small-block V8 and all-independent suspension. Evolution of the CERV idea continued through the '60s with ideas that were often incorporated into production Corvettes.

Chevy's '60s-era show cars were usually based on such models as the sporty Corvair Monza, the compact Chevy II Nova, and the Corvette.

The sleek rear-engined Monza GT fastback of 1962 offered an international flavor that directly influenced the

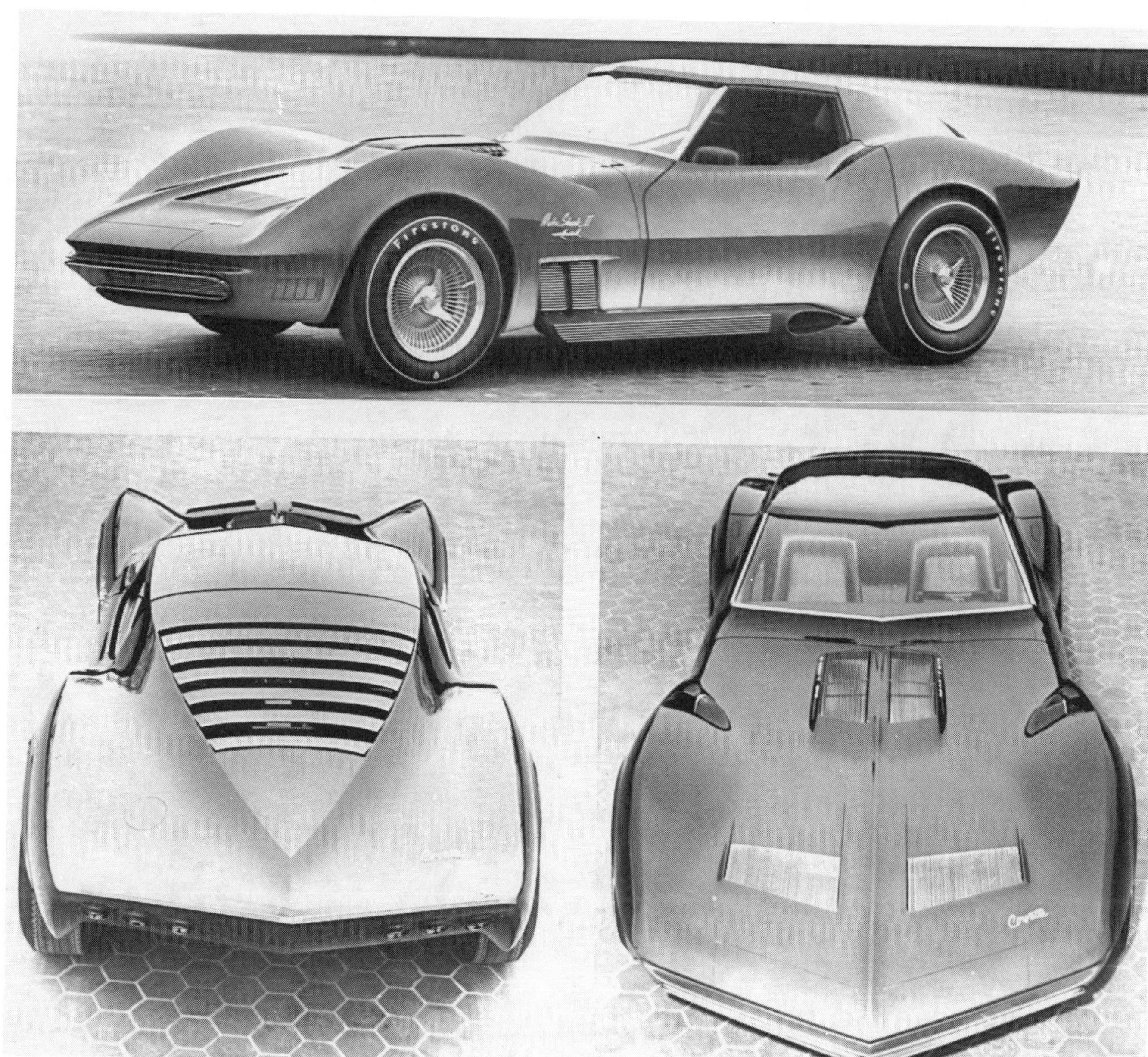

1967 Corvette XP mako Shark II

appearance of the 1965 Corvair Monza and the full-size '65 Chevrolet.

Super Nova was a sporty four-place coupe that figured heavily in the design of both '66 Chevy II Nova and '67 Camaro. In '65, the Mako Shark idea car signaled that a new, more voluptuous era was at hand for Corvette. In addition to showcasing a new 396 cu. in. V-8, the Mako accurately predicted the aggressive style of the 1968 Corvette.

During the '70s, Chevrolet engineers were busy meeting new regulations, improving fuel economy and downsizing.

Today's concept cars include the Corvette Indy, a look at one version of America's own sports car; Blazer XT-1, a 4x4 idea machine with four-wheel steering, a computerized "active" suspension and traction control to help eliminate wheel slip; and the Chevy "Express," a personalized expression of the bullet-train.

Attractive Car and Good Idea, The SS Saw Little of Racing

By Robert C. Ackerson

Duntov encased in the bubble top which was not used during the Sebring race.

Right from its very first public showing in January, 1953 at New York City's Waldorf Astoria, the Corvette was a visual sensation. Even now, nearly 25 years later, the original Corvettes deserve praise for their clean, simple, yet distinctive styling. However, styling doesn't win races and the early Corvettes lacked the mechanical sophistication needed to be a competitive sports car. In fairness, the old "Blue Flame" six provided performance that really wasn't all that bad, and in today's world of emission control equipped automobiles, it might even be called sparkling.

With the advent of Chevrolet's now classic 265 cid V-8 in 1955, the Corvette moved up several notches on the performance scale. While 1955 Corvettes with V-8 engines are extremely rare, even more so are those with the standard Chevrolet three-speed transmission, of which less that 20 were produced. This combination was far superior to the Powerglide models, and their rapid acceleration was a harbinger of things to come.

In the mid-fifties, Chevrolet was being influenced by two developments that were to be of great consequence in the decision to develop a competition version of the production Corvette. The first was Chevrolet's unaccustomed success in NASCAR stock car racing. The second factor, however was not based upon success, but defeat. Although this was not a route on the race track, it was a defeat in the race that mattered the most—the sales race between the Corvette and its arch-rival, the Ford Thunderbird.

The restyled and more powerful Corvette for 1956 provided Chevrolet the basis for a strong counter-attack. In fact, the very first 1956 Corvette off the assembly line at St. Louis was given a healthy dose of competition tonic that included the addition of a combination headrest-tail-fin (not unlike that of the D-type Jaguar), a racing screen and a fiberglass tonneau cover.

The Ford Thunderbird had been successful at the 1955 Daytona Beach speed trials and Chevrolet hoped to capitalize on the public interest in the speed runs over the measured mile with this modified "Daytona" Corvette. The result was most impressive: Zora Arkus-Duntov exceeded 150 mph on his run down the beach to set a new American sports car record.

Additional experience and encouragement came from participation in the 1956 Sebring race, where a Corvette dubbed the "Sebring Racing" (SR) Corvette, equipped with a larger engine and a ZF four-speed gearbox, finished a credible tenth overall. A second "stock" Corvette completed the twelve hour race first in its class. The SR model was further developed into an SR2 version, which was campaigned by Richard Thompson in SCCA events. But even a driver of Thompson's stature could not compensate for the excessive weight of the Corvette. Even with the V-8 output, the Corvette was still down on power and too heavy for serious competition.

All of these events provided the backdrop for the decision made in September, 1956, to embark on the XP-64 project, the object of which was to create a sports car capable of racing against the world's finest competition sports cars, and emerging victorious. The physical embodiment of project XP-64 was of course the Corvette Super Sport—the rarest of all Corvettes, whose formal racing career would consist of twenty-three laps at the 1957 Sebring endurance race.

From the very start, the Corvette SS program suffered from a shortage of both time and racing experience. It was already September and the goal was to have one car completed by December 1, 1956 in order that it could be displayed at the Automobile Manufacturers Association Show in New York City. Three additional SS models were to be constructed for competition in the 12 hour Sebring race scheduled for March, 1957. This ambitious goal was simply too much to hope for. As it turned out, the solitary SS that raced at Sebring had virtually no testing time on it, and any chance such an untried entity would have at winning was very, very slim.

A rather bizarre attempt by some members of Chevrolet's engineering and styling staff to disguise a D-Jaguar, replace its engine with a Corvette V-8 and hopefully achieve the desired racing success, is an indication of the pressure experienced by the XP-64 staff. Fortunately for all concerned, this idea was scrapped before it developed any serious momentum.

As it appeared at Sebring, the Corvette SS was a mixture of traditional, contemporary and some fairly advanced engineering and technology. Mounted in a 92 inch wheelbase, the engine was based on the standard 283 cid V-8, but featured a number of modifications resulting in increased output and a reduction in weight. Aluminum engine parts included the cylinder heads, clutch housing, water pump and radiator core. The oil pan was made of magnesium, as was the SS body. The fuel injection system's air metering valve faced toward the front, instead of its usual sideward location. This enabled the Chevrolet technicians to virtually eliminate any problems of fuel stoppage under competition conditions.

The SS frame, a tubular-truss type structure of welded chrome molybdenum steel tubing, was very closely patterned after that of the Mercedes-Benz 300-SL. While sturdy and rigid, it weighed a hefty 180 pounds.

The suspension of the SS was a straightforward design with no surprises or startling innovations. Integrated units, consisting of the coil springs, shock absorbers and spring pumpers, were used at all four wheels. The front suspension utilized non-parallel wishbones and a link-type stabilizer bar, while the rear axle was mounted in a de Dion tube arrangement. This type of rear suspension was neither exotic nor ultra-sophisticated, but it did have the advantage of resulting in a low ratio of unsprung to sprung weight. In addition, since the differential weight was carried on the springs, the remaining unsprung weight could be closely controlled for optimum cornering ability.

Since there was not sufficient time available to design a totally new braking system, the SS carried a normal brake system with two leading shoes, and a 12 inch diameter and 2½ inch width. The braking mechanism itself was a Chrysler design. Cast iron was used for the brake drums, which carried an outer casing of aluminum, fitted with heat dissipating fins. This arrangement was later adopted by Buick for its 1958 models. The rear brakes were mounted in an inboard location, which helped to reduce unsprung weight, but subjected the brakes to heat from the differential. A novel solution to the problem of uneven front and rear braking rates was the use of a mercury switch, which was sensitive to deceleration forces and could be adjusted to limit rear wheel braking to a predetermined amount. The result was better rear braking effectiveness at low speeds, and little danger of the rear wheels locking during rapid deceleration from high speeds.

While enough parts were made to construct five complete cars, only two made the trek to Sebring, where as *The Autocar* reported, the Corvette team appeared with "...a bevy of caravans (trailers), a crew of 150, enough spares to sink a battleship and a posse of guards." Perhaps it was just a matter of convenience, but the trailers were situated in the form of a large square, which was quite similar to the circles formed by the wagon trains when faced with an Indian attack in unfriendly territory. Mere coincidence or not, the Corvette team was in hostile territory, where the going was extremely tough.

Fortunately, Chevrolet had two top flight drivers in Piero Taruffi and John Fitch, both of whom put in numerous practice laps on the practice car, that was soon dubbed "the mule." Despite its crude bodywork and unkempt exterior, "the mule" was fast and possessed good handling characteristics. Unfortunately, there was no time for the knowledge gained from running "the mule" to be applied to the SS1, which was the actual car for the race. This was a pity, since the SS1 was a beautifully finished automobile, lighter and more powerful than the practice car, but totally lacking crucial modifications and refinements that come only from operation under actual racing conditions. Even a relatively minor, but important detail such as cockpit ventilation had been inadequately tested.

The SS Corvette's participation in the actual race was short-lived, and despite the best efforts of Fitch and Taruffi, their car was simply overwhelmed by all sorts of misfortunes. Fitch got off to a slow start, but on the second lap he was in sixth position. On the third time around, however, he had to stop to have his front tires replaced, since they had been severely damaged due to locking brakes. This was but the first of many pit-stops for fuel injection ills, a faulty ignition coil and finally overheating. After 23 laps, Taruffi retired the car, when a rubber bushing on one of the rear trailing arms collapsed and put the rear suspension in an unworkable condition. Fitch had turned a best lap of 3.29.8, whereas Jean Behra's record lap on the winning 4.5 liter Maserati V-8 was 3.24.5.

Unfortunately, the American Automobile Manufacturer's Association agreed to ban any further official racing efforts by its members after June, 1957.

Two Rare Vettes

Two rare Corvette prototypes are the Cerv I and the Cerv 2.

The Cerv I dates from 1960. It is a Corvette experimental research vehicle and was used to develop chassis and engine components for production models. It has engine no. 18004-241-B and chassis no. P-2152 and was donated to the museum by Chevrolet Division of General Motors Corp.

The Cerv II was the second in the series of Corvette experimental vehicles. It is a mid-engined prototype featuring a unique four-wheel-drive system with fluid couplings. The Cerv II was reported to be capable of going from zero-to-sixty miles per hour in just 2.8 seconds. It bears engine no. 11212EZ-92199-A and chassis no. P-3910.

These cars are just two of the more than 80 pedigreed autos on display at Briggs Cunningham's collection. Like the Cerv models, many of the cars have unique engineering or competition backgrounds.

To find out more about the Briggs Cunningham Automotive Museum write: 250 Baker St., Costa Mesa, CA 92626.

1960 CERV I

1963 CERV II A modified 327 cubic inch Chevrolet V-8 is mounted amidship in the Cerv II.

CERV I The racer that never got to race

By Bill Siuru

In the late 1950s and early '60s, Chevrolet and General Motors (GM) management were vacillating between "let's go racing" and "no racing" policies. However, this did not deter Zora Arkov-Duntov, known as Mr. Corvette, and a premiere racing enthusiast, from building a true racing machine around the Corvette.

This was the Chevrolet Experimental Racing Vehicle I, or CERV I. By the time the CERV I was introduced to the public, the R stood for Research to downplay the racing image.

Looking at the CERV I, there is no way to disguise the fact that this was an all-out racer, exactly what Duntov and senior Corvette engineers Harold Krieger and Walt Zetye had in mind when they designed the car.

The car's layout and dimensions came from the idea of someday racing the car at Indy. But the immediate goal was the Pikes Peak Hill Climb. Indeed, the CERV I was originally (but unofficially) called the "Hillclimber" around GM. The design was thought to be a natural for this race because its rear engine location gave a predominately rearward weight distribution; and its seating arrangement provided excellent visibility needed for the winding assault on the Peak.

Engine placement in the rear was also a selling ploy within GM management. The rationale being that it could show the public the full potential of a rear-engine car, to help in selling GM's new Corvair.

For power, Duntov turned to Chevy's small block 283 cid V-8. While the dimensions would be the same, the engine was almost entirely made of aluminum: block, heads, water-pump housing, flywheel, clutch pressure plate, and starter motor body.

Like the Vegas that would appear later, regular pistons were used in the aluminum block, a feat made possible by the high-silicon alloy used in the block. The results were impressive. Weight was cut by 175 pounds to a total of 350 pounds; and since the engine developed 353 hp, the magic 1:1 horsepower-to-weight ratio was achieved, while the horsepower-to displacement ratio exceeded it by 25 percent.

In later attempts to get even more performance out of the CERV I, horsepower was boosted to 420 through supercharging and 500 hp with twin TRW turbochargers.

The CERV I body design can be attributed to Larry Shinoda and Tony Lapine who were assigned many of GM's "special projects". The result was a fiberglass body that weighed an amazingly low 80 pounds. The entire CERV I weighed only 1450 pounds.

The chassis and running gear was a combination of pure race design and stock GM components. A tubular space frame was used. The suspension was fully independent, front and rear with inboard rear drum brakes. The car had one of the earliest dual braking systems. The four-speed transmission was stock. The car's bullet-shaped headrest is especially interesting. It covered the injection manifold plenum chamber with air scoops in the side.

The car made its "racing" debut at the United States Grand Prix at Riverside, Calif. in November 1960, with Duntov at the wheel. Of course, the engine was much too big for the 2½ liter Formula 1 displacement limit, so it was only driven a few exhibition laps around the track.

The CERV I's assault on the "Race to the Clouds" consisted of a few practice runs in September 1960. With the results being disappointing, further running was aborted. Monday-morning quarterbacking of the times on the unofficial runs, showed that they were a lot better than originally thought. Some even set records.

The CERV I's crew had put too much faith in the hearsay of the Peaks' "experts". Interestingly, GM was not officially involved in the Pikes Peak race, it only provided "a moving platform for the (Firestone) tires".

Of course, the CERV I never ran the Indianapolis 500 mile race, or any other official races. However, the car was used extensively to develop Firestone and Goodyear racing tires and thus was frequently seen on courses like Daytona and Sebring.

Before it was retired to the Briggs Cunningham Automotive Museum in Costa Mesa, Calif. in 1972, the car attained a top speed of 206 mph on GM's Milford Proving Grounds five-mile, circular banked track. For this feat, the 283 cid power plant had been replaced by a 377 cid V-8, a bored and stroked version of the 1964 vintage small block.

An official Chevrolet photo of Zora Arkus-Duntov with the CERV I.

Mako Shark I Previewed '63 Vette

By Wallace A. Wyss

The Corvette has always been GM's sort of "preview car," that is to say, you could look at it for a preview of what's to come in family cars.

But, back in the 60's, each Corvette would presage something to come in the production Chevrolet sedans and hardtops, and, in addition, each Corvette would give a hint of what was to come in Corvettes.

One of the most interesting show cars this writer has ever experienced first-hand was the Corvette Mako Shark I show car.

The Mako Shark I, code-named XP-755 (for "Experimental Project No. 755) was designed in 1961 by Larry Shinoda, working in Bill Mitchell's semi-secret basement studio at the GM Design Center. The studio was "semi-secret" because it was off-limits to people from, say, the Chevrolet studio or Pontiac studio, yet its own personnel had entree to any other studio they wanted. (Mainly because Shinoda reported to Mitchell and Mitchell was GM's VP in charge of Design.)

Mitchell wanted to build a show car that would give a good "preview" of the production Sting Ray to come in 1963, but not yet tip off the whole show. So the car was built on a 1961 Corvette solid-axle chassis, lest some over-eager journalist crawl underneath and find I.R.S. on the chassis had it been a prototype '63 chassis.

The styling theme — the shark — came reportedly because ace fisherman Mitchell had hooked a shark off Bimini. The author can vouch for this, having seen the actual stuffed mako shark in the den of Bill Mitchell's Birmingham, Michigan home.

The Mako Shark I was a fully driveable car—GM VP in charge of Design William L. Mitchell liked to have his show cars built that way so he could drive home from work in them, and occasionally, blow off a Cobra on Woodward Avenue . . .

The double-bubble roof canopy came straight from an earlier Corvette show car — the XP-700—but the big change was a flat downsweeping front nose with sharp-edged fenders rising out of it, actually inspired more by a clay model Corvette done back in 1957 called the "Q-Corvette." The '63 style roll-over headlights weren't necessary on a show car because a show car didn't have to conform to U.S. headlight height laws, so Mitchell had hideaway headlights put in the grille.

The turn signals were "fishy" in front because they were secreted in little gill-like shapes, just about where a real shark has them. In back, the Mako Shark I had three taillights per side, but then a really unusual feature—two little trapdoors on the rear deck that would pop open when you hit the brakes extra hard. Each trapdoor was mirrored on its inside surface and would reflect another set of brake lights secreted in the rear deck that were aimed straight up. Complicated? James Bond-ish? Perhaps, but Mitchell was a gadget-lover from the word "Go," and never took the simple route if there was a more novel way to do it.

You could say the same thing about the paint scheme. A real shark is usually dark blue on top so that the fish looking down can't see it against the bottom and white on the bottom so the fish looking up can't see it against the sky. Mitchell had the Mako Shark I painted this way, with a fadeaway "gradient density" effect joining the two.

Mitchell wanted to make certain that the Mako Shark I was fast. The first engine that went into it was a small block 327 fitted with a Roots-type "Jimmy" supercharger with eight pounds boost.

As time went on, various other engines were put into it, including a Rochester fuel-injected one and a hulking 427. It was a job to fit any engine because the see-through glass top made air conditioning mandatory and the car's heavy weight made power steering and power brakes almost necessities as well.

The author was invited for a ride in the car when visiting the GM Technical Center in the mid-60's. At that time, the car still had its original interior, which was characterized by lots of black crackle paint, metal grids on the floor in place of carpets and a leather-rimmed steering wheel was a Ferrari prancing horse (Mitchell proudly identified this as "a gift from Enzo Ferrari.")

The transparent top was tinted on top with a see-through tint, something like that on jet fighters. From the outside, the tint was opaque, mirror-like, like a Highway Patrolman's sunglasses.

The car was fast, and had a nice burble-like roar. Mitchell drove fast and with the sureness of a man who had driven everything that was fast, on both sides of the Atlantic. He didn't much care who I was—more or less a perfect stranger who had wandered into the Design area —indeed, one got the feeling he would demonstrate his toy to anyone, joyful at the excuse to wind it out on a bright sunny Michigan afternoon.

Rohm & Haas Chevy Concept Cars

by John Gunnell

Chevy buffs may be familiar with products from Rohm & Haas, the Pennsylvania firm that developed and trademarked Plexiglas. A few will even remember that R & H helped build a famous GM show car in 1939. But how many realize that the firm designed two Chevrolet concept cars in the 1960s?

One, the Explorer II, was based on a 1964 Corvette and may or may not have actually been built. R & H turned out a color brochure with a rendering of the car and sketches of its design details, but there's not evidence Explorer II ever went past the drawing board stage.

You're wondering if the name suggests there was an Explorer I? This would be logical and, also, right on the money. Such a vehicle was conceived in 1963. This time the car was a Corvair, and planning went beyond the drawing board.

The Explorer series of show cars was an outgrowth of R & H's long service to the auto industry as a materials supplier. Since its founding in 1909, the company had a deep and continuing interest in automobiles. Rohm & Haas's very first product was a bate (abating agent) for leather. It was used to produce the fine leather upholstery in early century cars. In the 1930s, the firm developed an acrylic plastic called Plexiglas.

Plexiglas seemed a natural replacement for the fragile glass lenses formerly used in taillights. To emphasize the qualities and properties of the new material, R & H helped make a GM show car for the 1939-1940 New York World's Fair. It was a see-through, Plexiglas-bodied Pontiac which has had much exposure in old car hobby magazines.

The Explorer I wasn't quite as radical as this so-called "Ghost Car," but the thinking behind it was virtually the same. The Philadelphia-based company wanted to use the customized Corvair to showcase innovative uses for Plexiglas in automobile design. Beginning as a stock 1963 coupe, the car was modified under the direction of R & H design engineers. The changes were basically limited to trim features.

For beginners, the car had a one-piece Plexiglas headlamp bezel. It was molded of transparent material which was deeply contoured. Reflector sections were metallized and the bezel was second-finished to match the black body finish. It incorporated the turn signal and parking lamp lenses.

A special sunroof was said to "provide daylight transmission" and provide a "convertible" feeling. Rectangular in shape, it consisted of two panels, the lower with a texture to eliminate reflections. The top panel had metallic flakes imbedded in it to reflect heat while enhancing appearance.

Perhaps the first ever plastic hubcaps were used on the show car. They were finished in flat black, giving the Corvair a "nasty" look. In the center was a circular plastic hub medallion bearing the Rohm & Haas corporate logo of two opposed arrowheads, one blue and the other magenta. The hub's three-dimensional finned background was translucent white. Around the hub were eight red Plexiglas reflectors added to increase night driving safety.

The circular medallion, in slightly smaller size, was also used in the steering wheel hub and on exterior sail panels. Front fender badges carried a smaller version of the symbol behind Explorer I nameplates.

Explorer I also appeared on the glove box trim panel made of another plastic "sandwich." The translucent white inner panel had a horizontally ribbed texture, but the outer panel was smooth to the touch. This made it easy to clean.

The Corvair also had a stock-looking curved rear window which was actually made of a single sheet of Plexiglas metallized, on the second surface, to reflect heat and light. It also significantly reduced weight.

Changes to the rear of the car consisted of a full-width decor panel and taillight ensemble with an oblong shape. The decor panel, in the center, matched the glove box door trim panel. On each side there were three taillight lenses consisting of a white rectangle, an amber rectangle and a lipstick-shaped red outer lens. They were surrounded and segmented by a metallized Plexiglas bezel. If nothing else, this treatment really brightened the Corvair's normally plain-looking rear. It was noted the center decor panel could be back-lighted.

The Explorer I brochure was published to be given to automotive engineers at trade shows. The purpose was to show how the characteristics of Plexiglas could be used to great advantage on cars of the future. There is no hint of any modifications other than cosmetic to the exterior or interior. The engine was probably left stock.

This means that the car was not as futuristic as other Detroit concept cars. Or was it? If you consider the changes that have taken place in the auto industry since 1963, many of them are the same ones suggested by the Explorer I: namely, greater use of plastics for improved appearance, better maintenance, more convenience and lighter weight.

When you look at things this way, the handsome black Corvair was a lot more predictive of the future than some other far out show cars. It's too bad someone didn't have the foresight to preserve this unique vehicle. Or is it possible that the car is still lingering in somebody's collection as is the Pontiac Ghost Car made by Rohm & Haas so many years before?

Racing & Pacing

Drag Race

By Bob Hovorka

A bright orange sun sparkled off the hood of the red '55 Chevy. Though it was eight years old, its V-8 barked through the twin glass packs as Tom Elton fingered the throttle linkage. He had been working on the car, modifying, revamping, improving, ever since he bought it two years ago. Now its engine compartment was filled with a rebuilt 283, that sported dual quads for more bite, and dual coils and points for more snap. It was honed and primed, fussed over and cared for, like some living entity. At first his friends looked at the two door sedan and wondered; later, they laughed as it spent more time in the garage than on the street. Now, it was ready! No one in the small town had a car that could compare with it; and this weekend everyone who laughed, would laugh no more.

This year's county fair would have one completely new event — a drag race — something that had never been done before. It might not be as fancy as the big city drag strips, but it was a measured quarter-mile, blocked off, where car could go against car.

Although drag racing had grown from the first official races after World War II, into a big spectator sport, the town council did not see it quite that way. In fact, they had voted down the idea of having such a race for several years. But somehow this year they agreed to give it a try; "To see if anyone was really interested in such foolishness," was their comment.

And was anyone interested? Well every young man who had a car of his own, or could borrow his father's, had been down to register for the big event. The official prize was a large gold and red trophy; but the most important prize was the unofficial recognition that the winner had the fastest car in the county.

Though the National Hot Rod Association had rules that separated cars into specific classes, this small, one day event just wouldn't have that many different cars. So the

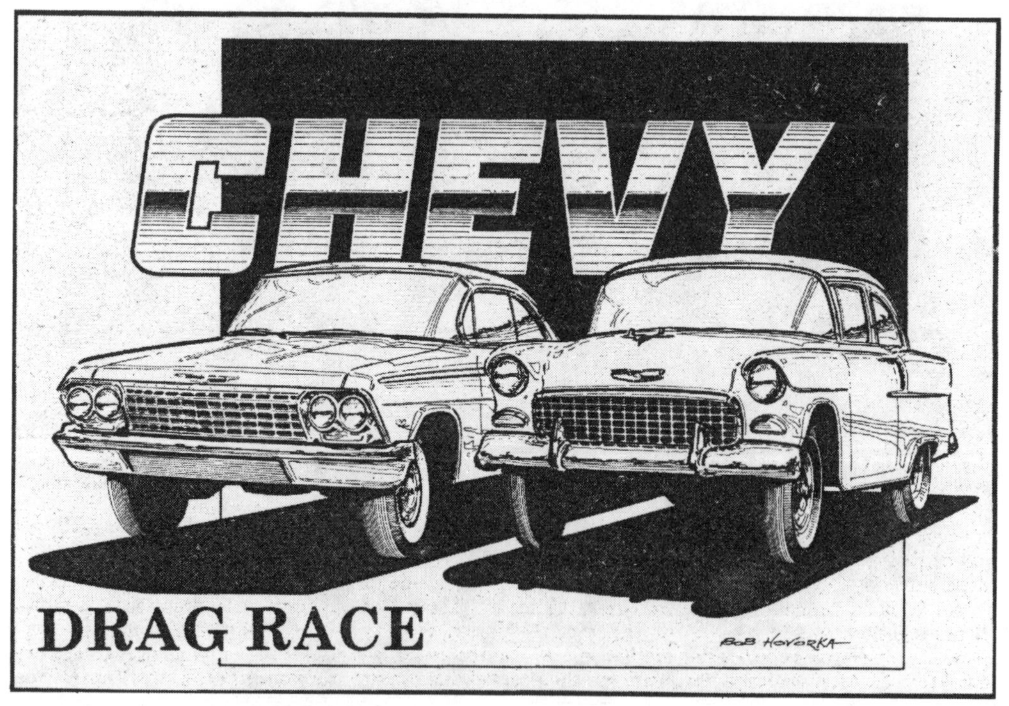

town council decided to make things simple; stock cars would race other stock cars of the same engine size; while any modification from stock, would make those cars race other modified cars. Not quite as fair as the official rules, but adequate for this local area.

Weeks before the race, cars began losing seats, hoods and many other things to save weight; things that were normally required to drive on the road. The committee quickly enacted its first rule change. "The cars had to meet state laws for motor vehicles *and* they had to be driven to the fairgrounds." This was an impressive sounding statement, but the local boys still found ways to shed a few pounds. Although the hoods went back on, some cars began showing up around town without much of an interior. Of course, if it was the family car, the interior stayed, though many a rear seat was pitched out on race day.

Tom wasn't worried. He still had one strong engine. In fact, that was one of the few problems with the car. It was difficult to get off the line without leaving a smoldering trail of fused rubber on the street. A set of cheater slicks might help, but he had put all his extra money in the engine, and now with the race just a week away, there was no chance of getting enough money for a set of tires. Yet, he still was confident that he could win — it was the best modified around — he was sure of it.

Everything was going great till the day before the race. He had stopped at the bakery on the way home when he first saw it. It rumbled slowly through town, bright red and looking mean. It stopped at the town's only traffic light, idling erratically, chrome lakers capped shut. The driver reached over with his right hand and took out the pack of cigarettes that were rolled in the left sleeve of his white T shirt. He lit one while he waited for the light.

Tom glanced at the front fender and the crossed checker flag emblems that rested above the chrome V. He both sighed in relief, and gasped in horror at the same instant. It wasn't a 409; it was a 327 and even if all the owner had done was to put on the lake plugs, it would be running in modified. He'd be up against it, he thought; that is, if the stranger had come to race. "What else would an outsider be doing here now," the words just popped out loud.

The '62 Bel Air had definitely come to race. It drove up main street, then turned at the corner, heading for Miller's Filling Station. Tom half ran, half flew up the street — and stood gasping for air on the corner. "He can't run it, he just can't!"

The '62 Chevy was filling up with ethyl, its owner was talking to Mr. Miller.

"He's asking directions to the fairgrounds; I just know it!" said Tom. He waited till the car left and then walked the remaining distance to the filling station; the bag of bakery squashed beneath his arm.

Mr. Miller looked up from the '52 Rambler he was working on, saw Tom's face, and answered the question Tom was afraid to ask. "Yep, he's come to run at the fairgrounds tomorrow."

Tom nodded his head; unable to speak.

"It's one of those 327 cubic inch V-8's. Three speed on the column."

Tom's head shook in dismay.

"What's the matter?" asked Mr. Miller.

Suddenly the fear that had swelled up inside of him since he saw the car, burst forth. "God, Mr. Miller, it's not fair! It's just not fair! I've saved and worked so hard on that old coupe — everyone laughed at me — but I wanted to show 'em — I know I could have won — if —"

"Hold on Tom. What do you mean, could have won. You've got quite an engine in that '55. That 283 you put in has got to count for something. There's care in the work you've done — much more care than just going out and buying a souped up automobile."

"I know — but that 327 — I mean it's practically a Corvette engine!"

"Whoa! Slow down my young friend. What do you really know about that '62 Chevrolet; I mean facts, not rumors."

"Well," there was a long pause.

"Well, what?"

"Well," again there was silence. "Well it's supposed to —"

Mr. Miller stopped him sort. "It's supposed to what? What are the facts? Are those statistics — it's supposed to! I'll tell you one thing, if you keep carrying on like this, you won't be able to win a race against this Rambler — and it's a flat head six! Now you set still for a minute, and let me check my files."

Tom followed Mr. Miller through the shop to the office. He watched as the grey haired mechanic opened a drawer and began looking through some papers. A damp sensation made him look away, and he noticed a red stain of raspberry jelly that had leaked from the bag he was carrying. He put down the bag and wiped at his sleeve with his handkerchief. Mr. Miller saw him from the corner of his eye and smiled. Tom looked up, saw his glance, and laughed out loud.

Mr. Miller brought a couple of papers from the file and sat down. "Now look Tom. That '62 automobile may have a reputation as a fast vehicle, but every automobile has some drawbacks. First of all, unless all my books are wrong, it's got a couple hundred pounds more weight to pull around. It can have 250 or 300 horsepower, let's figure 300 since I'm sure that fella wouldn't have bought the 250 engine."

"Now, your automobile originally had 162 horsepower, I remember it had a two barrel carburetor when you got it; but the two door coupe also had a lighter body. This, coupled with the 283 and the two 4 barrels you put on it, and I figure you've got to have somewhere between 250 and 270 horsepower — but remember the weight! You've got to have a couple hundred pounds less to move."

"Yeah, it might be lighter, but that's part of my problem. Everytime I really stomp on it, all I do is burn rubber — I can't get away from the line. Those new Chevy's have got positraction and everything!"

"Well that limited slip differential might be of some advantage, if he has one, but I tell you what; you stop at the bakery and get a couple new jelly biscuits — you can't bring those home all squashed like that — and go wash the jelly off your arm. Then you bring that old Chevrolet down here later tonight. You know I built a couple of hot speedsters in my time. There are still a few tricks I remember, and we just might be able to do a couple things this evening that will help you, *Get off the line,* as you call it, in front of that '62 that seems to be terrifying you."

Tom was back with the '55 Chevy in less than an hour. Mr. Miller had finished the Rambler and was waiting. He had Tom put the coupe on the grease rack.

"Now Tom, we're going to do a couple things tonight that will have to be changed back before you start driving this automobile on the street again."

Tom shot him a questioning glance.

"Oh, you'll be able to drive to the fairgrounds, that's not far, but you can't go driving around the roads like normal."

"What are you going to do? I mean there's really no time; tomorrow's the race."

"I'm not going to do anything major, just help get the power you've got in that engine to the road."

Mr. Miller began loosening the upper ends of the shock absorbers. Lifting the car on the hoist, he unfastened the lower end of the shocks and pulled them out. He removed the wheel assembly and began loosening the lower control arm cross shaft bushing bolts. In short order, he picked up a spring compressor and had the springs out. He then placed a metal disk, about ½ inch thick, above the coil springs and put them back.

"Tom, when you start out under heavy acceleration, does the right or left tire seem to be the one that leaves a strip of rubber?"

Tom thought only a moment."It's the right one that usually spins."

"You're sure?"

"Oh yes! I've got marks all down the driveway to prove it."

Mr. Miller went to one of the cabinets and brought out several rubber like blocks — the kind used to bolster sagging springs. He put them around the left front coil, so it wound up slightly higher than the right. Next, he brought out an old, dirty set of shock absorbers. Tom started to protest, but before he could really get started, Mr. Miller stopped him.

"These old worn shocks will help. Remember, I said there are some things that must be changed back before you go driving around the streets."

"But," Tom finally interrupted, "but why take out my good shocks and put in old, worn out ones? Mine are nearly new!"

Mr. Miller had moved to the rear of the car and was placing additional spring clips around the leaf springs. Tom followed, but let him work without further interruption.

Mr. Miller spoke, not really to Tom, more like thinking out loud. "It would be nice to get this back end down a little more, but we're somewhat limited."

After he finished, Mr. Miller rolled up two older tires. "We'll put these smaller tires on the front. That's about all we can do on such short notice."

Tom helped put on the tires, and they lowered the grease rack. Wiping off his hands, the old timer turned to Tom, "Well, it's time for a cup of coffee."

The two of them walked into the office and Tom was the first to speak. "I understand the extra spring clips at the rear — to help stiffen the springs — but what about the front?"

The wily old mechanic smiled. "You remember how you said you had trouble getting the power to the road? Well everything we did tonight was to that end. The metal spacers that I put above the springs in front, helped lift the front end. The worn shocks will let it come up even faster, which will help transfer the weight to the rear end."

"How come you only put those spring boosters on one side?"

"Well, do you remember how you said the right rear wheel always spins? By picking the left front spring up, we'll help increase the load on the right rear — getting better traction. The worn tires we put on the front will give you less rolling resistance. If you check, you'll find I put a little extra pressure in them. Make sure you're careful driving home tonight — and to the fairgrounds tomorrow."

* * *

The day was perfect. A cool front had passed through during the night, setting off a few showers that cut the heat. The trials ran all day without any serious problems. When it was all said and done, the modified class was down to two cars. A red '55 Chevy two door, and a red '62 Bel Air. Both cars sat at the line, the eyes of each driver glued to the starting flag. An air of excitement permeated far beyond the fenced off area; it reached nearly everyone at the fairgrounds. The starter was getting ready. Both car's engines began revving up, drivers half looking at the tach, half at the starter — ears straining above the yells of the crowd — trying to hear the engines. The flag man jumped higher and higher, till it looked like he'd clear the tops of the cars.

Suddenly the flag moved! Clouds of smoke billowed from the rear wheel wells, and it seemed an eternity before the cars left the line. Either the extra torque of the 327, or the nervousness of the '55 driver, let the '62 slip off a fraction before the '55 coupe. The revs climbed higher, and the '55 began to catch up. Tom watched the tach — pushing the 283 into regions it had rarely approached. He heard the 327 shift, and held on just a second longer. Then, he too punched the clutch and stretched for second.

Again the two Chevys revved higher and higher — louder and louder — fender to fender — the sound of open lakers shaking the very fencing that had been built to contain them. It was the old against the new — the local against the outsider — the loving care of one person against the factory's new, easy to buy power — and it was neck and neck!

Again the crescendo of power exploded from the open pipes, rising higher and higher; straining for the last bit of horsepower before the final shift. Then it comes! A slight faltering, and flat out for the final seconds. The crowd rises to its feet, screaming and stretching to see. The cars rocket past — both drivers taxing their cars for the last ounce of speed.

And then it's done!

The pulsating echoes of pounding pistons, reverberate for a few more seconds — before growing still. The cheering of the crowd, swells for the winner — before it too diminishes. And a grey haired mechanic and his wife slowly make their way towards a red Chevy two door — a smile on their faces.

25 Years Of Checkered Flags For the 1957 Chevrolet

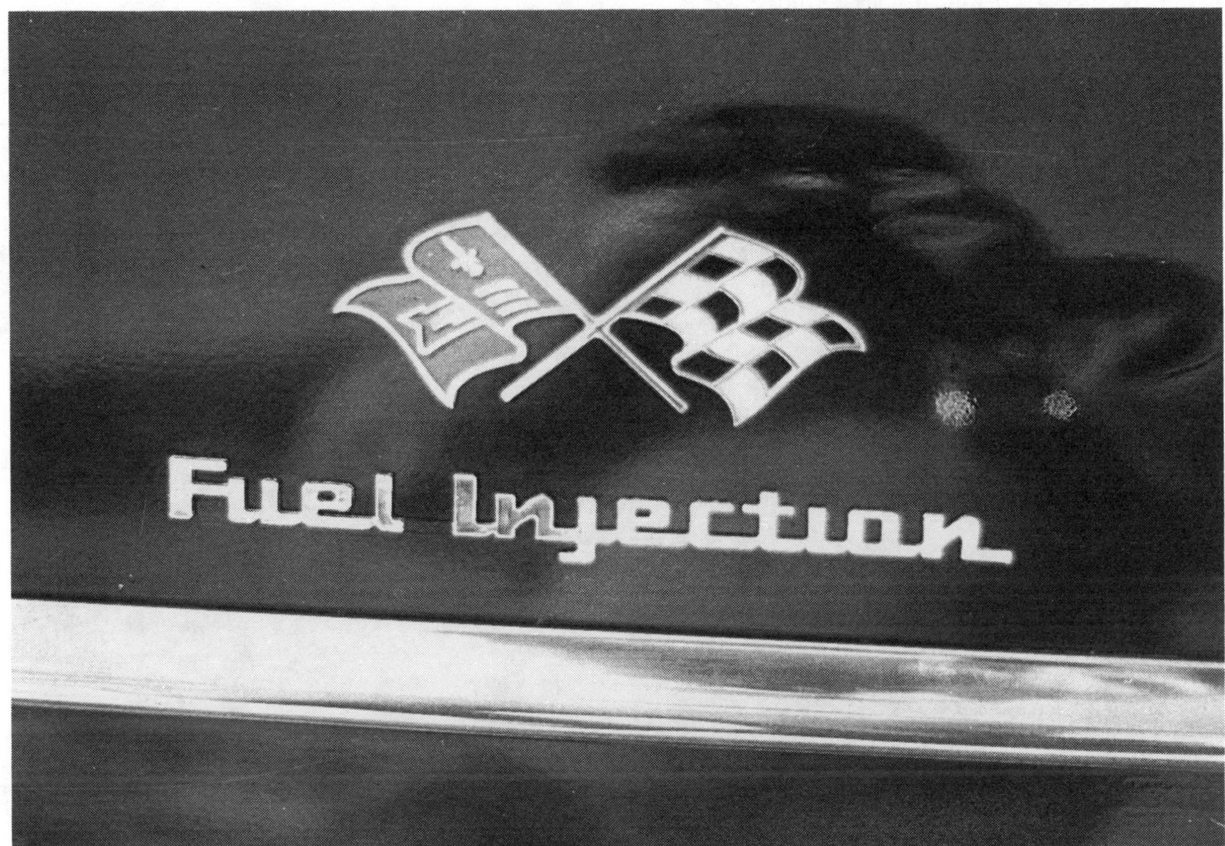

By Phil Hall

The closing of the 1981 season was a significant one for the classic 1957 Chevrolets, as it marked the completion of a quarter century of competition for the line of cars from Chevy, which was initially considered a disappointment.

As most Chevy fans know, the 1957 models represented the third year the 1955 basic body and chassis was used. The mid-1950s were years of tremendous change in styling and holding the facelifted 1957 models to compete with the really all-new 1957 offerings from Ford and Plymouth cost Chevy sales and its traditional first place in the sales race.

From a popularity standpoint at the time, the 1957 Chevrolet was a loser.

At first, things weren't much better on the race tracks of America. Chevrolet introduced its hottest engines of all time, but still fell short of the competition in engine size and advertised output.

Chevrolet's legendary 265 cubic inch V8 hit the market in the all-new 1955 models and grew for the first time with the 1957 introduction, with a 1/8-inch bore increase netting a boost to 283 cubic inches. The topper was a mechanical fuel injection system, which brought the advertised horsepower output up to 283, for a highly-promoted one horsepower per cubic inch.

While injected 1957s are ultra hot collector vehicles today, in 1957's charged performance atmosphere, they were just one of the pack. Ford's engines went up to 312 cubic inches, with a rare supercharger option bringing out 300 horsepower. Plymouth's V-800 option got 290 advertised horses from 318 cubes and medium and high priced cars got into even bigger numbers.

Two types of racing for new cars were popular at the time, oval track late model stock car competition and drag racing, on quarter-mile strips of pavement.

Chevrolet concentrated its factory-backed racing efforts on stock car racing, helping teams build race cars and doing development work to make sure the cars with the blue bow tie won on Sunday, so the showrooms could sell on Monday.

Drag racing was still in its formative stages with the competition still not organized to the point stock car racing was.

In drag racing, competing cars were broken down into classes, based on weight and horsepower. In stock car racing, oval track events threw all the competitors into one class and let them slug it out. If you won a major stock car race, you worked for it.

Chevrolet's introduction of the 1955 models coincided its first serious entry into the world of racing. The cars were light, the quick-winding small V8 engines could come off a turn fast and the conventional coils up front and leaf springs in the rear would be made to provide reasonable handling.

At first, Chevrolets couldn't outpower the giants of the day. Notably the big Chrysler 300s, but they could make fewer stops for fuel and tires, and could run circles around them on the shorter tracks.

Despite their small engine size, the 1955 and 1956 Chevys built a tough reputation in auto racing.

The 1957 models were an improvement over the 1955s and 1956s, with the more powerful 283s being the main factor in the evolution.

Racing rules of the era said that if you wanted to run a 283, it had to be in a 1957 model, thus the fastest stock and drag Chevrolets in 1957 were usually current models.

Normally, with performance technology advancing at a rapid rate, the 1957 Chevrolets would have been super-

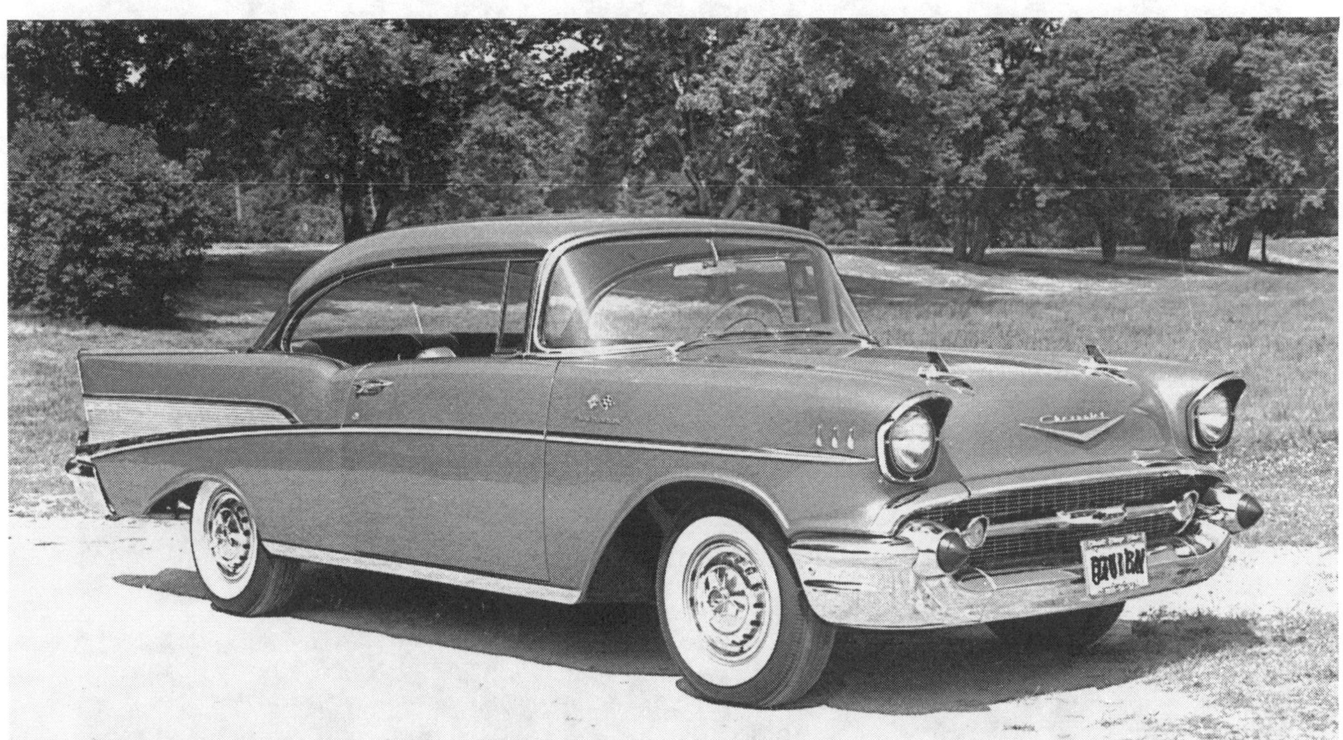

Today The Bel Air is the model most often seen with the crossed-flags emblem.

seded by the even better performing 1958 models and would have rapidly been forgotten in the highly competitive racing world.

However, a couple of events took place that would make the 1957 Chevrolet a legend, and neither had anything to do with the car itself.

The first was a political move by the domestic automobile manufacturers to take the heat off from the government. The open promoting of high performance cars and the backing of racing activities attracted the attention of legislators, both on a state and national level. With the highway death toll climbing, threats of legislation to regulate the auto industry were common.

In reaction to this, the Automobile Manufacturers Assn. agreed in June of 1957 to withdraw from the support of racing and back off in the promotion of high performance cars.

Race cars were cheaply sold or given to the teams and performance development programs were put on the back burner.

The second factor was perhaps the most important, the all-new 1958 Chevrolet. Had it not been for the 1958 Chevrolet, the 1957 never would have become the classic it is.

In an attempt to catch up with the lower, longer and wider competitors, Chevrolet introduced its 1958 models which were all of the above. Wheelbase went from 115 to 118 inches, length from 202.8 to 209.1, width from 73.9 to 77.7 and height from 59.1 to 56.4.

Mechanically, a new 348 cubic inch V8 became the top of the line powerplant. It was based on a design Chevrolet developed for trucks and it would be awhile before its performance potential could be unleashed.

The most controversial aspect of the 1958 models was the frame, which had coil springs on all four corners and was of X-design, meaning no side protection.

With the factory no longer supplying cars to race, or having its engineers help in getting the racers competitive, those racing Chevrolets found it easier to stay with the 1957 models.

The all-new again 1959 models provided no real help, as the radical-looking finned machines were even bigger than the 1958s, which turned out to be a rare one-year body.

With 1955-57 models a known entity and no real reason to advance to the 1958 and 1959 models, for one of the few times in the 1950s, the constant advancement to newer models in cars raced was halted.

As a result, 1957 models were raced longer than usual and developed a base that would propel them into a quarter century of competition in both stock car and drag racing.

While we cannot cover the racing accomplishments of the 1957 Chevy in detail here, as it would be impossible even to list the wins scored by this model, we can take a brief look at the phases it went through during the 25 years.

National cars were limited to a single four barrel carburetor, beginning in mid April of 1957.

Ford and Mercury dominated the early Grand National season, as their armada was too much for the Chevy teams and anyone else. When the factories pulled out, the tune changed.

With Chevrolet racing parts, which were available through its dealers, easier to obtain than Ford parts, which were sourced through Ford's performance outlets Holman & Moody in the South and Bill Stroppe in the West, teams faced with paying their own way fielded Chevrolets.

The lighter-weight "150" two-door sedan (restored example shown here) was the choice of most serious racers, but with the fuel-injected engine installed.

In 1957, as now, the most important stock car races were sanctioned by the National Association for Stock Car Auto Racing (NASCAR). There were several divisions, but the most important was the Grand National, for 1955-57 models.

The kickoff to the performance season was traditionally the Speed Weeks activities at Daytona Beach, Fla. in February. There the manufacturers traditionally paraded their newest performance cars for the press and fans and the brave entered them in the races.

Two kinds of events were held for new cars, Speed Trials on the beach, and an oval track race on a combination track consisting of beach and old country road.

Talk of the beach in 1957 was the fuel injected Chevrolets, the supercharged Fords and newly potent Pontiacs.

The Speed Trials were broken down into classes with the new Chevys running in Class 5 for cars with displacements from 259 to 305 cubic inches.

Chevrolets dominated Class 5 competition in the flying mile with Paul Goldsmith driving Smokey Yunick's new 1957 Chevy to an average speed of 131.076 mph. In standing start mile acceleration tests, T. Winston Parker topped the class with an average of 85.006 mph for his two-way runs. Both times were not far from the fastest cars of all that year, the 392 cubic inch Chrysler 300c.

NASCAR, sensing the impending pull back by the factories and wanting to avoid even more exotic setups than fuel injection and supercharging, declared that all Grand

As the 1957 season wore on, Chevrolets began winning like never before in Grand National. Two events in 1955 went to Chevy, three in 1956, but in 1957, 18 races were won by Chevrolets, among them the most prestigious of them all, the Labor Day Southern 500 on the pioneer superspeedway, the 1⅜-mile Darlington (S.C.) International Raceway, which was won by Speedy Thompson aboard a 1957 model.

Chevrolet-driving Buck Baker won the Grand National driving championship, marking the first time a Chevy pilot had done so.

The 1958 models got the cold shoulder from stock car teams, who were reluctant to experiment with all the new stuff, when they had a proven winner. The year 1958 turned out to be the best year yet for Chevrolet with 23 wins, more than any other make. Fireball Roberts drove his 1957 Chevy to victory in the Southern 500, a feat that would be repeated again in 1959 when Jim Reed won the event in a 1957 Chevy, marking three straight years of wins in the event by the same model.

In 1959, that last year 1957 Chevrolets were allowed to compete in Grand National, 14 events went to Chevy drivers, most in 1957 models, but some of the 1959s were creeping in, as development on the 348 was coming along.

Drag racing saw the 1957s downgraded out of the top classes, due to its small displacement, but the cars remained popular in whatever class they were legal in,

The fuel-injected 283 cubic inch 1957 Chevy V-8 produced 283 horsepower.

and would be so for decades to come.

In 1960, the 1957 models were too old for Grand National competition, but that didn't mean the end of their racing career, only the shifting of gears.

Back in 1955 it didn't take short track racers (using tracks a half-mile or so or less) to discover that the Chevrolet engine was ideally suited to the small ovals. It was lightweight and would wind up fast coming off a turn.

As late model stocks became more popular on the short tracks, replacing the cobbled up modifieds that were popular, the 1955-57 Chevrolet became the standard.

One neat feature which helped the 1957 models stay popular for years was the engine placement. The V8 in stock position sat with its number one spark plug behind the front balljoint, while most of the competitors had their engines also further forward. Since getting as much weight to the rear wheels as possible was desirable, the 1957 Chevy was a natural short tracker with a built-in engine setback.

In the early 1960s, Chevy ruled short track late model racing. It wasn't until the middle of the decade when Chevelles came on the scene, that the 1957s had any real competition.

Chevelles did gain the upper hand, as they were newer, were about the same size as the 1957s, had a lower center of gravity, had a conventional frame with coil springs all around and had plenty of room up front for both big and small blocks.

Coil spring technology advanced a great deal from the 1950s and came of age in the mid-1960s. Chevelles could beat the 1957s and become the standard of short track late model racing.

Did that mean retirement for the 1957s? No way. They were already popular in the classes for the less monied racers, which raced cars closer to stock with more restrictions than the late models. They were called hobby stocks, sportsmen or a variety of other names, and for the same reasons as before, the 1957 (and 1955-56 models) were popular.

Eventually Chevelles found their way into hobby stock/sportsman short track racing, as they themselves were being displaced from late model racing by the smaller Chevrolet Camaros.

As the 1970s came and went and the 1980s dawned, the number of 1957 Chevrolets still in the lower classes of stock car racing dwindled, but did not disappear. Many were still raced in 1981 and there were still a good number of short track events that are concluded with a 1957 Chevy driver carrying the checkered flag.

Over the years, rules have been relaxed so that a 1957 Chevy racing could have anything from a six cylinder engine, to a 454 cube big block, though as always, the small block V8 is the most popular powerplant.

Racing a 1957 Chevrolet today in short track stock car racing has its disadvantages. First, the Chevelles and Camaros are smaller, lighter and have a lower center of gravity, a very important factor on a short track.

Second, the parts situation. Even the supply of parts for a car as popular as as a 25-year-old Chevrolet become hard to get, especially when you are competing with the collector car market for such things as sheet metal, windshields and bumpers. Since short tracking is a contact sport, those items must be stocked for replacement after an accident. Searching over a radius of a couple hundred miles is not uncommon by racers.

Though the numbers of 1957 Chevrolets in stock car racing would likely continue to dwindle, as few are being built for racing anymore, there were enough to stretch well into the 1990s.

The idea of vintage stock car racing has not come of age, but if it ever does, the life of the 1957s could well be extended toward the end of the century.

In drag racing, life was a bit easier for the 1957 Chevrolets, as they were raced against cars in their classes, and the lack of bumping and crunching kept cars in good condition on the outside, leaving racers to concentrate on the inside. Also a variety of fiberglass parts were offered to cut weight and increase availability.

The glass body panels were allowed in the classes for modified cars, in which the 1957s were also popular, in addition to the stock categories.

As drag racing became more organized, national championship events were held and it became possible to chart the performance of certain models in major events.

The biggest of them all was (and still is) the National Hot Rod Assn. Nationals, held on Labor Day weekend.

Through the years, some of the 1957 Chevy wins included B/Stock Automatic in 1960 by Marilyn Clark, F/Stock Automatic in 1961 by James Watkins, E/Stock in 1963 by Charles Toth, H/Stock Automatic in 1964 by Gerry Robison, D/Stock by Jere Stahl and E/Stock by Joe DeLorenzo in 1965 and for its 10th anniversary, no less than six class wins in 1967.

Bracket racing is popular in drag racing today where classes are based on times, not specifications, and the 1957 Chevrolet is still hanging in there in the 1990s. They are also still raced in the lower stock classes and in modified form.

Chevy Wins NASCAR Grand Nats!

By Phil Hall

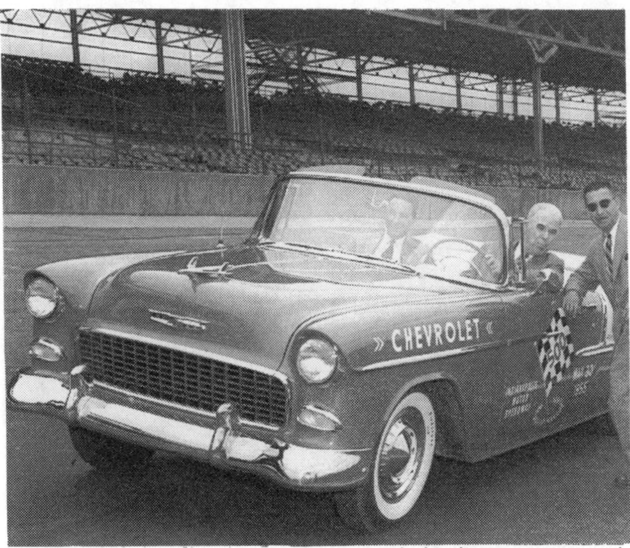

The '55 Chevy's enhanced performance led to its appearance at the Indianapolis Motor Speedway as the 500 mile race pace car that year.

According to a report in Speed Age, race driver Herb Thomas was spending an unpleasant May day in a hospital bed in 1955, after a crash which left him with a broken leg. Laying flat on his back, he predicted. "I'll race again in Darlington and win it for the third time — nobody's gonna beat me down there."

For a man of Thomas' stature in NASCAR Grand National stock car racing, the prediction wasn't to be taken lightly, but at the same time the world of stock car racing was revolving so fast in 1955, that while his leg was healing, things were happening to make Thomas' forecast look more and more like a dream than a statement.

When he was referring to Darlington, he meant the granddaddy of all NASCAR superspeedway races, the Labor Day Southern 500 at Darlington (S.C.) International Raceway. It started in 1950, when the paved, high-banked track was 1¼ miles. The track was enlarged to 1⅜ miles in 1953.

The Southern 500 was to the stock car racing set what the Indianapolis 500 was to open cockpit Indy car fans.

Driving a Hudson Hornet, Thomas won it in 1951 and again in 1954. His first win was a car owned by Marshall Teague and the latter in another Hornet prepped by a fellow named Smoky Yunick, who was making a name for himself as a top-notch mechanic.

With Hudson out of the racing biz in 1955, Yunick was experimenting with cars that year to find one which could win with the consistency of the Hornet. He tried Buick and Chevrolet.

Chevrolet, with its new 265 cubic inch V8 and an all-new body and chassis for 1955, was proving to be the sensation of the shorter tracks, but at Darlington, it was another ballgame.

Thomas' leg healed enough for him to return to racing and he proved he was still capable of winning by taking the 100-miler on Aug. 20 at the Raleigh (N.C.). The win was scored in a 1955 Buick.

Yunick announced that his choice for Darlington was the Chevrolet, a One-Fifty series two-door sedan. There was no question about it, Smokey and Herb really blew it this time. Everyone knew the Chrysler 300s of the Kiekhaefer team were the cars to beat, but otherwise it would take a big-engined Buick or Oldsmobile to win the 500.

Chevrolet had made the most of its short track victories, taking ads all over the place to let the world know that Chevrolet was the winner in the highly popular high performance game, which garnered weekly publicity, and hopefully sales, with each triumph.

Chevrolet's campaign did not go unnoticed by its major competitor, Ford, which had been cashing in on having the only V8 in the low-priced field since 1932. Suddenly, Ford's image as a performance car was being challenged.

With Chryslers winning the big races and Chevrolets the small, Ford's fortunes in stock car competition were not bountiful in 1955.

On August 25, 11 days before the 500, Ford announced a new high output engine available for police work and the like. The "Interceptor," as it was called, used the Thunderbird 292 cubic inch engine and put out 205 horsepower. This compared with Chevrolet's 195 rating for the power pack-equipped 265.

The timing was no accident, as a pair of factory-backed Fords just happened to be entered in the Southern 500 with Interceptors under the hoods. Drivers contracted were Curtis Turner and Joe Weatherly, two of the better shoes in the business.

On the first day of qualifying for the Southern 500, Fireball Roberts won the pole at an average speed of 110.628 mph in a 1955 Buick, with Buck Baker right behind in another Buick. Speedy Thompson was third in a 1954 Oldsmobile.

The big Chrysler 300s missed the first day of time trials,

but made up for it on the second. Tim Flock blew the track record away with a four-lap average of 112.041 mph, then his brother Fonty, aboard another 300, bettered the mark on a two-lap run that was cut short by rain. Tim's time held as the fastest and new record.

Neither the Chevrolets or Fords set the track on fire in qualifying, but Chevrolet's hopes were given a boost by the fact that 24 of the 69 starters were in its camp.

On race day, it ws cloudy and humid, but that didn't stop the fans. All seats were sold out and instead of the 35,000 turnout expected, reports put attendance at more than the 50,000 mark.

When the starting bomb went off, the place was packed,

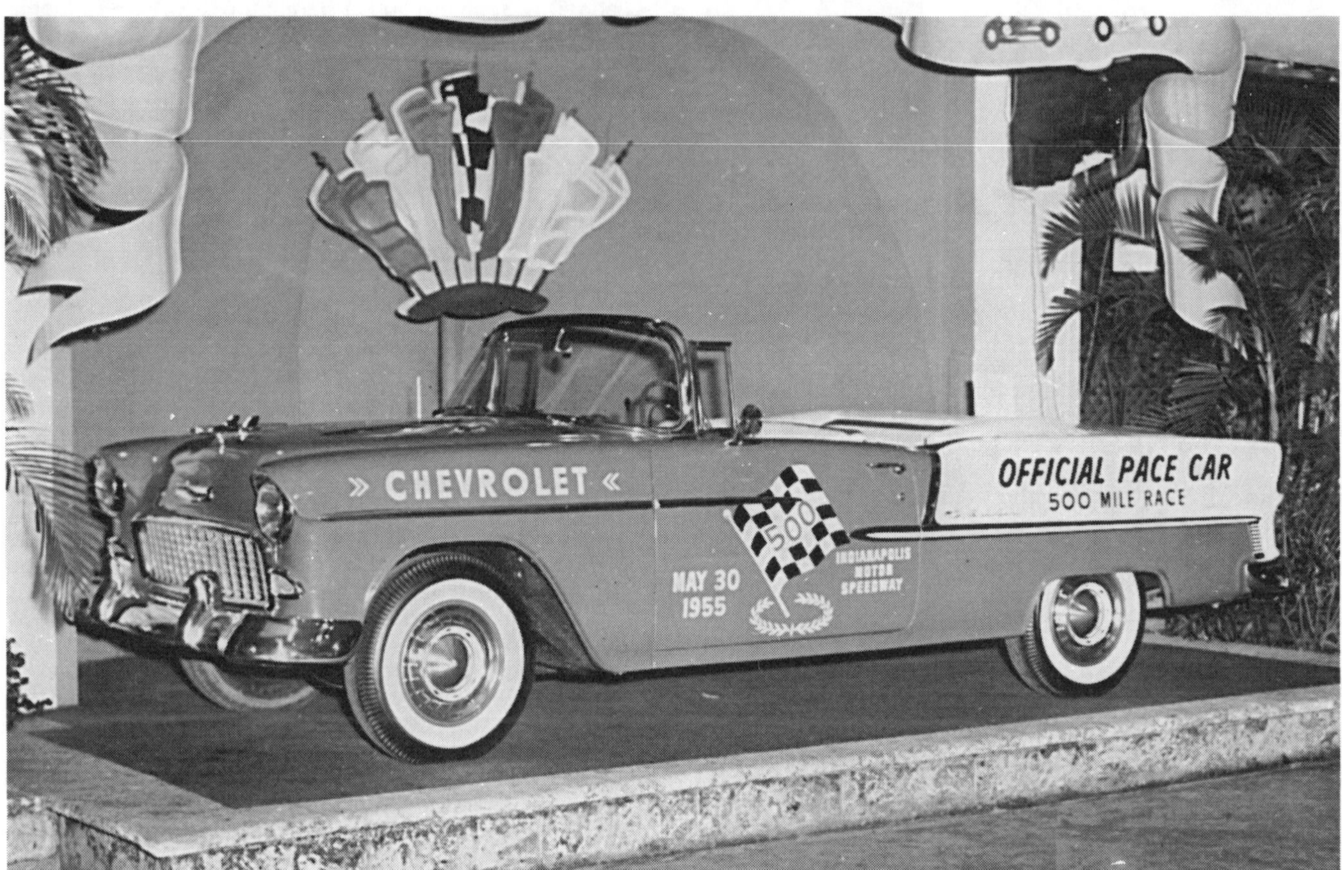

A racing image was appropriate for the first postwar Chevy V-8, which also turned up in races as well as parade laps.

the roads were jammed and the printed tickets were long gone. Ticket takers were just collecting cash. The infield was a sea of vehicles and people.

The 1955 Southern 500 was THE big showdown and everyone knew it.

There was no question that the Chryslers were the fastest cars, but Darlington was also hard on tires, especially on the heavier cars — and the 300s were heavy.

The Chrysler game plan was that Fonty Flock would intimidate the field in the early stages and brother Tim would lie back and win the race. Tim was running for the Grand National Championship that year and had to be conservative.

Ford's scheme, under factory guidance, was to go out and steal the thunder from everyone.

Yunick and Thomas figured their blue-green mount would handle well and be easy on tires and gas, which hopefully would make up for the power they were spotting the majority of the major competition.

When the pace car pulled off, Roberts put his Buick into the lead. Tim Flock challenged in the Kiekhaefer 300. Roberts' day was over quickly after he challenged the wall and lost after completing only 30 laps.

Fonty followed the script well, taking over the lead and throwing the big machine around with abandon, leaving the field in his wake. Fonty led the race for 84 laps, but back in the field the Fords were putting on a show. Weatherly started seventh and Turner, eight positions behind that. After 50 laps the loud and lavender machines were averaging 105 mph in traffic and passing everything but the Chryslers.

On lap 110, that happened with the Fords nailing the Chryslers to take first and second, in spectacular bumper-to-bumper fashion.

The packed house loved it.

Turner got a bumper job from another car and the resulting broken tie rod cut Ford's effort in half after 133 laps. Other frontrunners also fell by the wayside with Fonty Flock losing the battle with the third turn wall and Baker being taken out of the hunt with a flat tire.

All of a sudden, Chevrolets were in front, led by Bill Widenhouse, Jim Reed and Thomas.

Widenhouse and Weatherly then engaged in a classic Ford-Chevy battle over the next 130 laps, something race fans would be seeing countless times for the next two decades.

All but two of those laps were recorded with Weatherly in front.

With less than 100 laps to go, Widenhouse stopped for a tire change, which his crew blew — but good, taking him out of the action.

While Weatherly pitted, Thomas took over the lead and a few pit observers began to realize that Thomas hadn't changed tires so far.

Weatherly flew back into the track and went after Thomas, not only to take the lead, but to rub it in good by building up a one-lap cushion.

While the Ford crew was celebrating the upcoming victory in the pits, the front end on Weatherly's mount was coming unglued. He lost control, hit the wall and skidded across the track, wiping out a tire in the process.

Thomas was driving his calculated race and inherited the top spot with 48 laps to go. Five hours, 25 minutes and 25 seconds after the race started, Herb Thomas crossed the finish line — just as he predicted. He made only four fuel stops. His Firestone sports car tires went the distance.

Not only was it Chevrolet's first major Grand National win, but the domination of Chevrolets in the top 10 gave notice that the make had to be reckoned with from here on in.

Reed finished second, better than a lap off the pace. Tim Flock, in the first non-Chevy, was better than three laps off the pace in third in the 300. Gwyn Staley claimed fourth in another Chevy, followed by independent Ford driver Larry Flynn and Buick-riding Buck Baker. Positions seven through 10 were all 1955 Chevrolets.

After the race was over, Thomas said, "I could have gone 500 more miles." After his earlier quote in the hospital in May, there were few people around who would doubt him.

Chevrolet's NASCAR experiences span the years from 1955 to 1990. Here we see two NASCAR racers, a 1980 Lumina Coupe (right) and the current Monte Carlo in the famous #17 Tide colors of driver Darrell Waltrip.

Indianapolis 500

Pace Cars

1948: Chevrolet Fleetmaster convertible (IMS)

The Pace Car has been a part of the Indianapolis 500 race tradition for three-quarters of a century. During those years, Chevrolet has been given the Pace Car honor eight times. In 1990's Indy 500, the "screaming yellow" 1990 Beretta convertible paced the 74th running of this Indiana classic, so this seems an appropriate year to review Chevy's history as Pace Car.

For 1948 Chevy's Fleetmaster convertible powered by the trustworthy (and only choice) 216.5 cid Stovebolt Six served as the official Pace Car for the Indy 500.

What a change it was only seven years later when Chevy's all-new-in-and-out AND UNDER THE HOOD 1955 Bel Air convertible powered by the famous first time Chevy V-8 265 cid small block ohv engine paced the 1955 Indy 500.

By 1967, the first year for Chevy's performance car, the Camaro RS/SS became "leader of the pack" at Indy. Power for this handsome convertible came from its big-block 396 cid V-8.

For 1969, another Camaro served as Pace Car, a '69

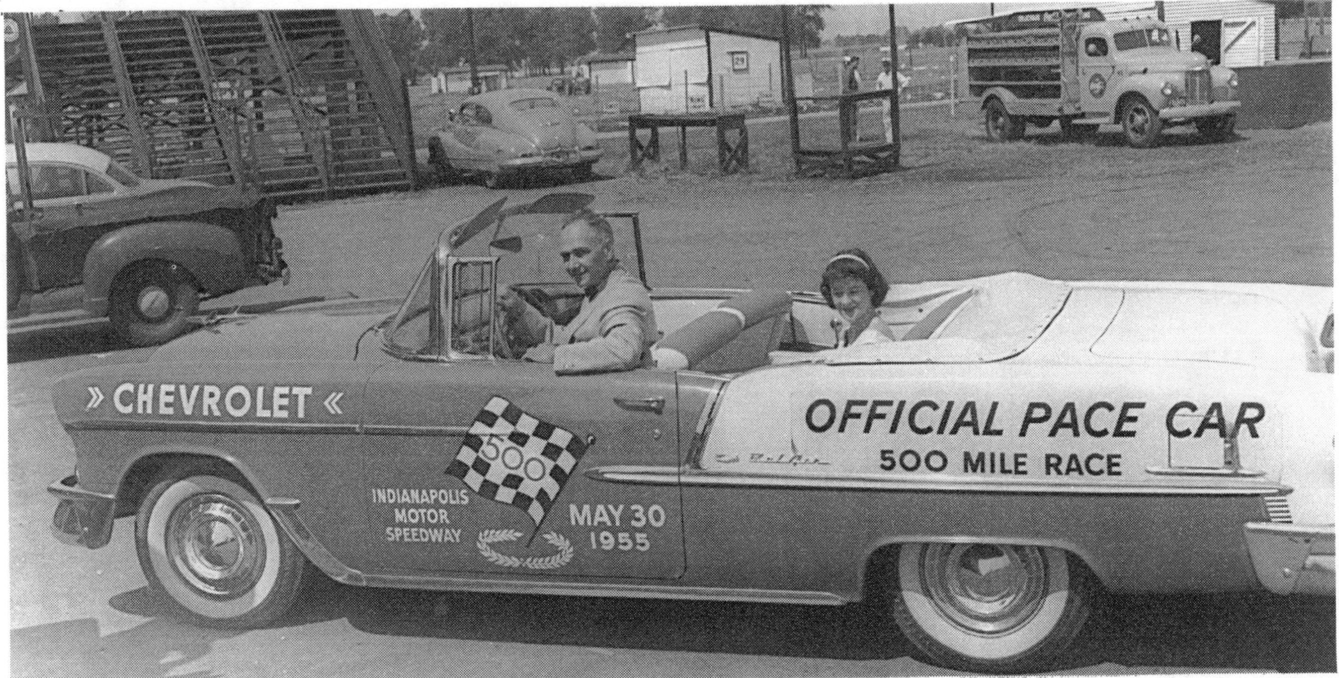

1955: Chevrolet Bel Air convertible (IMS)

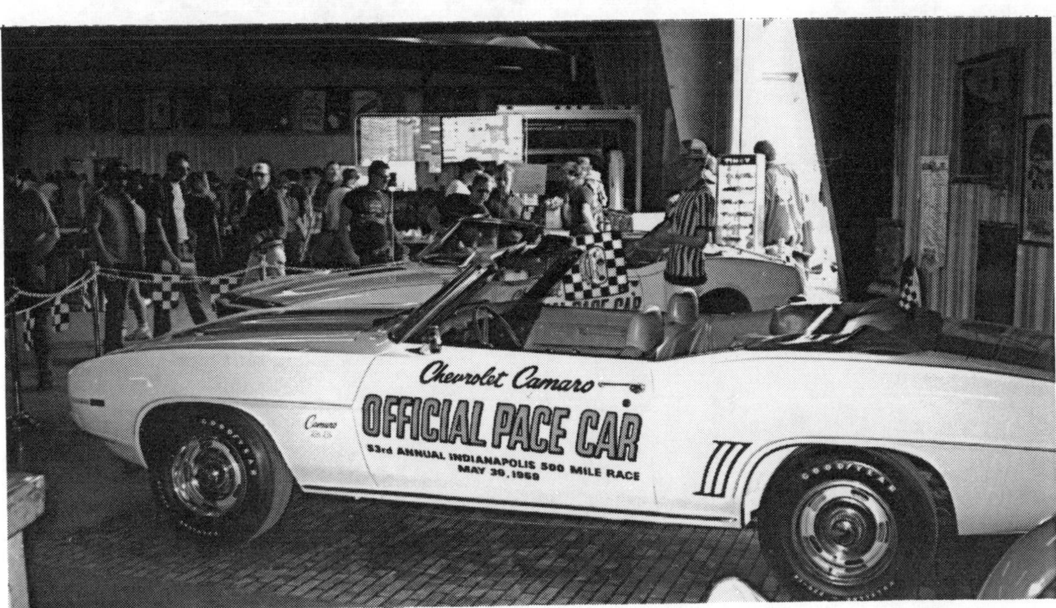

1969: Chevrolet Camaro SS396 convertible (IMS)

RS/SS. Storming down the track, it was again powered by the big-block 396 cid, 375 hp V-8.

In 1978, the Indy 500 was paced, finally, by America's Only Sports Car, the Corvette, which was by now full-grown and 25 years old, an entry long overdue as a Pace Car. The 350 cid 220 hp engine powered this handsome entry.

By 1982, the T-top Z28 Camaro made that model's third Indianapolis 500 appearance. An aluminum block and head example of Chevy's 350 cid small block which put out 250 hp propelled this Camaro.

A Corvette roadster was to appear in 1986 as Indy pacer, honoring a joint-anniversary of 75 years — for Chevrolet Division and the Indianapolis 500.

For 1990, appropriately but unplanned, Krause Publications' *Catalog of Chevrolet* was produced in the year of the 1990 Beretta convertible's Pace Car season. Powered by a 3.4 liter experimental V-6 engine bored out from the 3.1, this Beretta hopes to reinforce "The Hot One" image which started for Chevy in the mid-Fifties.

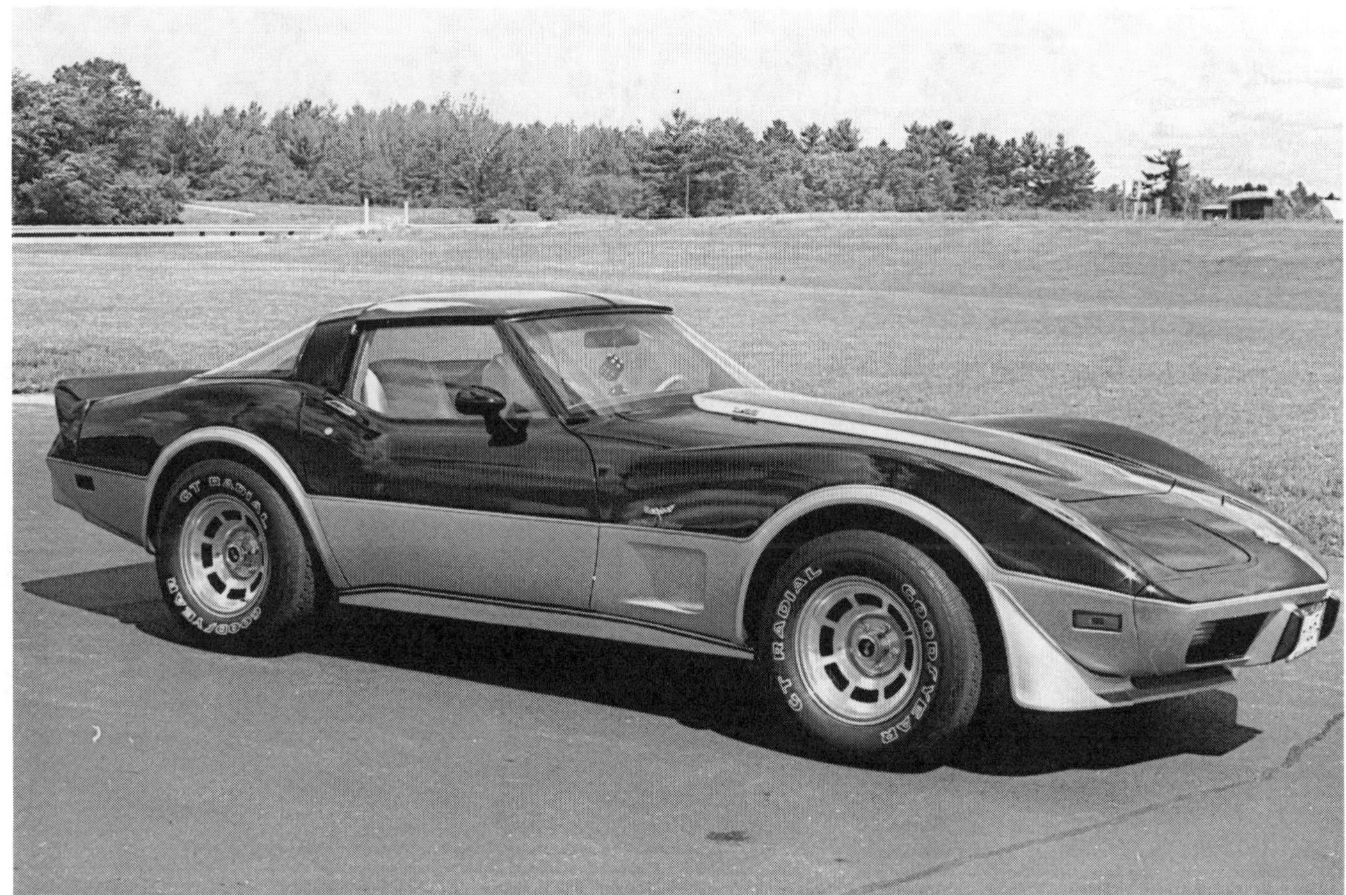

1978: Corvette Indy Pace Car (Tom and Cheryl Kell)

This electric-yellow Beretta convertible sports some incredible goodies under the hood. A specially modified 3.4 liter Chevy V6/60 produces 245 hp — admittedly almost twice the output of the production 3.1 liter 135 hp powerplant. This front-wheel drive Beretta is a stormer: it accelerates from 0-60 mph in 5.8 seconds, and it covers the quarter-mile in 13.8 seconds at 105 mph.

For the 1990 Indy 500, Chevrolet was also named "the official truck" for race day. Chevy's fleet of trucks and vans included the new Lumina APV, all-wheel-drive Astro vans, 454 SS pickups, Suburbans, 15-passenger vans, S-10 Blazers and full-size pickups.

Truly, 1990 at Indy turned out to be the Year of the Chevrolet, a vehicle whose name has been synonymous with performance since the birth of Ed Cole's 265 ohv V-8 engine in 1955!

1982: Camaro Z-28 T-top hatchback coupe Pace Car.

1986: Corvette Indy Pace Car convertible (CH)

STANDARD CATALOG OF

CHEVROLET

1912-1942

The Chevrolet was a car built for a purpose. It was the vehicle by which William C. Durant intended to regain control of General Motors, the corporation he had founded in 1908 and which he lost to the bankers in 1910. A businessman/entrepreneur of the swashbuckling adventurer sort, Billy Durant was not always wise, but he was ever resourceful. Initially his Chevrolet — which he envisioned as a light car of "French type" to be sold at popular prices — didn't work out exactly as planned, but that was Louis' fault.

By Beverly Rae Kimes

To put his plan into operation, Durant had contacted Louis Chevrolet, one of the stalwarts on the successful racing team Durant had established while heading Buick. Durant was aware that Chevrolet had ambitions to build a car of his own, and since the Chevrolet name was already well known in motor sport, and since Chevrolet had been born in Europe and knew what "French type" meant, Durant was sure he was the man for the job. Chevrolet hired a Frenchman to help him, Etienne Planche, whom he had known from his days with the Walter in Brooklyn and who had designed the Roebling-Planche (antecedent to the Mercer) — and this Billy thought boded well too.

In May of 1911 a Detroit newspaper leaked the news of the forthcoming Chevrolet car from Durant. Meanwhile Durant began organizing a whole bunch of companies: the Chevrolet Motor Company in Detroit (initially Chevrolet Motor Car but the "Car" was soon dropped), the Little Motor Car Company in Flint (to build a less expensive car called the Little to bring some quick cash into the coffers), the Mason Motor Company in Flint (to build engines for these cars, with former Buick engineer Arthur Mason at its head), the Republic Motor Company (for which he bought an entire block in New York City to be used as an auxiliary assembly plant), among others. And meanwhile, too, Louis was taking his time coming up with the new Chevrolet.

The Little arrived first, during the summer of 1912, as a $650 four.Some months later a $1285 Little Six was added, this a last-minute decision because the car Louis Chevrolet was building was turning out to be not a light French type at all, but a big car that Durant knew he couldn't sell for less than $2150. Still, when Louis Chevrolet finally had the car ready, Durant felt he had no other choice but to get it on the market right away, since a year-and-a-half had passed since that first press mention it was coming.

And thus it was, late in 1912, that the Chevrolet Six Type C Classic arrived, with an overhead valve T-head engine of 299 cubic inches (the largest displacement of any Chevrolet engine until introduction of the 348-cubic-inch V-8 in 1958) and a wheelbase of 120 inches (as long as any Chevy ever). The car was well built — three point motor suspension, a three-speed selective transmission on a full-floating rear axle — but it was also ponderous, and it didn't sell. Billy Durant definitely had a problem. With cheaper prices, the Little was selling, but it had been a shoestring operation and Durant was aware that the cars were not very durable. His solution was to combine the good points of the Chevrolet and the Little into one new car to be sold as a Chevrolet. And to gather all the various companies he had organized under the Chevrolet banner too, and to move the whole operation to Flint, where he had enjoyed boy-wonder status since his carriage-making days. This irritated Louis Chevrolet, who took off on his own to build the Frontenac; therefter Etienne Planche received an offer he couldn't refuse from Durant's old partner J. Dallas Dort and took off to build the Dort.

Subsequently Durant finished up the run of Chevrolet Classic Sixes for which parts remained, and introduced the Chevrolet Light Six or Model L for the 1914 model year (this the former Little Six, and the only L-head in Chevrolet history). More important in 1914 was the arrival of the H Series, powered by a 170.9-cubic-inch four-cylinder engine designed by Arthur Mason which would remain in production until 1928. These were the first Chevrolets not to include a self-starter as standard equipment (it was available optionally), but they were also the first Chevrolets to be sold for under a thousand dollars. Baby Grand for the $875 touring and Royal Mail for the $750 roadster were the delightful names for these automobiles and there was a sporty Amesbury Special available at $985 too.

All these cars carried a new emblem, the famous Chevrolet bowtie, which was Durant's idea and one which he'd carried around with him for a long time, having been inspired to it by either the wallpaper in a Paris hotel room (as he liked to say) or something he saw in the rotogravure section of a Hot Springs, Virginia newspaper (which is the way his wife remembered it).

Durant's plan to assemble Chevrolets in the heart of New York City, however, ran into an indisputable snag, the factory being located in one of the worst sections in town with the result that he had to buy protection from both Tammany Hall and street toughs. Thus when the former Maxwell-Briscoe plant became available in Tarrytown, he bought it up right away. A few months later, on December 16th, 1914, he introduced the Chevrolet Four-Ninety, that figure being its price tag and just happening to be also the price tag at which Henry Ford was selling his Model T.

The car — designed by Alfred Sturt, another former Buick man — was essentially a Series H stripped to essentials and offered in any color so long as it was black. This copycat approach from Chevrolet brought an immediate rejoinder from Ford; he lowered the Model T's price to $440. Durant began selling Four-Ninetys by the tens of thousands anyway, though by 1917 their price tags were $550, this including a self-starter which of course the Model T did not have.

Because of Henry Ford's headstart with mass production of the T, however, he could consistently lower his car's price tag with the result that the differential between the cars widened through the years — and the Model T swamped the Chevrolet in sales. But as this was happening, Billy Durant was otherwise occupied. Mysteriously, large chunks of General Motors stock were being bought up, and proxies procured, and on September 16th, 1915 — the seventh anniversary of Billy Durant's founding of General Motors — he had the corporation back again.

"Chevrolet Buys General Motors" was the headline — and though that was a simplification of the Durant maneuvers, it pretty much told the story. Unfortunately, with GM again his, Billy Durant began to neglect Chevrolet. The $1400 Model D ohv 90° V-8 on a 120-inch wheelbase — designed by Mason and Sturt, and an admirable car — was really a step backwards insofar as the Chevrolet marketing philosophy was concerned; introduced late in 1917, it was ushered out at the end of 1918.

The Series F had replaced the H for 1917, and was a bigger car, and bigger yet with the FB for 1919. Bigger, too, were the Chevrolet's price tags. Bigger yet was the trouble Billy Durant was getting himself into at the helm of General Motors. Just as the first time around, Durant was on a buying spree, and many of his purchases (especially Samson tractor which he hoped to be a competitor to the Fordson) proved disastrous.

When the postwar recession hit in 1920, Billy Durant lost everything: Chevrolet, General Motors, the whole works. Undaunted, he would come back, of course, with Durant Motors, but the question now was what would happen to Chevrolet. Heading GM was Pierre duPont who initially favored scuttling the car, but Alfred Sloan, Jr., the man duPont brought in to make sense of the wreckage of Durant's empire, talked him out of it. Instead of eliminating Chevrolet, Sloan eliminated most of the Durant men in the organization and replaced them with his own people: K.W. Zimmerscheid as Chevrolet General Manager and President, O.E. Hunt (formerly of Packard and Mercer) as Chief Engineer. And recognizing that tackling Henry Ford head-on was ludicrous ("suicidal," Sloan said), the decision was made to create a price class of its own for the Chevrolet, low but not the lowest, a step up in dollars but a step up also in refinement and creature comforts which those dollars bought and which the Model T didn't have.

Billy Durant himself had moved the Chevrolet toward this concept, but hadn't followed through. Sloan would — and it worked beautifully, though not immediately. First there was the misstep of the copper-cooled Chevrolet. It was an interesting idea; its engine, at 135 cubic inches, was the smallest in Chevrolet history but it promised fewer parts, less weight, lower cost and higher performance than a water-cooled unit; air cooling was certainly something the Model T didn't have, and the promotional potential for the car looked terrific. Unfortunately, the copper-cooled Chevrolet was terrible. Some 759 of the cars were built, 239 of which were scrapped before ever leaving the factory. Of the cars dispatched to dealers, in June 1923 the company asked for every one of them back, in the first massive recall in Chevrolet history.

Fortunately, there had been another Chevrolet to sell that year called Superior, successor to the Four-Ninety, the Model FB being dropped because it encroached on Olds and Oakland territory which was a market area in which Sloan didn't want the Chevrolet anyway. Meanwhile, Zimmerscheid, who had suffered a nervous breakdown during the copper-cooled fiasco, elected to retire — and on January 15th, 1924, Danish-born William S. Knudsen, Henry Ford's former production manager, became Chevrolet's President and General Manager. "I vant vun for vun," he said at a dealer meeting in Chicago. That would take a while, but unquestionably the Chevrolet was making inroads into Model T territory.

In 1924 Ford outsold Chevrolet by more than eight to one, in 1925 four to one, in 1926 less than three to one. Among the reasons for this was the, literally, superior Superior beginning in 1925 when the "infamous rear end," as Sloan called it — or the "Chevrolet hum" as had been the nickname for the noise made by the car's bevel gear rear axle since the first Four-Ninety days — was at last eliminated. Chevy's new rear axle was a one-piece banjo type with the entire differential mounted in a carrier which included the torque tube. Also new for '25 was variety of colors: Chevrolet was the first low-priced car to go Duco. And the car's standard transmission, sported since the beginning, was by now an even greater plus in the marketplace, since the jokes about the Model T's planetary were no longer as funny as they used to be.

In 1927 Knudsen went all out: "The Most Beautiful Chevrolet in Chevrolet History" read the ads. The bodies of the new Capitol series had a double belt, full crown fenders, bullet-shaped headlamps, and the $715 sport cabriolet was America's first low-priced car with a rumble seat. In 1927 Chevrolet built over 1.7 million cars. For the first time since 1906 a car other than a Ford was number one in the industry. But Ford had virtually given away the number one spot in 1927 by shutting down his factory for six months, and ensuing production delays with the new Model A Ford would give Chevrolet easy victory in 1928 too. Thereafter the top spot would have to be earned.

Like the new Model A, the new National series Chevrolet for '28 had four-wheel brakes. But the all-new Chevrolet for '29 had something the Ford didn't have: two more cylinders. The Cast Iron Wonder had arrived, Chevy now had a six for the price of a four, and a sturdy overhead valve engine that would endure into the early Fifties. The new cars were called International, appropriately since their body styling had the Continental flair that Harley Earl of GM's Art and Colour Department was trying to introduce to all corporation cars. Nonetheless, Ford, having sorted out the Model A production problems was now in full swing and delivering cars to the tens of thousands of people who had never driven anything else but a Ford and who had been desperately waiting for a new one since the T assembly line shutdown. Ford won the sales race in 1929 and in 1930, when the Chevrolet was called the Universal. In 1931 Chevy had it back with the Independence series, and retained the top spot in 1932 when Ford went to a V-8, which Chevy countered with the Confederate series offering synchromesh, free-wheeling, four-point rubber engine mounts, downdraft carburetion and further engine tweaks to get 60 hp out of the Cast Iron Wonder, only five less than Ford's V-8.

With the Great Depression in full cry, Chevrolet ushered in a cheaper six called the Standard in '33, which made a Master of the old six — and first place again in the industry. In 1933 the cast of characters in the Chevrolet management team changed, as the corporation moved top men around to troublespots within the GM family. William Knudsen was appointed Executive Vice-President for General Motors, his place at Chevrolet taken by his understudy of many years, Marvin Coyle. Harry Klingler, the super sales manager of Chevrolet since 1929, moved over to help troubled Pontiac, his place taken by the aptly named William Holler, who was a super salesman too. Only Chief Engineer Jim Crawford (who had replaced O.E. Hunt in 1929) remained at Chevy, and he begged Knudsen to do what he could to get Knee Action for Chevrolet for '34, initial thought having been that it should be reserved for the top-of-the-line GM cars. Knudsen won the argument, a good thing too, since Plymouth also went i.f.s. in '34. Ford stuck to transverse springs — and Chevy won the sales race again.

Chevy lost in '35, partly because of a labor strike, partly because the new Ford V-8 had pizzazz and was advertising 90 hp, as opposed to the 80 of Chevy's Blue Flame six (it had been called the Blue Streak in '34 and there was no explicable reason for the name change to Blue Flame, though probably both designations were coined by Chevrolet P.R. in hopes that people would start using them instead of Stovebolt Six, which Chevrolet's venerable engine was nicknamed).

Henry Ford helped Chevrolet regain the top spot in '36 by offering nothing new, which made Chevy's introduction of hydraulic brakes (Ford wouldn't have them until '39) something to shout about. But the 1937 Chevrolet gave William Holler even more crowing opportunity, because the car was all-new, with a more compact and powerful (85 hp) version of the Cast Iron Wonder, a stiffer box-girder frame and hypoid rear axle.

The 15,000,000th Chevrolet was built in 1939; in 1940 a General Motors dealer from Argentina, Juan Manuel Fangio, began his remarkable racing career behind the wheel of a Chevrolet Master 85 which he drove to victory in the 5900-mile Buenos Aires-Lima-Buenos Aires race at an average of 53.6 mph. From 1937 Chevrolet had remained solidly in first place in the industry, a position it would not relinquish for the remainder of the years before America's entrance into World War II brought a halt to automobile production. Postwar, Chevrolet's status as number one — indeed as the best-selling car in the world — would become a virtual tradition.

LITTLE

1912 Little, roadster, WLB

LITTLE — Flint, Michigan — (1912-1913) — The Little was one of two cars William C. Durant decided to build following his first ouster from General Motors. It was the first announced, on October 30th, 1911 — and the first to arrive, during late summer of 1912. The Little Motor Car Company was named for a huge bear of a man, William H. Little, Durant's former general manager at Buick. The car was more appropriately named than the man: it was little and cute as a button. A 20 hp $690 four on a 90-inch wheelbase, it was "simple to the point of innocence," according to Alex Hardy, the Durant man in charge of Little production. The car was produced at the Flint Wagon Works, which had previously seen manufacture of the Whiting. Meantime Bill Little himself was in Detroit, assigned as liaison to hurry Louis Chevrolet along in the design of the other car Billy Durant was planning to build. The new Chevrolet had been announced November 8th, 1911, a week after the Little, but Louis was taking his time finishing it. When finally during the summer of 1912 the prototype Chevrolet was completed, Durant was displeased. The car was too big, too heavy, too expensive; he knew he couldn't sell it for less than $2150. But at least it was a car to sell, so he ordered the Chevrolet into production. Meantime, aware of the costly direction the Chevrolet was taking, Durant had also decided to build a Little Six to sell for $1285, which was closer to his desired price range for the Chevrolet. Both cars arrived in the marketplace at the same time, which was unfortunate since each was a Durant car and tended to be confused or compared in the automotive press. This was to the benefit of neither, since the Chevrolet was sturdily built and expensive, and the Little was hastily built and inexpensive, Durant aware that it would be "driven to its death in less than 25,000 miles." A road test of that duration that Durant had ordered for the Little had proved it. Naturally, since the public was unaware of this, the Little's sales figures were far better than the Chevrolet's. Durant thus found himself with two cars, one that could be driven forever and wasn't selling, one that couldn't and was selling. His solution was to take the individual virtues of each car and combine them into one. Chevrolet was to be the one car. Among other factors, as Alex Hardy pointed out, the Little's name would ultimately have proved a negative, few people buying a small, inexpensive car wishing to be so pointedly reminded of it. And so the Little was discontinued without regrets in May of 1913 after approximately 3500 were built. All efforts now were focused on the Chevrolet. It appeared to be a wise decision.

1913 Little Six, touring, HAC

MONROE

1915 Monroe, model M-2, roadster, WLB

1917 Monroe, model M-3, roadster, WLB

MONROE — Flint, Michigan — (1914-1916) / Pontiac, Michigan — (1916-1918) / Indianapolis, Indiana — (1918-1923) — Initially, the Monroe was a collaboration. R.F. Monroe headed the Monroe Body Company in Pontiac, William C. Durant was the man behind the Chevrolet in Flint. Although the Monroe Motor Company, which was organized in Flint in August of 1914, was separate and distinct from Chevrolet, there were a good many ties that bound. Monroe's president was R.F. Monroe; its vice-president was Durant. All of the stockholders of the Monroe company were also stockholders of Chevrolet, manufacture of the Monroe was begun in a plant formerly used by Chevrolet in Flint, and distribution of the Monroe was through the Chevrolet sales organization. The Monroe-Durant collaboration was short-lived, however. In April of 1916 Durant resigned his Monroe vice-presidency, and Monroe moved his company into the former Welch plant in Pontiac. Capital stock in the reorganized Monroe Motor Car Company was increased to $1 million, and R.F. Monroe announced that henceforth he would sell his cars himself. This he did for the two years following, and then went bankrupt. In the fall of 1918, the Monroe assets were purchased by the William Small Company of Indianapolis, the former distributor for Monroes in that city. The plant at Pontiac was leased to General Motors for production of its Samson tractors, and Monroe now moved to Indianapolis. Monroe had begun as a small light car fitted with a proprietary engine and offered in open body styles only. Now it sported an engine of its own make, a sedan was added — and Louis Chevrolet was recruited by William Small as a consulting engineer to "work out designing problems for the Monroe car." There was a nice irony in this, Chevrolet long since having disassociated himself from William C. Durant. The extent of Chevrolet's influence on the Monroe production car was limited, but he did move into the Small premises in Indianapolis where, with the help of Corne-

1918 Monroe, model MM-6, sedan, HAC

1920 Monroe, model S, touring, HAC

lius Van Ranst, he put together seven race cars, four of them to be campaigned under the Monroe name, three as Frontenacs. His brother Gaston Chevrolet drove a Monroe to victory in the 1920 Indianapolis 500, the first win by an American car at the Brickyard since 1912. Unfortunately, three months later, in August of 1920 William Small went into receivership. Refinancing schemes were tried thereafter, but ultimately in January of 1922 the Monroe assets were acquired at the receiver's sale for $175,000 in cash by the Fletcher American National Bank in Indianapolis. By March of 1923, Monroe had a new owner: Strattan Motors Corporation which had just been organized by Frank E. Strattan, who was also reported to have his eye on purchase of the Premier plant in town. Strattan announced that he would continue the Monroe and introduce a new lower-priced car to be called the Strattan. By June, however, he had sold his interest in the Monroe in order to concentrate all energies on the new low-priced Strattan, which didn't survive the year. Meanwhile, Monroe had been bought from Strattan by Frederick Barrows of Premier. Initially, he organized this venture as Monroe Motors, Inc., but rather quickly the Monroe was simply absorbed into the Premier company. The last Monroes were sold as the Premier Model B.

1921 Monroe, model S, touring, JAC

1922 Monroe, model S, roadster, HAC

Chevrolet Data Compilation by M.G. "Pinky" Randall

1912 CHEVROLET

1912 Chevrolet, Classic Six, touring, OCW

CHEVROLET — CLASSIC SIX — SERIES C — SIX: The first Chevrolet bore a resemblance to the Republic Four, but was primarily an all-new automobile. Only one model — the Classic Six touring car — was available. It was built on a 120 inch wheelbase chassis. Features included ignition by dual system and dry cells, an English Air starter, drop-forged "I" front axle, full-floating rear axle and cone clutch. The springs were semi-elliptic up front and three-quarter platform in the rear. The steering gear was of the worm and gear type. The body, frame and wheels were finished in Chevrolet Blue-Black. The fenders, splash aprons and hood were black. A light gray stripe decorated the body and wheels. A German silver radiator bore the Chevrolet script, which was affixed to the dash on the right front. Standard equipment included a top, top boot, windshield, speedometer, electric speedometer light, self starter, demountable rims, extra tire holders, electric lights, gas gauge, two gallon auxiliary oil tank, 20 gallon gas tank and running board mounted tool kit.

I.D. DATA: Serial numbers were not used.

Model No.	Body Type & Seating	Price	Weight	Prod. Total
C	4-dr. Tr.-5P	2250	3500	2999

(Prod. total was the total for Littles and Chevrolets)

ENGINE: T-head. Twin cam. Six (Cast in three banks of two). Cast iron block. B & S: 3-9/16 x 5 in. Disp.: 299 cu. in. Brake H.P.: 40. Net H.P.: 30 NACC. Main bearings: Three. Valve lifters: Solid.

CHASSIS: W.B.: 120 in. Frt/Rear Tread: 56/56 in. Tires: 35 x 4.5.

TECHNICAL: Rear axle mounted selective sliding transmission. Speeds: 3F/1R. Floor-mounted gearshift controls. Cone type clutch. Full-floating rear axle. Internal expanding rear brakes. Wood spoke artillery wheels.

OPTIONS: Front bumper, Motometer. Spare tire(s). 60 in. Southern tread. OSRV mirror. Running board luggage gate. Whitewall tires.

HISTORICAL: Introduced Nov., 1911. Calendar year production: 2,999. Innovations: First car to bear Chevrolet nameplate. Chevrolet Motor Company was incorporated Nov. 3, 1911.

1913 CHEVROLET

1913 Chevrolet, Classic Six, touring, OCW

CHEVROLET — CLASSIC SIX — SERIES C — SIX: The 1913 Classic Six was virtually unchanged from the original, except for the design of the windshield. The method of mounting the windshield was now to bolt it to a swept back cowl, instead of directly to the dashboard. Also, the braces ran from the dash to the center hinges of the windshield frame. There is no record of exactly when the change took place — it may have been phased into production in late 1912. Thus, the later design cannot be used to date a car, but all 1913 models have swept back cowls. Colors and equipment were as in 1912.

I.D. DATA: Serial numbers were not used. Engine numbers identified the cars. Numbers are not available.

Model No.	Body Type & Seating	Price	Weight	Prod. Total
C	4-dr. Tr.-5P	2500	NA	5987

(Prod. total was the total for Chevrolet and Little. Chevrolet production alone was 402)

ENGINE: T-head. Twin cam. Six (Cast in three banks of two). Cast iron block. B & S: 3-9/16 x 5 in. Disp.: 299 cu. in. Brake H.P.: 40. Net H.P.: 30 NACC. Main bearings: Three. Valve lifters: Solid. Carb.: Stromberg (exhaust heated type).

CHASSIS: W.B.: 120 in.

TECHNICAL: Rear axle mounted selective sliding transmission. Speeds: 3F/1R. Floor-mounted gearshift controls. Cone type clutch. Full-floating rear axle. Internal expanding rear wheel brakes.

OPTIONS: Front bumper. Motormeter. Spare tire(s). 60 in. Southern tread. Rearview mirror. Running board luggage gate. Whitewall tires.

HISTORICAL: Introduced: Late 1912. Calendar year production: 5,987. Innovations: New windshield mounting and bracing system.W.C. Durant merged the Little Motor Car Company with Chevrolet in 1913. He gave the Chevrolet name to the Little car and moved the Detroit plant to his Flint Wagon Works. A second assembly plant was leased in New York City. The Chevrolet "Bow-Tie" trademark was used for the first time this year, on all Light Six models and "H" Series model for the 1914 model year.

1914 CHEVROLET

1914 Chevrolet, roadster, OCW PR (P.. Randall owner)

CHEVROLET — SERIES H — FOUR: The all-new 1914 H Series came in two body styles called the "Royal Mail" roadster and "Baby Grand" touring. (These names would be used on Chevrolet F, FA and FB models built through 1922). Early versions had a flat wooden dash. This was replaced in mid-year with a streamlined, all-metal dash and cowl. The folding windshield was braced to the cowl. The touring had a two-man top and came in Chevrolet gray or Plum color finish with black chassis and gray wheels. The roadster was finished only in Chevrolet gray with black chassis and gray wheels. Later model Royal Mails had Plum paint, also. The Royal Mails had a flat rear deck. "Standard" equipment included top, curtains, windshield, speedometer, horn, spare tire and complete tool kit. Early Royal Mails had 30 x 3-1/2 clincher type tires. Later model Royal Mails used straight side 30x3½ tires.

CHEVROLET — LIGHT SIX — SERIES L — SIX: Available only as a touring car, the new Light Six came in Chevrolet blue or Gun metal gray. The chassis and wheels were blue. Standard equipment included Mohair top, top boot, side curtains, ventilating windshield, foot rail, robe rail, speedometer, electric horn, demountable rims, spare tire carrier on rear, (with extra rim), two double bulb electric headlamps, electric taillamp, Auto-Lite starter, LBA battery and complete tool kit.

CHEVROLET — CLASSIC SIX — SERIES C — SIX: This large touring car was in the last season. The Chevrolet name appeared in script on the front. The radiator shell and Chevrolet nameplate were silver. The finish color was a dark (almost black) color called Chevrolet blue. It was used on the body, frame and wheels. The fenders and splash aprons and hood black. Light gray striping was seen on the body and wheels. Standard equipment included a top, boot, windshield, speedometer, electric lights, self-starter, demountable rims, extra tire holders, electric lights and gas gauge. A two gallon auxiliary oil tank was under the seat. Side curtains were stored in a compartment under the rear seat. Tools were stored in a box located under the runningboard, which was integral with it. There was a console-like storage fixture between the front seats.

I.D. DATA: [Series H] Serial numbers were not used. Engine numbers identified the cars. Starting: 1. Ending: 6243. [Series L] Serial numbers were not used. Engine numbers identified the cars. Starting: 1. Ending: 6243. [Series C] Serial numbers were not used. Engine numbers identified the cars. Engine numbers are not available.

1914 Chevrolet Baby Grand, PR (Pinky Randall, owner)

Model No.	Body Type & Seating	Price	Weight	Prod. Total
H-2	2-dr. Rds.-2P	750	1975	Note 3
H-4	4-dr. Tr.-5P	875	2500	Note 3
Note 1: Above price is for cars with Presto-Lite lights and magneto. With an Auto-Lite system the roadster was $875 and the touring was $1000.				
L	4-dr. Tr.-5P	1475	3050	490
Note 2: With Presto-Light lighting and magneto the price was $125 higher.				
C	4-dr tr.-5P	2500	3750	Note 3

Note 3: Total production was 5,005 Chevrolets of all models.

ENGINE: [Model H] Engine OHV. Inline. (Cast en bloc). Four cylinder. Cast iron block. B & S: 3-11/16 x 4 in. Disp.: 171 cu. in. Brake H.P.: 24. Net H.P.: 21.75 NACC. Main bearings: Three. Valve lifters: Solid. Carb.: Zenith two-jet. [Model L] Engine: L-head. Inline. (Cast in blocks of three). Six. cast iron block. B & S: 3-5/16 x 5-1/4 in. Disp.: 271 cu. in. Brake H.P.: 35. Net H.P. 26 NACC. Main bearings: Three. Valve lifters: Solid. Carb.: Zenith two-jet. [Model C] Engine T-head. Twin cam. Inline. Six (cast in three banks of two). Cast iron block. B & S: 3-9/16 x 5 in. Disp.: 299 cu. in. Brake H.P.: 40. Net H.P.: 30 NACC. Main bearings: Three. Valve lifters: Solid. Carb.: Stromberg (exhaust heated type).

CHASSIS: [Series H] W.B.: 104 in. Frt/Rear Tread: 56/56 in. Tires: 32 x 3.5. [Series L] W.B.: 112 in. Frt/Rear Tread: 56/56 in. Tires: 34 x 4. [Series C] W.B.: 120 in. Frt/Rear Tread: 56/56 in. Tires: 35 x 4.5. A special 60 in. thread for use on roads in the South was available.

1914 Chevrolet, roadster

TECHNICAL: Selective sliding (mounted on rear axle on Light/Classic sixes). Speeds: 3F/1R. Floor-mounted gearshift controls. Cone type clutch. [Model C] full-floating. Rear axle: [Model L] three-quarter floating. [Model H] semi-floating. [Classic Six] Internal expanding rear wheel brakes. [Others] External contracting rear wheel brakes. Wood spoke artillery wheels. Drivetrain options: Free-wheeling. Vacuum clutch. Hill-holder. Automatic transmission. Overdrive.

OPTIONS: Bumper front. Motometer. Auto-Lite electrical system. Spare tire(s). 60-in. Southern tread. Rearview mirror. Runningboard luggage gate. Houk wire wheels on "H" series.

HISTORICAL: Introduced: Late 1913. Calendar year production: (All) 5,005. Innovations: (H) First Chevrolet ohv four-cylinder engine. (L) only L-head Chevrolet ever built. Large 112 inch wheelbase. (C) Gray & Davis electric starter. Sims ignition. Longest wheel base in Chevrolet history (also used on 1917-19 V-8). Louis Chevrolet leaves company over dispute with W.C. Durant. In June 1914 the Maxwell Motor Company's Tarrytown, N.Y. plant was purchased by Chevrolet. A new sales office was set up in Oakland, Calif.

1915 CHEVROLET

CHEVROLET — SERIES H — FOUR: The 1915 Chevrolet fours had the same general appearance as 1914 editions, but the wheelbase grew to 106 in. Another change was the use of concealed door hinges. Larger tires with demountable rims were a new feature. The windshield cowl braces were removed. A starter became standard equip-

1916 Chevrolet, touring, OCW

ment. The diameter of the steering wheel went up to 17 inches. A new "Amesbury Special" roadster was introduced. It had the racy lines of an imported car and an exposed wooden dash board. A lockable rear deck was featured. The one piece windshield fitted behind the seat. Standard on all models were the top, top hood, windshield, speedometer and demountable rims.

CHEVROLET — SERIES L — SIX: The Light Six, Model L, was the only Chevrolet ever to use an L-head engine. It came only as a touring car available in Chevrolet blue or Gun metal gray. The chassis and wheels were blue. Standard equipment included Mohair top, cover, side curtains, ventilating windshield, foot rail, robe rail, speedometer, electric horn, demountable rims, spare tire carrier on rear, extra rim, two double-bulb electric headlamps, electric taillamp, Auto-Lite starter, LBA battery and complete tool equipment.

I.D. DATA: [Series H] Serial numbers were not used. Engine numbers located on flywheel and on the left front engine mount. Starting: 6244. Ending: 13000. [Series L] Serial numbers ran from 501 to 1000.

Model No.	Body Type & Seating	Price	Weight	Prod. Total
H-2	2-dr. Rds.-2P	750	2000	Note 1
H-4	4-dr. Tr.-5P	850	2500	Note 1
H-3	2-dr. Spl. Rds.-2P	985	2100	Note 1

Note 1: Total production for calendar 1915 was 13,605 Chevrolets including 313 cars built in Canada.
Note 2: Model H-2 also called "Royal Mail"; Model H-4 also called "Baby Grand"; Model H-3 also called "Amesbury Special".

Model No.	Body Type & Seating	Price	Weight	Prod. Total
L	4-dr. Tr.-5P	1475	3050	1000

ENGINE: [Series H] OHV. Inline. Four. Cast iron block. B & S: 3-11/16 x 4 in. Disp.: 171 cu. in. Brake H.P.: 24. Net H.P.: 21.75 N.A.C.C.: Main bearings: Three. Valve lifters: Solid. Carb.: Zenith two-jet. [Series L] L-head. Inline (Two banks of three each). Six. Cast iron block. B & S: 3-5/16 x 5-1/4 in. Disp.: 271 cu. in. Brake H.P.: 30. Net H.P.: 26.3. Main bearings: Three. Valve lifters: Solid. Carb.: Zenith double-jet.

CHASSIS: [Series H] W.B.: 106 in. Frt/Rear Tread: 56/56 in. Tires: 32 x 3.5. [Series L] W.B.: 112 in. Frt/Rear Tread: 56/56 in. Tires: 34 x 4.

TECHNICAL: Selective Sliding Gear transmission. Speeds: 3F/1R. Floor-mounted gearshift controls. Cone type clutch. Rear axles: (H) semi-floating; (L) three-quarter floating. Contracting and expanding rear wheel brakes. Wood artillery spoke wheels. Transaxle on Series L six.

OPTIONS: Front bumper. Spare tire. OSRV mirror. Houk quick-detachable wire wheels ($125). Auto lite electric system, on H ($60); on L ($125). Motometer. "Fat Man" steering wheel. Southern gauge (60 in. track).

HISTORICAL: Introduced: 1915 (490 introduced in Jan. 1915 and placed on sale June 1, 1915). Innovations: (H) Larger wheelbase. Starter option mounted on flywheel at rear of engine. New "Amesbury Special" roadster. Electric lights became standard equipment. Calendar year production: 13,605. Model year production: (H) 13,600; (L) 1000; (Total) 14,600.

Chevrolet sales offices opened in Kansas City, Mo. and Atlanta, Ga. New factories established in St. Louis, Mo. and Oshawa, Canada. Chevrolet also licensed Gardner Buggy Co. to assemble cars in St. Louis. Within 17 days of putting the new 490 on the market, Chevrolet Motor Co. had accepted 46,611 orders for the car valued at $23,329,390.

1916 CHEVROLET

CHEVROLET — SERIES 490 — FOUR: Named after the price of the two basic models, the Chevrolet 490 series was new for 1916. Neither the touring or the roadster had a left front door. A vertical windshield was one styling trait. Front fenders followed a straight line from behind the center of the front wheels to the front of the running boards and no splash guards were used. Standard equipment included a top, top hood and the windshield. The rear curtain in the top hood had a single celluloid window. With an electric lighting and starting system the price was $550. Cars so equipped had a Connecticut automatic ignition system instead of a magneto.

1916 Chevrolet, Series Four-Ninety, touring, HAC

CHEVROLET — SERIES H — FOUR: The Model H Chevrolet was about the same as in 1915. Both the flat deck "Royal Mail" and the "Baby Grand" touring were carried over. The Model H-2-1/2 Special Roadster replaced the "Amesbury Special." It had a conventional rear deck and Brewster Green finish. The other cars were finished in French gray with green patent leather upholstery. Standard equipment included a top, top hood, windshield, speedometer, ammeter and demountable rims on all models.

I.D. DATA: Serial numbers were not used on 1916 models in the 490 series. Series H Serial numbers were not used. Engine numbers located on the flywheel. Engine numbers for 1916 were 13001 to 29390.

Model No.	Body Type & Seating	Price	Weight	Prod. Total
490	1-dr. Rds.-2P	490	1820	Note 1
490	3-dr. Tr.-5P	490	1910	Note 1
H-2	2-dr. Rds.-2P	720	2000	Note 1
H-4	4-dr. Rds.-5P	720	2500	Note 1
H-2-1/2	2-dr. Spl. Rds.-2P	750	2100	Note 1

Note 1: Total production was 70,701 Chevrolets including 7,721 cars made in Canada.
Note 2: Model H-2 also called "Royal Mail"; Model H-4 also called "Baby Grand"; Model H-2-1/2 also called "Royal Mail" Turtledeck Roadster.

ENGINE: OHV. Inline. Four. Cast iron block. B & S: 3-11/16 x 4 in. Disp.: 171 cu. in. Brake H.P.: 24. Net H.P.: 21.74 N.A.C.C. Main bearings: Three. Valve lifters: Solid. Carb.: Zenith one-inch double-jet.

CHASSIS: [Series 490] W.B.: 102 in. Frt/Rear Tread: 56/56 in. Tires: (frt.) 30 x 3; (rear) 30 x 3.5. [Series H] W.B.: 106 in. Frt/Rear Tread: 56/56 in. Tires: 32 x 3.5.

TECHNICAL: Selective sliding transmission. Speeds: 3F/1R. Floor-mounted gearshift controls. Cone type clutch. Rear axles: (490) three-quarter floating; (H) semi-floating. External contracting rear wheel brakes. Wood spoke artillery wheels.

OPTIONS: Front bumper. Spare tire. OSRV mirror. Motometer. Southern gauge (60 in track). (H) A Simms high tension magneto was standard equipment. For $125 extra buyers could order the Auto-Lite starting, generating and lighting system with battery. Cars so equipped had a Connecticut coil and distributor in place of magneto. (490) similar electrical equipment was $60 extra. "Fat Man" steering wheel.

HISTORICAL: Introduced during late 1915. Calendar year production: 62,898. Model year production: (490) 18,000 approximate; (H) 52,000 approximate. Innovations: (490) New 490 Series designed as low cost auto to compete with Model T Ford. (H) Open Hotchkiss drive used on cars built at Tarrytown. Radius rods for improved rear axle alignment.

Chevrolet was now operating plants in Ft. Worth, Tex. and Bay City, Mich. The Warner Gear factory in Toledo, Ohio was purchased as a Chevrolet manufacturing plant. Chevrolet also opened the auto industry's first West Coast plant in Oakland, Calif. First closed car bodies built by Chevrolet this year. Production hits 70,701 unit mark.

1917 CHEVROLET

1917 Chevrolet, touring, HAC

CHEVROLET — SERIES 490 — EIGHT: For 1917 the 490 was changed little in appearance. A left front door was added. Electric lamps became standard equipment. A new model called the All-Season touring car had a permanent hardtop replacing the folding top. Flexible sliding windows disappeared into the roof and removable side sections were used. The top even had a dome lamp. The interior was trimmed in cloth upholstery. All models were finished in black. A self-starter was now standard equipment. New touring car body improvements included foot and robe rails, a tilted windshield, a one-man top with curtains of the improved type, protection flaps on the door tops, door storage pockets, a kickpad at the rear of the front seat and demountable rims.

CHEVROLET — SERIES F — FOUR: A new Series F replaced the Series H for the 1917 season. It had a longer wheelbase. Two models were offered. The "Royal Mail" was the roadster and the "Baby Grand" was the touring car. On both models the front fenders followed a straight line from just behind the center of the front wheels to the running board. A vertical, non-folding windshield was standard equipment. An Auto-Lite generator, starter and lighting system with Remy ignition was standard.

I.D. DATA: [Series 490] Serial number system same as on Model F except 490s were also built in St. Louis (code 3), Oakland (code 6) and Ft. Worth (code 7) plants. Serial numbers not used prior to July 1. Starting: 1-8972. Ending: 1-37468. Also: 2-22507 to 2-36488; 3-8512 to 3-15000; 6-5977 to 6-10089; 7-3001 to 7-5842 and 9-151 to 9-1935. Engine numbers located on flywheel. Engine numbers not available. [Series F] Serial number located on dashboard nameplate. Factory codes: 1 is Flint; 2 is Tarrytown and 9 is Oshawa (Canada). Starting: 1-1222. Ending: 1-3430. Also: 2-2894 to 2-4113 and 9-466 to 9-532. Engine numbers located on flywheel. Engine numbers not availble.

Model No.	Body Type & Seating	Price	Weight	Prod. Total
490	2-dr. Rds.-2P	535	1820	Note 1
490	4-dr. Tr.-5P	550	1890	Note 1
490	4-dr. A-Str.-5P	625	NA	Note 1
F-2	2-dr. Rds.-2P	800	2640	Note 1
F-5	4-dr. Tr.-5P	800	2745	Note 1

Note 1: Total production was 125,882 Chevrolets including 14,005 cars built in Canada.
Note 2: Price of both models increased to $875 during the year.

ENGINE: [Series 490] OHV. Inline. Four. Cast iron block. B & S: 3-11/16 x 4 in. Disp.: 171 cu. in. Brake H.P.: 24. Net H.P.: 21.75 N.A.C.C. Main bearings: Three. Valve lifters: Solid.. Carb.: Zenith double-jet. [Series F] OHV. Inline. Four. Cast iron block. B & S: 3-11/16 x 4 in. Disp.: 171 cu. in. Brake H.P.: 24. Net H.P.: 21.75 N.A.C.C. Main bearings: Three. Valve lifters: Solid. Carb.: Zenith double-jet.

CHASSIS: [Series F] W.B.: 108 in. Frt/Rear Tread: 56/56 in. Tires: 32 x 3-1/2. [Series 490] W.B.: 102 in. Frt/Rear Tread: 56/56 in. Tires: (frt.) 30 x 3; (rear) 30 x 3.5.

TECHNICAL: Selective sliding. Speeds: 3F/1R. Floor-mounted gearshift controls. Cone type clutch. Three-quarter floating rear axle. Overall ratio: 3.5:1. External contracting rear wheel brakes. Artillery spoke wood wheels.

OPTIONS: Self-starter and electric lights ($60). Motometer. OSRV mirror. Spare tire. Demountable rims (on roadster). Southern gauge (60 in. track). "Fat Man" steering wheel. Front bumper.

HISTORICAL: Introduced 1917. Innovations: (490) Plunger type oil pump. Open valve train. Cone type clutch. Ball bearing front wheels. Quarter elliptic springs. Duplex type front spring deleted. New All-Season car. (F) Larger wheelbase. Calendar year production: 110,839. Model year production: (490) 57,692; (F) 3,493; (Total) 61,185. Company President: William C. Durant.

Early in 1917 the Monroe Motor Co. was sold to William Small of Flint, Mich. Thereafter, this brand was no longer sold by Chevrolet dealers. Also on the business front, the Mason Motor Co., of Flint, merged with Chevrolet to build engines. Chevrolet was not yet part of General Motors. Chevrolet introduced its V-8 Model D in 1917. Specifications for this model are given in the 1918 Chapter.

1918 CHEVROLET

1918 Chevrolet, F series, center-door sedan, OCW

CHEVROLET — SERIES 490 — FOUR: New models this year were All-Season coupes and sedans with removable center posts. Open cars had a windshield with a 15° backwards slant. Wheel felloes were square and demountable rims were standardized. Closed cars featured a rear mounted gas tank. Standard equipment included a top, top hood, windshield, speedometer, ammeter, tire pump, electric horn and demountable rims. The bodies were built by Ionia Body Co. and finished by Chevrolet.

CHEVROLET — SERIES FA — FOUR: The FA series replaced the F. It was much the same as far as appearance. Open cars had a windshield with a 15° slant. The sedan had removable roof center posts. Standard equipment included top, top hood, windshield, speedometer, ammeter, tire pump, electric horn and demountable rims.

CHEVROLET — SERIES D — V-8: The Chevrolet V-8 Series D came in two models. The D-4 was a four-passenger roadster, the D-5 a five-passenger touring. Both were finished in Chevrolet green and had French-pleated leather upholstery. A 20-gallon gas tank was mounted at the rear of the frame. The touring was a four-door model. The roadster was actually more of a two-door "dual-cowl" touring car. Rear slanting hood louvers were used. The body was described as "a delight to the eye" and "a series of curves that blend harmoniously." All visible woodwork was of genuine mahogany and metal parts were nickel. The body foundation was of pressed steel. Standard equipment included a one-man waterproof top with side curtains and Bair brackets; windshield; sixteen candle power headlights; speedometer; demountable rims with extra rim; tire carrier; license holder and tools. Experts believe that production started late in 1917, and that the car was discontinued late in 1918. This was most likely the only full year for the model. To conserve space we are listing specifications in this book under 1918 only, although the Master Price Lists from Chevrolet include the model in 1917, 1918 and 1919. Production breakdown for those three years are indicated below..

1918 Chevrolet, Series 490, touring. Driver: Louis Chevrolet, JAC

I.D. DATA: [Series 490] Serial number located on dash nameplate. Factory codes were: 1 is Flint; 2 is Tarrytown; 3 is St. Louis; 6 is Oakland; 7 is Ft. Worth and 9 is Oshawa (Canada). Starting: 1-37469. Ending: 1-59674. Also: 2-36489 to 2-59958; 3-15001 to 3-24000; 6-10090 to 6-20097; 7-5843 to 7-15110 and 9-1936 to 9-1935. Engine numbers located on flywheel. Engine numbers not available. [Series FA] Serial number system same as on 490. Starting: 1-3431. Ending: 1-10241. Also: 2-4114 to 2-7432 and 9-772 to 9-2047. Engine numbers located on flywheel. Engine numbers not available. [Series D] Serial number system same as on 490 and FB. Starting: (1917) 1-8; (1918) 1-242. Ending: (1917) 1-241; (1918) 1-1557. Also: (1917) 2-2894 to 2-4112; (1918) 2-4113 to 2-7437 and (1917) 9-466 to 9-532; (1918) 9-533 to 9-727.

Model No.	Body Type & Seating	Price	Weight	Prod. Total
490	4-dr. Tr.-5P	685	1890	Note 1
490	2-dr. Rds.-2P	660	1820	Note 1
490	2-dr. A/W Cpe.-3P	1060	2040	Note 1
490	3-dr. A/W Sed.-4P	1060	2160	Note 1
FA-2	2-dr. Rds.-2P	935	2640	Note 1
FA-5	3-dr. Tr.-5P	935	2680	Note 1
FA-4	2-dr. A/W Sed.-4P	1475	2950	Note 1
D-4	2-dr. Rds.-4P	1550	3150	Note 1
D-5	4-dr. Tr.-5P	1550	3200	Note 1

Note 1: Total production of the Chevrolet 490 was 95,660 cars including 13,840 made in Canada. Total production of the Series D (V-8) was 511 in 1917; 2,199 in 1918 and 71 in 1919.
Note 2: Prices in 1917 were $1385 for both models.

ENGINE: [Series 490] OHV. Inline. Four. Cast iron block. B & S: 3-11/16 x 4 in. Disp.: 171 cu. in. Brake H.P.: 26 @ 1800 R.P.M. Net H.P.: 21.75 N.A.C.C. Main bearings: Three. Valve lifters: Solid. Carb.: 1V. [Series FA] OHV. Inline. Four. Cast iron block. B & S: 3-11/16 x 5-1/4 in. Disp.: 224. Brake H.P.: 37 @ 2000 R.P.M. Net H.P.: 21.75 N.A.C.C. Three main bearings. Solid valve lifters. Carb.: 1V. [Series D] 90# V-Block. OHV. Eight. Cast iron block. B & S: 3-3/8 x 4 in. Disp.: 288 cu. in. Net H.P.: 36 N.A.C.C. Main bearings: Three. Valve lifters: Solid. Carb.: Zenith double-jet.

CHASSIS: [Series 490] W.B.: 102 in. Frt/Rear Tread: 56/56 in. Tires: 30 x 3.5. [Series FA] W.B.: 108 in. Frt/Rear Tread: 56/56 in. Tires: 33 x 4. [Series D] W.B.: 120 in. Tires: 34 x 4 (non-skid on rear).

TECHNICAL: Selective sliding transmission. Speeds: 3F/1R. Floor-mounted gear shift controls. Cone type clutch. Three-quarter rear axle. Overall ratio: (490) 3.63:1; (FB) 4.62:1; (D) 4.25:1. External contracting rear wheel brakes. Wood spoke wheels.

OPTIONS: Spare tire. Motometer. OSRV mirror (fender mount). "Fat Man" steering wheel. Sixty inch Southern gauge.

HISTORICAL: Introduced late 1917. Calendar year production: 80,434. Model year production: (490) 86,200; (FA) 11,403; (D) 4833. Innovations: (490) New water pump. New gear oil pump. Spur and gear steering with one piece main shaft. New oil pressure gauge. (FA) larger displacement engine. New water pumps. (D) All new V-8 (introduced in late 1917 as 1917 model).

Chevrolet joined GM in 1918. St. Louis assembly plant opens. Truck production started, Chevrolet headquarters still at 57th St. and Broadway in N.Y.C. Royal Mail and Baby Grand names dropped. Same style continue as roadster and touring in FA series.

1919 CHEVROLET

CHEVROLET — SERIES 490 — FOUR: Only a few minor changes were made in 1919 models. On open cars a Bair top saddle replaced the old-fashioned, bolt-on type. The spare tire carrier was now of three-quarter circle design with a lever. Fixed center posts and a full frame door were now used on the 490 coupe. Prices included top, top hood, windshield, speedometer, ammeter, tire pump, electric horn and demountable rims.

CHEVROLET — SERIES FB — FOUR: The first 1,514 Chevrolet sedans built used the body and all chassis sheet metal from the FA. Later sedans and all other body types were completely new for 1919. New front fender featured a stylish reverse curve. A new 110 inch wheelbase was used. The later sedans were 4-door models. The new FB coupe had fixed center posts and a full frame door. Prices included top, top hood, windshield, speedometer, ammeter, tire pump, electric horn and demountable rims.

I.D. DATA: [Series 490] Serial number located on dash nameplate. Factory codes: 1 is Flint; 2 is Tarrytown; 3 is St. Louis; 6 is Oakland; 7 is Ft. Worth and 9 is Oshawa (Canada). Starting: 1-59675. Ending: 1-92474. Also: 2-59959 to 2-90421; 3-24001 to 3-47100; 6-20098 to 6-36684; 7-15111 to 7-25429 and 9-14187 to 9-28153. Engine numbers located on flywheel. Engine numbers not available. [Series FB] Serial number system was same as on 490. Starting: 1-100. Ending: 1-9384. Also: 2-100 to 2-4738; 6-1001 to 6-1289 and 9-104 to 9-1335. Engine numbers located on flywheel. Engine numbers unknown.

1919 Chevrolet, touring, HAC

Model No.	Body Type & Seating	Price	Weight	Prod. Total
490	2-dr. Rds.-2P	715	1820	Note 1
490	4-dr. Tr.-5P	735	1890	Note 1
490	4-dr. Sed.-4P	1185	2160	Note 1
490	2-dr. Cpe.-3P	1100	2040	Note 1
FB-20	2-dr. Rds.-2P	1110	2640	Note 1
FB-30	4-dr. Tr.-5P	1235	2880	Note 1
FB-50	2-dr. Cpe.-3P	1635	2820	Note 1
FB-40	4-dr. Sed.-4P	1685	2950	Note 1
FB-40	2-dr. Sed.-4P*	1685	2950	Note 1

Note 1: Total production of Chevrolets was 149,904 including 17,431 cars made in Canada.
Note 2: * This was the FB sedan using the old FA body with a center opening door on passenger side.

ENGINE: [Series 490] OHV. Inline. Four. Cast iron block. B & S: 3-11/16 x 4 in. Disp.: 171 cu. in. Brake H.P.: 26 @ 1800 R.P.M. Net H.P.: 21.75 N.A.C.C. Main bearings: Three. Valve lifters: Solid. Carb.: 1V. [Series FB] OHV. Inline. Four. Cast iron. B & S: 3-11/16 x 5-1/4 in. Disp.: 224 cu. in. Brake H.P.: 37 @ 2000 R.P.M. Net H.P.: 21.75. Main bearings: Three. Carb.: 1V.

CHASSIS: [Series 490] W.B.: 102 in. Frt/Rear Tread: 56/56 in. Tires: 30 x 3.5. [Series FB] W.B.: 110 in. Frt/Rear Tread: 56/56 in. Tires: 33 x 4.

TECHNICAL: Selective sliding. Speeds: 3F/1R. Floor-mounted gearshift controls. Cone type clutch. Three-quarter floating rear axle. Overall ratio: (490) 3.63:1; (FB) 4.62:1. External contracting two-wheel brakes. Artillery spoke wheels.

OPTIONS: OSRV mirror (fender mounted). Spare tire. Motometer. "Fat Man" steering wheel. Sixty inch Southern gauge.

HISTORICAL: Introduced late 1918. Calendar year production: 123,371. Model year production: [Series 490] 127,231; [Series FB] 14,516. Innovations: (490) Speedometer drive taken from universal joint. Four-button switch changed to lever type. Fixed center post coupe. (FB) completely new line introduced this year.
This was Chevrolet's first full year as a part of General Motors Corp. Some sources show the Series D V-8 as a 1919 model, but there are no 1919 serial numbers for V-8s. Some 1918 models may have been sold as 1919s.

1920 CHEVROLET

CHEVROLET — SERIES 490 — FOUR: Although automotive styling wasn't around in 1920, Chevrolet did make a change in the 490's appearance. It was done by replacing the old straight fenders with a reverse curve type. They also mounted the headlights on steel brackets and eliminated the tie-bar. New for open models was a top with two round windows in the rear.

CHEVROLET — SERIES FB — FOUR: Reverse curve front fenders were also used on the FB Series Chevrolets for 1920. Otherwise there was little change from first FB models of 1919.

I.D. DATA: [Series 490] Serial number located on nameplate on dash. Prefix indicates plant. 1 is Flint; 2 is Tarrytown; 3 is St. Louis; 6 is Oakland; 7 is Ft. Worth and 9 is Oshawa (Canada). Starting: 1-92475. Ending: 1A-20160. Also: 2-90422 to 2A-23673; 3-47101 to 3A-70100; 6-36685 to 6A-51094; 7-25430 to 7A-34121; 9-28154 to 9-A40225. Engine numbers located on flywheel. Engine numbers not available. [Series FB] Serial number system same as on 490 Series. Starting: 1-9385. Ending: 1-20516. Also: 2-4739 to 2-10634; 3-54 to 3-1600; 6-1290 to 6-4990 and 9-1336 to 9-4604. Engine numbers located on flywheel. Engine numbers not available.

1920 Chevrolet, coupe, HAC

Series 490 Model No.	Body Type & Seating	Price	Weight	Prod. Total
490	2-dr. Rds.-2P	795	1820	Note 2
490	4-dr. Tr.-5P	810	1895	Note 2
490	4-dr. Sed.-5P	1285	2160	Note 2
490	2-dr. Cpe.-3P	1210	2040	Note 2
Note 1: Prices dropped about $100 during 1920 model year.				
Series FB				
FB	2-dr. Rds.-2P	1270	2160	Note 2
FB	4-dr. Tr.-5P	1355	2800	Note 2
FB	4-dr. Sed.-5P	1885	2950	Note 2
FB	2-dr. Cpe.-3P	1855	2820	Note 2

Note 2: Total production was 150,226 Chevrolets including 18,847 cars made in Canada.
Note 3: Prices dropped $60-100 during 1921.

ENGINE: [Series 490] OHV. Inline. Four. Cast iron block. B & S: 3-11/16 x 4 in. Disp.: 171 cu. in. Brake H.P.: 26 @ 1800 R.P.M. Net H.P.: 21.75 N.A.C.C. Main bearings: Three. Valve lifters: Solid. Carb.: 1V. [Series FB] OHV. Inline. Four. Cast iron block. B & S: 3-11/16 x 5-1/4 in. Disp.: 224 cu. in. Brake H.P.: 37 @ 2000 R.P.M. Net H.P.: 21.75. Main bearings: Three. Valve lifters: Solid. Carb.: 1V.

CHASSIS: [Series 490] W.B.: 102. Tires: 30 x 3-1/2. [Series FB] W.B.: 110. Tires: 33 x 4.

TECHNICAL: Selective sliding. Speeds: 3F/1R. Floor-mounted gearshift controls. Cone type clutch. (490) two-piece rear axle. (FB) 3/4 floating rear axle. Overall ratio: (490) 3.63:1; (FB) 4.62:1. External contracting rear brakes. Wood spoke wheels.

OPTIONS: Front bumper. Rear bumper. Spare tire. Spare tire cover. Step plates. "Fat Man" steering wheel. Motometer. Cowl lights. Wind wings. OSRV mirror. Special paint.

HISTORICAL: Introduced: Jan. 1920. Model year production: (490) 129,106; (FB) 17,137; Total 146,243 approximate. Calendar year production: 121,908. Innovations: Gravity fuel feed on 490. Vacuum fuel feed on FB.
W.C. Durant leaves General Motors for second time. Karl W. Zimmerschield becomes president of Chevrolet.

1921 CHEVROLET

1921 Chevrolet, Series 490, sedan, HAC

CHEVROLET — SERIES 490 — FOUR: The 1921 Chevrolet 490 was virtually unchanged in appearance from last year. The passenger side door on the sedan was moved to a position in the center of the car. Larger size 31 x 4 tires were used on closed models only.

CHEVROLET — SERIES FB — FOUR: There were no basic changes in Series FB Chevrolets from 1920. The same four body styles remained in production.

I.D. DATA: [Series 490] Serial number located on nameplate on dash. Prefix indicates plant. 1A is Flint; 2A is Tarrytown; 3 is St. Louis; 6 is Oakland and 9 is Oshawa (Canada). Starting: 1A-20161. Ending: 1A-59938. Also: 2A-23674 to 2A-55239; 3-70101 to 3A-

53241; 6-51095 to 6A-54958; 9-40226 to 9A-47848. Engine numbers on flywheel. Engine numbers not available. [Series FB] The serial number system was the same as on the 490 series. Starting: 1-20517. Ending: 1-24853. Also: 2-10635 to 2-15651; 3-1601 to 3-2316; 6-4991 to 6-6121; 9-4605 to 9-6436. Engine numbers located on flywheel. Engine numbers not available.

Model No.	Body Type & Seating	Price	Weight	Prod. Total
Series 490				
490	Chassis	NA	NA	Note 2
490	2-dr. Rds.-2P	795	1820	Note 2
490	4-dr. Tr.-5P	820	1890	Note 2
490	2-dr. Cpe.-3P	1325	2040	Note 2
490	3-dr. Sed.-5P	1375	2160	Note 2

Note 1: During the year prices dropped to the 1922 factory prices.

Model No.	Body Type & Seating	Price	Weight	Prod. Total
Series FB				
FB	2-dr. Rds.-2P	1320	2640	Note 2
FB	4-dr. Trs.-5P	1345	2780	Note 2
FB	2-dr. Cpe.-3P	2075	2820	Note 2
FB	4-dr. Sed.-5P	2075	2950	Note 2

Note 2: Total production was 76,370 Chevrolets including 8,187 cars made in Canada.
Note 3: Prices dropped about $500 in late 1921 due to recession.

ENGINE: [Series 490] OHV. Inline. Four. Cast iron block. B & S: 3-11/16 x4 in. Disp.: 171 cu. in. Brake H.P.: 26 @ 1800 R.P.M. N.A.C.C. H.P.: 21.75. Main bearings: Three. Valve lifters: Solid. Carb.: 1V. [Series FB] OHV. Inline. Four. Cast iron block. B & S: 3-11/16 x 5-1/4 in. Disp.: 224 cu. in. Brake H.P.: 37 @ 2000 R.P.M. N.A.C.C. H.P.: 21.75. Main bearings: Three. Valve lifters: Solid. Carb.: 1V.

CHASSIS: [Series 490] W.B.: 102 in. Tires: 30 x 3-1/2 (open); 31 x 4 (closed). [Series FB] W.B.: 110 in. Tires: 33 x 4.

TECHNICAL: Selective sliding transmission. Speeds: 3F/1R. Floor mounted gear shift controls. Cone clutch. Shaft drive (torque tube). Rear axle: (FB) 3/4-Floating; (490) 2-piece. Overall Ratio: (FB) 4.62:1; (490) 3.63:1. External contracting rear brakes. 12-spoke wood artillery wheels.

OPTIONS: Spare tire. Spare tire cover. Step plates. "Fat Man" steering wheel. Motometer. Cowl lights. Wind wings. OSRV mirror. Special paint.

HISTORICAL: Introduced Jan. 1921. Innovations: New center door sedan. Larger tires on 490 closed models. Calendar year production: 61,717. Model year production: (490) 117,827 approximate; (FB) 13,028 approximate.
A management survey recommended the discontinuance of Chevrolet production.

1922 CHEVROLET

1922 Chevrolet, sedan, OCW

CHEVROLET — SERIES 490 — FOUR: The appearance of 490 models stayed about the same. Steel wheel felloes were new. The sedan became a 4-door model. Gypsy style rear curtains were now seen on open cars. Also, the windshield was lower and a hand-operated emergency brake was used for the first time. A Utility Coupe was added to the line in March, 1922.

CHEVROLET — SERIES FB — FOUR: This was the final season for the FB Chevrolet. There were no basic styling changes. New features included steel felloe wheels, a 10 gallon gas tank, a shorter steering column and a 4-1/2 in. lower seat cushion. New 32 x 4 size tires were introduced during the year.

I.D. DATA: [Series 490] Serial number located on name plate on dash. Prefixes indicated plant. 1 is Flint; 2 is Tarrytown; 3 is St. Louis; 6 is Oakland and 9 is Oshawa (Canada). Starting: 1A-59939. Ending: 1A-92881. Also: 2A-55240 to 2A-88765. 3A-33242 to 3A-66294. 6A-54959 to 6A-72319. 9A-47849 to 9A-70543. Engine numbers on flywheel. Engine numbers not available. [Series FB] Serial number system same as on 490 Series. Starting: 1-24854. Ending: 1A-39542. Also: 2-15652 to 2A-30267; 3-2317 to 3A-30599; 6-6122 to 6A-30704; 9-6436 to 9A-7593. Engine numbers located on flywheel. Engine numbers not available.

Model No.	Body Type & Seating	Price	Weight	Prod. Total
490	Chassis	NA	1435	Note 1
490	2-dr. Rds.-2P	510	1725	Note 1
490	4-dr. Tr.-5P	525	1770	Note 1
490	2-dr. Utl. Cpe.-2P	850	1945	Note 1
490	2-dr. Cpe.-4P	680	2015	Note 1
490	4-dr. Sed.-5P	875	2150	Note 1
FB	2-dr. Rds.-2P	865	2310	Note 1
FB	4-dr. Tr.-5P	885	2595	Note 1
FB	2-dr. Cpe.-4P	1325	2735	Note 1
FB	4-dr. Sed.-4P	1395	2890	Note 1

Note 1: Total production was 243,479 Chevrolets including 19,895 cars made in Canada.

1922 Chevrolet, touring, JAC

ENGINE: [Series 490] OHV. Inline. Four. Cast iron block. B & S: 3-11/16 x 4 in. Disp. 171 cu. in. Brake H.P.: 26 @ 1800 R.P.M. Main bearings: Three. Valve lifters: Solid. Carb.: 1V. [Series FB] OHV. Inline. Four. C.I. Block. B & S: 3-11/16 x 5-1/4 in. Disp.: 224 cu. in. Brake H.P.: 37 @ 2000 R.P.M. N.A.C.C. Horsepower 21.75. Main bearings: Three. Valve lifters: Solid. Carb.: 1V.

CHASSIS: [Series 490] W.B.: 102 in. Tires: 30 x 3-1/2 or 31 x 4. [Series FB] W.B.: 110 in. Tires: 32 x 4.

TECHNICAL: Selective sliding transmission. Speeds: 3F/1R. Floor mounted gear shift controls. Cone clutch. Shaft drive. (torque tube). Rear axle: (FB) 3/4-floating; (490) 2-piece. Overall Ratio: (FB) 4.62:1; (490) 3.63:1. External contracting rear brakes. Steel felloe wheels.

OPTIONS: Spare tire. Spare tire cover. Step plates. "Fat Man" steering wheel. Motometer. Cowl lights. Wind wings. OSRV mirror. Special paint.

HISTORICAL: Introduced: Jan. 1922. Innovations: (Series FB) New poured con rods. New crank w/two-inch longer throws. Improved cylinder head w/three exhaust ports. Reverse Elliot front axle. (Series 490) Valve adjustment on rocker arms. Larger diam. King pins. Single pedal brakes. Spiral cut ring and pinion. Calendar year production: 208,848. Model year production: (490) 109,473 approximate; (FB) 29,459 approximate. W.S. Knudsen became the new president of Chevrolet.

1923 CHEVROLET

1923 Chevrolet, Copper Cooled, coupe, HAC

CHEVROLET - COPPER-COOLED — SERIES C — FOUR: The Copper Cooled Chevrolet looked like a conventional 1923 Series B Superior model, except that the radiator was replaced by louvers and the "bow tie" emblem had a copper colored background. The word "Copper" appeared above the Chevrolet logo and the word "Cooled" was below it. There was a functional nickel plated hood ornament.

The unusual air-cooled engine in these Chevrolets was designed by Charles F. Kettering. The model evolved from two years of experimentation with the air-cooled concept, but the car was still unperfected when released for sale at the New York Automobile Show in Jan. 1923. Production was suspended five months later and a complete recall was issued.

Only 759 of the cars were built, of which 239 were scrapped before leaving the factory. Of the 500 cars shipped, 150 were used by Chevrolet representatives and about 300 were sent to dealerships. About 100 were sold before the recall. Two are known to survive today. One is part of the Harrah's Automobile Collection. The other is in the Henry Ford Museum. In addition, several engines still survive. Well-known Chevrolet collector "Pinky" Randall says, "I have one of them. They were used as stationary engines in Chevrolet factories."

1923 Chevrolet, Superior, roadster, JAC

CHEVROLET - SUPERIOR — MODEL B — FOUR: The 1923 Chevrolet Superior had much smoother lines for open models. The hood line was raised and the cowl section was narrowed. Drum type headlights were featured. The radiator was higher and had a flatter curvature at its top. Late in the year, deluxe versions of the touring, coupe and sedan were introduced. They featured disc wheels, bumpers, nickel plated radiator shells, deluxe radiator caps, motometers, running board kick plates and locking steering wheels. The Deluxe touring had outside door handles and deluxe upholstery.

I.D. DATA: [Series C] Serial numbers were located on a plate on the left side of the front seat frame. They took the form 1-C-1001 and up. Ending number is not recorded. The car in Mich. is 1-C-1109; the car in Nevada is 1-C-1268. The location of engine numbers is not recorded. [Series B] Serial number located on nameplate on the left side of front seat frame. Prefixes indicated the plant. 1 is Flint; 2 is New York; 3 is St. Louis; 6 is Oakland. Up to the later part of 1923 a 9 is Oshawa; later 9 is Norwood; 12 is Buffalo and 21 is Janesville. Starting: 1-B20391. Ending: 1-B98854. Also: 2-B19269 to 2-B111787; 3-B24459 to 3-B132178; 6-B8087 to 6-B51547; 9-B1928 to 9-B9077; 12-B1190 to 12-B7340 and 21-B1000 to 21-B38352. Engine numbers located on flywheel. Engine numbers not available.

Model No.	Body Type & Seating	Price	Weight	Prod. Total
M	2-dr. Rds.-2P	710	NA	Note 3
M	4-dr. Tr.-5P	695	NA	Note 3
M	4-dr. Sed.-5P	1060	NA	Note 3
M	2-dr. Coach-5P	1050	NA	Note 3
M	2-dr. Utl. Cpe.-2P	880	1700*	Note 3
M	4-dr. Del. Tr.-5P	725	NA	Note 3

Note 1: Based on *Special Interest Autos* "Drive Report" Sept.-Oct. 1975. Indicated that copper-cooled was 215 lbs. lighter than conventional Chevrolet.
Note 2: Total production: 500; Total Sales: 100.

Model No.	Body Type & Seating	Price	Weight	Prod. Total
B	Chassis	NA	1390	Note 3
B	2-dr. Rds.-2P	510	1715	Note 3
B	4-dr. Tr.-5P	495	1795	Note 3
B	2-dr. UH. Cpe.-2P	680	1915	Note 3
B	2-dr. S'net-4P	850	2055	Note 3
B	4-dr. Sed.-5P	860	2095	Note 3

Note 3: Total production was 480,737 Chevrolets including 25,751 cars made in Canada.
Note 4: Prices for Deluxe models slightly lower than prices for 1924 Deluxe models.

1923 Chevrolet, Superior, 4-dr. sedan, OCW

ENGINE: [Copper-Cooled] OHV. Inline. Four. Cast iron block w/bored copper fins. B & S: 3.5 x 3.5 in. Disp.: 135 cu. in. C.R.: 4.0:1. Brake H.P.: 22 @ 1750 R.P.M. Main bearings: Three. Valve lifters: Solid. Carb.: Carter 1V (updraft). Torque: 50 lbs.-ft. @ 1300 R.P.M. [Superior] OHV. Inline. Four. Cast iron block. B & S: 3-11/16 x 4 in. Disp.: 171 cu. in. Brake H.P.: 26 @ 2000 R.P.M. N.A.C.C. H.P.: 21.75. Main bearings: Three. Valve lifters: Solid. Carb.: Carter 1V.

CHASSIS: [Both Series] W.B.: 103 in. O.L.: 142 in. O.H.: 74.25 in. Frt/Rear Tread: 58/58 in. Tires: 30 x 3.5.

TECHNICAL: Selective sliding transmission. Speeds: 3F/1R. Floor-mounted gearshift controls. Cone clutch. Shaft drive. Semi-floating rear axle. Overall ratio: [Model M] 4.44:1; [Model B] 3.77:1. External contracting rear wheel brakes. Wood spoke 3.0 x 24.75 wheels.

OPTIONS: Front bumper. Rear bumper. Disc wheels. Plated radiator. Wind wings. Spare tire. Tire cover. Motometer. Kick plates. Deluxe upholstery. Deluxe radiator cap. Locking steering wheel. OSRV mirror. Sun visor (open cars). Special paint. Cowl lamps.

HISTORICAL: Superior B introduced Jan. 1923. Innovations: Increased wheelbase. Copper Cooled Series. New serial number system used letter or number to identify model year. Calendar year registrations: 291,761. Calendar year production: 415,814. Model year production: 323,182 (approx.)

New plants opened in Norwood, Ohio; Buffalo, N.Y. and Janesville, Wis. Some Model B engines had Holley carburetors.

1924 CHEVROLET

1924 Chevrolet, Superior, touring, OCW

CHEVROLET - SUPERIOR — SERIES F — FOUR: The Superior Series F was virtually unchanged in appearance from 1923 models. New body styles included a 2-door coach and four-passenger coupe. The sedanette was dropped. Standard equipment on open cars included tools; jack; speedometer; ammeter; oil pressure gauge; dashlight; choke pull; electric horn; ignition theft lock; demountable rims with extra rim; spare tire carrier; legal headlights; headlight dimmer; license bracket and double adjustable windshield. Closed models also had a windshield cleaner; plate glass windows; window regulator; sun visor and door locks. Deluxe equipment available for some mid-year models included disc wheels; bumpers; nickel radiator shells; runningboard kick plates and (on the touring) outside door handles.

I.D. DATA: Serial numbers were located on the right or left side of dash under cowl and seat frame. Starting: 1B72774. Ending: 1F38881. Also: 2B92892 to 2F51140; 3B98371 to 3F56585; 6B41756 to 6F29296; 9B1166 to 9F27125; 12B1064 to 12F35270 and 21B22374 to 21F33581. Note: Cars built late in the run were sold as 1925 models. They had the following serial numbers: 1F38882 to 1K-1; 2F51141 to 2K-1; 3F56586 to 3K-1; 6F297 to 6K-1; 9K27126 to 9K-1; 12F35271 to 12K-1 and 21F33582 to 21K-1.

Model No.	Body Type & Seating	Price	Weight	Prod. Total
F	2-dr. Rds.-2P	490	1690	Note 1
F	4-dr. Tr.-5P	495	1875	Note 1
F	4-dr. Sed.-5P	795	2070	Note 1
F	2-dr. Cpe.-2P	640	1880	Note 1
F	2-dr. Cpe.-4P	725	2005	Note 1
F	2-dr. Coach-5P	695	2030	Note 1
Deluxe Equipped				
F	4-dr. Del. Tr.-5P	640	1955	Note 1
F	4-dr. Del. Sed.-5P	940	2240	Note 1
F	2-dr. Del. Cpe.-4P	775	2050	Note 1

Note 1: Total production was 307,775 Chevrolets including 20,587 cars made in Canada.

ENGINE: OHV. En Bloc. Four. Cast iron block. B & S: 3-11/16 x 4 in. Disp.: 171 cu. in. Brake H.P.: 26 @ 2000 R.P.M. N.A.C.C. H.P.: 21.7. Main bearings: Three. Valve lifters: Solid. Carb.: 1V.

CHASSIS: W.B.: 103 in. Tires: 30 x 3-1/2 non-skid.

TECHNICAL: Selective sliding transmission. Speeds: 3F/1R. Floor mounted gear shift controls. Semi-floating rear axle. 3.82: 1. External contracting rear brakes. Steel felloe, woodspoke.

OPTIONS: Step plates. OSRV mirrors. Tire cover. Motometer. Special paint. Spare tire. Disc wheels. Deluxe equipment.

HISTORICAL: Introduced: Aug. 1, 1923. Innovations: New coach and four-passenger coupe. New Deluxe models. Improved front axle. Improved brakes. Calendar year registrations: 289,962. Calendar year production: 262,100. Model year production: 264,868 (Aug. 1, 1923 to Aug. 1, 1924).

Curved front axles and cable operated brakes characterized early models in this series. Straight front axles and brake rods were used on later Series F Superior Chevrolets. New plant in Norwood, Ohio opened this year. Cars built before Aug. 1, 1923 were Series B Superior Chevrolets.

1925 CHEVROLET

CHEVROLET - SUPERIOR — SERIES K — FOUR: The 1925 Chevrolet had a new radiator design. The upper part of the nickel plated shell curved down at the center. Fisher Body vertical ventilating (v.v.) windshields were used on closed cars. A Cadet style visor was another new feature. Wood spoke wheels were standard on open cars; sedans and coupes in late production had steel disc wheels. New Klaxon horns and a new steering wheel with walnut-like rim were other features of Superior K Chevrolets built after Aug. 1, 1925.

1925 Chevrolet, Superior, Series K, coupe, JAC

I.D. DATA: Serial numbers were located on the right or left side of dash under cowl and seat frame. Starting: 1K1000. Ending: 1K33571. Also: 2K1000 to 2K45727; 3K1000 to 3K48220; 6K1000 to 6K27866; 9K1000 to 9K27519; 12K1000 to 12K36081 and 21K1000 to 21K32544.

Note: Cars built late in the run were sold as 1926 models. They had the following serial numbers: 1K33752 to 1V-1; 2K45728 to 2V-1; 3K48221 to 3V-1; 6K27867 to 6V-1; 9K27520 to 9V-1; 12K36082 to 12V-1 and 21K32545 to 21V-1.

Model No.	Body Type & Seating	Price	Weight	Prod. Total
K	2-dr. Rds.-2P	525	1690	Note 1
K	4-dr. Tr.-5P	525	1855	Note 1
K	2-dr. Cpe.-2P	715	1880	Note 1
K	4-dr. Sed.-5P	825	2070	Note 1
K	2-dr. Coach-5P	735	2030	Note 1

Note 1: Total production was 519,229 Chevrolets including 30,968 cars made in Canada.

1925 Chevrolet, Superior, Series K, coach, OCW

ENGINE: OHV. Inline. Four. Cast iron block. B & S: 3-11/16 x 4 in. Disp.: 171 cu. in. Brake H.P.: 26 @ 2000 R.P.M. N.A.C.C. H.P.: 21.7. Main bearings: Three. Valve lifters: Solid. Carb.: 1V Model RXO.

CHASSIS: W.B.: 103 in. Tires: 30 x 3-1/2 (open cars); 29 x 4.40 (closed cars).

TECHNICAL: Selective sliding transmission. Speeds: 3F/1R. Floor-mounted gearshift controls. Clutch; single plate dry disc. Semi-floating rear axle. Overall Ratio: 3.82:1. External contracting rear wheel brakes. Spoke wheels (open); Disc wheels (closed).

OPTIONS: Front bumper. Rear bumper. Step plates. OSRV mirrors. Tire cover. Motometer. Special paint. Spare tire. Heater. Clock. Wood spoke wheels (closed cars). Steel disc wheels (open cars).

HISTORICAL: Introduced: Jan. 1925. Innovations: Redesigned engine with new block, rods and crank. New disc clutch. Semi-elliptic springs. Calendar year registrations: 341,281. Calendar year production: 444,671. Model year production: 306,479 (Jan. 1925 — Aug. 1925).

Cars built after August 1, 1925 had the new Klaxon horns and walnut steering wheel. They also had spark/throttle controls on the dash above the steering wheel and a headlight brace bar. They were sold as 1926 models. Bloomfield, N.J. factory purchased. First year of production over 500,000 units (incl. early 1926 models).

1926 CHEVROLET

CHEVROLET - SUPERIOR — SERIES V — FOUR: The Super Series V was introduced in mid-1926 and was marketed into the first part of the 1927 sales year. It was similar to the previous Series K except that a tie-bar connected the drum-shaped headlights.

I.D. DATA: Serial Number located on right or left side of dash under cowl and seat frame. Starting: 1V1000. Ending: 1V48499. Also: 2V1000 to 2V49550; 3V1000 to 3V83277; 6V1000 to 6V27138; 9V1000 to 9V52906; 12V1000 to 12V38701 and 21V1000 to 21V54755.

1926 Chevrolet, Superior, Landau Sedan V, 4-dr sedan, OCW

Model No.	Body Type & Seating	Price	Weight	Prod. Total
V	2-dr. Rds.-2P	510	1790	Note 1
V	4-dr. Tr.-5P	510	1950	Note 1
V	2-dr. Cpe.-2P	645	2035	Note 1
V	4-dr. Sed.-5P	735	2225	Note 1
V	2-dr. Coach-5P	645	2150	Note 1
V	4-dr. Lan. Sed.-5P	765	2220	NA

Note 1: Total production was 732,147 Chevrolets including 39.967 cars made in Canada.

ENGINE: OHV. Inline. Four cyl. Cast iron block. B & S: 3-11/16 x 4 in. Disp.: 171 cu. in. Brake H.P.: 26 @ 2000 R.P.M. Net H.P.: 21.7 N.A.C.C. Main bearings: Three. Valve lifters: Solid. Carb.: 1V.

CHASSIS: W.B. 103 in. Tires: 29 x 4.40.

TECHNICAL: Selective sliding transmission. Speeds: 3F/1R. Floor-mounted gearshift controls. Clutch: Single plate dry disc. Semi-floating rear axle. Overall ratio: 3.82:1. External Contracting rear wheel brakes. Wood spoke wheels.

OPTIONS: Step plates. OSRV mirror. Tire covers. Whitewall tires. Motometer. Special paint. Spare tire. Wood spoke wheels. Commercial pickup equipment.

HISTORICAL: Introduced: Mid-1926. Calendar year registrations: 486,366. Calendar year production: 588,962. Model year production: 547,724. Innovations: Belt driven generator. Cam operated oil pump. Improved brakes. New Landau Sedan.

Spark/throttle control moved above steering wheel on late models. Combination stop/taillamp (instead of round taillight) on late models. New Detroit axle factory. Eight million dollars appropriated to make Chevrolet more competitive with Ford.

1927 CHEVROLET

1927 Chevrolet, Capitol, landau sedan, AA

CHEVROLET - CAPITOL — SERIES AA — FOUR: The 1927 Chevrolets had a new radiator shell on which the top portion no longer bowed downwards. There was a downward pointing "peak" in the center of the upper shell. New bullet shaped headlight buckets were finished in black enamel with bright metal trim rings. Fuller crown fenders were seen. Rectangular brake and clutch pedals were used. There was a new parking brake release and a coincidental ignition/steering wheel lock. A new body style was the Sports Cabriolet. An Imperial Landau Sedan was introduced in May 1927. Equipment on open cars included tools; jack; speedometer; ammeter; oil pressure gauge, dash light; choke pull, electric horn, extra rim; spare tire carrier; bullet type cowl lamps; headlight dimmer; license brackets; double-adjustable windshield; foot accelerator; air cleaner; oil filter; pedal enclosure; rear-vision mirror; gas gauge and automatic stop light. Closed cars also had V.V. windshields; wipers; plate glass windows; window regulators; sunvisor; door locks; dome lights; rear window roller shade; door pockets and remote control door handles.

I.D. DATA: Serial Number located on right or left side of dash under cowl and seat frame. Starting: AA1 & up. Engine numbers located on base ahead of oil filter.

Model No.	Body Type & Seating	Price	Weight	Prod. Total
AA	2-dr. Rds.-2P	525	1960	41,313
AA	4-dr. Tr.-5P	525	1895	53,187

Model No.	Body Type & Seating	Price	Weight	Prod. Total
AA	2-dr. Cpe.-2P	625	2090	124,101
AA	2-dr. Spt. Cabr.-2/4P	715	2135	41,137
AA	2-dr. Coach-5P	695	2190	239,566
AA	4-dr. Sed.-5P	695	2275	99,400
AA	4-dr. Imp. Lan.-5P	NA	NA	37,426
AA	4-dr. Lan. Sed.-5P	745	2270	42,410

Note 1: The Sports Cabriolet was a closed car not a convertible.

1927 Chevrolet, Capital, coach (with Alfred Sloan), JAC

ENGINE: OHV. Inline. Four. Cast iron block. B & S: 3-11/16 x 4 in. Disp.: 171 cu. in. Brake H.P.: 26 @ 2000 R.P.M. Net H.P.: 21.7. Main bearings: Three. Valve lifters: Solid. Carb.: 1V; Model: Carter.

CHASSIS: W.B.: 103 in. Tires: 29 x 4.40 (balloon).

TECHNICAL: Selective sliding transmission. Speeds: 3F/1R. Floor-mounted gearshift controls. Single plate dry disc. Semi-floating rear axle. Overall ratio: 3.82:1. External Contracting rear-wheel brakes. Steel disc wheels.

OPTIONS: Window awnings. Step plates. Whitewall tires. Woodspoke wheels. Motometer. Special paint. OSRV mirror. Spare tire. Tire cover.

HISTORICAL: Introduced: Jan. 1927. Total production: 1,001,820 Chevrolets including 61,740 cars made in Canada. Innovations: First Chevrolet rumble seat on Capitol AA Sports Cabriolet. First year for natural wood spoke wheel option. New Remy distributor and Carter carburetor. Air and oil filters standard for first time.

In 1927, Chevrolet outsold Ford for the first time. Saginaw gray iron foundry was opened. First million car sales year for Chevrolet. General Manager: William S. Knudsen.

1928 CHEVROLET

1928 Chevrolet, National, Imperial landau, HAC

CHEVROLET — NATIONAL — MODEL AB — FOUR: The 1928 Chevrolets were larger cars. New, full crown fenders were used. There were larger, bullet type headlamps and a higher cowl line. Standard equipment included. Fisher V.V. windshield, vacuum wiper, inside rear view mirror, stop light, parking lights, door pockets and gas gauge. Smoking set and robe rails on sedans, Duco Finish.

I.D. DATA: Serial numbers on front seat heel board at left or right side. Starting: AB 1000 and up. A numerical prefix indicated assembly plant as follows: "1" - Flint, Mich.; "2" - Tarrytown, N.Y.; "3" - St. Louis; "5" - Kansas City, Mo.; "6" - Oakland, Calif.; "8" - Atlanta, Ga.; "9" - Norwood, Ohio; "12" - Buffalo, N.Y. and "21" - Janesville, Wis. Engine number on base ahead of oil filter. Codes not available.

Model No.	Body Type & Seating	Price	Weight	Prod. Total
AB	2-dr. Rds.-2P	495	2030	39,809
AB	4-dr. Tr.-5P	495	2090	26,973
AB	2-dr. Cpe.-2P	595	2235	150,356
AB	2-dr. Cabr.-2/4P	665	2270	NA
AB	2-dr. Cpe. Spt. Conv.-2P	695	2265	38,268
AB	2-dr. Coach-5P	585	2360	346,976
AB	4-dr. Sed-5P	675	2435	127,819
AB	4-dr. Imp. Lan.-5P	715	2405	54,998

ENGINE: OHV. Inline. Four. Cast iron block. B & S: 3-11/16 x 4 in. Disp.: 171 cu. in. Brake H.P.: 35 @ 2200 R.P.M. NACC H.P.: 21.7. Valve lifters: Solid. Carb. Carter 1V.

CHASSIS: W.B.: 107 in. Length: 156 in. (less bumpers). Tread: 56 in. Tires: 30 x 4.50 in.

TECHNICAL: Manual transmission. Straight cut gears. Speeds: 3F/1R. Floor shift controls. Overall Ratio: 3.82:1. Mechanical brakes on four wheels. Disc wheels.

OPTIONS: Front bumper. Rear bumper. Heater. Wood spoke wheels. Outside rear view mirror. Leatherette spare tire cover. Spare tire (rim std.). Fluid canisters. Runningboard step plates. Wind wings (open cars), Tire Lock, Two choices of radiator ornaments.

HISTORICAL: Introduced Jan. 1928. Indirect lighted instrument panel. Four-wheel brakes. Thermostat. Alemite chassis lubrication. Total production: 1,193,212 Chevrolets including 69,217 cars made in Canada. Hibbard & Darrin constructed at least one custom-bodied National series AB sedan. General Manager: W.S. Knudsen.

1929 CHEVROLET

1929 Chevrolet, International, 4-dr. sedan, HFM

CHEVROLET — INTERNATIONAL — MODEL AC — SIX: The 1929 Chevrolets had a more rectangular radiator with the company "bow-tie" logo in an upright oval at the top of the chrome plated radiator shell. Fewer vertical louvers were seen towards the rear of the hood side panels. Wider, single belt moldings decorated the body. New, one-piece full crown fenders and new bullet type lamps were used. A rumble seat Sport Roadster was a mid-year addition to the line.

I.D. DATA: Serial number on right body sill under floor mat, except roadster and phaeton (right side of seat frame on these models). Starting: AC1000 and up. Numerical prefixes used for each factory; same as 1928. Each factory built only one body style. Engine numbers on right side of block behind fuel pump. Codes not available.

Model No.	Body Type & Seating	Price	Weight	Prod. Total
1AC	2-dr. Rds.-2P	525	2175	27,988
2AC	4-dr. Phae.-5P	525	2240	8,632
3AC	2-dr. Cpe.-2P	595	2425	45,956
5AC	2-dr. Spt. Cpe.-2/4P	645	2470	Note 1
6AC	2-dr. Cabr.-2/4P	695	2440	45,956
8AC	2-dr. Coach-5P	595	2500	367,360
9AC	4-dr. Sed.-5P	675	2585	196,084
21AC	4-dr. Imp. Sed.-5P	695	2555	42,283
12AC	4-dr. Lan. Conv.-5P	725	2560	300
1AC	2-dr. Spt. Rds.-2/4P	545	2230	1,210

Note 1: Combined production total for coupe and Sport Coupe was 157,230 cars.
Note 2: Model number prefix shown above indicates assembly point. Refer to factory codes in 1928 Chevrolet serial number data.

ENGINE: OHV. Inline. Six. Cast iron block. B & S: 3-5/16 x 3-3/4 in. Disp.: 194 cu. in. Brake H.P.: 46 @ 2600 R.P.M. NACC H.P.: 26.3 Main bearings: Three. Valve lifters: Solid. Carb.: Carter 1V.

CHASSIS: W.B.: 107 in. Length: 156 in. (less bumpers). Tread: 56 in. Tires: 20 x 4.50.

TECHNICAL: Manual transmisson. Straight cut gears. Speeds: 3F/1R. Floor shift controls. Banjo rear axle. Single plate dry disc clutch. Overall ratio: 3.82:1. Four wheel mechanical brakes. Rod activated. Internal front/external rear. Disc wheels.

OPTIONS: Front bumper. Rear bumper. Single sidemount. Dual sidemount. Sidemount cover(s). Rear spare cover. Trunk rack. Steamer type trunk. Heater. Outside rear view mirror. Cigar lighter. Runingboard step plates. Wire spoke wheels. Wind wings (open cars). Accessory hood mascot.

HISTORICAL: Introduced: December 1928. Banjo type rear axle. Electro lock. Rubber covered 17-in. steering wheel. New six-cylinder engine. Total production: 1,328,605 Chevrolets including 73,918 cars made in Canada. Advertised as "A Six for the Price of a Four." Fuel consumption: App. 19 m.p.g. General Manager: W.S. Knudsen.

1930 CHEVROLET

1930 Chevrolet, Universal, coach, OCW

CHEVROLET — UNIVERSAL — SERIES AD — SIX: The major change in 1930 Chevrolets was the addition of a slanting, non-glare windshield. The gas gauge was moved to the dashboard. Other instruments had a new, circular shape with dark colored faces. Smaller tires were used. The Special Sedan replaced the Imperial Sedan. Its standard equipment included six wire wheels with fender wells, front and rear bumpers, robe rail, dome light and silk assist cords.

I.D. DATA: Serial numbers in same locations as 1929. AD 1000 and up. Numerical prefixes used for each factory; same as 1929. Each factory built one body style. Engine numbers same location; codes not available.

1930 Chevrolet, Universal, coupe, JAC

Model No.	Body Type & Seating	Price	Weight	Prod. Total
1AD	2-dr. Rds.-2P	495	2195	5,684
2AD	2-dr. Spt. Rds.-2/4P	515	2250	27,651
3AD	4-dr. Phae.-5P	495	2265	1,713
5AD	2-dr. Cpe.-2P	565	2415	100,373
6AD	2-dr. Spt. Cpe-2/4P	615	2525	45,311
8AD	2-dr. Coach-5P	565	2515	255,027
9AD	4-dr. Club Sed.-5P	625	2575	24,888
12AD	4-dr. Sed.-5P	675	2615	135,193
21AD	4-dr. Spec. Sed.-5P	685	2665	35,929
5AD	2-dr. R/S Cpe.-2/4P	—	—	9,211

Note 1: Model number prefix shown above indicates assembly point. Refer to factory codes in 1928 Chevrolet serial number data.

1930 Chevrolet, Universal, sport roadster, JAC

ENGINE: OHV. Inline. Six. Cast iron block. B & S: 3-5/16 x 3-3/4 in. Disp.: 194 cu. in. C.R.: 5.02:1. Brake H.P.: 50 @ 2600 R.P.M. NACC H.P.: 26.3. Main bearings: Three. Valve lifters: Solid. Carb.: Carter 1V.

CHASSIS: W.B.: 107 in. Tires: 19 x 4.75.

TECHNICAL: Manual transmission. Speeds: 3F/1R. Floor shift controls. Single plate clutch. Semi-floating rear axle. Overall ratio: 4.1:1. Four wheel internal (mechanical) brakes. Disc wheels.

OPTIONS: Front bumper. Rear bumper. Single sidemount. Dual sidemount. Sidemount cover(s). Trunk rack. Steamer trunk. Wood spoke wheels. Heater. Wire spoke wheels (std. on Sports models). Cigar lighter. Rear spare cover. Outside rear view mirror.

HISTORICAL: Introduced: Jan. 1930. New type manifold. Three-spoke steering wheel. Hydraulic shock absorbers added. Total production: 864,243 Chevrolets, including 39,773 cars made in Canada. The 7-millionth Chevrolet since 1912 was built on May 28, 1930 at Flint, Mich. General Manager: W.S. Knudsen.

1931 CHEVROLET

1931 Chevrolet, Independence, roadster, OCW

CHEVROLET — INDEPENDENCE — SERIES AE — SIX: The 1931 Chevrolet had a higher, larger radiator. The headlights were mounted on a bowed tie-bar. The hood sides featured multiple vertical louvers within a raised panel. There were new type panel and body moldings. 19" wire spoke wheels became standard equipment.

I.D. DATA: Serial numbers in same location as 1930. Starting: AE 1000 and up. Numerical prefixes used for each factory; same as 1929. Each factory built one body style. Engine numbers same location. Starting: 2100285. Ending: 2951552.

1931 Chevrolet, Independence, coupe, JAC

Model No.	Body Type & Seating	Price	Weight	Prod. Total
1AE	2-dr. Rds.-2P	475	2295	2,939
2AE	2-dr. Spt. Rds.-2/4P	495	2340	24,050
3AE	4-dr. Phae.-5P	510	2370	852
5AE	2-dr. Cpe.-2P	535	2490	57,741
6AE	2-dr. Spt. Cpe.-2/4P	575	2565	66,029
8AE	2-dr. 5-W Cpe.-2P	545	2490	28,379
21AE	2-dr. Cpe.-5P	595	2610	20,297
21AE	2-dr. Conv. Cabr.-2/4P	615	2520	23,077
9AE	2-dr. Coach-5P	545	2610	228,316
12AE	4-dr. Sed.-5P	635	2685	52,465
21AE	4-dr. Spec. Sed.-5P	650	2725	109,775
21AE	2-dr. Lan. Phae.-5P	650	2610	5,634

Note 1: Model number prefixes shown above indicate assembly point. Refer to factory codes in 1928 Chevrolet serial number data.

ENGINE: OHV. Inline. Six. Cast iron block. B & S: 3-5/16 x 3-3/4 in. Disp.: 194 cu. in. C.R.: 5.02:1. Brake H.P.: 50 @ 2600 R.P.M. NACC H.P.: 26.3. Main bearings: Three. Valve lifters: Solid. Carb.: Carter 1V.

1931 Chevrolet, Independence, sedan, JAC

CHASSIS: W.B.: 109 in. Tires: 19 x 4.75.

TECHNICAL: Manual transmission. Speeds: 3F/1R. Floor shift controls. Disc clutch. Semi-floating rear axle. Overall ratio: 4.1:1. Internal mechanical brakes on four wheels. Wire wheels standard.

OPTIONS: Front bumper. Rear bumper. Single sidemount. Dual sidemount. Sidemount cover(s). Rear spare cover. Pedestal mirrors. Dual taillamps. Heater. Dual chrome sidemount trim rings. Cigar lighter. Luggage rack. Touring trunk. Spotlight. Wind wings. Viking and Eagle radiator mascots. Guide lamps.

HISTORICAL: Introduced: Nov. 1930. Lovejoy shock absorbers. Semi-elliptic springs. Engine vibration dampener added. Heavier frame. More rigid crankshaft. Improved flywheel. New ribbed block and crankcase castings. Calendar year registrations: 583,429. Calendar year production: 627,104. Model year production: 623,901. General Managers: W.S. Knudsen and M.E. Coyle. Chevrolet produced its 8-millionth car on Aug. 25, 1931.

1932 CHEVROLET

1932 Chevrolet, Confederate, landau phaeton, OCW

CHEVROLET - CONFEDERATE — SERIES BA — SIX: Styling changes for 1932 Chevrolets included a longer hood and new deep crown front fenders. Door type louvers were used in the hood. They were chrome plated on Deluxe models. A built in radiator grille was part of the new design. New 18-inch wire wheels were adopted. Standard equipment included a built in sun visor, tilting windshield and adjustable seat. New technical features included a downdraft carburetor, counter-balanced crank shaft and added frame cross member.

I.D. DATA: Serial numbers on closed cars were on the right body sill under floor mat. Serial numbers on open cars were on the right side of the seat frame. Starting: BA 1000 and up. Numerical prefixes used for each factory; same as 1931. Each factory built one body style. Engine numbers in same location; codes not available.

Model No.	Body Type & Seating	Price	Weight	Prod. Total
1BA	4-dr. Phae.-5P	495	2495	419
1BA	2-dr. Rds.-2P	445	2410	1,118
2BA	2-dr. Spt. Rds.-2/4P	485	2480	8,552
5BA	2-dr. Cpe.-2P	490	2580	8,874
6BA	2-dr. Spt. Cpe.-2/4P	535	2645	2,226
8BA	2-dr. 5W Cpe.-2P	490	2580	34,796
21BA	2-dr. Cpe.-5P	575	2700	7,566
21BA	2-dr. Del. 5W Cpe.-2P	510	2580	26,623
21BA	2-dr. Conv.-2/4P	595	2590	7,066
9BA	2-dr. Coach-5P	495	2665	132,109
12BA	2-dr. Del. Coach-5P	515	2665	8,346
12BA	4-dr. Sed.-5P	590	2750	27,718
21BA	4-dr. Spec. Sed.-5P	615	2800	52,446
21BA	2-dr. Lan. Phae.-5P	625	2700	1,602

NOTE 1: Model number prefix shown above indicated assembly point. Refer to factory codes in 1928 Chevrolet serial number data.
NOTE 2: No production total available.

1932 Chevrolet, Confederate, coupe, JAC

ENGINE: OHV. Inline. Six. Cast iron block. B & S: 3-5/16 x 3-3/4 in. Disp.: 194 cu. in. C.R.: 5.2:1. Brake H.P.: 60 @ 3000 R.P.M. N.A.C.C. H.P.: 26.3. Main bearings: Three. Valve lifters: Solid. Carb.: Carter 1V Model 150S.

CHASSIS: W.B.: 109 in. Tires: 18 x 5.24.

TECHNICAL: Manual Synchromesh transmission. Speeds: 3F/1R. Floor shift controls. Single plate clutch. Semi-floating rear axle. Overall Ratio: 4.1:1. Four wheel internal (mechanical) brakes. Wire wheels standard. Drivetrain Options: Free-Wheeling was standard equipment.

1932 Chevrolet, Confederate, special sedan, JAC

OPTIONS: Front bumper. Rear bumper. Single sidemount. Dual sidemount. Trunk rack. Standard tire cover ($1). Deluxe tire cover ($2.50). Heater. Outside mirror. Pedastal mirrors. Dual wipers. Cowl lights. Dual horns. Metal tire covers ($6). Fender well tire lock ($5). Rear tire lock ($2.50). DeLuxe equipment included chrome hood louvers; two ash trays; assist cords; arm rests; curtains for rear and rear quarter windows and vanity case; clock; Eagle cap, chrome spoke covers; sport light; cigar lighter.

HISTORICAL: Introduced: Dec. 5, 1931. Innovations: Synchromesh transmission. Selective free wheeling. Counter-balanced crank shaft. Added frame member. Calendar registrations: 332,860. Calendar year production: 306,716. Model year production: 323,100. General Manager: M.E. Coyle.

The 1932 Chevrolet Sports Roadster could go from 0-35 mph in 6.7 seconds. Some station wagon bodies were constructed on Chevrolet chassis by Mifflinburg Body Co. of Mifflinburg, PA.

1933 CHEVROLET

1933 Chevrolet, Master Eagle, coach, OCW

CHEVROLET - MASTER EAGLE — SERIES CA — SIX: A slightly larger, more streamlined car was Chevrolet's Master Eagle series for 1933. New styling features included a V-shaped radiator, rear slanting hood door louvers, skirted fenders and a beaver tail back panel. This was called "Airstream" design. It also brought in a fixed position windshield and Fisher Body No-Draft ventilation system. Door lock buttons were on the window sills. Chrome headlight buckets were used. An eagle radiator mascot was available to identify cars in this series.

CHEVROLET — STANDARD MERCURY — SERIES-CC — SIX: Chevrolet introduced an all-new series in the middle of the year. These cars had slanting V-type radiators and skirted fenders. The headlight buckets were painted black and had chrome plated rims. Conventional hood louvers were featured. Overall dimensions were scaled down from those of the Master Eagle Series. Otherwise the two lines looked similar.

I.D. DATA: [Series CA] Serial numbers locations were as on 1932 models. Starting: CA 1000 & up. Engine numbers in same location; codes not available. [Series CC] Serial number locations were the same as on Master Eagle models. Starting: CC 1000 & up. Engine numbers in same location as on Master Eagle Motors; codes not available.

1933 Chevrolet, Master Eagle, phaeton, JAC

Model No.	Body Type & Seating	Price	Weight	Prod. Total
CA	2-dr. Spt. Rds.-2/4P	485	2555	2,876
CA	4-dr. Phae.-5P	515	2600	543
CA	2-dr. Cpe.-2P	495	2665	60,402
CA	2-dr. Spt. Cpe.-2/4P	535	2730	26,691
CA	2-dr. Conv.-2/4P	565	2820	4276
CA	2-dr. Coach-5P	515	2770	162,629
CA	4-dr. Sed.-5P	565	2830	162,361
CA	2-dr. Twn. Sed.-5P	545	2795	30,657
CC	2-dr. Cpe.-2P	445	2425	8909
CC	2-dr. Spt. Cpe.-2/4P	475	2485	1903
CC	2-dr. Sed.-5P	455	2515	25,033

ENGINE: [Series CA] OHV. Inline. Six. Cast iron block. B & S: 3-5/16 x 4 in. 194 cu. in. C.R.: 5.2:1. Brake H.P.: 65 @ 2800 R.P.M. N.A.C.C. H.P.: 26.3 Three main bearings. Valve lifters: solid. Carb.: Carter 1V Model W1. [Series CC] OHV. Inline. Six. Cast iron block. B & S: 3-5/16 x 3-1/2 in. Disp.:) 181 cu. in. C.R.: 5.2:1. Brake H.P.: 60 @ 3000 R.P.M. N.A.C.C. H.P.: 26.3. Main bearings: Three. Valve lifters: Solid. Carb.: Carter 1V Model W1.

CHASSIS: [Master Eagle Series] W.B.: 110 in. Tires: 18 x 5.25. [Mercury Series] W.B.: 107 in. Tires: 17 x 5.25.

TECHNICAL: Manual transmission (Synchromesh on Master Eagle). Speeds: 3F/1R. Floor shift controls. Single plate clutch. Semi-floating rear axle. Overall Ratio: (Master Eagle) 4.11:1; (Standard) 4.4:1. Four wheel internal mechanical brakes. Wire wheels standard. Selective standard on Master Eagle; not available on Standard Mercury. Note: Synchromesh transmission with Master Eagles. Selective constant mesh transmission on Mercury standard models.

1933 Chevrolet, Master Eagle, 2 dr. town sedan, JAC

OPTIONS: Oval wipers. Fog lights. Trunk rack. Twin horns. Outside mirrors. Sidemount pedestal mirrors; radio.
Note: Deluxe equipment for Chevrolets included dual horns, dual taillights, vanity set and other special interior furnishings.

HISTORICAL: (Master Eagle) Dec. 1932; (Mercury) Mar. 1933. Innovations: An airplane type dashboard was employed on Master Eagle models. Both Chevrolet engines featured an octane selector. Safety plate glass used in Mercury series windshield. Model year production: (Eagle Series) 450,530; (Mercury Series) 35,848; (Total) 486,378. General Manager: M.E. Coyle.
Chevrolet dealers sponsored the first Soap Box Derby in Dayton, Ohio this year. It was created by M.E. Scott, who later joined the company's public relations dept.

1934 CHEVROLET

1934 Chevrolet, roadster, OCW

CHEVROLET — MASTER — SERIES DA — SIX: Cars in Chevrolet's top priced series grew slightly larger in 1934, but the basic features of "Airstream" styling were unchanged. A new V-type radiator and grille appeared. The hood was even longer and wider, too. Deeper crown fenders were seen. There were three horizontal hood louvers which decreased in length from top to bottom. A new, winged hood ornament graced the radiator shell. Prices increased significantly this year.

CHEVROLET — STANDARD — SERIES DC — SIX: The Standard models for 1934 were much the same as last year. A new longer hood with horizontal streamlined louvers was used. The No-Draft ventilation system was also improved. A fancier, winged hood ornament made the cheaper Chevrolets look more like the expensive ones. The standard models had painted headlight buckets and less bright metal trim. The vertical grille bars were spaced wider apart than on the Master Series models.

I.D. DATA: [Series DA] Serial number locations were the same as on 1933 models. Starting: DA-1001 & up. Engine numbers were in the same location. Master series engine numbers were M-3964078 to M-4708994. [Series DC] Serial number locations were the same as on Master Series models. Starting: DC-1001 & up. Engine numbers were in same location as on Master Series motors. Starting: M-40549. Ending: M-166168.

1934 Chevrolet, coach, JAC

Model No.	Body Type & Seating	Price	Weight	Prod. Total
DA	2-dr. Rds.-2/4P	540	2830	1,974
DA	2-dr. Bus. Cpe.-2P	560	2895	53,018
DA	2-dr. Spt. Cpe.-2/4P	600	2995	18,365
DA	2-dr. Cabr.-2/4P	695	2990	3,276
DA	2-dr. Coach-5P	580	2995	163,948
DA	4-dr. Sed.-5P	640	3080	124,754
DA	2-dr. Twn. Sed.-5P	615	3020	49,431
DA	4-dr. Spt. Sed.-5P	675	3155	37,646
Note 1: The Sport Sedan was a touring sedan style with integral rear trunk.				
DC	2-dr. Spt. Rds.-2/4P	465	2380	1,038
DC	4-dr. Phae.-5P	520	2400	234
DC	2-dr. Cpe.-2P	485	2470	16,765
DC	2-dr. Coach-5P	495	2565	69,082
DC	4-dr. Sed.-5P	540	2655	11,840

Note 2: The 4-dr Sedan was added to the Standard Series as a mid-year model in Oct. 1934.

ENGINE: [Series DA] OHV. Inline. Six. Cast iron block. B & S: 3-5/16 x 4 in. Disp.: 206.8 cu. in. C.R.: 5.45:1. Brake H.P.: 80 @ 3300 R.P.M. N.A.C.C. H.P.: 26.3. Main bearings: Three. Valve lifters: Solid. Carb.: Carter 1V Model W1. [Series DC] OHV. Inline. Six. Cast iron block. B & S: 3-5/16 x 3-1/2 in. Disp.: 181 cu. in. C.R.: 5.2:1. Brake H.P.: 60 @ 3000 R.P.M. N.A.C.C. H.P.: 26.3. Main bearings: Three. Valve lifters: Solid. Carb.: Carter 1V Model W1.

CHASSIS: [Master Series] W.B.: 112 in. Tires: 5.50 x 17. Note: The Master Chevrolet featured "Knee Action" front suspension with coil springs. [Standard Series] W.B.: 107 in. Tires: 5.25 x 17.

1934 Chevrolet, 4-dr. sedan, JAC

TECHNICAL: Manual transmission. Speeds: 3F/1R. Floor shift controls. Single-plate clutch. Semi-floating rear axle. Overall ratio: 4.11:1. Four wheel mechanical brakes. Wire wheels. Selective free-wheeling optional on Master.

OPTIONS: Front bumper. Rear bumper. Dual taillights. Dual sidemount ($30). Sidemount cover(s). Fender skirts ($8). Bumper Guards. Radio. Heater. Clock. Cigar lighter. Radio antenna. Seat covers. Rear view mirror. Sportlight.

HISTORICAL: Introduced: (Master) Jan. 1934; (Standard) Jan. 1934. Innovations: Knee Action coil spring front suspension on Master Chevrolet. External horns not available. New X-Y frame on Master. New type valve and rocker arm arrangement for Master "Blue Flame" six. Calendar year registrations: 534,906. Calendar year production: 620,726. Model year production: (Master) 457,167; (Standard) 99,499; (Total) 556,666. General Manager: M.E. Coyle.

The phaeton, offered only in the Standard Series, is very rare today. Fender skirts were a new Chevrolet accessory in 1934. In an unusual promotion to prove the power of the improved Chevrolet engine, a 1934 Chevy six was used to tow a train called the Burlington Zephyr into a Chicago railroad station.

1935 CHEVROLET

1935 Chevrolet, Standard, coupe, OCW

CHEVROLET — STANDARD — SERIES EC — SIX: Standard series 1935 Chevrolets had styling that was very similar to 1934 models. Two changes were painted headlight shells and the repositioning of gauges in the center of the dashboard. Semi-elliptic front springs were carried over on these models. An 11-gallon fuel tank was used on standard Chevrolets.

CHEVROLET — MASTER DELUXE — SERIES ED/EA — SIX: The Master DeLuxe series 1935 Chevrolets had completely new styling. They featured Fisher Body Division's latest innovation — all-steel "Turret Top" body construction. It allowed smoother, rounder, more streamlined designs. Cars in the EA series featured "Knee-Action" front suspension with coil springs. (Dubonnet suspension). An option was semi-elliptic front springs and a straight front axle. Cars so equipped were designated ED series models and cost $20 less. A split type front windshield was part of the all-new body styling. The doors opened from the front in "suicide door" style. There were no open cars in the Master DeLuxe series. A 14-gallon fuel tank was used on Master DeLuxe models.

I.D. DATA: [Series EC] Serial numbers were on the body sill under the floor mat at right front door, near front seat; also on seat frame on right side. Starting: EC-1001. Ending: EC-39050. Engine numbers were on right side of block near fuel pump. Starting: M4709885. Ending: M5500178. [Series ED/EA] Serial numbers were in the same location as on Standard models. Starting: ED-1001/EA-1001. Ending: ED-3043/EA-54937. Engine numbers were in the same location as on Standard models. Starting: 4708995. Ending: 5500178.

1935 Chevrolet, Master DeLuxe, coupe, OCW

Model No.	Body Type & Seating	Price	Weight	Prod. Total
EC	2-dr. Spt. Rds.-2/4P	465	2410	1,176
EC	4-dr. Phae.-5P	485	2465	217
EC	2-dr. Cpe.-2P	475	2520	32,193
EC	2-dr. Coach-5P	485	2625	126,138
EC	4-dr. Sed.-5P	550	2675	42,049
Series ED (Without Knee-Action)				
ED	2-dr. Cpe.-2P	560	2910	40,201
ED	2-dr.Spt. Cpe.-2/4P	600	2940	11,901
ED	2-dr. Coach-5P	580	3010	102,996
ED	4-dr. Sed.-5P	640	3055	57,771
ED	2-dr. Twn. Sed.-5P	615	3050	66,231
ED	4-dr. Spt. Sed.-5P	675	3120	67,339

Note 1: Cars with "Knee Action" were designated EA models. They cost $20 more and weighed 30 pounds more. Production of ED and EA models was lumped together as a single total.

ENGINE: [Series EC] OHV. Inline. Cast iron block. B & S: 3-5/16 x 4 in. Disp.: 206.8 cu. in. C.R.: 5.45:1. Brake H.P.: 74 @ 3200 R.P.M. N.A.C.C. H.P.: 26.3. Main bearings: Three. Valve lifters: Solid. Carb.: Carter 1V Model 284S. [Series ED/EA] OHV. Inline. Six. Cast iron block. B & S: 3-5/16 x 4 in. Disp.: 206.8 cu. in. C.R.: 5.45:1. Brake H.P.: 80 @ 3300 R.P.M. N.A.C.C. H.P.: 26.3. Main bearings: Three. Valve lifters: Solid. Carb.: Carter 1V Model 284S.

CHASSIS: [Standard Series] W.B.: 107 in. Tires: 17 x 5.25. [Master DeLuxe ED Series] W.B.: 113 in. Tires: 17 x 5.50 without knee-action. Master DeLuxe EA Series W.B.: 113 in. Tires: 17 x 5.50 with knee-action.

TECHNICAL: Manual transmission. Speeds: 3F/1R. Floor shift controls. Single plate clutch. Semi-floating rear axle. Overall ratio: 4.11:1. Four wheel mechanical brakes. Wire wheels. Selective free-wheeling (optional on Master DeLuxe).

OPTIONS: Bumper guards. Radio. Heater. Clock. Cigar lighter. Radio antenna. Seat covers. Spotlight. Cowl lamps. Fender skirts. License plate frame. Wire wheels. Rear-view mirror. Dual sidemounts (rare).

HISTORICAL: Introduced: Dec. 15, 1934. Introduced Fisher Body with "Turret Top." The 1935 "Blue Flame" 6-cylinder engine had an improved head design, better lubrication and redesigned combustion chambers. Calendar year registrations: 656,698. Calendar year production: 793,437. Model year production: (standard) 207,976; (Master DeLuxe) 346,481; (Total) 554,457. General Manager: M.E. Coyle.

The 10 millionth Chevrolet ever produced was built on Nov. 13, 1934. The car — a 1935 model — was donated to the City of Flint (Mich.) for police safety patrol duties. The Standard Sports Roadster and Phaeton were discontinued in the early part of the 1935 production run. A new assembly plant (Code 14) opened in Baltimore. New manufacturing plants were added in Saginaw, Mich. and Muncie, Ind.

1936 CHEVROLET

1936 Chevrolet, convertible coupe, OCW

CHEVROLET — STANDARD — SERIES FC — SIX: The Standard series Chevrolets adopted the all-steel Fisher Body with "Turret Top" styling. They had more rounded front fenders and radiator grilles and shells. A split front windshield (as used on 1935 Master DeLuxes) was new. The number of horizontal hood louvers was reduced to two, with the top ones being longer. Rear fenders were skirted and more streamlined. Steel disc wheels were used this year. A 14-gallon fuel tank was now used on all Chevrolets.

MASTER DELUXE — SERIES FD/FA — SIX: A thicker, rounder radiator shell characterized cars in the Master DeLuxe lines. The grille was also larger and more rounded at the top; more pointed at the bottom. A lower hood ornament had its wings pointing back horizontally. The doors were now hinged toward the rear; no more "suicide" style front doors. The FD designation was for cars without coil spring front suspension; the FA designation was for cars with this feature. There were still no open cars in the Master DeLuxe series. In mid-year, steel spoke wheels were adopted for all models.

Model No.	Body Type & Seating	Price	Weight	Prod. Total
FC	2-dr. Cpe.-2P	495	2645	59,356
FC	2-dr. Cabr.-2/4P	595	2745	3629
FC	2-dr. Coach-5P	510	2750	76,646
FC	4-dr. Sed.-5P	575	2775	1,142
FC	2-dr. Twn. Sed.-5P	535	2775	220,884
FC	4-dr. Spt. Sed.-5P	600	2805	46,760
SERIES FD (WITHOUT KNEE-ACTION)				
FD	2-dr. Cpe.-2P	560	2895	49,319
FD	2-dr. Spt. Cpe.-2/4P	590	2940	10,985
FD	2-dr. Coach-5P	580	2985	40,814
FD	4-dr. Sed.-5P	640	3060	14,536
FD	2-dr. Twn. Sed.-5P	605	3030	244,134
FD	4-dr. Spt. Sed.-5P	665	3080	140,073

Note 1: Cars with "Knee Action" were designated FA models. They cost $20 more and weighed 30 pounds more. Production of FD and FA models was lumped together as a single total.

1936 Chevrolet, Master DeLuxe, sedan, HAC

ENGINE: OHV. Inline. Six. Cast iron block. B & S: 3-5/16 x 4 in. Disp.: 206.8 cu. in. C.R.: 6.0:1. Brake H.P.: 79 @ 3200 R.P.M. N.A.C.C. H.P.: 26.3. Main bearings: Three. Valve lifters: Solid. Carb.: Carter 1V Model 319S.
Note 2: The same engine was used in both series in 1936.

CHASSIS: [Standard Series] W.B.: 109 in. Tires: 17 x 5.25. [Master DeLuxe FD Series] W.B.: 113 in. Tires: 17 x 5.50 without knee-action. [Master DeLuxe FA Series] W.B.: 113 in. Tires: 17 x 5.50 with knee-action.

TECHNICAL: Manual transmission. Speeds: 3F/1R. Floor shift controls. Single-plate clutch. Semi-floating rear axle. Overall ratio: 4.11:1. Four-wheel hydraulic brakes. Steel spoke wheels (slotted).

OPTIONS: Fender skirts. Bumper guards. Radio. Heater. Clock. Cigar lighter. Radio antenna. Seat covers. External sun shade. Spotlight. Cowl lamps. Fog lamps. License plate frame. Wire wheels. Rear view mirror. Dual sidemounts. (Rare).

HISTORICAL: Introduced: Nov. 2, 1935. Innovations: Hydraulic brakes introduced for Chevrolets. Cabriolet reintroduced in Standard series. Boxgirder frame on standard models. Early Standards had composite wood/steel doors. Later cars were all-steel. Calendar year registrations: 930,250. Calendar year production: 975,238. Model year production: (Standard) 431,016; (Deluxe) 499,996; (Total) 975,238. General Manager: M.E. Coyle.
Chevrolet reclaimed the Number 1 position in U.S. automobile sales this season. A new transcontinental speed record was set by Bob McKenzie driving a 1936 Standard Chevrolet.

1937 CHEVROLET

CHEVROLET — MASTER — SERIES GB — SIX: Chevrolets had completely new "Diamond Crown" styling with safety glass in all windows and straight side fenders. A streamline groove ran from the fenders onto the doors, where it blended into the sheet metal. The grille was swept in on each side. Headlamp buckets on all models were painted body color. Master models had less trim, single taillamps, single wipers. Front fender parking lamps an option on all models. Inside there was no front seat armrest or dashboard heat indicator gauge. The sides of the hood were decorated with a tapering, spear-shaped panel incorporating cooling louvers. Semi-elliptic springs and a straight axle suspension were at the front of these cars. The standard Cabriolet featured Master DeLuxe style bumper guards. Safety-Plate glass was used in all Chevrolets. Trunks, on most models, were now larger, with enclosed spare tires.

MASTER DELUXE — SERIES GA — SIX: The Master DeLuxe models had the same size and styling features as Masters. Knee-Action front suspension was standard. Other standard equipment included dashboard heat indicator; front passenger armrest; dual taillamps; double wipers; twin sunvisors, fancy bumpers with guards.

I.D. DATA: Starting: GB-1001. Ending: GB-60674. Engine numbers were on the right side of block near fuel pump. Starting: 1. Ending: 1187821. Series GA Serial numbers were in the same location as on Master Models. Starting: GA-1001. Ending: GA-82134. Engine numbers were the same as on Master models.

1937 Chevrolet, 2-dr. sedan, AA

Model No.	Body Type & Seating	Price	Weight	Prod. Total
GB	2-dr. Cpe.-2P	619	2770	54,683
GB	2-dr. Cabr.-2/4P	725	2790	1724
GB	2-dr. Coach-5P	637	2800	15,349
GB	2-dr. Twn. Sed.-5P	655	2830	178,645
GB	4-dr. Sed.-5P	698	2845	2755
GB	4-dr. Spt. Tr. Sed.-5P	716	2885	43,240
GA	2-dr. Cpe.-2P	685	2840	56,166
GA	2-dr. Spt. Cpe.-2/4P	724	2870	8935
GA	2-dr. Coach-5P	703	2910	7260
GA	2-dr. Twn. Sed.-5P	721	2935	300,332
GA	4-dr. Sed.-5P	770	2935	2221
GA	4-dr. Spt. Sed.-5P	788	2960	144,110

ENGINE: [Series GA] OHV. Inline. Six. Cast iron block. B & S: 3-1/2 x 3-3/4 in. Disp.: 216.5 cu. in. C.R.: 6.25:1. Brake H.P.: 85 @ 3200 R.P.M. N.A.C.C. H.P.: 29.4 Main bearings: Four. Valve lifters: Solid. Carb.: Carter 1V Model W1.

CHASSIS: [Master Series] W.B.: 112-1/4 in. Tires: 16 x 6.00. [Master DeLuxe Series] W.B.: 112-1/4 in. Tires: 16 x 6.00.

1937 Chevrolet, Master, sport sedan, HAC

TECHNICAL: Manual transmission. Speeds: 3F/1R. Floor shift controls. Single-plate clutch. Semi-floating rear axle. Overall Ratio: (Master) 3.73:1; (Master DeLuxe) 4.22:1. Four wheel hydraulic brakes. Steel spoke wheels.

OPTIONS: Fender skirts. Bumper guards. Radio. Heater. Clock. Cigar lighter. Radio antenna. Seat covers. External sun shade. Spotlight. Fog lamps. License frames. Whitewall tires. Front fender marker lamps were mounted on top of fenders. Rear tire cover. Slide in express box. Wheel trim rings.
Note 1: Sidemounts were no longer a standard accessory.

HISTORICAL: Introduced: Nov. 1936. Innovations: Completely new all-steel Unisteel Body by Fisher with updated styling. Completely re-engineered 6-cylinder engine with larger bore; shorter stroke. Four main bearings. Boxgirder type frame now used on all models. Calendar year registrations: 768,040. Calendar year production: 868,250. Model year production: (Master) 306,024; (Master DeLuxe) 519,196; (Total) 825,220. General Manager: M.E. Coyle.
Chevrolet was again America's best selling automotibile.

1938 CHEVROLET

CHEVROLET — MASTER — SERIES HB — SIX: Chevrolet advertised that its 1938 models had new modern body styling. In reality, the body shell, fenders and running boards were the same as in 1937. A new grille was composed of horizontally arranged chromium bars, alternating one wide and four narrow. It was in two pieces, right and left. A center molding divided them. New bumper had a full width indentation, about one half inch wide, that was painted black. Headlights and taillamps were of a carryover design. The hood had ventilators highlighted by three chrome horizontal moldings. The bullet shaped headlights were mounted closely to the radiator grille. Inside the seats were two inches wider. Improved worm and roller sector steering was used. The front suspension was of semi-elliptic springs and a straight axle on all Master Series models, plus the Master DeLuxe cabriolet. Master Chevrolets had single taillamps as standard equipment.

1938 Chevrolet, Master DeLuxe, 4-dr. sedan, AA

CHEVROLET — MASTER DELUXE — SERIES HA — SIX: The Master DeLuxe featured styling changes identical to Master models. The main difference was that bumper guards were standard equipment on the Master DeLuxe. These guards were now braced to the frame. The Master DeLuxe designation appeared on the center chrome molding running across the oblong shaped hood ventilators. Dual taillamps were standard equipment.

I.D. DATA: [Series HB] Serial numbers were on a plate under hood on right side of cowl. Starting: HB-1001. Ending: HB-30097. Engine numbers were on the right side of block near fuel pump. National 1938 and later series on milled pad on crankcase to rear of distributor on right side of engine. Engines with a "B" prefix were built at Buffalo, N.Y. Starting: 1187822. Ending: 11915446; also B-1 to B-10502. [Series HA] Serial numbers were in the same location as on Master models. Starting: HA-1001. Ending: HA-46134. Engine numbers were the same as on Master models.

Model No.	Body Type & Seating	Price	Weight	Prod. Total
HB	2-dr. Cpe.-2P	648	2770	39,793
HB	2-dr. Cabr.-4P	755	2790	2,787
HB	2-dr. Coach-5P	668	2795	3,326
HB	2-dr. Twn. Sed.-5P	689	2825	95,050
HB	4-dr. Sed.-5P	730	2840	522
HB	4-dr. Spt. Sed.-5P	750	2845	20,952
HA	2-dr. Cpe.-2P	714	2840	36,106
HA	2-dr. Spt. Cpe.-4P	750	2855	2,790
HA	2-dr. Coach-5P	730	2900	1,038
HA	2-dr. Twn. Sed.-5P	750	2915	186,233
HA	4-dr. Sed.-5P	796	2915	236
HA	4-dr. Spt. Sed.-5P	817	2940	76,323

Note 1: The slant-back 2 and 4-door sedans were unusually rare Chevrolets. Other sedans were trunk-back models.

1938 Chevrolet, Master DeLuxe sport coupe, HAC

ENGINE: OHV. Inline. Six. Cast iron block. B & S: 3-1/2 x 3-3/4 in. Disp.: 216.5 cu. in. C.R.: 6.25:1. Brake H.P.: 85 @ 3200 R.P.M. N.A.C.C. H.P.: 29.4. Main bearings: Four. Valve lifters: Solid. Carb.: Carter 1V Model W1.

CHASSIS: [Master Series] W.B.: 112-1/4 in. Tires: 16 x 6.00. [Master DeLuxe Series] W.B.: 112-1/4 in. Tires: 16 x 6.00.

TECHNICAL: Manual transmission. Speeds: 3F/1R. Floor shift. Single-plate clutch. Semi-floating rear axle. Overall ratio: (Master) 3.73:1; (Master DeLuxe) 4.22:1. Four wheel hydraulic brakes. Steel spoke wheels.

OPTIONS: White sidewall tires. Fender marker lamps were mounted on top of fenders. Rear tire cover. Dual sidemount (rare). Sidemount cover (rare). Fender skirts ($8). Bumper Guards (std. on Master DeLuxe). Radio. Heater. Clock. Cigar lighter. Radio antenna. Seat covers. External sun shade. Spotlight. Fog lamps. wheel trim rings. License plate holder.
Note 2: At least one U.S. built 1938 Chevrolet had factory equipment dual sidemounts. This car is owned by a Dutch collector who lives in Holland.

HISTORICAL: Introduced: Oct. 23, 1937. Innovations: Heavier valve springs. Cutoff exhaust valve guides. Longer water pump shaft. New ball bearing water pump (mid-year). Improved generator and starter systems. New diaphragm spring type clutch. New Departure throw-out bearing. Lighter flywheel. Longer rear axle housing and shaft. Calendar year registrations: 464,337. Calendar year production: 490,447. Model year production: (Master) 167,926; (Master DeLuxe) 302,840; (Total) 470,766. General Manager: M.E. Coyle.

1939 CHEVROLET

CHEVROLET MASTER 85 — SERIES JB — SIX: The 1939 Chevrolets had longer hoods. Their redesigned hoods, fenders, wheels and runningboards made for a lower, longer appearance. The body shell was basically the same as 1938, but looked more modern. The grille extended back along the fender line at the top and narrowed to around four inches at the bottom. It had a well rounded look with horizontal grille mouldings and a horizontal bar effect on the splash aprons. The radiator was more upright. Headlights were mounted atop the front fenders. The door panel creases were eliminated and all four fenders were raised at the rear. Mounted at the center of the decklid, except on sedans and coaches, was the license plate lamp. Combination taillamps were of smaller size and incorporated stop lamps. The front bumpers had a more rounded face bar and were otherwise unchanged. Four spoke steel wheels replaced the old eight spoke type. Inside, the hand brake lever was moved to the cowl. A vacuum gearshift mounted on the steering column was a $10 option.

1939 Chevrolet, Master DeLuxe, 4-dr. sedan, AA

MASTER DELUXE — SERIES JA — SIX: The Master DeLuxe was a fancy version of the Master. It had bumper guards as standard equipment. Twin taillights were regular equipment. An all-new body style was the 4-passenger coupe with folding opera seats replacing the rumbleseat. The "Knee Action" coil spring front suspension was utilized.

I.D. DATA: [Series JB] Serial numbers were on a plate underhood on right side of cowl. Starting: JB-1001. Ending: JB-33221. Engine numbers were on the right side of engine on milled pad on crankcase near rear of distributor. Starting: 1915447. Ending: 2697267; also B-10503 to B-105461. [Series JA] Serial numbers were in the same location as on Master 85 models. Starting: JA-1001. Ending: JA-58510. Engine numbers were the same as on Master models.

Model No.	Body Type & Seating	Price	Weight	Prod. Total
JB	2-dr. Cpe.-2P	628	2780	41,770
JB	2-dr. Coach-5P	648	2795	1404
JB	2-dr. Twn. Sed.-5P	669	2820	124,059
JB	4-dr. Sed.-5P	689	2805	336
JB	4-dr. Spt. Sed.-5P	710	2845	22,623
JB	4-dr. Sta. Wag.-8P	848	3010	430

Note 1: The 4-door slant-back sedan continued to sell poorly. The new station wagon came in two variations. Production total given above includes 229 station wagons with folding end gates and 201 with rear door.

Model No.	Body Type & Seating	Price	Weight	Prod. Total
JA	2-dr. Bus. Cpe.-2P	684	2845	33,809
JA	2-dr. Spt. Cpe.-4P	715	2845	20,908
JA	2-dr. Coach-5P	699	2865	180
JA	2-dr. Twn. Sed.-5P	720	2875	220,181
JA	4-dr. Sed.-5P	745	2875	68
JA	4-dr. Spt. Sed.-5P	766	2910	110,521
JA	4-dr. Sta. Wag.-8P	883	3060	989

Note 2: Rare models included the Master DeLuxe coach and 4-dr slant-back sedan.

ENGINE: OHV. Inline. Six. Cast iron block. B & S: 3-1/2 x 3-3/4 in. Disp.: 216.5 cu. in. C.R.: 6.25:1. Brake H.P.: 85 @ 3200 R.P.M. N.A.C.C. H.P.: 29.4. Main bearings: Four. Valve lifters: Solid. Carb.: Carter IV Model W1-4205.

CHASSIS: [Master Series] W.B.: 112-1/4 in. Tires: 16 x 6.00. [Master DeLuxe Series] W.B.: 112-1/4 in. Tires: 16 x 6.00.

1939 Chevrolet, Master DeLuxe, coach, HAC

TECHNICAL: Manual transmission. Speeds: 3F/1R. Floor shift controls. Single-plate. Semi-floating rear axle. Overall Ratio: (Master) 3.23:1; (Master DeLuxe) 4.22:1. Four wheel hydralic brakes. Four spoke steel wheels. Vacuum clutch (10.00).
Note 3: Column gear shift used with vacuum clutch option.

OPTIONS: White sidewall tires. Rearview mirror. Single sidemount (standard on sta. wag.). License plate frame. Sidemount cover (on sta. wag.). Fender skirts (8.90). Bumper guards. Radio. Heater. Clock. Cigar lighter. Radio antenna. Seat covers. External sun shade. Spotlight. Fog lamps. Wheel trim rings. Slip-in coupe pickup box. Fender marker lamps were mounted on top of fenders.

HISTORICAL: Introduced: Oct. 1938. Innovations: Double-acting (airplane type) shock absorbers on Master 85. Rubber bushed front suspension on Master. Diaphragm clutch spring riveted to clutch cover. New open spring front suspension on Master DeLuxe. Double-acting rear shock absorbers. New folding trunk guard braced to frame. Town and Country DeLuxe horn package. Calendar year registrations: 598,341. Calendar year production: 648,471. Model year production: (Master) 200,058; (Master DeLuxe) 387,119, (Total) 587,177. General Manager: M.E. Coyle.
The new station wagon bodies were built by Mid-States Body Corp. The Master DeLuxe was said to be the fastest accelerating American passenger car of 1939. It went from 10 to 60 m.p.h. in high gear. A new manufacturing plant in Tonawanda, N.Y. was opened this year. The 15 millionth Chevrolet was built in 1939. No convertible cabriolets were built this year.

1940 CHEVROLET

1940 Chevrolet, Special DeLuxe, convertible coupe, OCW

CHEVROLET — MASTER 85 — SERIES KB — SIX: A longer wheelbase and completely new body and sheet metal were changes for 1940. The New "Royal Clipper" styling started with an "alligator" type front opening hood. The side panels were removable to get at the engine. The grille had a narrow vertical center bar, topped in name by a horizontal bar. It was of one piece design. The headlights were on top of the fenders and featured sealed beam bulbs. Parking lights were mounted on top of the front fenders. The trunk had more flowing lines with flush taillamps. The license plate lamp was again in the center of the trunk lid. The bumpers featured two black-finished indentations running the length of the face bar. The Master 85 models did not have stainless steel belt hood or running board moldings. They had plainer upholstery and slightly less standard equipment. Front suspension was still of the leaf-spring, I-beam axle design.

CHEVROLET — MASTER DELUXE — SERIES KH — SIX: Master DeLuxe was now Chevrolet's mid-priced line. These cars had the same styling as Master 85s, with more trim. Master DeLuxe identification appeared at the rear of the hood side ventilators. Stainless steel body and hood moldings were omitted. Knee-Action front suspension was standard equipment.

CHEVROLET — SPECIAL DELUXE — SERIES KA — SIX: The Special DeLuxe, Chevrolet's new top-priced line, was a fancier edition of the Master DeLuxe. Stainless steel moldings trimmed the hood and body belt line. Standard equipment included a 30 hour clock, front door arm rests, righthand windshield wiper, twin air horns and a deluxe steering wheel with horn ring. A convertible with a full width rear seat and power-operated top was new. The opera seat coupe was replaced with a 5-passenger coupe having a full rear seat. A choice of different colors of upholstery and convertible tops was offered for the first time by Chevrolet.

1940 Chevrolet, Special DeLuxe, coupe, JAC

I.D. DATA: [Series KB] Serial numbers were on a plate on right side of Floor pan in front of front seat. Starting: KB-1001. Ending: KB-20946. Engine numbers were on the right side of engine on milled pad on crankcase near rear of distributor. Starting: 2697268. Ending: 3665902; also B-105462 to B-221935. "B" prefix on engine number indicates Buffalo N.Y. factory. [Series KH] Serial numbers were in the same location as on Master 85 models. Starting: KH-1001. Ending: KH-37644. Engine numbers were the same as on Master 85 models. [Series KA] Serial numbers were in the same location as on other models. Starting: KA-1001. Ending: KA-72089. Engine numbers were the same as on other models.

Model No.	Body Type & Seating	Price	Weight	Prod. Total
KB	2-dr. Bus. Cpe.-2P	659	2865	25,734
KB	2-dr. Twn. Sed.-5P	699	2915	66,431
KB	4-dr. Spt. Sed.-5P	740	2930	11,468
KB	4-dr. Sta. Wag.-8P	903	3106	411
Note 1: Station wagon was low production model.				
KH	2-dr. Bus. Cpe.-2P	684	2920	28,090
KH	2-dr. Spt. Cpe.-2/4P	715	2925	17,234
KH	2-dr. Twn. Sed.-5P	725	2965	143,125
KH	4-dr. Spt. Sed.-5P	766	2990	40,924
KA	2-dr. Bus. Cpe.-2P	720	2930	25,537
KA	2-dr. Spt. Cpe.-4P	750	2945	46,628
KA	2-dr. Conv.-4P	898	3160	11,820
KA	2-dr. Twn. Sed.-5P	761	2980	205,910
KA	4-dr. Spt. Sed.-5P	802	3010	138,811
KA	4-dr. Sta. Wag.-8P	934	3158	2,493

Note 2: A total of 367 station wagons had double rear doors.

1940 Chevrolet, Master DeLuxe, 4-dr. sedan, OCW

ENGINE: OHV. Inline. Six. Cast iron block. B & S: 3-1/2 x 3-3/4 in. Disp.: 216.5 cu. in. Compression Ratio: 6.25:1. Brake H.P.: 85 @ 3400 R.P.M. N.A.C.C. H.P.: 29.4. Main bearings: Four. Valve lifters: Solid. Carb.: Carter 1V Model W1-420S.

CHASSIS: [Master 85 Series] W.B.: 113 in. Tires: 16 x 6.00. [Master DeLuxe Series] W.B.: 113 in. Tires: 16 x 6.00. [Special DeLuxe Series] W.B.: 113 in. Tires: 16 x 6.00.

TECHNICAL: Manual Synchromesh transmission. Speeds: 3F/1R. Column gearshift (vacuum type) controls. Single-plate clutch. Semi-floating rear axle. Overall ratio: (Master) 3.73:1; (Others) 4.11:1. Four wheel hydraulic brakes. Steel spoke wheels.

OPTIONS: Whitewall tires. Wheel trim rings. Rearview mirror. Master grille guard. Full wheel discs. Fender skirts. Bumper guards. Radio. Heater. Clock. Cigar lighter. Radio antenna. Seat covers. External sun shade. Spotlight. Fog lamps. Accessory (plastic) hood ornament.

HISTORICAL: Introduced Sept. 1939. Innovations: First use of plastic parts. First stainless steel trim. New shape oil pan. Redesigned valve lifters. Higher charging rate. Helical gear transmission. Cross trunion type u-joint. Redesigned front cross member. Calendar year registrations: 853,529. Calendar year production: 895,734. Model year production: (Master) 116,618; (Master DeLuxe) 232,510; (Special DeLuxe) 430,945; (Total) 775,073. General Manager: M.E. Coyle.

A Model 85 business coupe driven by Juan Manuel Fangio won the 6,000 mile Gran Primo Internacional Del Norte race in Argentina. Fangio averaged 55 mph. He came in over an hour ahead of the second place car. Three Chevys were among the top ten finishers in this contest. Chevrolet also signed its first contract for U.S. Government weapons production in April, 1940.

1941 CHEVROLET

1941 Chevrolet, Special DeLuxe, convertible coupe, OCW

CHEVROLET — MASTER DELUXE — SERIES AG — SIX: Longer, lower, wider bodies were mounted on a Chevrolet chassis with a three inch longer wheelbase. The grille resembled last years, but was new. It had six chrome plated die cast moldings. The hood was a front opening type with side panels eliminated. The headlights were now blended into the fenders. Chrome moldings decorated the front fender tops. There were parking lamps below each headlight. The new body featured concealed safety steps instead of runningboards. The slope of the windshield, rear window and upper bodysides was increased. Concealed hinges were used on the doors and hood. The Master DeLuxe had body belt moldings and model identification plates at the rear of the hood sides. Standard upholstery and trimmings were plain. There were no arm rests on the front doors.

SPECIAL DELUXE — SERIES AH — SIX: The Special DeLuxe had the same new body and basic styling as the Master DeLuxe. The series name appeared in chrome block letters on the rear sides of the hood. Additional standard equipment included a deluxe steering wheel with horn ring, stainless steel hood moldings, stainless steel window reveal moldings, a chrome plated license plate lamp and arm rests on the front doors. Richer upholstery material was used. In the spring, the Fleetline sedan was introduced. It was a close-coupled 4-door model without ventipanes.

1941 Chevrolet, Special DeLuxe, station wagon, JAC

I.D. DATA: [Series AG] Serial numbers were on a plate on right side of floor pan in front of front seat. Starting: AG-1001. Ending: AG-62708. Engine numbers were on the right side of engine on milled pad on crankcase near rear of distributor. Starting: AA-1001. Ending: AA-1163729. Engines built in Tonawanda factory were numbered AC-1001 to AC-195459. [Series AH] Serial numbers were in the same location as on Master DeLuxe. Starting: AH-1001. Ending: AH-02375. Engine number were the same as Master DeLuxe.

Model No.	Body Type & Seating	Price	Weight	Prod. Total
AG	2-dr. Bus. Cpe.-2P	712	3020	48,763
AG	2-dr. Cpe.-5P	743	3025	79,124
AG	2-dr. Twn. Sed.-5P	754	3050	219,438
AG	4-dr. Spt. Sed.-5P	795	3090	59,538
AH	2-dr. Bus. Cpe.-2P	769	3040	17,602
AH	2-dr. Cpe.-5P	800	3050	155,889
AH	2-dr. Cabr.-5P	949	3285	15,296
AH	2-dr. Twn. Sed.-5P	810	3095	228,458
AH	4-dr. Spt. Sed.-5P	851	3125	148,661
AH	4-dr. Sta. Wag.-8P	995	3410	2045
FLEETLINE SERIES				
AH	4-dr. Sed.-5P	877	3130	34,162

ENGINE: OHV. Inline. Six. Cast iron block. B & S: 3-1/2 x 3-3/4 in. Disp.: 216.5 cu. in. C.R.: 6.5:1. 90 @ 3300 R.P.M. N.A.C.C. H.P.: 29.4. Main bearings: Four. Valve lifters: Solid. Carter 1V Model W1483S.

CHASSIS: [Master DeLuxe] W.B.: 116. in. Tires: 16 x 6.00. [Special DeLuxe Series] W.B.: 116 in. Tires: 16 x 6.00.

TECHNICAL: Manual Synchromesh transmission. Speeds: 3F/1R. Column gear shift controls. Single-plate clutch. Semi-floating rear axle. Overall Ratio: 4.11:1. Four wheel hydraulic brakes. Steel spoke wheels.

OPTIONS: Whitewall tires. Stainless steel fender trim. Short wave radio. Exhaust deflector. Fender skirts. Bumper guards. Radio. Heater. Clock. Cigar lighter. Radio antenna. Seat covers. External sun shade. Spotlight. Fog lamps. Wheel trim rings. Full wheel discs. License plate frame. Accessory hood ornament. Bumper wing guards. Rearview mirror.

HISTORICAL: Introduced Sept. 1940. Innovations: Increased compression ratio. Flat top pistons. Smaller combustion chamber. New 10 mm. spark plugs. New design rocker arms. Redesigned water pump. Improved ignition points. Knee-Action front coil spring suspension standard on all Chevrolets. Calendar year registrations: 880,346. Calendar year production: 930,293. Model year production: (Master DeLuxe) 419,044; (Special DeLuxe) 602,327; (total) 1,021,371. General Manager: M.E. Coyle.

Last full production year prior to WWII. Chevrolet conducted a promotional contest in which Spencer Tracy was picked as America's top movie star. He was given a new Chevrolet station wagon.

1942 CHEVROLET

1942 Chevrolet, Special DeLuxe Fleetline, aerosedan, AA

1942 Chevrolet, Special DeLuxe, Fleetmaster cabriolet, HAC

CHEVROLET — MASTER DELUXE — SERIES BG — SIX: A heavier "American Eagle" grille with lower and wider horizontal bars characterized the 1942 Chevrolet. A front bumper gravel shield was added. Parking lights were in the grille side moldings. A new hood extended back to the edge of the door. The cowl panel was eliminated. Headlights were flush-mounted in the front fenders. Bolt-on caps extended the fenders onto the doors. At the rear the fenders and taillights were unchanged, but the license lamp and gravel shields were of new designs. There was no nameplate on the sides of the Master DeLuxe hood. Seats, steering wheel and interior trim were plain. On Jan. 1, 1942 all bright metal trim — with the exception of bumpers and guards — was eliminated as part of the war effort. These "black out" models had trim parts painted in body color.

CHEVROLET — SPECIAL DELUXE — SERIES BH — SIX: Better upholstery, more trim and a longer list of standard equipment were seen on Special DeLuxe Chevrolets. Extras included a deluxe steering wheel with horn ring, chrome hood nameplates, and front door arm rests. The Cabriolet now had rear quarter windows. A new model was a fastback 2-door Fleetline Aero sedan. Like the Fleetline Sportmaster sedan it had three stainless steel trim strips on the sides of the fenders and fender caps. After Jan. 1, Special DeLuxes were also sold with painted, rather than plated, trim.

I.D. DATA: [Series BG] Serial numbers were on a plate on right side of floor pan in front of front seat. Starting: BG-1001. Ending: BG-13310. Engine numbers were on the right side of engine on milled pad on crankcase near rear of distributor. Starting: 2AA-1001 & up; BA-1001 & up; 2AC-1001 & up. [Series BH] Serial numbers were in the same locations as on Master DeLuxe. Starting: BH-1001. Ending: BH-27530. Engine numbers were the same as on Master DeLuxe.

Model No.	Body Type & Seating	Price	Weight	Prod. Total
BG	2-dr. Cpe.-2P	760	3055	8,089
BG	2-dr. Cpe.-5P	790	3060	17,442
BG	2-dr. Twn. Sed.-6P	800	3090	41,872
BG	4-dr. Spt. Sed.-6P	840	3110	14,093
Fleetmaster Series				
BH	2-dr. Cpe.-2P	815	3070	1,716
BH	2-dr. Cpe.-5P	845	3085	22,187
BH	2-dr. Cabr.-5P	1080	3385	1,182
BH	2-dr. Twn. Sed.-6P	855	3120	39,421
BH	4-dr. Spt. Sed.-6P	895	3145	31,441
BH	4-dr. Sta. Wag.-8P	1095	3425	1,057
Fleetline Series				
BH	2-dr. Aerosedan-6P	880	3105	61,855
BH	4-dr. Spt. Master-6P	920	3165	14,530

Note 1: The new Aerosedan was a fastback model.

ENGINE: OHV. Inline. Six. Cast iron block. B & S: 3-1/2 x 3-3/4 in. Disp.: 216.5 cu. in. C.R.: 6.5:1. Brake H.P.: 90 @ 3300 R.P.M. N.A.C.C. H.P.: 29.4. Main bearings: Four. Valve lifters: Solid. Carb.: Carter 1X Model 483S.

CHASSIS: [Master DeLuxe Series] W.B.: 116 in. Tires: 16 x 6.00. [Special DeLuxe Series] W.B.: 116 in. Tires: 16 x 6.00.

TECHNICAL: Manual Synchromesh transmission. Speeds: 3F/1R. Column gear shift controls. Single-plate clutch. Semi-floating rear axle. Overall ratio: 4.11:1. Four wheel hydraulic brakes. Steel spoke wheels.

OPTIONS: Whitewall tires. Short wave radio. Signal-seeking radio. Exhaust deflector. Fender skirts. Bumper Guards. Radio. Heater. clock. Cigar lighter. Radio antenna. Seat covers. External sun shade. Spotlight. Fog lamps. Wheel trim rings. License plate lamp. Bumper wing guards. OSRV mirror.

HISTORICAL: Introduced: Sept. 1941. Innovations: Signal-seeking radio with station tuner introduced as an option. Aerosedan introduced. Calendar year production: 45,472. Model year production: (Master DeLuxe) 84,806; (Special DeLuxe) 173,989; (Total) 258,795. General Manager: M.E. Coyle.

All automobile production halted Feb. 1, 1942. Last pre-war Chevrolet built Jan. 30. All factories except Saginaw Service Mfg. plant converted for war production.

1943 - 1945 "WAR YEARS"

Because of war production, all civilian auto and truck manufacturing in the U.S. was curtailed by government order. Still, vehicles by the thousands were being produced. Many of these were strictly military, while others were former civilian models in "battle dress" of olive drab or Navy gray.

Chevrolet had already been involved in war production long before the government's order ending auto production was passed. In 1940, the first Chevrolet military contract was signed — but oddly, this was not for vehicles but for 76-MM high explosive shells. However, throughout the late 1930s and early 1940s, the government was buying more and more "civilian" Chevrolets for garrison use.

By mid-1941, Chevrolet had signed many more government contracts for military supplies, including specialized trucks, shells, parts for anti-aircraft guns, and Pratt & Whitney aircraft engines. Finally, in January, 1942, all Chevrolet factories except the plant at Saginaw, Mich., were completely converted to war production of various sorts. The Saginaw plant continued to supply maintenance parts for existing civilian Chevrolet trucks and cars.

Although most of Chevrolet's vehicle production was in the area of light and medium duty trucks, a few unusual vehicles were turned out. these included several models in the T17 Series of "Staghound" armored cars, several experimental versions of these cars, and an unusual extra-light vehicle along Jeep lines that was considered for airborne and glider delivery to troops.

While this was going on, a few civilian models were trickled out to buyers with high priority ratings — those in drastic need of new vehicles. Some of these were leftover 1942 vehicles which had been frozen in storage by the government, but which were slowly released after June, 1943. Others were ½-ton pickup trucks which were similar to those being produced for the military. These began to reach the priority public in mid-1944. On July 1, 1945, reconversion of the auto plants back to civilian production was begun, and work was started on the new cars — all of which were virtually identical to those produced in 1942, though all were called 1946 models.

Because Ford was able to get into gear ahead of General Motors, and because GM was hit by strike in late 1945, Chevrolet production was far exceeded by Ford this year — Chevrolet got only 12,776 cars off its lines during calendar year 1945, while Ford produced 34,439.

Shown in fore and aft views is an interesting example of the "blackout" models that were released in limited quantities to high priority buyers by the Office of Price Administration. The cars were all 1942 vehicles which had been frozen in storage until the OPA allowed a trickle release beginning in June, 1943. These models had no chrome whatever except on the bumpers and guards. The grille, hubcaps and mouldings are baked enamel with special pin striping. Later day accessories on this car include the

rearview mirror, exhaust deflector, and back-up lights. This restored model, the only remaining blackout Chevrolet know to exist, was owned by Bob Wingate of Covina, Calif., a former national president of Vintage Chevrolet Club of America, and noted Chevrolet collector and dealer.

In mid-1941, the War Production Board authorized the building of limited quantities of light trucks for high priority civilians — those in drastic need of vehicles for ther business. Among this limited production were these ½-ton Chevrolet pickup trucks, identical to the 1942 Series BK except for painted trim and certain components. For example, this model was delivered with a 4-speed transmission, overload springs, 7:00 x 16 1-ton truck wheels, and a left over 1940 truck grille guard and spotlight. The fog lights were a later addition. This version, appearing exactly as it left the dealer's floor, is owned by Walter R. Blair of Seattle.

Courtesy of Crestline Publishing, Sarasota, Fla.

STANDARD CATALOG OF

CHEVROLET

1946-1975

Although Chevrolet entered the postwar era with a warmed-over version of its 1942 model, the marque quickly assumed its traditional role as America's best selling car. The 1946-1948 Chevys were conservative in styling and engineering, but earned a reputation as value leaders in the low-price field. The Stovebolt Six, dating back to 1937, was not a performance engine, but provided dependable service.

By Tony Hossain

Chevrolet's brand new 1949 models were, once again, conservatively styled and ruggedly built. Although arch-rival Ford also fielded a new 1949 model, with more modern slab-sided body lines, Chevrolet remained far ahead in the sales race.

The big news for 1950 was the addition of a sporty Bel Air two-door hardtop and a new option, the fully automatic Powerglide transmission. Sales went over the 1.5 million mark for the first time in history.

Chevrolet strengthened its hold on the low-price field in the early Fifties, but these were not exciting years for enthusiasts . . . with one notable exception. In 1953, Chevy introduced the fiberglass Corvette sports car. The first Corvette used a Chevy sedan chassis, engine and Powerglide transmission, but the car would soon become a creditable sports car.

Nineteen fifty-five was Chevrolet's renaissance. It was year one for the hot Chevy and marked the Division's first assault on the growing youth market. With a sharp new style and a hot new 265 cubic inch V-8 under the hood, as optional power, Chevrolet was no longer Grandma's car. Model year production soared to over 1.7 million, a record figure for any automaker.

Chevrolet built upon a good thing in 1956, with an extensive facelift and some potent new power options for the 265 cubic inch 'Turbo Fire' V-8. But if there ever was a 'Classic Chevy', it was the 1957 model. In the Fifties, people regarded it as a 'baby Cadillac' and the Bel Air Sport Coupe, convertible and two-door Nomad station wagon quickly developed a cult following, that still lasts to this day. In a 1974 advertisement, Chevy referred to the 17-year old car as "the most popular used car in history." It still is.

Performance enthusiasts will remember 1957 as the year Chevy bored-out the small-block V-8 to 283 cubic inches and made available, that most prestigious of options, Ramjet Fuel Injection. Chevy claimed one horsepower per cubic inch.

The 1958 Chevrolet was totally redesigned, inside and out. The new Impala Sport Coupe and convertible replaced the Bel Air Series as Chevy's top-of-the-line offering. The Impala was immediately popular and, in ensuing years, would become known as 'the pre-eminent American car.'

Chevrolet called its 1959 models "all new all over again." Although they shared the cruciform frame design, which debuted in 1958, the 1959s' body styling was all new and highly controversial. Especially disconcerting, to many longtime Chevrolet buyers, were the extreme horizontal tailfins and dramatically larger size. While young people scoured used car markets for sharp 1955-1957 models in power-packed form, Chevrolet, responding to criticism of past performance merchandising, toned down the styling of its 1960 models.

The big news for 1960 was the introduction of the compact Corvair. Initially available in four-door sedan form only, the Corvair was a revolution in American automotive design with its rear-mounted aluminum Six, fully independent suspension and clean styling. At first sales were disappointing, but the mid-1960 addition of two-door models, and the luxurious Monza Club Coupe, sent sales upward. The Corvair quickly developed a following among automotive enthusiasts.

The Chevrolet product line continued to proliferate in the early Sixties with the addition of the traditionally engineered, compact Chevy II, in model year 1962. The came the popular Chevelle, two years later. Chevrolets from the early Sixties, that collectors find particularly appealing today, include the 1962-1964 Impala SS (Super-Sport), the Corvair Monza Spyder and all Corvettes.

Nineteen sixty-five would be known as the year of records for the Chevrolet Motor Division. Large Chevrolets were restyled with pleasing, flowing, lines. Also new, from the ground-up, was the Corvair. With continental-like styling and an all-new suspension system, the new Corvair received rave reviews from the motoring press. The 1965 Corvette received a four-wheel disc brake system and a robust 396 cubic inch V-8 became Chevy's latest stormer. It replaced the big Chevy's top-option '409'; an engine which had become a legend in the early Sixties.

The late 1960s were years of declining market share for Chevrolet products. Ralph Nader's attack on the Corvair, in 1965, hurt auto sales in general, but had a particularly severe impact on Chevrolet. The Corvair was quietly withdrawn from the market in 1969.

The Camaro, Chevy's belated answer to the enormously successful Ford Mustang, was introduced in model year 1967. First generation Camaros (1967-1969) are very popular among collectors today. Particularly desirable are the Z28 or SS performance packages and all convertible models.

Chevrolet regained lost market share in the early Seventies, with new products and aggressive marketing. New for 1970 was the Monte Carlo and a redesigned Camaro, hailed as a contemporary classic. The smart new, sporty design lasted, with few changes, through the 1981 model year. Chevrolet's combined car and truck sales, in 1971, totalled over 3 million units.

Chevy had entered the Seventies as the world's largest producer of motor vehicles. Notable new entries in 1971 included a redone full-size Chevrolet and the subcompact Vega. Although it was a strong contender in its market segment, the Vega suffered numerous quality and engineering problems and was withdrawn at the end of the 1977 model year. Highly desirable today, however, are the limited edition, high-performance 1975-1976 Cosworth Vegas.

Chevrolets from the 1970s attracting collector interest today include the 1970-1972 Monte Carlos, Chevelle SSs, Camaros of all years and the 1975 Caprice convertible. That car was Chevrolet's last production rag-top for the seventies.

1946 CHEVROLET

1946 Chevrolet, Stylemaster 4-dr sedan, 6-cyl

STYLEMASTER — SIX — SERIES DJ — The 1946 Chevrolet Stylemaster models were updated 1942 Master DeLuxes. The grille was modified, the parking lamps were relocated and chrome plated trim features returned to replace plastic parts used in pre-war cars. Plain fenders, notch back styling and Stylemaster block lettering on hood side moldings were identifiers. On the interior, three-spoke steering wheels, painted window sills and a minimum of bright metal trim moldings were used. Pile fabric upholstery, standard rubber floormats and single lefthand sun visors were seen.

STYLEMASTER I.D. NUMBERS: Serial numbers were stamped on a plate on the right front door hinge pillar. Motor numbers were stamped on the right side of block near fuel pump. The numerical prefix in serial number indicated assembly plant as follows: (1) — Flint, Mich.; (2) Tarrytown, N.Y.; (3) St. Louis, Mo.; (5) Kansas City, Mo.; (6) Oakland, Calif.; (8) Atlanta, Ga.; (9) Norwood, Ohio; (14) Baltimore, Md.; (21) Janesville, Wis. The letters on the number plate indicated year and model, for example: DJ was for 1946 Stylemasters. A Fisher Body Style Number was located on the vehicle data plate, on engine side of firewall. It began with a two-digit prefix designating model year, followed by a dash and four numbers indicating body type and sometimes having a letter suffix designating trim level or equipment installations. Serial numbers for Michigan built 1946 Stylemasters were DJ-1001 to 56896; motor numbers were DAA-1001 to 546865. Body Style Numbers corresponded to second column in charts below beginning with 1949 models. Chevrolet model number appear in this column for 1946-1948 models.

STYLEMASTER SIX SERIES DJ

Model Number	Body/Style Number	Body Type & Seating	Factory Price	Shipping Weight	Production Total
46-DJ	1504	2-dr Bus Cpe-2P	1022	3080	14,267
46-DJ	1524	2-dr Spt Cpe-5P	1059	3105	19,243
46-DJ	1502	2-dr Twn Sed-6P	1072	3145	61,104
46-DJ	1503	4-dr Spt Sed-6P	1123	3150	75,349

STYLEMASTER ENGINE
Six-cylinder. Overhead valves. Cast iron block. Displacement: 216.5 cubic inches. Bore and stroke: 3-1/2 x 3-3/4 inches. Compression ratio: 6.5:1. Brake horsepower: 90 at 3300 R.P.M. Four main bearings. Solid valve lifters. Carburetors: Carter one-barrel as follows: (standard transmision with Climate Control) YF-765S or YF-765SA; (manual choke with standard transmission) YF-787S or YF-787SA or YF-787SB; (all standard transmission) W1-684S or YF-787S or YF-787SB or YF-789S or YF-789SB.
NOTE: Carburetor availability listed above applies to all 1946-1951 Chevrolets with standard shift and will not be repeated in this book.

FLEETMASTER — SIX-SERIES DK — The Fleetmaster series replaced the prewar Special DeLuxe group. The moldings on sides of the hood carried this name. Richer upholstery trims were available and included two sun visors; front seat arm rests and wood-grained window sills. No business coupe was offered, but a convertible and station wagon were. A DeLuxe, two-spoke steering wheel, with a stylized "bird" horn button insert, was seen.

FLEETMASTER I.D. NUMBERS: Serial, motor and body style coding was based on the Stylemaster system, but different series codes and additional body nomenclature were used. Fleetmasters built in Michigan were numbered DK-1001 to 58678. The first two symbols in the main Style Number were '21' for Fleetmaster DK Series. Engine numbering range same as Stylemaster.

1946 Chevrolet, Stylemaster 4-dr sedan, 6-cyl

FLEETMASTER SIX SERIES DK

Model Number	Body/Style Number	Body Type & Seating	Factory Price	Shipping Weight	Production Total
46-DK	2124	2-dr Spt Cpe-5P	1130	3120	27,036
46-DK	2134	2-dr Cabriolet-5P	1381	3420	4,508
46-DK	2102	2-dr Twn Sedan-6P	1143	3165	56,538
46-DK	2103	4-dr Spt Sed-6P	1194	3200	73,746
46-DK	2109	4-dr Sta Wag-8P	1604	3435	804

FLEETMASTER ENGINE
See 1946 Stylemaster engine data.

1946 Chevrolet, Fleetline Sportmaster 4-dr sedan, 6-cyl

FLEETLINE — SIX — SUB-SERIES DK— As was the case in prewar times, a Fleetmaster sub-series was available as the two model Fleetline group. Both of these cars had the fastback GM 'Sport Dynamic' body shell and a Super DeLuxe level of trim. Fleetline lettering adorned the hood side molding. Triple speedline moldings were stacked on the flanks of all fenders. A distinctive bright metal windshield surround was seen. Interior appointments were generally of the Fleetmaster level, with special non-pile 'Fleet weave' fabrics used only in these two models. There was no way to overlook their extra-fancy appearance.

FLEETLINE I.D. NUMBERS: As a Fleetmaster sub-series, Fleetlines shared the same numbering system, except for style codes.

FLEETLINE SUB-SERIES DK

Model Number	Body/Style Number	Body Type & Seating	Factory Price	Shipping Weight	Production Total
46-DK	2113	4-dr SptMas Sed-6P	1222	3215	7,501
46-DK	2144	2-dr Aero Sed-6P	1165	3140	57,932

FLEETLINE ENGINE
See 1946 Stylemaster engine data.

CHEVROLET CHASSIS FEATURES: Three-speed manual transmission was exclusively available. Wheelbase: (all) 207-1/2 inches. Front tread: (all) 57.6 inches. Rear tread: (all) 60 inches. Rear axle ratio: 4.11:1. Tires: 16 x 6.00.

POWERTRAIN OPTIONS: Not available.

CONVENIENCE OPTIONS: Radio. Heater. Whitewall tire disks. Spotlight. Radio antenna. Fog lamps. Cowl windshield washer. Center bumper guards. DeLuxe steering wheel. DeLuxe pushbutton radio. Heater and defroster. Wheel trim rings. DeLuxe in-dash heater and defroster.

Historical footnotes: First postwar Chevy built October 3, 1945. The business coupe had front seat only. The Fleetmaster station wagon was a true 'woodie' wagon.

1947 CHEVROLET

1947 Chevrolet, Stylemaster 4-dr sedan, 6-cyl

STYLEMASTER — SIX — SERIES 1500 EJ — There was minimal change for 1947 at Chevrolet. The radiator grille had a softer, more horizontal appearance with the blades contoured into three distinct sections and Chevrolet lettering on the uppermost bar. A more horizontal hood emblem with bow-tie insignia was used. The horizontal moldings, which ran from hood to rear, were eliminated from all models, but a short, spear-shaped molding at the rear sides of the hood carried the series name in block letters. A three-spoke steering wheel with no horn ring was seen. Pile fabric upholstery was used. The floor mats lacked carpet inserts and a single lefthand sun visor appeared.

STYLEMASTER I.D. NUMBERS: Vehicle identification numbering was similar to the 1946 system, with new alphabetical codes adopted; 'EJ' for Stylemaster; 'EK' for Fleetmaster/Fleetline. Number plate locations unchanged. Serial numbers EJ-1001 to 33745. Motor numbers EA-1001 to 683120.

SYTLEMASTER SIX SERIES 1500 EJ

Model Number	Body/Style Number	Body Type & Seating	Factory Price	Shipping Weight	Production Total
47-EJ	1504	2-dr Bus Cpe-2P	1160	3050	27,403
47-EJ	1524	2-dr Spt Cpe-5P	1202	3060	34,513
47-EJ	1502	2-dr Twn Sed-6P	1219	3075	88,534
47-EJ	1503	4-dr Spt Sed-6P	1276	3130	42,571

STYLEMASTER ENGINE
See 1946 Stylemaster engine data.

FLEETMASTER — SIX — SERIES 2100 EK — Quick identification of Fleetmaster models came from the lettering on hood side spears, the appearance of bright metal windows reveal moldings and use of trim below taillamps. A DeLuxe two-spoke steering wheel was standard. Two-tone Bedford cloth upholstery was optional, with leatherette scuff covering used in all trim combinations on doors, front seats and rear seats. Carpet inserts highlighted Fleetmaster front floormats. Two sun visors were used. An illuminated radio grille and package compartment with lock was featured. Fleetline fastbacks lacked speedline fender trim, but again came with special "Fleetweave' upholstery and all Fleetmaster appointments.

FLEETMASTER I.D. NUMBERS: Followed same general system with new alphabeticl codes. Serial numbers EK-1001 to 72404. Motor numbers fit into the same sequence listed for Stylemaster above.

1947 Chevrolet, Fleetline Aerosedan 2-dr sedanette, 6-cyl

FLEETMASTER SIX SERIES 2100 EK

Model Number	Body/Style Number	Body Type & Seating	Factory Price	Shipping Weight	Production Total
47-EK	2103	4-dr Spt Sed-6P	1345	3185	91,440
47-EK	2102	2-dr Twn Sed-6P	1286	3125	80,128
47-EK	2124	2-dr Spt Cpe-5P	1281	3090	59,661
47-EK	2134	2-dr Conv Cpe-5P	1628	3390	28,443
47-EK	2109	4-dr Sta Wag-8P	1893	3465	4,912
FLEETLINE 2100 EK SUB-SERIES					
47-EK	2113	4-dr SptMas Sed-6P	1371	3150	54,531
47-EK	2144	2-dr Aero Sed-6P	1313	3125	159,407

FLEETLINE ENGINE
See 1946 Stylemaster engine data.

1947 Chevrolet, Fleetmaster 4-dr station wagon, 6-cyl

CHEVROLET CHASSIS FEATURES: Three-speed manual transmission was regular equipment; no options available. Wheelbase: (all) 116 inches. Overall length: (passenger cars) 197-3/4 inches; (station wagons) 207-1/2 inches. Front tread: (all) 57.6 inches. Rear tread: (all) 60 inches. Rear axle ratio: 4.11:1. Tires: 16 x 6.00.

POWERTRAIN OPTIONS: None available.

CONVENIENCE OPTIONS: Same as 1946.

Historical footnotes: Model year sales of 684,145 units made Chevrolet America's number 1 producer of autos. Dealer introductions held February 8, 1947. The business coupe had a front seat only. The Fleetmaster station wagon was a true 'woodie' wagon.

1948 CHEVROLET

1948 Chevrolet, Stylemaster 2-dr sport coupe, 6-cyl

STYLEMASTER — SIX — SERIES 1500 FJ — A T-shaped vertical center bar was added to the 1947 grille to make a 1948 Chevy. A new hood ornament and slightly revised nose emblem made appearances, as well. Black rubber windshield surrounds; plain side fenders; rubber mud guards and Stylemaster lettering on the rear hood side spears, characterized the exterior of the low-price Chevrolet. Inside was found a three-spoke steering wheel (without horn ring); painted dashboad; unlighted glove box; plainer trims; pile fabric upholstery; plain rubber floor mats; painted window sills and all-cloth seats without leather topped arm rests.

STYLEMASTER I.D. NUMBERS: Vehicle identification numbering was similar to the 1947 system, with new alphabetical codes adopted: 'FJ' for Stylemaster; 'FK' for Fleetmaster/Fleetline. Number plate locations unchanged. Serial numbers FJ-1001 to 30590. Motor numbers FA-1001 to 825234.

STYLE MASTER SIX SERIES 1500 FJ

Model Number	Body/Style Number	Body Type & Seating	Factory Price	Shipping Weight	Production Total
48-FJ	1503	4-dr Spt Sed-6P	1371	3115	48,456
48-FJ	1502	2-dr Twn Sed-6P	1313	3095	70,228
48-FJ	1524	2-dr Spt Cpe-6P	1323	3020	34,513
48-FJ	1504	2-dr Bus Cpe-3P	1244	3045	18,396

STYLEMASTER ENGINE
See 1946 Stylemaster engine data.

1948 Chevrolet, Fleetline 2-dr Aerosedan, 6-cyl (AA)

FLEETMASTER — SIX — SERIES 2100 FK — Short, stylized spears on the rear corners of hoods said 'Fleetmaster'. So did the inclusion of features such as chrome windshield surrounds; two-spoke DeLuxe steering wheel (with horn ring); wood-grained dashboard and window sills: illuminated glove locker; leatherette rear seat scuff covers; front floor mat carpet inserts and leather-topped front seat arm rests. An equipment change was that the clock and cigarette lighter were now considered standard on Fleetmasters and Fleetlines only. A dome lamp with automatic switch at driver's door was also a regular extra feature on these lines. On Fleetmaster, buyers could select two-tone Bedford cloth upholstery options, or stick with the standard pile fabric choice. Triple, stacked Speedline moldings once again graced front and rear fenders of Fleetline fastbacks. These cars had other Super DeLuxe features as well, such as five, vertical slashes of chrome beneath the taillights and Fleetline signature scripts on the center of deck lid. There was also a three-quarter length belt molding.

FLEETMASTER I.D. NUMBERS: Followed the same general system with new alphabetical codes. Serial numbers FK-1001 to 81603. Motor numbers fit into the same sequence listed for Stylemaster above.

FLEETMASTER SIX-SERIES 2100 FK

Model Number	Body/Style Number	Body Type & Seating	Factory Price	Shipping Weight	Production Total
48-FK	2103	4-dr Spt Sed-6P	1439	3150	93,142
48-FK	2102	2-dr Twn Sed-6P	1381	3110	66,208
48-FK	2124	2-dr Spt Cpe-6P	1402	3050	58,786
48-FK	2134	2-dr Conv Cpe-5P	1750	3340	20,471
48-FK	2109	4-dr Sta Wag-8P	2013	3430	10,171
FLEETLINE 2100 FK SUB-SERIES					
48-FK	2113	4-dr SptMas-6P	1492	3150	83,760
48-FK	2144	2-dr Aero Sed-5P	1434	3100	211,861

FLEETLINE ENGINE
See 1946 Stylemaster engine data.

1948 Chevrolet, Fleetline 2-dr Aerosedan, 6-cyl

CHEVROLET CHASSIS FEATURES: Same as 1946-1947.

POWERTRAIN OPTIONS: None available.

CONVENIENCE OPTIONS: Standard radio. DeLuxe pushbutton radio. Standard below dash heater and defroster. DeLuxe in-dash head and defroster. White sidewall tires. Spotlight cowl windshield washer. Low-pressure tires on wide rim 15 inch wheels. Bedford cord Fleetmaster upholstery. Front and rear bumper wing guards. Chrome plated gravel shields. Radio antenna. Clock in Stylemaster. Cigarette lighter in Stylemaster. Engine oil filter, external canister type. Oil bath air cleaner. Country Club trim package (see Historical footnotes for details). Wheel trim rings. Directional signals. External windshield sun shade (visor).

Historical footnotes: Model introductions were held February, 1948. Calendar sales of 775,982 units were recorded for the year. Precision interchangeable main engine bearings were adopted this season, in place of poured babbitt bearings. The business coupe had a front seat only. The Fleetmaster station wagon was a true 'woodie' wagon. An unique accessory sold by Chevolet dealers this year was the wood-grained 'Country Club' trim package, produced by Engineered Enterprises of Detroit, but sold only through factory authorized dealers for $149.50. It could be ordered for the Fleetline Aero Sedan and the Fleetmaster Town Sedan or convertible coupe, but very few cars were so-equipped.

1949 CHEVROLET

1949 Chevrolet, Styleline Special business coupe, 6-cyl

SPECIAL SERIES — SIX — 1500 GJ — Series designations were now determined by trim level, not body style. Each line had Styleline (notch back) and Fleetline (fastback) sub-series. All new, postwar designs were seen with integral front fenders and lower styling lines for fenders, roofs and hoods. The grille had a bowed upper bar with Chevrolet lettering; a horizontal center bar with round parking lamps (where bars intersected) and seven, short vertical bars dividing the lower opening. Standard equipment for Specials included dual tail and stop lights; dual license lights; dual windshield wipers; stainless steel body belt molding; body sill molding; rear fender crown moldings; front door pushbutton handles with integral key locks; black rubber rear fender shields; gas filler door in left rear fender; hood ornament and emblem; rear deck lid emblem; chrome headlamp rims; five extra-low pressure 6.70 x 15 tires on five-inch rims; front and rear bumpers and guards and license guard on front bumper. Seats were upholstered with tan, striped pattern, pile fabric with rubber-sized backs. Black rubber floor mats were used in the front compartment, carpets in rear of sedans and sport coupes. Three-spoke steering wheels with horn buttons appeared.

SPECIAL SERIES I.D. NUMBERS: Vehicle identification numbering was similar to the 1948 system, with new alphabetical codes adopted: 'GJ' for Special Series; 'GK' for DeLuxe. Number plate locations changed to lefthand door pillar. Engine number also stamped on crankcase to rear of distributor. Serial numbers GJ-1001 to 47213. Motor numbers GA-1001 to 1031807. Fisher Body Style Numbers now appear on second column of charts; Chevrolet model numbers in first column; Series code in head above.

SPECIAL SERIES 1500 GJ

Model Number	Body/Style Number	Body Type & Seating	Factory Price	Shipping Weight	Production Total
STYLELINE SUB-SERIES					
1503	49-1269	4-dr Sedan-6P	1460	3090	46,334
1502	49-1211	2-dr Sedan-6P	1413	3070	69,398
1524	49-1227	2-dr Spt Cpe-6P	1418	3030	40,239
1504	49-1227B	2-dr Bus Cpe-3P	1339	3015	20,337
FLEETLINE SUB-SERIES					
1553	49-1208	4-dr Sedan-6P	1460	3095	58,514
1552	49-1207	2-dr Sedan-5P	1413	3060	36,317

SPECIAL SERIES ENGINE
See 1946 Stylemaster engine data. Precision insert main engine bearings adopted 1948, used 1949 again.

1949 Chevrolet, Styleline DeLuxe convertible, 6-cyl (AA)

DELUXE SERIES — SIX — 2100 GK — In addition to body equipment found on Special Series models, DeLuxes had series nameplate (DeLuxe) on front fenders; stainless steel moldings on front fenders and doors; windshield reveal moldings; stainless steel rear fender shields (gravel guards); window reveal moldings (except station wagon and convertible); short lower belt molding sections; rear wheel cover panels (fender skirts); lefthand outside rear view mirror on convertible and chrome plated side window frames, also on convertible. Seats were upholstered with tan, striped pattern, flat cloth in sedans and coupe; genuine leather and tan Bedford cord in convertibles; tan leather fabric in station wagon. Also included were DeLuxe two-spoke steering wheel, two sun visors, simulated carpet floor mat inserts, two-tone tan and brown dashboard finish and many other DeLuxe appointments.

DELUXE SERIES I.D. NUMBERS: Followed same general system with new alphabetical code. Serial numbers GK-1001 to 128201. Motor numbers fit into the same sequence listed for Special Series above.

1949 Chevrolet, Fleetline DeLuxe 4-dr sedan, 6-cyl

DELUXE SERIES 2100 GK

Model Number	Body/Style Number	Body Type & Seating	Factory Price	Shipping Weight	Production Total
STYLELINE SUB-SERIES					
2103	49-1069	4-dr Sedan-6P	1539	3125	191,357
2102	49-1011	2-dr Sedan-6P	1492	3100	147,347
2124	49-1027	2-dr Spt Cpe-6P	1508	3065	78,785
2134	49-1067	2-dr Conv Cpe-5P	1857	3355	32,392
2109	49-1061	4-dr W-Sta Wag-8P	2267	3485	3,342
2119	49-1062	4-dr S-Sta Wag-8P	2267	3435	2,664
FLEETLINE SUB-SERIES					
2153	49-1008	4-dr Sedan-5P	1539	3135	130,323
2152	49-1007	2-dr Sedan-5P	1492	3100	180,251

NOTE: Body Style Number 1061, the wood station wagon, was replaced by Style Number 1062, the steel station wagon, in the middle of the model run, with both styles available concurrently early in the year.

DELUXE SERIES ENGINE
See 1946 Stylemaster engine data. Precision insert main engine bearings adopted 1948, used 1949 again.

CHEVROLET CHASSIS FEATURES: Box girder frame. In convertible a 'VK' structure of I-beam members takes place of engine rear support cross member. Knee-action front suspension with direct, double-acting shock absorbers. Ride stabilizer. Rubber insulated semi-elliptic rear springs with metal covers. Direct double-acting hydraulic rear shock absorbers. Four-wheel hydraulic brakes with 11 inch drums. Wheelbase: (all) 115 inches. Overall length: (passenger cars) 197 inches; (station wagon) 198 inches. Front tread: (all) 57 inches. Rear tread: (all) 58-3/4 inches. Rear axle: Semi-floating with hypoid drive and 4.11:1 gear ratio. Torque tube drive with tubular propeller shaft; both fully enclosed. Tires: 6.70 x 15 blackwall on widebase rims.

POWERTRAIN OPTIONS: Valve-in-head 90 horsepower inline Six and three-speed Synchromesh transmission with helical gears and manually operated steering column mounted controls used in all models. No other choices available.

CONVENIENCE OPTIONS: Standard manual radio. DeLuxe pushbutton radio. Radio antenna. Under dash heater and defroster. In-dash DeLuxe heater and defroster. White sidewall tires. Wheel trim rings. Spotlight. Fog lamps. Directional signals. Backup light. External windshield sun shade (visor), Tan striped pattern, free-breathing pile fabric DeLuxe Series upholstery trim. San-Toy seat covers. Outer bumper tips. Master grille guard. Locking gas filler cap. Other standard factory and/or dealer installed accessories.

Historical footnotes: Dealer introduction in January, 1949. Interior trims varied per body style and are fully explained in 1949 Chevrolet sales catalogs. Model year production, 1,037,600 units. Calendar year sales total 1,109,958. Chevrolet is America's Number 1 maker again. Steel station wagon (not wood) has front body side molding. Business Coupe has black rubber mat on rear compartment floor; single sun visor for driver. Lowering quarter windows in two-door sedans. Lowering forward sections and fixed ventipanes in four-door sedan rear door windows. Fixed quarter windows in coupes. Sliding rear quarter windows in sport coupe. Genuine carpet inserts for convertible front floor mat. Convertible features dome light in roof bow. Station wagon has sliding quarter windows; wood-grained leatherette headliner; tan rubber floor mats; tan linoleum cargo area deck and no rear seat arm rests, coat hooks or assist straps.

1950 CHEVROLET

SPECIAL SERIES — SIX — 1500 HJ — Few styling changes. New grille deletes vertical division bars, except for new triple ribbed type directly under front parking lamps. Nose and deck lid ornaments restyled; new hood ornament. Deck lid handle slightly revised for easier locking and lifting. Styleline Specials have bustle back; no chrome body strip. Fleetline Specials have sweeping fastback lines; no chrome body strip. Curved windshield with chrome center strip on both. Equipment features similar to list for 1949. Upholstery is gray-striped modern weave flat cloth with dark gray broadcloth; plain light gray fabric back, side and sidewall panels. Light gray control knobs replace ivory type used in 1949. Floor mat, lamp and steering wheel features follow trends of earlier years. Exact equipment varies per model and is fully outlined in 1950 factory sales literature.

SPECIAL CHASSIS I.D. NUMBERS: V.I.D. numbering system and number plate locations unchanged. Alphabetical codes 'HJ' for Special Series. Serial number HJ-1001 to 49801. Motor numbers HA-1001 to 1320152.

SPECIAL SERIES 1500 HJ

Model Number	Body/Style Number	Body Type & Seating	Factory Price	Shipping Weight	Production Total
STYLELINE SUB-SERIES					
1503	50-1269	4-dr Sedan-6P	1450	3120	55,644
1502	50-1211	2-dr Sedan-6P	1403	3085	89,897
1524	50-1227	2-dr Spt Cpe-6P	1408	3050	28,328
1504	50-1227B	2-dr Bus Cpe-3P	1329	3025	20,984
FLEETLINE SUB-SERIES					
1553	50-1208	4-dr Sedan-6P	1450	3115	23,277
1552	50-1207	2-dr Sedan-6P	1403	3080	43,682

NOTE: Body Style Number (second column above) begins with a two digit prefix designating model year; '50' = 1950. Main number identifies series (12 = Special) and body (69 = four-door sedan; 11 = two-door sedan, etc.). This number is located on vehicle data plate under hood and is the *best way* to positively identify Chevrolet body styles. Listings in this book for post-1950 models will drop the two-digit prefix designating model year for purpose of conserving space needed to include additional letter suffixes used for later Body Style Numbers. These letter suffixes are used to denote various things such as equipment and trim variations on similar body styles (e.g. B = business coupe with sliding rear quarter windows; F = Handyman station wagon with folding seat; D = Bel Air with DeLuxe trim).

SPECIAL ENGINE
See 1946 Stylemaster engine data. Precision insert bearings, adopted 1948, used again. Rochester one-barrel carburetor, model 7002050, used in mixed production with earlier type.

1950 Chevrolet, Styleline DeLuxe 4-dr sedan, 6-cyl

DELUXE SERIES — SIX — 2100 HK — Styleline DeLuxe models have bustleback; fender skirts; chrome body strip; word DeLuxe on fender and same extra equipment features outlined for 1949 DeLuxe series. Bel Air 'hardtop convertible', with three-piece wraparound curved backlight, is a new style. Fleetline DeLuxe models have sweeping fastback body with same higher trim level features inside and out. Bel Air interior features are same as in convertible coupe except two rear compartment lamps are used at roof quarter panels; neutral gray headliner with chrome roof bows appears and transmission lever knob is black plastic. Other DeLuxe models trimmed with gray striped broadcloth material having 'off-shoulder' dark gray broadcloth contrast panels and dark gray front seat back cushions, seat risers, upper sidewalls and center pillars. Light gray headliner and lower sidewalls used. Features vary per body style and are fully detailed in 1950 Chevrolet sales catalogs.

DELUXE SERIES I.E. NUMBERS: Followed same general system with new 'HK' alphabetical code. Serial numbers HK-1001 to 187118. Motor numbers fit into some sequence listed for Special Series above.

1950 Chevrolet, DeLuxe Bel Air 2-dr hardtop coupe, 6-cyl

DELUXE SERIES 2100 HK

Model Number	Body/Style Number	Body Type & Seating	Factory Price	Shipping Weight	Production Total
STYLELINE SUB-SERIES					
2103	50-1069	4-dr Sedan-6P	1529	3150	316,412
2102	50-1011	2-dr Sedan-6P	1482	3100	248,567
2124	50-1027	2-dr Spt Cpe-6P	1498	3090	81,536
2154	50-1037	2-dr BelAir-6P	1741	3225	76,662
2134	50-1067	2-dr Conv Cpe-5P	1847	3380	32,810
2119	50-1062	4-dr Sta Wag-8P	1994	3460	166,995
FLEETLINE SUB-SERIES					
2153	50-1008	4-dr Sedan-6P	1529	3145	124,287
2152	50-1007	2-dr Sedan-6P	1482	3115	189,509

NOTE: Style Number 50-1037 is a two-door pillarless hardtop coupe.

DELUXE ENGINE: See 1950 Special Series engine data, plus Powertrain Options below.

CHEVROLET CHASSIS FEATURES: Same as 1949 except overall length increases as follows: (passenger cars) 197-1/2 inches; (station wagon) 198-1/4 inches.

POWERTRAIN OPTIONS: Standard powertrain same as 1949. Powerglide two-speed automatic transmission was introduced as a $159 option for DeLuxe Series only. Cars so equipped were provided with a modified Chevrolet truck engine with 3-9/6 x 3-15/16 inch bore and stroke and 235 cubic inches of piston displacement. Hydraulic valve lifters and larger intake valves were used. Horsepower was rated the familiar 90 at 3300 R.P.M. A slightly lower 3.55:1 rear axle gear ratio was used on Powerglide equipped models. Also, 7.10 x 15 tires ($14.75 extra) were optional for convertibles equipped with Powerglide.

CONVENIENCE OPTIONS: Similar to 1949 in terms of availability, plus Powerglide automatic transmission as noted above.

Historical footnotes: Dealer introduction January 7, 1950. Model year production 1,371,535. Calendar year sales 1,520,577. Chevrolet is America's Number 1 maker again. Bel Air hardtop introduced. Powerglide automatic transmission introduced. Hydraulic valve lifters adopted for Powerglide six-cylinder engine. Body style features same as detailed under 1949 footnote. New Rochester carburetor was B or BC type ('C' indicating automatic choke). Some cars also had Stromberg BXVD-2 or BXXD-35 type carburetors.

1951 CHEVROLET

SPECIAL SERIES — SIX — 1500 JJ — A subtle, but attractive facelift characterized the 1951 Chevrolet. By moving the parking lamps into the lower grille opening, under the headlamps, a wider look was achieved. Styleline Specials had bustle backs and no chrome body strip. Fleetline Specials had fastbacks and no chrome body strip. Black rubber mud guards were seen on both Special lines. Two-tone gray interiors with light gray striped pattern cloth upholstery were used. Equipment features followed the 1949-1950 assortment. Variations are fully detailed in factory sales catalogs. New, smaller taillamps with a nearly square red plastic lens were used. A small, round reflector was positioned at the bottom of the same housing. Bendix 'Jumbo Drum' brakes replaced the old Huck units. A simplified trunk ornament bearing the Chevrolet bow-tie emblem was used. Specials still came only with the base engine and conventional transmission.

1951 Chevrolet, Styleline DeLuxe 2-dr sedan, 6-cyl

SPEICAL SERIES I.D. NUMBERS: V.I.D. numbering system and number plate locations unchanged. Alphabetical code 'JJ' for Special Series. Serial numbers JJ-1001 to 32061. Motor numbers JA-1001 to 1261301.

SPECIAL SERIES 1500 JJ

Model Number	Body/Style Number	Body Type & Seating	Factory Price	Shipping Weight	Production Total
STYLELINE SUB-SERIES					
1503	1269	4-dr Sedan-6P	1594	3110	63,718
1502	1211	2-dr Sedan-6P	1540	3070	75,566
1524	1227	2-dr Spt Cpe-6P	1545	3060	18,981
1504	1227B	2-dr Bus Cpe-3P	1460	3040	17,020
FLEETLINE SUB-SERIES					
1553	1208	4-dr Sedan-6P	1594	3130	3,364
1552	1207	2-dr Sedan-6P	1540	3090	6,441

SPECIAL ENGINE
Six. Overhead valves. Cast iron block. Displacement: 216.5 cubic inches. Bore and stroke: 3-1/2 x 3-3/4 inches. Compression ratio: 6.6:1. Brake horsepower: 92 at 3400 R.P.M. Four main bearings. Solid valve lifters. Carburetor: Single-barrel Rochester, Carter and Stromberg models used in mixed production.

1951 Chevrolet, Styleline DeLuxe 4-dr sedan, 6-cyl

DELUXE SERIES - SIX - 2100 JK — DeLuxe models also used the newly designed grille which had the lower two horizontal bars extended to form a circular frame for oblong parking lamps with five vertical sectioned bars beside the parking lamps. Chevrolet was written, in script, on the chrome grille frame molding. DeLuxes had a stainless steel molding starting above the front wheel openings and extending onto doors with a DeLuxe nameplate on front fenders. Chrome rear fender gravel shields and painted fender skirts were standard equipment. Interiors were two-tone gray with gray striped broadcloth upholstery. Four different, special two-tone combinations were offered for Bel Air interiors. Bel Air upholstery was in two-tone gray striped pile-cord fabric with genuine deep buff leather bolsters. Station wagons were trimmed with tan imitation pigskin. Cars with Powerglide had a special script, denoting this feature, on deck lids.

DELUXE SERIES I.D. NUMBERS: Followed same general system with new 'JK' alphabetical code. Serial numbers JK-1001 to 174408 motor numbers fit into same sequence listed for Special Series above.

DELUXE SERIES 1500 JK

Model Number	Body/Style Number	Body Type & Seating	Factory Price	Shipping Weight	Production Total
STYLELINE SUB-SERIES					
2103	1069	4-dr Sedan-6P	1680	3150	380,270
2102	1011	2-dr Sedan-6P	1629	3110	262,933
2124	1027	2-dr Spt Cpe-6P	1647	3090	64,976
2154	1037	2-dr BelAir-6P	1914	3215	103,356
2134	1067	2-dr Conv Cpe-5P	2030	3360	20,172
2119	1062	4-dr Sta Wag-8P	2191	3450	23,586
FLEETLINE SUB-SERIES					
2153	1008	4-dr Sedan-6P	1680	3155	57,693
2152	1007	2-dr Sedan-6P	1629	3125	131,910

NOTE: Style Number 1037 is a two-door pillarless hardtop coupe.

DELUXE ENGINE
For base engine data see 1951 Special Series engine data. For Powerglide engine, see Powertrain options.

CHASSIS FEATURES: Same as 1949-1950 except overall length changes as follows: (passenger car) 197-3/4 inches; (station wagon) 197-7/8 inches. Also, 7.10 x 15 tires standard on convertible.

POWERTRAIN OPTIONS: Two-speed Powerglide automatic transmission $169 extra as DeLuxe-only option. Powerglide engine: Inline Six. Overhead valves. Cast iron block. Displacement: 235.5 cubic inches. Bore and stroke: 3-9/16 x 3-15/16 inches. Four main bearings. Hydraulic valve lifters. Compression ratio: 6.7:1. Brake horsepower: 105 at 3600 R.P.M. Carburetor: Rochester one-barrel BC.

CONVENIENCE OPTIONS: Directional signals. Dash panel ash tray (standard in DeLuxe). Manual radio. DeLuxe pushbutton radio. Under dash heater and defroster. DeLuxe in-dash heater and defroster. Full wheel discs. Wheel trim rings. Whitewall tires. Thirty-nine hour stem wind clock (standard in DeLuxe). Fender skirts (standard on DeLuxe). No-Mar Fuel door guard. Door handle shields. Front and rear bumper wing tips. Master grille guard. Spot light. Fog lamps. External sun shade (visor). Locking gas filler door. Front fender stainless steel gravel shields. Impala-style hood ornament. Tissue dispenser. San-Toy seat covers. Left-hand outside rear view mirror (standard in convertible). Right-hand outside rear view mirror. Radio antenna. License plate frame. Backup lamp. Vacuumatic ash tray. Rubber heel protector. Underhood lamp. Luggage compartment lamp. Other standard factory and dealer-installed accessories.

Historical footnotes: Dealer introductions were held December 9, 1950. Model year production 1,250,803 units. Calendar year sales 1,118,096 cars. Chevrolet remains America's number 1 maker. Attractive new dashboard and steering wheel with 'bow tie' spoke and horn ring design (DeLuxe type). Parting seam makes first appearance on this body; located below headlamps.

1952 CHEVROLET

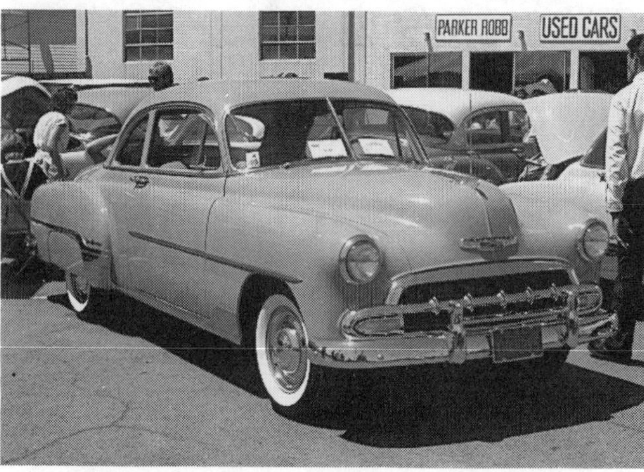

1952 Chevrolet, Styleline DeLuxe 2-dr sport coupe, 6-cyl

SPECIAL SERIES — SIX — 1500 KJ — A new grille for 1952 had five vertical bars that soon became known as Chevrolet "teeth". They were mounted to the horizontal center divider bar and equally spaced out from the center. The parking lamps were again in the lower grille opening and again oblong shaped, but now "floated" in their housings. The word Chevrolet trimmed a wider new nose emblem which still had a "bow-tie" logo. The Special Series no longer included fastback Fleetline models. Specials had notch back styling, no chrome body molding, rubber gravel deflectors and open rear wheel housings. Nine exteriors colors and four two-tone combinations were provided for all sedans, sport coupes and business coupes, including Styleline Specials. Two-tone gray interiors were featured, with seat upholstery of checkered pattern cloth.

SPECIAL SERIES I.D. NUMBERS: V.I.D. numbering system and number plate locations unchanged. Alphabetical code 'KJ' for Special Series. Serial numbers KJ-1001 to 19286. Motor numbers KA-1001 to 860773.

STYLELINE SPECIAL SERIES 1500 KJ

Model Number	Body/Style Number	Body Type & Seating	Factory Price	Shipping Weight	Production Total
1503	1269	4-dr Sedan-6P	1659	3115	35,460
1502	1211	2-dr Sedan-6P	1603	3085	54,781
1524	1227	2-dr Spt Cpe-6P	1609	3050	8,906
1504	1227B	2-dr Bus Cpe-6P	1519	3045	10,359

SPECIAL ENGINE
Inline Six. Overhead valves. Cast iron block. Displacement: 216.5 cubic inches. Bore and stroke: 3-1/2 x 3-3/4 inches Compression ratio: 6.6:1. Brake horsepower: 92 at 3400 R.P.M. Four main bearings. Solid valve lifters. Carburetor: Rochester one-barrel B or BC (automatic choke on BC); or Stromberg BXOV-2, model number 380286; or Stromberg BXOV-25, model number 380270.

1952 Chevrolet, DeLuxe Bel Air 2-dr hardtop coupe, 6-cyl

DELUXE SERIES — SIX — 2100 KK — The new 1952 styling was particularly attractive when packaged in DeLuxe trim. Easily noticed distinctions included body rub moldings on front fenders and doors: bright metal rear fender gravel guards (with long extension moldings sweeping up over the fender-skirted wheel housings) and DeLuxe script logos directly above the gravel guards on the rear fender pontoons. Bright metal windshield and window reveals were featured as well. A two-spoke steering wheel, with full blowing ring, replaced the three-spoke Special type with horn button. DeLuxes also had ivory plastic control knobs with bright metal inserts; dome lamps with automatic door switches; two inside sun visors and richer interior trims with foam rubber cushions. Upholstery combinations were reversed, with dark gray chevron pattern cloth and lighter toned upper contrast panels. As usual, convertibles, Bel Airs and station wagons had their own exclusive trim. There were also four exterior paint colors for Bel Airs and eleven two-tone combinations, while convertibles came in ten colors (with five different top tones) and wagons offered four types of finish in combination with wood grained trim panels. In the model lineup, the two-door Fleetline sedan was the sole fastback car in the Chevrolet line. It came only with DeLuxe trim, as did the Powerglide transmission option. Cars with Powerglide again had lettering to the effect attached on the rear deck lid.

DELUXE SERIES I.D. NUMBERS: Followed same general system with new 'KK' alphabetical code. Serial numbers KK-1001 to 115,255. Motor numbers fit into same sequence given for Special Series above.

DELUXE SERIES 2100 KK
STYLELINE SUB-SERIES

Model Number	Body/Style Number	Body Type & Seating	Factory Price	Shipping Weight	Production Total
2103	1069	4-dr Sedan-6P	1749	3145	319,736
2102	1011	2-dr Sedan-6P	1696	3110	215,417
2124	1027	2-dr Spt Cpe-6P	1715	3100	36,954
2154	1037	2-dr Bel Air-6P	1992	3215	74,634
2134	1067	2-dr Conv Cpe-5P	2113	3380	11,975
2119	1062	4-dr Sta Wag-8P	2281	3475	12,756
FLEETLINE SUB-SERIES					
2152	1007	2-dr Sedan-6P	1696	3110	37,164

NOTE: Style number 1037 is a two-door pillarless hardtop coupe.

DELUXE ENGINE
For base powerplant see 1952 Special Series engine data. For Powerglide engine, see Powertrain options.

CHASSIS FEATURES: Same as 1951 without change.

POWERTRAIN OPTIONS: Same as 1951 (Note: 3.55:1 gear ratio rear axle used with Powerglide transmission both years). Powerglide engine again displaced 235.5 cubic inches and produced 105 horsepower at 3600 R.P.M. Sales literature noted that special piston rings having one twist-type and one taper-face compression ring, one wide-slot oil control ring were used in Powerglide engine.

CONVENIENCE OPTIONS: Same as 1951 at about the same prices, with following variations: Price for Powerglide transmission increased to $178 extra. E-Z-Eye glass listed as optional. Ash tray (dash-type) now standard in both series. Availability of white walls limited.

Historical footnotes: Began January 19, 1952. Model year sales 827,317 despite Korean war manufacturing limitations. Calendar year sales 877,947 despite Korea. Whitewall tires uncommon. Inferior chrome plating process used this year. Chevrolet again number 1 American maker. In October, 1952 the millionth Powerglide equipped Chevrolet was assembled; the option was just 34 months old. The 28 millionth U.S. or Canadian Chevrolet car or truck was built in December, 1952.

1953 CHEVROLET

1953 Chevrolet, Two-Ten 4-dr sedan, 6-cyl

SPECIAL '150' SERIES — SIX — 1500A — The sub-series designations Styleline and Fleetline were dropped, since there was no fastback Chevrolet for 1953. Cars with Special level features and trim were 'One-Fifty' models or '150' models, this designation coming from the first three digits of the numerical series code. The sport coupe became the 'club coupe' and a 'Handyman' station wagon was a new Special model. New styling details included one-piece curved windshields: new chrome hood ornament and nose nameplate; new grille with three vertical fins on the center horizontal bar and extensions encircling the parking lamps and new vertical dual stop and taillamps. Easy identifiers included rubber windshield molding; plain body sides without moldings; rubber gravel guards; no rocker panel molding; unskirted rear wheel housings and no series nameplate. On the inside of Specials there was a standard steering wheel; single sun visor and plain upholstery. The 'One-Fifty' station wagon had safety sheet side door windows in place of Safety Plate glass and was rated a six-passenger model with a folding second seat.

SPECIAL '150' SERIES I.D. NUMBERS: V.I.N. numbering system and number plate locations unchanged. Alphabetical code 'A' for Special Series adopted and will no longer undergo annual change. Serial number A53(   )-001001 to A53-228961. Motor numbers LA-1001 to 1183450. The blank space (   ) in serial number is filled with a letter indicating assembly plant as follows: A = Atlanta; B = Baltimore; F = Flint; J = Janesville; K = Kansas City; L = Los Angeles; N = Norwood; O = Oakland; S = St. Louis; T = Tarrytown. It should be noted that engine numbers consisted of four to seven numbers with a prefix or suffix. The prefix or suffix indicated year, engine size, factory, type of valve lifter and other peculiaritites. It is impossible to tabulate all these codes in a small amount of space. Restorers can consult Chevrolet shop manuals or master parts catalogs for this type of information on 1946-1956 models.

SPECIAL '150' SERIES

Model Number	Body/Style Number	Body Type & Seating	Factory Price	Shipping Weight	Production Total
1503	1269	4-dr Sedan-6P	1670	3215	54,207
1502	1211	2-dr Sedan-6P	1613	3180	79,416
1524	1227	2-dr Clb Cpe-6P	1620	3140	6,993
1504	1227B	2-dr Bus Cpe-3P	1524	3140	13,555
1509	1262F	4-dr Sta Wag-6P	2010	3420	22,408

NOTES: Style Number 1227B has single seat (front), fixed rear quarter windows and rear storage space with raised floor. Style Number 1262F has two seats (folding second seat) and plexiglass 'Safety Seal" side windows.

1953 Chevrolet, Two-Ten 4-dr station wagon, 6-cyl

SPECIAL '150' SERIES ENGINE
Inline Six. Overhead valves. Cast iron block. Displacement: 235.5 cubic inches. Bore and stroke: 3-9/16 x 3-15/16. Compression ratio: 7.1:1. Brake horsepower: 108 at 3600 R.P.M. Four main bearings. Solid valve lifters. Carburetor: Rochester one-barrel B-type model 7007181 or Carter one-barrel model 2101S.

DELUXE '210' SERIES — SIX — 2100 B — Cars with DeLuxe level features and tirm were now called 'Two-Ten' or '210' models, the new designation taken from first three digits of numerical series code. The Sport Coupe became the 'Club Coupe'. The pillarless hardtop was *not* a Bel Air. The six-passenger station wagon with folding second seat was called the 'Handyman' (as was the same version with Special trim). The eight-passenger station wagon was called the 'Townsman'. The Townsman had three seats, the second and third units being stationary, but completely removable. The '210' convertible was deleted in mid-year and the '210' Townsman station wagon was also dropped for 1954, along with the '210' sport coupe. External identification of 'Two-Tens' was afforded by horizontal lower belt moldings running from front to rear; chrome windshield and window moldings; rocker panel moldings and bright metal rear gravel guards with short spears at the top. A two-spoke steering wheel with horn ring was used. Standard equipment also included cigarette lighter; dash panel ash tray; dual sun visors and 39-hour stem wind clock. Heaters and radios were optional and, when not fitted, blocker plates were used to cover the cutouts on the dash board for heater and radio controls. Interior door handles used on '210' models had bright metal inserts in the black plastic knobs. Other interior appointments included foam rubber seat cushion pads in front seats and in rear seats of sedans and coupes; front arm rests in all models; rear arm rests in sedans and coupes; rear compartment ash tray in four-door sedans; one ash tray in each armrest of two-door sedans and coupes and bright metal moldings on rear quarter panels of sedans and coupes.

DELUXE '210' SERIES I.D. NUMBERS: Followed same general system with new 'B' alphabetical code, which will no longer change annually. Serial numbers B53(   )-001001 to 228961 with blank (   ) showing assembly plant code. Motor numbers fit into same sequence given above for Special '150' Series.

DELUXE '210' SERIES

Model Number	Body/Style Number	Body Type & Seating	Factory Price	Shipping Weight	Production Total
z 2103	1069W	4-dr Sedan-6P	1761	3250	332,497
2102	1011W	2-dr Sedan-6P	1707	3215	247,455
2124	1027	2-dr Clb Cpe-6P	1726	3190	23,961
2154	1037	2-dr Spt Cpe-6P	1967	3295	14,045
2134	1067	2-dr Conv Cpe-5P	2093	3435	5,617
2109	1062F	4-dr Sta Wag-6P	2123	3450	18,258
2119	1062	4-dr Sta Wag-8P	2273	3495	7,988

NOTES: 'Two-Ten' body style numbers are similar to Bel Air Body Style numbers except for suffixes. Style Number 1011W. 1037 and 1067 have lowering rear quarter windows. The Style Number 1062F '210' Townsman station wagon varies from the '150' Townsman in that Safety Plate glass door windows are used.

DELUXE '210' ENGINE
See Special '150' engine data for Synchromesh engine specifications. See Powertrain Options for Powerglide engine specifications. Powerglide available on 'Two-Ten' and Bel Air lines only.

1953 Chevrolet, Bel Air 4-dr sedan, 6-cyl (AA)

BEL AIR — SIX — SERIES 2400 C— The Bel Air designation was applied to a four car lineup this season. It now identified a level of trim, instead of a particular body style. The numerical code 2400-C applied to all Bel Air models, but was rarely used in place of the descriptive series name. To identify this new luxury series, Chevrolet added a double molding on the rear fender pontoon. It enclosed a panel which was decorated with a short wide ribbed beauty molding. Bel Air script and Chevrolet crest on the leading edge above a chrome gravel shield. All 'Two-Ten' trim features and equipment were incorporated, plus rear fender skirts double windshield pillar moldings; extra wide window reveals on sedans and saddle moldings on sport coupes and convertibles. Exposed bright metal roof bows and dashboard mounted rear view mirrors were standard in Bel Air sport coupes.

BEL AIR SERIES I.D. NUMBERS: Followed the same general system with new 'C' alphabetical code, which will no longer change annually. Serial numbers C53(   )-001001 to 228961 with (   ) showing assembly plant code. Note that serial numbers as well as motor number, fit into same sequence given above for DeLuxe '210' Series.

BEL AIR 2400 C SERIES

Model Number	Body/Style Number	Body Type & Seating	Factory Price	Shipping Weight	Production Total
2403	1069WD	4-dr Sedan-6P	1874	3275	246,284
2402	1011WD	2-dr Sedan-6P	1820	3230	144,401
2454	1037D	2-dr Spt Cpe-6P	2051	3310	99,047
2434	1067D	2-dr Conv Cpe-5P	2175	3470	24,047

BEL AIR ENGINES
See Special '150' engine data for synchromesh engine specifications. See Powertrain Options for Powerglide engine specifications.

CHEVROLET CHASSIS FEATURES: Wheelbase: (all series) 115 inches. Overall length: (all passenger cars) 195-1/2 inches; (all station wagons) 197-7/8 inches. Front tread: (all) 56.69 inches. Rear tread: (all) 58.75 inches. Tires: (Convertible with Powerglide) 7.10 x 15 four-ply; (Townsman station wagon) 6.70 x 15 six-ply; (all others) 6.70 x 15 four-ply. Standard rear axle ratio: 3.7:1.

POWERTRAIN OPTIONS: Powerglide two-speed automatic transmission (cast iron type) was optional at $178 extra. A special engine, with following specifications, was used in conjunction with Powerglide Inline Six. Overhead valves. Cast iron block. Displacement: 235.5 cubic inches. Bore and stroke: 3-9/16 x 3-15/16 inches. Compression ratio: 7.5:1. Brake horsepower 115 at 3600 R.P.M. Four main bearings. Hydraulic valve lifters. Carburetor: Rochester BC type one-barrel model 7007200 or Carter one-barrel model 2101S. A transmission oil cooler and 3.55:1 axle ratio are used with Powerglide.

CONVENIENCE OPTIONS: Power steering ($178). Custom radio. Pushbutton Custom DeLuxe radio. Recirculating heater and defroster (under dash type). Air Flow heater and defroster (dashboard type) E-Z-Eye tinted glass. Autronic Eye automatic headlamp dimmer. White sidewall tires. Directional signals. Backup lights. Bumper guards (second pair, front or rear). Front fender gravel shields. Door handles shields. Windshield sunshade (visor). Full wheel discs. Accessory, "Bird type", hood ornament. Fender skirts on '150' models. License plate frame. Front and rear bumper tip guards. Stem wind clock on '150' models. Radio antenna. Locking gas filler door. Venti-pane wind deflectors. Left-hand outside rearview mirror. Fog lights. Traffic light viewer. Tissue dispenser. Vacuumatic ashtray. Non-glare rearview mirror. No-Mar fuel door trim. Underhood light. San-Toy seat covers. Other standard factory and dealer-installed accessories.

Historical footnotes: Dealer introduction January, 1953. Model year sales 1,356,413. Calendar year sales 1,477,287. Completely new body with wraparound backlight on all models except club coupe, convertible and station wagon. Chevrolet introduced Corvette marque. Powerglide models now have full-pressure lubrication. Powerglide available in Two-Ten and Bel Air only. Seventeen models are most ever offered by Chevrolet. First year for Chevrolet power steering. Chevrolet remains America's number 1 maker.

1954 CHEVROLET

1954 Chevrolet, One-Fifty 2-dr utility sedan, 6-cyl

SPECIAL '150' SERIES — SIX — 1500 A — Styling improvements for 1954 Chevrolets, although very minor, gave the impression of a wider, more modern car. New was a full-width horizontal center grille bar housing wraparound horizontal parking lamp housings at each outer end. Five vertical teeth were equally spaced from the center of the main bar out. The front bumper was redesigned with its ends bulged out to wraparound the body corners. New bumper guards, headlight rims, nose ornament and hood mascot were seen. The taillight housings were hooded to create a fin-like look in profile view. They housed a vertical red and white cigar-shaped lens, the white portion provided in case optional backup lamp wiring was added. Powerglide was now available in 'One-Fifty' models, cars so equipped having Powerglide — instead of the normal Chevrolet — scripts on the deck lid. Inside, the 150 Specials had black window crank knobs, and plainer interior appointments described as being "smartly fashioned of durable materials." Rubber windshield moldings; black rubber gravel guards; hub caps and plain body sides were a few ways to spot cars in this line. The club coupe was gone and the business coupe was renamed as the 'utility sedan', which had no back seat and a raised rear compartment load floor.

SPECIAL '150' SERIES I.D. NUMBERS: V.I.D. numbering system and numbering locatins unchanged. Serial numbers A54( )-001001 to 174684. Motor numbers 01001-Z54 to 1024930.

SPECIAL '150' SERIES

Model Number	Body/Style Number	Body Type & Seating	Factory Price	Shipping Weight	Production Total
1503	1269W	4-dr Sedan-6P	1680	3210	32,430
1502	1211W	2-dr Sedan-6P	1623	3165	64,855
1509	1262F	4-dr Sta Wag-6P	2020	3455	21,404
1512	1211WB	2-dr Utl Sedan-3P	1539	3145	10,770

NOTE: Style Number 1262F was the Handyman station wagon with two seats, the rear most a folding type.

SPECIAL '150' ENGINES
(Synchromesh)
Inline Six. Overhead valves. cast iron block. Displacement: 235.5 cubic inches. Bore and stroke: 3-9/16 x 3-15/16 inches. Compression ratio: 7.5:1. Brake horsepower: 115 at 3700 R.P.M. Four main bearings. Solid valve lifters. Carburetor: Rochester one-barrel 'B' type model 7007181 or Carter one-barrel model 2102S.
(Powerglide)
Same as above with following exceptions: Brake horsepower: 125 at 4000 R.P.M. Hydraulic valve lifters. Includes transmission oil cooler. New high-lift camshaft. Full-pressure lubrication. New 30-inch muffler. New aluminum pistons. Standard engine with Powerglide attachment, now available in all Chevrolet lines.

1954 Chevrolet, Two-Ten Del Ray 2-dr club coupe, 6-cyl

DELUXE '210' SERIES — SIX — 2100 B — 'Two-Ten' identification features were similar to 1953 and included chrome body side moldings; chrome windshield molding: chrome window moldings: rocker panel moldings: bright metal gravel guards; genuine carpets in rear compartment and durable cloth seats with vinyl contrasting panels in four different color schemes. The 'Two-Ten' club coupe was sometimes called the 'DelRay' and came with all-vinyl, waffle pattern upholstery and matching two-tone door panels. The Two-Ten 'Handyman' station wagon was upholstered with long-wearing vinyl materials of contrasting colors and textures including horizontally ribbed door panel inserts. The 'Two-Ten' convertible and 'Townsman' station wagon were dropped.

DELUXE '210' SERIES I.D. NUMBERS: Followed the same general system. Serial numbers B-54( )-001001 to 174684. Motor numbers fit into the same sequence given above for special '150' Series.

DELUXE '210' SERIES

Model Number	Body/Style Number	Body Type & Seating	Factory Price	Shipping Weight	Production Total
2103	1069W	4-dr Sedan-6P	1771	3230	235,146
2102	1011W	2-dr Sedan-6P	1717	3185	194,498
2124	1011WA	2-dr DelRay Cpe-6P	1782	3185	66,403
2109	1062F	4-dr Sta Wag-6P	2133	3470	27,175

NOTE: Style Number 1062F was the 'Handyman' station wagon with two seats, the rear most a folding type.

DELUXE '210' ENGINES
See 1954 Special '150' engine data.

1954 Chevrolet, Bel Air convertible, 6-cyl

BEL AIR — SIX — SERIES 2400 C — The new Bel Air had the traditional assortment of extra equipment and features such as full genuine carpeting; newly designed full wheel discs; horizontaly ribbed vinyl door panels and an electric clock. The sport coupe had special 'fashion fiesta' two-tone upholstery; rear pillar courtesy lights; chrome plated inside roof garnish moldings and rear window frame and bright metal exposed roof bows. The convertible interior seemed even richer, with two-tone all-vinyl trims and snap-on boot cover. The rear view mirror was no longer mounted atop the dashboard. Identifying all Bel-Airs externally were full-length sweepspear moldings with double moldings on rear fenders enclosing the name Bel Air and a Chevrolet crest; bright metal double windshield pillar moldings and window molding; body belt molding; rocker panel moldings; bright metal gravel guards and rear wheel fender skirts.

BEL AIR SERIES I.D. NUMBERS: Followed the same general system. Serial numbers C54( )-001001 to 174684. Motor numbers fit into the same sequence given above for Special '150' Series.

BEL AIR SERIES 2400 C

Model Number	Body/Style Number	Body Type & Seating	Factory Price	Shipping Weight	Production Total
2403	1069WD	4-dr Sedan—6P	1884	3255	248,750
2402	1011WD	2-dr Sedan-6P	1830	3220	143,573
2454	1037D	2-dr Spt Cpe-6P	2061	3300	66,378
2434	1067D	2-dr Conv Cpe-5P	2185	3445	19,383
2419	1062D	4-dr Sta Wag-8P	2283	3540	8,156

NOTE: Style Number 1062D was the Bel Air Townsman station wagon with Di-Noc simulated wood-grain exterior trim and color-keyed interior. It had three stationary seats, the rear two being entirely removable for extra cargo capacity.

BEL AIR ENGINE
See 1954 Chevrolet '150' Special engine data.

CORVETTE — SIX — SERIES 2900
See Corvette section.

CHEVROLET CHASSIS FEATURES: Same as 1953 Chevrolet chassis features with following exception: Overall length: (all passenger cars) 196-7/16 inches; (all station wagons) 198-15/16 inches.

POWERTRAIN OPTIONS: Powerglide ($178). External canister type oil filter. Powerglide 3.55:1 rear axle.

1954 Chevrolet, Bel Air 4-dr station wagon, 6-cyl

CONVENIENCE OPTIONS: All options available in 1953 were provided again at about the same prices. New options included: Power brakes ($38). Power operated front window lifts ($86). Power operated seat ($86). Some other options prices were: Power steering ($135). White sidewall tires ($27 exchange).

Historical footnotes: Introduced December, 1953. Model year sales 1,151,486. Calendar year sales 1,414,352. Ford actually out produced Chevrolet on a model year basis this season, but Chevrolet 'dumped' cars on dealers to increase factory shipments and capture first place on a calendar year basis. Thus, Ford was America's largest maker, but Chevrolet was the number 1 "selling" American car again. Last season for woodgrained station wagon trim through 1966 model year, when Caprice station wagon reintroduced this feature. First year automatic transmission was available in all Chevrolets. Last year for exclusive use of six-cylinder powerplants in Chevrolet.

1955 CHEVROLET

1955 Chevrolet, Two-Ten 4-dr sedan, V-8 (AA)

"ONE-FIFTY — SERIES 1500-A — The "One-Fifty" series was Chevrolet's lowest-priced line. Standard equipment included rubber floor mats front and rear; full-width all-steel seat frames with 'S' springs; all vinyl upholstery for station wagon and one piece wraparound windshield. Exterior bright metal decoration was limited to a Chevrolet script on front fender and standard chrome plated bumpers; grille; door handles; hood ornament; lamp rims and wheel hub center caps.

ONE-FIFTY I.D. NUMBERS: The beginning serial numbers for the 1955 "One-Fifty" series were A55-001001 (six cylinder) and VA55-001001 (V-8). Six-cylinder motor numbers began 01001-55Z and up V-8 motor numbers began 01001-55G and up.

ONE-FIFTY SERIES

Model Number	Body/Style Number	Body Type & Seating	Factory Price	Shipping Weight	Production Total
1503	55-1219	4-dr Sedan-6P	1728/1827	3165/3135	29,898
1502	44-1211	2-dr Sedan-6P	1685/1784	3110/3080	66,416
1512	55-1211B	2-dr Sedan-3P	1593/1692	3085/3055	11,196
1529	55-1263F	2-dr Wagon-6P	2030/2129	3290/3260	17,936

"ONE FIFTY" ENGINES
Six-Cylinder: Overhead valve. Cast iron block. Displacement: 235.5 cubic inches. Bore and stroke: 3-9/16 x 3-15/16 inches. Compression ratio: 7.5:1. Brake horsepower. 123 at 3800 R.P.M. (standard shift); 136 at 4200 R.P.M. (Powerglide). Four main bearings. Solid valve lifters (standard shift); Hydraulic valve lifters (Powerglide). Carburetor: Rochester model 7007181 one-barrel.

V-8: Overhead valve. Cast iron block. Displacement: 265 cubic inches. Bore and stroke: 3-¾ x 3 inches. Compression ratio: 8.0:1. Brake horsepower: 162 at 4400 R.P.M. (all V-8's). Five main bearings. Powerglide engine has hydraulic valve lifters. Carburetor: Rochester model 7008006 two-barrel.

NOTE: The V-8 was considered a separate series *not* an option. Factory Prices and Shipping Weights on charts give data for six-cylinder cars above slash and V-8 data below slash.

1955 Chevrolet, Bel Air 2-dr hardtop Sport Coupe, V-8

"TWO-TEN" — SERIES 2100 B — The "Two-Ten" series was Chevrolet's middle-priced line. Standard equipment included all "One-Fity;" equipment listed above plus stainless steel windshield and backlight reveals; chrome front seat and sidewall moldings glove compartment light; ash receptacles; cigarette lighter; arm rests and assist straps. Additional exterior bright metal decoration included upper belting and rear fender side and sash moldings.

"TWO-TEN" I.D. NUMBERS: The beginning serial numbers for the 1955 "Two-Ten" series were B55-001001 (six-cylinder) and VB55-001001 (V-8). The motor number sequence was the same for all series.

"TWO-TEN" SERIES 2100 B

Model Number	Body/Style Number	Body Type & Seating	Factory Price	Shipping Weight	Production Total
2103	55-1019	4-dr Sedan-6P	1819/1918	3180/3150	317,724
2102	55-1011	2-dr Sedan-6P	1775/1874	3145/3125	249,105
2124	55-1011A	2-dr Club Coupe-6P	1835/1934	3145/3115	115,584
2154	44-1037F	2-dr Spt Coupe-6P	1959/2058	3172/3144	11,675
2129	55-1063F	2-dr Wagon-6P	2079/2178	3330/3300	29,918
2109	55-1062F	4-dr Wagon-6P	2127/2226	3370/3340	82,303

"TWO-TEN" ENGINES
Engine availability for the "Two-Ten" series was the same as listed above for the "One-Fifty" line.

1955 Chevrolet, Bel Air 2-dr convertible coupe, V-8

BEL AIR — SERIES 2400-C — The "Bel Air" was Chevrolet's top series. Standard equipment included *most* features found on the lower-priced lines plus carpets on closed body styles; chrome ribbed headliner on Sport Coupe; richer upholstery fabrics; horizontal chrome strip on sides of front fender and doors; narrow white painted insert on rear fender horizontal side molding; gold Bel Air script and Chevrolet crest behind slanting vertical sash molding; ribbed vertical trim plate on sides above rear bumper ends; wide chrome window and door post reveals and full wheel discs.

BEL AIR I.D. NUMBERS: The beginning serial numbers for the 1955 Bel Air series were C55-001001 (six-cylinder) and VC55-001001 (V-8). The motor number sequence was the same for all series.

1955 Chevrolet, Bel Air 2-dr Nomad station wagon, V-8 (AA)

1955 Chevrolet, Bel Air Beauville 4-dr station wagon, 6-cyl

BEL AIR SERIES 2400-C

Model Number	Body/Style Number	Body Type & Seating	Factory Price	Shipping Weight	Production Total
2403	55-1019D	4-dr Sedan-6P	1932/2031	3200/3170	345,372
2402	55-1011D	2-dr Sedan-6P	1888/1987	3155/3125	168,313
2454	55-1037D	2-dr H.T. Spt Cpe-6P	2067/2166	3195/3165	185,562
2434	55-1067D	2-dr Conv-5P	2206/2305	3315/3285	41,292
2429	55-1064DF	2-dr Nomand Wgn-6P	2472/2571	3300/3270	6,103
2409	55-1062DF	4-dr Wagon-6P	2262/2361	3385/3355	24,313

BEL AIR ENGINES
Engine availability for the Bel Air series was the same as for other 1955 Chevrolet lines.

CHASSIS FEATURES: Wheelbase: 115 inches. Overall length: (passenger cars) 195.6 inches; (station wagons) 197.1 inches. Front tread: 58 inches. Rear tread: 58.8 inches. Tires: 6.70 x 15 tubeless.

POWERTRAIN OPTIONS: All three-speed manual gear box with column mounted gear shift was standard on all models. Overdrive was available on the manual transmission at $108 extra. Powerglide two-speed automatic transmission was available at $178 extra. The V-8 engine was available with an optional 'power-pack' that included single four-barrel carburetor and dual exhausts. Optional horsepower rating with 'power-pack' was 180 at 4600 R.P.M.

CONVENIENCE OPTIONS: Power steering ($92). Power brakes ($38). Directional signals. Electric windshield wipers. Power windows. Power seat. Heater and defroster. Air conditioning. White sidewall tires. Fender antenna. Locking gas cap. Continental tire kit. Outside sun visor. Self de-icing wiper blades. Wiring junction block. Electric clock. Compass. Seat covers. Accelerator pedal cover. Wire wheel covers. Tissue dispenser. Exhaust extension. Filter and element. License plate frame. Glare-shields. Grille guard. Fender guard. Door edge guard. Gasoline filler guard. Tool kit. Backup lamps. Courtesy lamps. Cigarette lighter. Floor mats. Outside rear view mirrors. Inside non-glare rear view mirrors. Vanity visor. Body sill. Manual radio. Pushbutton radio. Signal seeking radio. Automatic top riser. Arm rests. wheel trim rings. Safety light with mirror. Sport lamp. Electric shaver. Parking brake signal. Door handle shields. Front fender shields. Rear speaker. vent shades. Inside sun visor. Traffic light viewer. Foot operated windshield washer. Vacuum operated windshield washer.

Historical footnotes: Body style 55-1211B was a Utility Sedan: Body style 55-1263F was a Handyman wagon. Body style 55-1062F was a Handyman wagon. Body style 55-1063F was a Townsman wagon. Body style 55-1011A was the Del Ray. Body style 55-1037F was a mid-year model. Body style 55-1062DF was the Beauville wagon. Body Style 55-1064DF was the Nomad wagon, a two-door station wagon with special hardtop styling introduced as a mid-year model.

1956 CHEVROLET

1956 Chevrolet, One-Fifty 4-dr sedan, V-8 (AA)

'ONE-FIFTY' — SERIES 1500-A — A minor restyling for 1956 Chevrolets included a full-width grille; large, rectangular front parking lamps; new front and rear bumpers and guards (except station wagon guards); inward angled dome-shaped taillamp lenses set into chrome ribbed decorative housings (with backup lamp lens provided); new side trims that varied per series and squarer headlamp hoods. 'One-Fifty' models had Chevrolet rear fender nameplates; chrome moldings around the windshield and rear window and a horizontal body side molding. This chrome strip ran from just behind the headlamp hood crease line to a point below the rear side window, where it was intersected by a slanting sash molding embossed in windsplit style. Standard equipment included a two-spoke steering wheel with horn ring; lockable glove box; dome light and cloth and vinyl upholstery (all-vinyl on station wagon). Features such as the upholstery fabrics or provision of a dashboard ash tray varied per body style, but all had black rubber floor mats and small hub caps as standard features. Just one interior sun visor, on the driver's side, was provided as base 'One-Fifty' equipment.

'ONE-FIFTY' I.D. NUMBERS: The V.I.D. numbering system and numbering locations were unchanged. Serial numbers were A56-001001 to 220555 (six-cylinder) and VA56-001001 to 220555 (eight-cylinder). Six-cylinder motor numbers 01001-56Z to 525227 were used. V-8 motor numbers 01001-56G to 676997 were used.

'ONE-FIFTY' SERIES

Model Number	Body/Style Number	Body Type & Seating	Factory Price	Shipping Weight	Production Total
1503	1219	4-dr Sedan-6P	1869/1968	3206/3186	29,898
1502	1211	2-dr Sedan-6P	1826/3164	3164/3144	66,416
1512	1211B	2-dr Utl Sed-3P	1734/1833	3127/3107	11,196
1529	1263F	2-dr Sta Wag-6P	2171/2270	3309/3289	17,936

'ONE-FIFTY' ENGINES
Six-cylinder. Overhead valves. Cast iron block. Displacement: 235.5 cubic inches. Bore and stroke: 3-9/16 x 3-15/16 inches. Compression ratio: 8.0:1. Brake horsepower: 140 at 4200 R.P.M. Four main bearings. Hydraulic valve lifters. Carburetor: (Powerglide) Rochester model 7007200 one-barrel; or Carter 2101S one-barrel; (standard shift) Rochester model 7007181 one-barrel.
V-8. Overhead valves. Cast iron block. Displacement: 265 cubic inches. Bore and stroke: 3-3/4 x 3 inches. Compression ratio: 8.0:1. Brake horsepower: (standard transmission or 'Touch-Down' overdrive) 162 at 4400 R.P.M.; (Powerglide) 170 at 4400 R.P.M. Five main bearings. Hydraulic valve lifters. Carburetor: (Powerglide) Carter two-barrel model 2286S; Rochester two-barrel model 7009910; (standard shift) Rochester two-barrel model 7009909.

NOTE: The V-8 was considered a separate series *not* an option. Factory prices and shipping weights on charts give data for six-cylinder cars above slash and V-8 data below slash.

1956 Chevrolet, Two-Ten 2-dr hardtop Sport Coupe, V-8 (AA)

'TWO-TEN' — SERIES 2100 B — The 'Two-Ten' Series was Chevrolet's middle-priced line. These cars also carried Chevrolet rear fender nameplates and had chrome moldings around the windshield and backlight, plus on the side window sills. The side trim was distinctive in that the single horizontal molding swept downward, towards the rear bumper end, from the point where the sash molding intersected it below the rear side window. Exterior and interior details varied per body style, but all models had two sunshades (visors), ash trays and cigarette lighters and richer interior trims. The Del Ray coupe featured deep pile carpets and all vinyl upholstery, while others had vinyl coated rubber floor mats and vinyl and cloth trims. A two-spoke steering wheel with horn ring was used. Small hub caps were standard equipment. Specific interior colors were standard, but custom colored upholstery was optional. A brand new style was a pillarless four-door hardtop, which was called a Sport Sedan.

'TWO-TEN' I.D. NUMBERS: The Chevrolet numbering system and number locations were used and numbers assigned were the same as on 'One-Fifty' models, except the serial number prefix was a 'B'.

'TWO-TEN' SERIES

Model Number	Body/Style Number	Body Type & Seating	Factory Price	Shipping Weight	Production Total
2103	1019	4-dr Sedan-6P	1955/2054	3212/3192	283,125
2113	1039	4-dr H.T. Spt Sed	2117/2216	3262/3242	20,021
2102	1011	2-dr Sedan-6P	1912/2011	3177/3157	205,545
2124	1011A	2-dr Coupe-6P	1971/2070	3182/3162	56,382
2154	1037	2-dr H.T. Spt Cpe	2063/2162	3204/3184	18,616
2129	1063F	2-dr Sta Wag-6P	2215/2314	3344/3324	22,038
2109	1062F	4-dr Sta Wag-6P	2263/2362	3381/3361	113,656
2119	1062FC	4-dr Sta Wag-9P	2348/2447	3500/3480	17,988

REMINDER: As mentioned earlier, Fisher Body Style Numbers (second column) appear on vehicle data plates under the hood and reveal much about the car. They are preceeded by a two-digit prefix (not shown here) that indicates model year, '56' = 1956, etc. The first two digits of main number indicate series, for example 10 = 'Two-Ten' or Bel Air. The next two-digits indicate body type, for example 39 = Sport Sedan. Alphabetical suffixes indicate tirm or equipment features, for example F = folding seat in station wagon. Familiarity with such codes is highly recommended to hobbyists, restorers and collectors. These codes can be especially important when ordering N.O.S. (new old stock) parts.

1956 Chevrolet, Bel Air Nomad 2-dr station wagon, V-8

'TWO-TEN' ENGINES
Availability of base engines for the 'Two-Ten' series was the same as listed above for the 'One-Fifty' line.

1956 Chevrolet, Bel Air 4-dr hardtop Sport Sedan, V-8

BEL AIR — SERIES 2400 C — A real honey of a car, the luxurious Bel Air was richly appointed inside and out. Bel Air nameplates and emblems appeared on rear fenders. The slanting sash molding blended into a horizontal chrome belt that ran forward to the headlamp crease and doubled back, running horizontally to below rear side windows and then, sweeping down towards the rear bumper ends. Chrome wheel covers were standard equipment. There was an extra chrome treatment around and between all window groups. Three-spoke steering wheels and deep-pile carpets graced all models, but the Beauville nine-passenger station wagon. It had vinyl coated rubber floor mats as standard equipment. Exclusive Bel Air models included a convertible and the Milestone two-door Nomad station wagon, the latter having a unique two-door hardtop roof treatment. All Bel Airs had electric clocks and lighted, lockable glove compartments. All 1956 Chevrolets with V-8 power had large V-shaped emblems below the crest ornaments on the hood and deck, a feature which really looked great on Bel Airs.

BEL-AIR I.D. NUMBERS: The Chevrolet system was also used on Bel Air with the same range of numbers seen for other lines, but with a 'C' prefix for serial numbers.

BEL AIR SERIES

Model Number	Body/Style Number	Body Type & Seating	Factory Price	Shipping Weight	Production Total
2403	1019D	4-dr Sedan-6P	2068/2167	3231/3211	269,798
2413	1039D	4-dr H.T. Spt Sed	2230/2329	3280/3260	103,602
2402	1011D	2-dr Sedan-6P	2025/2124	3197/3177	104,849
2454	1037D	2-dr H.T. Spt Cpe	2176/2275	3232/3212	128,382
2434	1067D	2-dr Conv Cpe-6P	2344/2443	3340/3320	41,268
2429	1064DF	2-dr Nomad-6P	2608/2707	3362/3342	7,886
2419	1062DF	4-dr Sta Wag-9P	2482/2581	3516/3496	13,268

BEL AIR ENGINES
Base engines available for Bel Airs were the same as for other 1956 Chevrolet lines.

CHASSIS FEATURES: Wheelbase: 115 inches. Overall length: (station wagons) 200.8 inches; (all other models) 197.5 inches. Front tread: 58 inches. Rear tread: 58.9 inches. Tires: (station wagons) 6.70 x 15 six-ply on nine-passenger models; (all other models) 6.70 x 15 four-ply; (optional) 7.10 x 15 four-ply.

POWERTRAIN OPTIONS: Three-speed manual transmission with column mounted control was standard. Overdrive was available on the manual transmission at $108 extra. Powerglide two-speed automatic transmission was available at $189 extra. A four-barrel Super Turbo-Fire V-8 with 205 horsepower and 9.25:1 compression ratio was optional with all transmissions. Also a 225 horsepower dual four-barrel carburetor. Study of the specifications charts will reveal that Chevrolet V-8s were lighter than sixes. The resulting power-to-weight ratio is one reason 1956 Chevrolet V-8s became known as the 'Hot Ones.'

1956 Chevrolet, Bel Air Beauville 4-dr station wagon, V-8

CONVENIENCE OPTIONS: Power steering ($92). Power brakes ($38). Accelerator cover. Oil bath air cleaner. Air-conditioner (V-8 only). Arm rests for 'One-Fifty'. Autronic Eye. Backup lights. Chrome sill moldings. Park brake signal lamp. Power seat (except 'One-Fifty'). Lighted cigarette lighter. Electric clock (except Bel Air). Eleven-inch diameter heavy-duty clutch. Optional colors (paint or convertible top). Compass. Courtesy lights. Custom Color interior. Door edge guards. Door handle shields. Exhaust-extension. Fender guards. Fender top moldings. Floor mats. Locking gas cap. Heavy-duty generators. DeLuxe heater and defroster. Recirculating heater and defroster. Tinted glass. Glovebox lamp as option. Six-cylinder governor. Vibrator horn. License frames. Power convertible top. Vanity mirror. Oil filter. Chrome grille guard. Insect screen. Radio antennas. Radios (manual, pushbutton or signal-seeking). Rear speaker. Rain deflectors. Rearview mirrors (three-types). Seat covers. Ventilated seat pad. Electric shaver. Spotlights. Heavy-duty springs. Righthand sun visor for 'One-Fifty'. White wall and oversize tires. tissue dispenser. Tool Kit. Traffic light viewer. Trunk light. Underhood light. Continental wheel carrier. Wheel covers. Wire wheel covers. Power windows (except 'One-Fifty'). Plastic windshield glare shield. Outside sun visor. Windshield washers (automatic or foot operated). De-icing wiper blades. Dual electric wipers. wiring junction block.

Historical footnotes: Dealer introductions were held in November, 1955. Model year production equalled 1,574,740 units. Calendar year sales hit 1,621,004, Chevrolet was America's Number 1 maker. The 'Two-Ten' club coupe was called the Del Ray coupe. The 'One-Fifty' utility coupe was the equivalent of traditional business coupe and had a single front bench seat with raised storage compartment platform behind. All four-door hardtops were called Sport Sedans; two-door hardtops were Sport Coupes. Nine-passenger station wagons were called Beauvilles. Four-door conventional station wagons were called Townsman. Two-door conventional station wagons were called Handyman. The two-door Nomad station wagon had a slanting pillar roofline, cross ribbed roof and slanting tailgate with seven chrome 'slat' moldings. An innovation on all 1956 Chevrolets was that the lefthand taillamp functioned as the fuel filler door. The Nomad station wagon is a recognized Milestone Car. All 1955-57 Chevrolets are generally regarded as 'modern Classics', although not afforded traditional recognition as such by the Classic Car Club of America.

1957 CHEVROLET

1957 Chevrolet, One-Fifty 2-dr sedan, V-8 (AA)

'ONE-FIFTY' — SERIES 1500 — One of the most popular models in the modern collector car hobby, the 1957 Chevrolet was highlighed by a new oval shaped front bumper grille complete with bomb type bumper guards. Round front parking lamps were seen at each end of a horizontal center bar that seemed to float against the delicately cross-hatched grille insert. A Chevrolet medallion was set into a center cavity within this horizontal bar. Windsplit bulges ran along both sides of the flat hood panel, decorated in front by bomb sight ornaments. The headlamps were set into small 'grilles' housed in square-looking fender openings. New side moldings appeared, but varied for each series, looking a little richer as they moved up the scale. The rear fenders were shaped into broad, flat tailfins. Although based on the previous body structure, the new Chevrolet image seemed more modern and sportier. The 'One-Fifty' models were the plainest. They had exclusive use of the 1955-1956 style sash molding (below rear side windows), which intersected an approximately half-length, single horizontal molding. This strip of chrome ran from the front door region to the trailing edge of the tailfins. Chevrolet scripts were affixed to the upper sides of front fenders. The fins had only partial outline moldings near their rear tip, which dropped to the taillight housing. The grille insert was done in anodized aluminum finish. Interior trims were the most basic, although the Handyman station wagon had a two-tone look inside. Round horn buttons were used with standard steering wheels.

'ONE-FIFTY' I.D. NUMBERS: The V.I.D. numbering system and number locations were unchanged. Serial numbers used on 'One-Fifty' models were A57-100001 to 314393 for Sixes; VA57-100001 to 314393 for V-8s. Motor numbers are now difficult to catalog and factory shop manuals or master parts catalogs should be consulted.

'ONE-FIFTY' SERIES

Model Number	Body/Style Number	Body Type & Seating	Factory Price	Shipping Weight	Production Total
1503	1219	4-dr Sedan-6P	2048/2148	3241/3232	52,266
1502	1211	2-dr Sedan-6P	1996/2096	3216/3207	70,774
1512	1211B	2-dr Utl Sed-3P	1885/1985	3168/3159	8,300
1529	1263F	2-dr Sta Wag-6P	2307/2407	3411/3402	14,740

NOTE: The V-8 was considered a separate series, *not* an option. Factory prices and weights, on charts, give data for six-cylinder cars above slash and V-8 data below slash. Note that V-8s are now priced uniformly at $100 above six-cylinder models.

1957 Chevrolet, Bel Air 2-dr sedan, V-8

'ONE-FIFTY' ENGINES
Six-cylinder: See 1956 six-cylinder engine data. The 'Blue Flame' Six came with synchromesh, overdrive or Powerglide attachment.

V-8: See 1956 engine data applicable to the 265 cubic inch V-8. This 'Turbo-Fire 265' was available as the base V-8 powerplant for 1957 Chevrolets with synchromesh or overdrive transmissions only. It was not available with optional automatic transmissions according to the *1957 Chevrolet Passenger Car Shop Manual.* All other drive choices are listed under Powertrain Options below.

1957 Chevrolet, Two-Ten 2-dr station wagon, V-8 (AA)

'TWO-TEN' — SERIES 2100 — Distinguishing this line from the lowest series was the distinct side trim treatment; richer interiors and not really much else. The body rub moldings began just behind the headlight area and gently sloped to the rear bumper ends, although the sweep was most pronounced towards the rear half of the body. However, there was a second, upper molding, that branched off just below (and behind) the body belt dip. This top molding just about paralleled the general contour of the fins and ran, rearward, to hit the back edge of the fender. Inside the two moldings, near the taillamp, a Chevrolet script was placed. In many cases, this 'inside' area was painted a contrasting color, as part of many optional two-tone finish schemes. Other trim features were the same used on 'One-Fifty' models. For instance, rear fender top moldings on the rear third of the fins only and silver aluminized grilles. Three two-tone interior schemes, with cloth and vinyl combinations, were available at standard prices. Despite its kinship to the lowest priced line, this year's Two-Ten looked more Bel Air like, especially when done up in optional two-tone exterior finish. As in 1956, all Chevrolets with V-8 power had large, V-shaped hood and deck lid ornaments, which were bright metal finished on the lower series.

'TWO-TEN' I.D. NUMBERS: The only V.I.D. numbering variation for the mid-range models was a 'B' prefix (instead of 'A') for the serial numbers (with a 'VB' prefix indicating V-8 attachment). The range of numbers was the same used on 'One-Fifty' models, which indicates mixed production runs.

'TWO-TEN' SERIES

Model Number	Body/Style Number	Body Type & Seating	Factory Price	Shipping Weight	Production Total
2103	1019	4-dr Sedan-6P	2174/2274	3275/3266	260,401
2113	1039	4-dr HT Spt Sed-6P	2270/2370	3325/3316	16,178
2102	1011	2-dr Sedan-6P	2122/2222	3230/3221	162,090
2124	1011A	2-dr Del Ray Cpe-6P	2162/2262	3225/3216	25,664
2154	1037	2-dr HT Spt Cpe-6P	2204/2304	3265/3256	22,631
2109	1062F	4-dr Sta Wag-6P	2456/2556	3466/3457	27,803
2119	1062FC	4-dr Sta Wag-9P	2563/2663	3566/3557	21,083
2129	1063F	2-dr Sta Wag-6P	2402/2502	3411/3402	17,528

'TWO-TEN' ENGINES
Availability of base engines for the 'Two-Ten' Series was the same as listed above for the 'One-Fifty' line.

1957 Chevrolet, Bel Air 2-dr hardtop Sport Coupe, V-8

BEL AIR — SERIES 2400 C — Extra richness characterized the Bel Air line in all regards. Side trim was arranged as on 'Two-Tens', except the area between the molding 'branches' was filled with a silver anodized aluminum beauty panel Three gold chevrons marked the forward side of each front fender. Also done in gold were such things as the grille insert, V-8 ornaments (when used) and Bel Air beauty panel scripts. Rocker sills, roof and window outlines and the entire edge of the fins were all trimmed with bright metal moldings. There were also traditional Chevrolet/Bel Air crests on the rear fenders, near the golden script. Distinctive two-tone interiors were another highlight. The Nomad station wagon had carryover features with new 1957 styling and the convertible was a dream car come true.

BEL AIR I.D. NUMBERS: The Chevrolet numbering system was also used on Bel Airs with the same range of numbers seen for other lines, but with 'C' or 'VC' serial number prefixes.

1957 Chevrolet, Bel Air Nomad 2-dr station wagon, V-8

BEL AIR SERIES

Model Number	Body/Style Number	Body Type & Seating	Factory Price	Shipping Weight	Production Total
2403	1019D	4-dr Sedan-6P	2290/2390	3281/3272	254,331
2413	1039D	4-dr HT Spt Sed-6P		2364/2464	137,672
2402	1011D	2-dr Sedan-6P	2238/2338	3237/3228	62,751
2454	1037D	2-dr HT Spt Cpe-6P	2299/2399	3283/3274	166,426
2434	1067D	2-dr Conv Cpe-5P	2511/2611	3414/3405	47,562
2409	1062DFC	4-dr Sta Wag-6P	2580/2680	3465/3456	27,375
2429	1064DF	2-dr Nomad-6P	2757/2857	3470/3461	6,103

BEL AIR ENGINES
Base engines available for Bel Airs were the same as for other 1956 Chevrolet lines.

CHASSIS FEATURES: Wheelbase: 115 inches. Overall length: 200 inches. Front tread: 58 inches. Rear tread: 58.8 inches. Tires: 7.50 x 14 four-ply tubeless black wall.

1957 Chevrolet, Bel Air 4-dr hardtop Sport Sedan, V-8 (AA)

POWERTRAIN OPTIONS: According to the *1957 Chevrolet Passenger Car Shop Manual* six extra cost power options were available in conventional (non-Corvette) models, along with six gearbox selections. This provided a total of 17 optional engine/transmission combinations as follows:

C.I.D. Displ.	Comp. Ratio	Carb Barrels	Exhaust	H.P. @ R.P.M.	Trans Combo	Valve Lifters
TURBO-FIRE V-8						
283	8.5	2V	1	185 @ 4600	3-4	H
SUPER TURBO-FIRE V-8						
283	9.5	4V	2	220 @ 4800	1-2-3-4	H
CORVETTE V-8						
283	9.5	2 x 4V	2	245 @ 5000	1-2-4-5-6	H
283	9.5	F.I.	2	250 @ 5000	1-4-5-6	H
283	9.5	2 x 4V	2	270 @ 6000	5	S
283	10.5	F.I.	2	283 @ 6200	5	S

NOTES: F.I. = Fuel injection. Transmission choices: (1) — Three-speed manual; (2) — Overdrive; (3) — Regular Powerglide; (4) — Turboglide; (S) — Close-ratio three-speed and (6) — Corvette type Powerglide. H = hydraulic lifters. S = solid (mechanical) lifters. Covette V-8s were not available in sedan deliveries. Lightweight valves were used only with SR high-performance camshaft and solid lifters. Some collectors maintain that a limited number of 1957 Chevrolet passenger cars came with four-speed manual transmission attachments, perhaps dealer installed. This *cannot* be verified with normal factory literature and seems unlikely. Cars with fuel-injection engines wore special badges denoting this fact.

CONVENIENCE OPTIONS: Power brakes ($38). Power steering ($70). Overdrive ($108). Powerglide ($188). Turboglide ($231). Plus all other options listed in 1956 section at approximately the same prices. The fuel-injection V-8 was priced $484 over the base price of a Six. The more complete prices listed for 1958 Chevrolet optional equipement would be very close, if not the same, as prices for similar items in 1957. Safety seat belts and shoulder harnesses were new options this season.

Historical footnotes: Dealer introductions for 1957 Chevrolets were held October, 1956. Model year production peaked at 1,515,177 cars. Calendar year sales were counted at 1,522,536 units. Chevrolet outsold Ford by only 136 cars on a calendar year basis, but Ford actually built more 1957 specifications models than Chevrolet. It was a neck-and-neck battle between the Big Two this season. Turboglide transmission was a running production change, so some early cars may have had 265 cubic inch V-8s with Powerglide attachment. Chevrolet claimed that its solid lifter fuel-injection V-8 was the first American production car engine to provide one horsepower per cubic inch (283 cubic inches/283 horsepower). However, the 1956 Chrysler 300-B with optional V-8 had claimed the same achievement some six months earlier. This year the Chevrolet gas filler was incorporated into the chrome molding at the rear edge of the lefthand tailfin. Body style nomenclature (Sport Sedan; Sport Coupe; Del Ray; Beauville; Townsman; Handyman and Nomad) was similar, in application, to the year before.

1958 CHEVROLET

1958 Chevrolet, Del Ray 2-dr sedan, 6-cyl (AA)

DEL RAY — 1100 SERIES (6-CYL) — 1200 SERIES (V-8) — By adopting an all-new Safety Girder chassis for 1958, Chevrolet brought to market a completely reengineered and restyled line. Body revisions included lower, wider, longer sheet metal; a new front end with dual headlamps and a dream car look; gull-wing rear fender and deck sculpturing and revamped side trim treatments. New names, identified two-series, while models available within each line were altered, too. The sedan delivery was cataloged as a conventional model, but strangely, not with the station wagons — now a series unto themselves. Del Ray nameplates marked the rear fender coves (indentations) of four styles in the low-priced line, which had single belt moldings and lacked bright metal side window trim. Del Ray interior appointments were, needless to say, the most basic types with standard steering wheels, rubber floor mats and fewer bright highlights.

CHEVROLET I.D. NUMBERS: Serial number were stamped on a plate affixed to the left front door hinge pillar. The first symbol, a letter, identified series as follows: A = Del Ray Six; B = Del Ray V-8; C = Biscayne Six; D = Biscayne V-8; E = Bel Air Six; F = Bel Air V-8. The second and third symbols were '58' for 1958 model year. The fourth symbol indicated assembly plant, as follows: A = Baltimore; F = Flint; J = Janesville; K = Kansas City; L = Los Angeles; N = Norwood; O = Oakland: S = St. Louis and T = Tarrytown. The last six symbols were numbers indicating production sequence. Numbers for each series at each factory began at 100001 and up. For example, Number A58(F)-100101 = one hundredth Del Ray Six manufactured in Flint, Mich. Sedan deliveries used Body Style Number and letter prefix (G = Six; H = V-8). For example, 1171-G48(F)-100001 for Del Ray Six Sedan delivery built at Flint. Engine numbers are not given in general reference sources.

Model Number	Model Number	Body Type & Seating	Factory Price	Shipping Weight	Production Total
(PASSENGER CARS)					
1149	1249	4-dr Sedan-6P	2155/2262	3439/3442	Note 1
1141	1241	2-dr Sedan-6P	2101/2208	3396/3399	Note 1
1121	1221B	2-dr Utl Sed-3P	2013/2120	3351/3356	Note 1
1171	1271	2-dr Sed DeL-1P	2123/2230	3529/3531	Note 1
(STATION WAGONS)					
1193	1293	4-dr Sta Wag-6P	2467/2574	3740/3743	Note 1
1191	1291	2-dr Sta Wag-6P	2413/2520	3693/3696	Note 1

NOTE 1: Chevrolet production totals, after 1957, are available only in the following form, which indicates *all* series. There are no breakouts per series, model or engine type. For 1958, the totals were: Four-door sedan = 491,441; Two-door sedan = 256,182; Four-door station wagon = 170,473; Sports Coupe = 142,592; Sports Sedan = 83,330; Convertible = 55,989 and Two-door station wagon = 16,590.

ADDITIONAL NOTE: Chevrolet station wagons were officially listed as separate series, but will be grouped under passenger cars with the same level of trim in his catalog. Station wagons with Del Ray trim were called Yeoman models.

1958 Chevrolet, Bel Air Impala 2-dr hardtop Sport Coupe, V-8

ADDITIONAL NOTE: The model numbering system changed in 1958. Model numbers and Body Style Numbers are now identical. The first column in chart above now shows model/body numbers for Sixes. The second column in chart now shows model/body numbers for V-8s. This system will be applied for post 1958 models as well.

DEL RAY ENGINES
Six-cylinder. Overhead valves. Cast iron block. Displacement: 235.5 cubic inches. Bore and stroke: 3.56 x 3.94 inches. Compression ratio: 8.25:1. Brake horsepower: 145 at 4200 R.P.M. Four main bearings. Hydraulic valve lifters. Carburetor: Rochester two-barrel model 7012127.
V-8. Overhead valves. Cast iron block. Displacement: 283 cubic inches. Bore and stroke: 3.875 x 3 inches. Compression ratio: 8.5:1. Brake horsepower: 185 at 4600 R.P.M. Five main bearings. Hydraulic valve lifters. Carburetor: Rochester two-barrel model 7012133.

BISCAYNE — SERIES 1500 (6-CYL) — 1600 SERIES (V-8) — Only two body styles came under the Biscayne name, although two Brookwood station wagons wore the same level trim. Since Sixes and V-8s were considered separate series, the result is eight Biscayne level cars to catalog. The passenger styles wore Biscayne nameplates at the leading edge of the rear fender cove, but station wagons had Brookwood scripts in the same location. All 1958 Chevrolets with V-8 power had additional, large, V-shaped ornaments on the hood and deck (or tailgate). Biscayne side trim moldings outlined the upper and lower edges of the cove, but did not connect. Ahead of the cove, a bi-level belt molding, with slight forward taper, was seen. It was connected to the single, lower cove outline trim at the rear. Like the Del Ray models, Biscaynes came standard with small hub caps, no sill moldings, no chevrons and no fender ornaments, but they did feature slightly up-market interior trims.

BISCAYNE SERIES

Model Number	Model Number	Body Type & Seating	Factory Price	Shipping Weight	Production Total
(PASSENGER CARS)					
1549	1649	4-dr Sedan-6P	2290/2397	3447/3450	Note 1
1541	1641	2-dr Sedan-6P	2236/2343	3404/3407	Note 1
(STATION WAGONS)					
1593	1693	4-dr Sta Wag-6P	2571/2678	3748/3751	Note 1
1594	1694	4-dr Sta Wag-9P	2678/2785	3837/3839	Note 1

NOTE 1: See Del Ray, Note 1, production total data. **ADDITIONAL NOTE:** Station wagons with Biscayne trim are Brookwoods and were actually part of the separate Chevrolet station wagon series.

NOTE: The V-8 was considered a separate series *not* an option. Factory Prices and Shipping Weights on charts give data for six-cylinder cars above slash and V-8 data below slash.

BISCAYNE ENGINES
See 1958 Del Ray engine specifications.

1958 Chevrolet, Bel Air 4-dr hardtop Sport Sedan, V-8 (AA)

BEL AIR — 1700 SERIES (6-CYL) — 1800 SERIES (V-8) — This series was enriched over others and was also endowed with two, even more luxurious Impala models. The base Bel Air had a series name scripts and Chevrolet crests of the rear of the coves. The upper edge of the indentation was outlined with a single level molding that slashed down and back, below the body belt dip, to intersect an elaborated horizontal molding arrangement. This could best be described as spear-shaped moldings, with indented concave contrast band towards the rear, and a horizontally grooved, missle-shaped 'spear tip' at the front. Also seen were four chevrons on the sides of the front fenders; four short vertical strips on the lower rear fenders bulge; front fender top ornaments; chrome outlined side windows; grooved rear roof pillar beauty plates and full wheel discs. Interior appointments were rich and fancy. The Impala sport coupe and convertible were even more impressive. Trim features included Impala scripts, insignia and crossed-flag emblems at the front of the cove; broad, ribbed body sill panels; large dummy chrome plated chrome air scoops ahead of rear wheel wells; competition style two-spoke deep hub steering wheels (with Impala medallions); Impala dashboard script; standard rear radio speaker grille (with Impala script and medallion between rear seatback dip) and triple taillamp arrangments (replacing two taillights on other cars; one on all station wagons). The Impala sport coupe had a chrome-edged, rear facing dummy air scoop and curved contour crease molded into the back of the roof.

BEL AIR SERIES

Model Number	Model Number	Body Type & Seating	Factory Price	Shipping Weight	Production Total
(PASSENGER CARS)					
1749	1849	4-dr Sedan-6P	2440/2547	3467/3470	Note 1
1739	1839	4-dr HT SptSed-6P	2511/2618	3511/3514	Note 1
1741	1841	2-dr Sedan-6P	2386/2493	3424/3427	Note 1
1731	1831	2-dr HT Spt Cpe-6P	2447/2554	3455/3458	Note 1
(IMPALA)					
1747	1847	2-dr HT Spt Cpe-5P	2586/2693	3458/3459	Note 1
1767	1867	2-dr HT Spt Con-5P	2724/2841	3522/3523	Note 1
(STATION WAGON)					
1793	1893SD	4-dr Nomad-6P	2728/2835	3738/3771	Note 1

NOTE 1: See Del Ray, Note 1, production total data. **ADDITIONAL NOTES:** Impalas were considered part of the Bel Air line and were *not* listed as a sub-series. The Nomad station wagon was now a four-door style with conventional styling, but high-level trim. The Nomad was actually a part of the separate Station Wagon Series, but had Impala trim with Nomad rear fender nameplates.

CHASSIS FEATURES: Wheelbase: 117.5 inches. Overall length: 209.1 inches. Overall width: 77.7 inches. Overall height: (Impala Convertible) 56.5 inches; (Impala sport coupe) 56.4 inches; (other models) 57.4 inches. Tires: (convertibles and station wagons) 8.00 x 14; (other models) 7.50 x 14. Full coil spring suspension; high-level ventilation; anti-dive braking and built-in leveling and foot operated parking brakes were used this year.

POWERTRAIN OPTIONS: Optional engine and tranmission combinations were as follows:

C.I.D. Displ.	Comp. Ratio	Carb Barrels	Exhaust	H.P. @ R.P.M.	Trans Combo	Valve Lifter
SUPER TURBO-FIRE V-8						
283	9.5	4V	1	230 @ 4800	1-2-3-5	H
TURBO-THRUST V-8						
348	9.5	4V	2	250 @ 4400	1-4-5-6	H
SUPER TURBO-THURST V-8						
348	9.5	3 x 2V	2	280 @ 4800	1-4-5	H
348 (M)	11.0	3 x 2V	2	315 @ 5600	1-5	S
RAM-JET FUEL INJECTION V-8						
283	9.5	F.I.	1	250 @ 5000	1-4-5-6	H
283 (M)	10.5	F.I.	1	290 @ 6200	1-5	S

NOTES: (M) - Maximum performance V-8. F.I. - fuel injection. Transmission choices; (1) - Three-speed manual; (2) - Overdrive; (3) - Two-Speed Powerglide; (4) - Turboglide; (5) - Close-ratio three-speed; (6) - Corvette type Powerglide; H - Hydraulic lifters; S - Solid lifters. (M) - Includes special performance type cam shaft and high-speed valve trains. Some of the transmission attachment data that has been interpolated as normal factory literature is not specific about types of three-speed manual or automatic transmission used.

1958 Chevrolet, Bel Air Impala 2-dr convertible, V-8 (AA)

CONVENIENCE OPTIONS: Four-barrel carburetor for 283 cubic inch, 230 horsepower V-8 ($27). Turbo-thrust 250 horsepower V-8 ($59). Super Turbo-thrust 280 horsepowr V-8 ($70). Base fuel-injection 250 horsepower V-8 ($484). Powerglide transmission ($188). Turboglide transmission ($231). Overdrive ($108). Power steering ($70). Power brakes ($38). Power window control ($102). Front power seat ($43). Oil filter ($9). Oil bath air cleaner ($5). Dual exhaust as option ($16). DeLuxe heater ($77). Recirculating heater ($49). Whitewall tires, size 7.50 x 14, four-ply ($32). E-Z-I tinted glass ($38). Electric wipers ($7). Safety panel padding ($16). Manual radio ($61). Pushbutton radio ($84). Air conditioning ($468). Air suspension ($124). Two-tone paint ($32). Posi-traction rear axle with 3.36 or 3.55 ratio ($48). Other standard dealer installed accessories.

Historical footnotes: Dealer introductions of 1958 Chevrolets took place October, 1957. Model year total was 1,217,047 cars. Calendar year total was 1,255,935 cars. Gas filler now under door in trunk latch lid panel. On Impalas the center tail lens housed a backup lamp. A great deal of bright metal trim on 1958 Chevrolets was made of aluminum.

1959 CHEVROLET

BISCAYNE — SERIES 1100 (6-CYL) — 1200 SERIES (V-8) — Chevrolet for 1959 featured new slimline styling with wider, roomier bodies; new radiator grilles; seagull-wing rear ends; cat's eye taillights; increased glass area and flat-top roof styling on Sport Sedans. Standard equipment on Biscaynes included rear foam cushions; electric wipers and oil bath air cleaner for V-8s.

CHEVROLET I.D. NUMBERS: The V.I.D. numbers followed the 1958 system. A new assembly plant code 'W' was adopted for Willow Run, Mich. built cars. Other codes and starting numbers were unchanged.

BISCAYNE SERIES

Model Number	Model Number	Body Type & Seating	Factory Price	Shipping Weight	Production Total
(PASSENGER CARS)					
1119	1219	4-dr Sedan-6P	2301/2419	3605/3600	Note 1
1111	1211	2-dr Sedan-6P	2247/2365	3535/3530	Note 1
1121	1221	2-dr Utl Sed-3P	2160/2278	3480/3490	Note 1
(STATION WAGONS)					
1135	1235	4-dr Brookwd-6P	2638/2756	3955/3955	Note 1
1115	1215	2-dr Brookwd-6P	2571/2689	3870/3860	Note 1

NOTE 1: Chevrolet production totals are now available by body style only. For 1959, the totals were: Four-door sedan - 525,461; Two-door sedan - 281,924; Four-door station wagon - 188,623: Sports Sedan - 182,520; Sports Coupe - 164,901; Convertible - 72,765 and Two-door station wagon - 20,760. No breakouts by series, model or body style are available.

BISCAYNE ENGINE
Six-cylinder. Overhead valves. Cast iron block. Displacement: 235.5 cubic inches. Bore and stroke: 3-9/16 x 3-15/16 inches. Compression ratio: 8.25:1. Brake horsepower: 135 at 4000 R.P.M. Four main bearings, Hydraulic valve lifters. Carburetor: Rochester two-barrel model 7013003.

1959 Chevrolet, Impala 2-dr convertible, V-8

V-8: Overhead valves. Cast iron block. Displacement: 283 cubic inches. Bore and stroke: 3.875 x 3 inches. Compression ratio: 8.5:1. Brake horsepower: 185 at 4600 R.P.M. Five main bearings. Hydraulic valve lifters. Carburetor: Rochester two-barrel model 7013007.

1959 Chevrolet, Bel Air 4-dr sedan, 6-cyl (AA)

BEL AIR — SERIES 1500 (6-CYL) — SERIES 1600 (V-8) — Bel Airs had model script nameplates and crests on front fenders. While Biscayne side moldings ran from the headlights to center front doors, Bel Air moldings ran full length and had painted inserts. Another enrichment was front fender top ornaments. Kingswood and Parkwood station wagons had Bel Air trim, but their own model scripts on front fenders. Standard equipment was the same as Biscayne plus DeLuxe features, front foam seat cushions, DeLuxe steering wheel and power tailgate on Kingswood.

BEL AIR SERIES

Model Number	Model Number	Body Type & Seating	Factory Price	Shipping Weight	Production Total
(PASSENGER CARS)					
1519	1619	4-dr Sedan-6P	2440/2558	3600/3615	Note 1
1539	1639	4-dr HT Spt Sed-6P	2556/2674	3660/3630	Note 1
1511	1611	2-dr Sedan-6P	2386/2504	3515/3510	Note 1
(STATION WAGONS)					
1535	1635	4-dr Parkwd-6P	2749/2867	3965/3970	Note 1
1545	1645	4-dr Kingwd-9P	2852/2970	4020/4015	Note 1

NOTE 1: See 1959 Biscayne, Note 1, production total data.

BEL AIR ENGINES
See 1959 Chevrolet Biscayne engine data.

NOTE: The V-8 was considered a separate series *not* an option. Factory prices and shipping weights on charts give data for six-cylinder cars above slash and V-8 data below slash.

1959 Chevrolet, Impala 2-dr convertible, V-8 (AA)

IMPALA — SERIES 1700 (6-CYL) — SERIES 1700 (V-8) — For the "upper crust" Chevrolet, identification features included Impala nameplates and crossed racing flags emblems. Both identifiers were mounted inside the painted insert area of the full-length side trim moldings, below the rear side windows. The front fender top ornaments also had rear extension strips. Bright metal trim marked the deck lid center crease and taillamp lenses. Closed models had simulated Impala-style roof scoops. Nomads had Impala trim with different I.D. scripts. Standard equipment was the same as on Bel Airs, plus electric clock, dual sliding sun visors and aluminum trim.

IMPALA SERIES

Model Number	Model Number	Body Type & Seating	Factory Price	Shipping Weight	Production Total
(PASSENGER CARS)					
1719	1819	4-dr Sedan-6P	2592/2710	3625/3620	Note 1
1739	1839	4-dr HT Spt Sed-6P	2664/2782	3665/3670	Note 1
1737	1837	2-dr HT Spt Cpe-6P	2599/2717	3570/3580	Note 1
1767	1867	2-dr Conv Cpe-6P	2849/2967	3660/3650	Note 1
(STATION WAGONS)					
1735	1835	4-dr Nomad-6P	2891/3009	3980/3975	Note 1

NOTE 1: See 1959 Biscayne, Note 1, production total data.

IMPALA ENGINES
See 1959 Chevrolet Biscayne engine data.

CHASSIS FEATURES: Wheelbase: 119 inches. Overall length: 210.9 inches. Overall width: 79.9 inches. Overall height: (hardtops) 54 inches; (sedans) 56 inches; (station wagons) 56.3 inches. Tires: (convertible and station wagons) 8.00 x 14; (all other models) 7.50 x 14.

1959 Chevrolet, Bel Air 4-dr hardtop Sport Sedan, V-8

POWERPLANT OPTIONS: Optional engine and transmission combinations were as follows:

C.I.D. Displ.	Comp. Ratio	Carb Barrels	Exhaust	H.P. @ R.P.M.	Trans Combo	Valve Lifters
SUPER TURBO-FIRE V-8						
283	9.5	4V	1	230 @ 4800	1-2-3-4-5-6	H
RAM-JET FUEL INJECTION V-8						
283	9.5	F.I.	1	250 @ 5000	1-3-4-5-6-7	H
283	10.5	F.I.	1	290 @ 6200	1-5-7	H
TURBO-THRUST V-8						
348	9.5	4V	2	250 @ 4400	1-3-4-5-6-7	H
SUPER TURBO-THRUST V-8						
348	9.5	3 x 2V	2	280 @ 4800	1-3-4-5-6-7	H
SPECIAL TURBO-THRUST V-8						
348	11.0	4V	2	300@ 5600	1-3-5-6-7	S
SPECIAL SUPER TURBO-THRUST V-8						
348	11.0	3 x 2V	2	315 @ 5600	1-5-7	S

NOTES: F.I. - fuel injection. Transmission choices; (1) - Three-speed manual; (2) - Overdrive; (3) - Two-Speed Powerglide; (4) - Turboglide; (5) - Close-ratio three-speed; (6) - Corvette type Powerglide; (7) - Four-speed. Some of the transmission attachment data above is interpolated, as normal factory literature is not specific about types of three-speed manual or automatic transmissions used.

CONVENIENCE OPTIONS: Powerglide transmission ($199). Turboglide transmission ($242). Overdrive ($108). Super Turbo-fire V-8 ($147). Turbo-thrust V-8 ($199). Super Turbo-thrust V-8 ($269). Power steering ($75). Power brakes ($43). Power windows ($102). Power seat ($102). Oil filter ($9). Oil bath air cleaner ($5). Dual exhausts ($19). DeLuxe heater ($80). Recirculating heater ($52). Whitewall 7.50 x 14 tires ($32). Whitewalls 8.00 x 14 tires, for convertibles and station wagons ($35); other models ($51). E-Z-I tinted glass ($43). Windshield washer ($12). Padded dash ($18). Manual radio ($65). Pushbutton radio ($87). Air-conditioner including heater ($468). Air suspension ($135). Positraction with 3.36; 3.55 or 4.11 gears ($48). Two-tone paint, on Biscayne ($22); on Brookwood, Bel Air, Impala ($27); on Parkwood, Kingswood, Nomad ($32). Power tailgate window ($32). DeLuxe steering wheel ($4). Close-ratio four-speed transmission ($188). Wheel discs ($16). Two-speed wipers and washers ($16). Shaded rear window ($22). Front air foam cushion ($8). DeLuxe Group including sun visor; front arm rest; fender ornaments and cigarette lighter ($16). Heavy-duty 35-ampere generator($8).

Historical footnotes: Dealer introductions were held October, 1958. The Del Ray name was dropped. Calendar year sales were 1,528,592 units. Model year production equaled 1,481,071 cars. Ford and Chevy ran neck-and-neck, but Chevrolet turned out more cars built to 1959 specifications.

1960 CHEVROLET

BISCAYNE — SERIES 1100/1300 (6-CYL) — SERIES 1200/1400 (V-8) — This year a new oval grille enclosed dual headlamps. Missile inspired side trim was seen. The 'seagull' fins were more angular. Small circular taillamps were set into a beauty panel at the rear. Identification came from Biscayne front fender scripts; painted rear beauty panel and single molding quarter panel trim. Brookwoods, actually part of a separate station-wagon series, were trimmed like Biscaynes, except for front fender scripts. Cataloged as standard were dual sun visors, electric wipers, cigarette lighter and front arm rests, all formerly considered DeLuxe equipment. An economy sub-series for corporate fleet use was provided in two Fleetmasters, which were marketed without these DeLuxe type items.

BISCAYNE I.D. NUMBERS: The V.I.D. numbers followed the 1959 system.

BISCAYNE SERIES

Model Number	Model Number	Body Type & Seating	Factory Price	Shipping Weight	Production Total
(BASE PASSENGER CARS)					
1169	1269	4-dr Sedan-6P	2316/2423	3500/3505	Note 1
1111	1211	2-dr Sedan-6P	2262/2369	3415/3425	Note 1
1121	1221	2-dr Utl Sed-6P	2175/2282	3390/3395	Note 1
(FLEETMASTER 1300 SUB-SERIES)					
1369	1469	4-dr Sedan-6P	2284/2391	3495/3500	Note 1
1311	1411	2-dr Sedan-6P	2230/2337	3410/3415	Note 1
(STATION WAGONS)					
1145	1245	4-dr Brookwd-9P	2756/2863	3900/3895	Note 1
1135	1235	4-dr Brookwd-6P	2653/2760	3850/3845	Note 1

NOTE 1: Chevrolet production totals are again available by body style only. For 1960, the totals were: Four-door sedan - 497,048; Two-door sedan - 228,322; Sports Coupe - 204,467; Four-door station wagon - 198,066; Sports Sedan - 169,016; Convertible - 79,903 and Two-door station wagon - 14,663. No breakouts by series, model or engine are available.

BISCAYNE ENGINES
The 235 cubic inch six and 283 cubic inch V-8 remained the base engine for each series. There were no changes in specifications from 1959, except in Biscayne V-8 attachments, where a detuned 170 horsepower rating was cataloged for the '283'.

NOTE: The V-8 was considered a separate series *not* an option. Factory Prices and Shipping Weights on charts give data for six-cylinder cars above slash and V-8 data below slash.

1960 Chevrolet, Bel Air 2-dr hardtop sports coupe, 6-cyl

BEL AIR — SERIES 1500 (6-CYL) — SERIES 1600 (V-8) — A shield medallion split the words Bel Air on front fenders. A single rear quarter extension molding flew rearward from the missile ornament. The rear beauty panel was horizontally grooved and outlined with bright metal trim. All Biscayne features were standard, plus front foam cushions; DeLuxe steering wheel and power tailgate on Kingswood station wagon.

BEL AIR SERIES

Model Number	Model Number	Body Type & Seating	Factory Price	Shipping Weight	Production Total
(PASSENGER CARS)					
1519	1619	4-dr Sedan-6P	2438/2545	3565/3580	Note 1
1539	1639	4-dr HT Spt Cpe-6P	2554/2661	3605/3620	Note 1
1511	1611	2-dr Sed-6P	2384/2491	3490/3505	Note 1
1537	1637	2-dr HT Spt Cpe-5P	2489/2596	3515/3530	Note 1
(STATION WAGONS)					
1545	1645	4-dr Kingswd-9P	2850/2957	3990/4000	Note 1
1535	1635	4-dr Parkwd-6P	2747/2854	3945/3950	Note 1

NOTE 1: See 1960 Biscayne, Note 1, production total data.

BEL AIR ENGINE
See 1959 Chevrolet Biscayne engine data.

1960 Chevrolet, Impala 2-dr hardtop sports coupe, V-8 (AA)

IMPALA — SERIES 1700 (6-CYL) — SERIES 1800 (V-8) — The Impala was dressy from stem to stern. A short molding strip extended back from the headlights. Twin pairs of bar moldings were above and below this strip on the fender tips. The quarter panel missile ornaments had two moldings streaking rearward, the area between them filled with a white insert and Impala script with crossed racing flags insignia. Triple taillights and a vertically ribbed aluminum rear beauty panel were seen. All, but convertibles, had simulated vents on the lower rear window molding. Standard equipment was as on Bel Airs, plus parking brake, glove compartment and backup lights; anodized aluminum trim; electric clock and, on V-8s, oil filters and oil bath air cleaners.

IMPALA SERIES

Model Number	Model Number	Body Type & Seating	Factory Price	Shipping Weight	Production Total
(PASSENGER CARS)					
1719	1819	4-dr Sedan-6P	2590/2697	3575/3580	Note 1
1739	1839	4-dr HT Spt Sed-6P	2662/2769	3625/2625	Note 1
1737	1837	2-dr HT Spt Cpe-5P	2597/2704	3540/3530	Note 1
1767	1867	2-dr Conv Cpe-6P	2847/2954	3635/3625	Note 1
(STATION WAGONS)					
1735	1835	4-dr Nomad-6P	2889/2996	3960/3955	Note 1

NOTE 1: See 1960 Biscayne, Note 1, production total data.

CHASSIS FEATURES: Same as 1959 data except for a 0.1 inch reduction in overall length.

POWERTRAIN OPTIONS: Engine and transmission teams were similar to 1959, with the following changes: (1) The Ram Jet fuel injection system was *not* available. (2) The 348 cubic inch Special Super Turbo-Thrust V-8 came only in one variation; with 11.25:1 compression, Tri-Power carburetion, dual exhaust, highlift camshaft and mechanical lifters. It was now rated 335 horsepower at 5800 R.P.M. Consult 1959 Powertrain chart with these changes in mind.

1960 Chevrolet, Impala 2-dr convertible, V-8

CONVENIENCE OPTIONS: Oil bath air cleaner ($5). Air conditioner, including heater; requires automatic drive ($468). Positraction ($43). H-D battery ($8). Biscayne economy carburetor ($8). H-D clutch for Six ($5). Foam front cushion ($8). PCV valve ($12). Dual exhausts ($19). Temperature Control fan ($16). Generators, 35-amp ($8); 40-amp ($27). Tinted glass, windshield ($22); all windows($38); shaded backlight for Sport Coupe ($14). DeLuxe heater ($74). Recirculating heater ($46). Padded dash ($18). Non-glare inside mirror ($4). Six-cylinder oil filter ($9). Two-tone paint ($16). Power brakes ($43). Power seat, except 1100/1200/1300/1400, Six-Way ($97); Four-Way ($65). Power steering ($75). Power tailgate window ($32). Power windows, except 1100/1200/ 1300/1400 ($102). Manual radio ($56). Pushbutton radio ($72). H-D rear coil springs ($3). DeLuxe steering wheel ($4). Whitewalls, priced by size and model, ($16-36). Overdrive ($188). Powerglide on six ($188); on V-8 ($199). Turboglide V-8 only ($210). Four-speed close-ratio, V-8 only ($188). Wheel discs ($15). Windshield washer ($11). Electric wipers with washer ($16). Super Turbo-fire V-8 ($136). Turbo-thrust V-8 ($188). Special Turbo-thrust V-8 ($268). Special Turboglide thrust 320 horsepower V-8 ($311). Super turbo-thurst V-8 ($258). Special Super Turbo-thrust V-8 ($333). Seat belt ($16). Electric clock ($21). Wheel covers ($24). Edge guards, two-door ($4); four-door ($7). Lamps, ash tray ($3); backup ($13); courtesy ($7); glove box ($3); luggage ($4) and underhood ($4). Mats, front ($7); rear ($7). OSRV mirror, body-mounted ($6). Vanity mirror ($2). Body sill molding ($15). Brake signal ($5). Rear speaker ($15).

Historical footnotes: Model introduction October, 1959. Calendar year production 1,863,598. Model year production 1,391,485. Corvair introduced. Totals above include Corvettes and Corvairs, which are listed separately in this catalog.

1961 CHEVROLET

BISCAYNE — SERIES 1100/1300 (6-CYL) — SERIES 1200/1400 (V-8) — The 1961 Chevrolets followed the General Motors' pattern in adopting a brand new, downsized body, but varied from the corporate trend in that strictly carryover engineering was used. Grille and front areas were rather flat and square, while the rear end sported a flat V-type fin. At the front, a full-width air slot stretched above the grille, below the beveled front lip of the hood. The bevel line swept around the front body corners and ran, in a straight line, down and back towards the rear quarter panel. There, it angled upwards again, to connect with the flat V-type fin. Biscaynes had twin circular taillamps, small hub caps and model nameplates on upper rear fender tips, while lacking side body moldings along the bevel line. Rocker panel strips *were* used on 1100/1200 level cars, but not on the Series 1300/1400 Fleetmaster economy jobs. Standard equipment consisted on dual sun visors, electric windshield wipers, cigarette lighter, front arm rests and five 7.50 x 14 black tubeless tires.

CHEVROLET I.D. NUMBERS: Vehicle I.D. numbers were located at left front body hinge pillar. The first symbol was a '2' for 1962. The second through fifth symbols corresponded with the model/body number. The sixth symbol identified the final assembly plant as follows: A = Atlanta; B = Baltimore; F = Flint; G = Framingham; H = Fremont; J = Janesville; K = Kansas City; L = Los Angeles; N = Norwood; O = Oakland; R = Arlington; S = St. Louis; T = Tarrytown; U = Southgate; Y = Wilmington; W = Willow Run.

BISCAYNE SERIES

Model Number	Model Number	Body Type & Seating	Factory Price	Shipping Weight	Production Total
(FLEETMASTER LINE)					
1369	1469	4-dr Sedan-6P	2284/2391	3495/3500	Note 1
1311	1411	2-dr Sedan-6P	2230/2337	3410/3415	Note 1
(DELUXE LINE)					
1169	1269	4-dr Sedan-6P	2316/2423	3500/3505	Note 1
1111	1211	2-dr Sedan-6P	2262/2369	3415/3425	Note 1
1121	1221	2-dr Utl Sed-3P	2175/2282	3390/3395	Note 1
(STATION WAGONS)					
1145	1245	4-dr Brookwd-9P	2756/2863	3900/3895	Note 1
1135	1235	4-dr Brookwd-6P	2643/2760	3850/3845	Note 1

NOTE 1: Chevrolet production was recorded, by body style only, as follows: Four-door sedan = 452,251; Sport Coupe = 177,969; Sport Sedan = 174,141; four-door station wagon = 168,935; two-door sedan = 153,988 and convertible = 64,624. No further breakouts by model, series or engine were provided by Chevrolet, except in the case of Super Sport models, of which 453 were reported as built. Industry statistics provide *some* additional information. First, on a model year basis, approximately 137,300 station wagons were two-seat types and approximately 31,649 others had three-seats configuration. Second, Chevrolet production by series, again on a model year basis, included the following: (Fleetmaster) 3,000 units; (Biscayne) 201,006 units; (Bel Air) 330,000 units; (Impala) 491,000 units; and (Station Wagons) 169,000 units. These figures are slightly rounded-off, as is the figure of 513,000 six-cylinder Chevrolets built this season.

BISCAYNE ENGINE
Six-cylinder. Overhead valves. Cast iron block. Displacement: 235 cubic inches. Bore and stroke: 3.56 x 3.94 inches. Compression ratio: 8.25:1. Brake horsepower: 135 at 4000 R.P.M. Four main bearings. Hydraulic valve lifters. Carburetor: Rochester one-barrel model 7013003.

V-8: Overhead valves. Cast iron block. Displacement: 283 cubic inches. Bore and stroke: 3.875 x 3.00 inches. Compression ratio: 8.5:1. Brake horsepower: 170 at 4200 R.P.M. Five main bearings. Hydraulic valve lifters. Carburetor: Rochester two-barrel model 7019007.

NOTE: The V-8 was considered a separate series *not* an option. Factory Prices and Shipping Weights on charts give data for six-cylinder cars above slash and V-8 data below slash. Station wagons were grouped by the manufacturer as a separate series, but are being grouped under passenger cars with similar trim level in this catalog.

1961 Chevrolet, Bel Air 4-dr sedan, 6-cyl

BEL AIR — SERIES 1500 (6-CYL) — SERIES 1600 (V-8) — A chrome trim bar, extending from the front parking lights rearward to the trunk, distinguished Bel Airs from Biscaynes. Bel Air nameplates appeared at the upper rear fender; twin taillamps were seen; small hub caps were standard equipment and no rocker sill strips were used. As in other lines, regular sedans, Sport Sedans, Sport Coupes and station wagons all had individual rooflines with the flat-top look on regular sedans, a formal look on Sport Sedans, a rounded semi-fastback on Sport Coupes and boxy, conventional station wagon styling. Station wagons had Bel Air trim, but Parkwood rear fender scripts. Standard equipment matched that of Biscayne, plus foam seat cushions and DeLuxe steering wheel.

BEL AIR SERIES

Model Number	Model Number	Body Type & Seating	Factory Price	Shipping Weight	Production Total
(PASSENGER CARS)					
1569	1669	4-dr Sedan-6P	2438/2545	3515/3520	Note 1
1539	1639	4-dr HT Spt Sed-6P	2554/2661	3550/3555	Note 1
1511	1611	2-dr Sedan-6P	2384/2491	3430/3435	Note 1
1537	1637	2-dr HT Spt Cpe-5P	2489/2596	3475/3480	Note 1
(STATION WAGONS)					
1545	1645	4-dr Parkwd-9P	2850/2957	3910/3910	Note 1
1535	1635	4-dr Parkwd-6P	2747/2854	3865/3860	Note 1

NOTE 1: Chevrolet production was recorded only by body style. Chevrolet did not provide breakouts by model, series or engine. Industry statistics record that 330,000 Bel Air passenger cars were built. See Biscayne, Note 1, production totals for fuller details and station wagon production data.

BEL AIR ENGINES
See Biscayne engine data for 1961 Chevrolet base powerplants.

IMPALA — SERIES 1700 (6-CYL) — SERIES 1800 (V-8) — Impalas were easily identified by their triple taillight treatment. They also had crossed racing flags insignia at the center of the rear deck and at the rear fenders, with model identification scripts in the latter location as well. DeLuxe wheel discs and wide side moldings, with contrasting insert panels, were other visual distinctions of the top Chevrolet line. Nomad station wagons had Impala level trim, but Nomad rear fender signatures. Standard equipment lists began with Bel Air features and added parking brake, glovebox and backup lights; anodized aluminum trim; electric clock and 8.00 x 14 size tires on convertibles. By the way, all 1961 Chevrolet V-8s had oil filters and oil bath type air clenaers, all station wagons had 8.00 x 14 tires and nine-passenger jobs had power tailgates.

IMPALA SERIES

Model Number	Model Number	Body Type & Seating	Factory Price	Shipping Weight	Production Total
(PASSENGER CARS)					
1769	1869	4-dr Sedan-6P	2590/2697	3530/3525	Note 1
1739	1839	4-dr HT Spt Sed-6P	2662/2769	3575/2570	Note 1
1711	1811	2-dr Sedan-6P	2536/2643	3445/3440	Note 1
1737	1837	2-dr HT Spt Cpe-5P	2597/2704	3485/3480	Note 1
1767	1867	2-dr Conv Cpe-5P	2847/2954	3605/3600	Note 1
(STATION WAGONS)					
1745	1845	4-dr Nomad-9P	2922/3099	3935/3930	Note 1
1735	1835	4-dr Nomad-6P	2889/2996	3885/3885	Note 1

NOTE 1: Chevrolet production was recorded only by body style. Chevrolet did not provide breakouts by model, series or engine. Industry statistics record that approximately 491,000 Impala passenger cars (excluding station wagons) were built. Chevrolet has further revealed that 453 of these cars were equipped with a new 'Super Sport' option package. **SUPER SPORT NOTE:** The 1961 Super Sport package was a dealer installed kit available on any Impala model. It consisted of 'SS' emblems on rear fenders and deck lid; instrument panel pad; special wheel covers with spinners; power brakes and steering; heavy-duty springs and shocks; sintered metallic brake linings; 7,000 R.P.M. tachometer and 8.00 x 14 narrow band white sidewall tires. A choice of five performance power teams was available. Price for the equipment package was in the $54 range according to sources.

1961 Chevrolet, Impala 2-dr convertible, V-8

1961 Chevrolet, Impala 2-dr convertible, V-8

IMPALA SERIES ENGINES
See Biscayne engine data for 1961 Chevrolet base powerplants.

CHASSIS FEATURES: Wheelbase: 119 inches. Overall length: 209.3 inches. Front tread: 60.3 inches. Rear tread: 59.3 inches. Width: 78.4 inches. Height: 55.5 inches. Tires: Sizes are noted above.

1961 Chevrolet, Impala 4-dr hardtop Sport Sedan, V-8

POWERTRAIN OPTIONS: Six optional engine choices were provided for 1961 Chevrolets as follows:

C.I.D. Displ.	Comp. Ratio	Carb Barrels	Exhaust	H.P. @ R.P.M.	Trans Combo	Valve Lifters
SUPER TURBO-FIRE V-8						
283	9.5	4V	1	230 @ 4800	N.A.	H
TURBO-THRUST V-8						
348	9.5	4V	2	250 @ 4400	N.A.	H
SPECIAL TURBO-THRUST V-8						
348	9.5	4V	2	305 @ 5200	N.A.	S
348	11.25	4V	2	340 @ 5800	N.A.	S
SUPER TURBO-THRUST V-8						
348	11.25	3 x 2V	2	280 @ 4800	N.A.	H
SPECIAL SUPER TURBO-THRUST V-8						
348	11.25	3 x 2V	2	350 @ 6000	N.A.	S
TURBO-FIRE '409' V-8						
409	11.00	1x 4V	2	360 @ 5800	N.A.	S

1961 Chevrolet, Impala 2-dr convertible, V-8

CONVENIENCE OPTIONS: Oil bath air cleaner ($5). DeLuxe air-conditioner, with V-8 only, includes heater ($457). Cool pack air conditioner ($317). Positraction rear axle ($43). Heavy-Duty battery ($8). Group A body equipment package including OSRV mirror, front and rear bumper guards, grille guard and inside non-glare mirror, for all models except Impala and Nomad ($48). Group B body equipment package with electric clock, door guards and backup lights for all models except Impala and Nomad; two-door ($23); four-door ($26). Economy carburetor ($8). Heavy-duty clutch for six-cylinder models ($5). Crankcase ventilation system, required on California cars ($5). Air Foam front seat cushions for Biscayne and Brookwood models ($8). Positive engine ventilation for six-cylinder models ($12). Dual exhausts combined with 230 horsepower V-8 ($25). Temperature controlled radiator fan for V-8 models ($16). Optional generators, three types ($8-97). Tinted glass, all windows ($38); windshield only ($22); shaded rear windows on two-door Sport Coupe ($14). DeLuxe heater ($74); recirculating heater ($47). Padded instrument panel ($18). Oil filter with six-cylinder models ($9). Two- tone paint ($16). Power brakes ($43). Six-way power seat, except Biscayne and Brookwood, ($97); Four-way power seat, except Biscayne and Brookwood, ($65). Power steering ($75). Power tailgate window ($32). Power windows, except Biscayne and Brookwood, ($102). Heavy-Duty radiator ($11). Radios, manual ($54); pushbutton ($62). Heavy-Duty rear coil springs ($3). DeLuxe steering wheel ($4). Overdrive transmission ($108). Powerglide transmission with six-cylinder ($188). Powerglide transmission with V-8 ($199). Turboglide transmission with V-8 ($210). Four-speed, close ratio manual transmission with V-8 ($188). Wheel covers ($15). Windshield washers ($11). Two-speed electric windshield wipers and washers ($16). Super Turbofire V-8) ($136). Turbothrust V-8 ($201). Special Turbothrust V-8 ($317). Special Turbothrust, 340 horsepower V-8 ($344). Super Turbothrust V-8 ($271). Special Super Turbothrust V-8 ($365).

1961 Chevrolet, Impala 2-dr hardtop Sport Coupe

1961 Chevrolet, Impala, 4-dr Nomad Wagon.

Historical footnotes: Chevrolets were introduced to the public October 8, 1960. The Division's model year production output peaked at 1,204,917 cars, including Corvettes, but excluding 297,881 Corvairs. (See separate catalog listing for Corvettes and Corvairs). A total of 142 Impalas were manufactured with Super Sport equipment and the 409 cubic inch V-8. Production of models built to 1961 specifications ceased on August 2 of the year. Calendar year production of 1,604,805 units in all lines made Chevrolet America's Number 1 maker again. Semon E. 'Bunkie' Knudsen was general manager of the division this season.

1962 CHEVROLET

1962 Chevy II, Series '300' 4-dr station wagon, 6-cyl

CHEVY II — ALL SERIES — Designed to combat the popularity of the Falcon, Ford Motor Company's conventional compact car, the Chevy II line made its debut in 1962. This no nonsense economy job featured simple, squarish styling with unitized body frame construction. Major front end components, including fenders, were of bolt-on design for easy replacement. There were eleven basic models arranged in five different series, according to powerplant applications. At the bottom were the '100' Four or Six having, as standard equipment, five 6.00 x 13 tires; heater and defroster; front foam cushions; cigarette lighter; electric windshield wipers; oil filter and power tailgate on three-seat station wagons. These cars lacked moldings around the side windows, rear deck panel and body sides and had spartan interiors. The '300' Four and Six had all moldings mentioned above, plus slightly enriched interiors. The fifth series was the Nova 400, which came only with six-cylinder power. Identification features included Nova rear fender nameplates; side body, window and deck trim; rocker sill strips; front fender tip windsplit moldings and full wheel discs. Nova equipment included all found on the lower series plus 6.50 x 13 tires (also used on base station wagons); rear foam seat cushions; floor carpets and special interior upholstery and trim. The engines used in all Chevy IIs were completely new.

CHEVY II I.D. NUMBERS: Vehicle numbers were on the left front body hinge pillar. Motor numbers, for both engines, were on the right side of the block to the rear of distributor. The first symbol was a '2' indicating model year. The next four symbols corresponded to model numbers in the chart below. Note that '300' Six and Nova 400s both use 400 numbering, but with distinct body codes. The sixth symbol was a standard Chevrolet assembly plant code (See 1961 section), with Chevy II production limited to factories in Willow Run, Michigan and Norwood, Ohio. The last six numbers were the sequential production code starting with 100001 at each plant.

CHEVY II SERIES (ALL)

Model Number	Model Number	Body Type & Seating	Factory Price	Shipping Weight	Production Total
SERIES 100 (4-CYL)/SERIES 100 (6-CYL)					
0169	0269	4-dr Sedan-6P	2041/2101	2445/2535	Note 1
0111	0211	2-dr Sedan-6P	2003/2063	2410/2500	Note 1
0135	0235	2-dr Sta Wag-6P	2339/2399	2665/2755	Note 1
SERIES 300 (4-CYL)/SERIES 300 (6-CYL)					
0369	0469	4-dr Sedan-6P	2122/2182	2460/2550	Note 1
0311	0411	2-dr Sedan-6P	2084/2144	2425/2515	Note 1
0345	0445	2-dr Sta Wag-9P	2517/2577	2765/2855	Note 1
SERIES NOVA 400 (6-CYL)					
NA	0449	4-dr Sedan-6P	2236	2575	Note 1
NA	0441	2-dr Sedan-6P	2198	2540	Note 1
NA	0437	2-dr Spt Cpe-5P	2264	2550	Note 1
NA	0467	2-dr Conv-5P	2475	2745	Note 1
NA	0435	4-dr Sta Wag-6P	2497	2775	Note 1

NOTE 1: Production totals were recorded by body style only, with no breakouts by series, model or engine. Totals for 1962 were as follows: Four-door sedan = 139,004; Four-door station wagons = 59,886; Two-door Sport Coupe = 59,586; Two-door sedan = 44,390 and Two-door convertible = 23,741. See Historical footnotes for additional 1962 Chevy II production data.

1962 Chevrolet, Chevy II Nova 2-dr convertible, 6-cyl

ADDITIONAL NOTES: Since Chevrolet Model Numbers and Body Style Numbers were the same, Column 1 above has been used to list four-cylinder model codes and Column 2 above has been used to list six-cylinder model codes. Factory Prices and Shipping Weights above slash are for Fours, below slash for Sixes. The Nova 400 line came only with six-cylinder power, so no slashes are used.

CHEVY II ENGINES

Four-cylinder. Overhead valves. Cast iron block. Displacement: 153.3 cubic inches. Bore and stroke: 3.875 x 3.25 inches. Compression ratio: 8.5:1. Brake horsepower: 90 at 4000 R.P.M. Five main bearings. Hydraulic valve liftes. Carburetor: Rochester one-barrel model 7020103.

Six-cylinder. Overhead valves. Cast iron block. Displacement: 194.4 cubic inches. Bore and stroke: 3.562 x 3.25 inches. Compression ratio: 8.5:1. Brake horsepower: 120 at 4400 R.P.M. Seven main bearings. Hydraulic valve lifters. Carburetor: Rochester one-barrel Model 7020105.

NOTE: There was a factory-offered kit for dealer installation for either a 283 to 327 cubic inch V-8 engine with horsepower up to 360 h.p.

BISCAYNE — SERIES 1100 (6-CYL) — SERIES 1200 (V-8) — The plainest full-sized Chevrolet benefited from the body side sculpturing of the 1962 design. Standard features included heater and defroster; dual sun visors; crank operated ventipanes; directional signals; parallel action windshield wipers; front door arm rests; ash tray; coat hooks and color keyed vinyl-coated rubber floor coverings. Interiors were trimmed in cloth and leather grain vinyl with all vinyl sidewalls. Exterior bright metal decoration included an anodized aluminum grille with pairs of headlamps flanking. Biscaynes had a slender, full length lower body sill molding and four taillights at the rear. The series script appeared on the rear fenders. Small hub caps were standard.

BISCAYNE I.D. NUMBERS: Serial numbers began with 211( )( )-( )100001 for the six-cylinder cars; 212( )( )-( )100001 for the V-8s. The numbers were coded with the first five symbols representing the year, series and style number. The sixth symbol was the alphabetical assembly plant code and the last six symbols represented the sequential assembly number, with series in mixed production.

BISCAYNE SERIES

Model Number	Model Number	Body Type & Seating	Factory Price	Shipping Weight	Production Total
(PASSENGER CARS)					
1169	1269	4-dr Sedan-6P	2378/2485	3480/3475	Note 1
1111	1211	2-dr Sedan-6P	2324/2431	3405/3400	Note 1
(STATION WAGONS)					
1135	1235	4-dr Biscayne-6P	2725/2832	3845/3840	Note 1

1962 Chevrolet, Impala 2-dr convertible, V-8

NOTE: Production totals were recorded by body style only, with no breakouts by series, model or engine. Totals for 1962 'Regular Chevrolets' were as follows: Four-door sedan = 533,349; Two-door hardtop Sport Coupe = 323,427; Four-door station wagon = 187,566; Four-door hardtop Sport Sedan = 176,077; Two-door sedan = 127,870 and Two-door convertible = 75,719. Model year statistics kept by the industry tell us additional information about production by series, body style and engine in rounded off figures. Production of Biscaynes, excluding station wagons was, for example, approximately 166,000 units. Production of *all* full-sized Chevy V-8s was 921,900 units. Production of *all* full-sized Chevy Sixes was 502,100 units. Production of *all* Chevrolet station wagons was 187,600. **ADDITIONAL NOTE:** The V-8 was considered a separate series *not* an option. Factory Prices and Shipping Weights above slash are for Sixes, below slash for V-8s. Since Chevrolet Model Numbers and Body Style Numbers were the same, the first column in each chart has been used to list six-cylinder model codes and the second column in each chart has been used to list V-8 model codes.

BISCAYNE ENGINE

Six-cylinder. Overhead valves. Cast iron block. Displacement: 235 cubic inches. Bore and stroke: 3.56 x 3.94 inches. Compression ratio: 8.25:1. Brake horsepower: 135 at 4000 R.P.M. Four main bearings. Hydraulic valve lifters. Carburetor: Rochester one-barrel model 7013003.

V-8. Overhead valves. Cast iron block. Displacement: 283.0 cubic inches. Bore and stroke: 3.875 x 3.00 inches. Compression ratio: 8.5:1. Brake horsepower: 170 at 4200 R.P.M. Five main bearings. Hydraulic valve lifters. Carburetor: Rochester two-barrel Model 7020007.

1962 Chevrolet, Bel Air 2-dr hardtop Sport Coupe, V-8

BEL AIR — SERIES 1500 (6-CYL) — SERIES 1600 (V-8) — This was Chevrolet's popular mid-priced line. Standard equipment included all Biscayne features plus extra quality interior appointments; foam front and rear seats; color keyed carpeting; foam backed luggage compartment mat and a specific steering wheel hub. Interiors were higher grade cloth and vinyl combinations. A full-length upper body side molding was used with Bel Air script appearing on the rear fenders just below it. A stainless bright gutter cap molding was another Bel Air feature. Four taillights, arranged two on each side, were seen. A bright rear cove molding added a touch of distinction.

BEL AIR I.D. NUMBERS: Followed the Chevrolet system with second pair of symbols '15' for Sixes and '16' for V-8s.

BEL AIR SERIES

Model Number	Model Number	Body Type & Seating	Factory Price	Shipping Weight	Production Total
(PASSENGER CARS)					
1569	1669	4-dr Sedan-6P	2510/2617	3480/3475	Note 1
1511	1611	2-dr Sedan-6P	2456/2563	3410/3405	Note 1
1537	1637	2-dr HT Spt Cpe-6P	2561/2668	3445/3440	Note 1
(STATION WAGONS)					
1545	1645	4-dr Sta Wag-9P	2922/3029	3895/3890	Note 1
1535	1635	4-dr Sta Wag-6P	2819/2926	3845/3840	Note 1

NOTE 1: Production totals were recorded by body style only, with no breakouts by series, model or engine. See Biscayne, Note 1, for 'Regular Chevrolet' overall production totals. Model year statistics kept by the industry tell us additional information about production in rounded off figures. For example, production of 1962 Bel Airs, excluding station wagons, was approximately 166,000 units.

BEL AIR ENGINES

Base engines for Bel Airs were the same as for Biscaynes. See 1962 Biscayne engine data.

1962 Chevrolet, Impala 4-dr sedan, V-8

IMPALA — SERIES 1700 (6-CYL) — SERIES 1800 (V-8) — Chevrolet's top models were in the Impala line. Standard equipment included most features found on lower priced lines plus bright aluminum front seat end panels; bright metal backed rear view mirror; extra long front and rear arm rests with finger-tip door release handles; built-in door safety panel reflectors; rear seat radio grille built into Sport Coupe and convertible styles and Sports type steering wheel with Impala center emblem. The instrument panel included an electric clock; parking brake warning light; glove compartment light and bright metal valance panels. Interiors were plusher cloth and leather grain vinyl combinations with embossed vinyl headlining. Exterior body side trim consisted of a full-length body side upper molding with color keyed insert; a wide, ribbed body sill molding; stainless steel window reveals (except convertible) and Impala script badge on the rear fenders. Front fender ornaments were standard, while, at the rear, a brushed aluminum cove panel with six taillamps was found. Backup lights were built-in. A simulated rear window vent was seen, below the glass, on all styles, but the convertible.

IMPALA I.D. NUMBERS: Followed the Chevrolet system with second pair of symbols '17' for Sixes and '18' for V-8s.

IMPALA SERIES

Model Number	Model Number	Body Type & Seating	Factory Price	Shipping Weight	Production Total
(PASSENGER CARS)					
1769	1869	4-dr Sedan-6P	2662/2769	3510/3505	Note 1
1739	1839	4-dr HT Spt Sed-6P	2734/2841	3540/3535	Note 1
1747	1847	2-dr HT Spt Cpe-5P	2669/2776	3455/3450	Note 1
1767	1867	2-dr Conv-5P	2919/3026	3565/3560	Note 1
(STATION WAGONS)					
1745	1845	4-dr Sta Wag-9P	3064/3171	3935/3930	Note 1
1735	1835	4-dr Sta Wag-6P	2961/3068	3870/3865	Note 1

NOTE 1: Production totals were reported by body style only, with no breakouts by series, model or engine. See Biscayne, Note 1, for 'Regular Chevrolet' overall production totals. Model year statistics kept by the industry tell us additional information about production in rounded off figures. For example, production of 1962 Impalas, excluding station wagons, was approximately 704,900 units. Chevrolet records also reveal that 99,311 Impalas were manufactured with optional Super Sport equipment packages. Also, of interest to collectors, a total of 15,019 cars had the 409 cubic inch V-8 installed during the 1962 model year.

1962 Chevrolet, Impala 4-dr hardtop Sport Sedan, V-8

IMPALA ENGINES

Base engines for Impalas were the same as for Biscaynes. See 1962 Biscayne engine data.

CHASSIS FEATURES: Wheelbase: (Chevy II) 110 inches; (Chevrolet) 119 inches. Overall length: (Chevy II station wagon) 197.4 inches; (all other Chevy IIs) 183 inches; (Chevrolet, all models) 209.6 inches. Front tread: (Chevy II) 56.8 inches; (Chevrolet) 60.3 inches. Rear tread: (Chevy II) 56.3 inches; (Chevrolet) 59.3 inches. Tires: (Chevy II, all station wagons and Sport models) 6.50 x 13; (all other Chevy II) 6.00 x 13; (Biscayne) 7.00 x 14; (Chevrolet station wagons) 8.00 x 14; (all other Chevrolets) 7.50 x 14.

CHEVROLET POWERTRAIN OPTIONS: Turbo-Fire 250 horsepower 327 cubic inch V-8 with four-barrel carburetor and dual exhausts ($191). Turbo-Fire 300 horsepower 327 cubic inch V-8 with four-barrel carburetor and dual exhausts ($245). Turbo-Fire 380 horsepower 409 cubic inch V-8 with four-barrel carburetor, dual exhausts, high-lift camshaft and solid valve lifters ($428). Turbo-Fire 409 horsepower 409 cubic inch V-8 with dual four-barrel carburetors, light weight valve train, dual exhausts and solid valve lifters ($484). Economy carburetor ($8). Heavy-duty six-cylinder clutch ($30). Positive crankcase ventilation system ($5). Positive six-cylinder engine ventilation ($12). Heavy-duty battery ($8). Oil bath air cleaner ($5). Temperature controlled 170 horsepower V-8 radiator fan ($16). Generator 35-amp ($8). Delcotron 45-amp generator ($27). Delcotron 52-amp generator, with DeLuxe air-conditioner ($8); without air ($34). Note: Generator options not available with 409 cubic inch V-8s. Heavy-duty radiator ($11). Positraction rear axle ($43). Overdrive transmission ($108). Six-cylinder Powerglide attachment ($188). V-8 Powerglide attachment, not available with 409 cubic inch engine ($199). Close-ratio four-speed transmission with Turbo-Fire V-8 ($188).

CHEVY II POWERTRAIN OPTIONS: Rear axles with 3.36 or 3.55 gear ratio ($2). Positraction rear axle ($40). Heavy-duty battery ($8). Heavy-duty clutch ($5). Crankcase ventilation ($4). Generator, 35-amp ($8). Delcotron generator 42-amp ($27). Heavy-duty radiator ($3). Powerglide transmission ($167).

CHEVROLET CONVENIENCE OPTIONS: DeLuxe air-conditioning with automatic transmission, includes heater ($364). Cool Pack air-conditioner ($317). Group A body equipment including OSRV mirror, rear bumper guards, grille guard and inside non-glare mirror, for station wagons ($29); other models ($34). Heavy-duty metallic-faced brakes ($38). Impala Comfort and Convenience Group ($30); same for Bel Air ($41); same for Biscayne ($44). Air foam front seat cushions for Biscayne ($8). Tinted glass, all windows ($38); windshield only ($22). Shaded Sport Coupe backlight ($14). Padded dash ($16). Lockable station wagon rear compartment ($11). Two-tone paint ($16). Power brakes ($43). Six-Way power seat ($97). Power steering ($75). Power tailgate window ($32). Power windows, except Biscayne ($102). Manual radio ($48). Pushbutton radio ($57). Station wagon divided second seat ($38). Impala Sport Coupe and convertible bucket seats ($102). Heavy-duty front and rear shock absorbers, except station wagons ($1). Heavy-duty front coil springs ($1). Heavy-duty rear coil springs ($3). DeLuxe steering wheel for Biscayne ($4). Tachometer for V-8s ($49). Vinyl trim for Biscayne sedan ($5). Wheel discs ($18). Electric two-speed wipers with washers ($17). Various whitewall and oversize tire options ($31-36). The Option Code 240 Super Sport package added or substituted the following items on regular Impala equipment: Swirl-patten body side moldings; 'SS' rear fender emblems; 'SS' deck lip badge; specific Super Sport full wheel discs with simulated knock-off spinners; locking center console and passenger assist bar. Super Sport equipment was available on the Impala Sport Coupe and convertible at $53.80 extra, plus $102.25 for bucket seats.

CHEVY II CONVENIENCE OPTIONS: Air-conditioning ($317). Rear arm rest for '100' models only ($10). Front seat driver's safety belt ($11). Two front seat safety belts ($20). Group A body equipment, station wagons ($29); passenger cars ($34). Heavy-duty brakes ($38). Comfort and Convenience group ($39). Tinted glass, all windows ($27); windshield only ($13). Padded dash ($16). Two-tone paint, except convertible ($11). Power brakes ($43). Power steering ($75). Power tailgate window on six-passenger station wagon ($27). Manual radio and antenna ($48). Pushbutton radio and antenna ($57). Station wagon divided second seat ($38). Nova 400 front bucket seats, except station wagon ($70). Heavy-duty rear shock absorbers ($1). Heavy-duty springs, front ($1); rear ($3). Whitewall tires ($30). Full wheel covers ($13) and wire wheel covers ($38).

Historical footnotes: Chevrolets and Chevy IIs built to 1962 specifications appeared in dealer showrooms September 29, 1961. Model year production hit 1,424,000 units, excluding Corvairs, Corvettes and Chevy IIs. The new Chevy II series saw production of 326,600 additional units for the model year, which included 47,000 cars in the '100' Series (35,500 Sixes); 103,200 cars in the '300' Series (92,800 Sixes); 116,500 Nova 400s (all Sixes) and 59,900 station wagons (57,800 Sixes), in rounded-off totals. Consult separate Corvair and Corvette sections of this catalog for production of these models. Calendar year output peaked at 2,161,398 units, making Chevrolet America's Number 1 automaker by a substantial margin.

1963 CHEVROLET

1963 Chevy II, Nova 400 2-dr hardtop Sport Coupe, 6-cyl

CHEVY II — ALL SERIES — Detail refinements and new freshness for its basically simple lines were the major exterior changes for this year's Chevy II. On the inside, new upholstery and trim set the cars off. The three series, '100,' '300' and Nova 400 were continued with a total of ten regular models plus a new Super Sport option exclusive to Nova 400 Sports models. A new grille consisted of five, slightly thicker, horizontal bars and the main divider bar of the previous year was gone. Chevrolet lettering on the front of the hood replaced the thin, wide medallion of 1962. Base level '100' Series models were very plain, without body side trim. Series '300' models had moldings along the body sides, window reveals and edges of the rear cove panel. Novas had similar trim plus wheel discs and rocker sill moldings, with identification scripts on the rear fenders. Cars with the Super Sport option had special finned wheel covers, wider body side moldings, aluminized rear panels and 'SS' badges on the rear fenders and right-hand side of the deck lid. Standard equipment included five 6.00 x 13 black tubeless tires on most cars (6.50 x 13 on station wagons and Nova 400 Sports models); heater; defroster; front foam cushions; cigarette lighter; electric windshield wipers; oil filter and power tailgate windows on three-seat station wagons. In addition, Nova 400s had rear foam seats; floor carpets; special upholstery; DeLuxe trims and backup lights.

CHEVY II I.D. NUMBERS: Vehicle numbers took the same form and were found in the same locations as in 1962. The first symbol was changed to a '3' to indicate 1963 model year. Chevy II models were built at two assembly plants in Willow Run, Michigan and Norwood, Ohio.

CHEVY II SERIES (ALL)

Model Number	Model Number	Body Type & Seating	Factory Price	Shipping Weight	Production Total
SERIES 100 (4-CYL)/SERIES 100 (6-CYL)					
0169	0269	4-dr Sedan-6P	2040/2099	2455/2545	Note 1
0111	0211	2-dr Sedan-6P	2003/2062	2430/2520	Note 1
0135	0235	4-dr Sta Wag-6P	2338/2397	2725/2810	Note 1
SERIES 300 (4-CYL)/SERIES 300 (6-CYL)					
0369	0469	4-dr Sedan-6P	2121/2180	2470/2560	Note 1
0311	0411	2-dr Sedan-6P	2084/2143	2440/2530	Note 1
0345	0445	4-dr Sta Wag-9P	2516/2575	2810/2900	Note 1
SERIES NOVA 400 (6-CYL)					
NA	0449	4-dr Sedan-6P	2235	2590	Note 1
NA	0437	2-dr HT Spt Cpe-5P	2262	2590	Note 1
NA	0467	2-dr Conv-5P	2472	2760	Note 1
NA	0435	4-dr Sta Wag-6P	2494	2835	Note 1

NOTE 1: Chevy II production totals were recorded by body style only, with no breakouts by series, model or engine. Totals for 1963 were as follows: Four-door sedan = 146,097; Two-door hardtop Sport Coupe = 87,415; Four-door station wagon = 72,274; Two-door sedan = 42,017 and Two-door convertible = 24,823. Chevrolet Motor Division later released the information that 42,432 cars (out of the above totals) were manufactured with Super Sport equipment, but did not indicate how many were Sport Coupes or convertibles. Model year statistics kept by the industry tell us additional information about production by series, body style and engines, in round figures. For example, the total output of 1963 Chevy IIs was approximately 375,600 cars. This included 50,400 in the '100' Series (48,200 Sixes); 78,800 in the '300' Series (77,700

1963 Chevrolet, Chevy II Nova SS 2-dr hardtop, 6-cyl

Sixes); 171,100 in the Nova 400 Series (all Sixes) and 75,300 station wagons (74,800 Sixes). Of these station wagons (all lines) a total of 67,347 were two-seat types and only 7,927 were three-seat types. Also, a mere 470 station wagons with four-cylinder engines were made. **ADDITIONAL NOTES:** Since Chevy II Model Numbers and Body Style Numbers were the same, Column 1 above has been used to list four-cylinder model codes and Column 2 above has been used to list six-cylinder model codes. Factory Prices and Shipping Weights above slash are for Fours, below slash for Sixes. The Nova 400 line came only with six-cylinder power, so no slashes are used.

CHEVY II ENGINES
Four-cylinder. Overhead valves. Cast iron block. Displacement: 153.3 cubic iches. Bore and stroke: 3.875 x 3.25 inches. Compression ratio: 8.5:1. Brake horsepower: 90 at 4000 R.P.M. Five main bearings. Hydraulic valve lifters. Carburetor: Rochester one-barrel Model 7020103.

Six-cylinder: Overhead valves. Cast iron block. Displacement: 194.4 cubic inches. Bore and stroke: 3.562 x 3.25 inches. Compression ratio: 8.5:1. Brake horsepower: 120 at 4400 R.P.M. Seven main bearings. Hydraulic valve lifters. Carburetor: Rochester one-barrel Model 7023103.

BISCAYNE — SERIES 1100 (6-CYL) — SERIES 1200 (V-8) — Chevrolet's new 1963 styling was seen as a move to make the company's products look more like luxury cars. Grilles, bumpers, hoods, sculptured side panels and rear deck contours were all new, yet the overall alteration level was minor. Seen in profile, both front and rear fenders had a 'Vee' shape. The basic Biscayne was a little brighter this year with its slender, full-length upper body molding. Standard features included heater and defroster; dual sun visors; crank operated ventipanes, directional signals; parallel action electric windshield wipers; front door arm rests; vinyl embossed headliners; ash tray and color coordinated vinyl-coated rubber front covering. Interiors were trimmed in cloth and leather grained vinyls (all vinyl on station wagons) with full vinyl door panels. The front seat was foam-cushioned. Exterior brightwork included the full-length body trim strip; anodized bright grille, hood, and deck emblems and bright trim rings for the twin unit taillights. A series script and Chevrolet badge were seen on rear fenders and small hub caps were standard.

CHEVROLET I.D. NUMBERS: Vehicle numbers took the same form and were found in the same locations as in 1962. The first symbol was changed to a '3' to designate the 1963 model year. The next pair of symbols correspond to the first two digits in the Model/Style Number code and identified the series. The following pair of symbols corresponded to the last two digits in the Model/Style Number code and identified the type of body. The sixth symbol was a letter designating the assembly plant. The final six numers represented the sequential production number, with series in mixed production.

BISCAYNE SERIES

Model Number	Model Number	Body Type & Seating	Factory Price	Shipping Weight	Production Total
(PASSENGER CARS)					
1169	1269	4-dr Sedan-6P	2376/2483	3280/3415	Note 1
1111	1211	2-dr Sedan-6P	2322/2429	3205/3340	Note 1
(STATION WAGON)					
1135	1235	4-dr Sta Wag-6P	2723/2830	3685/3810	Note 1

NOTE 1: Production totals were recorded by body style only, with no breakouts by series, model or engine. Totals for 1963 'Regular Chevrolets' were as follows: Four-door sedan = 561,511; Two-door hardtop Sports Coupe = 399,224; Four-door station wagon = 198,542; Four-door hardtop Sports Sedan = 194,158; Two-door sedan = 135,636 and Two-door convertible = 82,659. Model year statistics kept by the industry tell us additional information about production by series and body style, etc. in round figures. Production of Biscaynes, excluding station wagons, was approximately 186,500 cars, of which 37,000 were V-8s and 149,500 Sixes. Production of station wagons (all trim levels) was approximately 198,500 cars, of which 146,200 were V-8s and 52,300 Sixes. **ADDITIONAL NOTE:** The V-8 was considered a separate series *not* an option. Factory Prices and Shipping Weights above the slash are for Sixes, below the slash for V-8s. Since Chevrolet Model Numbers and Body Numbers were the same, the first column in each chart has been used to list six-cylinder model codes and the second column in each chart has been used to list V-8 model codes.

BISCAYNE ENGINES
Six-cylinder. Overhead valves. Cast iron block. Displacement: 230 cubic inches. Bore and stroke: 3.875 x 3.25 inches. Compression ratio: 9.25:1. Brake horsepower: 140 at 4400 R.P.M. Seven main bearings. Hydraulic valve lifters. Carburetor: Rochester one-barrel Model 7023003.

V-8. Overhead valves. Cast iron block. Displacement: 283 cubic inches. Bore and stroke: 3.875 x 3.00 inches. Compression ratio: 9.25:1. Brake horsepower: 195 at 4800 R.P.M. Five main bearings. Hydraulic valve lifters. Carburetor: Rochester two-barrel Model 7023007.

BEL AIR SERIES — SERIES 1500 (6-CYL) — SERIES 1600 (V-8) — Chevrolet's medium priced line was refined for 1963. Standard equipment included most Biscayne features plus extra-quality interior trims; front and rear foam seat cushions; DeLuxe steering wheel; glove compartment light; carpets; automatic dome light and dual rear ash trays. A foam backed luggage compartment mat was another Bel Air additive. A bright metal lower body ridge molding, with accent stripe, was used. Bel Air signature scripts and Chevrolet badges appeared on the rear fenders. Stainless steel drip gutter moldings were found above the side windows. A bright finished rear cove with embossed Chevrolet lettering was seen at the rear, as well as twin unit taillights.

BEL AIR SERIES

Model Number	Model Number	Body Type & Seating	Factory Price	Shipping Weight	Production Total
(PASSENGER CARS)					
1569	1669	4-dr Sedan-6P	2508/2615	3280/3415	Note 1
1511	1611	2-dr Sedan-6P	2454/2561	3215/3345	Note 1
(STATION WAGONS)					
1545	1645	4-dr Sta Wag-9P	2921/3028	3720/3850	Note 1
1535	1635	4-dr Sta Wag-6P	2818/2925	3685/3810	Note 1

NOTE 1: Production totals were recorded by body style only, with no breakouts by series, model or engine. See Biscayne, Note 1, for 'Regular Chevrolet' overall production totals. Model year statistics kept by the industry tell us additional information about production in round figures. For example, production of 1963 Bel Airs, excluding station wagons, was approximately 354,100 cars, of which 177,200 were V-8s and 176,900 were Sixes. Station wagon series totals, listed under Biscayne, Note 1, include Bel Air station wagons.

BEL AIR ENGINES
Base engines for Bel Airs were the same as for Biscaynes. See 1963 Biscayne engine data.

1963 Chevrolet, Impala 2-dr convertible with 'SS' equipment, V-8

IMPALA — SERIES 1700 (6-CYL) — SERIES 1800 (V-8) — Chevrolet's plushest line had most standard equipment found on lower lines, plus bright aluminum front seat end panels; patterned cloth and leather grained vinyl upholstery (in color coordinated materials); extra thick foam seat cushions; tufted grain and cobble pattern vinyl door and side panels; paddle type arm rests with lift-up door releases; bright metal rear view mirror backing; added insulation and foam backed trunk mats. A specific Sports style steering wheel with half-circle, thumb control horn ring was used. Other extras included electric clock; parking brake warning lamp; glove box lamp; bright metal, textured, instrument cluster accents and dashboard face panels, of similar texture. The steering wheel had duo-tone finish on cars with Fawn, Aqua, Green and Blue interiors. Exterior body side trim included front fender accent bars; stainless steel belt moldings with stainless steel drip caps (except convertible); a full-length lower body molding with colored insert and Impala lettering on the rear quarter section. An Impala emblem also appeared high on rear fenders. The rear cove was filled with satin aluminum finish and trimmed by bright metal outline moldings. Triple unit taillight groups were used and incorporated built-in backup lamps.

IMPALA SERIES

Model Number	Body/Style Number	Body Type & Seating	Factory Price	Shipping Weight	Production Total
(PASSENGER CARS)					
1769	1869	4-dr Sedan-6P	2662/2768	3310/3435	Note 1
1739	1839	4-dr HT Spt Sed-6P	2732/2839	3350/3475	Note 1
1747	1847	2-dr HT Spt Cpe-5P	2667/2774	3265/3390	Note 1
1767	1867	2-dr Conv Cpe-5P	2917/3024	3400/3870	Note 1
(STATION WAGON)					
1745	1845	4-dr Sta Wag-9P	2063/3170	3745/3870	Note 1
1735	1835	4-dr Sta Wag-6P	2960/3067	3705/3835	Note 1

NOTE 1: Production totals were recorded by body style only, with no breakout by series, model or engine. See Biscayne, Note 1, for 'Regular Chevrolet' overall production totals. Model year statistics kept by the industry tell us additional information about production in round figures. For example, production of 1963 Impalas, excluding station wagons, was approximately 832,600 cars, of which 735,900 were V-8s and 96,700 were Sixes. Station wagon series totals, listed under Biscayne, Note 1, included Impala station wagons. Chevrolet Motor Division had also released a specific figure of 153,271 cars built, in 1963, with the Super Sport equipment package, but no breakout per body style. A total of 16,920 cars had the 409 cubic inch V-8 installed during the 1963 model run. Most of these units were Super Sports.

IMPALA ENGINES
Base engines for Impalas were the same as for Biscaynes. See 1963 Biscayne engine data.

CHEVROLET CHASSIS FEATURES: Wheelbase: (Chevy II) 110 inches; (Chevrolet) 119 inches. Overall length: (Chevy II station wagon) 187.4 inches; (other Chevy IIs) 183 inches; (all Chevrolets) 210.4 inches. Front tread: (Chevy II) 56.8 inches ; (Chevrolet) 60.3 inches. Rear tread: (Chevy II) 56.3 inches; (Chevrolet) 59.3 inches. Tires: (Chevy II station wagon) 6.50 x 13; (Chevy II) 6.00 x 13; (Chevrolet station wagon) 8.00 x 14; (Chevrolet convertible) 7.50 x 14; (Chevrolet) 7.00 x 14.

1963 Chevrolet, Impala 4-dr hardtop Sport Sedan, V-8

1963 Chevrolet, Impala 4-dr hardtop Sport Sedan, V-8

CHEVROLET POWERTRAIN OPTIONS: Turbo-Fire 250 horsepower 327 cubic inch V-8 with four-barrel carburetor and dual exhausts ($191). Turbo-Fire 300 horsepower 327 cubic inch V-8 with four-barrel carburetor and dual exhausts ($245). Turbo-Fire 340 horsepower 327 cubic inch V-8 with four-barrel carburetor and dual exhausts ($349). Turbo-Fire 400 horsepower 409 cubic inch V-8 with four-barrel carburetor, dual exhausts, high lift camshaft and solid valve lifters ($428). Turbo-Fire 425 horsepower 409 cubic inch V-8 with dual four-barrel carburetors, dual exhausts, high lift camshaft and solid valve lifters ($484). Overdrive transmission with six-cylinder or 283 cubic inch V-8 engines ($108). Six-cylinder Powerglide ($188). Powerglide with 283/327 cubic inch V-8s ($199). Close-ratio four-speed manual transmission with 250 horsepower V-8 ($188). Four-speed transmission with 340/400/425 horsepower V-8s ($237). Positraction rear axle ($43). Delcotron 42-amp generator, standard with air-conditioning, optional on others at ($11). Heavy-duty radiator ($11). Heavy-duty battery, standard with 340 horsepower V-8, optional on others at ($8). Six-cylinder temperature controlled cooling fan ($16). Delcotron 52-amp generator ($32). Delcotron 62-amp generator ($65-75).

CHEVY II POWERTRAIN OPTIONS: Positraction rear axle ($38). Heavy-duty clutch ($5). Delcotron 42-amp generator ($11). Heavy-duty radiator ($3). Powerglide transmission ($167).

CHEVROLET CONVENIENCE OPTIONS: DeLuxe air-conditioning, including heater ($364). Cool Pack air-conditioning ($317). Driver seat belt ($10). Pair of front seat belts ($19). Heavy-duty brakes with metallic facings ($38). Comfort and Convenience Group, for Impala ($31); for Bel Air ($41); for Biscayne ($44). Biscayne front air foam seat cushion ($8). Tinted glass, all windows ($38); windshield only ($22). Grille guard ($19). Passenger car rear bumper guard ($10). Padded dash ($18). Station wagon luggage locker ($11). Station wagon luggage carrier ($43). Two-tone paint ($16). Power brakes ($43). Six-Way power seat ($97). Power steering, except Biscayne ($75). Power tailgate window ($32). Power windows, except Biscayne ($102). Manual radio ($48). Pushbutton radio ($57). Pushbutton radio with antenna and rear speaker ($70). Vinyl roof for Impala Sport Coupes ($75). Station wagon divided second seat ($38). DeLuxe steering wheel ($4). Super Sport equipment package ($161). Tachometer with V-8s ($48). Wheel discs ($18). Wire wheel discs on super Sport ($25); on others ($43). Two-speed electric washers and wipers ($17).

1963 Chevrolet, Impala 2-dr hardtop Sport Coupe, V-8

CHEVY II CONVENIENCE OPTIONS: Air conditioning ($317). Rear arm rests ($10). Pair of front seat belts ($19). Heavy-Duty brakes ($38). Comfort and Convenience Group, on Nova ($28); on others ($39). Tinted glass, all windows ($27); windshield only ($13); Grille guard ($15); Rear bumper guard ($10). Padded dash ($16). Station wagon roof luggage rack ($43). Two-tone paint, except convertible ($11). Power brakes ($3). Power steering ($75). Power tailgate window ($27). Power convertible top ($54). Pushbutton radio with antenna and rear speaker ($70). Manual radio and antenna ($48). Pushbutton radio and antenna ($57). Station wagon divided second seat ($38). Super Sport equipment for Nova Sports Coupe and Convertible ($161). Full wheel covers ($13). Wire design wheel covers ($13). Various whitewall and oversize tire options ($9-42).

Historical footnotes: For 1963 the widest range of Chevrolets ever offered in history was available in dealer showrooms on September 28, 1962. The division sold three out of every ten cars retailed in the U.S. this season. Model year sales of Chevrolets and Chevy IIs peaked at 1,947,300 units. Calendar year production reached 2,303,343 cars, including Corvettes and Corvairs, which are covered separately in this catalog. Semon E. Knudsen remained General Manager of Chevrolet Motor Division. In July, 1963, prototypes for a new, intermediate sized line, to be called Chevelle, were introduced at the long-lead press preview. The cast iron crankshaft, used in the all-new seven main bearing six-cylinder engine, was a first for Chevrolet. The 1963 Super Sport equipment package (RPO Z03) was expanded this season. It now included swirl pattern side molding inserts; matching cove inserts; red-filled 'SS' overlays for rear fender Impala emblems; specific full wheel covers; all-vinyl front bucket seat interiors and also, a center console with locking storage compartment when optional Powerglide or four-speed manual transmissions were ordered. In addition, the Super Sport's dashboard was trimmed with bright, swirl pattern inserts and 'SS' steering wheel center hubs were used.

1963 was also a peak for factory racing options such as the Z11 drag package (RPOZ11) available for the model 1847 Impala Sport Coupe. This $1245 option had aluminum front sheet metal, a special 427 C.I. 430 h.p. version of the 409, achieving the 18 C.I. increase via a .15 inch stroke for a bore and stroke of 4.312 x 3.65. This engine also including a new dual 4 bbl. intake manifold that isolated the intake runners from the engine valve that was covered by a separate valve cover. The cylinder heads were slightly different on the intake manifold mating the surface to match this new manifold set up. Dec. 1, 1962, 25 Z11 were issued. January 1, 1963, 25 more were issued, and 7 more were sold after that date for a total of 57. The aluminum front end saved 112 lbs., other weight saving measures such as the lack of center bumper backing and bracing reduced another 121 lbs. The shipping weight was 3345 pounds.

Also in 1963, 5 Mark II NASCAR 427 "mystery engines" were also built and raced at Daytona, winning the two 100 mile preliminary races and setting the track stock car speed record.

1963 Chevrolet, Impala 4-dr Sedan, V-8

While these engines were very rare, they were the prototype of the 396 C.I. 1965 engine that was brought up to 427 C.I. In 1966 and 454 C.I. in 1970. These first 5 engines were closely related to the 409 and the Z11 427, and even shared crankshaft and piston rods with the Z11, but differed completely in the cylinder head having the combustion chamber in the cylinder head. That means the cylinder block deck surfaces were angled to parallel the piston dome, and also incorporated the stagger valve or "porcupine" valve layout. The bore and stroke was the same as the Z11, 4.312 x 3.65. The GM decision to adhere strictly to the AMA anti-racing ban put a tragic end to these great engines, but not before the cat was, at least briefly, out of the bag.

1964 CHEVROLET

1964 Chevrolet, Chevy II Nova 4-dr sedan, 6-cyl

CHEVY II — ALL SERIES — The 1964 Chevy II had a redesigned grille. Nine vertical bars were equally spaced along the five, full-width horizontal blades. This gave a quadrant effect. Side trim treatments were more like the 1962 look than the immediately previous appearance. The base level '100' Series models had no belt moldings. The '300' Series was gone. Nova 400 models had constant-width belt moldings and Nova signature scripts at the upper, trailing edge of front fenders. The top series consisted of only one model, the Nova Super Sport Sports Coupe, with 'SS' trim and equipment. Body style and engine availability was shuffled as indicated by the chart below. New technical features included an optional 283 cubic inch V-8 and self-adjusting 9.6 inch drum brakes.

CHEVY II I.D. NUMBERS: Serial numbers and number locations followed the previous system. The first symbol in the serial number was changed to a '4' to indicate the 1964 model year. (Some sources refer to '100' Series models with six-cylinder or V-8 power as '200', based on the Model Number designations).

CHEVY II ALL SERIES

Model Number	Model Number	Body Type & Seating	Factory Price	Shipping Weight	Production Total
SERIES 100 (4-CYL)/SERIES 100 (6-CYL)					
0169	0269	4-dr Sedan-6P	2048/2108	2495/2580	Note 1
0111	0211	2-dr Sedan-6P	2011/2070	2455/2540	Note 1
NA	0235	4-dr Sta Wag-6P	NA/2406	NA/2840	Note 1
NOVA 400 SERIES (6-CYL)					
NA	0469	4-dr Sedan-6P	NA/2243	NA/2595	Note 1
NA	0411	2-dr Sedan	NA/2206	NA/2560	Note 1
NA	0437	2-dr Spt Cpe-5P	NA/2271	NA/2660	Note 1
NA	0435	4-dr Sta Wag-6P	NA/2503	NA/2860	Note 1
NOVA SUPER SPORT SERIES					
NA	0447	2-dr Spt Cpe-4P	NA/2433	NA/2675	Note 1

NOTE 1: Production was recorded only by body styles, as follows; Four-door sedan - 84,846; Two-door sedan - 40,348; Four-door station wagon - 35,670 and Two-door Sport Coupe - 30,827. Industry statistics giving breakouts do not correspond with each other. For example, one source indicates production, by engine, as 165,487 Sixes; 1,121 Fours and 25,083 V-8s. A second source indicates production of 800 Fours; and 190,900 Sixes with no indication of V-8 installations. Series production, as indicated by the latter source, includes 800 Fours in the '100' Series; 52,300 cars in the '100' Series (with 0200 Model Numbers); 102,900 cars in the Nova Series (including Super Sports) and 35,700 station wagons. Apparently, the new V-8 option caused some confusion in record keeping. **ADDITIONAL NOTE:** Fours and Sixes were consid-

ered separate series; the Six was *not* an option. On the charts above, Factory Prices and Shipping Weights above slash are for Fours, below slash for Sixes. The V-8 was considered an *option*, not a separate series. See Chevy II Powertrain Options. Since Chevy II Model Numbers and Body Style Number were the same, Column 1 in the chart lists the model codes for Fours and Column 2 in the chart lists the model codes for Sixes. The Series '100' station wagon and all Novas were available with the base Six or optional V-8, but not with the four-cylinder motor.

CHEVY II BASE ENGINES
Four-cylinder. Overhead valves. Cast iron block. Displacement: 153 cubic inches. Bore and stroke: 3.875 x 2.35 inches. Compression ratio: 8.5:1. Brake horsepower: 90 at 4000 R.P.M. Five main bearings. Hydraulic valve lifters. Carburetor: Carter one-barrel model 3379.

Six-cylinder. Overhead valves. Cast iron block. Displacement: 194.4 cubic inches. Bore and stroke: 3.562 x 3.25 inches. Compression ratio: 8.5:1. Brake horsepower: 120 at 4400 R.P.M. Seven main bearings. Hydraulic valve lifters. Carburetor: Rochester one-barrel model 7023105.

1964 Chevelle, Malibu 'SS' 2-dr hardtop sports coupe, V-8

CHEVELLE — ALL SERIES — Anticipating a general improvement in the market for cars priced and sized below regular models, Chevrolet introduced its all-new Chevelle, a car that fit between the compact Chevy II and full-size models and was soon being called a 'senior compact.' Assembly was quartered at plants in Baltimore and Kansas City and a brand new factory in Fremont, California. The car was styled with square looking lines in the Chevy II model, but curved side window glass and an emphasis on width provided a distinctive look. Eleven models were available in two basic lines, called Chevelle '300' and Chevelle Malibu, with a convertible as an exclusive upper level offering. Base editions lacked body side moldings. Malibu models had a full-length strip of bright metal along the lower belt line, with an insert at the rear and Malibu rear fender script. A Super Sport option was released and cars so-equipped had no lower belt trim. Instead, there was a molding running along the full length of the upper body ridge and continuing along the rear fender edge, plus 'SS' rear fender and rear panel badges and specifically styled wheel covers. Bucket front seats were popular features in the Chevelle Malibu Super Sport.

CHEVELLE I.D. NUMBERS: The normal Chevrolet system was used to encode Chevelles. The first serial number symbol was a '4' to designate the 1964 model year. The next pair of symbols designated the series and was '53' on Chevelle '300' Sixes; '54' on Chevelle '300' V-8s; '55' on Malibu Sixes and '56' on Malibu V-8s. The next pair of symbols designated body style and corresponds to the chart listings below. The sixth symbol was an alphabetical assembly plant code: 'B' for Baltimore: 'K' for Kansas City and 'Z' for Freemont. The last six digits were the sequential production number.

CHEVELLE ALL SERIES

Model Number	Model Number	Body Type & Seating	Factory Price	Shipping Weight	Production Total
(SERIES 300 (6-CYL)/SERIES 300 (V-8)					
5369	5490	4-dr Sedan-6P	2268/2376	2850/2980	Note 1
5311	5411	2-dr Sedan-6P	2231/2339	2825/2955	Note 1
5335	5435	4-dr Sta Wag-6P	2566/2674	3130/3250	Note 1
5315	5415	2-dr Sta Wag-6P	2528/2636	3050/3170	Note 1
MALIBU SERIES (6-CYL)/MALIBU SERIES (V-8)					
5569	5669	4-dr Sedan-6P	2349/2457	2870/2995	Note 1
5537	5637	2-dr Spt Cpe-5P	2376/2484	2850/2975	Note 1
5567	5667	2-dr Conv-5P	2587/2695	2995/3120	Note 1
5545	5645	4-dr Sta Wag-8P	2744/2852	3240/3365	Note 1
5535	5635	2-dr Sta Wag-6P	2647/2755	3140/3265	Note 1

NOTE 1: Production was recorded only by body style, as follows: Two-door Sport Coupe = 134,670; Four-door sedan = 113,816; Four-door station wagon = 41,374; Two-door convertible = 23,158; Two-door sedan = 22,588 and Two-door station wagon = 2,710. Industry statistical breakouts show 142,034 Chevelle Sixes and 196,252 Chevelle V-8s were built. Additional statistics record series production, in rounded off figures, as follows: (Chevelle 300) 53,000 Sixes and 15,300 V-8s; (Malibu) 62,100 Sixes and 86,900 V-8s; (Malibu SS) 67,100 V-8s and (Station wagons) 17,100 Sixes and 26,900 V-8s. **ADDITIONAL NOTE:** Sixes and V-8s were considered separate series. Factory Prices and Shipping Weights above slash are for Sixes, below slash for V-8s. Since Chevelle Model Numbers and Body Style Numbers were the same, the first column on chart shows model codes for Sixes and the second column on chart shows model codes for V-8.

CHEVELLE BASE ENGINES
Six-cylinder. Overhead valves. Cast iron block. Displacement: 194.4 cubic inches. Bore and stroke: 3.562 x 3.25 inches. Compression ratio: 8.5:1. Brake horsepower: 120 at 4400 R.P.M. Seven main bearings. Hydraulic valve lifters. Carburetor: Rochester one-barrel model 7023105.

V-8. Overhead valves. Cast iron block. Displacement: 283 cubic inches. Bore and stroke: 3.875 x 3.00 inches. Compression ratio: 9.25:1. Brake horsepower: 195 at 4800 R.P.M. Four main bearings. Hydraulic valve lifters. Carburetor: Rochester one-barrel model 7024101.

BISCAYNE — SERIES 1100 (6-CYL) — SERIES 1200 (V-8) — Chevrolet's most inexpensive line. Standard features included heater and defroster; dual sunvisors; color-keyed floor carpeting; foam-cushioned seats: cigarette lighter; glove compartment lock; dual-spoke steering wheel with horn ring; front and rear arm rests; ash tray; crank-operated ventipanes and two coat hooks. Interiors were trimmed in patterned cloth and leather grain vinyl combinations, with all-vinyl door panels and embossed vinyl headliners. Spatter pattern paint was used in the luggage compartment. Exterior bright metal decoration included a full-length lower body molding; rear cove upper molding; twin style taillights; hood and deck emblems and nameplates; Biscayne rear fender signatures with Chevrolet emblems; small wheel center hubcaps and bright windshield, rear window and ventipane frames.

CHEVROLET I.D. NUMBERS: Serial numbers and number locations followed the previous system. The first symbol was changed to a '4' to indicate the 1964 model year.

BISCAYNE SERIES

Model Number	Model Number	Body Type & Seating	Factory Price	Shipping Weight	Production Total
1169	1269	4-dr Sedan-6P	2417/2524	3300/3430	Note 1
1111	1211	2-dr Sedan-6P	2363/2471	3230/3365	Note 1
1135	1235	4-dr Sta Wag-6P	2763/2871	3700/3820	Note 1

NOTE 1: Production (for all full-sized Chevrolets) was recorded by body style only, as follows: Four-door sedan = 536,329; Two-door Sport Coupe = 442,292; Four-door Sport Sedan = 200,172. Four-door station wagon = 192,827; Two-door sedan = 120,951 and Two-door convertible = 81,897. Industry statistical breakouts show 383,647 Chevrolet Sixes and 1,190,821 Chevrolet V-8s were built. Additional statistics record series production, in rounded off figures, as follows: (Biscayne Six) 132,500; (Biscyane V-8) 41,400; (Station wagon Six) 39,700 and (Station wagon V-8) 153,100. As usual, the station wagon totals are for Chevrolet wagons of all trim levels and not Biscayne wagons only. **ADDITIONAL NOTE:** In all charts covering full-sized Chevrolets, the first column shows six-cylinder model codes and the second column shows V-8 model codes. Sixes and V-8s were considered separate series. Factory Prices and Shipping Weights above slashes are for Sixes, below slash for V-8.

BISCAYNE ENGINES
The base six-cylinder engine for 1964 Chevrolets was the same powerplant used in 1963. The base V-8 for Chevrolets was the same powerplant used in 1963 Chevrolets (and also in 1964 Chevy IIs and Chevelles). Consult 1963 Biscayne engine data for specifications.

BEL AIR — SERIES 1500 (6-CYL) — SERIES 1600 (V-8) — Chevrolet's middle-priced line had less exterior distinction, but a plusher interior for 1964. Standard equipment included all the Biscayne features listed above plus bright door trim accents; plastic cowl side panels with molded-in ventilation grilles; a bright instrument panel molding; glove compartment light; dome light door switches; DeLuxe quality interior handles and a patterned rubber luggage compartment mat. Interior trim was of a brighter, color-keyed patterned, cloth and leather-grained vinyl combination on the seats, with all-vinyl door panels and embossed headliner. A narrow, full-length upper body bright molding and a slender body sill molding were used. Bel Air script and Chevrolet badges appeared on the rear fenders. Dual rear cove moldings were used, with twin-unit taillights. Bright roof drip cap moldings were a Bel Air feature.

BEL AIR SERIES

Model Number	Model Number	Body Type & Seating	Factory Price	Shipping Weight	Production Total
1569	1669	4-dr Sedan-6P	2519/2626	3305/3440	Note 1
1511	1611	2-dr Sedan-6P	2465/2573	3235/3370	Note 1
1535	1635	4-dr Sta Wag-6P	2828/2935	3705/3825	Note 1
1545	1645	4-dr Sta Wag-9P	2931/3039	3845/3865	Note 1

NOTE 1: Production was recorded by body style only. See Biscayne, Note 1, for overall Chevrolet production totals. Industry statistical breakouts show series production of passenger cars, in rounded off figures, as follows: (Bel Air Six) 137,800 and (Bel Air V-8) 180,300. Bel Air station wagons are included in combined total previously noted.

BEL AIR ENGINES
Engine availability for the Bel Air was the same as listed for the Biscayne line. See 1963 Biscayne engine data.

1964 Chevrolet, Impala 2-dr hardtop Sport Coupe, V-8

IMPALA — SERIES 1700 (6-CYL) — SERIES 1800 (V-8) — The separation of Impala Super Sport models into their own series made the regular Impala the second most expensive Chevrolet line for 1964. Standard equipment included most features found on lower-priced lines, plus extra-thick foam cushion seats; bright aluminum front seat end panels; bright instrument panel insert with nameplate molding; electric clock; parking brake warning light; Impala center emblem on steering wheel; chrome backed rear view mirror; specific paddle-type front and rear arm rests (with finger-tip door release lever); dual dome lights; bright windshield, rear window and upper side window interior garnish moldings and an automatic luggage compartment light. Interiors were of cloth and leather-grain vinyl, in a more intricate design, with bright-accented all-vinyl door panels and vinyl embossed headliner. (Convertible and Station wagons had all-vinyl trim). Exterior trim included color-accented body side moldings; hood and deck windsplit moldings; rear cove outline moldings; satin-finish anodized cove insert; triple unit taillights (with backup light built in); Impala lettering and emblem on rear fenders; roof rail and drip cap moldings; bright door windows glass edges (hardtop styles) and bright belt moldings/

1964 Chevrolet, Impala 4-dr station wagon, V-8

IMPALA SERIES

Model Number	Model Number	Body Type & Seating	Factory Price	Shipping Weight	Production Total
1769	1869	4-dr Sedan-6P	2671/2779	3340/3460	Note 1
1739	1839	4-dr HT Spt Sed-6P	2742/2850	3370/3490	Note 1
1747	1847	2-dr HT Spt Cpe-6P	2678/2786	3295/3415	Note 1
1767	1867	2-dr Conv-6P	2927/3035	3400/3525	Note 1
1735	1835	4-dr Sta Wag-6P	2970/3077	3725/3850	Note 1
1745	1845	4-dr Sta Wag-9P	3073/3181	3770/3895	Note 1

NOTE 1: Production was recorded by body style only. See Biscayne, Note 1, for overall Chevrolet production totals. Industry statistical breakouts show series production of passenger cars, in rounded off figures, as follows: (Impala Six) 73,600 and (Impala V-8) 816,000. Impala station wagons are included in combined total for all trim level wagons, as noted under Biscayne production data. Impala Super Sports *are* included in above breakout.

IMPALA ENGINE
Engine availability for Impalas was the same as listed for the Biscayne line. See 1963 Biscayne engine data.

1964 Chevrolet, Impala 'SS' 2-dr hardtop sports coupe, V-8

IMPALA SUPER SPORT — SERIES 1300 (6-CYL) — SERIES 1400 (V-8) — Chevrolet's plushest and most sporting model was available only in two-door styles. Standard equipment approximated that of the Impala, with added interior features including leather-grained vinyl upholstery with individual front bucket seats and locking compartment in a center console. Swirl-pattern instrument panel inserts and moldings were used. A built-in rear seat radio speaker grille was featured. Dual dome and floor courtesy lamps, with automatic door switches, or manual instrument panel controls, were used. Door safety reflectors were found on the all-vinyl door panels. Special 'SS' emblems appeared on the console and door panels. Exterior distinction came from the use of a wider upper body molding, filled with a swirl-pattern silver anoidized insert. Impala lettering and the 'SS' badge appeared on the rear fenders, with another badge appearing on the deck lid. The rear cove outline moldings were filled with silver-anodized inserts. Full wheel covers of specific Super Sport design were used.

IMPALA SUPER SERIES

Model Number	Body/Style Number	Body Type & Seating	Factory Price	Shipping Weight	Production Total
1347	1447	2-dr HT Spt Cpe-5P	2839/2947	3325/3450	Note 1
1367	1467	2-dr Conv-5P	3088/3196	3435/3555	Note 1

NOTE 1: Chevrolet Motor Division recorded the production of 185,325 Impala Super Sport models in 1964. There is no breakout, by body style, available at this time. It is most likely that six to ten percent of these units were convertibles; the rest two-door hardtop Sport Coupes. A total of 8,684 Chevrolets were equipped with 409 cubic inch engines during the 1964 model run, the majority being Impala Super Sports.

1964 Chevrolet, Impala SS 2-dr convertible, V-8

IMPALA SUPER SPORT ENGINES
Engine availability for Impala Super Sports was the same as listed for the Biscayne line. See 1963 Biscayne engine data.

CHASSIS FEATURES: Wheelbase: (Chevy II) 110 inches; (Chevelle) 115 inches; (Chevrolet) 119 inches. Overall length: (Chevy II station wagon) 187.6 inches; (Chevy II) 182.9 inches; (Chevelle station wagon) 198.8 inches; (Chevelle) 193.9 inches; (Chevrolet station wagon) 210.8 inches; (Chevrolet) 209.9 inches. Width: (Chevy II) 69.9 inches; (Chevelle) 74.6 inches; (Chevrolet) 79.6 inches. Tires: (Chevy II station wagons and Novas) 6.50 x 13; (Chevy II) 6.00 x 13; (Chevelle station wagons) 7.00 x 14; (Chevelles) 6.50 x 14; (Chevrolet station wagons) 8.00 x 14; (Chevrolet convertibles) 7.50 x 14; (other Chevrolets) 7.00 x 14.

CHEVY II POWERTRAIN OPTIONS: The 230 cubic inch six-cylinder engine with one-barrel carburetor and 155 horsepower was $43 extra. The 283 cubic inch V-8 with two-barrel carburetor and 195 horsepower was $108 extra. Other powertrain options were the same as in 1963 at similar prices.

CHEVELLE POWERTRAIN OPTIONS: The 230 cubic inch six-cylinder engine with one-barrel carburetor and 155 horsepower was $43 extra. The 283 cubic inch V-8 with four-barrel carburetor, 9.25:1 compression and 220 horsepower returned as a $54 extra. The 327 cubic inch V-8 with four-barrel carburetor, 10.5:1 compression and 250 horsepower was a $95 extra. The 327 cubic inch V-8 with four-barrel carburetor, 10.5:1 compression and 300 horsepower was a $138 option which may have been installed in a limited number of Malibu Super Sports after mid-year.

CHEVROLET POWERTRAIN OPTIONS: Power teams available for full-sized 1964 Chevrolets were the same as in 1963 at about the same prices.

CONVENIENCE OPTIONS: Chevy II and Chevrolet convenience options for 1964 were about the same selection available the previous season at approximately the same prices. An obvious exception was the offering of tilt steering wheels on the conventional lines, as a new accessory. Factory installed optional equipment for Chevelles was nearly the same selection available for Chevy IIs at similar prices. Additional information on 1964 convenience options was not available at the time this catalog was published.

1965 CHEVROLET

BISCAYNE — (6-CYL/V-8) — SERIES 153/154 — Chevrolets had larger bodies for 1965. A new stamped grille had a lower extension below the bumper, which was slightly veed. Curved window glass and taillamps mounted high at the rear characterized the new styling. Rear fender lines had a prominent kick up end, overall a blunter and more rounded shape. Biscaynes had thin body sill moldings, thin rear fender ridge moldings, bright windshield moldings and dual-style rear lamps with the Biscayne script on the rear quarters. Standard equipment for all Biscaynes included heater and defroster; foam-cushioned front seat; oil filter; electric wipers; front seat belts and five blackwall tires. Convertibles and all 327 cubic inch V-8 cars had 7.75 x 14 tires, station wagons and 409 cubic inch V-8 cars had a 8.25 x 14 tires. Interiors were vinyl and pattern cloth (all-vinyl on station wagons).

VEHICLE IDENTIFICATION NUMBERS: The numbering system and code locations were changed as follows: 13 symbols, the first five digits indicate the model, the sixth designates the year, the seventh (a letter) is the assembly plant and the last six digits are the sequential number. The first number symbol designated make, (1) = Chevrolet. The second and third number symbols designated series. The fourth and fifth number symbols designated Fisher Body code. The sixth number symbol designated year '5' = 1965. The following group of symbols was the sequential unit production number, with series in mixed (pre-assigned). Body Style Numbers were used and are extrapolated in the specifications charts below.

BISCAYNE SERIES

Model Number	Body/Style Number	Body Type & Seating	Factory Price	Shipping Weight	Production Total
153/4	15369	4-dr Sed-6P	2417/2524	3365/3515	Note 1
153/4	15311	2-dr Sed-6P	2363/2470	3305/3455	Note 1
153/4	15335	4-dr Sta Wag-6P	2417/2871	3765/3900	Note 2

NOTE 1: Some 107,700 six-cylinder and 37,600 V-8 Biscaynes were built. Total production, in figures rounded-off to the nearest 100 units, was 145,300 excluding station wagons (all full-sized Chevrolet station wagons being contained in a separate series).
NOTE 2: Some 29,400 six-cylinder and 155,000 V-8 full-sized Chevrolet station wagons were built during the 1965 model year. Total station wagon output, in figures rounded-off to the nearest 100 units, was 184,400 cars. This includes Biscayne; Bel Air and Impala station wagons.

ADDITIONAL NOTE: V-8s have the numeral '4' as the third digit of their series, model and serial number.

BISCAYNE SERIES ENGINE DATA

SIX-CYLINDER
Inline six-cylinder. Overhead valves. Cast iron block. Displacement: 230 cubic inches. Bore and stroke: 3.87 x 3.25 inches. Compression ratio: 8.5:1. Brake horsepower: 140 at 4200 R.P.M. Seven main bearings. Hydraulic valve lifters. Carburetor: Rochester one-barrel Model 7025003.

V-8
V-8. Overhead valves. Cast iron block. Displacement: 283 cubic inches. Bore and stroke: 3.875 x 3.0 inches. Compression ratio: 9.25:1. Brake horsepower: 195 at 4800 R.P.M. Five main bearings. Carburetor: Rochester two-barrel Model 7024101.

BEL AIR — (6-CYL/V-8) — SERIES 155/156 — External decor on the Bel Air included a narrow full-length bodyside molding; roof drip rail moldings; rear accent band and Bel Air script (with Chevrolet emblems on rear quarters). All features found on Biscaynes were included, plus a glove compartment light and power tailgate window on nine-passenger station wagons. Interiors were plusher, with vinyl and pattern cloth trims.

BEL AIR SERIES

Model Number	Body/Style Number	Body Type & Seating	Factory Price	Shipping Weight	Production Total
155/6	15569	4-dr Sed-6P	2519/2626	3380/3530	Note 1
155/6	15511	2-dr Sed-6P	2465/2573	3310/3460	Note 1
155/6	15535	4-dr Sta Wag-6P	2970/2936	3810/3950	Note 2
155/6	15545	4-dr Sta Wag-6P	3073/3039	3765/3905	Note 2

NOTE 1: Some 107,800 six-cylinder and 163,600 V-8 Bel Airs were built. Total production, in figures rounded-off to the nearest 100 units, was 271,400, excluding station wagons (all full-sized Chevrolet station wagons being contained in a separate series).
NOTE 2:
See full-sized station wagon production Note 2 under Biscayne Series listing above.

ADDITIONAL NOTES: V-8s have the numeral '6' as the third digit of their series, model and serial numbers.

1965 Chevrolet, Impala 2-dr convertible, V-8

IMPALA — (6-CYL/V-8) — SERIES 163/164 — Impala features included wide, lower, bright bodyside moldings (with rear fender extensions); bright wheelhouse moldings; bright rear cove panel trim; triple-unit taillamps and full wheel covers. Interiors were more detailed and plusher. Instrument panels had bright center panel moldings and wood-grained lower panel facings. Bright garnish moldings were seen. Extra features included on Impala were electric clock; parking brake light; trunk and backup lights. Luxurious vinyl/pattern cloth trim combinations were used in pillared sedan models. Both convertibles and station wagons featured all-vinyl trims. Black all-vinyl upholstery was available in sport coupes and pillarless sport sedans. The four-door (hardtop) sport sedans had dual roof side rail lamps.

IMPALA SERIES

Model Number	Body/Style Number	Body Type & Seating	Factory Price	Shipping Weight	Production Total
163/4	16369	4-dr Sed-6P	2672/2779	3460/3595	Note 1
163/4	16337	2-dr HT-6P	2678/2785	3385/3630	Note 1
163/4	16339	4-dr HT-6P	2742/2850	3490/3525	Note 1
163/4	16337	Conv-6P	2943/3051	3470/3605	Note 2
163/4	16335	4-dr Sta Wag-6P	2970/3078	3825/3960	Note 3
163/4	16345	4-dr Sta Wag-9P	3073/3181	3865/4005	Note 3

NOTE 1: Some 56,600 six-cylinder and 746,800 V-8 Impalas were built. Total production, in figures rounded off to the nearest 100 units, was 803,400, excluding station wagons (all full-sized Chevrolet station wagons being contained in a separate series).
NOTE 2: A total of 72,760 full-sized Chevrolet convertibles were built, including both Impalas and Impala Super Sports. About 45,800 of these were Impalas and about 27,000 were Impala Super Sports.
NOTE 3:
See full-sized station wagon production Note 2 under Biscayne Series listing above.

IMPALA SUPER SPORT — (6-CYL/V-8) — SERIES 165/166 — The prestige Chevrolet was noted by its bright wheelhouse moldings (without bright lower body moldings); Super Sport front fender scripts; black-filled rear cove band with Impala SS badge at right and a similar badge on the radiator grille, at the left. Specific Super Sport full wheel covers were used. The SS interior featured full carpeting; all-vinyl trim with front bucket seats and bright seatback outline moldings; combination vinyl and carpet door trim (with bright accents); foam cushions; courtesy lights; SS identification on the door panels and a console with a built-in, Rally-type clock. A vacuum gauge was standard as well.

IMPALA SUPER SPORT

Model Number	Body/Style Number	Body Type & Seating	Factory Price	Shipping Weight	Production Total
165/6	16537	2-dr HT-6P	2839/2947	3435/3570	Note 1
165/6	16567	Conv-6P	3104/3212	3505/3645	Note 2

NOTE 1: 3,600 six-cylinder and 239,500 V-8 Impala Super Sports were built. Total production was exactly 243,114 units.
NOTE 2: Approximately 27,000 Impala Super Sport convertibles were built.
ADDITIONAL NOTES: V-8 models have the numeral '6' as the third digit of their series, style and serial number.

CHEVELLE '300' — (6-CYL/V8) — SERIES 131/132 — Chevelles were mildly restyled for their second year. The nose was veed slightly outward and a new grille was used. At the rear were new taillamps. '300' models had lower body sill moldings; Chevelle '300' rear fender nameplates and emblems; bright ventipanes; windshield and rear window reveal moldings; single unit taillamps with bright bezels; rear bumper backup light opening covers and small hubcaps. Interiors were pattern cloth and vinyl trim (all vinyl on station wagons) in a standard grade, with vinyl floor covering. Standard equipment included; heater and defroster; front foam cushions; electric windshield wipers; front seat belts and five 6.95 x 14 blackwall tires (station wagons had 7.35 x 14 blackwall tires).

CHEVELLE '300' I.D. NUMBERS: Serial Numbers took the same general form as on full-sized Chevrolets with applicable Chevelle Series codes used for the second and third symbols. Chevelle Serial Numbers were mixed in production.

CHEVELLE '300'

Model Number	Body/Style Number	Body Type & Seating	Factory Price	Shipping Weight	Production Total
131/2	13169	4-dr Sed-6P	2193/2251	2910/3035	Note 1
131/2	1311	2-dr Sed-6P	2156/2215	2870/3010	Note 1
131/2	13115	2-dr Sta Wag-6P	2453/2505	3185/3275	Note 2

NOTE 1: Some 26,500 Chevelle '300' Sixes and 5,100 V-8s were built. Total production, in figures rounded-off to the nearest 100 units, was 31,600 cars, excluding station wagons (all Chevelle station wagons being contained in a separate series).
NOTE 2: Some 13,800 six-cylinder and 23,800 V-8 Chevelle station wagons were built during the 1965 model year. Total Chevelle station wagon output, in figures rounded-off to the nearest 100 units, was 37,600 cars. This includes all station wagons in the Chevelle '300', Chevelle '300' DeLuxe and Chevelle Malibu Series.

CHEVELLE

SIX-CYLINDER
Inline six-cylinder. Overhead valves. Cast iron block. Displacement: 194 cubic inches. Bore and stroke: 3.563 x 3.25 inches. Compression ratio: 8.5:1. Brake horsepower: 120 at 4400 R.P.M. Seven main bearings. Hydraulic valve lifters. Carburetor: Rochester one-barrel Model 7023105.

V-8
V-8. Overhead valves. Cast iron block. Displacement: 283 cubic inches. Bore and stroke: 3.875 x 3.00 inches. Compression ratio: 9.25:1. Brake horsepower: 195 at 4800 R.P.M. Hydraulic valve lifters. Carburetor: Rochester two-barrel Model 7024101.

CHEVELLE '300' DELUXE — (6-CYL/V-8) — SERIES 133/134 — Chevelle '300' DeLuxe models had higher bright bodyside trim strips; Chevelle 300 rear fender emblems; roof drip cap moldings and rear cove outline moldings (except station wagons). Interiors were a plusher vinyl and cloth, with all-vinyl door trim and a unique dual-spoke steering wheel with horn ring. Standard equipment, in addition to that found on the Chevelle '300', included padded arm rests.

CHEVELLE '300' DELUXE

Model Number	Body/Style Number	Body Type & Seating	Factory Price	Shipping Weight	Production Total
133/4	13369	4-dr Sed-6P	2220/2236	2910/3050	Note 1
133/4	13311	2-dr Sed-6P	2183/2288	2870/3010	Note 1
133/4	13335	4-dr Sta Wag-6P	2511/2616	3185/3320	Note 2

NOTE 1: Some 32,000 six-cylinder and 9,600 V-8 Chevelle '300' DeLuxes were built. Total production, in figures rounded-off to the nearest 100, was 41,600 cars, excluding station wagons (All Chevelle station wagons being contained in a separate series).
NOTE 2: See Chevelle station wagon production Note 2 under Chevelle '300' Series listing above.

ADDITIONAL NOTES: V-8 models have the numeral '4' as the third digit of the series, model and serial numbers.

1965 Chevelle, Malibu SS 2-dr convertible, V-8

CHEVELLE MALIBU — (6-CYL/V-8) — SERIES 135/136 — Series features added to, or replacing 300 DeLuxe equipment, included color-accented bodyside moldings; bright wheelhouse moldings; Malibu rear fender scripts (with Chevelle emblems); hood windsplit moldings; ribbed upper and lower cove trim panels; ribbed tailgate lower trim panel on station wagon; backup lights in rear bumper; luxurious pattern cloth and vinyl interior trims; color-keyed deep twist floor carpeting; foam cushioned rear seat; specific dual- spoke steering wheel (with horn ring); electric clock; bright glove compartment facing molding (with series nameplate) and glovebox light.

CHEVELLE MALIBU

Model Number	Body/Style Number	Body Type & Seating	Factory Price	Shipping Weight	Production Total
135/6	13569	4-dr Sed-6P	2299/2405	2945/3080	Note 1
135/6	13537	2-dr HT-6P	2326/2431	2930/3065	Note 1
135/6	13567	Conv-6P	2532/2637	3025/3160	Note 2
135/6	13535	Sta Wag-6P	2590/2695	3225/3355	Note 3

NOTE 1: Some 56,400 six-cylinder and 95,800 V-8 Malibus were built. Total production, in figures rounded-off to the nearest 100 units, was 152,200 cars, excluding station wagons (all Chevelle station wagons being contained in a separate series).
NOTE 2: Exactly 19,765 Chevelle convertibles were built during the 1965 model year. However, this total includes both Malibu and Malibu Super Sport convertibles.
NOTE 3: See Chevelle station wagon production Note 2 under Chevelle '300' Series listing above.

1965 Chevrolet, Malibu SS 2-dr convertible, V-8

CHEVELLE SUPER SPORT — (6-CYL/V-8) — SERIES 137/138 — A clean, sporty appearance was obtained by the use of wide bright body sill moldings; rear lower fender moldings; Malibu SS rear fender scripts; deck lid SS emblems; black-accented grille and rear cove (except silver rear cove with black exterior); specific Super Sport full wheel covers; front bucket seats with bright trim ends; center console with four-speed or automatic transmissions and all-vinyl luxury interiors. Special instrument panel features included temperature, ammeter and oil pressure gauges.

CHEVELLE SS

Model Number	Body/Style Number	Body Type & Seating	Factory Price	Shipping Weight	Production Total
137/8	13737	2-dr HT-6P	2484/2590	2980/3115	Note 1
137/8	13767	Conv-6P	2690/2796	3075/3210	Note 2

NOTE 1: Some 58,600 six-cylinder and 72,500 V-8 Malibus were built. total production, infigures rounded-off to the nearest 100, was 81,100 units.
NOTE 2: See convertible production Note 2 under Chevelle Malibu Series listing above.
ADDITIONAL NOTES: V-8 models have the numeral '8' as the third digit of their series, model and serial numbers.
NOTE: RPO Z16 was the mid-year SS-396 package, which included a 375 horsepower, 396 cubic inch V-8, with dual exhausts and chrome accents; four-speed transmission; special shocks and suspension; 160 miles per hour speedometer and AM/FM stereo multiplex radio. Specific exterior trim included Malibu SS emblems mounted on front fenders; special rear cove panel and '396 Turbo-Jet' front fender emblems. An SS 396 emblem was mounted in the dash. Fifteen inch wide simulated mag style wheel covers were included. The cost for RPO Z16 was $1,501 and a total of just 201 cars were equipped with it.

CHEVY II — 100-4/100-6 — (4-CYL/6-CYL) — SERIES 111/113 — Chevy IIs for 1965 were mildly restyled with a new grille, new rear cove treatment and revised bright trim. Sedans benefited from a new roof line. Chevy II 100 Series models featured rear fender script emblems; bright ventipane frames; windshield and rear window reveal moldings (side and upper tailgate reveal moldings on station wagons); anodized aluminum grille with special emblems; single unit headlights with anodized aluminum bezels; grille opening moldings with Chevrolet hood nameplate; front fender engine identification emblems (with optional Six and V-8); front bumper mounted parking and directional signal lights; small, bright hub caps; cove divider molding (with nameplate and emblem); single-unit taillights with matching backup light opening cover plates optional; backup lights; cloth and vinyl trim interior; all-vinyl interior on station wagons; black rubber floor covering and dual-spoke steering wheel with horn button. Standard equipment included heater and defroster; front seat belts; foam cushioned front seats;

dual sun visors; 6.00 x 13 blackwall tubeless tires on four-cylinder models and 6.50 x 13 blackwall tires on six-cylinder models. Station wagons had size 7.00 x 13 blackwall tires.

CHEVY II 100 I.D. NUMBERS: Serial Numbers took the same general form as on full-sized Chevrolets with applicable Chevy II Series codes used for the second and third symbols. Chevy II Serial Numbers were mixed in production.

CHEVY II 100 SERIES ENGINE DATA

FOUR-CYLINDER
Inline four-cylinder. Overhead valves. Cast alloy iron block. Displacement: 153 cubic inches. Bore and stroke: 3.875 x 3.25 inches. Compression ratio: 8.5:1. Brake horsepower: 90 at 4000 R.P.M. Five main bearings. Hydraulic valve lifters. Carburetor: Carter one-barrel Model 3379.

SIX-CYLINDER
Inline six-cylinder. Cast alloy block. Displacement: 194 cubic inches. Bore and stroke: 3.563 x 3.25 inches. Compression ratio: 8.5:1. Brake horsepower: 177 at 2400 R.P.M. Seven main bearings. Hydraulic valve lifters. Carburetor: Rochester one-barrel Model 7023105.

CHEVY II '100' SERIES

Model Number	Body/Style Number	Body Type & Seating	Factory Price	Shipping Weight	Production Total
111	11169	4-dr Sed-6P	2005	2520	Note 1
111	11111	2-dr Sed-6P	1968	2505	Note 1
113	11369	4-dr Sed-6P	2070	2620	Note 1
113	11311	2-dr Sed-6P	2033	2605	Note 1
113	11335	4-dr Sta Wag-6P	2362	2875	Note 2

NOTE 1: Total production, in figures rounded-off to the nearest 100 units, was 40,500 cars (excluding station wagons).
NOTE 2: A total of 21,500 Chevy II station wagons were built during the 1965 model year. This includes station wagons Chevy II '100' and Chevy II Nova Series.

ADDITIONAL NOTES: Six-cylinder models have the numeral '3' as the third digit of the series, style and serial numbers.

CHEVY II NOVA — (6-CYL) — SERIES 115 — Nova features used in place of, or in addition to, Chevy II 100 Series equipment included: full-length, color-accented bodyside moldings; rear quarter crown moldings; Nova nameplates and emblems on rear fenders; roof drip cap moldings; hood windsplit moldings; ribbed cove divider panel with nameplate and emblem; single-unit taillights with matching backup lights; luxury pattern cloth and vinyl trim (all-vinyl on station wagons); bright accents on sidewall trim panels; arm rests with built in ash trays; series nameplate on glove compartment door; full-width instrument panel trim molding; specific dual-spoke steering wheel with horn ring and color-keyed deep-twist carpet floor covering.

CHEVY II NOVA

Model Number	Body/Style Number	Body Type & Seating	Factory Price	Shipping Weight	Production Total
115	11569	4-dr Sed-6P	2195	2645	Note 1
115	11537	2-dr HT-5P	2222	2645	115
115	11535	4-dr Sta Wag	2456	2880	Note 2

NOTE 1: Total production, in figures rounded-off to the nearest 100 units, was 51,700 cars (excluding station wagons).
NOTE 2: See Chevy II station wagon production Note 2 under Chevy II '100' Series listing above.

1965 Chevy II, Nova SS 2-dr hardtop sports coupe, V-8 (PH)

CHEVY II NOVA SUPER SPORT — (6-CYL) — SERIES 117 — Additional to, or replacing, Nova equipment were features including color-accented bodyside and rear quarter moldings; front and rear wheel opening moldings; belt moldings; Nova SS rear fender nameplates and SS emblems; Nova SS deck lid nameplate and emblem; rear cove outline molding; silver-painted rear cove area; special Super Sport wheel covers with 14 inch wheels and tires; luxurious all-vinyl trim and headliner; front bucket seats; floor-mounted shift and special trim plate (with optional four-speed and Powerglide transmissions); oil pressure, temperature and ammeter gauges (in place of warning lights); bright front seat outer end panels; SS glove compartment door nameplates and electric clock.

CHEVY II NOVA SUPER SPORT

Model Number	Body/Style Number	Body Type & Seating	Factory Price	Shipping Weight	Production Total
117	11737	2-dr HT-5P	2381	2690	4,300

CHASSIS FEATURES: Wheelbase: (full-size Chevrolets) 119 inches; (Chevelle) 115 inches; (Chevy II) 110 inches. Overall length: (full-size Chevrolet passenger cars) 213.1 inches; (full-size Chevrolet station wagons) 213.3 inches; (Chevelle passenger cars) 196.6 inches; (Chevelle station wagons) 201.4 inches; (Chevy II passenger cars) 182.9 inches; (Chevy II station wagons) 187.6 inches. Front tread: (full-size Chevrolets) 61.2 inches; (Chevelle) 58.0 inches; (Chevy II) 56.8 inches. Rear tread: (full-size Chevrolets) 61.6 inches; (Chevelle) 58.0 inches; (Chevy II) 56.3 inches. Tires: (full-size six-cylinder passenger cars) 7.35 x 14; (full-size V-8 passenger cars) 7.35 x 14; (convertibles) 7.75 x14; (full-size station wagons) 8.25 x 14; (Chevelle passenger cars) 6.95 x 14; (Chevelle station wagons) 7.35 x 14; (Chevy II 100-4) 6.00 x 13; (Chevy II, Nova passenger cars) 6.50 x 13; (Chevy II Nova SS) 6.95 x 14; (Chevy II and Nova station wagons) 7.00 x 13.

FULL-SIZE CHEVROLET POWERTRAIN OPTIONS: Three-speed manual transmission was standard in all models. Overdrive transmission ($107.60). Automatic transmission. Powerglide on six-cylinder models ($188.30); on V-8 models ($199.10). Turbo-Hydramatic with 325 and 396. Four-speed manual floor shift transmission with 240 horsepower ($188.30); with 300, 340 and 400 horsepower engine ($236.75). Six-cylinder 250 cubic inch 150 horsepower L22 engine. V-8 283 cubic inch 220 horsepower L77 engine. V-8 327 cubic inch 250 horsepower L30 engine ($95). V-8 327 cubic inch 300 horsepower L74 engine ($138). V-8 396 cubic inch 325 horsepower L35 engine. V-8 396 cubic inch 425 horsepower L78 engine. V-8 409 cubic inch 340 horsepower L33 engine ($242.10). V-8 409 cubic inch 400 horsepower L31 engine ($320.65). V-8 425 h.p. 409 cubic inch L31-L80. V-8 425 h.p. 396 cubic inch L78. Positive traction rear axle ($43). Heavy-duty air cleaner ($5.40). Heavy-duty clutch ($11). Available rear axle gear ratios: 3.35:1; 3.55:1.

CHEVELLE POWERTRAIN OPTIONS: Three-speed manual transmission was standard. Overdrive transmission ($108). Powerglide automatic transmission on six-cylinder ($188); on V-8s ($199). Four-speed manual floor shift transmission ($188). Six-cylinder 230 cubic inch 140 horsepower L26 engine. V-8 283 cubic inch 220 horsepower RPO L77 engine. V-8 327 cubic inch 250 horsepower L30 engine. V-8 327 cubic inch 300 horsepower L74 engine. V-8 327 cubic inch 250 horsepower L79 engine. Positive traction rear axle ($38). Heavy-duty clutch, on six-cylinder only ($5). Available rear axle gear ratios: 3.08:1; 3.31:1; 4.70:1; 2.73:1.

CHEVY II/NOVA POWERTRAIN OPTIONS: Three-speed manual transmission was standard. Automatic transmission, on V-8s ($178); on six and four-cylinder ($167). Four-speed manual floor shift transmission on V-8 only ($188). Six-cylinder 230 cubic inch 140 horsepower RPO L26 engine. V-8 283 cubic inch 220 horsepower L77 engine. V-8 327 cubic inch 250 horsepower L30 engine. V-8 327 cubic inch 300 horsepower L74 engine. Positive traction rear axle ($38). Heavy-duty clutch, not available on V-8, AC ($5). Available rear axle gear ratios: 3.08:1; 3.55:1; 3.36:1; 3.07:1.

FULL-SIZE CHEVROLET CONVENIENCE OPTIONS: Power brakes ($43). Power steering ($96). Four-season air conditioning, not available with 400 horsepower 409 ($363). Size 7.75 or larger tires required. DeLuxe front seat belts with retractors ($8). Rear window defroster ($22). Tinted glass on all windows ($38); windshield only ($22). Rear bumper guards, not available on wagons ($10). Front bumper guards ($16). Heater/defroster delete ($72 credit). Tri-volume horn ($14). Padded instrument panel ($18.30). Rear luggage compartment lock on six-passenger wagons ($11). Roof luggage rack on wagons ($43). Six-Way power seat, not available on Biscayne, Super Sport or with four speed transmission ($97). Power windows, not available on Biscayne ($102.25). Manual radio ($50). Pushbutton radio ($59). AM/FM pushbutton radio ($137). AM/FM radio with stereo ($244). Rear seat speaker ($13). Vinyl roof cover on Impala, SS sport coupe, Impala Sport Sedan ($75). Foam front seat cushion on Biscayne ($8). Divided second seat on wagons ($38). Sport styled steering wheel ($32). Comfort-tilt steering wheel ($43). Vinyl interior on Biscayne sedan ($5). Wire design wheel covers, not available on Impala SS ($75). Wire wheel design wheel covers on Impalla SS ($57). Electric two-speed windshield wipers with washer ($17). **NOTE:** RPO Z-18 was the Caprice Custom Sedan option for model 16439 (Impala four-door hardtop) and included a heavier stiffer frame, suspension changes, black-accented front grille and rear trim panel with Caprice nameplate, slender body sill moldings, Fleur-de-lis roof quarter emblems, color-keyed body side stripes, specific full wheel covers and Caprice hood and dash emblems.

CHEVELLE CONVENIENCE OPTIONS: Power brakes ($43). Power steering ($86). Four-season air conditioning ($364). Rear antenna, not available on station wagons (no charge). Front bumper guards ($10); rear bumper guards, not available on wagons ($10). Rear windshield defroster ($22). Tinted glass on all windows ($31); windshield only ($20). Heater and defroster deletion ($72 credit, not available with air). Tri-volume horn ($14). Instrument panel safety pad ($18). Luggage rack on station wagons ($43). Two-tone paint ($16). Four-way power seat, not available on four-speed, SS or 300 Series) ($64). Power tailgate window on wagons ($27). Power top on convertible ($54). Power windows, not available on 300 Series ($102). Manual radio ($50). Pushbutton radio ($58). Pushbutton radio with rear seat speaker, not available on convertibles ($72). AM/FM radio ($137). Black vinyl roof cover on Sport Coupes ($75). DeLuxe seat belts with retractors ($8). Divided second seat on wagons ($38). Sport-styled steering wheel ($32). Comfort-lift steering wheel with four-speed or Powerglide ($43). Tachometer on V-8s ($48). Full wheel covers, excluding Super Sport ($22). Simultated wire wheels, excluding Super Sport ($75). Simulated wire wheel covers, excluding Super Sport ($57).

CHEVY II/NOVA CONVENIENCE OPTIONS: Power brakes ($43). Power steering, not available on four-cylinder ($86). Air conditioning, not available on four-cylinder ($317). Rear antenna, not available on station wagon (no charge). Rear arm rest, 100 Series only ($10, standard on Novas). Front Custom DeLuxe retractable seat belts ($8). Tinted glass on all windows ($27); on windshield only ($13). Grille guard ($15). Rear bumper guard, not available on station wagons ($10). Tri-Volume horn, not available on AC ($14). Padded instrument panel ($16). Roof luggage rack on station wagons ($43). Two-tone paint ($11). Power tailgate window on station wagons ($27). Pushbutton radio with front speaker ($59). Manual radio ($50). Pushbutton radio with front and rear speakers ($72). Pushbutton AM/FM radio ($137). Divided second seat on station wagons ($37). Tachometer ($48). Super Sport wire wheel covers ($57). Wire wheel covers on Nova and 100 Series ($75). Wheel covers, not available on Nova and Super Sport ($13). Wheel covers for 13" wheels ($70).

Historical footnotes: Model year production peaked at 2,382,509 units. Calendar year sales of 2,587,487 cars were recorded. E.M. Estes was the Chief Executive Officer of the company this year. Chevy built 155,000 V-8 models including all Chevrolet, Chevelle and Chevy II models and station wagons. They built 29,400 six-cylinders. Total production was 184,400 units. Chevy built 59,650 of its 396 cid V-8s and 2,828 of its 409 cid V-8s for 1965. This year was also the end of an era. The great W-block introduced in 1958 as a 348 cubic inch, later the 409 of 1961, was phased out, and the Mark IV production version of the '63 Mark II NASCAR engine in its 396 cubic inch version superseded the 409.

1966 CHEVROLET

BISCYANE — (6-CYL/V-8) — SERIES 153/154 — Chevrolet was in the second season of a totally new body change, so mild face lifting sufficed. Front fenders were given blunt, forward-thrusting while the four-unit headlamp system was placed in new anodized bezels flanking a revised anodized aluminum grille. At the rear a break with the now traditional round taillamp units were made; the 1966 full-size cars had horizontal rectangle assemblies, with backup lights built in on Biscayne and Bel Air models. Other Biscayne features included series rear fender script, bright ventipane frames, windshield and rear window reveal moldings, (tailgate and side reveal moldings on station wagons), and grille opening moldings. Interiors were upholstered in vinyl and cloth, with DeLuxe door release handles featured, and a foam-cushioned front seat only. A silver-painted shatter-resistant rearview mirror was suspended above the instrument panel, which had a glove compartment lock, bright instrument cluster housing and padding. A dual-spoke steering wheel with horn ring was standard, as was carpeting on the floor, dual sun visors and embossed vinyl headlining. A heater and defroster unit, front and rear ashtrays, front and rear seatbelts and five tubeless blackwall tires were included in the base equipment.

VEHICLE IDENTIFICATION NUMBERS: The numbering system and code locations were the same as for previous models with the sixth symbol changed as follows to '6' to indicate the 1966 model year.

BISCAYNE SERIES

Model Number	Body/Style Number	Body Type & Seating	Factory Price	Shipping Weight	Production Total
153/4	15369	4-dr Sed-6P	2431/2537	3375/3510	Note 1
153/4	15311	2-dr Sed-6P	2379/2484	3310/3445	Note 1
153/4	15335	4-dr Sta Wag-6P	2772/2877	3770/3895	Note 1

NOTE 1: 83,200 six-cylinder Biscaynes and 39,200 V-8 Biscaynes were built, excluding station wagons.
ADDITIONAL NOTES: V-8 models have the numeral '4' as the third digit of their model, series, style and serial numbers.

BISCAYNE SERIES ENGINE DATA

SIX-CYLINDER
Inline six-cylinder. Overhead valves. Cast-iron block. Displacement: 250 cubic inches. Bore and stroke: 3.87 x 3.53 inches. Compression ratio: 8.5:1. Brake horsepower: 155 at 4200 R.P.M. Hydraulic valve lifters. Carburetor: Downdraft single-barrel.

V-8
V-8. Overhead valves. Cast iron block. Displacement: 283 cubic inches. Bore and stroke: 3.875 x 3.0 inches. Compression ratio: 9.25:1. Brake horsepower: 195 at 4800 R.P.M. Five main bearings. Carburetor: Downdraft two-barrel.

BEL AIR — (6-CYL/V-8) — SERIES 155/156 — A step up Chevrolet's price and prestige ladder was the Bel Air, readily distinguished from the Biscayne by its full-length body side molding along the dent-prone body side flare. In addition, Bel Air script and Chevrolet emblems were used on the rear fenders, while roof drip gutter moldings and a deck lip molding were also added. Interiors were a bit plusher, in cloth and vinyl (except the station wagon, which was all-vinyl) and features added to or replacing Biscayne equipment included: a glove box lamp, automatic front door courtesy/dome lamp switches, third seat courtesy lamp and third seat foam padding on station wagons.

BEL AIR SERIES

Model Number	Body/Style Number	Body Type & Seating	Factory Price	Shipping Weight	Production Total
155/6	15569	4-dr Sed-6P	2531/2636	3390/3525	Note 1
155/6	15511	2-dr Sed-6P	2479/2584	3315/3445	Note 1
155/6	15545	4-dr Sta Wag-9P	2948/3053	3815/3990	Note 1
155/6	15535	4-dr Sta Wag-6P	2835/2940	3770/3895	Note 1

NOTE 1: Base Bel Air engines were the same as listed for the 1966 Biscayne.
ADDITIONAL NOTES: V-8 models had the numeral '6' as the third digit of their series, style and serial numbers. 236,600 Bel Airs were built, (excluding station wagons), of which 164,500 had V-8 engines and 72,100 had six-cylinder engine.

1966 Chevrolet, Impala 4-dr station wagon, V-8

IMPALA — (6-CYL/V-8) — SERIES 163/164 — A more DeLuxe Chevrolet, with a color-accented full-length body side molding on the body flare peak, body sill bright moldings, front and rear wheel opening moldings, bright side window accents, Impala front fender nameplates and emblems, belt moldings, deck lid molding with color accent, triple-unit wraparound rear taillamps (dual unit on station wagon), backup lamps in the rear bumper, hood windsplit molding and station wagon lower reveal molding. Interiors were plusher cloth and vinyl (all-vinyl on station wagon and convertible), with following features added to or replacing Bel Air equipment: brushed aluminum lower instrument panel insert with bright bezel, fingertip door releases, foam-cushioned rear seat, bright aluminum seat end panels, chrome-plated rearview mirror housings, bright windshield header (on convertible), rear seat speaker grille (convertible and two-door hardtop), and dual roof rear quarter panel interior lights on two-door hardtops which also had dual instrument panel courtesy lamps along with the convertible.

IMPALA SERIES

Model Number	Body/Style Number	Body Type & Seating	Factory Price	Shipping Weight	Production Total
163/4	16369	4-dr Sed-6P	2678/2783	3425/3565	Note 1
163/4	16339	4-dr HT-6P	2747/2852	3525/3650	Note 1
163/4	16337	2-dr HT-6P	2684/2789	3430/3535	Note 1
163/4	16367	Conv-6P	2935/3041	3485/3610	Note 1
163/4	16345	4-dr Sta Wag-9P	3083/3189	3860/3985	Note 1
163/4	16335	4-dr Sta Wag-9P	2971/3076	3805/3930	Note 1

NOTE 1: Impala production totalled 654,900, of which 33,100 were six-cylinders and 621,800 were V-8s.
ADDITIONAL NOTES: V-8 models have the numeral '4' as the third digit of their series, model and serial numbers.

1966 Chevrolet, Impala 2-dr convertible, V-8

IMPALA SUPER SPORT — (6-CYL/V-8) — SERIES 167/168 — The sporting Impala lost some of its exterior distinction this year, with only the addition of Super Sport front fender nameplates, grille Impala SS indention bar, deck badge and specific tri-bar Super Sport wheel covers giving distinction. Interiors again featured all-vinyl trim, with front bucket seats, with console and SS identification on the instrument panel. Standard features added to those found on base-line Chevrolets were the same as on the Impala models.

IMPALA SUPER SPORT SERIES

Model Number	Body/Style Number	Body Type & Seating	Factory Price	Shipping Weight	Production Total
167/8	16737	2-dr HT-6P	2842/2947	3460/3485	Note 1
167/8	16767	Conv-6P	3093/3199	3505/3630	Note 1

NOTE 1: Impala Super Sport production totaled 119,300 of which 900 were six-cylinder and 118,400 were V-8s.
ADDITIONAL NOTES: V-8 models have the numeral '8' as the third digit of their series, style and serial numbers.

1966 Chevrolet, Caprice 2-dr hardtop coupe, V-8

CAPRICE — (V-8) — SERIES 166 — A very popular Sport Sedan option in 1965, the Caprice was expanded to series status for 1966, including a new Coupe with special formal roofline and two station wagon models with woodgrain body side trim. Interiors were plush cloth in the four-door hardtop Sport Sedan (bench front seat standard, Strato-back front seat optional), all-vinyl or cloth in the two-door hardtop Custom Coupe, and all-vinyl in the station wagons. A wood-look lower instrument panel insert was used, with wood-accented combination vinyl and carpet door panels (except on wagons) added. Exterior distinction came from color-keyed body side striping, wide, ribbed body sill moldings, Caprice front fender and deck signatures, wrap-around rear taillamps with bright horizontal ribs, specific Caprice wheelcovers, roof rear quarter emblems, twin simulated exhaust ports below Custom Coupe backlight and a Caprice tailgate nameplate on the Custom Wagons.

CAPRICE SERIES

Model Number	Body/Style Number	Body Type & Seating	Factory Price	Shipping Weight	Production Total
166	16639	4-dr HT-6P	3063	3675	Note 1
166	16647	2-dr Cpe-6P	3000	3585	Note 1
166	16645	4-dr Sta Wag-9P	3347	4020	Note 1
166	16635	4-dr Sta Wag—6P	3234	3970	Note 1

NOTE 1: 181,000 Caprices were built, excluding station wagons.

CAPRICE ENGINES
Base Caprice engines were the same as listed for the 1966 Biscayne, except the six-cylinder was not available.

CHEVELLE '300' — (6-CYL/V-8) — SERIES 131/132 — A new body graced 1966 Chevelles, with forward thrusting front fenders, new body contour lines, wider-appearing anodized aluminum grille and new rear body cove treatment. Chevelle '300' models were relatively lacking in ornamentation with Series rear fender emblems, bright ventipane frames, windshield and rear window moldings, outside rearview mirror, four headlamps with anodized aluminum bezels, grille outline moldings, recar cover Chevelle nameplate, front bumper mounted park/turn lights, small hubcaps, single-unit rear lights with bright bezels and built-in back-up lights. Interiors were pattern cloth and vinyl trimmed, black rubber floor covering, plus all GM safety features and five blackwall tires, heater and defroster.

CHEVELLE I.D. NUMBERS: Serial Numbers took the same general form as used on full-sized Chevrolets, with applicable Chevelle Series codes used for the second and third symbols.

CHEVELLE '300' SERIES

Model Number	Body/Style Number	Body Type & Seating	Factory Price	Shipping Weight	Production Total
131/2	13169	4-dr Sed—6P	2202/2308	2935/3080	Note 1
131/2	13111	2-dr Sed-6P	2165/2271	2895/3040	Note 1

NOTE 1: A total of 28,600 Chevelle '300s' were built of which 23,300 were six-cylinder and 5,300 were V-8.
ADDITIONAL NOTES: V-8 models have the numeral '2' as the third digit of their serial numbers and style numbers.

CHEVELLE '300' ENGINES
The base engines were the same as listed for the 1965 Chevelle. Both six and eight-cylinder were offered.

CHEVELLE '300' DELUXE — (6-CYL/V-8) — SERIES 133/134 — A slightly upgraded Chevelle '300', with full-length body side moldings, Chevelle '300' DeLuxe rear fender nameplates and painted rear quarter reveal moldings, bright tailgate molding and emblem on station wagon. A dual-spoke steering wheel was specific to this model, with horn ring, as was the color-keyed upper instrument panel with bright lower panel trim strip. Doors had bright accents on the trim panels and the rear arm rests had built in ashtrays. Interiors were cloth and vinyl upholstered.

CHEVELLE '300' DELUXE SERIES

Model Number	Body/Style Number	Body Type & Seating	Factory Price	Shipping Weight	Production Total
133/4	13369	4-dr Sed-6P	2276/2382	2945/3095	Note 1
133/4	13311	2-dr Sed-6P	2239/2345	2910/3060	Note 1
133/4	13335	4-dr Sta Wag-6P	2575/2681	3210/3350	Note 1

NOTE 1: A total of 37,500 Chevelle '300s' were built (excluding station wagons), of which 27,100 were six-cylinders and 10,500 were V-8s.
ADDITIONAL NOTES: V-8 models had the numeral '4' as the third digit of their style and serial numbers.

CHEVELLE MALIBU — (6-CYL/V-8) — This nicely trimmed series added to or replaced equipment on the Chevelle '300' DeLuxe as follows: slender body sill and wheelhouse molding were added, along with Malibu rear fender nameplates and a hood windsplit molding. A rear cove outline molding surrounded the single-unit rear lights with built-in backup lamps (vertical light units were used on the station wagons), and a rear cove emblem was used, with Chevrolet script above on the deck lid. Station wagons in this series had a full-width ribbed molding and emblem and tailgate Chevelle nameplate. Interiors were plusher cloth and vinyl (all-vinyl on convertible and station wagon). A distinctive dual-spoke steering wheel was used. Black crackle finish was used on the instrument panel upper section, a glove compartment light, bright back rearview mirror, bright roof rails and floor carpeting were additional Malibu features.

CHEVELLE MALIBU

Model Number	Body/Style Number	Body Type & Seating	Factory Price	Shipping Weight	Production Total
135/6	13569	4-dr Sed-6P	2352/2458	2960/3110	Note 1
135/6	13569	4-dr HT-6P	2458/2564	3035/3180	Note 1
135/6	13517	2-dr HT-6P	2378/2484	2935/3075	Note 1
135	13567	Conv	2588/2693	3030/3175	Note 1
135/6	13535	4-dr Sta Wag-6P	2651/2756	2651/3375	Note 1

NOTE 1: A total of 241,500 Chevelle Malibus were built (excluding station wagons), of which 52,300 were six-cylinders and 189,300 were V-8s.
ADDITIONAL NOTES: V-8 models had the numeral '6' as the third digit of their style and serial numbers.

1966 Chevelle, SS-396 2-dr hardtop sports coupe, V-8

CHEVELLE SUPER SPORT 396 — (V-8) — SERIES 138 — Chevelle's performance package for this year included twin simulated air intakes, ribbed color-accented body sill and rear fender lower moldings, SS-396 grille and rear cover emblems and Super Sport script on the rear fenders. Specific wheel covers were included, as were five nylon red-stripe tires. Interiors were all-vinyl, with bench front seat standard and included all Malibu features (except for color-keyed vinyl-coated cargo floor mat and textured vinyl cargo area sidewalls.)

CHEVELLE SUPER SPORT 396 (SERIES 138)

Model Number	Body/Style Number	Body Type & Seating	Factory Price	Shipping Weight	Production Total
136	13617	2-dr HT-6P	2276	3375	Note 1
136	13667	Conv	2984	3470	Note 1

NOTE 1: Chevelle Super Sport production was 72,272 units in both styles.

CHEVELLE SUPER SPORT 396 ENGINE
V-8. Overhead valves. Cast iron block. Displacement: 396 cubic inches. Bore and stroke: 4.094 x 3.76 inches. Compression ratio: 10.25:1. Brake horsepower: 325 at 4800 R.P.M. Five main bearings. Hydraulic valve lifters. Downdraft four-barrel carburetor.

CHEVY II — 100-4/100-6 — (4-CYL/6-CYL) — SERIES 111/113 — A new body was used for 1966, featuring single unit headlamps in new bright bezels, a refined anodized aluminum front grille, and turn directional signal lights in the front bumper. At the rear were new vertical-type taillights, of the single unit type with built-in backup lamps. Chevy II '100' models had Chevy II rear fender emblems, bright ventipane frames, windshield and rear window reveal moldings, bright outside rearview mirror, grille opening moldings, small bright hubcaps, deck lid Chevy II emblem tailgate on wagons and cloth and vinyl interiors (all-vinyl on station wagons) and cloth and vinyl interiors (all-vinyl on station wagon). Standard features included a dual spoke steering wheel with horn button, padded instrument panel, glove compartment lock, vinyl door and sidewall trim panels, DeLuxe type door handles and regulators, foam-cushioned front seat, dual sun visors, two coat hooks and other convenience items.

CHEVY II I.D. NUMBERS: Serial numbers took the same general form as on full-sized Chevrolets with applicable Chevy II series codes used for the second and third symbols.

CHEVY II

Model Number	Body/Style Number	Body Type & Seating	Factory Price	Shipping Weight	Production Total
111/3	11169	4-dr Sed-6P	2065/2127	2535/2635	Note 1
111/3	11111	2-dr Sed-6P	2028/2090	2520/2630	Note 1
113	11335	Sta Wag-6P	2430	2855	Note 1

NOTE 1: Six-cylinder and optional V-8 units had the numeral '3' as the third digit of their style and serial numbers.
ADDITIONAL NOTES: A total of 47,000 Chevy II '100s' were produced, of which 44,500 were six-cylinders and 4,900 were optional V-8s.

CHEVY II NOVA — (6-CYL) — SERIES 115 — Plusher models, with exterior distinction derived from a color accent-full length body side molding, body sill moldings, Nova rear fender script and model badge, hood emblem, roof drip gutter bright moldings, door and rear quarter upper side moldings (on two-door hardtop Sport Coupe), bright roof rear quarter belt molding (on sedan), and full width-color accented deck trim with Chevy II nameplate. Interiors were cloth and vinyl (all vinyl on sport coupe and station wagon), with the following features added to equipment found on the Chevy II '100': distinctive dual-spoke steering wheel with horn ring, glove compartment door trim panel and nameplate, bright accents on door and sidewall trim, rear armrests with built-in ashtrays, foam cushioned rear seat, color-keyed floor carpeting and automatic front door dome light switches.

1966 Chevy II, Nova Super Sport 2-dr hardtop sports coupe, V-8

CHEVY II NOVA SERIES

Model Number	Body/Style Number	Body Type & Seating	Factory Price	Shipping Weight	Production Total
115	11569	4-dr Sed-6P	2245	2640	Note 1
115	11537	2-dr HT-6P	2271	2675	Note 1
115	11535	4-dr Sta Wag-6P	2518	2885	Note 1

NOTE 1: A total of 73,900 Chevy II Novas were built, excluding station wagons. Of these, 54,300 were six-cylinders and 19,600 were V-8s.
ADDITIONAL NOTES: V-8s were a Nova option, and are listed under Powertrain Options.

NOVA SUPER SPORT — (6-CYL) — SERIES 117 — The sporty Nova was identified on the exterior by color-accented wide body sill moldings, front and rear wheel opening moldings, with extension on both lower fenders, door and rear quarter upper body side moldings, an SS grille emblem, Nova SS rear fender script, a full width, ribbed rear deck panel with Chevy II nameplate and SS badge and special 14" Super Sport wheelcovers. Interiors included all-vinyl front bucket seats (console with four-speed or automatic) and most features found on Nova models. An SS emblem was found on the glove box door.

NOVA SUPER SPORT SERIES

Model Number	Body/Style Number	Body Type & Seating	Factory Price	Shipping Weight	Production Total
117	11737	2-dr HT	2430	2740	10,100

NOTE: V-8s were a Nova SS option and are included in Powertrain Options.

CHASSIS FEATURES: Wheelbase: (full-size Chevrolets) 119.0 inches; (Chevelle) 115.0 inches; (Chevy II) 110.0 inches. Overall length: (full-size Chevrolet) 213.2; (full-size wagons) 212.4 inches; (Chevelle) 197.0 inches; (wagons) 197.6 inches; (Chevy II) 183.0 inches; (wagons) 187.4 inches. Front tread: (full-size Chevrolet) 62.5 inches; (full-size wagons) 63.5 inches; (Chevelle) 58.0 inches; (Chevy II) 56.8 inches; (wagons) 56.3 inches. Rear tread: (full-size Chevrolet) 62.4 inches; (full-size wagons) 63.4 inches; (Chevelle) 58.0 inches; (Chevy II) 56.3 inches; (wagons) 55.8 inches. Tires: (full-size Chevrolet) 7.35 x 14, 7.75 x 14, 8.25 x 14, 8.55 x 14 (depending on model, engine and options); (Chevelle) 6.95 x 14 or 7.35 x 14, (SS-396) 7.75 x 14; (Chevy II) six-cylinder 6.50 x 13; on V-8 6.95 x 14.

FULL-SIZE CHEVROLET POWERTRAIN OPTIONS: A three-speed manual transmission, with column shift, was standard on six-cylinder and 283 and 327 cubic inch V-8 models. A heavy-duty three-speed, with floor shift was optional (required) with 396 and 427 cubic inch V-8s ($79). Overdrive was optional for standard engines ($115). A four-speed manual transmission was optional for V-8 engines ($184). Close ratio version (2.20:1 low) was available for 396-427 V-8s. Powerglide two-speed automatic transmission was available with column shift (floor lever on bucket-seat equipped Series 163, 163, 166 cars) for six-cylinder ($184); for 283, 327 and 325 horsepower 396 V-8s ($195). Turbo Hydra-Matic was optional on 296 and 390 horsepower 427 cubic inch V-8s ($226). Optional engines included: 283 cubic inch, 220 horsepower Turbo-Fire V-8 (RPO L77). 327 cubic inch, 275 horsepower Turbo-Fire V-8 (RPO-L30) ($93). 396 cubic inch, 325 horsepower Turbo-Jet V-8 (RPO L35) ($158). 427 cubic inch, 390 horsepower Turbo-Jet V-8 (RPO L36) ($316). 427 cubic inch, 425 horsepower Turbo-Jet V-8 (RPO L72).

CHEVELLE POWERTRAIN OPTIONS: A three-speed manual transmission, with column mounted shift, was standard on all Chevelle models. Overdrive was optional with standard engines ($116). A four-speed manual transmission, close ratio or wide range with floor shift was available for all V-8s ($184; $105 on SS-396). Powerglide two-speed automatic transmission was offered for six-cylinder and all cataloged V-8 engines except the 360 horsepower, 396 cubic inch V-8 ($184; $195 on SS-396). Optional engines included: 230 cubic inch, 140 horsepower six-cylinder (RPO L26) ($37). 283 cubic inch, 220 horsepower V-8 (RPO L77). 327 cubic inch, 275 horsepower V-8 (RPO L30) ($93). 327 cubic inch, 350 horsepower V-8 (RPO L79) ($198). 396 cubic inch, 360 horsepower V-8 (RPO L34 SS-396 only) ($105) 396 cubic inch 375 horsepower V-8 (RPO L78 SS-396 only).

CHEVY II POWERTRAIN OPTIONS: A three-speed manual transmission was standard in all models. A four-speed manual transmission was optional for cars equipped with V-8s ($184). Powerglide two-speed automatic transmission was optional for all engines ($164-$174). Optional engines included: 230 cubic inch, 140 horsepower six-cylinder (RPO L26) ($37). 283 cubic inch, 220 horsepower V-8 (RPO L77). 327 cubic inch, 275 horsepower V-8 (RPO L30) ($93). 327 cubic inch, 350 horsepower V-8 (RPO L79) (only 200 were built).

CHEVROLET FULL-SIZE CONVENIENCE OPTIONS: Power brakes ($42). Power steering ($95). Four-Season comfort on air conditioning. Power rear antenna ($28). Rear window defroster. Emergency road kit. Tinted Soft-Ray glass on all windows ($37); windshield only ($21). Front bumper guards ($16); rear bumper guards ($16). Strato-ease front seat headrests ($53). Deletion heater and defroster ($71 credit). Tri-volume horn ($14). Special instrumentation ($79). Spare wheel lock. AM/FM pushbutton radio with front antenna ($134). AM/FM pushbutton radio with front antenna and rear speaker ($147). AM/FM pushbutton stereo radio with front antenna ($239). AM pushbutton radio with front antenna ($57). AM pushbutton radio with front antenna and rear speaker ($71). Vinyl roof cover in black or beige ($79). Front and rear Custom DeLuxe color matched seat belts with front retractors. Four-Way power drivers seat ($70). Comfort-Tilt steering wheel ($42). Sport-styled steering wheel ($32). Tilt-telescopic steering wheel. Tachometer. Traffic hazard warning system. Set of five 14-inch wheels with 6JK rims ($21). Mag style wheel covers ($53). Simulated wire wheel covers ($56). Power windows ($100).

CHEVELLE AND CHEVY II CONVENIENCE OPTIONS: Power brakes ($42). Power steering ($84). Four-Season air conditioning on Chevelle; All-Weather on Chevy II ($310). Center console for strato-bucket seats. Rear window defroster. Tinted Soft-Ray glass on all windows ($31); on windshield only ($21). Front bumper guards ($10); rear bumper guards ($10). Strato-Rest headrest ($53). Tri-volume horn. AM/FM pushbutton radio, not available in Chevy II. AM/FM pushbutton radio with rear speaker, not available in Nova. AM pushbutton radio ($57). AM pushbutton radio with rear seat speaker ($71). Vinyl roof cover ($74). Custom DeLuxe color matched seat belts ($8). Four-way power front seat, not available in Chevy II. Strato-bucket front seats, not available in Chevy II. Comfort-Tilt steering wheel, not available in Chevy II. Sports-styled steering wheel ($32). Tachometer, not available in Chevy II. Power operated convertible top. Wheel covers ($21). Mag styled wheel covers ($74). Simulated wire wheel covers ($73). Power windows, Chevelle only.

Historical footnotes: Model year production peaked at 2,215,979 units. Calendar year sales of 2,202,758 cars were recorded. E.M. Estes was the Chief Executive Officer of the company this year. Of the total production of 1966 Chevrolets, 1,499,876 were full size cars, 18,100 were six-cylinder station wagons. 167,400 were full-size V-8 Chevrolet station wagons, 8,900 were six-cylinder Chevelles, 23,000 were V-8 Chevelles, 16,500 were six-cylinder Chevy II/Novas and 4,900 were Chevy II/Nova V-8s. Chevrolet called their two-door hardtops 'Sport Coupes' in all lines. Style 16647 was the Caprice Custom Coupe.

1967 CHEVROLET

BISCAYNE — (6-CYL/V-8) — SERIES 153/154 — Chevrolet featured a new body for 1967. The Biscayne was the base line. It had an anodized aluminum grille, at the front, with a bright bumper carrying the parking/turn signal lamps below. Grille opening moldings were used, as were bright windshield and rear window reveal moldings. Biscayne script appeared on the rear fenders, while Chevrolet script was found on the deck lid and hood. Small bright metal hub caps were standard and a chrome outside rearview mirror was included. Ventipane frames were plated. Dual unit taillamps were found at the rear with built-in backup lights. Station wagons had tailgate reveal moldings and script on the tailgate. Interiors were cloth and vinyl, or all-vinyl on station wagons. Standard features included a brake system warning light; cigarette lighter; illuminated heater control panel; padded instrument panel; glove compartment lock; front door arm rests; rear arm rests with built-in ash trays, foam -cushioned front seat (with seatback latches on two-door models) and color-keyed floor carpeting.

VEHICLE IDENTIFICATION NUMBERS: The numbering system and code locations were the same as for previous models with the sixth symbol changed to the numeral '7' to indicate the 1967 model year.

BISCAYNE SERIES

Series Number	Body/Style Number	Body Type & Seating	Factory Price	Shipping Weight	Production Total
153/154	69	4-dr Sed-6P	2484/2589	3410/3525	Note 1
153/154	11	2-dr Sed-6P	2442/2547	3335/3465	Note 1
153/154	35	Sta Wag-6P	2817/2923	3765/3885	Note 2

NOTE 1: Some 92,800 Biscayne passenger cars were built in the 1967 model year. In figures rounded-off to the nearest 100 units, this total included 54,200 Sixes and 38,600 V-8s. This does not include station wagons.
NOTE 2: Some 155,100 full-sized station wagons were built in the 1968 model year. In figures rounded-off to the nearest 100 units, this included 11,400 Sixes and 140,700 V-8s. Since production of all station wagons was totaled separately, this includes Biscayne, Bel air and Impala output.

ADDITIONAL NOTES: In all the specifications charts in this section, Series Numbers, prices and weights above slash apply to Sixes/below slash to V-8s. The Chevrolet 'Model Number' is the combination of the Series and Body Style designations. Therefore, making reference to the chart above, a six-cylinder Biscayne four-door sedan would be Model Number 15369 priced at $2,484 and weighing 3410 pounds. The same basic system is used for listing all 1967 Chevrolets in this catalog.

BISCAYNE ENGINES
Standard engines were the same as those listed for 1965-1966 Biscaynes.

BEL AIR — (6-CYL/V-8) — SERIES 155/156 — The middle-priced Chevrolet line had a narrow full-length bodyside molding; roof drip cap moldings; triple unit taillamps with center backup lights; lower deck lid or tailgate moldings and Bel Air script on the rear fenders to give it distinction. Interiors were somewhat refined and standard equipment, added to that found on the Biscaynes, included a glove compartment light; illuminated ignition switch and the following station wagon features: foam-cushioned third seat; color-keyed textured vinyl cargo area sidewalls (except two-seat wagon) and a third seat courtesy light.

BEL AIR SERIES

Series Number	Body/Style Number	Body Type & Seating	Factory Price	Shipping Weight	Production Total
155/156	69	4-dr Sed-6P	2484/2689	3395/3535	Note 1
155/156	11	2-dr Sed-6P	2542/2647	3340/3470	Note 1
155/156	45	Sta Wag-9P	2993/3098	3825/3940	Note 2

NOTE 1: Some 179,700 Bel Air passenger cars were built in the 1967 model year. In figures rounded-off to the nearest 100 units, this total included 41,500 Sixes and 138,200 V-8s.

NOTE 2: Production of Bel Air station wagons was included with that of the other full-sized Chevrolet station wagons. See 1967 Biscayne Series listing Note 2 above.

BEL AIR ENGINES
Standard engines were the same as for the Biscayne.

IMPALA — (6-CYL/V-8) — SERIES 163/164 — Exterior items giving the Impala its status included bright lower bodyside moldings; roof drip cap and reveal moldings on hardtops; bright side window accents on station wagon and sedan; deck lid center panel accents in silver (with Chevrolet center emblem flanking rear cove); black accented-taillamp surrounds and lower tailgate reveal molding (on the station wagon). Full wheel covers were included. Interiors were cloth and vinyl, or all-vinyl, depending on the model. These features were added to (or replaced) the equipment found on lower-priced lines: a brushed metal, bright-outlined lower instrument panel facing; electric clock; finger-tip door releases; foam-cushioned rear seat; bright seat end panels; bright garnished moldings on hardtop styles; bright foot pedal trim outlines (with power brakes); roof side rail lights; courtesy lamps under instrument panel (on two-door hardtop and convertible) and a power-operated convertible top.

1967 Chevrolet, Impala SS 2-dr convertible, V-8

IMPALA SERIES

Series Number	Body/Style Number	Body Type & Seating	Factory Price	Shipping Weight	Production Total
163/164	69	4-dr Sed-6P	2723/2828	3455/3575	Note 1
163/164	39	4-dr HT-6P	2793/2899	3540/3660	Note 1
163/164	37	2-dr HT-6P	2740/2845	3475/3590	Note 1
163/164	67	2-dr Conv-6P	2991/3097	3515/3625	Note 2
163/164	45	Sta Wag-9P	3129/3234	3860/3980	Note 3
163/164	35	Sta Wag-6P	3016/3122	3805/3920	Note 3

NOTE 1: Some 575,600 Impala passenger cars were built in the 1967 model year. In figures rounded-off to the nearest 100 units, this total included 18,800 Sixes and 556,800 V-8s. This includes convertibles, but does not include station wagons.
NOTE 2: Exactly 29,937 full-sized Chevrolet convertibles were built in the 1967 model year. This total is included in the rounded-off total given above and covers both Impala and Impala SS convertibles. There are no further breakouts available as to how many convertibles were Sixes, V-8s or Super Sports.
NOTE 3: Production of Impala station wagons was included with that of other full-sized Chevrolet station wagons. See 1967 Biscayne Series listing Note 2.

IMPALA ENGINES
Base engines were the same as listed for the Biscayne.

1967 Chevrolet, Impala SS 2-dr hardtop Sport Coupe, V-8

IMPALA SUPER SPORT — (6-CYL/V-8) — SERIES 167/168 — The sporting Impala once again featured an all-vinyl interior, with front Strato bucket seats and a division console housing the shift lever as standard equipment (Strato bench seating was a no charge substitution). Exterior identification was made by the use of black accents on the grille (with bright horizontal bars remaining); front and rear wheelhouse moldings; black-accented body sill and lower rear fender bright moldings; a black-accent deck lid latch panel; SS deck lid and grille badges and specific Impala SS full wheel covers.

IMPALA SUPER SPORT

Series Number	Body/Style Number	Body Type & Seating	Factory Price	Shipping Weight	Production Total
167/168	37	2-dr HT-6P	2898/3003	3500/3615	66,510
167/168	67	2-dr Conv-6P	3149/3254	3535/3650	9,545

NOTES: A total of exactly 2,124 Impala Super Sports were equipped with the SS-427 option. In figures rounded-off to the nearest 100 units, total model year production of Impala Super Sports included some 400 Sixes and 75,600 V-8s.

IMPALA SUPER SPORT ENGINES
Base engines were the same as for the 1967 Biscayne.

CAPRICE — (V-8) — SERIES 116 — This posh Chevrolet included these exterior features on the Custom Sedan and Custom Coupe: Front fender lights; front and rear wheelhouse moldings; bright lower bodyside moldings with rear quarter extensions; color-keyed bodyside stripes; belt reveal molding on Custom Coupe; black- accented deck lid panel with bright highlight trim, triple-unit taillights with backup lights in the rear bumper; Caprice deck lid signatures; roof side panel nameplates and specific Caprice full wheel covers. Interiors were very plush, being trimmed in cloth; cloth and vinyl or all-vinyl, depending on model. Caprice Custom station wagons had wood panels, with bright outline moldings, on the bodysides and tailgate, plus Caprice tailgate nameplates. Interior features, in addition to (or replacing) those found on lower-priced models included walnut-look lower instrument panel facing (with bright outline); pattern coth and vinyl door panels; wood-look door panel trim in sedan and coupe (wagons were all-vinyl) and front seat fold-down center arm rest (on sedans).

CAPRICE SERIES

Model Number	Body/Style Number	Body Type & Seating	Factory Price	Shipping Weight	Production Total
166	39	4-dr HT-6P	3130	3710	Note 1
166	47	2-dr HT-6P	3078	3605	Note 1
166	45	Sta Wag-9P	3413	3990	Note 2
166	35	Sta Wag-6P	3301	3935	Note 2

NOTE 1: In figures rounded-off to the nearest 100 units, a total of some 124,500 Caprice passenger cars were built in the 1967 model year. All were V-8 powered. This does not include Caprice station wagons.
NOTE 2: Production of Caprice station wagons was included with that of other full-sized Chevrolet station wagons. See 1967 Biscayne Series listing Note 2.

CAPRICE ENGINE
The base engine was the same as the Biscayne V-8.

CHEVELLE '300' — (6-CYL/V-8) — SERIES 131/132 — Very slight sheetmetal changes, primarily in the front and rear fender edges, were made for Chevelle in 1967. A new anodized aluminum grille was used and all Chevelles had grille opening moldings with a Chevrolet badge; front bumper-mounted parking and directional signals; windshield bright reveal moldings; bright ventipane frames; rear window reveal moldings and backup lights in the rear bumper. Chevelle '300' models had rear fender series identification; single-unit taillights with bright bezels; a chromed outside rearview mirror and Chevelle lettering in the deck cove. Interiors were trimmed in cloth and vinyl and included these features: parking brake and brake system warning light; cigarette lighter; glove compartment lock; lever-type door handles; front door arm rests, foam-cushioned front seat; padded sun visors; black rubber floor covering; day/night rearview mirror; four-way hazard flasher system and center dome light.

CHEVELLE '300' SERIES

Series Number	Body/Style Number	Body Type & Seating	Factory Price	Shipping Weight	Production Total
131/132	69	4-dr Sed-6P	2250/2356	2955/3090	Note 1
131/132	11	2-dr Sed-6P	2221/2326	2935/3360	Note 1

NOTE 1: Some 24,700 Chevelle '300' models were built for the 1967 model year. In figures rounded-off to the nearest 100 units, this total included 19,900 Sixes and 4,800 V-8s.

CHEVELLE '300' ENGINES
Base six-cylinder and V-8 engines were the same as listed for 1966 Chevelle '300's.

CHEVELLE '300' DELUXE — (6-CYL/V-8) — SERIES 133/134 — A slightly embellished Chevelle. Series features, in addition to (or replacing) those of the Chevelle '300' included bright exterior body sill moldings; rear cove lower trim moldings on the sedan; Chevelle '300' DeLuxe rear fender nameplates and a rear cove or tailgate center emblem. Interiors were cloth and vinyl (all-vinyl in station wagon) and the instrument panel had a silver-finished upper accent. Rear arm rests had built-in ash trays, while the floor was covered with color-keyed vinyl-coated rubber. Automatic interior light switches were found on the door jambs. Bodies had Flush and Dry rocker panels and inner fenders.

CHEVELLE 300 DELUXE SERIES

Series Number	Body/Style Number	Body Type & Seating	Factory Price	Shipping Weight	Production Total
133/134	69	4-dr Sed-6P	2324/2930	2980/3110	Note 1
133/134	11	2-dr Sed-6P	2295/2400	2955/3090	Note 1
133/1344	35	Sta Wag-6P	2619/2725	3230/3360	Note 2

NOTE 1: Some 26,300 Chevelle '300' DeLuxe models were built during the 1967 model year. In figures rounded-off to the nearest 100 units, this total included 19,300 Sixes and 7,000 V-8s. Station wagons are not included.
NOTE 2: Some 27,300 Chevelle station wagons were built during the 1967 model year. In figures rounded-off to the nearest 100 units, this included 5,900 Sixes and 21,400 V-8s. Since production of station wagons for all Chevelle series was counted as a single total, these figures include both Chevelle 300 DeLuxe and Chevelle Malibu station wagons.

MALIBU — (6-CYL/V-8) — SERIES 135/136 — A nicely appointed Chevelle, the Malibu found exterior distinction by the use of bright lower bodyside and rear quarter moldings; roof drip cap moldings; bright rear quarter window reveal moldings (on station wagons); Malibu rear fender nameplates; black-accented rear cove outline panel; single-unit taillights with black-accented bezels and bright horizontal strips; rear cove or tailgate Chevelle badge (to the right) and a tailgate molding on the station wagon. Full wheel covers were included. Interiors were plusher and included a specific steering wheel; a walnut-finish upper panel on the instrument panel; illuminated heater control panel; electric clock; bright accents on the vinyl sidewall and door panel trim; bright bases on front arm rests; a foam-cushioned rear seat; color-keyed floor carpeting and courtesy lights in the convertible.

MALIBU SERIES

Series Number	Body/Style Number	Body Type & Seating	Factory Price	Shipping Weight	Production Total
135/136	69	4-dr Sed-6P	2400/2506	3000/3130	Note 1
135/136	17	2-dr HT-6P	2434/2540	2980/3115	Note 1
135/136	67	2-dr Conv-6P	2637/2743	3050/3185	Note 2
135/136	35	Sta Wag-6P	2695/2801	3260/3390	Note 3
135/136	39	4-dr HT-6P	2506/2611	3065/3200	Note 1

NOTE 1: Some 227,800 Malibu passenger cars were built during the 1967 model year. In figures rounded-off to the nearest 100 units, this total included 40,600 Sixes and 187,200 V-8s. This does not include station wagons.
NOTE 2: Exactly 12,772 convertibles were built, for the 1967 model year, in the Chevelle Malibu and Malibu SS Series. This figure is included in the rounded-off totals given above.There is no breakout available to indicate how many Chevelle convertibles were Malibu SS models.
NOTE 3: Production of station wagons in the Malibu Series was included with that of Chevelle 300 DeLuxe station wagons. See Chevelle 300 DeLuxe Series listing Note 2.

1967 Chevelle, Concours Estate, 4-dr station wagon, V-8

CONCOURS — (6-CYL/V-8) — SERIES 137/138 — This was a luxury station wagon of the Chevelle line, featuring special black-accented grille; synthetic wood-grain exterior side and tailgate panelling (with bright outline trim); front and rear wheelhouse moldings; ribbed,grey-accented, body sill moldings; tailgate emblem; badge for Concours identification and rear fender Concours script. Interiors were trimmed in textured vinyl. The passenger floor was carpeted and the cargo load floor had a vinyl coating.

CONCOURS SERIES

Series Number	Body/Style Number	Body Type & Seating	Factory Price	Shipping Weight	Production Total
137/138	35	Sta Wag-6P	2827/2933	3270/3405	Note 1

NOTE 1: Concours production was included with that of all other Chevelle station wagons. See Chevelle '300' DeLuxe listing Note 2.

CHEVELLE SS 396 — (V-8) — SERIES 138 — The Chevelle had a youthful flair and was identifiable by these exterior additions or changes from other Chevelles: special black-accented grille with SS 396 badge; front and rear wheelhouse bright outlines; ribbed, gray-accented body sill moldings; color-keyed bodyside accent stripes; simulated air intakes on the domed hood; Super Sport rear fender emblems; black-painted rear cove panel (with SS 396 center medallion); five Red-Stripe special tires and specific full wheel covers. Interiors were all-vinyl, with a black-accent upper panel on the instrument board. Bucket seats were an option.

CHEVELLE SS 396 SERIES

Series Number	Body/Style Number	Body Type & Seating	Factory Price	Shipping Weight	Production Total
138	17	2-dr HT-6P	2825	3415	Note 1
138	67	2-dr Conv-6P	3033	3495	Notes 1/2

NOTE 1: Exactly 63,006 Chevelle SS 396 models were built during the 1967 model year. This includes both hardtop coupes and convertibles. All were V-8 powered. No further body style breakouts are currently available.
NOTE 2: Given the available figures, the only conclusion that can be made about Chevelle SS 396 convertible production is that no more than 29,937 were built. (See 1967 Chevelle Malibu Series listing Note 2 for further explanation).

CHEVELLE SS 396 ENGINE
Engine had same dimensions as the 1966 Chevelle SS 396, however, the 375 h.p. version was dropped and the 360 h.p. engine was now rated at 350 h.p.

CHEVY II 100 — (4-CYL./6-CYL) — SERIES 111/113 — Very minor trim changes occurred for the second year of the 1966's styling cycle. A new anodized aluminum grille had a distinct horizontal center bar motif, with a Chevy II nameplate to the driver's side. Chevy II '100' standard items included grille opening moldings; front bumper mounted parking and directional signal lamps; windshield bright reveal molding; small, bright hubcaps; bright ventipane frames; chromed outside rearview mirror; vertical, single-unit taillights (with built-in backup lights); rearview reveal molding and deck lid or tailgate Chevy II emblems. Chevy II rear fender emblems gave side identification. Interiors were trimmed in cloth and vinyl or all-vinyl, depending on model. Standard interior features included bright instrument cluster bezel; brake system warning light; glove compartment lock; front door arm rests; foam-cushioned front seat; folding front seatback latches (on two-door sedan); black rubber floor covering; four-way hazard flasher and center dome light.

CHEVY II '100' SERIES

Series Number	Body/Style Number	Body Type & Seating	Factory Price	Shipping Weight	Production Total
111/113	69	4-dr Sed-6P	2120/2182	2560/2650	Note 1
111/113	11	2-dr Sed-6P	2090/2152	2555/2640	Note 1
111/113	35	Sta Wag-6P	2478	2865	Note 2

NOTE 1: Some 35,900 Chevy II '100' passenger cars were built for the 1967 model year. In figures rounded-off to the nearest 100 units, this included 480 Fours, 33,720 Sixes and 1,700 V-8s. This does not include station wagons.
NOTE 2: Some 12,900 Chevy II station wagons were built during model year 1967. In figures rounded-off to the nearest 100 units, this included no Fours, 10,000 Sixes and 2,900 V-8s. Since station wagon production for all series were combined as a single total, this includes Chevy II '100' and Nova Series station wagons.

CHEVY II 100 ENGINES
Base four-cylinder and six-cylinder engines were the same as for 1966 Chevy II 100.

CHEVY II NOVA — (6-CYL) — SERIES 115 — A more DeLuxe Chevy II, the Nova had these features in addition to (or replacing) those found on the Chevy II '100': black-accented bodyside moldings; body sill moldings; roof drip cap bright moldings; door and rear quarter moldings on two-door hardtops; bright roof rear quarter belt molding on sedan; full-width deck lid or tailgate trim panel (with Chevy II badge and emblem) and bright metal extensions under station wagon rear lights. Interiors were cloth and vinyl (all-vinyl in station wagon). Standard features, in addition to those on lower-priced models, included an illuminated heater control panel; cigarette lighter; glove compartment door trim panel; glove compartment light; instrument panel nameplate; more distinctive door panels and sidewall trim (with bright accents); bright bases on front padded arm rests; rear arm rest bright bases and built-in ash trays; foam-cushioned rear seat; color-keyed floor carpeting and automatic front door dome light switches.

CHEVY II NOVA SERIES

Series Number	Body/Style Number	Body Type & Seating	Factory Price	Shipping Weight	Production Total
115	69	4-dr Sed-6P	2298	2660	Note 1
115	37	2-dr HT Cpe-6P	2330	2660	Note 1
115	35	Sta Wag-6P	2566	2890	Note 2

NOTE 1: Some 47,600 Nova passenger cars were built in the 1967 model year. In figures rounded-off to the nearest 100 units, this total included 34,400 Sixes and 13,200 V-8s. This does not include station wagons.

1967 Chevy II, Nova SS 2-dr hardtop sports coupe, V-8 (AA)

NOTE 2: Production of Nova station wagons is included with that of other Chevy II station wagons. See Chevy II '100' Series listing Note 2.

NOVA SUPER SPORT — (6-CYL) — SERIES 117 Revised for 1967, the taut, small Nova continued to make an excellent high-performance car when based on this model. The 1967 Nova Super Sport had these exterior distinctions: special black-accented grille (with Nova SS emblem low on the driver's side); lower body moldings (above black-painted sill area); bodyside accent stripes; front and rear bright wheelhouse moldings (with extensions along lower fender edges); specific Super Sport full wheel covers; Super Sport rear fender scripts and full-width color accent deck lid trim panel (with center emblem and Nova SS signature). Interiors were all-vinyl, with front Strato-bucket seats and bright seat end panels standard. A floor shift trim plate was included on cars with four-speed or automatic transmission. A three-spoke steering wheel was used. Other standard features were the same as Nova.

CHEVY II NOVA SUPER SPORT SERIES

Series Number	Body/Style Number	Body Type & Seating	Factory Price	Shipping Weight	Production Total
117	11737	2-dr HT Cpe-5P	2487	2690	10,100

NOTE: Total Nova SS production for the 1967 model year was 10,100 units. In figures rounded-off to the nearest 100 units, this included 1,900 Sixes and 8,200 V-8s.

1967 Chevrolet, Camaro SS 2-dr hardtop, V-8

CAMARO — (6-CYL/V-8) — SERIES 123/124 — Chevrolet entered the pony car race with their sporty Camaro for 1967. A 'building block' system of options allowed the creation of many varied and distinctive vehicles (see Camaro Convenience Options). The base models featured: slender body sill moldings; black plastic grille; single-unit headlights; grille-mounted parking lights; small, bright metal hubcaps; tail-lights with bright bezels and built-in backup lights; windshield pillar and rear belt moldings and manual-operation top (on convertible). Standard interior features included color-keyed all vinyl trim with Strato-bucket front seats and scuff-resistant cowl side panels with ventilator grilles; color-keyed carpeting; front arm rests with bright bases; cigarette lighter; built-in instrument panel ash tray; automatic front door switches for dome or courtesy lights; locking glove compartment; friction-type venti-panes and, in convertibles, built-in arm rests and dual courtesy lights.

CAMARO I.D. NUMBERS: Serial Numbers took the same general form as on full-size Chevrolets.

CAMARO SERIES

Series Number	Body/Style Number	Body Type & Seating	Factory Price	Shipping Weight	Production Total
123/124	37	2-dr HT Spt Cpe-5P	2466/2572	2770/2920	195,765
123/124	67	2-dr Conv-5P	2704/2809	3025/3180	25,141

ADDITIONAL NOTES: Total production included 602 Camaro coupes with the Z-28 option; 64,842 Camaros with the Rally Sport trim option (of which 10,675 were convertibles); 34,411 Camaros (coupes and convertibles) with the super Sport option (many with Rally Sport option also) and approximately 1000-1500 were produced and Z-10 pace Car replica hardtops.

CAMARO ENGINES

SIX-CYLINDER
Inline six-cylinder. Overhead valves. Cast iron block. Displacement: 230 cubic inches. Bore and stroke: 3.88 x 3.25 inches. Compression ratio: 8.5:1. Brake horsepower: 140 at 4400 R.P.M. Seven main bearings. Hydraulic valve lifters. Carburetor: Downdraft one-barrel.

V-8
V-8. Overhead valves. Cast iron block. Displacement: 327 cubic inches. Bore and stroke: 4.0 x 3.25 inches. Compression ratio: 8.8:1. Brake horsepower: 210 at 4600 R.P.M. Five main bearings. Carburetor: Downdraft two-barrel.

CHEVROLET FULL-SIZE POWERTRAIN OPTIONS: A three-speed manual transmission with floor shift was standard with six-cylinder and 283-327 cubic-inch V-8s. A three-speed manual transmission with floor shift was optional for 396 and 427 cubic inch V-8s (PRO M13). Overdrive was optional for the base six-cylinder and base 283 V-8 ($16). A four-speed manual transmission with floor shift was optional for all V-8 engines (RPO M20) ($184). Powerglide two-speed automatic transmission was optional for all engines except the 427 cubic inch versions ($184 with six-cylinder; $195 with V-8). Turbo HydraMatic ($226). Three-speed automatic transmissions were available with 327, 396 and 427 cubic inch V-8s. Optional engines included: RPO L30/ 327 cubic inch 275 horsepower V-8 ($92.70). RPO L35 396/ cubic inch 325 horsepower V-8 ($158). RPO L36/ 427 cubic inch 385 horsepower V-8, included with SS 427 package ($316). Posi-Traction rear axle.

CHEVELLE POWERTRAIN OPTIONS: A three-speed manual transmission, with column shift, was standard on six-cylinder, 283 and 327 cubic inch V-8s cars. A three-speed, heavy-duty manual transmission, with floor shift, was standard with 396 cubic inch V-8s (optional other models for $79). An overdrive transmission was available with base six-cylinder and 283 V-8 engines ($116). A four-speed manual transmission, with floor shift, was optional for all V-8 engines (wide or close ratio SS 396 $105; others $184). Powerglide two-speed automatic transmission was available with all engines ($116 with Six; $195 with V-8 except SS 396). Turbo HydraMatic three-speed automatic transmission was available with 396 cubic inch V-8s ($147). Optional engines included: 250 cubic inch, 155 horsepower six-cylnder /RPO L22 ($26). 327 cubic inch 275 horsepower V-8 /RPO L30 ($198). 327 cubic inch 325 horsepower V-8 /RPO L79 ($93). 396 cubic inch 350 horsepower V-8/RPO L34, for SS 396 only. ($105). Posi-Traction rear axle ($42.15).

CHEVY II POWERTRAIN OPTIONS: A three-speed manual transmission, with column shift, was standard on all models. A four-speed manual transmission was available with optional V-8s ($184). Powerglide two-speed automatic transmission was available with all engines ($164, $174 on V-8). Optional engines included; 250 cubic inch 155 horsepower six-cylinder /RPO L22 ($37). 327 cubic inch 275 horsepower V-8 /RPO L30 ($93). Posi-Traction rear axle ($42).

CAMARO POWERTRAIN OPTIONS: A three-speed manual transmission was standard on all models except Z-28. A three-speed heavy-duty manual transmission with floor shift was available for 350 and 396 cubic inch V-8 engines. A four-speed manual transmission was optional for all engines ($184 with SS 350). Powerglide two-speed automatic transmission was available for six-cylinder, 327 and 350 cubic inch V-8s ($184; $195 with V-8). Turbo HydraMatic was optional with the 325 horsepower 396 V-8. Optional engines included: 302 cubic inch 290 horsepower V-8 / RPO Z28. 327 cubic inch 275 horsepower V-8 / RPO L30 ($93). 350 cubic inch 295 horsepower V-8 / RPO L48 — SS 350. 396 cubic inch 325 horsepwoer V-8 / RPO L35 — SS 396. 396 cubic inch 375 horsepwoer V-8 / RPO L78 — SS 396. Posi-Traction rear axle ($42).

CHASSIS FEATURES: Wheelbase: (all full-size Chevrolets) 119.0 inches; (Chevelle) 115.0 inches; (Chevy II) 110.0 inches; (Camaro) 108.1 inches. Overall length: (all full-size Chevrolet passenger cars) 213.2 inches; (full-size wagons) 212.4 inches; (Chevelle passenger cars) 197.0 inches; (Chevy II) 183.0 inches; (Camaro) 184.6 inches. Front tread: (all full-size Chevrolet passenger cars) 62.5 inches; (full-size wagons) 63.5 inches; (Chevelle) 58.0 inches; (Chevy II) 56.8 inches; (Chevy II wagons) 56.3 inches; (Camaro) 59.0 inches. Rear tread: (all full-size Chevrolet passenger cars) 62.4 inches; (full-size wagons) 63.4 inches; (Chevy II) 56.3 inches; (Chevy II wagons) 55.8 inches; (Camaro) 58.9 inches. Tires: (full-size Chevrolets) 8.25 x 14, with disc brakes 8.15 x 15, on SS-427 6.70 x 15, on station wagons 8.55 x 14; (Chevelles) 7.35 x 14, with 384 Sport Sedan, convertible, 327 and wagons 7.75 x 14, SS-396 F70 x 14; (Chevy II) 6.95 x 14; (Caramo) 7.35 x 14, SS-350 D70 x 14 and Z-28 7.75 x 15.

FULL-SIZE CHEVROLET CONVENIENCE OPTIONS: Power brakes ($42). Power steering ($95). Four-Season air conditioning ($356). Comfort-On air conditioning ($435). Rear window air deflector on wagons ($19). Rear manual antenna, not available on wagons or with AM/FM radio ($9.50). Custom DeLuxe front and rear seat belts ($6). Front shoulder belts ($23). Load area carpets on Caprice and Impala wagons ($53). Electric clock on Biscayne and Bel Air ($16). Rear window defroster ($21). Tinted glass on all windows ($37); windshield only ($21). Door edge guards on two-doors ($3); on four-doors ($6). Rear bumper guards ($16). front bumper guards ($16). Head rest with Strato-Back or buckets ($53). Head rests with standard bench front seats ($42). Heater and defroster deletion ($71 credit). Tri-Volume horn ($14). Special instrumentation, V-8 only ($79). Automatic superlift level control, not available on six-cylinder ($79). Roof luggage rack on wagons ($42). Color-keyed floor mats ($11). LH outside remote control mirror ($10). Two-tone paint ($16). Rear power antenna ($28). Six-Way power seat, not available on Biscayne or with bucket seats ($95). Four-Way power seat on Impala, Super Sport with bucket seats ($70). Power tailgate window, standard on three-seat wagons ($32). Power windows, not available on Biscayne ($100). Pushbutton radio with front antenna ($57). Pushbutton AM/FM radio with front antenna ($134). Pushbutton AM/FM radio with front antenna and rear speaker ($147). AM/FM stereo radio with front antenna ($239). Rear seat speaker ($13). Vinyl roof cover on black or beige hardtops ($79). Divided second seat on wagons ($37). Strato-back vinyl seat in Caprice Custom sedan ($116). Strato-back vinyl seat in Impala SS (no charge). Strato-back cloth seat, Caprice Custom sedan and coupe ($105). Strato-back seats, included console, floor mounted shift ($158). Rear fender skirts ($26). Speed and cruise control ($50). Speed warning indicator ($11). Comfort-lift steering wheel with Powerglide. HydraMatic or four-speed transmission required ($42). Sport styled steering wheel ($32). Stereo tape system with four speakers ($129). Wheel covers, not available on Impala SS or Caprice ($21). Mag style wheel covers, on all Chevrolets except Super Sports and Caprice ($74). Mag style wheel covers, Impala SS and Caprice ($53). Simulated white wheel covers on Super Sports and Caprice ($56). Simulated wire wheel covers, all except Superports and Caprice ($74).

CHEVELLE/CHEVY II CONVENIENCE OPTIONS: Power brakes ($42). Power steering ($84). Four-Season air conditioning, Chevelle ($356). All-Weather air conditioning, Chevy II ($311). Rear antenna ($10). Custom DeLuxe front and rear seat belts ($6). Driver and passenger front shoulder belts, Standard ($23); Custom DeLuxe ($26). front bumper guards, Chevelle ($13); Chevy II ($10). Rear bumper guards, Chevelle ($13 not available in wagons); Chevy II ($10). Electric clock, Chevelle 300 and 300 DeLuxe ($16); Chevy II and Nova ($16). Rear window defroster, sedan and sport coupes ($21). Door edge guards, two-doors ($3); four-doors ($6). Tinted glass on all windows ($31); windshield only ($21). Driver and passenger Strato-Ease headrests, Chevelle with bucket seats and Nova SS ($53); Chevelle, Nova and 100 with standard bench front seat ($42). Heater and defroster deletion ($70 credit). Tri-Volume horn, all Chevelle except 300 ($14). Special instrumentation on Chevelle V-8 sport coupes and convertibles ($79). Luggage rack, wagons ($42). Front and rear color-keyed floor mats ($11). LH outside remote control mirror ($10). Two-tone paint ($16). Power tailgate window, wagons ($32). Pushbutton radio with front antenna and rear speaker ($71). Pushbutton radio with front antenna ($57). Pushbutton AM/FM radio with front antenna. Chevelle only ($134). Rear speaker ($13). Vinyl roof cover, Chevelle ($74). Strato bucket seats, Chevelle sport coupe and convertible ($111). Speed and cruise control, Chevelle V-8 models ($50). Speed warning indicator ($10). Sport styled steering wheel ($32). Stereo tape system with four speakers. Chevelle ($129). Tachometer Chevelle V-8 models ($47). Wheel covers, not available with disc brakes ($21). Mag styled wheel covers. Chevy II, Super Sport, not available with disc brakes, ($53). Nova and 100 Series ($74); Chevelle ($74). Simulated wire wheel covers, Chevy II, Super Sport, not available with disc brakes ($56); Nova and 100 Series ($74); Chevelle ($74).

CAMARO CONVENIENCE OPTIONS: All-weather air conditioning ($356). Manual rear antenna, not available with AM-FM radio ($10). Custom DeLuxe seat belts ($6). Standard front shoulder belts ($23). Custom DeLuxe front shoulder belts ($26). Electric clock, not available with stereo ($16). Floor console with shifter ($47). Rear window defroster, coupe ($21). Tinted glass on all windows ($31); windshield only ($21). Rear bumper guards ($10); front bumper guards ($13). Door edge guards ($3). Strato-Ease headrests ($53). Heater and defroster deletion ($32 credit). Tri-Volume horn, coupe only ($14). Ashtray light, coupe only ($1.60). Courtesy lights ($4). Glove compartment light, when not included ($2.65). Front and rear floor mats ($42). Power steering ($84). Power windows ($100). Manual pushbutton radio ($57). Manual pushbutton radio with rear seat speaker ($71). AM-FM radio ($133). Vinyl roof cover, black or beige for sport coupe only ($74). Folding rear seat ($32). Strato-back front seat, not available on convertible with console ($26). Speed and cruise control with V-8 on Powerglide only ($50). Speed warning indicator ($11). Comfort-tilt steering wheel ($42). Sports style steering wheel ($32). Stereo tape system with four speakers ($128). Simulated wire wheel covers, not available with disc brake ($74). Simulated mag wheel covers, not available with disc brakes ($74). Special instrumentation group included ammeter, temperature, oil and fuel gauges; electric clock mounted on console; fuel indicator light and tachometer in instrument panel ($79) and much more.

CAMARO OPTION PACKAGES: Style trim group (RPO Z21): adds front and rear wheel house moldings, drip gutter moldings on coupe, and body side accent stripes. ($29).
Special interior group (RPO Z23): replaces standard equipment with these items: bright pedal pad frames, windshield pillar moldings in bright metal and roof rail moldings in coupe ($11).
Custom interior (RPO Z87): replaces standard equipment with these special items: roof rear quarter dome lights on sport coupe, recessed door handles, color-keyed accent bands on front and rear seats, special front armrests, glove compartment light, three-spoke oval steering wheel with ornaments, carpeted scuff panels on doors, molded luggage compartment mat ($95).
Camaro Rally Sport (RPO Z22): includes style trim group and parking lights below

bumper, special grille with electrically controlled panels concealing headlamps, 'RS' grille, fender and gas cap emblems, wide lower body moldings, hood drip bright moldings on coupe, body side accent strips, black-painted specific taillight bezels and backup lights below rear bumper ($105).
Camaro SS 350 (RPO L48): featured these additions: 295 horsepower Turbo-Fire 350 V-8, 'SS' grille, fender and gas cap emblems (even when 'RS' group is included), special hood and simulated intake grids, front hood stripes and five special D70 x 14 red-stripe tires ($105). (SS 36 RPO L34 was similar).

Historical footnotes: All Chevrolets appeared in dealer showrooms September 29, 1966. Model year production peaked at 1,900,049 units. Calendar year sales of 1,978,550 cars were recorded. E.M. Estes was the Chief Executive Officer of the company this year. Station wagon production was 155,100 of which 11,400 were six-cylinders and 140,700 were V-8s.

1968 CHEVROLET

BISCAYNE — (SIX/V-8) — SERIES 153/154 — Chevrolets grew longer in 1968, with the addition of some bumper, grille, hood and fender modifications. The change that stood out the most was in the taillamp design, which now featured recessed lenses housed in rear bumper apertures. The hood was restyled to cover recessed windshield wipers. The front end featured a 'floating' type bumper design, in which a grille with slightly finer gridwork showed through below the bumper bar. Headlights were now mounted in rectangular bezels. The size of the parking lamps, notched into the front corners of the body, was reduced from 1967 and the lens was now smooth and light colored. Biscayne was the base series with standard equipment including all GM safety features; front seat shoulder belts; door-actuated light switches; heater and defroster; cigarette lighter; locking glove box; carpeting; arm rests; center dome light; Flush and Dry rocker panels and either the base Six or V-8. Passenger cars wore 8.25 x 14 blackwall tires, while station wagons had size 8.55 x 14.

VEHICLE I.D. NUMBERS: The numbering system and code locations were the same as on previous models. The Vehicle Identification Number had thirteen symbols. The first five symbols were digits representing the Chevrolet 'Model Number' (and were the same as the combination of the first and second columns in the specifications charts below). The sixth symbol was changed to an '8' to indicate 1968 model year. The seventh symbol, a letter, designated the assembly plant. The last six symbols were digits representing the sequential unit production number, beginning at 100001 and up at each factory.

BISCAYNE SERIES

Series Number	Body/Style Number	Body Type & Seating	Factory Price	Shipping Weight	Production Total
153/154	69	4-dr Sed-6P	2484/2589	3395/3525	Note 1
153/154	11	2-dr Sed-6P	2442/2547	3335/3465	Note 1
153/154	35	4-dr Sta Wag-6P	2817/2923	3765/3885	Note 2

NOTE 1: Some 82,100 Biscayne passenger cars were built in the 1968 model year. In figures rounded-off to the nearest 100 units, this total included 44,500 Sixes and 37,600 V-8s. This does not include station wagons.
NOTE 2: Some 175,600 full-sized Chevrolet station wagons were built in the 1968 model year. In figures rounded-off to the nearest 100 units, this total included 7,700 Sixes and 167,900 V-8s. Since production of station wagons was totaled separately, this includes Biscayne, Bel Air and Impala output.
ADDITIONAL NOTE: In all specifications charts in this section, Series Numbers, prices and weights above slash apply to Sixes/below slash to V-8s. The Chevrolet 'Model Number' is the combination of the Series and Body Style designations. Therefore, making reference to the chart above, a six-cylinder 1968 Biscayne four-door sedan would be Model Number 15369 priced at $2,484 and weighing 3395 pounds. The same basic system is used for listing all 1968 Chevrolets in this catalog.

BISCAYNE ENGINES
Inline Six. Overhead valve. Cast iron block. Displacement: 250 cubic inches. Bore and stroke: 3.875 x 3.53 inches. Compression ratio: 8.5:1. Brake horsepower: 155 at 4200 R.P.M. Seven main bearings. Hydraulic valve lifters. Carburetor: Carter one-barrel Model 3891593.

V-8. Overhead valves. Cast iron block. Displacement: 307 cubic inches. Bore and stroke: 3.875 x 3.25 inches. Compression ratio: 10.0:1. Brake horsepower: 200 at 4600 R.P.M. Five main bearings. Carburetor: Rochester two-barrel Model 7028101.

BEL AIR — (SIX/V-8) — SERIES 155/156 — The Bel Air Series was Chevrolet's moderate-priced, full size line for 1968. Bel Air had all standard equipment found in Biscaynes, plus mid-bodyside moldings; bright metal rear window, roof drip and windshield moldings; front and rear side marker lamps; glove box and ignition switch lights and upgraded interior trims. Station wagons featured all-vinyl interior; seat belts for all passengers and automatic ignition key alarms. The three-seat station wagon also had a power tailgate window.

VEHICLE I.D. NUMBERS: The numbering system and code locations were the same as on Biscayne models, with the first five symbols changed to Bel Air nomenclature.

BEL AIR SERIES

Series Number	Body/Style Number	Body Type & Seating	Factory Price	Shipping Weight	Production Total
155/156	69	4-dr Sed-6P	2723/2828	3466/3582	Note 1
155/156	11	2-dr Sed-6P	2681/2786	3404/3518	Note 1
155/156	45	4-dr Sta Wag-9P	3183/3238	3878/3981	Note 2
155/156	35	4-dr Sta Wag-6P	3020/3125	3823/3926	Note 2

NOTE 1: Some 152,200 BelAir passenger cars were built in the 1968 model year. In figures rounded-off to the nearest 100 units, this total included 28,900 Sixes and 123,400 V-8s. This does not include station wagons.
NOTE 2: Production of Bel Air station wagons was included with that of the other full-sized Chevrolet station wagons. See Biscayne Series listing Note 2 above.

BEL AIR ENGINES
See 1968 Biscayne Series engine data.

IMPALA — (SIX/V-8) — SERIES 163/164 — The Impala Series was Chevrolet's top-selling full-sized line. It had the same general styling features as the other big cars, except that a new format-top roofline treatment was available. This gave buyers a choice between a fastback or coach style motif. Standard equipment began, in a basic sense, with everything incuded for the Bel Air. However, bright roof drip moldings were not used on Impala two-door sedans or four-door sedans and station wagons. Additional features for the volume series included DeLuxe steering wheel; door and window frame moldings; ignition switch and luggage lights and front and rear foam seat cushions. The Impala sport coupe also had thin, bright metal rocker panel accent moldings, below the doors, and bright metal wheel lip trim. The convertible featured courtesy lights, all-vinyl upholstery and carpeting on lower door panels. The three-seat Impala station wagon had a built-in rear bumper step. Super Sport equipment returned to its original status as an optional equipment package.

1968 Chevrolet, Impala 2-dr convertible, V-8

VEHICLE I.D. NUMBERS: The numbering system and code locations were the same as on Bel Air models, with the first five symbols changed to Impala nomenclature.

IMPALA SERIES

Series Number	Body/Style Number	Body Type & Seating	Factory Price	Shipping Weight	Production Total
163/164	69	4-dr Sed-6P	2846/2951	3513/3623	Note 1
163/164	39	4-dr HT Sed-6P	2917/3022	3601/3711	Note 1
163/164	87	2-dr HT Cpe-6P	2863/2968	3517/3623	Note 1
164	47	2-dr FT Cpe-6P	3021	3628	Note 1
164	67	2-dr Conv-6P	3197	3677	Note 2
164	45	4-dr Sta Wag-9P	3358	4042	Note 3
164	35	4-dr Sta Wag-6P	3245	3984	Note 3

NOTE 1: Some 710,900 Impala passenger cars were built in the 1968 model year. In figures rounded-off to the nearest 100 units, this total included 11,500 Sixes and 699,500 V-8s. This includes convertibles, but does not include station wagons.
NOTE 2: Exactly 24,730 Impala convertibles were built in the 1968 model year. This figure is included in the rounded-off figures given above. There are no further breakouts available as to how many of these cars were Sixes, V-8s or equipped with Super Sport options.
NOTE 3: Production of Impala station wagons was included with that of other full-sized Chevrolet station wagons. See Biscayne Series listing Note 2 above.
ADDITIONAL NOTES: Style Number 47, the Formal-Top (FT) coupe was called the Custom coupe. The Impala Super Sport option, RPO Z03 was available for styles 87, 47 and 67 at $179.05 extra. The Impala SS 427 package, RPO Z24 with 385 horsepower L36 Turbo-jet 427 V-8 was available for the same models at $358.10 extra. The Impala SS 427 package, RPO Z24 with 425 horsepower L72 Turbo-Jet 427 V-8 was available for the same models at $542.45 extra. A total of 38,210 Impalas had one of these options installed. There are no further breakouts available as to how many cars were equipped with each specific option or as to which body styles the Super Sport packages were added to at the factory.

IMPALA ENGINES
See 1968 Biscayne Series engine data for specifications that apply to the base Six and base V-8 used in the Impala Series.

1968 Chevrolet, Caprice 2-dr hardtop sports coupe, V-8 (GM)

CAPRICE — (V-8) — SERIES 166 — The Caprice represented the top of the full-sized Chevrolet line. Its equipment assortment began with all Impala features, plus full wheel covers; courtesy and ash tray lamps; Caprice signature scripts fender lights; distinctive side moldings; electric clock and front center arm rest seat. The Caprice coupe also included the Astro Ventilation system. Caprice station wagons had instrument panel courtesy lamps and, in three-seat styles, courtesy lights in the auxilliary passenger area.

VEHICLE I.D. NUMBERS: The numbering system and code locations were the same as on Impala models, with the first five symbols changed to Caprice nomenclature.

CAPRICE SERIES

Series Number	Body/Style Number	Body Type & Seating	Factory Price	Shipping Weight	Production Total
166	39	4-dr HT Sed—6P	3271	3754	Note 1
166	47	2-dr FT Cpe-6P	3219	3648	Note 1
166	45	4-dr Sta Wag-9P	3570	4062	Note 2
166	35	4-dr Sta Wag-6P	3458	4003	Note 2

NOTE 1: In figures rounded-off to the nearest 100 units, some 115,500 Caprice passenger cars were built. All were V-8 powered. This does not include station wagons.
NOTE 2: Production of Caprice station wagons was included with that of other full-sized Chevrolet station wagons. See Biscayne Series listing Note 2 above.

CAPRICE ENGINES
See 1968 Biscayne Series V-8 engine data for specifications that apply to the base V-8 used in Caprice Series.

1968 Chevrolet, Caprice 2-dr hardtop sports coupe, V-8

CHEVELLE 300 — (SIX/V-8) — SERIES 131/132 — The Chevelle was completely and very attractively restyled for model year 1968, with one additional body style added to the line in a new station wagon. Characteristics of the latest appearance included long hood/short deck characteristics with the front fenders swept back and cut under the feature line. Two wheelbases were provided, the shorter for two-doors and the longer for four-doors. The standard V-8 now displaced 307 cubic inches. Lowest in price was the base '300' line on which, other than the windshield surround and ventipane frames, practically no chrome moldings were used. A new front bumper was straighter-lined, with the only openings being large squares flanking the license plate, plus smaller, outboard rectangles incorporating amber parking light lenses. The horizontal, dual headlamps were mounted in individual, bright metal bezels of square shape and the full-width grille featured a fine gridwork of cross-hatched moldings with black-finished air slot directly above. Chevelle scripts appeared on the front fenders behind the wheel openings (at mid-body height) and above the left headlight. Standard equipment included all GM safety features, front arm rests; heater and defroster; base Six or V-8 and 7.35 x 14 two-ply (four-ply rated) tires. Base station wagons, however, used 7.75 x 14 blackwalls. Standard interiors were all textured vinyl in Blue, Gold or Black.

VEHICLE I.D. NUMBERS: The numbering system and code locations were the same as on full-sized Chevrolets, with the first five symbols changed to Chevelle nomenclature.

CHEVELLE 300 SERIES

Series Number	Body/Style Number	Body Type & Seating	Factory Price	Shipping Weight	Production Total
131/132	27	2-dr Cpe-6P	2341/2447	3988/3124	Note 1
131/132	35	4-dr Nomad Wag-6P	2625/2731	3350/2731	Note 1

NOTE 1: Some 12,600 Chevelle 300 passenger cars were built in the 1968 model year. In figures rounded-off to the nearest 100 units, this total included 9,700 Sixes and 2,900 V-8s. This does not include the four-door Nomad station wagon.
NOTE 2: Some 45,500 Chevelle station wagons were built in model year 1968. In figures rounded-off to the nearest 100 units, this includes 10,700 Sixes and 34,800 V-8s. Since station wagon production was separately totaled, this includes Chevelle 300, Chevelle 300 DeLuxe, Chevelle Malibu and Chevelle Concours station wagons.

CHEVELLE 300 ENGINES
Inline Six. Overhead valve. Cast iron block. Displacement: 230 cubic inches. Bore and stroke 3.875 x 3.25 inches. Compression ratio 8.5:1. Brake horsepower 140 at 4400 R.P.M. Seven main bearings. Hydraulic valve lifters. Carburetor; Rochester one-barrel Model 7028017.

V-8. See 1968 Biscayne Series base V-8 engine data.

CHEVELLE 300 DELUXE — (SIX/V-8) — SERIES 133/134 — The easiest way to distinguish the Chevelle 300 DeLuxe was to look for the ribbed, bright metal rocker panels below the door. These were promoted as the Flush and Dry type. Other equipment, above the most basic assortment, included a lefthand outside rearview mirror; front shoulder belts; Chevrolet badge on grille center and rear deck latch panel; door switch dome lamp; lane change turn signals; keyless door locking; suspended accelerator pedal; backup lights and self-adjusting brakes. Four-doors had chrome window sill moldings, while two-doors had chrome trim along the upper window frame. As on all Chevelles, when the base V-8 was added, a black, rectangular engine call-out badge was positioned ahead of the front fender side marker lens and framed in the same band of bright metal. The all-vinyl textured seating surfaces used in Chevelle 300 DeLuxes came only in Black, although Blue, Black or Gold fabric/vinyl combinations were also provided.

VEHICLE I.D. NUMBERS: The numbering system and code locations were the same as on Chevelle 300s, with the first five symbols changed to DeLuxe nomenclature.

CHEVELLE 300 DELUXE SERIES

Series Number	Body/Style Number	Body Type & Seating	Factory Price	Shipping Weight	Production Total
133/134	69	4-dr Sed-6P	2445/2550	3071/3207	Note 1
133/134	37	2-dr HT Cpe-6P	2479/2584	3036/3171	Note 1
133/134	27	2-dr Cpe-6P	2415/2521	3005/3141	Note 1
133/134	35	4-dr Nomad Wag-6P	2736/2841	3409/3554	Note 1

NOTE 1: Some 43,200 Chevelle 300 DeLuxe passenger cars were built in the 1968 model year. In figures rounded-off to the nearest 100 units, this total included 25,500 Sixes and 17,700 V-8s. This does not include station wagons.

NOTE 2: Production of station wagons in this series was included with that of the other Chevelle station wagons. See Chevelle 300 Series listing Note 2 above.

CHEVELLE 300 DELUXE ENGINES
See 1968 Chevelle 300 Series engine data for base Six specifications.

See 1968 Biscayne Series engine data for base V-8 specifications.

1968 Chevelle, Malibu 4-dr sedan, V-8

CHEVELLE MALIBU — (SIX/V-8) — SERIES 135/136 — The new Malibu was trimmed to play its role as the top, non-super high-performance car in the Chevelle lineup. Like the 300 DeLuxe, a Chevrolet insignia was carried in the center of its grille. The Malibu however, did not have the 300 DeLuxe's matching insignia on the rear deck latch panel. Instead, the panel was banded in chrome, with a Chevelle signature near the right rear taillamp. And the taillamps themselves were different, as Malibu backup lights were repositioned into the back bumper. Other added highlights included Malibu scripts on the front fender sides; chrome trim along the front feature line (also extending along the lower side feature line); twin pinstripes along the upper side feature line and additional window frame accents. Standard equipment began at the DeLuxe level and added hide-away two-speed wipers; DeLuxe steering wheel; illuminated heater controls; ignition alarm system; crank-operated ventipanes; side marker lights; high-level ventilation and wheel covers. Interior trim choices varied with body style and there was also a very special Concours four-door hardtop. It came with all-vinyl seating; lockable glove box with light; extra-thick foam cushioned seats; color-keyed to wall carpeting; black-accented wheel openings; black-trimmed lower body accents; ribbed bright metal rear deck lid latch panel plate; Concours signature scripts; chrome wheel lip moldings; special oval steering wheel with horn tabs and wood-grained dash panel inlays. It was called the Concours Sport Sedan and had a lot of extra appeal. Malibu interior trims included the regular fabric/vinyl patterns in Gold, Black, Blue and Grey Green; or all-vinyl in Teal, Gold, Black, Blue, Red and Parchment/Black or the Concours Sport Sedan's special Custom fabric choice in Gold, Blue, Black or Grey-Green.

VEHICLE I.D. NUMBERS: The numbering system and code locations were the same on Chevelle DeLuxe 300 models, wth the first five symbols changed to Malibu nomenclature.

MALIBU SERIES

Series Number	Body/Style Number	Body Type & Seating	Factory Price	Shipping Weight	Production Total
135/136	69	4-dr Sed-6P	2524/2629	3090/3223	Note 1
135/136	39	4-dr HT Sed-6P	2929/2735	3165/3298	Note 1
135/136	37	2-dr HT Cpe-6P	2558/2663	3037/3170	Note 1
135/136	67	2-dr Conv-6P	2757/2863	3115/3245	Note 2
135/136	35	4-dr Sta Wag-6P	2846/2951	3421/3554	Note 3

NOTE 1: Some 266,400 Chevelle Malibu passenger cars were built in the 1968 model year. In figures rounded-off to the nearest 100 units, this total included 33,100 Sixes and 233,200 V-8s. This includes convertibles, but does not include station wagons.
NOTE 2: Exactly 10,080 Chevelle convertibles were built in the 1968 model year. This figure is *partially* included in the rounded-off totals above. The additional portion of the convertible total is included below, in the Chevelle SS-396 Series. No additional breakouts are available to indicate how many convertibles were Malibus and how many were SS-396s.
NOTE 3: Production of Chevelle Malibu station wagons is included with that of other Chevelle station wagons. See Chevelle 300 Series listing Note 2 above.

MALIBU ENGINES
See 1968 Chevelle 300 Series base Six or V-8 engine data.

CHEVELLE CONCOURS — (SIX/V-8) — SERIES 137/138 — In addition to the Concours Sport Sedan, in the regular model line, there was a separate Concours Estate sub-series for 1968. It included only one model, a luxurious station wagon which was specially trimmed. It came standard with all GM safety features, plus all-vinyl upholstery; lighted glovebox light; extra-thick foam cushioned seats; simulated Walnut exterior side and rear paneling; hide-away two-speed wipers; chrome wheel lip moldings and the special oval steering wheel with the horn tabs.

VEHICLE I.D. NUMBERS: The numbering system and code locations were the same as for Malibu models, with the first five symbols changed to Concours Estate Wagon nomenclature.

CONCOURS ESTATE SUB-SERIES

Series Number	Body/Style Number	Body Type & Seating	Factory Price	Shipping Weight	Production Total
137/138	35	4-dr Cus Sta Wag-6P	2978/3083	3543/3561	Note 1

NOTE 1: The production of Chevelle Concours Estate station wagons was included with that of other Chevelle station wagons. See Chevelle 300 Series listing Note 2 above.

CONCOURS ESTATE ENGINES
See 1968 Chevelle 300 Series base Six or V-8 engine data.

CHEVELLE SS 396 — (V-8) — SERIES 138 — Quick-size convenience; floor-mounted shift; vinyl upholstery; carpeting and brand-new looks characterized the high-performance Chevelle SS 396 Series. Other standard extras on the two models in the line included fender mounted side marker lamps; lower bodyside moldings with front and rear extensions; black-accented finish below the feature line, front to rear; specific SS 396 identification at grille and latch panel centers; black-out grille treatment; black-finished deck panel plate; F70 x 14 four-ply rated special Red Stripe (or White Stripe) tires; concealed windshield wipers; 325 horsepower 396 cubic inch V-8; full wheel covers with SS center medallions and 396 engine call-out badges ahead of side marker lenses.

VEHICLE I.D. NUMBERS: The numbering system and code locations were the same as on Chevelle Concours Estate model, with the first five symbols changed to SS 396 nomenclature.

CHEVELLE SS 396 SERIES

Series Number	Body/Style Number	Body Type & Seating	Factory Price	Shipping Weight	Production Total
138	37	2-dr HT Cpe-6P	2899	3475	Note 1
138	67	2-dr Conv-6P	3102	3551	Notes 1/2

NOTE 1: In figures rounded-off to the nearest 100 units, some 57,600 Chevelle SS 396 models were built in the 1968 model year according to *industry* statistics. However, other statistics, released by Chevrolet Motor Division, indicate production of 62,785 Chevelle Super Sports. This seems to indicate one of two things: A) a possible error in reporting figures to *industry* sources or B) that some cars were possibly sold with

Super Sport equipment, less the 396 cubic inch V-8. There is no breakout as to how many Chevelle SS-396s were convertibles or sport coupes.
NOTE 2: Given available figures, the only conclusion that can be made about SS 396 convertible production is that no more than 10,080 were built. However, the exact figure is probably much lower. (See 1968 Chevelle Malibu Series listing Note 2 above for further explanation).
ADDITIONAL NOTE: Chevrolet Motor Division built a total of 131,700 of their 396 cubic inch V-8s during the 1968 model year, but some were installed in SS 396 Camaros and Chevy IIs. In addition, a small percentage of these engines may have been used in U.S. built cars marketed in Canada.

CHEVELLE SS 396 SERIES ENGINE
V-8. Overhead valves. Cast iron block. Displacement: 396 cubic inches. Bore and stroke: 4.09 x 3.76 inches. Compression ratio: 10.25:1 Brake horsepower: 325 at 4800 R.P.M. Five main bearings. Hydraulic valve lifters. Carburetor: Rochester Quadra-Jet four-barrel.

1968 Nova, 2-dr sedan, V-8

CHEVY II NOVA — (FOUR/SIX) — SERIES 111/113 — Chevrolet's senior-sized 'compact' underwent a basic styling change in 1968. The new body was longer and wider and featured a Chevelle-inspired semi-fastback roofline with wide, flaring sail panels. Another change was a reduction in base model offerings, with only two and four-door sedans remaining. The four-cylinder engine remained available, but only slightly more than one thousand units were sold so-equipped. So, for all intents and purposes, the 230 cubic inch Six was the essential Chevy II powerplant, but the 307 and 396 cubic inch V-8s were optional, as was a Super Sport equipment package. The Chevy II would stay with this basic body through 1974 and a just slightly modified one thereafter. However, the 1968 models are easy to spot by the positioning of the Chevy II name at the center of the upper grille surround. Other features included single headlamps set into square bezels; a full-width multiple bar grille and the Chevelle-like rear end look. Standard equipment included all GM safety features; heater and defroster; front arm rests; foot-operated emergency brake; ignition alarm system; concealed fuel filler; front and rear side marker lights and 7.35 x 14 four-ply rated (two-ply) blackwall tires.

VEHICLE I.D. NUMBERS: The numbering system and code locations were the same as on othe Chevrolet products, with the first five symbols changed to Chevy II nomenclature. Apparently, at some point during the year, the cars equipped with V-8 power were marketed as a separate, third line, Series 114.

CHEVY II SERIES

Series Number	Body/Style Number	Body Type & Seating	Factory Price	Shipping Weight	Production Total
FOUR					
111	69	4-dr Sed-6P	2229	2790	Note 1
111	27	2-dr Sed-6P	2199	2760	Note 1
SIX					
113	69	4-dr Sed-6P	2291	2890	Note 2
113	27	2-dr Sed-6P	2261	2860	Note 2
V-8					
114	69	4-dr Sed-6P	2396	NA	Note 3
114	27	2-dr Sed-6P	2367	NA	Note 3

NOTE 1: Exactly 1,270 four-cylinder Chevy IIs were built in the 1968 model year. No breakout per body style is available.
NOTE 2: In figures rounded-off to the nearest 100 units, a total of 146,300 six-cylinder Chevy IIs were built in the 1968 model year.
NOTE 3: In figures rounded-off to the nearest 100 units, a total of 53,400 Chevy II V-8s were built during the 1968 model year.
ADDITIONAL NOTES: A Nova SS option package, RPO L48, was available for Model Number 11427 only, at a price of $210.65 extra. It included special steering wheel; hood ornaments; black-accented grille and rear deck latch panel plate; hood insulation; SS nameplates; SS deck emblems; black-out style SS grille treatment; Red Stripe tire on 6 inch wide rims and a 295 horsepower 350 cubic inch Turbo-Fire V-8. There is no record of how many 1968 Nova SS coupes were built. However, there are statistics showing that only 2.7 percent of the 105,858 Chevy IIs made for domestic sale had dual exhausts and, based on this, we might estimate that 2,858 of these cars were made.

CHEVY II ENGINES
Inline Four. Overhead valves. Cast iron block. Displacement: 153 cubic inches. Bore and stroke: 3.875 x 3.25 inches. Compression ratio: 8.5:1. Brake horsepower: 90 at 4000 R.P.M. Five main bearings. Hydraulic valve lifters. Carburetor: Rochester one-barrel Model 7028009.

Six. See 1968 Chevelle Series 300 base Six engine data.

V-8. See 1968 Chevelle 300 Series base V-8 engine data.

CAMARO — (SIX/V-8) — The Camaro was virtually unchanged as it entered its second model year, although close inspection would show the addition of the new front and rear side marker lights and ventless door glass. Standard equipment included all GM safety features; integrated front headlamps and parking lights; Strato-Bucket front seats; all-vinyl interior; carpeting; Astro Ventilation system; front shoulder belts; outside rearview mirror; the new side marker lights; heater and defroster; five 7.35 x 14 (two-ply) four-ply rated blackwall tires and courtesy lights in the convertible.

VEHICLE IDENTIFICATION NUMBERS: The numbering system and code locations were the same as on other Chevrolet products, with the first five symbols changed to Camaro nomenclature.

1968 Camaro, 2-dr SS-350 hardtop sports coupe, V-8 (AA)

CAMARO SERIES

Series Number	Body/Style Number	Body Type & Seating	Factory Price	Shipping Weight	Production Total
123/124	37	2-dr HT Spt Cpe-4P	2638/2727	3040/3050	214,711
123/124	67	2-dr Conv-4P	2852/2941	3160/3295	20,440

ADDITIONAL NOTES: The figures above are exact totals. Production included 50,937 Sixes and 184,178 V-8s; 40,977 cars with Rally Sport option; 27,884 cars with SS option; 7,199 cars with Z-28 option; 12,997 cars for export; 54,948 cars with three-speed manual transmission; 47,572 cars with four-speed transmission; 132,631 cars with automatic transmission; 35,866 cars with air conditioning; 115,280 cars with power steering and 3,304 cars with power windows.

CAMARO ENGINES
Six. See 1968 Chevelle 300 Series six-cylinder engine data.

V-8. Overhead valves. Cast iron block. Displacement: 326.7 cubic inches. Bore and stroke: 4.00 x 3.25 inches. Compression ratio: 8.75:1. Brake horsepower: 210 at 4000 R.P.M. Five main bearings. Hydraulic valve lifters. Carburetor: Rochester two-barrel. Model 7028101.

CHASSIS FEATURES: Wheelbase: (Chevrolet) 119 inches; (Chevelle two-door) 112 inches; (Chevelle four-door) 116 inches; (Nova) 111 inches; (Camaro) 108 inches. Overall length: (Chevrolet wagon) 214 inches; (Chevrolet) 215 inches; (Chevelle wagon) 208 inches; (Chevelle four-door) 202 inches; (Chevelle two-door) 198 inches; (Nova) 190 inches; (Camaro) 185 inches. Front tread: (Chevrolet) 62.5 inches; (Chevelle) 59 inches; (Nova) 59 inches; (Camaro) 59 inches. Rear tread: (Chevrolet) 62.4 inches; (Chevelle) 59 inches; (Nova) 58.9 inches; (Camaro 58 inches. Tires: Refer to text.

CHEVROLET OPTIONS: Dual stage air cleaner, with Six ($5.30). Four Season air conditioning, except with 425 horsepower V-8 ($368.65). Comfortron automatic temperature control air conditioning, except with 425 horsepower V-8 ($447.65). Positraction rear axle ($42.15). Station wagon load area carpeting ($52.70). Heavy-duty chassis equipment on Biscayne ($36.90). Electric clock, standard in Caprice ($15.80). Heavy-duty clutch ($10.55). Rear window defroster ($21.10). Turbo-Fire 250 horsepower 327 cubic inch V-8 ($63.20). Turbo-Fire 275 horsepower 327 cubic inch V-8 ($92.70). Turbo-Jet 325 horsepower 396 cubic inch V-8 ($158). Turbo-Jet 385 horsepower 427 cubic inch V-8, included with SS-427 option ($263.30). Turbo-Jet 425 horsepower 427 cubic inch V-8 ($447.65). Dual exhausts with 250, 275, Or 325 horsepower V-8 ($27.40). Tinted glass, windshield ($25.30); all windows ($39.50). Caprice retractable headlights ($79). Head rests with Strato bucket seats ($52.70); with bench seats ($42.15). Special instrumentation including ammeter, oil pressure, temperature gauges and tachometer, in Caprice ($79); in other models, including clock, ($94.80). Remote control lefthand OSRV mirror ($9.50). Station wagon rooftop luggage rack, fixed type ($44.25); adjustable type ($63.20). Power rear antenna ($28.45). Power drum brakes ($42.15). Power disc brakes, includes 15 inch hub caps, wheels and tires ($121.15). Power door lock system, two-door ($44.80); four door ($68.50). Six-Way power seat, except Biscaynes, cars with bucket seats or cars with four-speed manual transmission ($94.80). Four-Way power lefthand bucket seat ($69.55). Power steering ($94.80). Power tailgate window ($31.60). Power windows, except Biscayne and Styles 15511-611 ($100.10). Heavy-duty radiator ($13.70). Pushbutton AM radio with antenna ($61.10). Pushbutton AM/FM radio with front antenna ($133.80). AM/FM radio and stereo ($239.15). Rear manual antenna ($9.50). Rear speaker ($13.20). Stereo tape system with four speakers ($133.80). White or black vinyl roof for all hardtops ($89.55). Cloth Strato-Back seats ($105.35). Strato-Back seats, bucket style ($158). Superlift shock absorbers, standard type ($42.15); automatic level control type ($89.55). Cruise Master speed control ($52.70). Rear fender skirts, except station wagons and disc brakes ($26.35). Speed warning indicator ($10.55). DeLuxe steering wheel ($4.25). Comfort-Tilt steering wheel ($42.15). Sport steering wheel ($31.60). Front and rear special purpose suspension ($21.10). Overdrive tranmission ($115.90). Powerglide transmission, with Six ($184.35); with V-8s, except '427' ($194.85). Close-Range four-speed manual transmission with '427' V-8 ($184.35). Heavy-duty Close-Range four-speed manual transmission with '427' V-8 only ($310.70). Wide-Range four-speed manual transmission, in all V-8 models ($184.35). Turbo-Hydramatic transmission ($226.45-$237). All-vinyl interior trim ($5.30-$10.55). Wheel covers, standard 14 inch ($21.10); mag-style 14 inch — Caprice or Super Sport ($52.70); others ($73.75); simulated wire type — Caprice or Super Sport ($55.85); others ($73.75). Mag spoke 14 inch wheel covers. Caprice or Super Sport ($52.70); others ($73.75). Rally wheels, on Caprice or SS-427 without disc brakes; ($21.10); others ($31.60); with discs ($10.55). Appearance Guard Group ($26.35-$49.55). Auxillary Lighting Group ($2.65-$39). Convenience Operating Group ($9.50-46.40). Decor Group ($21.10-$72.80). RPO Z03 Impala Super Sport Option, includes special all-vinyl interior; Strato-Bucket seats; center console; SS wheel covers and console shift with automatic or four-speed manual transmissions, on Impala Custom coupe, sport coupe or convertible ($179.05). RPO Z24 Impala SS 427 Option, includes all above, plus special hood; Red Stripe tires; ornamentation; special suspension features and 15 inch wheels, with RPO L36 Turbo-Jet 385 horsepower V-8 ($358.10); with RPO L72 Turbo-Jet 425 horsepower V-8 ($542.45).

NOTES: V-8 engine option prices are in addition to cost of base V-8. Where a range of prices is indicated, retail varied according to model, trim level, body style or inclusion of other features. It was usually slightly less expensive to add some options to the topline models. Numerous tire options were provided for all 1968 Chevrolets.

CHEVELLE OPTIONS: Four-Season air conditioning ($360.20). Station wagon air deflector ($19). Positraction rear axle ($42.15). Economy or performance axle ($2.15). Heavy-duty battery ($7.40). Station wagon rooftop carrier ($44.25). Electric clock ($15.80). Heavy-duty clutch, with Six ($5.30); with V-8 ($10.55). Center console, including electric clock and with bucket seats, gear shift lever is mounted in console/available with three-speed only in SS 396 ($50.60). Rear windshield defroster ($21.10). RPO L22/ 250 cubic inch 155 horsepower Six ($26.35). RPO L73/ 327 cubic inch 250 horsepower V-8 ($63.20). RPO L30/ 327 cubic inch 275 horsepower V-8 ($92.70). RPO L79/ 327 cubic inch 325 horsepower V-8 ($198.05). RPO L34/ 396 cubic inch 350 horsepower V-8, in SS 396 only ($105.35). RPO L78/ 396 cubic inch 375 horsepower V-8, in SS 396 only ($237). Dual exhausts ($27.40). Temperature-controled fan ($15.80). Tinted glass, all windows ($34.80); windshield only ($26.35). Special instrumentation, Malibu V-8s and SS 396 only ($94.80). Light monitoring system ($26.35). Remote-control lefthand outside rearview mirror ($9.50). Two-tone paint ($21.10). Power disc front brakes ($100.10). Power front drum brakes ($42.15). Power steering ($94.80). Power convertible top ($52.70). Power windows, in Concours/Malibu/SS396 only ($100.10). AM/FM radio with front antenna($61.10). AM/FM radio with front antenna ($133.80). AM/FM radio with stereo and front antenna ($239.15). Rear seat speaker ($13.20). White or black vinyl top on hardtops ($84.30). Strato bucket seats in Malibu/SS396 ($110.60). Superlift shock absorbers ($42.15). Speed and Cruise Control, automatic transmission required ($52.70). Speed warning indicator ($10.55). Comfortilt steering wheel ($42.15). Sport style steering wheel ($31.60). SS 396 accent striping ($29.50). Four-speed manual transmissions: special close-ratio type for SS396 with 375 horsepower V-8 ($237); close-ratio for all models with 325-350-375 horsepower V-8s ($184.35); Wide-Range type ($184.35). Turbo-Hydramatic in SS 396 with 325-350 horsepower V-8s ($237). Three-speed manual transmission with floor-shift ($79). Powerglide transmission, with Six ($184.35); with small V-8s ($194.85). Overdrive ($115.90). Vinyl interior trim, Malibu or 300s ($10.55). Wheel covers, regular type ($6.35); mag style ($21.10); simulated wire/mag-spoke Rally styles, all ($73.75). Rally wheels with special hub caps and trim rings ($31.60). Hidden windshield wipers ($19).

CHEVY II OPTIONS: All-Season air conditioning, except four-cylinders ($347.60). Rear positraction axle ($42.15). Console with floor mounted shift, except four-cylinders, (bucket seats required) not available on 295 or 325 horsepower engine with standard transmission ($50.60). Electric clock ($15.80). Heavy-duty clutch ($5.30). 155 horsepower, 250 six-cylinder ($26.35). 275 horsepower, 327 V-8 ($92.70). 325 horsepower, 327 V-8 ($198.05). Dual exhaust, V-8 models with standard or 275 horsepower engine only ($27.40). Tinted glass, all windows ($30.55); windshield only ($21.10). Special instrumentation, V-8 coupes with console ($94.80). LH outside remote-control mirror ($9.50). Power brakes, all with drum-type brakes except four-cylinder ($42.15). Power brakes, all with disc-type brakes except four-cylinder ($100.10). Power steering, except four-cylinder ($84.30). Vinyl roof cover in white or black, all except four-cylinder ($73.75). Sports styled steering wheel ($31.60). Stereo tape system ($133.80). Powerglide, four and six-cylinder models ($163.70). Powerglide, with 200, 275, 295 and 325 horsepower engines ($174.25). Four-speed wide range, with 200, 275, 295 and 325 horsepower engines ($184.35). Four-speed close range, with 325 horsepower engines ($79.00). Simulated wire wheel covers ($73.75). Mag-style wheel covers ($73.75). Mag spoke wheel covers ($31.60). Custom Exterior Group ($68.50). Exterior Decor Package ($31.60). Nova SS Option includes: 295 horsepower Turbo-Fire 350 engine, special steering wheel, hood ornaments, black accented grille and rear deck plate, hood insulation, nameplate, deck emblems, SS grille, red stripe tires on six inch rims. Special Interior Group ($15.80).

CAMARO OPTIONS: Four-Season air conditioning ($360.20). Positraction rear axle ($42.15). Electric clock ($15.80). Rear window defroster ($21.10). 155 horsepower Turbo-Thrift, six-cylinder ($26.25). 275 horsepower, Turbo-Fire, V-8 ($92.70). Dual exhaust with deep tone mufflers, with 210 or 275 horsepower engines ($27.40). Dual exhaust, with 210 or 275 horsepower engines ($27.40). Tinted glass on all windows, with air conditioning ($26.35); windshield only ($30.55). Special instrumentation not available with 375 horsepower or 302" engine. Includes ammeter, temperature, oil pressure and fuel gauges mounted on console, electric clock and tachometer mounted in instrument panel, in V-8 models with console ($94.80). Light monitoring system ($26.35). Power drum brakes ($42.15). Power disc brakes ($100.10). Power steering ($84.30). Power top in White, Black or Blue on convertible ($52.70). Power windows ($100.10). Heavy-duty radiator, standard with air; not available with 302" or 396" engines ($13.70). Pushbutton AM radio ($61.10). Pushbutton AM/FM radio ($133.80). Pushbutton AM/FM stereo radio ($239.15). Manual rear antenna, not available with AM/FM or Aux. Panel and Valance, ($9.50). Stereo tape system ($133.80). White or Black vinyl roof cover, Sport Coupe ($73.75). Rear folding seat ($42.15). Strato-back front seat, Sport Coupe, not available with console ($32.65). Speed and Cruise-Control, V-8 only, Powerglide required ($52.70). Speed warning indicator ($10.55). Special rear springs, included rear bumper guards ($20.05). Special steering with quick response ($15.80). Comfort-Tilt steering wheel, automatic or floor mounted transmission required ($42.15). Sport style steering wheel ($31.60). Accent striping ($13.70). Powerglide, six-cylinder ($184.35). Powerglide, with all 210, 275 and 295 horsepower V-8 ($194.85). Three-speed Special with 295, 325, 350 and 375 horsepower engines ($79.00). Four-speed wide range, except with 375 horsepower engines ($184.35). Four-speed close ratio, with 350, 375 horsepower and 302 engines ($184.35). Four-speed heavy-duty close ratio, with 375 horsepower engine ($310.70). Turbo HydraMatic, with 325 and 350 horsepower engines ($237.00). Rally wheels ($31.60). Bright metal wheel covers (21.10). Simulated wire wheel covers ($73.75). Mag-styled wheel covers ($73.75). Mag spoke wheel covers ($73.75). Appearance Guard Group ($40.10). Camaro SS Option includes: special hood, special red stripe tires, SS emblems, hood insulation, black accented grille, front accent band, engine accents, special suspension, V-8 engine, (dual exhausts, no charge) with 295 horsepower L48 V-8 ($210.65); with 325 horsepower L35 V-8 ($263.30); with 350 horsepower L34 V-8 ($368.65); with 375 horsepower L78 V-8 ($500.30). Rally Sport Group ($105.35).

1969 CHEVROLET

BISCAYNE — (SIX/V-8) — SERIES 153/154 — Full-sized Chevrolets were completely redesigned. While wheelbase was unchanged, cars grew an inch in length; station wagons three inches. A new, integrated bumper/grille imparted a narrower look, although the width of 80 inches was the same as the previous year. The area around the front and rear wheelhousings was flared out, giving a more highly sculptured appearance. The lower body feature line kicked-up, between the flares, giving a 'pinched' bodyside effect. A straight, upper feature line ran between the wraparound ends of the front and back bumpers. The grille surround was a heavy chrome molding, completely encircling headlamps and grille. The grille insert was a grid-patterened type, with bright, prominent cross-hatched moldings forming large, square openings which were filled with multiple, smaller blades. Parking lamps were set into the front gravel pan, which had a wide slot at the center, allowing a portion of the grille to show through. Vertical, rectangular, side markers were positioned at the extreme forward edge of front fenders. Taillights were of a round-cornered rectangular shape and set into the rear bumper. Twin lamps were seen on lower-priced models; triple lamps on the richer cars. Identification trim consisted of a Chevrolet insignia at the center of the grille; Chevrolet scripts on the left hood and right deck lid edges and a model script behind the front wheel well, at mid-fender height. New transmissions, some new engines, ventless side window glass and an anti-theft steering column were promoted advances. New options included a headlight washing device and automatic, liquid 'tire chain' dispensing system. Basic equipment on the Biscayne included all GM safety features; head restraints (as a mandatory option); door-actuated light switches; heater and defroster; cigarette lighter; locking glove box; carpeting; arm rests; center dome light; 8.25 x 14 two-ply (four-ply rated) black sidewall tires and either the 155 horsepower Six or 235 horsepower V-8 as base powerplants.

VEHICLE I.D. NUMBERS: Serial Numbers on all Chevrolet products were now found on the top lefthand surface of the instrument panel. They were visible through the windshield. The Vehicle Identification Number had thirteen symbols. The first five symbols were the same as the Chevrolet Model Number. This was the same as the combinations of the applicable nomenclature from the first and second columns shown in the specifications charts below. The sixth symbol was changed to a '9' to indicate 1969 model year. The seventh symbol indicated the assembly plant. The last six symbols were digits giving the sequential production number. Numbers began at 100001 at each factory.

BISCAYNE SERIES

Series Number	Body/Style Number	Body Type & Seating	Factory Price	Shipping Weight	Production Total
153/154	69	4-dr Sed-6P	2687/2793	3590/3725	Note 1
153/154	11	2-dr Sed-6P	2645/2751	3630/3670	Note 1
153/154	36	4-dr Sta Wag-6P	3064/3169	4045/4170	Note 1

NOTE 1: Some 68,700 Biscayne were built during the 1969 model year. In figures rounded-off to the nearest 100 units, this included 27,400 Sixes and 41,300 V-8s. This includes station wagons.

ADDITIONAL NOTES: In all specifications charts in this section, Series Numbers, prices and weights above slash apply to Sixes/below slash to V-8s. The Chevrolet 'Model Number' is the combination of Series and Body Style designations. Therefore, making reference to the chart above, a V-8 1969 Biscayne two-door sedan would be Model Number 15411 priced at $2,751 and weighing 3,670 pounds. The same basic system is used for listing all 1969 Chevrolets in this catalog.

BISCAYNE ENGINE
Inline Six. Overhead valves. Cast iron block. Displacement: 250 cubic inches. Bore and stroke: 3.88 x 3.53 inches. Compression ratio: 8.5:1. Brake horsepower: 155 at 4200 R.P.M. Seven main bearings. Hydraulic valve lifters. Carburetor: Rochester one-barrel Model 7029017.

V-8. Overhead valves. Cast iron block. Displacement: 326.7 (327) cubic inches. Bore and stroke: 4.00 x 3.25 inches. Compression ratio: 9.0:1. Brake horsepower: 235 at 4800 R.P.M. Five main bearings. Hydraulic valve lifters. Carburetor: Rochester two-barrel Model 7029127.

BEL AIR — (SIX/V-8) — SERIES 155/156 — The Bel Air represented the next step up from Biscayne. Cars in this line featured a thin, horizontal molding along the full-length of the upper body feature line; Bel Air front fender side scripts and twin taillamps. Interiors were slightly upgraded. Standard equipment included all items found on Biscaynes, plus side moldings; bright metal rear window, roof drip and windshield moldings; front and rear side marker lamps and glove box light. Base powerplants were the same as in Biscaynes, but the Bel Air level Townsman station wagon came only with the V-8 this season.

VEHICLE I.D. NUMBERS: The numbering system and code locations were the same as Biscaynes, with the first three symbols changed to Bel Air nomenclature.

BEL AIR SERIES

Series Number	Body/Style Number	Body Type & Seating	Factory Price	Shipping Weight	Production Total
155/156	69	4-dr Sed-6P	2787/2893	3590/3725	Note 1
155/156	11	2-dr Sed-6P	2745/2851	3540/3670	Note 1
156	46	4-dr Sta Wag-9P	3345	4230	Note 1
156	36	4-dr Sta Wag-6P	3232	4175	Note 1

NOTE 1: Some 155,700 Bel Airs were built during the 1969 model year. In figures rounded-off to the nearest 100 units, this total included 16,000 Sixes and 139,700 V-8s. This includes station wagons.

BEL AIR ENGINES
See 1969 Biscayne Series engine data.

1969 Chevrolet, Impala 2-dr Custom (Formal) coupe, V-8

IMPALA — (SIX/V-8) — SERIES 163/164 — The Impala, being a bit fancier than Biscayne/Bel Air models, came with the triple taillight arrangement. There were also wide, bright metal underscores along the lower portion of the body, between the wheel openings. Naturally, the bodyside scripts bore the proper model name. The two-door sedan was not offered in Impala trim, but four other styles joined the four-door sedan in this line. The sportier models, such as the convertible and Custom coupe with formal (blind rear quarter) type roofline came with V-8 power only. Other models, including two and four-door hardtops, offered buyers the choice of a Six or V-8. Impala level (Kingswood) station wagons also came solely with V-8 engines. Standard equipment included everything used for Bel Airs, except that bright roof drip moldings were deleted from all the full-pillared models. In addition, all Impalas added a DeLuxe steering wheel; door and window frame moldings; glove box and luggage compartment lighting and extra-thick front foam seat cushions. The sport coupe also had bright metal moldings below the doors combined with wheel lip moldings. The convertible had all of this, plus all-vinyl upholstery and carpeted lower door panels.

VEHICLE I.D. NUMBERS: The numbering system and code locations were the same as on Bel Airs, with the first three symbols changed to Impala nomenclature.

IMPALA SERIES

Series Number	Body/Style Number	Body Type & Seating	Factory Price	Shipping Weight	Production Total
163/164	69	4-dr Sed-6P	2911/3016	3640/3760	Note 1
163/164	39	4-dr HT Sed-6P	2981/3086	3735/3855	Note 1
163/164	37	2-dr HT Cpe-6P	2927/3033	3650/3775	Note 1
164	47	2-dr FT Cpe-6P	3085	3800	Note 1
164	67	2-dr Conv-6P	3261	3835	Note 1/2
164	46	4-dr Sta Wag-9P	3465	4285	Note 1
164	36	4-dr Sta Wag-6P	3352	4225	Note 1

NOTE 1: Some 777,000 Impalas were built during the 1969 model year. In figures rounded-off to the nearest 100 units, this included 8,700 Sixes and 768,300 V-8s. This includes convertibles and Kingswood station wagons.
NOTE 2: Exactly 14,415 full-size Chevrolet Impala convertibles were built during the 1969 model year. This figure is also included in the rounded-off total given above. There is no further breakout as to how many of these cars were Sixes, V-8s or Super Sport equipped units.
ADDITIONAL NOTES: Standard equipment in all full-size Chevrolet station wagons included all GM safety features; heater and defroster; front head restraints (mandatory option); all-vinyl trim; dual-speed electric wipers and washers; carpeting; Hide-Away windshield wipers; Astro Ventilation; dual-action tailgate and ash tray light. Townsman (Bel Air) and Kingsman (Impala) station wagons also had courtesy lights; bodyside moldings and, on Kingswood only, DeLuxe steering wheel and extra thick front foam seat cushions.
ADDITIONAL NOTES: A total of only 2,425 full-sized Chevrolets built during the 1969 model year were equipped with the Super Sport option. Style Number 39 was called the Sports Sedan; Style Number 37 was called the Sports Coupe and Style Number 47 was called the Custom Coupe.

IMPALA ENGINES
See 1969 Biscayne Series engine data for base Six or base V-8 specifications.

CAPRICE — (V-8) — SERIES 166 — The Caprice was the top-rung offering in the Chevrolet full-sized lineup. Standard features included the complete assortment of Impala equipment, plus full wheel covers; Caprice signature scripts; front fender marker lamps; distinctive side molding treatment; electric clock and front seat with center arm rest. The Caprice Sport Coupe also provided the Astro Ventilation system at its base price. The Caprice-level station wagon was the luxurious Kingswood Estate, which came with all items used on Impala-level Kingswood models, plus full wheel covers; electric clock; glove box light; window moldings; two-spoke steering wheel; scultpured wheel openings; Look-of-Wood side paneling; recessed step-in boarding type rear bumper; wheel lip moldings and Kingswood Estate identification scripts on the rear fender sides. Passenger styles had rear fender skirts, but the Estate wagons did not. Retractable headlights were optional on all Caprices. Variable ratio power steering was a new extra-cost feature offered for Impala/Caprice models only.

VEHICLE I.D. NUMBERS: The numbering system and code locations were the same as on Impalas, with the first three symbols changed to Caprice V-8 nomenclature.

CAPRICE SERIES

Series Number	Body/Style Number	Body Type & Seating	Factory Price	Shipping Weight	Production Total
166	39	4-dr HT Sed-6P	3346	3895	Note 1
166	47	2-dr FT Cpe-6P	3294	3815	Note 1
166	46	4-dr Sta Wag-9P	3678	4300	Note 1
166	36	4-dr Sta Wag-6P	3565	4245	Note 1

NOTE 1: In figures rounded-off to the nearest 100 units, a total of 166,900 Caprice models were built during the 1969 model year. All were V-8 powered. This figure includes Kingswood Estate station wagons.

ADDITIONAL NOTES: Style Number 39 is called the Sport sedan; Style Number 47, the Formal Top (FT) coupe is called the Custom hardtop coupe; Style Numbers 46 and 36 are called Kingswood Estate station wagons.

CAPRICE ENGINE
See 1969 Biscayne Series engine data for the Caprice base V-8 specifications.

CHEVELLE 300 DELUXE — (SIX/V-8) — SERIES 133/134 — For 1969, the Chevrolet intermediate size car had new frontal styling. The forward edge of the hood and fenders was more beveled than 1968. The square-shaped housings containing the circular headlight lenses were changed from the former bright-finished appearance, with the new dull-finish look emphasizing negative space effects. This treament was carried to the grille insert, which also had a dull-finish treatment that gave prominence to a bright, horizontal molding stretching, full-width, between the headlights. A Chevrolet insignia was placed at the center of this bar. A new front bumper with wider, horizontal slots on either side of the license plate area was seen. The parking lamps were set into the slots. At the rear, there were larger taillight lenses mounted in the body corners. The front side marker lamps, although still rectangular, grew smaller and were repositioned closer to the upper feature line. Different wheelbases once again appeared: 112 inches on two-door styles and 116 inches on four-doors. Standard equipment on Chevelle 300 DeLuxe models included all GM safety features; head restraints (as a mandatory option); heater and defroster; front arm rests; dual headlights; 7.35 x 14 four-ply rated blackwall tires and either a 140 horsepower Six or 200 horsepower V-8 as base powerplant. The low-level Chevelles were characterized, externally, by thin rocker panel moldings; bright metal windshield and rear window framing; bright metal roof drip moldings and series identification badges on the front fenders, behind the wheel opening. With all factors totaled, the 1969 Chevelle was a very handsome machine, even in its most basic forms.

VEHICLE I.D. NUMBERS: The numbering system and code locations were the same as on full-size Chevrolets, with the first three symbols changed to Chevelle Six or V-8 nomenclature.

CHEVELLE 300 DELUXE SERIES

Series Number	Body/Style Number	Body Type & Seating	Factory Price	Shipping Weight	Production Total
133/134	69	4-dr Sed-6P	2488/2577	3100/3230	Note 1
133/134	37	2-dr HT Spt Cpe-6P	2521/2611	3075/3205	Note 1
133/134	27	2-dr Cpe-6P	2458/2548	3035/3165	Note 1
131/132	35	4-dr Nomad-6P	2668/2758	3390/3515	Note 2
131/132	36	4-dr Nomad/D-6P	2710/2800	NA/NA	Note 2
133/134	35	4-dr GB Sta Wag-6P	2779/2869	3445/2585	Note 2
133/134	36	4-dr GB/D Sta Wag	2821/2911	NA/NA	Note 2
134	46	4-dr GB/D Sta Wag	3024	3740	Note 2

NOTE 1: Some 42,000 Chevelle 300 DeLuxe passenger cars were built during the 1969 model year. In figures rounded-off to the nearest 100 units, this included 21,000 Sixes and 21,000 V-8s. This does not include station wagons.
NOTE 2: Some 45,900 Chevelle station wagons were built during the 1969 model year. In figures rounded-off to the nearest 100 units, this included 7,400 Sixes and 38,500 V-8s. Since station wagon production was separately totaled without regard to series, this figure includes all Nomad, Greenbrier, Concours and Concours Estate station wagons.
ADDITIONAL NOTE: The Chevelle station wagon offerings proliferated during 1969. Although the non-DeLuxe Chevelle 300 passenger cars were dropped, the comparable Nomad station wagon was carried over as an economy sub-model, which is listed with the 300 DeLuxe line in this Catalog. Extra station wagon features included all-vinyl interior trim; dual-speed electric wipers and windshield washers. Note that Nomad Series nomenclature is the same as that of 1968 Chevelle standard 300 models. Nomad Style Number 36 included the new, Dual-Action type tailgate (Nomad/D = Nomad Dual). The Greenbrier was the true Chevelle 300 DeLuxe level station wagon and came in three forms; Style Number 35 two-seat (GB Sta Wag-6P); Style Number 36 two-seat with Dual-Action tailgate (GB/D Sta Wag-6P) and Style Number 46 three-seat (V-8 only) with Dual-Action tailgate (GB/D Sta Wag-9P).

CHEVELLE 300 DELUXE ENGINES
Inline Six. Overhead valves. Cast iron block. Displacement 230 cubic inches. Bore and stroke: 3.875 x 3.25 inches. Compression ratio: 8.5:1. Brake horsepower: 140 at 4400 R.P.M. Seven main bearings. Hydraulic valve lifters. Carburetor: Rochester one-barrel Model 7029017.

V-8. Overhead valves. Cast iron block. Displacement: 306.6 (307) cubic inches. Bore and stroke: 3.875 x 3.25 inches. Compression ratio: 9.0:1. Brake horsepower 200 at 4600 R.P.M. Five main bearings. Hydraulic valve lifters. Carburetor: Rochester two-barrel.

1969 Chevelle, SS 396 2-dr hardtop sports coupe, V-8

CHEVELLE MALIBU — (SIX-V-8) — SERIES 135/136 — The Malibu was the mid-priced, mid-sized series and included all equipment found on the base line, plus Hide-Away two-speed wipers; DeLuxe steering wheel; glove box light; window moldings; and carpets. It is not easy to pinpoint specific identification features as such details varied according to body type and the optional equipment packages that a buyer ordered. In fact, it was possible to order Chevelles (including Malibus and all other models) in over 300 different variations. Some that collectors look for are the Malibu four-door hardtop (Sports sedan) with the RPO Z16 Concours package or the Malibu two-door hardtop (Sports coupe) with Argent Silver lower bodyside treatment, both of which added greatly to a sporty appearance. To confuse matters even more, several pages of new or revised options packages were released by Chevrolet in May, 1969. A convertible was also available in Malibu trim and had all of the above standard equipment, plus courtesy lights. The SS 396 (Z-25) was still offered as an option package.

VEHICLE I.D. NUMBERS: The numbering system and code locations were the same as on Chevelle 300 DeLuxe models, with the first three symbols changed to Malibu Six or V-8 nomenclature.

MALIBU SERIES

Series Number	Body/Style Number	Body Type & Seating	Factory Price	Shipping Weight	Production Total
135/136	69	4-dr Sed-6P	2567/2657	3130/3265	Note 1
135/136	39	4-dr HT Sed-6P	2672/2762	3205/3340	Note 1
135/136	37	2-dr HT Spt Cpe-6P	2601/2690	3095/3230	Note 1
135/136	67	2-dr Conv-6P	2800/2889	3175/3300	Note 1/2
136	46	4-dr Estate Wag-9P	3266	3730	Note 3
136	36	4-dr Estate Wag-6P	3153	3680	Note 3

NOTE 1: Some 367,100 Chevelle Malibu passenger cars were built during the 1969 model year. In figures rounded-off to the nearest 100 units, this total included 23,500 Sixes and 343,600 V-8s. This includes Malibu convertibles, but does not include Concours Estate station wagon.
NOTE 2: Exactly 8,927 Malibu convertibles were built during the 1969 model year. No further breakout is available to indicate how many of these cars were Sixes or V-8s. This total is included in the rounded-off figures given above.
NOTE 3: Production of Chevelle Malibu Concours Estate station wagons is included with that of the other Chevelle station wagons. See 1969 Chevelle 300 DeLuxe Series listing Note 2.
ADDITIONAL NOTES: Exactly 86,307 Chevelle Malibus were equipped with the SS 396 option package. These cars are included in the rounded-off totals given above in Note 1. (Also, partially, in the Malibu convertible breakout above). There is no indication as to how many SS 396 packages were installed on specific body styles.

CHEVELLE MALIBU ENGINES
See 1969 Chevelle 300 DeLuxe Series engine data for specifications covering Malibu base Six and V-8. The SS-396 package included the special, high-performance engine, with following specifications:
V-8. Overhead valves. Cast iron block. (Aluminum cylinder heads optional after mid-year). Displacement: 396 cubic inches. Bore and stroke: 4.09 x 3.76 inches. Compression ratio: 10.25:1. Brake horsepower: 325 at 4800 R.P.M. Hydraulic valve lifters. Five main bearings. Carburetor: Rochester four-barrel Quadra-Jet.

1969 Chevrolet, Nova 2-dr sedan, V-8 (AA)

NOVA — (FOUR/SIX/V-8) — The Chevy II name was dropped from the 'senior' compact offerings, which were now simply called Novas. Due to this change, a Chevrolet emblem was placed on the center of the upper grille bar. Vertical louvers were optional on the side of the cowl, behind the front wheel opening. A Nova script was seen on the righthand corner of the deck lid. The front sidemarker lights were enlarged and moved slightly closer to the body corner. A vast selection of options, including Super Sport equipment, could be ordered. Standard equipment included the corporate safety assortment; head restraints (mandatory option); heater and defroster; front arm rests; concealed fuel filler and 7.35 x 14 four-ply rated black sidewall tires. Base engines were the 90 horsepower Four; 140 horsepower Six or 200 horsepower V-8 from the Chevrolet power team lineup.

VEHICLE I.D. NUMBERS: The numbering system and code locations were the same as on Chevelles, with the first three symbols changed to the appropriate Nova nomenclature.

NOVA SERIES

Series Number	Body/Style Number	Body Type & Seating	Factory Price	Shipping Weight	Production Total
FOUR					
111	69	4-dr Sed-6P	2267	2810	Note 1
111	27	2-dr Cpe-6P	2237	2785	Note 1
SIX					
113	69	4-dr Sed-6P	2345	2920	Note 2
113	27	2-dr Cpe-6P	2315	2895	Note 2
V-8					
114	69	4-dr Sed-6P	2434	NA	Note 3
114	27	2-dr Cpe-6P	2405	NA	Note 3

NOTE 1: Exacty 6,103 four-cylinder Novas were built during the 1969 model year. No breakout per body style is available.
NOTE 2: In figures rounded-off to the nearest 100 units, a total of 157,400 six-cylinder Novas were built in the 1969 model year. No breakout per body style is available.
NOTE 3: In figures rounded-off to the nearest 100 units, a total of 88,400 Nova V-8s were built during the 1969 model year. No breakout per body style is available.
ADDITIONAL NOTE: A total of 17,654 of the Novas included in the above Notes were equipped with the Super Sport Option package.

NOVA ENGINES
See 1968 Chevy II Series engine data for four-cylinder specifications. See 1969 Chevelle 300 DeLuxe Series for Six and V-8 specifications.

1969 Camaro, Z28 2-dr hardtop sports coupe, V-8 (AA)

CAMARO — (SIX/V-8) — SERIES 123/124 — A new body gave the 1969 Camaro a longer and lower appearance. Sport coupe and convertible styles were offered, with option package selections having a great effect on final appearance features. The formerly smooth-sided body was now more highly sculptured, with a side feature line tracing the forward edge of the front wheel housing and running straight from the top of the opning to the rear of the car. A second line traced the front of the rear wheel opening and blended into the main one. Simulated vertical air slots were positioned ahead of the rear wheel. The Rally Sport option offered a special black grille with concealed headlights, the retractable headlamp doors being decorated by a triple-slot design motif. A funtional 'Super Scoop' hood was available with Z-28 or Super Sport (SS) packages. Standard equipment began at the safety-oriented level and included the mandatory head rest option plus, heater and defroster; integrated front headlight and parking light unit; Strato-Bucket front seats; all-vinyl interior; carpeting; Astro Ventilation system; front shoulder safety belts; lefthand OSRV mirror; side marker lights; E78 x 14 two-ply (four-ply rated) black sidewall tires; 140 horsepower Six or 210 horsepower V-8 and, in convertibles, interior courtesy lights. In terms of power, the rare ZL-1 Camaros became one of the year's hottest and most collectible cars. Optioned with a 427 cubic inch V-8 featuring aluminum block construction and three two-barrel carburetors, these 425 horsepower jobs were built in limited numbers for factory experimental racing purposes. Production of only 69 units has been reported. Nearly as desirable to car collectors, although not quite as rare, is the Indianapolis Pace Car replica Camaro. According to several articles, about 100 original editions were built and provided as official cars for dignitaries and press personalities attending the 500 Mile Race. The actual Pace Car was an RS/SS 396 convertible and most of the rest were SS 350 rag-tops. However, experts on the marque seem to universally agree that a Pace Car package was later marketed for the general public, leading to the sale of about 2,000 more of these specially-trimmed models. Unfortunately, this package does not show-up on either the initial factory options sheets, or the May 1, 1969 revised sheets, that were used in researching this Catalog. Therefore, it is currently impossible to document exactly what equipment was included, or the prices in effect.

VEHICLE I.D. NUMBERS: The numbering system and code locations were the same as on other 1969 Chevrolet products, with the first three symbols changed to Camaro nomenclature.

1969 Chevrolet, Camaro RS 2-dr convertible, V-8

CAMARO SERIES

Series Number	Body/Style Number	Body Type & Seating	Factory Price	Shipping Weight	Production Total
123/124	37	2-dr HT Spt Cpe-4P	2638/2727	3040/3050	214,280
123/124	67	2-dr Conv-4P	2852/2941	3160/3295	16,519

ADDITIONAL NOTES: The figures above are for domestic market units only. Production included 65,008 Sixes; 178,087 V-8s; 37,773 Rally Sports; 33,980 Super Sports (some cars had both Rally Sport and Super Sport packages); 19,014 cars with the Z-28 option; 72,395 cars with three-speed manual transmission; 50,128 cars with four-speed manual transmission; 120,572 cars with automatic transmission; 37,878 cars with air conditioning; 120,060 cars with power steering and 2,913 cars with power windows. A total of 12,316 Camaros were built for export.

CAMARO ENGINES
Base Six. See 1969 Chevelle 300 DeLuxe Series engine data.

Base V-8. Overhead valves. Cast iron block. Displacement: 326.7 (327) cubic inches. Bore and stroke: 4.00 x 3.25 inches. Compression ratio: 9.0:1. Brake horsepower: 210 at 4600 R.P.M. Five main bearings. Hydraulic valve lifters. Carburetor: Rochester two-barrel.

CHASSIS FEATURES: Wheelbase: (Chevrolet) 119 inches; (Chevelle two-door) 112 inches; (Chevelle four-door) 116 inches; (Nova) 111 inches; (Camaro) 108 inches. Overall length: (Chevrolet wagon) 217 inches; (Chevrolet) 216 inches; (Chevelle two-door) 197 inches; (Chevelle wagon) 208 inches; (Chevelle four-door) 201 inches; (Nova) 190 inches; (Camaro) 186 inches. Front and rear tread: Same as 1968. Tires: Refer to text.

POWERTRAIN OPTIONS (EARLY 1969): Turbo-Thrift '250' Six, in Chevelle/Camaro/Nova ($26.35). Turbo-Fire '350' V-8 in Chevrolet/Camaro ($52.70); in Chevelle/Nova ($68.50). RPO L66/396 cubic inch Turbo-Jet 265 horsepower V-8, in Chevrolets ($68.50). RPO L48/350 cubic inch 300 horsepower V-8, in Chevrolet ($52.70); in Chevelle ($68.50). RPO L35/396 cubic inch Turbo-Jet 325 horsepower V-8 in Camaro SS only ($63.20). RPO LS1/427 cubic inch 355 horsepower V-8, in Chevrolets only ($163.25). RPO L34/396 cubic inch Turbo-Jet 350 horsepower V-8, in Chevelle SS 396 only ($121.15); in Camaro SS/Nova SS ($184.35). RPO L78/396 cubic inch Turob-Jet 375 horsepower V-8, in Chevelle SS 396 ($252.80); in Camaro SS/Nova SS ($316). RPO L78-89/375 horsepower Turbo-Jet V-8 with special aluminum cylinder heads, in Chevelle SS 396 ($647.75); in Camaro SS ($710.95). RPO L36/427 cubic inch 390 horsepower Turbo-Jet V-8, in Chevrolet ($237). RPO L72/427 cubic inch 425 horsepower Turbo-Jet V-8, in Chevrolet ($447.65); in Chevrolet with SS option ($183.35). Dual exhausts ($30.55). Wide-Range four-speed manual transmission, in Camaro ($195.40); in others ($184.80). Close-ratio four-speed manual transmission, in Camaro ($195.40); in others ($184.80). Heavy-duty four-speed manual transmission, in Nova ($312.55); in Camaro ($322.10); in Chevelle ($264); in Chevrolet ($313). Powerglide automatic transmission, with Nova V-8 ($158.40); with Nova Four/Six ($147.85); with other V-8s ($174.25); with other Sixes ($163.70). Special three-speed manual transmission, standard with SS 427/396 and Camaro/ Nova SS; in others ($79). Torque-Drive, in Camaro/Nova Six only ($68.65). Turbo-HydraMatic (M40 type), in Nova Six ($174.25); in other Six ($190.10); in all, except Nova, with 255/300 horsepower V-8 ($200.65); in Nova with 255/300 horsepower V-8 ($190.10); in all with 375/425 horsepower V-8 ($290.40); in all with other V-8s ($221.80). Floor-mounted shift lever, as optional equipment ($10.55). Posi-Traction axle ($42.15).

POWERTRAIN OPTIONS (May 1, 1969 changes): PO L65/250 cubic inch Turbo-Fire 250 horsepower V-8, in Chevelle/Nova/Camaro ($21.10); RPO LM1/350 cubic inch Turbo-Fire 255 horsepower V-8, in Chevrolet and Camaro ($52.70); in Chevelle/Nova ($68.50). RPO NC8 dual chambered exhaust system, in Chevelle SS396/Z28/Camaro SS with 325/350/375 horsepower V-8 ($15.80).

CONVENIENCE OPTIONS: Four-Season air conditioning ($363.40-$384.45). Comfortron air conditioning ($463.45). Station wagon rear deflector ($19). Custom DeLuxe shoulder belts ($12.15-$16.90). Power drum brakes, except Nova Four ($42.15). Power front disc brakes, except Nova Four ($64.25). Special Camaro front bumper ($42.15). Load floor carpeting in Kingswood and Estate ($52.70). Adjustable roof rack ($52.70). Electric clock ($15.80). Heavy-duty clutch ($47.50-$52.70). Console with courtesy light ($53.75). Electro-Clear rear defroster ($32.65). Power door locks, Chevrolet/Chevelle two-door ($44.80); four-door ($68.50). Retractable headlights, Caprice/Estate ($79). Headlight washer ($15.80). Special instrumentation; in Chevelle/Camaro ($94.80). Light monitoring system ($26.35). Two-tone paint, all except Camaro ($23.20); on Camaro, includes roof molding, ($31.60). AM pushbutton radio ($61.10). AM/FM pushbutton radio ($133.80). AM/FM radio and stereo ($239.10). Rear manual antenna ($9.50-$10.55). Vinyl roof ($79-$88.55). Camaro folding rear seat ($42.15). Six-Way power seat ($100.10). Strato Bucket seat, in Caprice, includes front center arm rest and Custom knit black cloth trim ($115.90). Strato Bucket, in Malibu coupe/convertible ($121.15); in Caprice, including console with shift if automatic or four-speed, plus center console ($168.55). Automatic level control, Chevrolets ($89.66). Rear fender skirts, Chevrolets with 14 inch wheels ($31.60). Speed and Cruise Control, V-8 and automatic required, ($57.95). Power steering ($89.55-$105.35). Special steering with Quick-Response feature in Camaro, power steering required with air conditioner or 396 cubic inch V-8, ($15.80). Comfort-Tilt steering column ($45.30). Sport styled steering wheel, except Nova ($34.80). Chevelle SS 396 fender accent striping ($26.35). Camaro, front accent or Sport striping ($25.30). Liquid tire chain ($23.20). Power convertible top, on Chevelle/Camaro ($52.70). Power trunk opener, on Chevrolet ($14.75). Power tailgate window, standard in three seat wagon; in two-seat styles ($34.80). Hide-Away wipers as option ($19). Full wheel covers ($21.10). Mag-spoke wheel covers, Caprice and Kingswood Estate ($52.70); all others ($73.75); Simulated wire wheels, Caprice and Kingswood Estate ($55.85). Special wheel covers and Caprice and Kingswood Estate ($57.95); on other full-sized Chevrolets ($79).

CONVENIENCE OPTIONS (May 1, 1969 changes): Adjustable wagon roof rack ($52.70). Electro-Clear rear defroster ($47.40). Special ducted hood for Camaro SS with performance package ($79). Front and rear spoiler, Camaro without performance package ($32.65). Special rear springs, on Camaro, includes rear bumper guards ($20.05).

OPTION PACKAGES
RPO Z27 Camaro SS 350 Option included: special hood; sport striping: hood insulation: F70 x 14 white letter tires; 14 x 7 inch wheels; power disc brakes; special three-speed manual transmission; bright fender louvers; engine accents; emblems and 300 horsepower '350' V-8 ($295.95); after May 1, 1969 ($311.75).
RPO Z16 Chevelle Concours sedan (hardtop) included: luxury cloth seat and sidewall trim; steering wheel emblem; panel trim plate; black accented lower body side and wheel opening moldings; deck lid nameplate and special insulation ($131.65).
RPO ZJ2 Nova Custom exterior package included: simulated front fender louvers with bright accents; bodysill and rear fender moldings; black bodysill and lower rear fender trim panels; accent striping. Coupe also had bright side window moldings and lower body accent band. Sedan also had bodyside molding with black vinyl insert, on Coupe ($97.95); on Sedan ($79).
RPO Z87 (Camaro)/ZJ1 (Nova with bench)/A51 (Nova with buckets) Custom interior trim. Included on Camaro: molded vinyl door panel with built-in arm rest; assist grip; carpeted lower door panel; wood-grain panel accents; wood-grain steering wheel; bright pedal trim; glove box light; insulation and baggage mat. Included, on Nova, luxury seats and sidewalls; bright accents; rear arm rest ash trays; carpets; DeLuxe mirror; interior or light switches; baggage mat; insulation. Price for bucket seat Nova ($231.75); price for other ($110.60).

RPO Z24 Impala SS 427 Option, on Custom Coupe, Sport Coupe or convertible included: power disc brakes; special three-speed transmission; ornamentation; chassis and suspension features; 15 inch wheels; Red Stripe tires and 390 horsepower 427 cubic inch V-8 ($422.35).
RPO Z26 Nova SS Option package, on coupe only included: simulated air intakes on hood; simulated front fender louvers; black accents; black accent grille and rear panel; SS emblems; Red Stripe F70 x 14 tires; 14 x 7 inch wheels; special suspension and three-speed gear box; power disc brakes; bright engine accents; hood insulation and 300 horsepower '350' V-8 ($280.20).
RPO Z22 Camaro Rally Sport (R/S) Option package included: special grille with concealed headlights; headlight washers; fender striping (except with SS); bright accents on simulated rear fender louvers; front and rear wheel lip moldings; black body sills; RS emblems; nameplates; accented tail and parking lights; backup lights below bumper; steering wheel accents and coupe roof drip moldings ($131.65).
RPO Z35, Camaro SS 396 Option included: special hood, ornamentation and suspension; Sport wheels; white letter tires (Wide-Oval); power disc brakes; special three-speed transmission; black accented grille and 325 horsepower '396' V-8 ($347.60).
RPO Z28, Camaro Special Performance Package included: dual exhaust with deep-toned muffler; special front and rear suspension; heavy-duty radiator and temperature controlled fan; quick-ratio steering; 15 x 7 inch Rally wheels; E70 x 15 white letter tires; 3.73 ratio axle; Rally stripes on hood and rear deck and special 302 cubic inch V-8 (estimated horsepower rating 350). Four-speed manual transmission and power disc brake options were additional mandatory options (at regular price in *addition* to Z-28 retail). Posi-Traction rear axle was also recommended. Cost ($458.15); after May 1, 1969 ($506.60). A total of 503 were equipped with disc brakes.

Historical footnotes: The 1969 Chevrolet lineup was introduced September 26, 1968. John Z. DeLorean was General Manager of Chevrolet Division. Model year output figures included exactly 1,109,013 full-sized Chevrolets; 439,611 Chevelles; 269,988 Novas and 243,085 Camaros. Market penetration, including Corvettes and Corvairs, was an even 25 percent. The 1969 Camaro captured top honors in SCCA Trans-Am Championship racing for cars in the over 2.5 liter class. Mark Donahue and Roger Penske were the top Chevrolet drivers.

1970 CHEVROLET

NOTE: *A fundamental shift in automotive marketing took place in the 1970s. Increasing emphasis was placed on introducing new chassis lines, while distinctions between different series built off the same platform became less obvious and less significant. Chevrolet, for example, introduced its Monte Carlo sports/personal car in 1970, its subcompact Vega in 1971 and the Monza in 1975. At the same time, it became harder to tell apart the lowest and highest-priced models in the Nova, Chevelle and Chevrolet lines. Generally speaking, the low-level cars came with more standard features each season, while the top-level cars were distinguished, primarily, by minor appointment and trim differences. Enthusiasts became more interested in rare and desirable options packages (which give certain cars extra collector value in the hobby market today), than in the small details and variations . Therefore, in order to cover the most important aspects of 1970-1975 Chevrolet product history in the allotted amount of space, this Catalog will group the cars according to chassis lines from this point on.*

1970 Chevrolet, Caprice 2-dr Custom coupe, V-8

FULL-SIZED CHEVROLET — (SIX/V-8) — ALL SERIES — The 'big' Chevrolets were the same, in size, as the previous models. There were changes to the front and rear. The front fender line, hood and grille were redone, eliminating the encircling, integrated bumper/grille look. Round, horizontal dual headlamps were set in square bezels flanking a somewhat finer textured griile, although a cross-hatched insert design was retained. The gravel pan was reshaped to round the front body corners and incorporate slightly enlarged parking lights as well as triple-slit side marker lights. At the rear, the taillights took a new vertical-slot shape and were recessed into the bumper. A base '350' V-8, optional regular-fuel '400' V-8 and transmission controlled vacuum spark advance were technical refinements. Standard equipment for Biscaynes included all safety features; windshield antenna; Astro Ventilation; Hide-Away wipers; Delco-Eye battery; side-guard door beams; heater/defroster: cigarette lighter; locking glove box; carpets; ash tray light; center dome lamp; F78-15 blackwalls and either the '250' Six or '350' V-8. The Bel Air was equipped likewise, plus having side and roof drip moldings and a glove box light. The Impala had all above, plus foam seat cushions; fabric and vinyl trim (all-vinyl in convertible); DeLuxe steering wheel; trunk light; door/window frame moldings; vinyl-insert bodyside moldings and luggage lamps. The sport coupe also had bright metal moldings below the doors and on its wheel lips. The Custom coupe had power front disc brakes and the convertible had courtesy lights and carpeted lower door panels. Tires were size F78-15 on Sixes; G78-15 on V-8s. The Caprice was equipped with all of the above, plus power front disc brakes; distinctive side moldings; color-keyed wheel covers; electric clock; G78-15/B bias-belted blackwalls; 250 horsepower base engine and, in sedans, a center arm rest seat. Station wagons had such items as vinyl trim; Dual-Action tailgates and glove box light, plus all Biscayne passenger car equipment. The Kingswood wagon compared to the Impala trim level, with courtesy lights; bodyside moldings and foam cushions included. The Kingswood Estate was the Caprice-level counterpart and, thus, had a DeLuxe steering wheel; clock and window moldings, plus exterior wood-grain paneling. Base engine for all wagons was the '350' V-8 and H78-15/D tires were used. Power disc brakes were standard with Kingswood Estates.

VEHICLE I.D. NUMBERS: The numbering system and code locations were the same as on previous models. The sixth symbol was changed to '0' to indicate 1970 model year. In the specifications charts below, the first column lists the applicable series nomenclature. Six-cylinder series codes are given above slash/V-8 series codes below slash. In cases where a certain model came only with V-8 power no slash is used. The second column lists the Body Style Number. The Chevrolet Model Number is the combination of these two columns. This same basic system is used for all 1970 Chevrolet listings in this Catalog.

1970 Chevrolet, Impala 2-dr convertible, V-8

FULL-SIZED CHEVROLET

Series Number	Body/Style Number	Body Type & Seating	Factory Price	Shipping Weight	Production Total
BISCAYNE SERIES (INCLUDES BROOKWOOD WAGON)					
153/154	69	4-dr Sed-6P	2787/2998	3600/3759	Note 1
154	36	4-dr Sta Wag-6P	3294	4204	Note 2
BEL AIR SERIES (INCLUDES TOWNSMAN WAGONS)					
155/156	69	4-dr Sed-6P	2887/2998	3604/3763	Note 3
156	46	4-dr Sta Wag-9P	3469	4263	Note 2
156	36	4-dr Sta Wag-6P	3357	4208	Note 2
IMPALA SERIES (INCLUDES KINGSWOOD WAGONS)					
163/164	69	4-dr Sed-6P	3021/3132	3655/3802	Note 4
163/164	37	2-dr HT Spt Cpe-6P	3038/3149	3641/3788	Note 4
164	39	4-dr HT Spt Sed-5P	3203	3871	Note 4
164	47	2-dr Cus Cpe-6P	3266	3801	Note 4
164	67	2-dr Conv-6P	3377	3843	Note 4/5
164	46	4-dr Sta Wag-9P	3589	4321	Note 2
164	36	4-dr Sta Wag-6P	3477	4269	Note 2
CAPRICE SERIES (INCLUDES KINGSWOOD ESTATE)					
166	39	4-dr HT Sed-6P	3527	3905	Note 6
166	47	2-dr HT Sed-6P	3474	3821	Note 6
166	46	4-dr Sta Wag-9P	3866	4361	Note 2
166	36	4-dr Sta Wag-6P	3753	4295	Note 2

GENERAL NOTE: All series production totals given below are expressed in figures rounded-off to the nearest 100 units. Note 5 provides the exact number of convertibles built, but convertible production is also included in Note 4. On all 1970 Chevrolet product specifications charts in this Catalog, Serial Numbers, prices and weights above slash apply to Sixes/below slash to V-8s.

NOTE 1: Biscayne model year production was some 35,400 units, including 12,300 Sixes and 23,100 V-8s.
NOTE 2: Chevrolet returned to the practice of recording production of all station wagons built off the same platform as a lumped sum. In figures rounded-off to the nearest 100 units, a total of 162,600 full-sized station wagons were built during the 1970 model year. This included Brookwood, Townsman, Kingswood and Kingswood Estate models. All full-sized station wagons were V-8s.
NOTE 3: Bel Air model year production was some 75,800 units, including 9,000 Sixes and 66,800 V-8s.
NOTE 4: Impala model year production was some 612,800 units, including 6,500 Sixes and 606,300 V-8s.
NOTE 5: Exactly 9,562 Impala convertibles were built. This breakout is included in Note 4 above.
NOTE 6: Caprice V-8 Series model year production was some 92,000 units.

CHEVROLET ENGINES
Inline Six. Overhead valves. Cast iron block. Displacement: 250 cubic inches. Bore and stroke: 3.875 x 3.53 inches. Compression ratio: 8.5:1. Brake horsepower: 155 at 4200 R.P.M. Seven main bearings. Hydraulic valve lifters. Carburetor: Rochester one-barrel.

V-8. Overhead valves. Cast iron block. Displacement: 350 cubic inches. Bore and stroke: 4.00 x 3.48 inches. Compression ratio: 9.0:1. Brake horsepower: 250 at 4500 R.P.M. Five main bearings. Hydraulic valve lifters. Carburetor: Rochester two-barrel.

1970 Chevrolet, Monte Carlo 2-dr hardtop coupe, V-8

MONTE CARLO — (V-8) — SERIES 138 — The original Monte Carlo was said to combine action and elegance in a sporty, personal luxury package. Based on the same platform as the redesigned 1969 Pontiac Grand Prix, the Monte Carlo was bigger than the Chevelle and had a price tag in the Impala range. A long hood/short deck image and smart interior and exterior appointments were incorporated. Styling features included large, single headlamps mounted in square-shaped bright housings; a rectangular front opening with a grid-textured grille of thin, bright horizontal moldings (with a center badge) and a profile emphasizing the popular 'venturi' shape (enhanced by a crispy sculptured upper feature line). Although mainly luxurious in overall character, the Monte Carlo turned out to be quite a fine high-performance machine. The potent, SS 454 version was capable of 0 to 60 miles per hour in under eight seconds and the overall package was found to be extremely suitable in short track stock car racing. This was due to a combination of good power-to-weight distribution along with aerodynamic factors. The only available body style was a coupe which had, as standard equipment, all features found on Chevelle Malibus (See Malibu listing), plus power front disc brakes; electric clock; assist straps; elm-burl dash panel inlays; G78-15/B bias-belted black sidewall tires and a 350 cubic inch V-8. Although commonly seen on most Monte Carlos that sold, fender skirts were optional.

VEHICLE I.D. NUMBERS: The numbering system and code locations were the same as on full-sized Chevrolets, with the first five symbols changed to Monte Carlo nomenclature.

MONTE CARLO SERIES

Series Number	Body/Style Number	Body Type & Seating	Factory Price	Shipping Weight	Production Total
138	57	2-dr HT Cpe-5P	3123	3460	145,975

NOTE: The production figure given above is the exact model year total.

MONTE CARLO ENGINE
See 1970 full-sized Chevrolet Series base V-8 engine data.

1970 Chevelle, SS 396 2-dr hardtop sports coupe, V-8

INTERMEDIATE-SIZED CHEVELLE — (SIX/V-8) — ALL SERIES — The more highly sculptured 1970 Chevelle featured a bold-looking frontal treatment with split grille and dual, blending headlights. A new, slotless front bumper incorporated rectangular parking lamps directly below the headlamps. The swept-back front fender look was gone, replaced by a blunter image. An upper feature line ran from above the headlight level to the top of the back bumper, with a prominent dip at mid-waist height. Rear side markers with a slotted and segmented look were seen. The Chevelle 300 DeLuxe name was dropped. The Chevelle was the base model and the Malibu was one step up. A wide range of station wagons included the Nomad (comparable to the long gone standard 300 line); the Greenbriers (counterparts to the recently deleted DeLuxes); Malibu-level Concours models and the top-of-the-line Concours Estate Wagon (which carried nomenclature indicating Monte Carlo-level appointments). Obviously, while Chevrolet had trouble selling some types of Chevelles as passenger cars, it was still able to market them in station wagon styles. This created an unusual Chevelle wagon lineup. Chevelle level standard equipment included the safety assortment; heater/defroster; locking glove box; cigarette lighter; rubber floor mats and either a 155 horsepower 250 cubic inch Six or 200 horsepower 307 cubic inch V-8. The blackwall tires were size E78-14/B on both Sixes and V-8s. Sources used in researching this Catalog indicate that the base Chevelle wasn't available at the beginning of the model year, but was added at a mid-season date. The Chevelle Malibu Series, on the other hand, was marketed throughout the year. It had all of the above features, plus hidden antenna; Astro Ventilation; side-guard door beam construction; Delco-Eye battery; Hide-Away wipers and a glove box light. The convertible also came with interior courtesy lights. Malibu engines were the same described above as were tire sizes for the Six. On Malibu V-8s, larger F78-14/B rubber was used. All station wagons came with GM safety features; Dual-Action tailgates; in-the-windshield hidden antenna; Hide-Away wipers; side beam doors; heater/defroster; all-vinyl trim and cigarette lighter. Base Concours models had courtesy lights. The Concours Estate added carpeting; door edge moldings and simulated wood-grain exterior paneling. Engines were the same used on passenger cars and V-8s had power front disc brakes. All station wagons had G78-14/G blackwalls.

VEHICLE I.D. NUMBERS: The numbering system and code locations were the same as on previous models, with the first five symbols changed to Chevelle/Malibu nomenclature.

INTERMEDIATE-SIZED SERIES

Series Number	Body/Style Number	Body Type & Seating	Factory Price	Shipping Weight	Production Total
NOMAD STATION WAGONS					
131/132	36	4-dr Sta Wag-6P	2835/2925	3615/3718	Note 1
CHEVELLE (GREENBRIER STATION WAGONS)					
133/134	69	4-dr Sed-6P	2537/2627	3196/3312	Note 2
133/134	37	2-dr Cpe-6P	2572/2662	3142/3260	Note 2
133/134	36	4-dr Sta Wag-6P	2946/3100	3644/3748	Note 1
134	46	4-dr Sta Wag-9P	3213	3794	Note 1
CHEVELLE MALIBU SERIES (CONCOURS STATION WAGON)					
135/136	69	4-dr Sed-6P	2685/2775	3221/3330	Note 3
135/136	39	4-dr HT Sed-6P	2790/2881	3302/3409	Note 3
135/136	37	2-dr Spt Cpe-6P	2719/2809	3197/3307	Note 3
135/136	67	2-dr Conv-6P	2919/3009	3243/3352	Note 3/4
135/136	36	4-dr Sta Wag-6P	3056/3210	3687/3794	Note 1
136	46	4-dr Sta Wag-9P	3323	3836	Note 1
CONCOURS ESTATE STATION WAGON					
138	46	4-dr Sta Wag-9P	3455	3880	Note 1
138	36	4-dr Sta Wag-6P	3342	3821	Note 1

GENERAL NOTE: All series production totals given below are expressed in figures rounded-off to the nearest 100 units. Note 4 provides the exact number of convertibles built, but convertible production is also included in Note 3.
NOTE 1: A total of some 40,600 intermediate-sized Chevelle station wagons were built in the 1970 model year. This included 5,600 Sixes and 35,000 V-8s. This also includes all Nomad/Greenbrier/Concours and Concours Estate models, with no additional breakouts, as to series, available at this time.
NOTE 2: Base Chevelle model year production was some 23,900 units, including 10,700 Sixes and 13,200 V-8s (passenger cars only).
NOTE 3: Chevelle Malibu model year production was some 375,800 units, including 21,100 Sixes and 354,700 V-8s (passenger cars only).
NOTE 4: Exactly 7,511 Chevelle convertibles were built. This breakout is included in the rounded-off totals in Note 3 above.

1970 Chevrolet, Chevelle Malibu 4-dr hardtop Sport Sedan, V-8

CHEVELLE ENGINES
Six. See 1970 Chevrolet engine data for Chevelle Six specifications.

V-8. Overhead valves. Cast iron block. Displacement: 307 cubic inches. Bore and stroke: 3.875 x 3.53 inches. Compression ratio: 9.0:1. Brake horsepower: 200 at 4600 R.P.M. Five main bearings. Hydraulic valve lifters. Carburetor: Rochester two-barrel.

1970 Chevrolet, Nova 2-dr sedan, V-8

NOVA — (FOUR/SIX/V-8) — SERIES 111/113/114 — The 1970 Nova had a grille insert with squarer openings than the previous model. The Chevrolet badge at the center of the upper grille molding was slightly fatter and not quite as wide as before. Options included simulated bright vertical cowlside louvers; in-the-windshield radio antennas and, new for the year, variable ratio power steering. The sporty Nova SS option package included a hefty 300 horsepower '350' V-8. Regular equipment included GM safety hardware; front arm rests; heater/defroster; Delco-Eye battery and E78-14 black sidewall tires. Base engines were the 90 horsepower Four; 140 horsepower '230' Six and the 307 cubic inch V-8.

VEHICLE I.D. NUMBERS: The numbering system and code locations were the same as on other Chevrolet products, with the first five symbols changed to Nova nomenclature.

NOVA SERIES

Model Number	Body/Style Number	Body Type & Seating	Factory Price	Shipping Weight	Production Total
FOUR					
111	69	4-dr Sed-6P	2205	2843	Note 1
111	27	2-dr Cpe-6P	2176	2820	Note 1
SIX					
113	69	4-dr Sed-6P	2284	2942	Note 2
113	27	2-dr Cpe-6P	2254	2919	Note 2
V-8					
114	69	4-dr Sed-6P	2533	NA	Note 3
114	27	2-dr Sed-6P	2503	NA	Note 3

NOTE 1: Exactly 2,247 Nova Fours were built for the U.S. market during the 1970 model year.
NOTE 2: Exactly 173, 632 Nova Sixes were built for the U.S. market during the 1970 model year.
NOTE 3: Exactly 139,243 Nova V-8s were built for the U.S. market during the 1970 model year.
ADDITIONAL NOTE: There are no breakouts currently available to indicate how many Novas in each series were four-door sedans or two-door coupes.

1970 Chevrolet, Nova 2-dr sedan, V-8

NOVA SERIES ENGINES
Four. See 1969 Nova Series four-cylinder engine data.

Six. See 1970 Chevrolet Series six-cylinder engine data.

Base V-8. See 1970 Chevelle Series base V-8 engine data.

1970 Camaro, 2-dr hardtop sports coupe, V-8

CAMARO SERIES — (SIX/V-8) — Due to slow sales of 1969 Camaros, no new design was introduced for this series at model introduction time in the fall of 1969. Chevrolet dealers continued to sell leftover units until supplies ran out. This may have led to some cars with 1969 specifications being sold and titled as 1970s. The true 1970 models (often called 1970-1/2 Camaros) did not go on sale until February 26, 1970. They had completely new styling with high-intensity headlamps; a semi-fastback roofline; snout-styled grille (with egg crate insert) and a much smoother-looking rear end. The only body style available was the sport coupe. Standard equipment included all GM safety features; Strato-Bucket front seats; all-vinyl interior; carpetings; Astro Ventilation; lefthand OSRV mirror; side marker lights and E78-14/B bias-belted blackwall tires. The 155 horsepower six was base engine in the Camaro six, while the '307' V-8 was standard in the second line. Desirable options packages were the Camaro SS equipment group; the Rally Sport assortment and the RPO Code Z28 special performance package. The latter carried a retail price of $572.95 and featured the 360 horsepower 350 cubic inch V-8.

VEHICLE I.D. NUMBERS: The numbering system and code locations were the same as on other Chevrolet products, with the first five symbols changed to Camaro nomenclature.

CAMARO SERIES

Model Number	Body/Style Number	Body Type & Seating	Factory Price	Shipping Weight	Production Total
123/124	87	2-dr HT Spt Cpe-4P	2749/2839	3058/3172	117,604

NOTE: The production total above is for domestic market units only. Production included 27,135 cars with Rally Sport equipment; 12,476 cars with Super Sport equipment; 8,733 cars with Z-28 equipment; 112,323 V-8s; 12,566 Sixes; 14,859 cars with three-speed manual transmission; 18,678 cars with four-speed manual transmission; 91,352 cars with automatic tranmission; 38,565 cars with air conditioning; 92,640 car with power steering and 7,295 cars built in the United States for export marketing.

CAMARO SERIES ENGINE
Six. See 1970 Chevrolet Series six-cylinder engine data.

Base V-8. See 1970 Chevelle Series base V-8 engine data.

1970 Chevrolet, Monte Carlo 2-dr hardtop Sport Coupe, V-8

CHASSIS FEATURES: Wheelbase: (Chevrolet) 119 inches; (Chevelle two-door) 112 inches; (Chevelle four-door) 116 inches; (Monte Carlo) 116 inches; (Nova) 111 inches; (Camaro) 108 inches. Overall length: (Chevrolet wagon) 217 inches; (Chevrolet) 216 inches; (Chevelle wagon) 207 inches; (Chevelle two-door) 198 inches; (Chevelle four-door) 202 inches; (Monte Carlo) 206 inches; (Nova) 190 inches; (Camaro) 188 inches. Width: (Chevrolet) 80 inches; (Chevelle) 76 inches; (Monte Carlo) 76 inches; (Nova) 73 inches; (Camaro) 75 inches. Tires: Refer to text.

POWERTRAIN OPTIONS: RPO L65/250 horsepower '350' V-8, in 1970-1/2 Camaro ($31.60); in base Chevelle ($21.10); in Malibu and Nova ($16.70). RPO L34/350 horsepower '396' V-8, in 1970-1/2 Camaro with RPO Z27 ($152.75). RPO L78/375 horsepower '396' V-8, in 1970-1/2 Camaro with RPO Z27, positraction required ($385.50). RPO L48/300 horsepower Turbo-Fire V-8, in 1970-1/2 Chevelles and Malibus ($68.50). RPO LS3/330 horsepower 400 cubic inch Turbo-Jet V-8, in 1970-1/2 Chevelles ($162.20); in Malibu and Chevelle wagons ($128.32); in Monte Carlo ($111.67). RPO LS6/450 horsepower 454 cubic inch Turbo-Jet V-8, in 1970-1/2 Chevelle with SS 454 Option package ($263.30). PRO LF6/265 horsepower Turbo-Fire-400 ($50). RPO LS4/345 horsepower 454 cubic inch Turbo-Jet V-8, except Novas and Chevelles ($133.35). RPO Code L22/155 horsepower 250 cubic inch Turbo-Thrift Six, in Camaro and Nova ($20.85). **NOTE:** Option RPO L78/L89 was available for the 1969 style Camaro sold in the 1970 model year. This included the 375 horsepower Turbo-Jet 396 V-8 with aluminum heads ($562.45). Wide-range type four-speed manual transmission, in 1970-1/2 Camaro ($205.96); in 1970-1/2 Chevelle ($184.80); in Malibu/Nova/Monte Carlo ($184.80); in 1969 style Camaro sold in 1970 model year, includes Hurst shifter on last model ($195.40). Special close-ratio four-speed manual transmission, in 1970-1/2 Chevelle ($221.80); in 1970-1/2 Camaro ($232.35). Regular close-ratio four-speed manual transmission, in Malibu/Nova ($184.80); in 1970-1/2 Camaro ($205.95); in 1970-1/2 Chevelle ($184.80); in 1969 style Camaro, including Hurst shifter ($195.40). Turbo-Hydramatic transmission, in 1970-1/2 Chevelle with 330/350/360 horsepower V-8s ($221.80); in same model with 450 horsepower V-8 ($290.40); in Nova Six ($174.25); in other Sixes ($190.10); in 200/250/300 horsepower V-8s, except Nova ($200.65); in Nova with 250/300 horsepower V-8 ($190.10); in all with 265/330/345/350/390 horsepower V-8 ($221.80); in all with 325/425 horsepower V-8. Torque-Drive transmission, in Nova Four/Six and 1969 style Camaro Six ($68.65). Powerglide transmission, Sixes except Nova ($163.70); V-8s except Nova ($174.25); Nova Six ($147.85); in Nova V-8 ($158.40). RPO ZL2 Chevelle cowl-induction hood, SS 396 option required ($147.45). Positraction axle ($42.15). Heavy-duty battery ($15.80). Dual exhausts ($24.17). 63 ampere generator, without air conditioning ($21); with air conditioning ($4). Engine block heater ($10.55). Special ducted hood for 1969 Camaro sold in 1970 model year, requires Z28 ($79). Heavy-duty radiator ($15-$32, per size of car).

CONVENIENCE OPTIONS: Comfortron air conditioning ($463.45). Four Season air conditioning ($363.40-$384.15). Wagon defector ($19). Power drum brakes ($41.15-$43.05). Power front disc brakes ($64.25-$65.65). Carpeted load floor ($52.70). Monte Carlo console ($53.75). Console in Malibu/Nova with bucket seats ($53.75). Electro Clear rear defroster ($41.70). Standard rear defroster ($20.85-$29.20). Power door locks, two-door ($35.45); four-door ($54.12). Tinted glass ($24.83-$30). Headlight delay system ($18.36). Special instrumentation, includes tachometer, ammeter and temperature gauges, Malibu coupe/convertible ($84.30); Monte Carlo ($68.50); Camaro and Nova V-8 with console ($94.80). Vigilante light monitoring system, except Nova ($26.35). AM pushbutton radio ($61.10). AM/FM pushbutton radio ($133.80). AM/FM radio with FM stereo ($239.10). Stereo tape, with AM radio ($194.85); with AM/FM radio and FM stereo ($372.85). Black, Blue, Dark Gold, Green or white vinyl tops; on Monte Carlo ($126.40); on Chevrolet ($105.35); on Nova Six/V-8 ($84.30); on Camaro sport coupe, includes roof rail molding ($84.30); on Chevelle ($94.80). Six-Way power front seat ($100.10). Power Strato Bucket seat ($121.15). Rear fender skirts; on Monte Carlo and Chevrolet, except wagons ($31.60). Power steering ($89.55-$105.35). Comfort-Tilt steering wheel ($46). Wheel covers ($21). Monte Carlo color-keyed wheel covers ($15.80). Special wheel covers ($57.95-$80.70). Six 15 x 7JK wheels on Monte Carlo ($10.55). Rally styled wheels, on Caprice and Kingswood Estate ($21); others ($36). Nova Sport styled wheels ($79). Fingertip windshield wiper control ($19). Rear deck lid spoiler, on 1970-1/2 Camaro, standard with Z28 package ($32.65). Air conditioning, 1970-1/2 Camaro ($380.25). Console, including compartment, ash tray and automatic shift lever, in 1970-1/2 Camaro ($59). Vinyl roof, on 1970-1/2 Camaro ($89.55).

CONVENIENCE OPTION PACKAGES:
Nova Custom Exterior Package, includes simulated front fender louvers; bright accents; rear panel trim plate; body sill and rear fender moldings; black body sill and lower rear fender; accent striping on coupe; bright side window and lower body moldings; black lower accent band and black vinyl insert type side molding on sedan; on coupes ($97.95); on sedans ($79).
Nova Custom Interior Package, includes luxury seat and sidewall trim with bright accents; rear arm rest ash trays; carpeting; bright rear view mirror support, dome light bezel and pedal trim; right front hood light switch; glove box light; trunk mat and insulation.
RPO Z27 Camaro Super Sport Package (1969 style), includes 300 horsepower '350' V-8; special hood; insulation; F70-14 white letter tires; 14-7 wheels; special suspension; power disc brakes; special three-speed manual transmission; bright fender louvers; engine accents and simulated rear fender louvers ($311.75). RPO Z27 Camaro Super Sport package (1970-1/2 style), includes 300 horsepower '350' V-8; bright engine accents; power brakes; special ornamentation; hood insulation; F70-14 white letter tires; 14-7 wheels; black-painted grille; Hide-A-Way wipers with black arms and SS emblems ($289.65).
RPO Z23 1970-1/2 Camaro interior accent group, includes additional instrument cluster lighting; wood-grain dash accents and steering wheel ($21.10) or included with Z28 package at no charge.
RPO Z22 1970-1/2 Camaro Rally Sport package, includes black painted grille with rubber-tipped vertical center bar and resilient body-color grille frame; independent left and right front bumpers; license plate bracket mounted below right front bumper; parking lights with bright accents molded on grille panel; Hide-A-Way wipers; bright window, hood panel and body sill moldings; body-colored door handle inserts; RS emblems; nameplate; bright accented taillamps and backup lamps, F78-14 or E70-14 tires required ($188.35).
PRO Z28 1970-1/2 Camaro Special Performance Package, includes special 360 horsepower '350' V-8 with bright engine accents; heavy-duty radiator; dual exhausts; black-painted grille; Z28 emblems; special performance suspension; heavy-duty front and rear springs; 15 x 7 inch wheels; special center caps and trim rings; hood insulation; F60-15B white-lettered tires; rear deck spoiler and special paint stripes on hood and deck ($572.95).
RPO Z15, 1970-1/2 Chevelle SS 454 Package, includes bright engine accents; dual exhausts with bright tips; black-painted grille; wheel opening moldings; power front disc brakes; special rear suspension and rear bumper with black insert; special 'power bulge' hood; SS emblems; 360 horsepower 454 cubic inch Turbo-Jet V-8; heavy-duty battery; F70-14 white letter tires; 14 x 7 wheels (sport type); deletion of body sill molding and deletion of belt line molding, on Malibu V-8 Sport coupe or convertible with M40 Turbo-Hydramatic or four-speed manual transmissions ($503.45).
RPO Z20 Monte Carlo SS Package, includes 360 horsepower '454' V-8; Superlift with Automatic Level Control; dual exhausts; G70-15/B white letter tires; 15 x 7 wheels; 454 emblems on body sill moldings and requires Turbo-Hydramatic ($420.25).
RPO Z26 Nova SS Package, includes 300 horsepower '350' V-8; dual exhausts: power front disc brakes; simulated air intake on hood; simulated front fender louvers; bright accents; black-finished grille and rear panel; 14-7 wheels; E70-14 White Stripe tires; hood insulation and SS emblems. Four-speed manual or Turbo-Hydramatic transmission required ($290.70).
RPO L34 Nova SS 396 package, includes same as above with 350 horsepower Turbo-Jet V-8 ($184.35 extra).
RPO L38 Nova SS 396 package, includes same as above with 375 horsepower Turbo-Jet V-8 ($316.00).
RPO Z25 Chevelle SS 396 package, includes 350 horsepower 396 cubic inch Turbo-Jet V-8; power front disc brakes; dual exhausts with bright tips; black-painted grille; wheel opening moldings; special rear bumper with black inserts; 'power dome' hood; special suspension; 14 x 7 inch Sport style wheels; G70-14 white lettered tires and SS emblems. Four-speed or Turbo-Hydramatic required ($445.55).
RPO Z25 with L78 Chevelle SS 396 with 375 horsepower V-8 and cast iron heads. Includes same as above, except engine ($210.65).
RPO Z25 with L78/L89 Chevelle SS 396, includes same as above with 375 horsepower V-8 and aluminum heads ($394.95).

Historical footnotes: The 1970-1/2 Camaro was not introduced until February 26, 1970, while the other new Chevrolet products hit the showrooms on September 18, 1969. John Z. DeLorean was General Manager of the Chevrolet Motor Division this year. Calendar year production of models included in this section was as follows: (Chevrolet) 550,596; (Monte Carlo) 130,659; (Nova) 247,344; (Chevelle) 354,839 and Camaro (143,675). Model year output included 143,664 Camaros; 354,855 Chevelles; 130,657 Monte Carlos; 550,571 Chevrolets and 254,242 Novas. A total of 53,599 Chevelle SS 396 models left the factory, including 3,733 with the 454 cubic inch V-8. Also carrying Super Sport equipment were 3,823 Monte Carlos and 19,558 Novas.

1971 CHEVROLET

1971 Chevrolet, Kingswood Estate 4-dr station wagon, V-8

FULL-SIZED CHEVROLET — (SIX/V-8) — ALL SERIES — All-new styling and increased size were characteristics of the big Chevrolets for 1971. All models grew, but the station wagon showed the largest gain in inches and was now on a longer wheelbase than passenger cars. The grille had an egg crate look and was higher, but narrower. Parking lamps were resituated on the front body corners, where the large, ribbed, vertical lenses were set into fender extension caps. The dual, horizontal headlamps were housed in square bezels. The hood panel bulged at the center and carried Chevrolet block lettering on its front edge. Bodyside contours were more rounded and straighter. The rear fenders kicked-up at the upper rear quarter region, then slanted back towards the tail. New taillight treatments were seen. Power disc brakes became standard on all full-sized models, as well as on Monte Carlos and Camaros. Standard equipment for Bel Airs included hidden (in-the-windshield) antenna; Astro-Ventilation; concealed wipers; side-guard beam doors; heater and defroster; cigarette lighter; locking glove box; center dome light; arm rests; 145 horsepower Six or 245 horsepower V-8; inside hood release and lefthand OSRV mirror. Bel Airs had all these features, plus glove box light and cloth with vinyl trim interior. Impalas had the same equipment as Bel Airs, plus luggage compartment light; vinyl-trimmed pattern cloth upholstery; wood-grain accented dash; DeLuxe steering wheel; foam front seat cushions and, on convertibles, courtesy lights; lower door carpeting and all-vinyl seats. Tires were F78 x 15 on Bel Air/Biscayne, G78 x 15 on Impala. The Caprice added ash tray and courtesy lights; electric clock; rear fender skirts; distinctive cloth and vinyl trim; color-keyed wheel covers; 225 horsepower V-8 and also used G78 x 15 tires. The Caprice sedan was equipped with a fold-down center arm rest in the front seat. Features of full-sized station wagons were concealed storage bin; cushioned-center steering wheel; flush and dry rocker panels; all-vinyl interior; power disc/drum brakes; Hide-Away wipers; Glide-Away tailgate (with power window); Air-Flow rear contour; recessed dual headlights; flush-style curved side glass; Flow-through power ventilation; open rocker panels; inside hood release; forward-facing rear seat (on nine-passenger styles); 245 horsepower '350') V-8 and L78 x 15 tires mounted on 15 x 6 inch wheels. Brookwoods added a map light. Townsman/Kingswood models added mirror map and glove box lights and the Kingswood Estate also had ash tray, courtesy, glove box and mirror map lights; door edge guards; electric clock and wood-grained side and rear panels.

VEHICLE IDENTIFICATION NUMBERS: The numbering system and code locatons were the same as for previous models with the sixth symbol changed to a '1' to indicate 1971 model year.

FULL-SIZED CHEVROLET SERIES

Series Number	Body/Style Number	Body Type & Seating	Factory Price	Shipping Weight	Production Total
BISCAYNE (BROOKWOOD STATION WAGON)					
153/154	69	4-dr Sed-6P	3096/3448	3732/3888	Note 1
154	35	4-dr Sta Wag-6P	3929	4542	Note 2
BEL AIR (TOWNSMAN STATION WAGON)					
155/156	69	4-dr Sed-6P	3232/3585	3732/3888	Note 3
156	45	4-dr Sta Wag-9P	4135	4598	Note 2
156	35	4-dr Sta Wag-6P	4020	4544	Note 2
IMPALA (KINGSWOOD STATION WAGON)					
163/164	69	4-dr Sed-6P	3391/3742	3760/3914	Note 4
163/164	57	2-dr HT Cpe-6P	3408/3759	3742/3896	Note 4
164	39	4-dr HT Sed-6P	3813	3978	Note 4
164	47	2-dr Cus Cpe-6P	3826	3912	Note 4
164	67	2-dr Conv-6P	4021	3960	Note 4/5
164	45	4-dr Sta Wag-9P	4227	4648	Note 2
164	35	4-dr Sta Wag-6P	4112	4588	Note 2
CAPRICE (KINGSWOOD ESTATE WAGON)					
166	39	4-dr HT Sed-6P	4134	4040	Note 6
166	47	2-dr Cus Cpe-6P	4081	3964	Note 6
166	45	4-dr Sta Wag-9P	4498	4738	Note 2
166	35	4-dr Sta Wag-6P	4384	4678	Note 2

GENERAL NOTE: All model year production totals given below are expressed in figures rounded-off to the nearest 100 units.
NOTE 1: Some 37,600 Biscaynes were built during the 1971 model year. This total included 2,900 Sixes and 34,700 V-8s.
NOTE 2: Some 91,300 full-sized Chevrolet station wagons were built during the 1971 model year. All were V-8s. This includes Brookwood, Townsman, Kingswood and Kingswood Estate models, with no breakouts available as to series production.
NOTE 3: Some 20,000 Bel Airs were built during the 1971 model year. This included 5,000 Sixes and 15,000 V-8s.
NOTE 4: Some 427,700 Impalas were built during the 1971 model year. This included 2,300 Sixes and 425,400 V-8s.**NOTE 5:** Exactly 4,576 Impala Chevrolet convertibles were built during the 1971 Model year. This breakout is included in the rounded-off totals in Note 4 above. All convertibles were V-8s.
NOTE 6: Some 91,300 Caprices were built during the 1971 model run. This included all V-8s.
ADDITIONAL NOTES: In all specifications charts in this section the Series Numbers, prices and weights above slash are for Sixes/below slash for V-8s. This sytem is used for all 1971 Chevrolet product listings in this catalog.

FULL-SIZED CHEVROLET ENGINE DATA

SIX
Inline Six. Cast iron block. Displacement: 250 cubic inches. Bore and stroke: 3.875 x 3.53 inches. Compression ratio: 8.5:1. Brake horsepower: 145 at 4200 R.P.M. Seven main bearings. Hydraulic valve lifters. Carburetor: Rochester one-barrel.

V-8 BISCAYNE/BEL AIR/IMPALA
V-8. Overhead valves. Cast iron block. Displacement: 350 cubic inches. Bore and stroke: 4.00 x 3.48 inches. Compression ratio: 8.5:1. Brake horsepower 245 at 4800 R.P.M. Five main bearings. Hydraulic valve lifters. Carburetor: Rochester two-barrel.

V-8 CAPRICE AND STATION WAGONS
V-8. Overhead valves. Cast iron block. Displacement: 400 cubic inches. Bore and stroke: 4.125 x 3.75 inches. Compression ratio: 8.5:1. Brake horsepower: 255 at 4400 R.P.M. Five main bearings. Hydraulic valve lifters. Carburetor: Rochester two-barrel.

1971 Chevrolet, Monte Carlo 2-dr hardtop coupe, V-8

MONTE CARLO — (V-8) — SERIES 138 — A new grille with a finer insert mesh appeared on 1971 Monte Carlos. A front bumper with rectangular parking lamps was used in this model's second year. Another change was a raised hood ornament. The original wheelbase was carried over, but overall length grew an inch. The headlight bezels were squarer. This was the last year for the Monte Carlo SS 454, of which only 1,919 examples were built in 1971. Standard Monte Carlo features included all safety equipment; power front disc brakes; power ventilation system; electric clock; side-guard door beam structure; assist straps; vinyl burled elm finish instrument panel; concealed wipers; 245 horsepower '350' V-8; glove box light and lefthand OSRV mirror.Size G78 x 15 tires were used.

VEHICLE I.D. NUMBERS: The numbering system and code locations were the same as on full-sized Chevrolets, with the first five digits changed to Monte Carlo nomenclature.

MONTE CARLO SERIES

Series Number	Body/Style Number	Body Type & Seating	Factory Price	Shipping Weight	Production Total
138	57	2-dr HT Cpe-5P	3416	3488	112,599

NOTE: The production figure above is the exact model year output and includes 1,919 cars with Monte Carlo SS 454 equipment.

MONTE CARLO ENGINE
See 1971 Chevrolet Series Biscayne/Bel Air/Impala engine data (V-8 only).

1971 Chevelle, Malibu 2-dr hardtop sports coupe, V-8

INTERMEDIATE-SIZED CHEVELLE — (SIX/V-8) — ALL SERIES — The Chevelle models received changes to the front and rear for 1971. A new, twin level grille was divided by a bright, horizontal bar with a Chevrolet 'bow tie' insignia at the middle. The grille inserts were of multiple, horizontal blades segmented by wide-spaced vertical dividers. Single headlamps in square bezels were used. Parking lamps were moved, from the previous bumper location, into the front fenders. There were two parking lamps lenses, set into individual rectangular housings that wrapped around the body corners. The upper lens was amber; the lower lens was white. At the rear, circular taillights were deeply recessed into the bumper. Standard equipment for base editions consisted of Astro-Ventilation; cigarette lighter; side-guard door beam structure; concealed wipers and either the 145 horsepower '250' Six or 200 horsepower '307' V-8. The Malibu convertible also had interior courtesy lamps, while all Malibus featured a glovebox light and left OSRV mirror. Size E78 x 14 tires were used. Equipment included on Nomad, Concours and Greenbriers was comprised of Dual-Action tailgate; concealed storage compartment; cushioned-center steering wheel; flush and dry rocker panels; all-vinyl interior; bias-belted G78 x 14 tires; carpeting; vinyl-coated textured metal cargo floor and side-beam door construction. The Nomad came as a Six or V-8, while the others came V-8 only. Concours and Concours Estates also had Hide-Away wipers; power front disc/rear drum brakes and glove box light. The Estate also included door edge guards and wood-grained exterior paneling, with rear-facing third seats and power tailgate window in nine-passenger jobs.

VEHICLE I.D. NUMBERS: The numbering system and code locations were the same as on Monte Carlos, with the first five digits changed to Chevelle nomenclature.

INTERMEDIATE-SIZED CHEVELLE SERIES

Series Number	Body/Style Number	Body Type & Seating	Factory Price	Shipping Weight	Production Total
NOMAD STATION WAGONS					
131/132	36	4-dr Sta Wag-6P	2997/3097	3632/3746	Note 1

1971 Chevrolet, Chevelle Malibu SS 2-dr hardtop, V-8

Model Number	Model Number	Body Type & Seating	Factory Price	Shipping Weight	Production Total
CHEVELLE (GREENBRIER WAGONS)					
133/134	69	4-dr Sed-6P	2677/2773	3210/3338	Note 2
133/134	37	2-dr HT Cpe-6P	2712/2807	3166/3296	Note 2
134	46	4-dr Sta Wag-9P	3340	3882	Note 1
134	36	4-dr Sta Wag-6P	3228	3820	Note 1
CHEVELLE MALIBU (CONCOURS WAGON)					
135/136	69	4-dr Sed-6P	2851/2947	3250/3380	Note 3
135/136	37	2-dr H.T. Cpe-6P	2885/2980	3212/3342	Note 3
136	39	4-dr HT Sed-6P	3052	3450	Note 3
136	67	2-dr Conv-6P	3260	3390	Note 3/4
136	46	4-dr Sta Wag-9P	3450	3908	Note 1
136	36	4-dr Sta Wag-6P	3337	3864	Note 1
CONCOURS ESTATE WAGON					
138	46	4-dr Sta Wag-9P	3626	3944	Note 1
138	36	4-dr Sta Wag-6P	3514	3892	Note 1

GENERAL NOTE: All model year production figures given below are expressed to the nearest 100 units. No body style breakouts are available, except for convertibles.
NOTE 1: Some 42,300 Chevelle intermediate-sized station wagons were built during the 1971 model year. This includes 2,800 Sixes (all Nomads) and 39,500 V-8s. This includes all Nomad, Greenbrier, Concours and Concours Estate wagons, with no additional breakout by series available at the current time.
NOTE 2: Some 35,600 base Chevelles were built during the 1971 model year. This included 11,500 Sixes and 24,100 V-8s.
NOTE 3: Some 249,300 Chevelle Malibus were built during the 1971 model year. This included 9,100 Sixes and 240,200 V-8s.
NOTE 4: Exactly 5,089 Chevelle Malibu convertibles were built during the 1971 model year. This breakout is included in the rounded-off totals in Note 3 above. All convertibles were V-8s. There is no additional breakout available as to the number of Super Sport convertibles built.
ADDITIONAL NOTE: In rounded-off figures, a total of some 80,000 Chevelles were sold with Super Sport equipment packages. Exactly 19,992 of these cars were Chevelle SS 454s.

CHEVELLE SERIES ENGINES
Inline Six. Overhead valves. Cast iron block. Displacement: 250 cubic inches. Bore and stroke: 3.875 x 3.53 inches. Compression ratio: 8.5:1. Brake horsepower: 145 at 4200 R.P.M. Seven main bearings. hydraulic valve lifters. Carburetor: Rochester one-barrel.

V-8. Overhead valves. Cast iron block. Displacement: 307 cubic inches. Bore and stroke: 3.875 x 3.25 inches. Compression ratio: 8.5:1. Brake horsepower: 200 at 4600 R.P.M. Five main bearings. Hydraulic valve lifters. Carburetor: Rochester two-barrel.

1971 Chevrolet, Nova 2-dr sedan, V-8

NOVA SERIES — (SIX/V-8) — SERIES 113/114 — The disappearance of the Nova Four was one change for the 'senior' compact models. There was also a very slight amount of revision to the grille. It seemed to highlight the vertical elements more than the year before. A vertical molding was also seen in the front fender corner trim panels. Amber plastic parking lamp lenses were new. Simulated fenderside louvers were off the optional equipment list, but many new packages were added. The body was essentially the same design introduced in 1968. Standard features included front arm rests; foot-operated brake; ignition key alarm system; anti-theft steering wheel column lock; heater and defroster and either the '250' Six or '307' V-8. The Nova wore E78 x 14 tires in standard trim.

VEHICLE I.D. NUMBERS: The numbering system and code locations were the same as on Chevelles, with the first symbols changed to Nova nomenclature.

1971 Chevrolet, Nova 2-dr sedan, V-8

NOVA SIX/V-8 SERIES

Series Number	Body/Style Number	Body Type & Seating	Factory Price	Shipping Weight	Production Total
111/113	69	4-dr Sed-6P	2205/2284	2843/2942	Note 1
111/113	27	2-dr Cpe-6P	2176/2254	2820/2919	Note 1

NOTE 1: Exactly 194,878 Novas were built in the 1971 model year. This included exactly 94,928 Sixes and 99,950 V-8s. No additional body style breakouts are available at the current time.
ADDITIONAL NOTE: Exactly 7,015 cars included in the total above were sold with Super Sport equipment packages.

NOVA SERIES ENGINES
See 1971 Chevelle Series engine data.

1971 Chevrolet, 2-dr Vega 2300 notch back sedan, 4-cyl

VEGA 2300 — (FOUR) — SERIES 2300 — The Vega was a completely new sub-compact car from Chevrolet. Three two-door models, notch back sedan, hatch back coupe and kamm back station wagon were offered. Single headlights, round parking lamps and a slightly 'veed' rectangular grille with egg-crate insert characterized the front of the car. A full-width, wraparound bumper ran across the grille. The rear panel had a slightly concave treatment, with twin rectangular taillamps at each side. Three sets of louvers were punched in the deck of the notch back and on the rear quarter of wagons. The hatch back had its louvers at the rear roof pillar. Power came from an aluminum Four with overhead camshaft. A dome-shaped bulge was on the hood of all three styles. A nameplate was placed ahead of the forward hood seam, above the upper lefthand corner of the grille. It read 'Chevrolet Vega 2300'. Standard features included side marker lights and reflectors; functional vent louvers; flush and dry rocker panels; left OSRV mirror; front bucket seats; rear bucket-style bench seats; Flow-Through ventilation; three-speed manual transmission with floor shift control; windshield washers; dual speed wipers; ash tray; all-vinyl upholstery; exhaust emission control system; storage well in driver's door and 80 horsepower Four. The coupe also had hatch back rear deck construction; fold-down back seat; front area carpeting; passenger sliding seat adjustment; cargo area rubber mats and concealed, under floor storage area. Sedans and wagons had front manual disc brakes; the wagon included carpeting and all featured a three-point safety belt system. Size 6.00 x 13 tires were used as standard equipment.

1971 Chevrolet, Vega 2300 2-dr Kammback Wagon, 4-cyl

VEGA 2300 SERIES

Series Number	Body/Style Number	Body Type & Seating	Factory Price	Shipping Weight	Production Total
141	11	2-dr Sed-4P	2090	2146	58,800
141	77	2-dr Cpe-4P	2196	2190	168,300
141	15	2-dr Sta Wag-4P	2328	2230	42,800

NOTE 1:
A total of exactly 2,747 Vegas were built during the 1971 model year. In figures rounded-off to the nearest 100 units, this includes the body style breakouts shown in the chart above, plus 7,800 panel wagons.

VEGA 2300 SERIES ENGINE
Inline OHC-Four. Aluminum block. Displacement: 140 cubic inches. Bore and stroke: 3.501 x 3.625 inches. Compression ratio: 8.0:1. Brake horsepower: 90 at 46-4800 R.P.M. Hydraulic valve lifters. Carburetor: one-barrel.

CAMARO — (SIX/V-8) — SERIES 123/124 — There was hardly any change in the 1971 Camaro. As on other Chevrolets, the grille insert seemed to have a more vertical character, although the design elements remained basically unchanged. Trim details varied according to the options ordered for each car. New options were Brown or Blue vinyl top coverings. Power disc brakes were standard. So was side marker lights; reflectors; defroster; washers and dual speed wipers; inside day/nite mirror; outside rear view mirror; all-vinyl interior; bucket seats; rear bucket style seat cushions; front disc brakes; steel side guard rails; three-speed manual transmission with floor shift; cigarette lighter; carpeting; Astro-Ventilation and either the '250' Six or '307' V-8. Size E78 x 14 tires were standard equipment. The Camaro SS package included dual exhausts; power brakes; lefthand remote-control sport mirror; special ornamentation and hood insulation; F70-14 tires (white-lettered); 14 x 7 inch wheels; black-finished grille; Hide-Away wipers and the 270 horsepower 350 cubic inch V-8 with bright engine accents. Rally Sport equipment included special black-finished grille with rubber-tipped vertical center bar and resilient body-color grille frame; independent front left and righthand bumpers; license plate bracket below right bumper; parking lights with bright accents mounted on grille panel; Hide-Away wipers; bright roof drip, window and hood

1971 Camaro SS 396, 2-dr hardtop sports coupe, V-8

panel moldings; body-color insert on door handles; RS emblem on steering wheel; RS front fender nameplates and bright accented taillights and backup lamps (RS emblems are deleted when Camaro SS or Z/28 package is ordered). The Z/28 package also included special 330 horsepower '350' V-8 with bright engine trim; remote-control lefthand OSRV mirror; special instrumentation; power brakes; 3.73:1 ratio Positraction rear axle; heavy-duty cooling; dual exhausts; black accented grille; Z/28 front fender **emblems; rear bumper guards; sport suspension; rear deck spoiler with Z/28 decal; special paint stripes on hood and rear deck (choice of either black or white stripes, except with vinyl top or roof with black or white paint finish); heavy-duty front and rear springs; 15 x 7 inch wheels with chrome lug nuts; special center hub caps with trim rings and F60-15/B bias-belted white-letter tires.**

VEHICLE I.D. NUMBERS: The numbering system and code locations were the same as on other Chevrolet products, with the first five symbols changed to Camaro nomenclature.

CAMARO SERIES SIX/V-8

Series Number	Body/Style Number	Body Type & Seating	Factory Price	Shipping Weight	Production Total
123/124	87	2-dr HT Cpe-4P	2921/3016	3094/3218	107,496

NOTE: The Camaro production total listed above is an exact figure covering cars built for the domestic market. It includes 18,404 Rally Sports; 8,377 Super Sports; 4,862 Z-28s; 103,452 cars with V-8s: 11,191 Sixes; 13,042 cars with three-speeds; 10,614 cars with four-speeds; 90,987 cars with automatic; 42,537 cars with air-conditioning and 93,163 cars with power steering. In addition, a total of 7,147 cars were built in the U.S. for export market sales.

CAMARO SERIES ENGINES
See 1971 Chevelle Series engine data.

CHASSIS FEATURES: Wheelbase: (Chevrolet wagon) 125 inches; (Chevrolet) 121.5 inches; (Monte Carlo/Chevelle four-door) 116 inches; (Chevelle two-door) 112 inches; (Nova) 111 inches; (Camaro) 108 inches; (Vega) 97 inches. Overall length: (Chevrolet wagon) 224 inches; (Chevrolet) 217 inches; (Monte Carlo/Chevelle wagon) 207 inches; (Chevelle two-door) 198 inches; (Chevelle four-door) 202 inches; (Nova) 190 inches; (Camaro) 188 inches; (Vega) 170 inches. Width: (Chevrolet) 80 inches; (Monte Carlo/Chevelle) 76 inches; (Nova) 73 inches; (Camaro) 75 inches; (Vega) 66 inches. Tires: Refer to text.

POWERTRAIN OPTIONS: Three-speed manual transmission was standard. Automatic transmission. Special three-speed manual floor shift transmission. Four-speed manual floor shift transmission. Wide-ratio four-speed manual transmission with floor shift. Close-ratio four-speed manual transmission with floor shift . Vega Four 140 cubic inch 110 horsepower two-barrel engine. Chevrolet V-8 400 cubic inch 255 horsepower two-barrel engine. Chevrolet V-8 402 cubic inch 300 horsepower four-barrel engine. Chevrolet V-8 454 cubic inch 365 horsepower four-barrel engine. Monte Carlo/Corvette 402 cubic inch 300 horsepower four-barrel engine . Monte Carlo/Chevelle V-8 454 cubic inch 365 horsepower four-barrel engine . Chevelle V-8 350 cubic inch 245 horsepower two-barrel engine. Chevelle V-8 350 cubic inch 270 horsepower four-barrel engine. Nova V-8 350 cubic inch 245 horsepower two-barrel engine. Camaro V-8 350 cubic inch 245 horsepower two-barrel engine. Camaro V-8 350 cubic inch 270 horsepower four-barrel engine . Camaro V-8 350 cubic inch 330 horsepower four-barrel engine. Camaro V-8 402 cubic inch 300 horsepower four-barrel engine.

CONVENIENCE OPTIONS: Vega power steering ($95). Vega air conditioning ($360). Nova vinyl top ($84). Nova power steering ($103). Nova air conditioning ($392). Chevelle vinyl top ($95). Monte Carlo/Camaro/Chevelle air conditioning ($408). Camaro vinyl top ($90). Monte Carlo vinyl top ($126). Chevrolet AM/FM stereo ($239). Chevrolet power windows ($127). Vega GT coupe package ($349). Nova SS package ($328). Chevelle SS package ($357). Malibu SS package ($357). Camaro SS package ($314). Monte Carlo SS 445 package ($485). Camaro RS package ($179).

Historical footnotes: The full-sized Chevrolets were introduced on September 29, 1970 and the Vega appeared in dealer showrooms September 10. Calendar year production of 2,275,694 cars was recorded. John L. DeLorean was the Chief Executive Officer of the company this year. In the high-performance car field, Chevrolet built some 80,000 Chevelle Super Sports; 7,015 Nova Super Sports; 1,919 Monte Carlo SS 454 models and 8,377 Camaro Super Sports. Only 19,292 Chevelle SS models had the 454 cubic inch V-8 installed. Monte Carlos continued to compete and win on the horsepower reduced to 425 due to lower 9.0:1 compression ratio. This compared to 460 horsepower in the late 1970 LS6-equipped Chevelles. Most other Chevrolets were limited to an 8.5:1 maximum compression ratio, to insure adaptability of the new motors to low-lead or no-lead fuel. However, the Camaro Z-28 was another exception. It came with a 9.0:1/350 cubic inch job that produced 330 horsepower.

1972 CHEVROLET

FULL-SIZED CHEVROLET — (SIX/V-8) — ALL SERIES — Chevrolet's standard models continued to get bigger, with a slight increase in passenger car wheelbase as well. The front lip of the hood dipped deeper, creating a slimmer grille above the full-width bumper. However, more of the grille showed through underneath. Parking lamps, while still in the fender extension caps, were smaller. The grille had a finer texture and a Chevrolet insignia was seen at the center of the hood. A lower body feature line was used on the body sides and the upper rear fender edge was somewhat raised. Tires were size G78 x 15/B on Impala/Caprice; F78 x 15/B on Biscayne/Bel Air and H78 x 5 on station wagons. Power brakes, power steering and automatic transmission became standard in all full-sized lines. For this season only, horsepower ratings were expressed in both the traditional way, and the new S.A.E. Net form.

1972 Chevrolet, Caprice 2-dr hardtop coupe, V-8

VEHICLE IDENTIFICATION NUMBERS: The code locations were the same as for previous models with the sixth symbol changed to a '2' to indicate 1972 model year. A change in the Serial Number system was seen. The first symbol remained a '1' to indicate Chevrolet manufacture. The second and third symbols (formerly designating series) were replaced by a single letter, as shown in the second column of the charts below. The third and fourth symbols designated Body Style Number. The fifth symbol designated the type of engine. The sixth symbol designated the model year. The seventh symbol designated assembly plant. The following group of six symbols was the sequential unit production number, beginning at 100001 and up at each plant. The Chevrolet 'Model' Number was now the combination of numbers and letters shown in the first two columns of the charts below.

1972 Chevrolet, Caprice 4-dr hardtop sedan, V-8

FULL-SIZED CHEVROLET SERIES K-L-M-N

Series Number	Body/Style Number	Body Type & Seating	Factory Price	Shipping Weight	Production Total
BISCAYNE (BROOKWOOD STATION WAGON)					
1K	69	4-dr Sed-6P	3074/3408	3857/4045	Note 1
1K	35	4-dr Sta Wag-6P	3882	4686	Note 2
BEL AIR (TOWNSMAN STATION WAGON)					
1L	69	4-dr Sed-6P	3204/3538	3854/4042	Note 3
1L	45	4-dr Sta Wag-9P	4078	4769	Note 2
1L	35	4-dr Sta Wag-6P	3969	4687	Note 2
IMPALA (KINGSWOOD STATION WAGONS)					
1M	69	4-dr Sed-6P	3369/3704	3928/4113	Note 4
1M	57	2-dr HT Cpe-6P	3385/3720	3864/4049	Note 4
1M	39	4-dr HT Sed-6P	3771	4150	Note 4
1M	47	2-dr Cus Cpe-6P	3787	4053	Note 4
1M	67	2-dr Conv-6P	3979	4125	Notes 4/5
1M	45	4-dr Sta Wag-9P	4165	4817	Note 2
1M	35	4-dr Sta Wag-6P	4056	4734	Note 2
CAPRICE (KINGSWOOD ESTATE WAGON)					
1N	69	4-dr Sed-6P	4009	NA	Note 6
1N	47	2-dr Cus Cpe-6P	4026	4102	Note 6
1N	45	4-dr Sta Wag-9P	4423	4883	Note 2
1N	35	4-dr Sta Wag-6P	4314	4798	Note 2

1972 Chevrolet, Impala 2-dr convertible, V-8

1972 Chevrolet, Impala Custom Coupe 2-dr hardtop, V-8

GENERAL NOTE: Unless otherwise noted, all model year production totals given in the 1972 Chevrolet section are expressed in figures rounded-off to the nearest 100 units and are series production totals with no body style breakouts available.
NOTE 2: Production of Brookwood/Townsman/Kingswood and Estate wagons was counted as a lumped sum and included 171,700 units, all of which were V-8 powered. No breakout by trim level is available at this time.
NOTE 1: Some 20,500 Biscayne passenger cars were built during the 1972 model year, including 1,500 Sixes and 19,000 V-8s.
NOTE 3: Some 41,900 Bel Air passenger cars were built during the 1972 model year, including 900 Sixes and 41,000 V-8s.
NOTE 4: Some 597,500 Impala passenger cars were built during the 1972 model year, including 1,500 Sixes and 596,000 V-8s.
NOTE 5: Exactly 6,456 Impala convertibles were built during the 1972 model year. This breakout is included in the rounded-off totals in Note 3 above. All convertibles were V-8s.
NOTE 6: Some 178,500 Caprice passenger cars were built during the 1972 model year. All were V-8s.
ADDITIONAL NOTES: In all specifications charts in this section the prices and weights above slash are for Sixes/below slash for V-8s. This system is used for all 1972 Chevrolets products listings in the Catalog. Beginning in 1972, Chevrolet Sixes and V-8s used the same alpha-numerical Series Code and the fifth symbol in the Serial Number then designated engine type.

1972 Chevrolet, Caprice Estate 4-dr station wagon, V-8

FULL-SIZE CHEVROLET ENGINES
Inline Six. Overhead valves. Cast iron block. Displacement: 250 cubic inches. Bore and stroke: 3.875 x 3.53 inches. SAE Net horsepower: 110. Seven main bearings. Hydraulic valve lifters. Carburetor: one-barrel.

V-8 (BISCAYNE/BEL AIR/IMPALA)
V-8. Overhead valves. Cast iron block. Displacement: 350 cubic inches. Bore and stroke: 4.00 x 3.48 inches. SAE Net horsepower: 165. Five main bearings. Hydraulic valve lifters.

V-8 (CAPRICE/ALL STATION WAGONS)
V-8. Overhead valves. Cast iron block. Displacement: 400 cubic inches. Bore and stroke: 4.126 x 3.75 inces. SAE Net horsepower: 170. Five main bearings. Hydraulic valve lifters. Carburetor: two-barrel.

MONTE CARLO — (V-8) — SERIES 1H — The new Monte Carlo grille covered the entire area between the square-bezeled headlamps. It had horizontal blades divided by prominent vertical blades. Parking lamps were moved from the bumper and were vertically positioned at the outboard grille segments. It was the last season for the original Monte Carlo body style. Standard equipment tires were size G78 x 15/B blackwalls.

VEHICLE I.D. NUMBERS: The numbering system and code locations were the same as on full-sized Chevrolets, with the first four symbols changed to Monte Carlo nomenclature. Sequential unit production numbers for Monte Carlos (and Chevelles) began at 400001 at each factory.

MONTE CARLO SERIES H

Series Number	Body/Style Number	Body Type & Seating	Factory Price	Shipping Weight	Production Total
1H	57	2-dr HT Cpe-6P	3362	3506	180,819

NOTE: The production total above is an exact model year figure.

MONTE CARLO ENGINE
See 1972 Chevrolet Biscayne/Bel Air/Impala V-8 engine data.

1972 Chevelle, Malibu 2-dr hardtop sports coupe, V-8

INTERMEDIATE-SIZED CHEVELLE — (SIX/V-8) — ALL SERIES — Changes to the Chevelle were of a minor nature. The grille had a new texture and was divided, horizontally, by two even-spaced moldings giving a three-tier look. Parking lamps were still found in the fender cap, but now had a larger, one piece plastic lens of square shape. It wrapped around the body corner, serving double duty as a side marker lamp. A new molding treatment, with some trim levels, included a stainless steel spear, at mid-body height, that ran only between the front and rear wheel openings. Tires for base models were size E78 x 14/B blackwalls. Station wagons had G78 x 14/B tires. Chevelle V-8s built for California sale were equipped with the 350 cubic inch engine in 165 or 175 horsepower form. Federal cars had either the '250' Six or the '307' two-barrel V-8.

VEHICLE I.D. NUMBERS: The numbering system and code locations were the same as on Monte Carlos, with the first four symbols changed to Chevelle nomenclature.

INTERMEDIATE-SIZED CHEVELLE SERIES B-C-D-H

Series Number	Body/Style Number	Body Type & Seating	Factory Price	Shipping Weight	Production Total
NOMAD STATION WAGON					
1B	36	4-dr Sta Wag-6P	2926/3016	3605/3732	Note 1
CHEVELLE (GREENBRIER STATION WAGON)					
1C	69	4-dr Sed-6P	2636/2726	3204/3332	Note 2
1C	37	2-dr HT Cpe-6P	2669/2759	3172/3300	Note 2
1C	46	4-dr Sta Wag-9P	3247	3870	Note 1
1C	36	4-dr Sta Wag-6P	3140	3814	Note 1

1972 Chevrolet, Chevelle Malibu 2-dr hardtop, V-8

Model Number	Model Number	Body Type & Seating	Factory Price	Shipping Weight	Production Total
MALIBU (CONCOURS STATION WAGONS)					
1D	69	4-dr Sed-6P	2801/2891	3240/3371	Note 3
1D	39	4-dr HT Sed-6P	2991	3438	Note 3
1D	37	2-dr HT Cpe-6P	2833/2923	3194/3327	Note 3
1D	67	2-dr Conv-6P	3187	3379	Notes 3/4
1D	46	4-dr Sta Wag-9P	3351	3909	Note 1
1D	36	4-dr Sta Wag-6P	3244	3857	Note 1
CONCOURS ESTATE WAGON					
1H	46	4-dr Sta Wag-9P	3588	3943	Note 1
1H	36	4-dr Sta Wag-6P	3431	3887	Note 1

NOTE 1: A total of some 54,400 Chevelle intermediate-sized station wagons were built during the 1972 model run, including 3,000 Sixes and 51,400 V-8s. This includes all Greenbrier, Concours and Concours Estate wagons, with no further breakout by trim level.
NOTE 2: Some 49,400 standard Chevelle passenger cars were built during the 1972 model year, including 13,800 Sixes and 35,600 V-8s.
NOTE 3: Some 290,100 Chevelle Malibus were built during the 1972 model year, including 8,400 Sixes and 281,700 V-8s.
NOTE 4: Exactly 4,853 Malibu convertibles were built during the 1972 model year. This breakout is included in the rounded-off totals in Note 3 above. All convertibles were V-8s. There is no additional breakout available as to the number of Super Sport convertibles built.
ADDITIONAL NOTE: Exactly 24,946 of the Chevelles included in the rounded-off figures above were sold with Super Sport equipment packages. A total of 3,000 of these cars were also Chevelle SS-454s.

CHEVELLE SERIES ENGINES
Six. See 1972 Chevrolet Series six-cylinder engine data.
Federal V-8. See 1972 Nova Series V-8 engine data.
California V-8. See 1972 Chevrolet Series V-8 engine data.

1972 Chevrolet, Nova 2-dr sedan, V-8

NOVA — (SIX/V-8) — SERIES X — The Nova was carried over from 1971 without any obvious change, except for an indented license plate housing on the front bumper. If closely examined, a slight change in the bevel of the hood could be seen. There were numerous decor packages available to create anything from a hot rod to personal/luxury car look. However, the true high-performance hardware was no longer provided above, or under, the parts counter. Base engines in all states were the '250' Six or '307' V-8. A 245 horsepower '350' V-8 was optional. Regular tires were E78 x 14/B blackwalls.

VEHICLE I.D. NUMBERS: The numbering system and code locations were the same as on Chevelles, with the first four digits changed to Nova nomenclature.

1972 Chevrolet, Nova 2-dr sedan, V-8

NOVA SERIES X

Series Number	Body/Style Number	Body Type & Seating	Factory Price	Shipping Weight	Production Total
1X	69	4-dr Sed-6P	2405/2501	2976/3108	Note 1
1X	27	2-dr Cpe-6P	2376/2471	2952/3084	Note 1

NOTE 1: Exactly 349,733 Novas were built during the 1972 model year. In exact figures this included 139,769 Sixes and 209,964 V-8s. No additional breakouts by body style are available.
ADDITIONAL NOTE: Exactly 12,309 of these cars were sold with Nova SS equipment packages.

NOVA ENGINES
Six. See 1972 Chevrolet Series six-cylinder engine data.

V-8. Overhead valves. Cast iron block. Displacement: 307 cubic inches. Bore and stroke: 3.875 x 3.25 inches. Brake horsepower: 200. Five main bearings. Hydraulic valve lifters. Carburetor: two-barrel.

1972 Chevrolet, Vega 2300 2-dr coupe, 4-cyl

VEGA 2300 — (FOUR) — SERIES 1V — The grille on the Vega was finished in a manner that made its vertical elements slightly less prominent. A model identification emblem was positioned on the side of the cowl. A change to AZ8 x 13 tires was made for standard equipment. Otherwise, there was very little difference from 1971.

1972 Chevrolet, Vega 2-dr coupe, 4-cyl

VEHICLE I.D. NUMBERS: The numbering system and code locations were the same as on Novas, with the first four symbols changed to Vega nomenclature.

VEGA 2300 SERIES 1V

Series Number	Body/Style Number	Body Type & Seating	Factory Price	Shipping Weight	Production Total
1V	11	2-dr Sed-4P	2060	2158	55,800
1V	77	2-dr Cpe-4P	2160	2294	262,700
1V	15	2-dr Sta Wag-4P	2285	2333	72,000

NOTE: The exact model year output of Vegas was 394,592 units, which included 4,114 panel express trucks. The figures in the chart above are body style breakouts rounded-off to the nearest 100 units.

VEGA 2300 SERIES ENGINE
Inline Four. Overhead valves. Cast aluminum block. Displacement: 140 cubic inches. Bore and stroke: 3.50 x 3.625 inches. Brake horsepower 80. Carburetor: one-barrel.

1972 Camaro SS, 2-dr hardtop sport coupe, V-8

CAMARO — (SIX/V-8) — SERIES Q — The Camaro, for 1972, had a slightly different grille mesh and new high-back bucket seats. The fate of the car was said to be in danger, since a strike at the Camaro assembly plant (Lordstown, Ohio) turned into a disaster. The walkout stranded thousands of bodies on the assembly line and, by the time it was over, these cars were unfit for sale under new Federal safety standards. General Motors was forced to scrap the bodies and almost decided to do the same with the Camaro/Firebird program. Chevrolet engineer, Alex Mair, fought successfully for survival of the nameplate, which later went on to much greater achievements in sales. Camaros wore E78 x 14 tires, in standard trim and base engine selections were the same as in Chevelles, with different V-8s used for Federal and California cars.

VEHICLE I.D. NUMBERS: The numbering system and code locations were the same as on Vegas, with the first four symbols changed to Camaro nomenclature.

CAMARO SERIES Q

Series Number	Body/Style Number	Body Type & Seating	Factory Price	Shipping Weight	Production Total
1Q	87	2-dr HT Cpe-4P	2730/2820	3121/3248	68.656

NOTE: The Camaro production total listed above is an exact figure covering cars built for the domestic market. It includes 11,364 Rally Sports; 6,562 Super Sports; 2,575 Camaro Z28s; 63,832 cars with V-8s; 4,824 cars with Sixes, 6,053 cars with three speeds; 5,835 cars with four-speed; 56,768 cars with automatics, 31,737 cars with air conditioning and 59,857 cars with power steering. In addition, a total of 3,698 cars were built in the U.S. for export sales.

1972 Chevrolet, Camaro 2-dr sports coupe, V-8

CAMARO SERIES ENGINES
See 1972 Chevelle Series engine data.

CHASSIS FEATURES: Wheelbase: (Chevrolet passenger) 122 inches; (all other models) same as 1971. Overall length: (Chevrolet wagon) 226 inches; (Chevrolet) 220 inches; (all other models) same as 1971. Tires: (all models) Refer to text.

POWERTRAIN OPTIONS: Three-speed manual transmission was standard on all Sixes and non-full-sized lines. Automatic transmission was standard on full-sized V-8s. Overdrive transmisson. Automatic transmission. Three-speed manual floor shift transmission. Four-speed manual floor shift transmission. Wide-ratio four-speed manual transmission with floor shift. Close-ratio four-speed manual transmission with floor shift. Vega four-cylinder 140 cubic inch 90 horsepower two-barrel engine. Chevrolet V-8 350 cubic inch 255 horsepower four-barrel engine ($168). Chevrolet V-8 400 cubic inch 170 horsepower four-barrel engine. Chevrolet V-8 402 cubic inch 210 horsepower four-barrel engine. Chevrolet V-8 454 cubic inch 270 horsepower four-barrel engine. Monte Carlo V-8 350 cubic inch 175 horsepower two-barrel dual-exhaust. Monte Carlo V-8 402 cubic inch 240 horsepower four-barrel engine ($142). Monte Carlo V-8 454 cubic inch 270 horsepower four-barrel engine ($261). V-8 cubic inch horsepower four-barrel engine. Chevelle V-8 350 cubic inch 165 horsepower two-barrel engine. Chevelle V-8 350 cubic inch 175 horsepower two-barrel dual exhaust. Chevelle V-8 402 cubic inch 240 horsepower four-barrel engine ($168). Chevelle V-8 454 cubic inch 270 horsepower four-barrel engine ($272). Nova V-8 350 cubic inch 165 horsepower two-barrel engine. Camaro V-8 350 cubic inch 165 horsepower two-barrel engine. Camaro V-8 350 cubic inch 200 horsepower four-barrel engine. Camaro V-8 350 cubic inch 255 horsepower high-output engine. Camaro V-8 402 cubic inch 240 horsepower four-barrel engine.

CONVENIENCE OPTIONS: Vega power steering ($92). Vega air conditioning ($349). Nova vinyl top ($82). Nova power steering ($100). Nova air conditioning ($381). Nova Super Sport Package ($320). Chevelle vinyl top ($92). Monte Carlo/Chevelle air conditioning ($397). Chevelle SS Package ($350). Chevrolet/Monte Carlo/Chevelle AM/FM stereo ($233). Chevrolet/Monte Carlo/Chevelle AM/FM Stereo with tape ($363). Camaro vinyl top ($87). Camaro air conditioning ($397). Camaro SS Package ($306). Camaro RS Package ($118). Monte Carlo vinyl top ($123). Monte Carlo Custom trim ($350). Chevrolet vinyl top ($106). Chevrolet air conditioning ($405). Chevrolet power windows ($113). Vega GT Package ($339). Camaro Z28 Special Performance option ($598).

Historical footnotes: The full-sized Chevrolets were introduced on September 23, 1971 and the other models appeared in dealer showrooms at the same time. Calendar year production of 2,252,892 cars was recorded. Sales of models covered here, by U.S. franchised dealers in calendar 1973, peaked at 2,300,812 cars. This figure excludes Corvettes and Sports Vans, which Chevrolet Motor Division normally accounted with auto production. F. James McDonald was the Chief Executive Officer of the company this year.

1973 CHEVROLET

1973 Chevrolet, Caprice 2-dr Custom Coupe, V-8

FULL-SIZED CHEVROLET — (SIX/V-8) — ALL SERIES — New styling, front and rear, characterized 1973 Chevrolet model offerings made up of Bel Airs, Impalas, Caprice Classics and three station wagon lines. A wider, bolder grille design was featured. On Caprice Classics, the grille had an open grid texture and a Caprice medallion was placed at the center of the hood lip. Grilles on other Series had additional vertical bars and a Chevrolet 'bow tie' badge at the grille center, instead of the hood medallion. On all cars, the upper grille border was at a level even with the top of the headlamp surrounds. The front lamp treatment used dual, round lenses housed in side-by-side square bezels. Parking lamps were moved from the fender extension caps, into the bumper, which was a new hydraulically-cushioned, energy-absorbing type. The rear bumper panel slanted forward and housed rectangular lamps. Following the pattern established in 1958, the higher-priced models had triple taillamps, while Biscaynes and Bel Airs had a dual lens design. All station wagons had single-unit taillights in the fenders and Dual-Action tailgate construction. At the front of all models, the license plate housing was moved to the center of the bumper, instead of to one side. The only full-sized convertible remaining was in the Caprice Classic lineup. Power steering and power front disc brakes were standard equipment. All V-8 models included automatic transmission at base price. A new, 22 gallon fuel tank provided a longer cruising range. The first cars of the year were assembled August 7, 1972. With the discontinuance of the Biscayne, the Bel Air became the low-priced Chevrolet and the only model available with the 250 cubic inch Six. A 145 horsepower 350 cubic inch V-8 was base powerplant in the Bel Air station wagon and all Impalas. The 400 cubic inch V-8, now rated at 150 SAE Net horsepower, was standard in all Caprice Classics and Caprice Estate wagons. The station wagons no longer used distinctive nameplates, such as Brookwood or Kingswood. Standard sized tires were G78-15B on Bel Air; H78-15B on Bel Air station wagons and L78-15B on Impala coupes/Caprice/Estate and Impala station wagons.

VEHICLE IDENTIFICATION NUMBERS: The numbering system and code locations were the same as for previous models with the sixth symbol changed to '3' to indicate 1973 model year. The first symbol '1' designated Chevrolet products. The second symbol designed series. The third and fourth symbols designated Body Style Number. The fifth symbol designated engine type. The sixth symbol designated model year. The seventh symbol designated assembly plant. The following group of symbols was the sequential unit production number, beginning with 100001 at each plant. The Chevrolet Model Number was the combination of the first four symbols.

1973 Chevrolet, Caprice Classic 2-dr convertible, V-8

FULL-SIZED CHEVROLET SERIES

Series Number	Body/Style Number	Body Type & Seating	Factory Price	Shipping Weight	Production Total
BEL AIR SERIES					
1K	69	4-dr Sed-6P	3247/3595	3895/4087	Note 1
1K	45	4-dr Sta Wag-9P	4136	4770	Note 1
1K	35	4-dr Sta Wag-6P	4022	4717	Note 1
IMPALA SERIES					
1L	69	4-dr Sed-6P	3752	4138	Note 1
1L	39	4-dr HT Sed-6P	3822	4162	Note 1
1L	57	2-dr Spt Cpe-6P	3769	4096	Note 1
1L	47	2-dr Cus Cpe-6P	3836	4110	Note 1
1L	45	4-dr Sta Wag-9P	4233	4807	Note 1
1L	35	4-dr Sta Wag-6P	4119	4742	Note 1
CAPRICE CLASSIC SERIES					
1N	69	4-dr Sed-6P	4064	4176	Note 1
1N	39	4-dr HT Sed-6P	4134	4208	Note 1
1N	47	2-dr Cus Cpe-6P	4082	4143	Note 1
1N	67	2-dr Conv-6P	4345	4191	Notes 1/2
1N	45	4-dr Sta Wag-9P	4496	4858	Note 1
1N	35	4-dr Sta Wag-6P	3282	4779	Note 1

NOTE 1: Domestic model year production of all full-sized Chevrolets totaled 941,104 units. Due to the effects of a new trade agreement between the two countries, some cars for the Canadian market may have been built in the United States, while some cars for the U.S. market may have been built in Canada. No body style breakouts, except for convertibles, are available at the current time.
NOTE 2: Exactly 7,339 Caprice Classic convertibles were built in the 1973 model run. This breakout is included in the total model year production figure given in Note 1.
ADDITIONAL NOTES: The Bel Air sedan was the only 1973 Chevrolet available with a six-cylinder engine. For this model the prices and weights above slash are for Six/below slash for V-8s.

FULL-SIZED SERIES ENGINES

BEL AIR SIX
Inline Six. Cast iron block. Displacement: 250 cubic inches. Bore and stroke: 3.875 x 3.53 inches. Compression ratio: 8.25:1. SAE Net horsepower: 100 at 3600 R.P.M. Seven main bearings. Hydraulic valve lifters. Carburetor: one-barrel.

BEL AIR/IMPALA V-8
V-8. Overhead valves. Cast iron block. Displacement: 350 cubic inches. Bore and stroke: 4.00 x 3.48 inches. Compression ratio: 8.5:1. SAE Net horsepower: 145 at 4000 R.P.M. Five main bearings. Hydraulic valve lifters. Carburetor: two-barrel.

CAPRICE V-8
V-8. Overhead valves. Cast iron block. Displacement: 400 cubic inches. Bore and stroke: 4.126 x 3.75 inches. Compression ratio: 8.5:1. SAE Net horsepower: 150 at 3200 R.P.M. Five main bearings. Hydraulic valve lifters. Carburetor: two-barrel.

1973 Chevrolet, Monte Carlo 2-dr hardtop coupe, V-8

MONTE CARLO — (V-8) — SERIES 1H — The 1973 Monte Carlo saw extensive styling changes. It was four inches longer and had a heavily sculptured look with new rear quarter sheetmetal. The upper grille border was lowered and the front lip of the hood extended down to meet it. Parking lamps were placed, vertically, in the front fender ends. The grille insert had a neat, cross-hatched texture. There was a badge at its center, plus a script on the left side of the hood. A wide, 'U' shaped guard was built into the new front bumper, which was re-engineered to conform with Federal standards. Headlights were round units set into circular housings, which blended in the rounded upper fender contour. The outer fender surface swooped in a radical curve, to the middle of the door. The rear fenderline had a prominent kick-up, with extra crisp sculpturing seen here as well. A V-shaped rear window was used and opera window treatments were optional. At the back, the fenders tapered to a crisply shaped tail, which was highlighted by a U-shaped panel that curved upwards around the trapezoidal taillamps (which were accented with multiple horizontal moldings). Backup lights were incorporated into the bumper again. The Monte Carlo was now offered in three basic levels of trim, with countless options packages available. There was the base Monte Carlo, the 'S' Series and the Landau. The latter model featured wide lower body accents and bright wheel lip moldings. Standard equipment included power disc front brakes, power steering and automatic transmission. The base engine was the same '350' V-8 used in Impalas. Regular tires were G78 x 15 blackwalls.

VEHICLE I.D. NUMBERS: The numbering system and code locations were the same as on Chevrolets, with the first four symbols changed to Monte Carlo nomenclature. Sequential numbers for Monte Carlos (and Chevelles) began with 400001 at each assembly plant.

MONTE CARLO SERIES

Series Number	Body/Style Number	Body Type & Seating	Factory Price	Shipping Weight	Production Total
MONTE CARLO					
1H	57	2-dr HT Cpe-5P	3415	3713	Note 1
MONTE CARLO 'S'					
1H	57	2-dr HT Cpe-5P	3562	3720	Note 1
MONTE CARLO LANDAU					
1H	57	2-dr HT Cpe-5P	3806	3722	Note 1

NOTE 1: Exactly 233,689 Monte Carlos were built in the 1973 model year. No breakouts by trim level or engine are available at the current time.

MONTE CARLO SERIES ENGINE
See 1973 Chevrolet Bel Air/Impala Series engine data.

1973 Chevelle, 2-dr Laguna Colonnade coupe, V-8

CHEVELLE INTERMEDIATES — (SIX/V-8) — ALL SERIES — Totally new 'Colonnade hardtop' styling was seen on 1973 Chevelles. Primarily a safety advance engineered to meet new Federal roll-over standards, this innovative design consisted of a body with inner and outer shells; side guard door beam construction and improved fuel tank isolation. Extremely heavy roof pillars and a side window treatment similar to that used in building limousines, created a car that looked like a hardtop, but was really not. The 'Colonnade' look was great on coupes and sedans, but seemed somewhat awkward for station wagons. General styling highlights included cross-hatched grilles (with a very flat look) that continued below the single headlights with extremely narrow extensions. Bodysides were quite plain, with Malibus wearing rocker panel moldings. All models carried their nameplates at the left of the grille and on the fenders, in back of the front wheel opening. New energy-absorbing front bumpers incorporated retangular parking lights at the outer ends. Taillamps were circular units, recessed into a back panel that was 'veed', horizontally, along its full-width centerline. The top-of-the line entry was the Laguna, with a special die-cast grille accented with double horizontal moldings and circular rally lights. It had a racy, European flavor. The Chevelle convertible was discontinued. Each of three Series — Chevelle DeLuxe,Malibu and Laguna — included Colonnade coupe, sedan and station wagons. Base powerplants in the DeLuxe and Malibu lines were eight the '250' Six, or the '307' V-8. Laguna offerings started with the '350' V-8 under the hood, but the top option, the '454' V-8, was down to a 245 Net horsepower rating. Tire sizes varied by model: E78-14 on most passenger cars; G78-14 on most wagons and Lagunas and H78-14 on the Laguna Estate.

VEHICLE I.D. NUMBERS: The numbering system and code locations were the same as on Monte Carlos, with the first four symbols changed to Chevelle nomenclature.

CHEVELLE SERIES

Series Number	Body/Style Number	Body Type & Seating	Factory Price	Shipping Weight	Production Total
DELUXE SERIES					
1C	29	4-dr Col Sed-6P	2719/2835	3435/3585	Note 1
1C	37	2-dr Col Cpe-6P	2743/2860	3423/3580	Note 1
1C	35	4-dr Sta Wag-8P	3331	4054	Note 1
1C	35	4-dr Sta Wag-6P	3106/3198	3849/4006	Note 1
MALIBU SERIES					
1D	29	4-dr Col Sed-6P	2871/2987	3477/3627	Note 1
1D	37	2-dr Col Cpe-6P	2894/3010	3430/3580	Note 1
1D	35	4-dr Sta Wag-8P	3423	4075	Note 1
1D	35	4-dr Sta Wag-6P	3290	4027	Note 1
MALIBU ESTATE					
1G	35	4-dr Sta Wag-8P	3608	4080	Note 1
1G	35	4-dr Sta Wag-6P	3475	4032	Note 1
LAGUNA SERIES					
1E	29	4-dr Col Sed-6P	3179	3627	Note 1
1E	37	2-dr Col Cpe-6P	3203	3678	Note 1
1E	35	4-dr Sta Wag-8P	3616	4158	Note 1
1E	35	4-dr Sta Wag-6P	3483	4110	Note 1
LAGUNA ESTATE					
1H	35	4-dr Sta Wag-8P	3795	4189	Note 1
1H	35	4-dr Sta Wag-6P	3662	4141	Note 1

NOTE 1: Exactly 328,533 Chevelles were built in the 1973 model year. No breakouts by body style, trim level or engine are available at the current time.
ADDITIONAL NOTES: A total of exactly 28,647 Chevelle SS 396 option packages were installed on the above cars. Approximately 2,500 Chevelle SS 454 packages were also installed on the above cars.

CHEVELLE
SIX
See 1975 Chevrolet Series Bel Air Six engine data.

V-8 (DELUXE/MALIBU)
V-8. Overhead valves. Cast iron block. Displacement: 306 cubic inches. Bore and stroke: 3.87 x 3.25 inches. Compression ratio: 8.5:1. SAE Net horsepower: 115 at 3600 R.P.M. Five main bearings. Hydraulic valve lifters. Carburetor: two-barrel.

V-8 (LAGUNA/ESTATE)
See 1975 Chevrolet Bel Air/Impala V-8 engine data.

1973 Chevrolet, Nova 2-dr hatch back coupe, V-8

NOVA — (SIX/V-8) — ALL SERIES — The Nova was 'customized' this season, but could still be purchased in standard trim, too. The new Nova Custom Series was simply a bit richer inside and out. General appearance changes were 'hatched' out of a program that emphasized refinements, instead of major revamps. One change, in fact,was a hatch back coupe with an easily lifted, counter-balanced panel that flipped-up to give rear compartment access. Side guard beam door construction; flow-through ventilation; improved sound deadening and a 21-gallon fuel tank were standard equipment revisions. A new grille design featured a more open cross-hatch texture and built-in parking lights. Dual, rectangular taillight treatments were seen, on each side at the rear. A heftier, safer bumper protected both ends of the car, with the rear unit having a new center dip and both using black vinyl impact strips. The Nova nameplate was above the left side of the grille. Attractive half-vinyl tops made the options list. Base engines were the '250' Six or '307' V-8. Standard tires were E78-14 blackwalls.

VEHICLE I.D. NUMBERS: The numbering system and code locations were the same as on Chevelles, with the first four symbols changed to Nova nomenclature.

NOVA SERIES

Series Number	Body/Style Number	Body Type & Seating	Factory Price	Shipping Weight	Production Total
NOVA					
1X	69	4-dr Sed-6P	2407/2497	3065/3194	Note 1
1X	27	2-dr Cpe-6P	2377/2467	3033/3162	Note 1
1X	17	2-dr Hatch-6P	2528/2618	3145/3274	Note 1
NOVA CUSTOM					
1Y	69	4-dr Sed-6P	2580/2671	3105/3234	Note 1
1Y	27	2-dr Cpe-6P	2551/2641	3073/3203	Note 1
1Y	17	2-dr Hatch-6P	2701/2791	3152/3281	Note 1

NOTE 1: Exactly 369,511 Novas were built in the 1973 model year. No breakouts by body style, trim level or engine are available at the current time.
ADDITIONAL NOTES: A total of exactly 35,542 Nova Super Sports were built for the 1973 model year.

NOVA ENGINES
See 1973 Chevelle Series engine data.

1973 Chevrolet, Vega 2300 2-dr sedan, 4-cyl

VEGA — FOUR — The 1973 Vega had a new front bumper with stronger mountings. It provided better protection for the carry over sheetmetal. The nameplate was changed to read 'Vega by Chevrolet' with the '2300' engine size call-out being dropped. Unaccustomed to using cubic centimeter measurements for engine displacement, American buyers had trouble relating to the meaning of the original nomenclature. New, Chevrolet-built three and four-speed transmissions, with improved shift linkages and a better emissions control system were featured in the third generation Vega. Using the new SAE system, the base, one-barrel Four was rated at just 72 horsepower; the optional, two-barrel engine at 85. The standard tire size was, again, A78-13. Vega's new grille had a handsome, egg crate texture.

1973 Chevrolet, Vega 2-dr Kammback GT station wagon, 4-cyl

VEHICLE I.D. NUMBERS: The numbering system and code locations were the same as on Nova, with the first four symbols changed to Vega nomenclature.

VEGA SERIES

Series Number	Body/Style Number	Body Type & Seating	Factory Price	Shipping Weight	Production Total
1V	11	2-dr Notch-4P	2087	2219	Note 1
1V	77	2-dr Hatch-4P	2192	2313	Note 1
1V	15	2-dr Sta Wag-4P	2323	2327	Note 1

NOTE 1: Exactly 395,792 Vegas were built during the 1973 model year. No breakout as to body style is available at the current time. All Vegas utilized four-cylinder engines.

VEGA SERIES ENGINE
Inline Four. Overhead camshaft. Aluminum block. Displacement: 140 cubic inches. Bore and stroke: 3.501 x 3.625 inches. Compression ratio: 8.0:1. Brake horsepower: 72 at 4400 R.P.M. Hydraulic valve lifters. Carburetor: one-barrel.

1973 Chevrolet, Camaro 2-dr sports coupe, V-8

CAMARO — (SIX/V-8) — SERIES 1Q — The 1973 Camaro had very few changes from the previous style. The texture of the grille insert was modified by using slightly heavier, deeper moldings and reducing the number of vertical moldings from 12 to seven. Those trim packages featuring a full-width front bumper bar had new, black rubber faced guards. They protruded both above and below the bumper, housing the license plate at the bottom, center. Fifteen new colors were available, a new soft-rim steering wheel with four spokes was used and the rear seats received a bit more foam padding. A new decor treatment was the 'luxuring touring' Camaro LT package, which included rocker panel accents; dual outside rearview mirrors; Hide-Away wipers; full instrumentation (with tachometer); 14 x 7 inch Rally wheel rims and extra sound-deadening insulation. A new option was a set of Turbine I wheels, for all models except those with the Z/28 package. Air conditioning was, however, available for the first time with Z/28 'special performance' equipment. Base Camaro engines were the '250' Six or '307' V-8 and E78 x 14 tires were used. Standard in Z/28s was a hydraulic lifter '350' V-8 with a new low-restriction air cleaner and 245 SAE Net horsepower.

VEHICLE IDENTIFICATION NUMBERS: The numbering system and code locations were the same as for Vegas with the first four symbols changed to Camaro nomenclature.

1973 Camaro, 2-dr LT hardtop sports coupe, V-8

CAMARO SERIES

Series Number	Body/Style Number	Body Type & Seating	Factory Price	Shipping Weight	Production Total
BASE LEVEL					
1Q	87	2-dr Spt Cpe-4P	2781/2872	3119/3238	Note 1
LT LEVEL					
1S	87	2-dr Spt Cpe-4P	3268	3349	Note 1

NOTE 1: Exactly 89,988 Camaros were built in the United States, for domestic market sales, during the 1973 model year. This total includes 16,133 cars with Rally Sport equipment; 11,574 cars with the Z/28 package; 93,138 V-8s; 3,618 Sixes; 5,964 cars with three-speeds; 11,388 with four-speeds; 79,404 with automatics; 49,504 with air conditioning; 96,752 with power steering 217 with power windows and 6,768 cars made in the U.S. for export markets. The Camaro SS package was discontinued and the number of Camaro LT equipped cars is not available at the current time.

CAMARO SERIES ENGINES
See 1975 Chevelle Series engine data for base Six and V-8 specifications.

CHASSIS FEATURES: Wheelbase: (Chevrolet wagon) 125 inches; (Chevrolet) 121.5 inches; (Monte Carlo/Chevelle four-door) 116 inches; (Chevelle two-door) 112 inches; (Nova) 111 inches (Vega) 97 inches; (Camaro) 108 inches. Overall length: (Chevelle wagon) 229 inches; (Chevrolet) 223 inches; (Monte Carlo) 211 inches; (Chevelle four-door) 207 inches; (Chevelle two-door) 203 inches; (Chevelle wagon) 214 inches; (Nova) 195 inches; (Vega) 173 inches; (Camaro) 189 inches. Width: (Chevrolet) 80 inches; (Monte Carlo) 78 inches; (Chevelles) 77 inches; (Novas) 73 inches; (Vega) 66 inches; (Camaro) 75 inches. Tires: Refer to text.

POWERTRAIN OPTIONS: Three-speed manual transmission was standard in Vega/Nova/Chevrolet/Chevelle/Monte Carlo and Camaro with Fours or Sixes. Automatic transmission was standard in Chevrolet V-8s and Camaro LTs and was, also a no-cost option in the Z/28. Automatic transmission was optional, except in above models. Four-speed manual floor shift transmission was optional in Vega/Nova/Monte Carlo/Chevelle/Camaro. Vega four-cylinder 140 cubic inch 85 horsepower two-barrel engine ($41 *). Chevrolet V-8 350 cubic inch 175 horsepower four-barrel engine. Chevrolet V-8 400 cubic inch 150 horsepower two-barrel engine. Chevrolet V-8 454 cubic inch 215 horsepower four-barrel engine ($231). Chevrolet V-8 454 cubic inch 245 horsepower four-barrel dual-exhaust engine. Monte Carlo V-8 350 cubic inch 175 horsepower four-barrel engine. Monte Carlo V-8 454 cubic inch 245 horsepower four-barrel dual-exhaust engine ($209). Chevelle V-8 350 cubic inch 145 horsepower two-barrel engine. Chevelle V-8 350 cubic inch 175 horsepower four-barrel engine. Chevelle V-8 454 cubic inch 24 horsepower four-barrel engine ($235). Camaro V-8 350 cubic inch 145 horsepower two-barrel engine. Camaro V-8 350 cubic inch 175 horsepower four-barrel engine. Camaro V-8 350 cubic inch 245 horsepower Z/28 engine (*). Nova V-8 350 cubic inch 145 horsepower two-barrel engine. Nova V-8 350 cubic inch 175 horsepower four-barrel engine. Positive traction rear axle. **NOTE:** The Vega GT package included the two-barrel Four. The Camaro Z/28 package included the 245 horsepower '350' V-8.

POPULAR CONVENIENCE OPTIONS: Vega power steering ($92). Vega air-conditioning ($349). Vega Estate Wagon package ($212). Vega hatchback GT package ($340). Vega station wagon GT package ($314). Vega Custom interior ($115). Nova vinyl top ($82). Nova air conditioning ($381). Nova Super Sport package ($123). Nova skyroof ($179). Chevelle/Camaro/Nova power brakes ($46). Nova power brakes with front discs ($68). Chevelle vinyl top ($92). Chevelle/Monte Carlo/Camaro AM/FM stereo ($233). Chevrolet/Monte Carlo/Chevelle AM/FM stereo with tape ($363). Chevelle Malibu SS package ($243). Monte Carlo vinyl top ($123). Chevelle/Monte Carlo skyroof ($325). Camaro vinyl top ($87). Monte Carlo/Camaro air conditioning ($397). Camaro LT Special Performance package ($502). Camaro Z/28 Special Performance package ($598). Chevrolet vinyl top ($106). Chevrolet power seats ($103). Chevrolet power windows ($124). Chevrolet air conditioning ($482). Nova power steering ($100).

Historical footnotes: The 1973 Chevrolets were introduced on September 21, 1972. Model year production peaked at 2,365,381 units. Calendar year sales of 2,434,890 cars were recorded. F. J. MacDonald was the Chief Executive Officer of the company this year. Early (1971 and 1972) Vegas came with steel head gaskets which were easily 'done-in' by water and heat. The result was that dealers had to replace many motors under the original 12,000 miles engine warranty. The early motors earned such a bad reputation that the warranty was later extended to 50,000 miles to help prevent a too large drop in sales due to the problem.
NOTE: The model year production and calendar year sales figures given above have been adjusted to exclude Corvette and Sport Van totals. See the Corvette section of the is Catalog for additional data. See Krause Publications *Complete Encyclopedia of Commercial Vehicles* for Chevrolet truck information.

1974 CHEVROLET

1974 Chevrolet, Impala 2-dr hardtop coupe, V-8

FULL-SIZED CHEVROLET — (V-8) — ALL SERIES — Caprice Classics had a different appearance than Bel Airs and Impalas this year and all models were changed at the front and rear. A new grille on the low/medium-priced cars was completely above the bumper and the number of vertical bars was cut more than 50 percent. Their new front bumper had no parking light or grille reveal openings, but rubber-faced protective guards were standard. The license plate attachment was moved from the center to the left. On these Bel Airs and Impalas, the parking lamps were placed in the fender extension caps, outboard of the dual, square headlamp housings. A 'bow tie' insignia was at the center of the grille, with a Chevrolet inscription on the left side of the upper grille frame molding. A model identification script was seen behind the front wheel housings. Standard equipment for Bel Airs included all regulation safety features; body sill moldings; power steering; power brakes (with front disc and rear finned drums); inside day/nite mirror; foam seats; power ventilation system; glove box light; cigar lighter; recessed wipers; inside hood release; lefthand OSRV mirror; windshield antenna; pattern cloth and vinyl interior; and Turbo-Hydramatic transmission on V-8s. Most sources indicate that all big Chevrolets were V-8 powered, but the Bel Air sedan was available with a Six and three-speed manual gear box, at least at the beginning of the year. There is no record of any such cars being built and sold. The Impalas had all of the above, plus bright bodyside moldings (with a black vinyl insert on the Custom coupe); triple taillights with silver accents; front and rear wheel lip moldings (on Custom coupe) and a luggage compartment mat. The base V-8 was the two-barrel 350 cubic inch and regular tire were G78-15 blackwalls. All front end sheetmetal on the Caprice was distinctive and had a more swept back look with different fenders; hood; grille; header bar and lamps. The grille was more elaborate with 11 prominent bright moldings forming a dozen segments. Each segment was filled with multiple horizontal and vertical members. A signature script was placed in the lefthand side of the grille and a Caprice crest was seen at the center of the wider, upper border bar. The Caprice parking lights wer moved to a position between the headlights and the grille. The Custom Coupe had a form of a Colonnade styling, in which over-sized opera windows were used at the upper rear roof quarters. Body sides were decorated with a low, full length molding, which was extra-wide and carried color-keyed vinyl protective strips. A Caprice crest was placed on the coupes central roof pillar. The Caprice had the same

1974 Chevrolet, Caprice Classic 2-dr Custom coupe, V-8

equipment as Impalas, plus ash tray and courtesy lights; electric clock; rear fender skirts; distinctive cloth and vinyl interior; color-keyed wheel covers; GT8-15/B tires and a 400 cubic inch V-8. The sedan used a fold-down center arm rest seat. Station wagons were equipped like their passenger car counterparts, plus hidden storage compartment; Glide-Away tailgate; all-vinyl upholstery; power taillight window; L78-15/B tires and forward-facing rear seat on nine passenger styles. The Caprice Estate also had a vertical bar grille; electric clock; ash tray and courtesy lights and 400 cubic inch two-barrel V-8 engine. Wood-grained siding was optional.

VEHICLE IDENTIFICATION NUMBERS: The numbering system and code locations were the same as for previous models with the sixth symbol changed to a '4' to indicate 1974 model year. The first symbol '1' designated Chevrolet product. The second symbol designated Series. The third and fouth symbols designated Body Style Number. The fifth symbol designated engine type. The sixth symbol designated model year. The seventh symbol designated assembly plant. The following group of symbols was the sequential unit production number, beginning with 100001 at each plant. The Chevrolet Model was the combination of the first four symbols.

1974 Chevrolet, Caprice Estate 4-dr station wagon, V-8

FULL-SIZED CHEVROLET SERIES

Series Number	Body/Style Number	Body Type & Seating	Factory Price	Shipping Weight	Production Total
BEL AIR SERIES					
1K	69	4-dr Sed-6P	3960	4148	Note 1
1K	45	4-dr Sta Wag-9P	4578	4884	Note 2
1K	35	4-dr Sta Wag-6P	4464	4829	Note 2
IMPALA SERIES					
1L	69	4-dr Sed-6P	4135	4205	Note 3
1L	39	4-dr HT Sed-6P	4215	4256	Note 3
1L	57	2-dr Spt Cpe-6P	4162	4167	Note 3
1L	47	2-dr Cus Cpe-6P	4229	4169	Note 3
1L	45	4-dr Sta Wag-9P	4675	4936	Note 2
1L	35	4-dr Sta Wag-6P	4561	4891	Note 2
CAPRICE CLASSIC					
1N	69	4-dr Sed-6P	4465	4294	Note 4
1N	39	4-dr HT Sed-6P	4534	4344	Note 4
1N	47	2-dr Cus Cpe-6P	4483	4245	Note 4
1N	67	2-dr Conv-6P	4745	4308	Notes 4/5
1N	45	4-dr Sta Wag-9P	4914	5004	Note 2
1N	35	4-dr Sta Wag-6P	4800	4960	Note 2

GENERAL NOTE: Domestic model year production of full-sized Chevrolets totaled exactly 630,861 units. This total is again distorted, by the fact that production of some models for U.S. Sales was quartered in Canada. The exact number of full-sized Chevrolets sold by dealers holding U.S. franchises was 565,376 cars. This means that some 65,485 Bel Airs, Impalas and Caprice Classics built in U.S. factories were shipped to Canada under the new trade agreements. A similar situation existed in other Chevrolet model lines. This should be kept in mind when using the series output figures given below.
NOTE 1: Exactly 34,095 Bel Air passenger cars were built for the 1974 model year. All were V-8s.
NOTE 2: Exactly 35,331 full-sized wagons were built for the 1974 model year. All were V-8s. This includes all station wagons with no further breakout, by series, available at this time.
NOTE 3: Exactly 405,286 Impala passenger cars were built for the 1974 model year. All were V-8s.
NOTE 4: Exactly 155,860 Caprice passenger cars were built for the 1974 Model year. All were V-8s.
NOTE 5: Exactly 4,670 Caprice Classic covertibles were built for the 1974 model year. All were V-8s.
ADDITIONAL NOTE: Though listed as available early in the year, standard reference sources do not indicate the price or weight of a Bel Air Six and Chevrolet production records indicate that no such cars were built.

FULL-SIZED SERIES ENGINES

BEL AIR/IMPALA
V-8. Overhead valves. Cast iron block. Displacement: 350 cubic inches. Bore and stroke: 4.00 x 3.48 inches. Compression ratio: 8.5:1. SAE Net horsepower: 145 at 2400 R.P.M. Five main bearings. Hydraulic valve lifters. Carburetor: two-barrel.

1974 Chevrolet, Caprice Classic 2-dr convertible, V-8

CAPRICE
V-8. Overhead valves. Cast iron block. Displacement: 400 cubic inches. Bore and stroke: 4.126 x 3.75 inches. Compression ratio: 8.5:1 SAE Net horsepower: 150 at 2400 R.P.M. Five main bearings. Hydraulic valve lifers. Carburetor: two-barrel.

1974 Chevrolet, Monte Carlo 2-dr sport coupe, V-8

MONTE CARLO — (V-8) — SERIES 1H — The 1974 Monte Carlo received minor appearance changes, the most obvious a new egg crate grille. Body side moldings use with some decor packages were of a new design that extended completely forward to hit the rear edge of the front wheel housing. The front lip of the hood was decorated with a center medallion, instead of the former left side script. Landau or Monte Carlo 'S' packages replaced the mid-bodyside molding (described above) with wide, bright rocker panel accents having both front and rear extensions. At the rear, a new bumper was used. It incorporated two, full-width vinyl impact strips and protruded out further, giving the cars three extra inches of length. Rubber faced rear bumper guards were also new. The backup lights were moved, from the bumper, to a license-plate-flanking position on the deck latch panel. The design of the trunk lock was simplified and the multiple, short accent moldings were removed from the taillights. Crests and chrome signatures called-out the various levels of trim. Standard equipment included Power-Beam single-unit headlights; formal coupe roofline; rear quarter 'coach' style windows; Hide-Away wipers; rear stabilizer; power front disc brakes; power steering; ignition key alarm; flow-thru power ventilation; electric clock; wood-burl dash and steering wheel accents; Delco-Eye battery; carpets; door map pockets; knit cloth and vinyl trim; cigar lighter; inside hood release; GR70-15 radial tires and '350' V-8. The Landau also had a landau vinyl top; color-keyed rear window and belt moldings; fender accent stripes; body-color Sport mirrors (left remote-control); wheel covers; visor/vanity mirror; 15 x 7 Turbine II wheels; radial tuned suspension; passenger assist grips and door map pockets.

VEHICLE IDENTIFICATION NUMBERS: The numbering system and code locations were the same as for previous models with the first-four symbols changed to Monte Carlo nomenclature. Sequential production numbers on Monte Carlos began with 400001, as in 1973.

MONTE CARLO SERIES

Series Number	Body/Style Number	Body Type & Seating	Factory Price	Shipping Weight	Production Total
MONTE CARLO 'S'					
1H	57	2-dr HT Cpe-5P	3885	3926	Note 1
MONTE CARLO LANDAU					
1H	57	2-dr HT Cpe-5P	4129	3950	Note 1

NOTE 1: Exactly 312,217 Monte Carlos were built for the 1974 Model year. All were V-8s. No additional breakouts per trim level are available. Monte Carlo sales by U.S. dealers peaked at 284,867 cars. This indicates that over 25,000 U.S. built cars were shipped to Canada.

MONTE CARLO SERIES ENGINES
See 1974 Bel Air/Impala Series engine data.

1974 Chevelle, Malibu Classic 4-dr station wagon, V-8

INTERMEDIATE-SIZED CHEVELLES — (SIX/V-8) — ALL SERIES — The Nomad and Chevelle DeLuxe Series model were dropped in 1974 and the intermediate-sized Chevrolet products now came in Malibu, Malibu Classic, Malibu Classic Estate and Laguna decor levels. Basic styling changes were modest. They included a bumper without the flattened license plate attachment panel in the center; twin-slot side marker lamps and a radiator-style grille that looked like a Mercedes-Benz unit stretched-out sideways. Decor option packages, however, had a big effect on final appearances. Chevelles came in a variety of 'flavors' ranging from the 'unmarked police car' look to the race-ready image of the Laguna Type S-3 coupe. One way to spot a 1974 model for sure, was to eyeball the round-corner traphezoid shape of the large rear lamps. Early models had round taillights; later versions became more rectangular, so the 1974 types are very distinctive. A new, stand-up hood ornament decorated the Malibu Classic, which also had wide, lower body accent panels. Optional innovations included the canopy top or louvered rear 'coach' window treatments. Standard equipment on the base Malibu included regulation safety equipment; flow-through power ventilation system; double panel steel accoustical roof; inside hood release; manual front disc brakes; side marker lamps and reflectors; defroster; dual speed wipers with washers; inside day/nite mirror; left OSRV mirror; full foam rubber seats; color-keyed vinyl roof covering; cigar lighter; Hide-Away wipers; windshield radio antenna; Delcotron generator; E78-14/B tires and either the '250' Six or '350' two-barrel V-8. Malibu V-8s wore G78-14/B tires. The Malibu Classic came with all of the above, plus carpeting; glove box light; mixed pattern cloth and vinyl interior; bodyside, roof drip and wheel opening moldings and DeLuxe center arm in rest front seat. The Laguna Colonnade Coupe came only in V-8 form. It featured, in addition to the above, patterned cloth and vinyl (or all-vinyl) interior; wood-grain vinyl accents on dash (with elm-burl center vinyl inlay); full wheel covers; bright accented dual-unit taillights; wheel lips and scalp-moldings; GR70-15/B steel-belted radial tires and the two-barrel '350' V-8. The high-performance image Laguna type S-3 coupe added a custom eggcrate grille isolated within a body-color front end panel; bright grille cross bar with Square Rally lights at each end; nerf-bar bumper treatment; louvered 'coach' window styling; swivel bucket seats; variable-ratio power steering; heavy-duty Pliacell shock absorbers; radial-tuned suspension; Specific Type S-3 nameplates at grille center and behind front wheels; engine callout decals above side markers; lower body perimeter striping and black-accent treatment; body-color twin Sport mirros (left remote-controlled); Red or white Stripe radial tires; body color reveal moldings; full-instrumentation (with round-faced gauges); four-spoke steering wheel and 15 x 7 Turbine II wheels. Top power option was the detuned — SAE rated — 235 horsepower 454 cubic inch V-8.

1974 Chevrolet, Chevelle Malibu Classic Colonnade coupe, V-8

VEHICLE IDENTIFICATION NUMBERS: The numbering system and code locations were the same as for previous models with the first four symbols changed to Chevelle nomenclature. Sequential unit production numbers on Chevelles began with 400001 and up.

1974 Chevrolet, Chevelle Laguna S-3 Colonnade coupe, V-8

CHEVELLE INTERMEDIATE SERIES

Series Number	Body/Style Number	Body Type & Seating	Factory Price	Shipping Weight	Production Total
MALIBU					
1C	29	4-dr Col Sed-6P	3049/3340	3638/3788	Note 1
1C	37	2-dr Col Cpe-6P	3054/3345	3573/3723	Note 1
1C	35	4-dr Sta Wag-8P	3834	4223	Note 2
1C	35	4-dr Sta Wag-6P	3701	4191	Note 2
MALIBU CLASSIC					
1D	29	4-dr Col Sed-6P	3304/3595	3695/3845	Note 3
1D	37	2-dr Col Cpe-6P	3307/3598	3609/3759	Note 3
1D	37	2-dr Lan Cpe-6P	3518/3800	NA/NA	Note 3
1D	35	4-dr Sta Wag-9P	4251	4315	Note 2
1D	35	4-dr Sta Wag-6P	4118	4283	Note 2
MALIBU CLASSIC ESTATE					
1G	35	4-dr Sta Wag-9P	4424	4338	Note 2
1G	35	4-dr Sta Wag-6P	4291	4306	Note 2
LAGUNA					
1E	37	2-dr Col Cpe-6P	3723	3951	Note 4
LAGUNA TYPE S-3					
1E	37	2-dr Col Cpe-5P	4504	NA	Note 4

NOTE 1: Exactly 91,612 Malibu passenger cars were built for the 1974 Model year, including 27,188 Sixes and 64,424 V-8s.
NOTE 2: Exactly 44,108 Chevelle intermediate-sized station wagons were built for the 1974 Model year. All were V-8s. This includes all Malibu, Malibu Classic and Malibu Classic Estate wagons, with no breakouts per trim level available at this time.
NOTE 3: Exacly 204,870 Malibu Classic passenger cars were built for the 1974 model year, including 8,940 Sixes and 195,930 V-8s.
NOTE 4: Exactly 21,902 Lagunas were built for the 1974 model year. All were V-8s. No breakout per trim level is avaialble at this time.

CHEVELLE SERIES ENGINES
Six. See 1973 Chevelle Series six-cylinder engine data.

V-8. See 1974 Chevrolet Series engine data.

1974 Chevrolet, Nova 2-dr sedan with 'Spirit of America' option, V-8

NOVA — (SIX/V-8) — ALL SERIES — Never a car to change for the sake of change, the 1974 Nova was basically unaltered. A 'bow tie' badge was added at the center of the grille and the nameplate on the lefthand side of the hood lip read 'Nova by Chevrolet''. Rubber-faced front bumper guards were standard, now, and eleven new colors were available. Coupes or hatchbacks with Super Sport options received the black-out grille treatment with prominent horizontal moldings bridging the rectangular parking lamps top and bottom. Two-tone finish was available for Body Style Number 17. The designers also added new hub caps, with a bright annodized look. Two-speed Powerglide automatic transmission was no longer offered. Standard equipment included color-keyed rubber floor coverings; flow-through ventilation system; full-foam front seats; foam rear seats; dual-speed electric wipers; left OSRV mirror; cargo-guard luggage compartment (except hatchback) and '250' Six. The hatch back added the swing-up rear deck and fold-down rear seat. The Nova Custom also had bright parking light and liftgate accents; body sill and scalp moldings; DeLuxe bumpers with black vinyl impact strips; carpets; inside day/nite mirror; glove box light; right front door light switch; cigarette lighter and trunk mat. Standard tire were size E78-14/B blackwalls and the two-barrel '350' was base V-8.

VEHICLE IDENTIFICATION NUMBERS: The numbering system and code locations were the same as for previous models with the first four symbols changed to Nova nomenclature. Sequential unit numbers on Novas began at 100001 and up at each factory.

NOVA SERIES

Series Number	Body/Style Number	Body Type & Seating	Factory Price	Shipping Weight	Production Total
NOVA					
1X	69	4-dr Sed-6P	2841/2949	3192/3330	Note 1
1X	27	2-dr Cpe-6P	2811/2919	3150/3288	Note 1
1X	17	2-dr Hatch-6P	2935/3043	3260/3398	Note 1
NOVA CUSTOM					
1Y	69	4-dr Sed-6P	3014/3123	3233/3371	Note 1
1Y	27	2-dr Cpe-6P	2985/3093	3206/3344	Note 1
1Y	17	2-dr Hatch-6P	3108/3217	3299/3437	Note 1

NOTE 1: Exactly 390,537 Novas were built during the 1974 model year, including 171,430 Sixes and 219,107 V-8s. No breakouts per body style or trim level are available at the current time.
ADDITIONAL NOTE: Included in the total given above were exactly 21,419 cars equipped with the Nova SS option package. No additional breakout per coupes and hatch back styles is available at the current time.

NOVA ENGINES
Six. See 1973 Chevelle Series six-cylinder engine data.

V-8. See 1974 Chevelle Series V-8 engine data.

1974 Chevrolet, Vega 2-dr Estate wagon, 4-cyl

VEGA — (FOUR) — SERIES 1V — New for the Vega sub-compact was a shovel nosed look with a quad-level, air-slot style grille, divided into two halves with a vertical, body-colored center divider strip. The headlamps were recessed into slanting, square-shaped housings finished in bright metal style. A much thicker, full-width wraparound bumper incorporated black rubber guards and vinyl black impact strips. Single-unit square taillamps (or vertical fender-mount lamps on wagons) were seen at the rear, where a more protrusive bumper — with vinyl impact strips, was used. A three-inch length increase resulted. Standard equipment included all regulation safety devices; side marker lights and reflectors; left OSRV mirror; backup lights; bright hub caps; foam-filled front bucket/rear bucket style seats; storage well in driver's door; glove box; power vent system; folding seatback latches; steel side guard beams; ashtray;

inside windshield moldings; carpets; heater and defroster; windshield washer and electric wipers; inside hood release; manual front disc brakes; three-speed manual transmission with floor shift; OHC-Four engine and AT78-13 black sidewall tires. The hatch back added a fold-down rear seat and stowage compartment. The station wagon (Kammback) also had a swing-up tailgate and folding rear seat. The Estate wagon featured DeLuxe interior and exterior trim; full carpeting and concealed storage compartment.

VEHICLE IDENTIFICATION NUMBERS: The numbering system and code locations were the same as for previous models with the first four symbols changed to Vega nomenclature. Sequential unit production numbers on Vegas began at 100001 at each factory.

VEGA SERIES

Series Number	Body/Style Number	Body Type & Seating	Factory Price	Shipping Weight	Production Total
1V	11	2-dr Cpe-4P	2087	2219	63,591
1V	77	2-dr Hatch-4P	2192	2313	271,682
1V	15	2-dr Sta Wag-4P	2323	2327	113,326
1HV	05	2-dr Panel-2P	2404	2402	4,289

NOTE: The production totals given in the chart above are the exact model year output figures per body style. The panel delivery is included to indicate Model Number, price and weight characteristics of this particular body style. The panel truck was marketed strictly as a commercial vehicle, although this model is very popular with many involved in the modified vehicles, segment of the old car hobby.

VEGA ENGINE
See 1973 Vega Series engine data. Specifications were basically unchanged, though a 75 horsepower rating was advertised in 1974.

1974 Chevrolet, Camaro 2-dr sports coupe, V-8

CAMARO — (SIX/V-8) — ALL SERIES — The Camaro got a major restyling for the 1974 model year. It followed the Vega's shovel nosed theme and included a soft urethane-cushioned front panel. The forward angled grille featured an egg crate motif, with grille texture reveal below the new, widened front bumper. At the rear, a new appearance was also achieved. The four round taillamps from previous models gave way to large lenses that slid around the body corners to serve double-duty as side marker lights. The area between the lamps was flattened. The Z/28 option included a bolder graphics treatment with decals calling-out the model nomenclature within stripes that dominated the hood and deck lids. Parking lamps were now circular and housed inside slanting, scooped-out square recesses between the grille and front fenders. Standard equipment included safety features; side markers and reflectors; rear markers; rocker moldings; Astro vents; day/nite inside mirror; double-panel roof; pull-type door handles; color-keyed carpets; front bumper guards; bucket seats; all-vinyl interior; dual wipers and washers; left OSRV mirror; rear bucket cushions; manual front disc brakes; three-speed with floor-shift; E78-14 tires and '250' Six or '350' two-barrel V-8. The Camaro LT Coupe added electric clock; special instrumentation; OSRV Sport mirrors (left remote-controlled); Rally wheels and Hide-Away wipers; plus the base V-8 as standard equipment.

VEHICLE IDENTIFICATION NUMBERS: The numbering system and code locations were the same as for previous models with the first four symbols changed to Camaro nomenclature. Sequential unit production numbers on Camaros began with 100001 and up.

CAMARO SERIES

Series Number	Body/Style Number	Body Type & Seating	Factory Price	Shipping Weight	Production Total
CAMARO LEVEL					
1Q	87	2-dr HT Cpe-4P	3162/3366	3309/3450	Note 1
CAMARO LT LEVEL					
1S	87	2-dr HT Cpe-4P	3713	3566	Note 1

NOTE 1: Exactly 146,595 Camaros were built for the U.S. market in the 1974 model year. Exactly 4,412 Camaros were built for export, bringing total output to 151,008 units. This included 13,802 Camaros with the Z/28 package; 128,810 V-8s; 22,198 Sixes: 11,174 with three-speeds, 11,175 with four-speeds; 128,659 with automatic; 79,279 with air conditioning and 151,008 with power steering. No breakout is currently available as to the number of cars equipped in LT level trim.

1974 Camaro, 2-dr LT hardtop sports coupe, V-8

CAMARO ENGINES
Six. See 1973 Chevrolet Series six-cylinder engine data.

V-8. See 1974 Chevrolet Series V-8 engine data.

CHASSIS FEATURES: Wheelbase: (Chevrolet wagon) 125 inches; (Chevrolet) 121.5 inches; (Monte Carlo/Chevelle four-door) 116 inches; (Nova/Nova Custom) 111 inches; (Vega) 97 inches; (Camaro) 108 inches. Overall length: (Chevrolet wagon) 229 inches; (Chevrolet) 223 inches; (Monte Carlo) 214 inches; (Chevelle wagon) 216 inches; (Chevelle four-door) 211 inches; (Chevelle two-door) 207 inches; (Nova) 197 inches; (Nova Custom) 198 inches; (Vega) 176 inches; (Camaro) 196 inches. Width: Same as 1973 for all styles. Tires: Refer to text.

POWERTRAIN OPTIONS: Three-speed manual transmission was standard in Chevelle/Nova/Camaro Six. Automatic transmission was standard in Bel Air/Impala/Caprice. Automatic transmission optional in others. Three-speed manual floor shift transmission, standard in Vega. Four-speed manual floor shift transmission was optional in Nova/Camaro/Vega. Vega four-cylinder 140 cubic inch 85 horsepower two-barrel engine. Chevrolet V-8 350 cubic inch 160 horsepower four-barrel engine. Chevrolet V8 400 cubic inch 150 horsepower two-barrel engine. Chevrolet V-8 400 cubic inch 180 horsepower four-barrel engine. Chevrolet V-8 454 cubic inch 235 horsepower four-barrel engine ($248). Monte Carlo V-8 350 cubic inch 160 horsepower four-barrel engine. Monte Carlo V-8 400 cubic inch 150 horsepower two-barrel engine. Monte Carlo V-8 400 cubic inch 180 horsepower four-barrel engine. Monte Carlo 454 cubic inch 235 horsepower four-barrel engine ($241). Chevelle V-8 400 cubic inch 150 horsepower two-barrel engine. Chevelle V-8 400 cubic inch 180 horsepower four-barrel engine. Chevelle V-8 454 cubic inch 235 horsepower four-barrel engine ($293). Nova V-8 350 cubic inch 160 horsepower four-barrel engine. Nova V-8 350 cubic inch 185 horsepower four-barrel dual-exhaust engine. Camaro V-8 350 cubic inch 160 horsepower four-barrel engine. Camaro V-8 350 cubic inch 185 horsepower four-barrel dual-exhaust engine. Positive traction rear axle.

CONVENIENCE OPTIONS: Power brakes. Power steering. Monte Carlo/Camaro/Chevelle/Chevrolet AM/FM stereo ($233). Monte Carlo/Chevelle/Chevrolet AM/FM stereo with tape ($363). Chevrolet power seats ($106). Chevrolet wagon luggage rack ($77). Impala 'Spirit of America' sport coupe package ($399). Vega vinyl top ($75). Vega power steering ($95). Vega air conditioning ($362). Vega GT package ($359). Nova air conditioning ($396). Nova SS package ($140). Chevelle vinyl top ($92). Monte Carlo/Chevelle sky roof ($325). Camaro vinyl top ($87). Camaro air conditioning ($412).

Historical footnotes: The 1974 Chevrolets were introduced September 22, 1973. Model year production peaked at 2,396,284 units. Calendar year sales of 2,156,460 cars were recorded. Robert L. Lund was the Chief Executive Officer of the company this year. Sales of Chevrolet's full-line of cars. Sport vans, and Vega panel experess models dropped 12.3 percent from 1973 levels. **NOTE:** The model year production and calendar year sales figures given above cover only models included in this section, excluding Corvette and Sport van production and sales. Vega panel express models are, however, included in both totals.

1975 CHEVROLET

1975 Chevrolet, Caprice 4-dr hardtop sedan, V-8

FULL-SIZED CHEVROLET — (SIX/V-8) — ALL SERIES — Model year 1975 is best known as the season of the catalytic converter and the 'last' Chevrolet convertible. Additional innovations included introduction of the standard High-Energy ignition system and new, Colonnade style rooflines for four-door sedans and Sport sedans (four-door hardtops). The Bel Air and Impala received a revised frontal treatment which was similar to that of the 1974 Caprice Classic. This brought changes including the placement of parking lamps between grille and headlamps; a bright signature script on the lefthand face of the grille and repositioning of the Chevrolet 'bow tie' near the center of the hood lip.Bel Airs had no side spears and stuck with a two-unit taillight design. Impalas were highlighted with three-quarter length, bodyside moldings that ran from behind the front upper wheel lip to the rear of the car and bright-accented, triple taillamps were used. The Caprice Classic again had distinctive appearance features including a vertical barred grille that was even with the upper headlamp borders and partially revealed through an opening below the front bumper. A bright signature script was placed on the left of the grille; a Caprice Crest was seen at the upper center and parking lamps were moved into the bumper, directly under the headlamps. Tires were HR78-15/B blackwalls on passenger cars and LR78-15/C size on station wagons. The standard V-8 in all models was the 145 horsepower job of 350 cubic inch displacement. Other equipment features were comparable to those listed in 1974.

VEHICLE IDENTIFICATION NUMBERS: The numbering system and code locations were the same as for previous models with the sixth symbol changed to a '5' to indicate 1975 model year. The first symbol '1' designated Chevrolet product. The second symbol designated the series. The third and fourth symbols designated the Body Style Number. The fifth symbol designated type of engine. The sixth symbol designated model year. The seventh symbol designated assembly plant. The following group of six symbols was the sequential unit production number beginning with 100001 at each factory.

FULL-SIZED CHEVROLET

Series Number	Body/Style Number	Body Type & Seating	Factory Price	Shipping Weight	Production Total
BEL AIR					
1K	69	4-dr Sed-6P	4345	4179	Note 1
1K	45	4-dr Sta Wag-9P	4998	4913	Note 2
1K	35	4-dr Sta Wag-6P	4878	4856	Note 2
IMPALA					
1L	69	4-dr Sed-6P	4548	4218	Note 3
1L	39	4-dr HT Sed-6P	4631	4265	Note 3
1L	57	2-dr Spt Cpe-6P	4575	4207	Note 3
1L	47	2-dr Cus Cpe-6P	4626	4190	Note 3
1L	47	2-dr Lan Cpe-6P	4901	NA	Note 3
1L	45	4-dr Sta Wag-9P	5121	4959	Note 2
1L	35	4-dr Sta Wag-6P	5001	4910	Note 2
CAPRICE					
1N	69	4-dr Sed-6P	4819	4311	Note 4
1N	39	4-dr HT Sed-6P	4891	4360	Note 4
1N	47	2-dr Cus Cpe-6P	4837	4275	Note 4
1N	47	2-dr Lan Cpe-6P	5075	NA	Note 4
1N	67	2-dr Conv-6P	5113	4342	Note 4/5
1N	45	4-dr Sta Wag-9P	5351	5036	Note 2
1N	35	4-dr Sta Wag-6P	5231	4978	Note 2

NOTE 1: Exactly 13,168 Bel Air four-door sedans were built during the 1975 model year. All were V-8s.
NOTE 2: Exactly 58,529 full-sized Chevrolet station wagons were built during the 1975 model year. All were V-8s. This total includes Bel Air, Impala and Caprice Classic Estate wagons, with no additional breakouts, per trim level, available at the current time.
NOTE 3: Exactly 176,376 Impala passenger cars were built during the 1975 model year. All were V-8s. No breakouts per body style are available at the current time.
NOTE 4: Exactly 103,944 Caprice Classic passenger cars were built during the 1975 model year. All were V-8s. No breakouts per body style (except convertible) are available at the current time.
NOTE 5: Exactly 8,349 Caprice Classic convertibles were built during the 1975 model year. All were V-8s. This breakout is included in Note 4 above.
ADDITIONAL NOTE: All 1975 Chevrolet Series production totals in this catalog may include same cars built in Canada for the U.S. market.

BEL AIR/IMPALA/CAPRICE ENGINE
See 1974 Bel Air/Impala Series engine data.

1975 Chevrolet, Monte Carlo 2-dr sport coupe, V-8

MONTE CARLO (V-8) SERIES H — Chevrolet's personal/luxury car was refined for model year 1975. A new grille treatment featured two rows of 14 chrome-framed squares, arranged horizontally above the bumper with an additional row revealed through a long, oval slot below. Each of the 42 square segments was highlighted with three, short vertical moldings. A shield-shaped medallion was placed at the center of the upper grille opening, with a Monte Carlo signature on the lefthand hood lip. Parking lamps were housed at the front fender corners, with a strip of body colored sheetmetal dividing the lens vertically. A new taillight treatment featured a stack of four horizontal slats that wrapped around the rear body edges. The Monte Carlo signature was removed from the righthand trunk corner and dropped to the rear deck lid latch panel, directly below. Wheel cover design details were changed. Luxurious interiors featured new trim and fabrics and a choice of options such as 50/50 reclining passenger seats or swivel bucket seats. Standard engine was the '350' V-8 in its two-barrel form. Power front disc brakes were included.

VEHICLE I.D. NUMBERS: The numbering system and code locations were the same as previous models, with the first four symbols changed to Monte Carlo nomenclature. Sequential unit numbers began at 400001 at each plant.

MONTE CARLO

Series Number	Body/Style Number	Body Type & Seating	Factory Price	Shipping Weight	Production Total
MONTE CARLO 'S'					
1H	57	2-dr HT Cpe-5P	4249	3927	Note 1
MONTE CARLO LANDAU					
1H	57	2-dr HT Cpe-5P	4519	3950	Note 1

NOTE 1: Exactly 258,909 Monte Carlos were built during the 1975 model year. All were V-8s. No additional breakouts per trim level are available at the current time.

MONTE CARLO ENGINE
See 1974 Bel Air/Impala Series engine data.

CHEVELLE — (SIX/V-8) — ALL SERIES — Appearance features of Chevelles were changed in small details from 1974. The grille was still of the Mercedes chromed radiator shell type, but modified with prominent division bars forming ten vertical segments. Each segment had a screen-like texture within. On Malibu Classics, the screening was black-finished, making the bright metal elements stand-out more for a look of increased elegance. The Classic models also featured stand-up hood ornaments. Taillamp designs were again based on a horizontal, rectangular shaped lens. The lamps, however, were somewhat longer and narrower, with nearly square backup lights added at the inboard side. On Malibu Classics, the rectangular panel housing the taillights (and center license plate indentation) received a satin silver finish and held a model identifying signature script on the right side. It was mid-year before the Laguna Type S-3 coupe was reintroduced, again featuring a unique styling treatment. Prime among its special touches was a sloping, urethane plastic front end with a grille opening that was divided, both horizontally and vertically, to form four large, rectangular slots with screen-textured inserts. Also included were Rally wheels, louvered opera windows and radial tuned suspension. The S-3 came in a choice of six colors with specific body striping and half-vinyl roofs on the optional equipment list. Technical innovations for Chevelles were a more efficient Six, High-Energy ignition and catalytic converter. Base V-8 was the '350' two-barrel and tire sizes were FR78-15/B on passenger cars; HR78-15/B on wagons and special GR70-15/B wide profile type on Laguna Type S-3.

VEHICLE IDENTIFICATION NUMBERS: The numbering system and code locations were the same as for previous models with the first four symbols changed to Chevelle nomenclature. Sequential unit numbers on Chevelles began with 400001 and up at each factory.

CHEVELLE SERIES

Series Number	Body/Style Number	Body Type & Seating	Factory Price	Shipping Weight	Production Total
MALIBU					
1C	29	4-dr Col Sed-6P	3402/3652	3713/3833	Note 1
1C	37	2-dr Col Cpe-6P	3407/3657	3642/3762	Note 1
1C	35	4-dr Sta Wag-6P	4463	NA	Note 2
1C	35	4-dr Sta Wag-6P	4318	4207	Note 2
MALIBUE CLASSIC					
1D	29	4-dr Col Sed-6P	3695/3945	3713/3898	Note 3
1D	37	2-dr Col Cpe-6P	3698/3948	3681/3801	Note 3
1D	37	2-dr Lan Cpe-6P	3930/4180	NA/NA	Note 3
1D	35	4-dr Sta Wag-9P	4701	NA	Note 2
1D	35	4-dr Sta Wag-6P	4556	4275	Note 2
MALIBU CLASSIC ESTATE					
1G	35	4-dr Sta Wag-9P	4893	NA	Note 2
1G	35	4-dr Sta Wag-6P	4748	4301	Note 2
LAGUNA TYPE S-3					
1E	37	2-dr Col Cpe-5P	4113	3908	Note 4

NOTE 1: Exactly 63,530 Chevelle Malibu passenger cars were built for the 1975 model year, including 21,804 Sixes and 41,726 V-8s. No additional breakouts per body style are available at the current time.
NOTE 2: Exactly 45,582 Chevelle station wagons were built during the 1975 model year. All were V-8s. This total includes Malibu, Malibu Classic and Malibu Classic Estate wagons with no additional breakout, per trim level, available at the current time.
NOTE 3: Exactly 131,455 Malibu Classic passenger cars were built during the 1975 model year, including 3,844 Sixes and 127,611 V-8s. No further breakouts, per body style, are available at the current time.
NOTE 4: Exactly 6,714 Chevelle Laguna coupes were built during the 1975 model year. All were V-8s.
ADDITIONAL NOTE: In all 1975 Chevelle, Nova and Camaro listings in this catalog the prices and weights above slash are for Sixes/below slash for V-8s. The 8-9 passenger, intermediate sized station wagon was no longer a distinct model offering as the rear seat was now optional equipment. Therefore, weights for this particular car are not recorded.

CHEVELLE SERIES ENGINES
Six: See 1975 Nova Series six-cylinder engine data.
V-8: See 1974 Bel Air/Impala V-8 engine data.

1975 Chevrolet, Nova LN 2-dr sedan, V-8

NOVA — (SIX/V-8) — ALL SERIES — The 'Senior Compact' Novas underwent the most change in the Chevrolet lineup receiving, for the first time in eight years, revised body styling. Patterned after the German Mercedes-Benz, the body was squarer and more luxurious looking. Roof lines received the major share of attention, with thinner pillars seen on all models, as well as a slimmer roof panel, increasing the total area of glass. The windshield, alone, measured 15 percent larger. A functional, louver treatment (for venting stale air from the interior) was featured on two-door Novas. Swing-out rear quarter windows were optional on coupes, while the hatch back had lift gate improvements. The new Nova grille was a simple, but elegant rectangular with two, full-width bright accent moldings and a bright vertical center trim bar. Rectangular parking lamps stood-up in the outboard ends of the grille and circular headlights were placed into large, square, bright-finished housings. Rectangular taillamps were seen. Available lines included the base models, Nova Custom (with thin rocker moldings) and 'Luxury Nova' LN (with fancy fender medallions and lower perimeter moldings which accented the front and rear quarters and wheel lips, plus the area between the wheel openings and above the rock panel trim). The Noval LN also featured thick window reveal moldings and vertically grooved trim plates on the center body pillar. Technical innovations included either the improved six-cylinder engine or an all-new 262 cubic inch (4.3 litre) V-8, except on cars certified for California sale. Three-speed manual transmission was standard (automatic with '350' V-8 in California cars); Turbo Hydramatic was optional and a 'Muncie' four-speed could be ordered for attachment with only the most powerful optional engine. The High-Energy electronic ignition system was standard equipment. Regular tire equipment was size E78 x 14 bias-belted blackwalls. The new Nova Six had an EPA fuel economy rating of 16 city/23 highway miles per gallon.

VEHICLE I.D. NUMBERS: The numbering system and code locations were the same as on previous models, with the first four symbols changed to Nova nomenclature. Sequential production numbers on Novas began with 100001.

NOVA SERIES

Series Number	Body/Style Number	Body Type & Seating	Factory Price	Shipping Weight	Production Total
NOVA 'S'					
1X	27	2-dr Cpe-5P	3099/3174	NA/NA	Note 1
NOVA					
1X	69	4-dr Sed-5P	3209/3284	3306/3408	Note 1
1X	27	2-dr Cpe-5P	3205/3280	3276/3378	Note 1
1X	17	2-dr Hatch-5P	3347/3422	3391/3493	Note 1
NOVA CUSTOM					
1Y	69	4-dr Sed-5P	3415/3490	3367/3469	Note 1
1Y	27	2-dr Cpe-5P	3402/3477	3335/3437	Note 1
1Y	17	2-dr Hatch-5P	3541/3616	3421/3523	Note 1
NOVA LN					
1Y	69	4-dr Sed-5P	3795/3870	NA/NA	Note 1
1Y	27	2-dr Cpe-5P	3782/3857	NA/NA	Note 1

NOTE 1: Exactly 272,982 Novas were built in the 1975 model year, including 138,879 Sixes and 134,103 V-8s. No breakouts per body style or trim level are available at the current time. Exactly 9,067 Novas were sold with the Super Sport option.
ADDITIONAL NOTES: Ajusted on a new Cumulative model year basis, the above total increased slightly to 273,014 units for the 1975 model year. In cases where shipping weights are not available NA, the car listed was not a distinct model, but a decor package (or decor package deletion, in the case of the stripped-down Nova 'S').

NOVA SERIES ENGINES

SIX
Inline, L-head Six. Cast iron block. Displacement: 250 cubic inches. Bore and stroke: 3.875 x 3.53 inches. Compression ratio: 8.2:1. SAE Net horsepower: 105 at 1800 R.P.M. Seven main bearings. Hydraulic valve lifters. Carburetor: one-barrel.

'FEDERAL' V-8
V-8. Overhead valves. Cast iron block. Displacement: 262 cubic inches. Bore and stroke: 3.671 x 3.10 inches. Compression ratio: 8.5:1. SAE Net horsepower: 110 at 3600 R.P.M. Five main bearings. Hydraulic valve lifters. Carburetor: Rochester two-barrel.

'CALIFORNIA' V-8
V-8. Overhead valves. Cast iron block. Displacement: 350 cubic inches. Bore and stroke: 4.00 x 3.48 inches. Compression ratio: 8.5:1. SAE Net horsepower: 155 at 3800 R.P.M. Five main bearings. Hydraulic valve lifters. Carburetor: four-barrel.

1975 Chevrolet, Vega GT 2-dr hatchback coupe, 4-cyl

VEGA — (FOUR) — SERIES V — While unchanged, in a basic sense when it appeared in the fall of 1974, the Vega built to 1975 specifications included a number of refinements ranging from a new catalytic converter and spark and carburetion improvements to redesigned front suspension equipment. Power brakes and a tilt steering wheel were optional for the first time. In the middle of the year, a special, limited-edition Cosworth Vega appeared on the scene (2,061 built). Its double overhead camshaft, sixteen valve four-cyliner engine was designed by England's famed Cosworth Engineering, Ltd. (a renowned race car building firm) and underwent final development in the Chevrolet Engineering laboratories. A true, high-performance machine, the Cosworth Vega also featured a Bendix electronic fuel injection system; special pulse air injection hardware; Vega heavy-duty front suspension; Chevrolet torque-arm rear suspension; stainless steel exhaust headers; breaker less High-Energy ignition; onboard Motorola computer; black vinyl interior with adjustable driver's seat back; black carpeting; padded Sport steering wheel; 8000 R.P.M. tachometer; electric clock; temperature gauges; volt meter; passenger grab bar; gold-colored cast aluminum wheels; black exterior finish with specific gold pin striping; dual Sport mirrors; black-finished wiper arms; blacked-out headlamp bezels and instruent panel 'Twin Cam' nameplate finished in gold and engraved with owner's name and car Serial number. The Vega engine in the Cosworth was extensively modified so as to qualify as a virtually handcrafted powerplant. The engines were, infact, built by hand assembly methods at Chevrolet's Tonawanda, New York plant. They were then shipped to Lordstown, Ohio, where the installation took place in bodies constructed off-line, apart from the regular production models. Special components included shot-peened rods; forged and magna-fluxed crank shaft; the computer-controlled induction setup; 16-valve aluminum Cosworth cylinder head; deep-dished high-compression pistons; low-lift design performance cam shaft (for smooth idle); solid valve lifters and over-sized, oval-shaped exhaust ports connected to scavenging type steel tube headers and low-restriction pipes and mufflers. Engine displacement was actually reduced to 122 cubic inches (2 liters) and specifications included 3.16 x 3.50 bore and stroke, 8.5:1 compression ratio and 120 horsepower at 5200 R.P.M. However, experimental racing versions prepared by Cosworth Engineering's Keith Duckworth, featured 11.5:1 compression and 270 horsepower at 8.750 R.P.M. The production version (which was orginally scheduled for 1974½ introduction, but failed to achieve government certification due to a burned exhaust valve in the test prototype) came with a close-ratio four-speed manual transmission and rode on six inch wide spoked wheels. The regular, single cam Vega, on the other hand, featured 78 horsepower in one-barrel carburetor/base engine form and had standard three-speed manual attachment and A78-13/B blackwall tires on conventional rims.

VEHICLE IDENTIFICATION NUMBERS: The numbering system and code locations were the same as for previous models with the first four symbols changed to Vega nomenclature. Sequential unit production numbers for 1975 Vegas began with 100001 with all assemblies quartered at the Lordstown, Ohio factory.

1975 Chevrolet, Vega Kammback GT 2-dr station wagon, 4-cyl

VEGA SERIES

Series Number	Body/Style Number	Body Type & Seating	Factory Price	Shipping Weight	Production Total
VEGA					
1V	11	2-dr Cpe-4P	2786	2415	35,133
1V	77	2-dr Hatch-4P	2899	2478	112,912
1V	15	2-dr Sta Wag-4P	3016	2531	56,133
VEGA ESTATE					
1V	15	2-dr Sta Wag-4P	3255	NA	Note 1
VEGA 'LX'					
1V		112-dr Cpe-4P	3119	NA	Note 2
COSWORTH VEGA					
1V	77	2-dr Hatch-4P	5916	NA	2,061
VEGA PANEL EXPRESS					
1HV	05	2-dr Panel-2P	2822	2401	1,525

NOTE 1: Included in two-door station wagon total. No breakout is available for number of wagons equipped with 'Estate' trim package.
NOTE 2: Included in two-door (notch back) coupe total. No breakout is available for number of coupes equipped with 'LX' decor package.

VEGA ENGINE
See 1974 Vega Series engine data. Brake horsepower for the 1975 one-barrel Four was 78 at 4200 R.P.M., but other specifications were unchanged. The two-barrel Four (87 horsepower at 4400 R.P.M.) was standard in cars built for California sale and was also included in Vega Estate and Vega LX packages. Refer to text for Cosworth Vega specifications.

1975 Chevrolet, 2-dr Monza 2+2 hatchback, 4-cyl.

MONZA — (FOUR) — ALL SERIES — A popular Chevrolet nameplate of the past appeared again in the fall of 1974, on an all-new sub-compact with a sporty, European-like body. Originally planned to be called the Chaparral, this fastback 2+2 coupe was built-off the Vega platform, but bore an uncanny resemblance to the Ferrari GTC-4. It was some four-inches longer and 180 pounds heavier than its Vega counterpart, which left enough room for a small block V-8 under the hood. Base engine, however, was the aluminum 2.3 liter Four and the same V-8s used for Novas were optional. Standard features included front bucket seats in leather-look vinyl; arm rests; door map pockets; added Sport steering wheel; wood-grain dash inserts; three-speed manual floor-shift transmission; manual front disc/rear drum brakes; Firestone BR78 x 13 steel-belted radial tires on 6 inch wide rims; tight-sealing rear hatch panel; carpeting and fold down rear seat back. In April, 1975, to answer the threat of the new Mustang II Ghia coupe, the mid-year Monza 'S' notch back was introduced as an addition to the line. This style was 1.5 inches shorter and 135 pounds lighter than the 2+2 and had increased headroom, a new instrument panel and single, round headlights in place of the fastback's dual, rectangular type. It was classified as the 'Towne Coupe'.

VEHICLE IDENTIFICATION NUMBERS: The numbering system and code locations were the same as for previous models with the first four symbols changed to Monza nomenclature. Sequential unit numbers used on 1975 Monzas began at 100001 and production was quartered at the Chevrolet factory in Saint Therese, Quebec, Canada. The Monza, however, was more an American car than a 'captive import'.

MONZA SERIES

Series Number	Body/Style Number	Body Type & Seating	Factory Price	Shipping Weight	Production Total
MONZA 'S'					
1M	27	2-dr Twn Cpe-4P	3570	2675	Note 1
1M	07	2-dr Hatch-4P	3648	NA	Note 1
MONZA (2+2)					
1R	07	2-dr Hach-4P	3953	2753	Note 1

NOTE: Exactly 66,615 Monzas were built during the 1975 model year, including 41,658 Fours and 24,957 V-8s. No breakouts by body style or trim level are available at the current time.

MONZA ENGINES
Four. See 1974 and 1975 Vega Series engine data.

V-8. See 1975 Nova Series engine data.

CAMARO — (SIX/V-8) — ALL SERIES — The Camaro featured a new, wraparound backlight for 1975. It provided a ten percent increase in rear visibility. The Z/28 'Special Performance Package' was (temporarily) dropped, but the Rally Sport option was reissued to fill the gap. Standard equipment echoed that of the previous season, plus High-Energy ignition and the catalytic converter. The R/S added Rally wheels; radial-tuned suspension; specific ornamentation and graphics including black paint accents for the grille; hood; front fender tops; headlamp bezels; window reveal area; forward sail panels and roof header. Engine selections were down to just three EPA-era choices: improved 105 horsepower '140' Six; RPO L65/145 horsepower two-barrel '350' V-8 (not available in cars for California sale) and the RPO LM1/155 horsepower four-barrel '350' V-8 (in California and high-altitude counties only).

VEHICLE IDENTIFICARTION NUMBERS: The numbering system and code locations were the same as for previous models with the first four symbols changed to Camaro nomenclature. Sequential unit production numbers on 1975 Camaros began with 500001 and up.

CAMARO SERIES

Series Number	Body/Style Number	Body Type & Seating	Factory Price	Shipping Weight	Production Total
CAMARO					
1Q	87	2-dr HT Cpe-4P	3540/3685	3421/3532	141,629
CAMARO TYPE LT					
1S	87	2-dr HT Cpe-4P	4057	3616	Note 1

NOTE 1: Production of the Camaro LT is included in the total figure given for base Camaro in chart above. This represents domestic production for the U.S. market. An additional 4,160 cars were built for export. Of the full total, 29,359 were Sixes and 116,430 were V-8s.

1975 Camaro, 2-dr hardtop sports coupe, V-8

ADDITIONAL NOTES: The total above also included 8,688 cars with four speeds; 10,568 with three-speeds; 126,533 with automatics; 77,290 with air conditioning; 7,000 with Rally Sport equipment; 145,755 with power steering and 10,598 with power windows.

CAMARO SERIES ENGINES
Six. See 1975 Nova Series six-cylinder engine data.

V-8. See 1975 Nova Series 'California' V-8 engine.

CHASSIS FEATURES: Wheelbase: (Chevrolets / Monte Carlo / Camaros / Novas / Vegas / Chevelles) same as 1974; (Monza) 97 inches. Overall length: (Chevrolets / Monte Carlos / Camaros / Novas / Vegas / Chevelle wagons) same as 1974; (Chevelles two-doors) 206 inches; (Chevelle four-doors) 210 inches; (Monza 2+2) 180 inches; (Monza Town Coupe) 179 inches. Width: (Monza) 66 inches; (all other models) same as 1974. Tires: Refer to text.

POWERTRAIN OPTIONS: Refer to text for changes.

CONVENIENCE OPTIONS: Vega vinyl top ($79). Vega power steering ($111). Monza / Vega air conditioning ($398). Vega wagon luggage rack ($50). Monza / Vega AM/FM stereo ($213). Vega hatch back GT packages ($425). Monza 5.7 liter engine ($298). Camaro / Nova vinyl top ($87). Nova air conditioning ($435). Nova tape deck ($199). Nova AM/FM stereo ($223). Chevelle wagons 454 V-8 engines ($285). Chevelle 454 V-8 engine ($340). Chevelle vinyl top ($96). Chevrolet / Monte Carlo / Camaro / Chevelle AM/FM stereo ($233). Chevrolet / Monte Carlo / Camaro / Chevelle AM/FM stereo with tape ($363). Monte Carlo / Chevelle sky roof ($350). Chevelle wagon luggage rack ($65). Chevrolet / Monte Carlo / Chevelle power seats ($113). Camaro / Chevelle Rally wheels ($46). Monte Carlo / Camaro power windows ($91). Monte Carlo vinyl top ($123). Monte Carlo 454 V-8 engine ($285). Chevrolet Group 454 V-8 engine ($315). Chevrolet wagon luggage rack ($77). Chevrolet Group wagson 454 V-8 engine ($172).

Historical footnotes: The full-sized Chevrolets were introduced in September, 1974 and the Cosworth Vega, Laguna Type S-3 and Monza Towne Coupe appeared in dealer showrooms during April, 1975. Model year production peaked at 1,600,878 units. Calendar year production of 1,639,490 cars were recorded R.L. Lund was the Chief Executive Officer of the company this year. The Monza 2 + 2 coupe was selected as 1975 Car of the Year by *Motor Trend* magazine.

STANDARD CATALOG OF

CHEVROLET

1976-1986

When Monte Carlo and the restyled Camaro appeared in 1970, few were surprised by their popularity. Similarly high expectations greeted the subcompact Vega when it emerged a year later, only to fizzle through half a dozen seasons, victim of unresolved technical difficulties (including its aluminum four-cylinder engine). Monza, an alternate subcompact, came to life for 1975. But Chevrolet's modest new Chevette for 1976 may have been most significant of all, heralding a trend toward small cars to rival the imports, which would eventually take over the industry. Based on GM's German-built Opel Kadett, Chevette even came in a two-passenger Scooter version, priced as low as $2899.

By Jim Flammang

1980 Monte Carlo Landau Coupe (CP)

In 1973, Chevrolet had turned away from the pillarless two-door hardtop, switching to the "Colonnade" design. This would be the final year for the true pillarless four-door hardtop in Impala/Caprice form. After a poor 1975, Chevrolet sales rose amply this year, but Oldsmobile's Cutlass was GM's best seller.

1980 Citation X11 Club Coupe (CP)

Full-size Chevrolets of 1976 were still mighty big, carrying V-8 engines up to 400 and 454 cu. in. displacement. Mid-sizes and Camaro, on the other hand, switched from a 350 to 305 cu. in. standard V-8. Nova compacts could have either a 305 or 350 V-8 instead of the basic inline six. Among the most noteworthy models was the Cosworth Vega with Twin Cam (16-valve) engine, in its final year. *Motor Trend* had named Monza Car of the Year for 1975. Monzas with the Spyder package draw the most interest today. So does the Nova Super Sport (SS) coupe and hatchback. Also of interest to enthusiasts: the last Chevelle Laguna S-3, sporting a "soft" aero front end and louvered coach windows. Camaro came in base of Luxury Touring (LT) trim, but the Z28 had faded away (temporarily).

1981 Caprice Classic sedan (AA)

Full-size Chevrolets weren't quite full after their 1977 downsizing, as the 350 became Impala/Caprice's biggest V-8. Caprice earned the *Motor Trend* honors this year, as overall Chevrolet sales rose moderately — and full-size models considerably. A Borg-Warner four-speed gearbox went into some Camaros, which didn't change at first. Later in the year, though, the Z28 was back, carrying a four-barrel 350 V-8. Though not so potent as its forerunners, it attracted considerable attention. For its final season, Vegas's Cosworth was gone, but twin GT packages were available. Chevette's Scooter added a back seat. Monza's Spyder came in two separate packages; one for appearance, another for performance.

1982 Camaro Z28 Sport Coupe (CH)

Downsizing hit the mid-size Malibu and Monte Carlo for 1978. Base engines were new too: a 200 cu. in V-6 for Malibu, 231 V-6 (from Buick) for Monte. Chevrolet sales reached their third highest point ever for the model year, led by a whopping rise in Chevette interest. Monza continued in its previous form, and added the former Vega's hatchback and wagon. Both Spyder and GT packages were available, as was a new 196 cu. in. Buick-built V-6. Monza's base four-cylinder engine came from Pontiac, but the 305 V-8 was Chevrolet's. Chevette supplemented the original two-door with a four-door hatchback, and lengthened its standard equipment list. Camaro's Z28 added slanted fender louvers, rear spoiler and hood air scoop.

Except for a new small-block 267 cu. in. V-8 available under Monte Carlo hoods, not much changed for 1979. A new Berlinetta replaced Camaro's Type LT, while Z28 featured new flared front wheel openings and air dam.

Full-size models switched from the old familiar inline six-cylinder engine to a new standard 229 cu. in. V-6 for 1980, and enjoyed an aero restyle. That news was minor, though, compared to the introduction of the Citation X-car. Widely praised at first, Chevrolet's first front-drive model soon suffered a variety of recalls and charges of seriously flawed brakes — charges that were never fully resolved, even years later. For the moment, though, Citation found plenty of buyers, including nearly 25,000 for its sporty X-11 package. Monza Spyders were available again, but V-8 engines were not. Camaro's Z28 took on further bodily changes, this time rear fender flares and a rear-facing hood scoop. California Z28 fans couldn't have the 350 V-8. Both 267 and 305 V-8s were available in other Camaros, though, along with the new base V-6. Monte Carlos could now get Buick's turbocharged 231 cu. in. V-6, which delivered 55 more horsepower than the standard 229 cu. in engine. Turbo-powered Chevrolets never quite took hold, as they did in other makes. Oldsmobile diesels were available in full-size wagons. Overall, Chevrolet sales declined by some 20 percent in this rough year for the industry.

Citation's X-11 package included a high-output V-6 engine for 1981, but the recalls were already having an impact on sales. Monte Carlo got a wedge-shape aero restyle, but little else was new. A diesel engine, supplied by Isuzu, became available in Chevettes, with five-speed gearbox. Sales slipped again — even worse for full-size models, which seemed in danger of extinction. Within the next couple of years, however, they would enjoy a rebirth of popularity.

1983 Cavalier Type 10 hatchback coupe (AA)

Front-wheel drive took on two additional forms for 1982: subcompact Cavalier and family-size Celebrity, both of which quickly became popular. A downsized Camaro looked even sleeker than its predecessor, if also a lot more expensive. It was named Car of the Year by *Motor Trend*. Powerplants ranged from the base Pontiac "Iron Duke" four (now fuel-injected), to 173 cu. in. V-6 and 305 V-8. More than 6,300 Indy 500 Commemorative Editions of the Z28 were built. Z28 Camaros could also get a Cross-Fire fuel-injected engine, churning out 165 horsepower.

Most noteworthy event of the 1983 model year was the arrival of a Cavalier convertible. A new high-output, 190-horsepower 305 V-8 became available under Camaro hoods. Monte Carlo added an SS model, which gained a strong following, also with a high-output 305 V-8. Only four-door full-size models were offered this year, but Caprice's coupe would return for '84. Five-speed gearboxes were available on Chevette, Cavalier and Camaro. Malibu, a long-standing nameplate, was in its final season. NHTSA's order to recall Citations for the alleged brake problems helped sales to plunge. Chevrolet sales went up somewhat, but largely as a result of increases in larger models.

A more powerful Monte Carlo SS lured youthful customers for 1984, with its wind-tunnel nose and lack of brightwork. Cross-Fire injection had lasted only two years as a Z28 option, but a four-barrel V-8 took its place. Camaro Berlinettas turned to a Corvette-inspired cockpit with digital instruments. A Eurosport option was added to Celebrity's possibilities; a Type 10 hatchback model to Cavalier's. So was a Celebrity station wagon. No more Chevette Scooters were built — hardly a major loss.

1984 Celebrity Eurosport coupe (CP)

Cavalier was America's best selling car, with Celebrity a strong second.

Excitement marked the 1985 model year, with the arrival of the IROC-Z Camaro. This Z28 option was styled like racing models, with foglamps, low air dam, and full-circle "ground effects" skirting. Three 305 cu. in V-8s were available, including one with tuned-port fuel injection. A performance-oriented Z24 Cavalier was announced, but didn't arrive until later. Chevrolet's market share dropped by a percentage point, to 19 percent. Two new Chevrolet imports hit the market: the three-cylinder Sprint (from Suzuki) and four-cylinder Spectrum (from Isuzu). The new Astro van also appeared.

1985 Monte Carlo SS Sport Coupe (AA)

Citation finally bit the dust after 1985, but something quite different emerged: the joint-venture Nova, produced in partnership with Toyota. One more nameplate disappeared: Impala. Cavalier had its Z24, with port-injected 173 cu. in. V-6 engine; and an RS series replaced the former Type 10. Monte Carlo added a luxurious and stylish LS model. On the sales front, Celebrity took over Cavalier's spot as No. 1. Early in 1987, the Chevette dropped away. Even pioneers can't last forever, especially when front-drive had become the standard for small cars — and more than a few big ones.

As always, Chevrolet offered quite a selection of cars to tempt later collectors. All Camaros are pleasing, with Z28s the most desirable — even those that lacked the performance of earlier (and later) models. The recent IROC-Z has already attracted considerable attention. Monte Carlo SS coupes, especially the more stark looking, minimally-trimmed models, are likely to remain in demand. Rarest is Monte's SS Aerocoupe fastback, with only 200 built in 1986; but most enthusiasts have never even seen one. Surely a Cosworth Vega is worth hanging onto, while Monza Spyders may be too numerous to rise much in value. A V-8 Spyder may be more curiosity than collectible — an example of stuffing a full-size engine where it might not belong. In view of the imminent shrinking of engine sizes, one of the final 454 V-8s might be worth acquiring; too bad there weren't any '76 convertibles to put one in. A latter-day Cavalier ragtop might be nice to have a few year hence. Keep a Chevette in your garage? They played a powerful role in paving the way for small domestic cars, but it's hard to imagine one as truly collectible.

1976 CHEVROLET

Chevrolet's lineup was largely a carryover from 1975, with one big (actually small) exception: the new subcompact Chevette. Throughout the line, improved gas mileage was the year's primary theme. Chevrolet also reduced its total number of models. A new 305 cu. in. engine replaced the former 350 as base V-8 under Chevelle, Monte Carlo and Camaro hoods. Vega and Monza also got new engines this year. Most models could have optional low axle ratios. Rectangular headlamps, first offered on full-size 1975 models, were now stacked vertically on Malibu Classic and Monte Carlo. All Chevrolets had a new roll-over fuel spillage control system. Brake materials were improved. Monza offered a sporty new Spyder option package. Rust resistance got considerable attention this year. Chevettes were protected by 17 anti-corrosion methods including wax base spray; epoxy paint; front inner fender plastic liners; zinc coated cowl side panels, hood, roof side rails and rear quarter panels; zinc-rich primer; galvanized metal front side rails, front valance and rocker panels; and oil base coating on rear springs. Promoted for Vega was a zinc-rich pre-prime coating on door surfaces; Plastisol- sealed door edges; aluminum wax spray applied to inner door areas after painting; plus four-layer fender protection, zinc-coated steel for lower radiator support and front fenders, and galvanized steel rocker panels.

1976 Chevette Rally 1.6 hatchback coupe (CH)

CHEVETTE — SERIES 1T — FOUR — "A new kind of American car" was promised by Chevette's catalog, "international in design and heritage." Target market was buyers of Datsun B210, Toyota Corolla, and VW Rabbit. In addition to the basic four-passenger two-door hatchback, Chevrolet offered Sport, Woody and Rallye options, as well as a bare-bones two-passenger (no back seat) Scooter with a base price of just $2899. Chevette's design was based on GM's German-built Opel Kadett. Powered by a base 85 cu. in. (1.4-liter) four-cylinder overhead-cam engine, Chevette carried a fully synchronized four-speed manual transmission, rack-and-pinion steering, and front disc brakes. Chevrolet's new subcompact measured almost 17 inches shorter than Vega (formerly the smallest Chevrolet), and weighed over 600 pounds less (just under one ton). As for economy, EPA estimates with the base 1.4-liter engine and four-speed manual gearbox came to 28 MPG city and 40 MPG highway. And the optional 97.6 cu. in. (1.6-liter) OHC four was thriftier yet, reaching a 48 MPG highway estimate. Styling features included an aero-designed front spoiler and flush-type door handles. Chevette's simple grille consisted of four wide openings (two on each side) in an angled body-color panel. Front fenders held small marker lenses; rear quarters, similar red lenses. Round headlamps were recessed; park/signal lamps mounted below the bumper area. Front fenders held 'Chevette' script near rear edges. At the rear were "international" horizontal tri-color taillamps (red, amber and white). The full-width (48 in.) rear hatch had pneumatic supports. This was Chevrolet's first metric-measurement car, supplied with a simple self-servicing booklet. A built-in diagnostic connector (first one on a domestic car) helped do- it-yourselfers or mechanics analyze electrical system problems. The optional Four-Season air conditioner had its own diagnostic connector. Unibody construction plus a combined hood and grille gave easy underhood accessibility. Front fenders bolted on. High-strength bumpers were mounted on shock absorbers, which connected to solid underbody rails. The front suspension had a stabilizer bar, low-friction ball joints and high-caster geometry, mounted on a heavy-gauge crossmember. At the rear were variable-rate coil springs and torque tube axle. Chevette was the first Chevrolet to get a fingertip "Smart Switch" on the steering column to control headlamp dimmer, turn signals, lane-change and "flash-to-pass" signals, and wiper/washer. Up front were full-form, shell- type bucket seats; in back, a full-width seat with folding backrest. Body color choices were: antique white, silver, light or dark blue metallic, lime green, bright yellow, cream, burnt orange, medium orange, firethorn metallic, light red, black, buckskin, or dark green metallic. (Light blue metallic, lime green, burnt orange and light red were Chevette exclusives.) Soft vinyl upholstery came in black, dark blue, light buckskin or dark firethorn. Cloth-and-vinyl upholstery came in light buckskin or dark firethorn. The optional Custom interior was rattan-pattern vinyl in black, light buckskin, dark blue, dark firethorn or white; or Rutledge cloth-and- vinyl in the same colors (except white). Standard equipment included the 1.4-liter engine; four- speed manual gearbox with floor lever; blackwall tires on 13 x 5 in. disc wheels; heater/defroster; fuel gauge; courtesy light in windshield header; easy-access instrument panel; spare tire below cargo floor; mini do-it-yourself service manual; color-keyed wall-to-wall carpeting; fold-down rear seat; glove compartment with door latch; bright bumpers and trim moldings; and acoustical insulation. The Sport Coupe added bold sport stripes and black accents. The Rally Coupe package came with a 1.6-liter engine, special suspension with rear stabilizer bar, special instruments including tachometer and temperature gauge, sport shifter and steering wheel, passenger assist grip, Rally wheel covers, and black rocker panels. Woody Coupes had woodgrain vinyl body trim, custom interior with woodgrain vinyl accents on the instrument cluster, sport steering wheel, day/night mirror, bright window moldings, wheel trim rings, and deluxe grille with bright accents. The low-budget Scooter had only two bucket seats and less standard equipment, including an open glove compartment. It came only in light blue, antique white, cream, or light red. Chevette options included the larger 1.6-liter engine, AM/FM radio, twin sport mirrors, Four-Season air conditioning, sport steering wheel, deluxe bumpers with impact strips, bumper guards, rooftop luggage rack, rear defogger, custom exterior trim package, and swing-out rear quarter windows. Also optional: a sport shifter (with console), the $306 Woody package, and Rally equipment. Turbo Hydra-matic cost an extra $244.

1976 Chevette 2-dr hatchback coupe, 4-cyl

1976 Vega GT hatchback coupe (CH)

VEGA — SERIES 1H — FOUR — Chevrolet's first subcompact coupe, introduced in 1971, never quite managed to overcome its early so-so reputation. Vegas came in sport and hatchback coupe form, as well as a two-door station wagon and Estate wagon. The LX model was dropped this year. The base aluminum-block four added new hydraulic valve lifters, eliminating the need for tappet adjustment. Crankcase ventilation was improved to ease engine breathing. New valve stem seals improved overhead oil control. Instead of a catalytic converter, the base four used an air pump and manifold injection for emissions control. Torque arm rear suspension was new this year (introduced on the '75 Monza). Brakes used larger (91/2 x 2 in.) rear drums and new organo-metallic front disc pad material. Power brakes were optional. So was a new lightweight, aluminum-case four-speed manual gearbox, as well as a five-speed on the Cosworth twin-cam model (and others with the optional two- barrel engine). The four-speed came with a new 2.53:1 axle ratio, plus long 3.75:1 low-gear ratio. A new box-section design front cross-member added structural rigidity. Vega's new grille consisted of three wide louvered openings that reached almost to the recessed round headlamps, giving the car an ultra-wide appearance. Parking lamps sat behind the grille. At the back, new multi-color lights were divided into three top-to-bottom sections, with tiny square backup lenses in lower sections. (Wagons had narrower vertical taillamps.) Vega's unitized body had bolt-on front fenders. Body colors this year were antique white, silver, black, buckskin, cream, bright yellow, medium orange, and seven metallics: light or dark blue, firethorn, mahogany, lime green, medium saddle, and dark green. Both 140 cu. in. four-cylinder engines were called Dura- built: with one-barrel (70 horsepower) or two-barrel (84 horsepower) carburetion. Vegas rode 13 x 5 in. steel wheels, except 13 x 6 in. on the GT. Cosworths had 13 x 6 in. cast aluminum wheels. Standard equipment included the 140 cu. in. four with 1Bbl. carburetor, three-speed manual transmission (floor shift), electric fuel pump, heater/defroster, front bucket seats, and A78 x 13 blackwall tires. All models could have five-speed manual or Turbo Hydra-matic for the same $244 extra cost. All could get a new heavy-duty sealed Freedom battery. Vega's GT package included the two-barrel version of the 140 engine, F41 sport suspension, special instruments, woodgrain accents on instrument cluster, dual sport mirrors (left remote-controlled), black headlamp bezels, bright grille header moldings, 13 x 6 in. wheels with trim rings, and A70 x 13/B white-letter tires. Offered for both hatchback coupes and wagons, the GT package also included a sport steering wheel, belt and wheel opening moldings, adjustable driver's seatback, and black sill and lower bodyside moldings. Sport coupes could have a new Cabriolet appearance option. This would be the final season for the Cosworth Twin Cam Vega. Cosworths carried an aluminum 122 cu. in. engine developed by Chevrolet and Cosworth Engineering of England. It had twin overhead camshafts, 16 valves, electronic fuel injection and mechanical valve lifters, and developed 110 horsepower at 5600 R.P.M. Four-speed manual shift was standard. To boost performance, the axle ratio switched from the former 3.73:1 to a new 4.10:1. Cosworths came in nine colors with gold pinstriping. Included were special gold- color aluminum wheels; 'Cosworth Twin Cam' decals on rear and both sides; gold-colored wheel opening stripes; and end panel striping. Custom interiors came in black or white, with Cosworth insert in the sport steering wheel. Also standard: an 8000 R.P.M. tachometer and adjustable driver's seatback.

1976 Monza Towne Coupe (CP)

MONZA - SERIES 1H — FOUR/V8 — Monza's 2 + 2 hatchback had been named Motor Trend "Car of the Year" after introduction in 1975. Part way through that model year, the Towne Coupe debuted, with much different notchback styling. Both returned for 1976, along with a formal Cabriolet version of the Towne Coupe. The base Towne Coupe had large rear quarter windows, hard bumpers, plus a sound-deadening and acoustical package. The $256 Cabriolet option included opera-type rear quarter windows and a vinyl top that covered the rear half of the roof, plus bright moldings, sport equipment, and woodgrain steering wheel shroud. Hatchbacks had a low body-color grille: just two rows of four wide holes, with that pattern repeated below the bumper. On the solid panel above the grille was a round emblem, plus 'Chevrolet' lettering off toward the driver's side. Parking lamps with rounded outer lower edges sat below the bumper. An engine identification plaque was at the front of front fenders, above the marker lens; 'Monza 2+2' lettering farther back, at the cowl. Quad rectangular headlamps were inset into a soft, resilient urethane front- end skin. The hood sloped down between the headlamps, but contained a bulge farther back. The 2+2 had bright-trimmed wraparound taillamps that tapered to a point on the bodyside, with square backup lenses toward the center. Towne Coupes had an entirely different front-end and side look, including bright chrome bumpers and single headlamp bezels. A classic grid grille (six holes wide) held hidden parking/signal lights. Rear bumper cover and rocker panels were body-colored. Monza body colors were cream, bright yellow, medium orange, black, buckskin, silver and antique white, plus metallic light or dark blue, firethorn, mahogany, lime green, saddle brown, and dark green. Refinements for the aluminum-block 140 cu. in. (2.3- liter) four included new hydraulic lifters for quieter running, new valve stem seals to improve oil control, and improved crankcase ventilation. That engine again had a 60,000-mile, five-year

1976 Monza 2+2 hatchback coupe (CP)

guarantee. Monza also offered options of a two-barrel version of the 140 four, a 262 cu. in. (4.3- liter) V-8, or even a 305 (5.0-liter) V-8. That big V-8 was smaller in size, yet considerably stronger in horsepower, than the 350 offered in 1975. No V-8s were available on the base Towne Coupe. The two-barrel four was included in Sport and Cabriolet packages. Transmission choices included a new four-speed manual gearbox with aluminum case for the four- cylinder engine, plus an economy five-speed that had been introduced during the 1975 model year. A new underbody lowered the floor hump between bucket seats by more than two inches. An all-new brake system included larger rear drums with increased torque capacity, a new vented front rotor, new front disc pad material and front-to-rear proportioning. A muffler replaced the catalytic converter on the Towne Coupe's base four. Models that retained converters lost their exhaust system resonators this year. All models had a new floor shift and parking brake console. The new lighter weight four-speed gearbox, used with four-cylinder engines, had a 3.75:1 low gear. Monza standard equipment included the 2.3-liter four with one-barrel carburetor, three-speed manual transmission, heater/defroster, bucket seats, cigarette lighter, front disc brakes, A78 x 13/B tires, and cut-pile carpeting. Hatchback 2+2 models included Euro-style finned wheel covers with GT center hub and bright nuts. Towne Coupes had bright metallic wheel covers. The 4.3-liter V-8 engine cost an extra $224. Four- and five-speed manual gearboxes were optional, as was Turbo Hydra-matic. So were aluminum wheels, as well as a widened choice of entertainment options including AM/FM stereo radio and tape player. Inside, the 2+2 had a new deluxe "stitched" instrument panel pad, with woodgrain vinyl ornamentation color-keyed to the car interior. A two-spoke steering wheel had woodgrain vinyl insert. The 2+2 had knit cloth and vinyl upholstery in black, buckskin or firethorn; or all-vinyl in black, buckskin, firethorn or white Towne Coupes had sport cloth upholstery in black or buckskin. Cabriolet equipment for the Towne Coupe included the padded vinyl roof in firethorn, mahogany, white, silver metallic, buckskin, or blue. Monza's Spyder package, available on the 2+2 or Towne Coupe with sport equipment, had the two-barrel four; floor console; F41 suspension with large front and rear stabilizer bars and special shocks; wheel opening moldings; day/night mirror; sport steering wheel; distinctive Spyder identification; special instrumentation and stitched instrument panel pad with woodgrain vinyl accents; and BR70 or BR78 radial tires. Spyders required a five-speed manual gearbox or turbo Hydra-matic. A total of 2,339 were produced. Towne Coupes with sport equipment had a black pillar applique with argent edges, ahead of large rear quarter windows. The package included body-colored finned wheel covers with argent painted edges; front stablizer bar; plus body-contoured high-back front bucket seats. Knit cloth/vinyl upholstery came in black, buckskin or firethorn; all-vinyl in black, buckskin, firethorn or white.

1976 Nova Concours coupe (CH)

NOVA — SERIES 1X — SIX/V-8 — Nova Concours joined the lineup this year as top-of-the- line member of the compact family. Both 111 in. wheelbase models showed a new front-end look. Novas displayed a new six-row crosshatch grille (6 x 12 pattern) split in half by a heavier horizontal bar, with single round headlamps. Regular Novas had vertical amber parking lamp lenses at grille ends. Twin side-by-side rectangular taillamps were split by two horizontal dividers. Concours models added chrome trim around the headlamps and hood areas, as well as a special NC insignia and upright three-dimensional hood ornament. Concours' similar but bold grille had 24 square holes in two rows, each square containing 3 x 3 crosshatching, also with vertical parking lamps between grille and headlamps. Concours had a wide bright panel above the grille; regular Novas did not. Identifying features also included a fender nameplate, wheel cover insignia, and NC shield on the rear panel. Concours models also carried bumper guards and impact strips, bright moldings, plus dark-accented full-length bodyside louvers and rocker panel moldings. Inside, the Concours had rosewood-grain vinyl accents on the dash, steering wheel and upper door panels, along with identification on the right side of the instrument panel. A new 305 cu. in. engine became the basic V-8, replacing the former 262. Base engine continued to be the inline 250 cu. in. six. A four-barrel 350 V-8 was also optional again. Power brakes moved from the option list to standard equipment for V-8 Novas this year, and were available on six-cylinder models. Brake systems had new front disc

1976 Nova SS coupe (CP)

pads and rear lining material, and larger-diameter rear cylinders. Air conditioners had a new seven-mode setting and maximum cooling position. Otherwise, changes were modest this year: altered fuel and exhaust system mountings, new interior colors and trim materials, and new instrument panel knobs. Nova's body colors were: medium orange, buckskin, cream, antique white, bright yellow, black and silver; plus metallic light or dark blue, firethorn, mahogany, lime green, saddle, and dark green. Regular Nova interiors came in three cloth and vinyl colors: black, buckskin or firethorn. All-vinyl colors were buckskin, blue or firethorn. Hatchbacks came only with all-vinyl interiors. Concours had three knit cloth and vinyl interiors: black, buckskin or firethorn. Or all-vinyl in buckskin or firethorn. White interiors were available in coupe and hatchback only. Optional: new high-pile deluxe carpeting. Standard equipment included the 250 cu. in. six-cylinder engine (one-barrel carb), three-speed manual shift, heater/defroster, front disc brakes, and cut-pile carpeting. Nova V-8s had power brakes. Four-speed wide-range manual shift cost $242, while a floor shift lever cost $29 extra. Both cabriolet and vinyl roofs were optional. So were heavy- duty and sport suspensions. The 350 cu. in. V-8 was available for $85 more than the standard 305 V-8. Nova Concours carried similar equipment but added bright moldings, front/rear bumper guards, full wheel covers, cigarette lighter, and FR78 x 14 steel-belted radial tires. Nova's Super Sport (SS) coupe and hatchback had a new black-finished diamond-mesh pattern grille with 'Nova SS' emblem, plus other black-accented trim. Styling features included black headlamp bezels and side window frame moldings; distinctive lower body side striping; Nova SS decals on fenders and rear end panel; dual black sport mirrors (left remote controlled); horizontal parking lamps with clear lenses; heavy-duty suspension; and four-spoke sport steering wheel. The $187 SS coupe package also included roof drip moldings, rally wheels with trim rings, and heavy- duty F40 front/rear suspension. All told, 7,416 SS Novas came off the line.

1976 Camaro Type LT coupe (CP)

CAMARO — SERIES 1F — SIX/V-8 — Chevrolet's sport coupe, in base or Type LT (Luxury Touring) form, looked similar to the 1975 version. The crosshatch grille was made up of thin bars peaked forward at the center, surrounded by a bright molding with rounded upper corners. Round, deeply recessed parking lamps sat between the grille and the recessed round headlamps. Front fenders held small side marker lenses. Taillamps with bright moldings wrapped around the side, tapering to a point. Small vertical backup lights were in the taillamp housings. Rectangular emblems sat on hood and deck. Type LT had a 'TYPE LT' nameplate on the right side of the bright rear end panel, but could also be spotted by its brushed aluminum applique across the full width of the rear end panel. LT seat trim now used vertical stitching for both cloth and vinyl upholstery (three knit cloth/vinyl choices or three all-vinyl). Standard sport coupes came with two cloth/vinyl interiors or four in all- vinyl. Styling features included a long hood and short deck, with swept-back roofline. Sport Coupes had new narrow bright rocker panel moldings, 14 x 6 in. wheels, contoured Strato- bucket front seats, cut-pile carpeting, padded vinyl-covered four-spoke steering wheel with crest, and a left outside mirror. Type LT added Hide-A-Way wipers and sport mirrors (left one remote-controlled), and 14 x 7 in. Rally wheels. Inside LT were a tachometer, clock, voltmeter and temp gauge, plus color-keyed steering wheel, glove compartment light, and simulated leather instrument panel trim. LT interiors also had special bucket seats with deep-contour backs and built-in padded armrests. A new small-block V-8 engine was available this year: a 305 cu. in. (5.0-liter) version that replaced the 350 as standard eight-cylinder engine. It came with either the standard or high-performance

1976 Camaro Rally Sport coupe (CP)

axle ratio. As before, the 250 cu. in. inline six was the base (Sport Coupe) powerplant, while a 350 (5.7-liter) V-8 with four-barrel carburetor was available for both models. Transmission choices were the same as in 1975, except that the four-speed manual gearbox came with a 2.85:1 low-gear ratio (formerly 2.54:1). Power brakes (front disc) were now standard with V-8s. Brake improvements included new front disc pad material and new rear linings, plus larger-diameter rear wheel cylinders. Base Sport Coupes had the standard inline six; LT the new 305 V-8. Standard equipment included a heater/defroster, variable-ratio power steering, finned rear brake drums, contoured Strato bucket seats, four-spoke steering wheel, and FR78 x 14 steel-belted radial tires. Three-speed manual transmission (floor shift) was standard. Turbo Hydra-matic was optional on all models, wide-range four-speed manual available with the optional 350 cu. in. engine (which cost $85 more than the 305). Both transmissions were priced at $260. Cruise-Master speed control was optional for the first time. Also available: Rally or styled wheels, sport suspension, power windows and door locks, Four-Season air conditioning, rear defogger, tinted glass, white-letter tires, front and rear spoilers, Positraction, two-position driver's seatback, and center console with storage area. This year's vinyl Sport Roof covered only the front, leaving a painted band exposed at the back. Of the 14 Camaro body colors this year, ten were new. Choices were: light or dark blue metallic, firethorn metallic, mahogany metallic, lime green or dark green metallic, buckskin, cream, bright yellow, medium orange or saddle metallic, black, silver, and antique white. Sport Coupes came with black or dark firethorn cloth/vinyl upholstery, or all-vinyl in black, white, dark firethorn or light buckskin. Type LT offered three Dover knit cloth/vinyl choices (black, dark blue and dark firethorn) or all-vinyl in black, white or light buckskin. A Rally Sport package, available on both models, included low-gloss black finish on forward roof, hood, grille, header panel, headlamp bezels, upper fenders, rockers and rear panel, as well as Rally wheels. Tri-color striping separated the black-accented areas from the basic body color. The package also included bright headlamp trim, 'Rally Sport' decals on decklid and front fender, and argent paint. Rally Camaros came in white, silver, light blue metallic, firethorn metallic, or bright yellow body colors.

1976 Chevelle Malibu Classic Landau Coupe (CP)

CHEVELLE — SERIES 1A — SIX/V-8 — Two Chevelle series were offered for 1976, Malibu and Malibu Classic, plus (for the last time) the sportier Laguna S3. The Malibu Classic lineup included a Colonnade coupe and sedan, plus Landau coupe, two- and three-seat wagons, and two- or three-seat Estate wagons. Base Malibus came in coupe, sedan or wagon form (also two- or three-seat). Malibu Classic's restyled front end displayed new stacked rectangular headlamps, plus a lightweight diamond-pattern grille with script in lower corner, "classic" hood ornament, and new bumpers. Standard Malibus added a new horizontally-ribbed grille, but kept their single round headlamps with bright bezels. Both displayed a restyled rear end with tapered rear panel, with new horizontal rectangular taillamps and bumper in integrated design. Parking lamps were inset in the lower bumper. Landau coupes had new color-keyed paint stripes at front and rear, coach window styling, and distinctive vinyl roof. Malibu Classics had wide bright rocker panel moldings and window moldings, while base Malibus were plain. Biggest change in the powerplant parade was a new small- block 305 cu. in. (5.0-liter) standard V-8, which was supposed to emit fewer hydrocarbons as well as deliver better economy than the prior 350 V-8. Though the stroke of the 305 was the same as the 350, it was the only Chevrolet engine to have a 3.74 inch bore. Base engine was again the 250 cu. in. inline six, hooked to either three-speed manual or optional Turbo Hydra-matic. (V-8 Chevelles came only with automatic.) A 350 V-8 with two-barrel remained optional, as did a four- barrel 400 cu. in. V-8. Only in California was the four- barrel 350 offered. The big 454 was dropped as a Chevelle option this year. All Chevelles except the basic six-cylinder Malibu coupe and sedan now had standard power brakes. The brake system used new lining materials, plus larger rear drums in coupes and sedans. Standard equipment included the six-cylinder engine, three-speed manual (column) shift, front disc brakes, heater/defroster, cut-pile carpeting, lighter, hide-away wipers, and FR78 x 15/B steel-belted radial tires. Chevelle V-8s had a standard 305 engine and Turbo Hydra-matic, GR78 tires, as well as power brakes and steering. Wagons carried the 350 V-8. The Malibu Classic Landau added a vinyl roof, body-color sport mirrors (left one remote-controlled), deluxe bumpers, dual horns, and full wheel covers. 70-series radial tires and sport suspension were available at extra cost. All models could have the 400 cu. in. V-8 powerplant for $148 or less. Of the 14 body colors this year, nine were new. Available were metallic light or dark blue, firethorn, mahogany, lime green, medium saddle, and dark green; plus cream, medium red, buckskin, cream gold, antique white, silver, and black. Interiors came in new knit vinyls as well as patterned cloths and expanded vinyls. Light buckskin, dark mahogany and lime white were new interior trim colors. Base Malibu interiors were sport cloth and vinyl, in black and buckskin. All-vinyl upholstery came in black, buckskin or blue, plus mahogany and white (with accents of black, lime or mahogany) for coupes only. Malibu Classic's interior was standard knit cloth and vinyl in black, blue or mahogany. (Coupes could have buckskin.) Or buyers could get all-vinyl in buckskin and blue, plus black, mahogany and white (with accents of black, blue, mahogany or lime) for coupe only. For its final season, the sporty Laguna S3 added the new Chevelle rear end but otherwise looked largely the same as in 1975. Laguna had an angled, aerodynamically styled "soft" urethane front end, louvered coach windows, sport mirrors (driver's remote), rally wheels, color-keyed bumper impact strips, plus S3 identification on grille, front fenders and rear panel. Optional on Laguna: sport roof and sport striping. Inside was a round-dial instrument panel and woodgrain vinyl accents. The radial-tuned suspension had large-diameter stabilizer bars and revalved shock absorbers. Not available on Laguna bodies were light blue metallic, cream, medium saddle metallic, dark green metallic, medium red, buckskin, and cream gold. Laguna interiors were sport cloth and vinyl in black and buckskin; or all-vinyl in black, buckskin, blue and mahogany; plus white with accents of black, lime or mahogany.

1976 Monte Carlo Landau Coupe (CP)

MONTE CARLO — SERIES 1A — V-8 — Chevrolet's personal-luxury coupe, in the lineup since 1970, came in regular 'S' or Landau coupe form. New front-end styling focused on new vertically-stacked rectangular headlamps, plus an integrated-look bumper. This year's grille was made up of three wide segments, one above the other, each with internal crosshatching. Both parking and backup lamps were repositioned. Rounded horizontal parking lamps sat below the bumper. New tapered vertical taillamps had emblems in the center and small rectangular backup lenses below. A characteristic bodyside bulge tapered from front fenders into doors, continuing again on the rear quarters. Base engine was the 305 cu. in. (5.0-liter) V-8 with two-barrel carburetor; optional, either a 350 two-barrel or 400 four-barrel. Only in California was the 350 with four- barrel carb available. The 454 cu. in. V-8 available in 1975 was dropped this year. Standard powertrain included Turbo Hydra-matic with a 2.73:1 axle ratio. Montes also had standard power steering and brakes, electric clock, hideaway wipers, cut-pile carpeting, full wheel covers, and 15x7 in. wheels with GR70 x 15/B steel-belted radial tires. The Landau model added a landau vinyl roof and body-color sport mirrors (left remote), visor vanity mirror, plus Turbine II wheels, pinstripe accents, dual horns, and landau body identification. The 350 cu. in. V-8 engines cost an extra $30 (two-barrel) or $85 (four-barrel); the 400 V-8, an extra $148. New to the option list: an electric rear window defogger. Of the 14 Monte body colors, nine were new. They included cream, buckskin, cream gold, medium red, white, black and silver; plus metallic mahogany, firethorn, medium saddle, lime green, light blue, dark blue, or dark green. Two-tones were available. Standard interiors had a full-foam bench seat; deep cut pile carpeting; color-keyed instrument panel and steering wheel; and tailored knit cloth or vinyl upholstery in choice of three shades. Optional swivel bucket seats could have rich velour fabric. Custom interiors came in velour, knit cloth or vinyl fabric; or three all-vinyl colors.

1976 Impala S sedan (CP)

IMPALA/CAPRICE — SERIES 1B — V-8 — Full-size Chevrolets got new front styling and engine/brake refinements. For 1976 there were 13 models in two series (down from 17 in three series the year before). Bel Air sedans and wagons were dropped, as was the Caprice convertible. Impala's sport coupe was dropped; a new Impala sedan added. Impala's lineup now included a Custom coupe, Custom Landau coupe, sport sedan, four-door sedan, 'S' sedan, and station wagons (two or three seat). On the higher-priced Caprice Classic side, the choices were a coupe, sport sedan, four-door sedan, and Landau coupe; plus Caprice Estate station wagons (two or three seat). This would be the final year for the "true" pillarless four-door hardtop body. Impala refined its "swept back" front end look with round quad headlamps (as on the '75 Caprice). The grille had four full-width segments that appeared unconnected to each other. At the rear were triple-unit wraparound taillamps. The new Caprice front-end look featured new quad rectangular headlamps, plus a new grille with bold chrome horizontal and vertical bars and smaller inner bars. Both grilles repeated themselves in twin segments down in the front bumper. Both lines had hideaway windshield wipers. Caprice had wide bodyside moldings with color-keyed textured vinyl inserts (which could match the vinyl roof, if desired). Four V-8 choices were available: 350 cu. in. (5.7-liter) with two- or four-barrel carburetor; 400 cu. in. (6.6-liter) 4Bbl.; and big 454 (7.4-liter) with 4Bbl. Three-speed Turbo Hydra-matic was standard with each engine. Wagons kept the 400 V-8 as standard powerplant. Like all Chevrolet engines, the 454 V-8 got revised ignition tuning and carburetor metering, plus refinements to improve economy and performance at low- and mid-range speeds. Some models with the 454 got different brake lining materials and heavier brake drums, plus a new brake pedal ratio. Standard Caprice equipment included the 350 V-8 with two-barrel, power steering and brakes, carpeting, heater/defroster, deluxe bumpers, and accent stripes. Caprice also had rear fender skirts, a quiet sound group, electric clock, and GR78 x 15/B steel-belted radial tires. Wagons came with glide-away tailgate and LR78 x 15/C tires. Landau coupes added twin sport mirrors (left remote-controlled). The big 454 V-8 was optional on all models, priced from $223 to $375. Inside, Caprice Classic sported new bright steering wheel trim; plus new simulated rosewood accents on instrument cluster, steering wheel, and above the glove compartment. Impala's standard equipment was similar to Caprice, but the low-budget 'S' version had bias-ply tires rather than radials, and less acoustical material. Impala 'S' also had no bodyside chrome strip or door window trim. Impala had a soft- rimmed steering wheel with cushioned center; but the same dash as Caprice, with simulated rosewood. Landau

1976 Caprice Classic Sport Sedan (CP)

versions of both coupes had an elk-grain padded vinyl roof cover in choice of colors to complement the body. Also included: landau identification on quarter-window glass, body-colored wheel covers with landau markings, twin body- color sport mirrors, deluxe bumpers with impact strips, accent stripes and bright moldings. Sport sedans had a bright metal vinyl top molding. Of the 14 Caprice/Impala body colors, nine were new this year. The list included cream, antique white, silver, black, medium red, buckskin and cream gold; plus metallic light or dark blue, lime or dark green, medium saddle, firethorn, and mahogany. Impala upholstery was new standard knit cloth and vinyl in black, dark blue, or dark firethorn; or buckskin sport cloth. Caprice's knit cloth and vinyl came in black, dark blue, or dark mahogany. All-vinyl white trim was now available in the Caprice Classic coupe. Wagons added a cargo light as auxiliary lighting, while an illuminated visor vanity mirror was available on all models. Options included aluminum door edge guards.

I.D. DATA: Like other GM passenger cars, Chevrolets used a 13- symbol Vehicle Identification Number (VIN) displayed on the upper left surface of the instrument panel, visible through the windshield. the first digit ('1') indicates Chevrolet Division. Next is a letter identifying the series (car line): 'B' Chevette; 'J' Chevette Scooter; 'V' Vega; 'M' Monza; 'R' Monza 2+2; 'X' Nova; 'Q' Camaro; 'S' Camaro Type LT; 'Y' Nova Concours; 'C' Chevelle Malibu; 'D' Malibu Classic; 'E' Laguna S3; 'H' Monte Carlo; 'L' Impala; 'N' Caprice Classic. Symbols 34 indicate body type: '08' Chevette 2-dr. hatchback coupe; '11' Vega 2-dr. notchback pillar coupe; '77' Vega 2-dr. hatchback coupe; '07' Monza hatchback pillar coupe; '17' Nova 2-dr. hatchback coupe; '27' 2-dr. notchback coupe; '87' Camaro 2-dr. hardtop sport coupe; '37' Chevelle 2-dr. notchback hardtop coupe; '47' Caprice/Impala 2-dr. notchback hardtop coupe; '57' Monte Carlo 2-dr. hardtop coupe; '69' 4-dr. (4-window) pillar sedan; '39' 4-dr. (4-window) hardtop sedan; '29' Chevelle 4-dr. sedan; '35' 4-dr. 2-seat station wagon; '45' 4-dr. 3-seat wagon; '15' Vega 2-dr. station wagon. Symbol five is the engine code: '1' L485 1Bbl.; 'E' L497.6 1Bbl.; 'O' L4122 EFI; 'A' L4140 1Bbl.; 'B' L4140 2Bbl.; 'D' L6250 1Bbl.; 'G' V8262 2Bbl.; 'Q' V8305 2Bbl.; 'V' V8350 2Bbl.; 'L' V8350 4Bbl.; 'U' V8400 4Bbl.; 'S' V8454 4Bbl. Next is a code for model year ('6' 1976). Symbol seven denotes assembly plant: 'B' Baltimore, MD; 'C' South Gate, CA; 'D' Doraville, GA; 'J' Janesville, WI; 'K' Leeds, MO; 'U' Lordstown, OH; 'L' Van Nuys, CA; 'N' Norwood, OH; 'R' Arlington, TX; 'S' St. Louis, MO; 'T' Tarrytown, NY; 'W' Willow Run, MI; 'Y' Wilmington, DE; 'Z' Fremont, CA; '1' Oshawa, Ontario; '2' St. Therese, Quebec; '4' Scarborough, Canada. The last six digits are the sequential serial number. A Body Number Plate on the upper horizontal surface of the shroud (except X-bodies, on the vertical surface) identifies model year, car division, series, style, body assembly plant, body number, trim combination, modular seat code, paint code, and date build code. A three-symbol (sometimes two) code combined with a serial number identifies each engine. Inline sixes have that number on a pad at front right of block, at rear of distributor. On V-8s, it's on a pad at front right side of block. Chevette engine numbers are on a pad at right of block, below No. 1 spark plug. Vega numbers are on a pad at right side of block below No. 3 plug at head parting line.

VEGA (FOUR)

Model Number	Body/Style Number	Body Type & Seating	Factory Price	Shipping Weight	Production Total
1H	V11	2-dr. Spt Cpe-4P	2984	2443	27,619
1H	V77	2-dr. Hatch-4P	3099	2534	77,409
1H	V15	2-dr. Sta Wag-4P	3227	2578	46,114
1H	V15	2-dr. Est Wag-4P	3450	N/A	7,935

1976 Cosworth Vega hatchback coupe (CP)

CHEVETTE (FOUR)

1T	B08	2-dr. Hatch-rP	3098	1924	178,007

CHEVETTE SCOOTER (FOUR)

1T	J08	2-dr. Hatch-4P	2899	1870	9,810

Chevette Production Note: 7,523 Chevettes were built for the Canadian market, called Acadians.

COSWORTH VEGA (FOUR)

1H	V77	2-dr. Hatch-4P	6066	N/A	1,446

MONZA (FOUR/V-8)

1H	M27	2-dr. Twn Cpe-4P	3359	2625	46,735
1H	R07	2-dr. Hatch 22-4P	3727	2668	34,170

Monza Engine Note: Prices shown are for four-cylinder. Only 7,277 Towne Coupes and 10,085 hatchbacks had a V-8 engine, which cost an additional $224. Production totals include four-cylinder Monzas built in Canada.

NOVA (SIX/V-8)

Model Number	Body/Style Number	Body Type & Seating	Factory Price	Shipping Weight	Production Total
1X	X27	2-dr. Cpe-6P	3248/3413	3188/3272	131,859
1X	X17	2-dr. Hatch-6P	3417/3579	3391/3475	18,719
1X	X69	4-dr. Sedan-6P	3283/3448	3221/3305	123,767

NOVA CONCOURS (SIX/V-8)

1X	Y27	2-dr. Cpe-6P	3795/3960	3324/3408	22,298
1X	Y17	2-dr. Hatch-6P	3972/4134	3401/3485	7,574
1X	Y69	4-dr. Sedan-6P	3830/3995	3367/3451	30,511

CAMARO (SIX/V-8)

1F	Q87	2-dr. Spt Cpe-4P	3762/3927	3421/3511	130,538
1F	S87	2-dr. LT Cpe-4P	-- /4320	-- /3576	52,421

CHEVELLE MALIBU (SIX/V-8)

1A	C37	2-dr. Col Cpe-6P	3636/4166	3650/3755	30,592
1A	C29	4-dr. Col Sed-6P	3671/4201	3729/3834	38,469
1A	C35	4-dr. Sta Wag-6P	-- /4543	-- /4238	13,581
1A	C35	4-dr. 3S Wag-9P	-- /4686	-- / N/A	2,984

CHEVELLE MALIBU CLASSIC (SIX/V-8)

1A	D37	2-dr. Col Cpe-6P	3926/4455	3688/3793	82,634
1A	D37	2-dr. Lan Cpe-6P	4124/4640	N/A	30,167
1A	D29	4-dr. Col Sed-6P	4196/4490	3827/3932	77,560
1A	D35	4-dr. Sta Wag-6P	-- /4776	-- /4300	24,635
1A	D35	4-dr. 3S Wag-9P	-- /4919	-- / N/A	11,617
1A	G35	4-dr. Est Wag-6P	-- /4971	-- /4326	5,518
1A	G35	4-dr. 3S Est Wag-6P	-- /5114	-- /N/A	

Malibu Classic Engine Note: Only 672 Landau coupes, 5,791 regular coupes and 4,253 sedans had a six-cylinder engine.

LAGUNA S-3 (V-8)

1A	E37	2-dr. Col Cpe-5P	4622	3978	9,100

Laguna Production Note: Total includes 864 built in Canada.

MONTE CARLO (V-8)

1A	H57	2-dr. 'S' Cpe-6P	4673	3907	191,370
1A	H57	2-dr. Lan Cpe-6P	4966	N/A	161,902

FULL-SIZE CHEVROLETS IMPALA (V-8)

1B	L47	2-dr. Cust Cpe-6P	4763	4175	43,219
1B	L47	2-dr. Lan Cpe-6P	5058	N/A	10,841
1B	L69	4-dr. Sedan-6P	4706	4222	86,057
1B	L69	4-dr. 'S' Sed-6P	4507	N/A	18,265
1B	L39	4-dr. Spt Sed-6P	4798	4245	39,849
1B	L35	4-dr. Sta Wag-6P	5166	4912	19,657
1B	L45	4-dr. 3S Wag-9P	5283	4972	21,329

CAPRICE CLASSIC (V-8)

1B	N47	2-dr. Coupe-6P	5043	4244	28,161
1B	N47	2-dr. Lan Cpe-6P	5284	N/A	21,926
1B	N69	4-dr. Sedan-6P	5013	4285	47,411
1B	N39	4-dr. Spt Sed-6P	5078	4314	55,308
1B	N35	4-dr. Est Wag-6P	5429	4948	10,029
1B	N45	4-dr. 3S Est-6P	5546	5007	21,804

FACTORY PRICE AND WEIGHT NOTE: Where two prices and weights are shown, the figure to the left of the slash is for six-cylinder model, to right of slash for V-8 (except Monza, four-cylinder and V-8). **PRODUCTION NOTE:** Chevelle and full-size totals include models built in Canada.

ENGINE DATA: BASE FOUR (Chevette): Inline. Overhead cam. Four-cylinder. Cast iron block and head. Displacement: 85.0 cu. in. (1.4 liters). Bore & stroke: 3.23 x 2.61 in. Compression ratio: 8.5:1. Brake horsepower: 52 at 5200 R.P.M. Torque: 70 lbs.-ft. at 3600 R.P.M. Five main bearings. Hydraulic valve lifters. Carburetor: 1Bbl. Rochester 1ME. VIN Code: 1. OPTIONAL FOUR (Chevette): Inline. Overhead cam. Four-cylinder. Cast iron block and head. Displacement: 97.6 cu. in. (1.6 liters). Bore & stroke: 3.23 x 2.98 in. Compression ratio: 8.5:1. Brake horsepower: 60 at 4800 R.P.M. Torque: 82 lbs.-ft. at 3400 R.P.M. Five main bearings. Hydraulic valve lifters. Carburetor: 1Bbl. Roch. 1ME. VIN Code: E. BASE FOUR (Cosworth Vega): Inline vee-slanted. Dual overhead cam. Four-cylinder 16valve (four valves per cylinder). Cast aluminum alloy block and head. Displacement: 122 cu. in. (2.0 liters). Bore & stroke: 3.50 x 3.16 in. Compression ratio: 8.0:1. Brake horsepower: 110 at 5600 R.P.M. Torque: 107 lbs.-ft. at 4800 R.P.M. Five main bearings. Solid valve lifters. Electronic fuel injection. VIN Code: O. BASE FOUR (Vega, Monza): Inline. Overhead cam. Four-cylinder. Aluminum block, cast iron head. Displacement: 140 cu. in. (2.3 liters). Bore & stroke: 3.50 x 3.63 in. Compression ratio: 8.0:1. Brake horsepower: 70 at 4400 R.P.M. Torque: 107 lbs.-ft. at 2400 R.P.M. Five main bearings. Hydraulic valve lifters. Carburetor: 1Bbl. Rochester 1MV. VIN Code: A. OPTIONAL FOUR (Vega, Monza): Same as 140 cu. in. four above, except Brake H.P.: 84 at 4400 R.P.M. Torque: 113 lbs.-ft. at 3200 R.P.M. Carb: 2Bbl. Holley 5210C. BASE SIX (Nova, Chevelle, Camaro): Inline. OHV. Six-cylinder. Cast iron block and head. Displacement: 250 cu. in. (4.1 liters). Bore & stroke: 3.88 x 3.53 in. Compression ratio: 8.25:1. Brake horsepower: 105 at 3800 R.P.M. Torque: 185 lbs.-ft. at 1200 R.P.M. Seven main bearings. Hydraulic valve lifters. Carburetor: 1Bbl. Roch. 1MV. VIN Code: D. OPTIONAL V-8 (Monza): 90-degree, overhead valve V-8. Cast iron block and head. Displacement: 262 cu. in. (4.3 liters). Bore & stroke: 3.67 x 3.10 in. Compression ratio: 8.5:1. Brake horsepower: 110 at 3600 R.P.M. Torque: 195 lbs.-ft. at 2000 R.P.M. Five main bearings. Hydraulic valve lifters. Carburetor: 2Bbl. Roch. 2GC. VIN Code: G. BASE V-8 (Monte Carlo); OPTIONAL (Monza, Nova, Camaro, Chevelle): 90-degree, overhead valve V-8. Cast iron block and head. Displacement: 305 cu. in. (5.0 liters). Bore & stroke: 3.74 x 3.48 in. Compression ratio: 8.5:1. Brake horsepower: 140 at 3800 R.P.M. Torque: 245 lbs.-ft. at 2000 R.P.M. Five main bearings. Hydraulic valve lifters. Carburetor: 2Bbl. Roch. 2GC. VIN Code: Q. BASE V-8 (Chevelle wagon, Caprice, Impala); OPTIONAL (Chevelle, Monte Carlo): 90-degree, overhead valve V-8. Cast iron block and head. Displacement: 350 cu. in. (5.7 liters). Bore & stroke: 4.00 x 3.48 in. Compression ratio: 8.5:1. Brake horsepower: 145 at 3800 R.P.M. Torque: 250 lbs.-ft. at 2200 R.P.M. Five main bearings. Hydraulic valve lifters. Carburetor: 2Bbl. Roch. 2GC. VIN Code: V. OPTIONAL V-8 (Nova, Camaro, Chevelle, Monte Carlo, Caprice, Impala): Same as 350 cu. in. V-8 above, except four-barrel carburetor Brake H.P.: 165 at 3800 R.P.M. Torque: 260 lbs.-ft. at 2400 R.P.M. Carb: 4Bbl. Roch. M4MC. VIN Code: L. BASE V-8 (Caprice/Impala wagon); OPTIONAL (Chevelle, Monte Carlo, Caprice, Impala): 90-degree, overhead valve V-8. Cast iron block and head. Displacement: 400 cu. in. (6.6 liters). Bore & stroke: 4.13 x 3.75 in. Compression ratio: 8.5:1. Brake horsepower: 175 at 3600 R.P.M. Torque: 305 lbs.-ft. at 2000 R.P.M. Five main bearings. Hydraulic valve lifters. Carburetor: 4Bbl. Roch. M4MC. VIN Code: U. OPTIONAL V-8 (Caprice, Impala): 90-degree, overhead valve V-8. Cast iron block and head. Displacement: 454 cu. in. (7.4 liters). Bore & stroke: 4.25 x 4.00 in. Compression ratio: 8.25:1. Brake horsepower: 225 at 3800 R.P.M. Torque: 360 lbs.-ft. at 2400 R.P.M. Five main bearings. Hydraulic valve lifters. Carburetor: 4Bbl. Roch. M4ME. VIN Code: S.

CHASSIS DATA: Wheelbase: (Chevette) 94.3 in.; (Vega/Monza) 97.0 in.; (Camaro) 108.0 in.; (Nova) 111.0 in.; (Chevelle cpe) 112.0 in.; (Chevelle sed/wag, Monte Carlo) 116.0 in.; (Imp/Capr) 121.5 in.; (Imp/Capr wag) 125.0 in. Overall length: (Chvt) 158.7 in.; (Vega) 175.4 in.; (Monza Twne cpe) 177.8 in.; (Monza hatch) 179.3 in.; (Camaro) 195.4 in.; (Nova) 196.7 in.; (Nova Concours) 197.7 in.; (Camaro) 195.4 in.; (Chevelle cpe) 205.3 in.; (Laguna) 207.3 in.; (Chevelle sed) 209.3 in.; (Chevelle wag) 215.2 in.; (Monte) 212.7 in.; (Imp/Capr) 222.9 in.; (Imp/Capr wag) 228.6 in. Height: (Chvt) 52.3 in.; (Vega spt cpe/wag) 51.8 in.; (Vega hatch) 50.0 in.; (Monza Twne cpe) 49.8 in.; (Monza hatch) 50.2 in.; (Nova) 54.3 in.; (Camaro) 49.2 in.; (Chevelle/Laguna cpe) 53.1 in.; (Chevelle sed) 53.8 in.; (Chevelle wag) 55.7 in.; (Monte) 52.7 in.; (Imp/Capr cpe) 53.7 in.; (Imp/Capr sed) 54.4 in.; (Imp/Capr spt sed) 53.9 in.; (Imp/Capr 2S wag) 58.1 in.; (Imp/Capr 3S wag) 57.4 in. Width: (Chvt) 61.8 in.; (Vega/Monza) 65.4 in.; (Nova) 72.2 in.; (Camaro) 74.4 in.; (Chevelle) 76.6 in.; (Chevelle wag) 76.8 in.; (Monte) 77.6 in.; (Imp/Capr) 79.5 in. Front Tread: (Chvt) 51.2 in.; (Vega/Monza) 54.8 in.; (Nova/Camaro) 61.3 in.; (Camaro LT) 61.6 in.; (Chevelle) 61.5 in.; (Monte) 61.9 in.; (Imp/Capr) 64.1 in. Rear Tread: (Chvt) 51.2 in.; (Vega/Monza) 53.6 in.; (Nova) 59.0 in.; (Camaro) 60.0 in.; (Camaro LT) 60.3 in.; (Chevelle/Monte) 60.7 in.; (Imp/Capr) 64.0 in. Standard Tires: (Chvt) 155/8013B; (Vega/Monza) A78 x 13/B; (Nova) E78 x 14/B; (Nova Concours, Camaro) FR78 x 14/B; (Chevelle six) FR78 x 15/B; (Chevelle V-8) GR78 x 15/B; (Chevelle wag) HR78 x 15/B; (Monte) GR70 x 15/B; (Imp/Capr) G78 x 15/B; (Imp/Capr wag) LR78 x 15/C.

TECHNICAL: Transmission: Three-speed floor shift standard on Vega/Monza four and Camaro; column shift on Chevelle/Nova; floor shift available on Nova. Gear ratios: (1st) 3.11:1; (2nd) 1.84:1; (3rd) 1.00:1; (Rev) 3.22:1; except Nova V8350 (1st) 2.85:1; (2nd) 1.84:1; (3rd) 1.00:1; (Rev) 2.95:1. Four-speed floor shift standard on Chevette, optional on Vega/Monza four: (1st) 3.75:1; (2nd) 2.16:1; (3rd) 1.38:1; (4th) 1.00:1; (Rev) 3.82:1. Four-speed floor shift optional on Monza V-8, Cosworth: (1st) 3.11:1; (2nd) 2.20:1; (3rd) 1.47:1; (4th) 1.00:1; (Rev) 3.11:1. Four-speed floor shift optional on Nova/Camaro V8350: (1st) 2.85:1; (2nd) 2.02:1; (3rd) 1.35:1; (4th) 1.00:1; (Rev) 2.85:1. Five-speed floor shift on Vega/Monza: (1st) 3.10:1; (2nd) 1.89:1; (3rd) 1.27:1; (4th) 1.00:1; (5th) 0.80:1; (Rev) 3.06:1. Three-speed Turbo Hydra- matic standard on Chevelle V-8 and Monte/Caprice/Impala, optional on others. Gear ratios: (1st) 2.52:1; (2nd) 1.52:1; (3rd) 1.00:1; (Rev) 1.94:1 except Caprice/Impala w/V8454: (1st) 2.48:1; (2nd) 1.48:1; (3rd) 1.00:1; (Rev) 2.08:1. Chevette and Nova (exc. V8350) THM gear ratios: (1st) 2.74:1; (2nd) 1.57:1; (3rd) 1.00:1; (Rev) 2.07:1. Standard final drive ratio: (Chevette) 3.70:1 exc. 4.11:1 w/1.6 engine; (Vega) 2.92:1 exc. 2.53:1 w/4-spd, 2.93:1 w/5- spd, 2.92:1 or 3.42:1 w/auto.; (Cosworth Vega) 4.10:1; (Monza) 2.92:1 exc. 2.56:1 or 2.93:1 w/5-spd or auto., 3.42:1 w/2Bbl. four, 2.56:1 w/V-8; (Nova) 2.73:1 exc. 3.08:1 w/V8350, 2.73:1 or 3.08:1 w/auto.; (Camaro) 2.73:1 exc. 2.73:1 or 3.08:1 w/auto., 2.85:1 w/4-spd; (Chevelle) 2.73:1 exc. 2.73:1 or 3.08:1 w/auto.; (Monte) 2.73:1; (Caprice/Imp) 2.73:1 or 3.08:1. Steering: (Chevette) rack and pinion; (others) recirculating ball. Front Suspension: unequal length control arms, coin springs stabilizer bar. Rear Suspension: (Chevette) rigid axle, torque tube, longitudinal trailing radius arms, coil springs, transverse linkage bar; (Vega) rigid axle, lower trailing radius arms, upper oblique torque arms, coil springs, transverse linkage bar; (Monza) similar to Vega, with stablilizer bar; (Nova/Camaro) semi-elliptic leaf springs, stabilizer bar on Camaro; (others) rigid axle, lower trailing radius arms, upper oblique torque arms and coil springs, plus stabilizer bar on Laguna, Monte and Caprice Classic. Brakes: front disc, rear drum. Ignition: High energy electronic. Body construction: (Chvt/Vega/Monza) unitized; (Nova/Camaro) integral, with separate partial front box frame; (Chevelle/Monte/Impala/Caprice) perimeter box frame with cross-members. Fuel tank: (Chvt) 13 gal.; (Vega) 16 gal.; (Monza) 18.5 gal.; (Nova/Camaro) 21 gal.; (Chevelle/Monte) 22 gal.; (Imp/Capr) 26 gal.' (Imp/Capr wag) 22 gal.

DRIVETRAIN OPTIONS: Engines: 1.6-liter four: Chevette ($51). 140 cu. in., 2Bbl. four: Vega/Monza ($56). 262 cu. in., 2Bbl. V-8: Monza ($224). 350 cu. in., 2Bbl. V-8: Chevelle/Monte ($30). 350 cu. in., 4Bbl. V-8: Nova/Camaro/Chevelle/Monte ($85); Chevelle wag ($55); Imp/Caprice cpe/sed ($56). 400 cu. in., 4Bbl. V-8: Chevelle/Monte ($148); Chevelle wag ($118); Imp/Capr cpe/sed ($120). 454 cu. in., 4Bbl. V-8: Imp ($375); Caprice ($350); Imp/Capr wag ($223). Transmission/Differential: Four-speed manual shift: Vega/Monza ($60). Four-speed wide-range manual shift: Nova ($242); Camaro ($260). Five-speed manual shift: Vega/Monza ($244). Turbo Hydra-matic transmission: Chevette/Vega/Monza ($244); Nova/Camaro, Chevelle six ($260). Sport shifter w/console: Chevette ($40). Floor shift lever: Nova ($29). Positraction axle: Vega/Monza ($48); Nova/Camaro/Chevelle/Monte ($51); Imp/Capr ($55). High-altitude or highway axle ratio: Chvt/Vega/Monza ($12); Chevelle/Monte/Imp/Capr ($13). High- altitude axle ratio: Nova/Camaro ($13). Power Accessories: Power brakes: Chvt/Vega/Monza ($55); Nova/Camaro/Chevelle six ($58). Power steering (variable ratio): Vega/Monza ($120); Nova/Chevelle ($136). Suspension: F40 H.D. suspension: Nova ($6-$29); Chevelle/Monte/Imp/Capr ($18). F41 sport suspension: Vega ($141); Monza ($26); Nova/Camaro ($25-$32); Imp ($32); Caprice ($7). FE8 radial-tuned suspension: Chevelle ($27); Imp/Capr cpe/sed ($25). Superlift rear shock absorbers: Imp/Caprice ($44). Rear stabilizer bar: Chevette ($26). Other: Heavy-duty radiator ($25-$34). H.D. alternator (61amp): Chevelle/Monte/Imp/Capr ($27). H.D. battery ($15-$16). California emission certification ($50).

CHEVETTE/VEGA/MONZA CONVENIENCE/APPEARANCE OPTIONS: Option Packages: Woody package: Chevette ($306). Rally equipment: Chevette ($230-$251). GT pkg.: Vega hatch ($457); Vega wagon ($340-$429). Cabriolet equipment (vinyl roof, opera windows, bright moldings, woodgrain steering wheel shroud, sport equipment): Monza ($256). Sport equipment: Monza ($118). Spyder equipment: Monza Twn Cpe ($421-$430); Monza hatch ($333-$342). Quiet sound group: Chvt ($29- $39); Vega ($32-$43). Comfort/Convenience: Air conditioning ($424). Rear defogger ($66). Tinted glass ($44). Sport steering wheel ($15). Comfortilt steering wheel: Vega/Monza ($48). Special instrumentation: Chvt ($56); Vega ($72); Monza ($56-$72). Econominder gauge: Monza ($10-$26). Electric clock: Chvt/Monza ($16). Cigarette lighter: Chvt ($5). Glove compartment lock: Chvt ($3). Lighting and Mirrors: Aux. lighting: Vega ($15-$29); Monza ($15). Twin sport mirrors, left remote: Vega/Monza ($25). Driver's remote sport mirror: Chvt ($19). Twin remote sport mirrors: Chvt ($43). Day/night mirror ($7). Entertainment: Pushbutton AM radio ($70). Pushbutton AM/FM radio ($129). AM/FM stereo radio: Vega/Monza ($212). Stereo tape player w/AM radio: Monza ($196). Rear speaker ($20). Windshield antenna: Vega/Monza ($15); incl. w/radios. Exterior Trim: Vinyl roof: Chvt ($90). Swing-out windows: Chvt ($45); Vega cpe ($29-$35). Custom exterior: Chvt ($82); Vega ($59-$88). Decor group: Vega ($6-$34). Sport decor: Chvt ($77). Sport stripes: Vega ($76). Bodyside moldings ($36). Wheel opening moldings: Vega/Monza ($19). Side window reveal moldings: Chvt ($59). Door edge guards ($7). Roof carrier: Chvt/Vega ($53). Rear air deflector: Vega ($23). Deluxe bumpers, front/rear: Chvt ($27); Vega ($44). Deluxe bumpers w/guards: Monza ($60). Deluxe front bumper guards: Vega ($17). Deluxe bumper guards, front/rear: Chvt ($34-$61); Monza ($34). Interior Trim/Upholstery: Custom interior trim: Chevette ($152-$164). Console: Chvt ($16); Monza ($73). Bucket seats: Vega ($126-$158); Monza ($124-$140). Adjustable driver's seatback: Vega/Monza ($17). Load floor carpet: Chvt ($40). Color-keyed floor mats ($14). Front mats: Chvt ($8). Deluxe seatbelts ($15). Trunk mat: Monza ($10). Wheels and Tires: Aluminum wheels: Monza ($173-$204). Rally II wheels: Vega ($97). Wheel covers: Vega ($28). Sport wheel covers: Chvt ($36-$66). Wheel trim rings: Chvt ($30); Vega ($3-$30). 155/8013/B WSW: Chvt ($32). 155/8013/B SBR: Chvt ($99). 155/8013/B SBR WSW: Chvt ($131). 155/8013/B SBR WLT: Chvt ($145). A78 x 13/B WSW: Vega ($32); Monza ($26-$32). A78 x 13/B belted WSW: Vega ($53); Monza ($43-$53). BR78 x 13/B SBR: Vega ($34-$122); Monza ($98-$122). BR78 x 13/B SBR WSW: Vega ($66-$154); Monza ($123-$154). BR78 x 13/B SBR WLT: Vega ($80-$168); Monza ($135-$168). BR78 x 13/C SBR: Monza ($114- $146). BR78 x 13/C SBR WSW: Monza ($25-$178). BR78 x 13/C SBR WLT: Monza ($36-$192). BR70 x 13/B SBR WLT: Monza ($36-$46). Stowaway spare: Monza ($23).

NOVA/CAMARO/CHEVELLE/MONTE CARLO CONVENIENCE/APPEARANCE OPTIONS: Option Packages: SS equipment: Nova ($187). Rally Sport equipment: base Camaro ($260); Camaro LT ($173). Interior decor/quiet sound group: base Camaro ($53). Comfort/Convenience: Air conditioning ($452-$479). Rear defogger (forced-air): Nova/Camaro/Monte ($43); Chevelle ($43-$47). Rear defogger (electric): Monte ($77). Cruise- Master speed control: Nova/Chevelle/Monte ($73). Tinted glass: Nova/Camaro ($46); Chevelle ($49); Monte ($53). Sport steering wheel: base Nova, Chevelle ($16). Comfortilt steering wheel ($52). Six-way power seat: Chevelle/Monte ($124). Power windows ($99-$140). Power door locks: Nova/Chevelle ($62-$89); Camaro/Monte ($62). Power trunk release: Monte ($17). Power tailgate release: Chevelle 2S wag ($20). Electric clock: Nova/Camaro ($18); Chevelle ($19). Special instrumentation (incl. tach and console): Nova ($160); Concours ($89). Special instrumentation (incl. tach and clock): base Camaro ($92). Econominder gauge pkg.: Chevelle/Monte ($45). Econominder light: Nova ($16). Intermittent wipers: Nova/Monte ($28). Hide-a-way wipers: base Camaro ($22). Lighting, Horns and Mirrors: Aux. lighting ($21-$41). Dual horns: Nova/Camaro-/Chevelle ($6). Remote-control driver's mirror: Nova/Chevelle/Monte ($14). Twin sport mirrors, left remote ($27). Twin remote sport mirrors (body-color): Nova/Chevelle/Monte ($20-$46). Day/night mirror: Nova ($7). Visor vanity mirror: Chevelle/Monte ($4). Lighted visor mirror: Chevelle ($26); Monte ($23-$26). Entertainment: Pushbutton AM radio ($75). AM/FM radio: Nova/Camaro/Chevelle ($137); Monte ($146). AM/FM stereo radio ($226). Stereo 8track tape player w/AM radio: Nova/Camaro/Chevelle ($209); Monte ($225). Stereo tape player with AM/FM stereo radio ($324). Rear speaker ($21). Windshield antenna ($16); incl. w/radios. Exterior Trim: Electric sky roof: Monte ($370). Vinyl roof: Nova/Camaro ($96); Chevelle ($109); Monte ($129). Cabriolet roof: Nova ($150). Spoilers, front/rear: Camaro ($81). Exterior decor pkg.: Nova ($73); Chevelle ($19-$51). Custom appearance group: Nova Concours ($65-$75). Exterior style trim: Camaro ($58). Fashion-tone paint: Monte ($104-$233). Two-tone paint: Nova/Chevelle ($40). Swing-out rear side windows: Nova ($48). Bodyside moldings: Nova/Camaro-/Chevelle ($38); Nova Concours, Monte ($49). Door edge guards ($7-$11). Wheel opening moldings: Nova ($19). Roof drip moldings: base Nova, Camaro ($16). Bodyside pinstriping: Nova ($26). Sport stripes: Chevelle cpe/sed ($81). Rear window air deflector: Chevelle wag ($23). Roof carrier: Chevelle wag ($68). Deluxe bumpers: Chevelle/Monte ($29). Deluxe bumpers w/guards, front/rear: Nova ($63). Bumper guards, front/rear: Camaro/Chevelle/Monte ($36); Chevelle wag ($18). Interior Trim/Upholstery: Interior decor pkg.: base Nova ($25). Console: base Nova, Camaro/Chevelle/Monte ($71). Bench seat w/custom interior: base Nova ($180). Bucket seats: Nova ($255); Nova Concours ($204). Knit or sport cloth seats: Camaro, Chevelle wag ($20). Vinyl bucket seats: Chevelle ($20). Bucket seats w/knit cloth or vinyl: Chevelle ($102- $140); Monte ($140). Custom cloth bucket seats: Monte ($265). 50/50 reclining passenger seat: Monte ($273). Adj. driver's seatback: Camaro ($19). Litter container: Chevelle/Monte ($6). Deluxe carpet: Nova/Camaro ($32). Removable load-floor carpeting: Chevelle wag ($42). Color-keyed mats ($15). Deluxe seatbelts ($14-$20). Wheels and Tires: Custom styled wheels: Nova ($116); Nova Concours ($86); Camaro ($79-$116). Rally wheels: base Nova/Camaro ($60); Nova Concours ($38); Chevelle ($35-$60); Monte ($46). Wire wheel covers: Chevelle ($59-$89); Monte ($79); Monte Landau ($23 credit). Full wheel covers: base Nova, Camaro ($30). Deluxe wheel covers: Monte ($19). Wheel trim rings: base Nova ($33). E78 x 14/B BSW: Camaro ($84-$106 credit). E78 x 14/B WSW: base Nova ($26-$33); Camaro ($58-$73 redit). FR78 x 14/B SBR: base Nova ($84-$106). FR78 x 14/B SBR WSW: Nova ($112-$141); Nova Concours, Camaro ($28-$35); Chevelle six ($30-$37). FR78 x 14/B SBR WLT: Nova ($123- $155); Nova Concours, Camaro ($39-$49). GR78 x 15/B SBR WSW: Chevelle/Laguna V-8 ($30-$37). HR78 x 15/B SBR BSW: Chevelle/Laguna V-8 ($38). HR78 x 15/B SBR WSW: Chevelle/Laguna V-8 ($78); Chevelle wag ($40). GR70 x 15/B SBR BSW: Chevelle V-8 ($43-$54); Laguna ($14-$17). GR70 x 15/B SBR WSW: Chevelle V-8 ($73-$91); Laguna ($43-$54); Monte ($30-$37). GR70 x 15/B SBR WLT: Chevelle V-8 ($84-$105); Laguna ($55-$68). Stowaway spare: base Nova, Camaro ($15); Concours/Chevelle/Monte (NC). NOTE: Chevelle/Laguna GR70 tires included sport suspension.

1976 Impala Custom Coupe (CP)

IMPALA/CAPRICE CONVENIENCE/APPEARANCE OPTIONS: Comfort/Convenience: Four season air cond. ($485). Comfortron auto-temp air cond. ($567). Rear defogger, forced-air ($44- $48). Cruise-Master speed control ($74). Tinted glass ($63). Comfortilt steering wheel ($53). Power door locks ($63-$90). Six-way power seat ($126). Power windows ($105-$159). Power trunk release ($17). Power tailgate: wag ($52). Electric clock: Imp ($19). Econominder gauge pkg. ($34). Intermittent wipers ($28). Quiet sound group ($33-$45). Lighting, Horns and Mirrors: Aux. lighting ($20-$37). Dome reading light ($14). Dual horns: Imp ($6). Driver's remote mirror ($14). Dual remote mirrors ($42). Dual remote body- color sport mirrors ($19-$47). Visor vanity mirror ($4). Lighted visor mirror ($26). Entertainment: Pushbutton AM radio ($76). AM/FM radio ($148). AM/FM stereo radio ($229). Stereo 8-track tape player w/AM radio ($228); with AM/FM stereo radio ($328). Rear speaker ($21). Windshield antenna ($16); incl. w/radios. Exterior Trim: Vinyl roof ($125-$150). Rear fender skirts ($33); std. on Caprice. Two-tone paint ($41) incl. bright outline moldings. Roof carrier: wag ($82). Bodyside moldings: wag ($39). Deluxe bodyside moldings: Imp ($25-$50). Door edge guards ($7-$11). Wheel opening moldings: Imp ($19); std. on cpe. Deluxe bumpers ($40). Bumper guards ($43). Interior Trim/Upholstery: 50/50 reclining passenger seat ($142). Deluxe load-floor carpet: wag ($61). Removable load- floor carpet: wag ($43). Color-keyed mats ($15). Litter container ($6). Color-keyed deluxe seatbelts ($17-$20). Deluxe trunk trim ($35-$43). Wheels and Tires: Full wheel covers ($31). Wire wheel covers ($69-$100). G78 x 15/B WSW: cpe/sed ($37). HR78 x 15/B SBR BSW: Imp S ($132); others (NC). HR78 x 15/B SBR WSW: Imp S ($172); other cpe/sed ($41). LR78 x 15/C SBR BSW (NC); std. on wag. LR78 x 15/C SBR WSW ($47).

HISTORY: Introduced: Oct. 2, 1975. Model year production (U.S.): 1,920,200 (incl. Corvettes but not incl. 7,523 Acadians). Of total vehicles built for U.S. market, 411,883 were four- cylinder, 278,775 six, and 1,341,112 had a V-8. Calendar year production: 2,012,024 (incl. 47,425 Corvettes, 5,311 Acadians and 27,677 Sportvans). Calendar year sales by U.S. dealers: 2,104,142 for a 24.4 percent market share, down from almost 26 percent in 1975. (That total included 30,337 Sportvans and 41,673 Corvettes.) Model year sales by U.S. dealers: 2,077,119 (including 27,416 Sportvans and 41,027 Corvettes), up from 1,714,593 in 1975.

Historical Footnotes: Chevrolet hoped to sell 275,000 Chevettes in its initial season, taking 185,000 sales away from imports, to help the company into a strong year after poor sales in 1975. Only 1,686,062 Chevrolets had been built in calendar year 1975, the lowest total since 1970. Model year production was lower yet for 1975: just 1,614,491, far below the 2.4 million Chevrolets produced in model year 1973. As it turned out, neither Chevette nor Vega sold well in 1976. This year did indeed see a resurgence in sales, but GM's best seller was now the Olds Cutlass, not a Chevrolet. In fact, Chevrolet sales amounted to only 42.6 percent of the GM total, one of the lowest figures posted in recent years. Model year sales were up, however, by 21.1 percent over the 1975 total. Why? Because big cars continued to sell rather well. The new 305 cu. in. V-8 was particularly well received by the public. R.L. Lund was Chevrolet's General Manager. Appearing at the Detroit Auto Show was an experimental (but fully operational) Monza Super Spyder, crafted from a 1975 Monza 2 + 2. Powered by the Cosworth Twin Cam four and five-speed gearbox, it featured a hand-built fiberglass nose and tail panels, magnesium wheels, and fluorescent tube lighting up front. This was one more GM show car that never made it into production.

1977 CHEVROLET

Full-size Chevrolets were downsized for 1977, leading the first wave of shrinkage that would hit the entire domestic lineup in the next few years. The old reliable inline six and the 305 cu. in. V-8 each added five horsepower. At mid-year the renowned Camaro Z28 returned, adorned with graphics and carrying a four-barrel 350 V-8 under the hood. The one-barrel 140 cu. in. four and 262 V-8 were dropped. Intermittent wipers became optional on subcompact to compact models. A new "Pulse Air" system replaced air injection on Chevette, Vega and Monza fours.

1977 Chevette hatchback coupe (CH)

CHEVETTE — SERIES 1T — FOUR — As in its opening season, Chevette came in two models: standard four-passenger hatchback coupe, and Scooter. But this year, the Scooter added a standard back seat for the same four-passenger capacity (though the back seat could be deleted). The Woody option was dropped, but the Rally Sport was offered again. A new "Sandpiper" appearance package, available with white or yellow-gold body paint (a color not offered on other models) wasn't hard to spot with foot-long 'Sandpiper' decals on quarter panels. A custom interior included yellow-gold "Reef" vinyl seat trim with cloth insert, plus yellow-gold carpeting, instrument panel and door panels. Also in the package: a sport steering wheel, day/night mirror, and carpeted cargo area. Two engines were available again this year: the base 85 cu. in. (1.4-liter) four and bigger 97 cu. in. (1.6-liter). Both could have either standard four-speed manual gearbox or optional three-speed automatic. (In California and high-altitude regions, only the 1.6 was available.) The 1.4 gained five horsepower this year as a result of a larger carburetor flow capacity and revised hot air intake system. Positive carburetor outside air control also improved cold-weather driveability. The 1.4 had similar changes but a smaller power boost. New front disc brake pad and rear brake lining materials were meant to increase lining life. A smaller rear wheel cylinder was said to improve front-to-rear braking balance. Joining Chevette's option list: an intermittent "pulse" windshield wiper that operated either from the "smart switch" on the column or a separate dash control. Interiors had a new pattern of vinyl cloth, while custom interiors used perforated vinyl. Of the 14 Chevette body colors, nine were new: light lime, red, bright orange, light buckskin, and five metallics (silver, dark blue, brown, orange, and dark aqua). Carryover colors, were white, black, firethorn metallic, light blue, and bright yellow.

1977 Vega GT hatchback coupe (CP)

VEGA — SERIES 1H — FOUR — For its seventh and final try at luring buyers, Vega again came in three body styles: notchback or hatchback coupe, plus station wagon and Estate wagon. The Cosworth Vega was gone. So were the GT Estate Wagon options and Cabriolet equipment package. This year's GT package came in two levels: one subtle, the other bold. The subtler one had a blacked-out trim theme with black paint around window openings, windshield and doors, plus black sport mirrors and wheels. For a more noticeable look, the alternate package featured bold horizontal stripes that broke along the bodyside to display huge 'Vega GT' lettering. It was hard to miss, since the lower-bodyside decal ran the full distance between wheel openings.

1977 Vega 2-dr coupe, 4-cyl

Standard engine was the 140 cu. in. (2.3-liter) Dura- Built four with two-barrel carburetor, plus four-speed manual gearbox. A five-speed manual and three-speed automatic transmission were available. The one-barrel carb engine and three-speed manual shift, formerly standard, were dropped this year. A new, simpler Pulse-Air manifold injection system was standard on the base engine, replacing the Air Injection Reactor system. Vega was the only domestic production car with an all-aluminum engine block. Vega's standard interior added a color-keyed steering column, steering wheel, instrument cluster face, and parking brake cover. Of the 14 body colors this year, eight were new: dark blue, brown, orange, silver or dark aqua metallic; light buckskin; light lime; and bright orange. Carryover colors were white, black, firethorn metallic, light blue, red, and bright yellow. Vega's GT package included woodgrained dash accents, sport mirrors (left remote), black headlamp bezels, bright grille header molding, F41 sport suspension, Rally II wheels with trim rings and special center caps, black sill and lower bodyside moldings, gauge set (including tachometer and clock), and white-letter tires. The price was $401 for hatchbacks (including belt moldings) and $373 for wagons.

1977 Monza Sport Spyder hatchback coupe (CH)

MONZA — SERIES 1H — FOUR — Once again, Monza fielded a notchback Towne Coupe and a 2+2 hatchback, with no significant styling changes this year. Towne Coupes had a new rear look with functional tri- color taillamps. A Sport Front End Appearance option package, introduced late in the prior model year, gave Towne Coupes the same soft-fascia front end and rectangular headlamps as the 2+2, along with a rear bumper impact strip. Other carryover options: large rear quarter windows, or opera windows. The Cabriolet Equipment package was dropped, but a Cabriolet vinyl roof and opera windows remained available. Two intertwined all-new options were offered, however: the Monza Spyder appearance and performance packages. The appearance package included bold striping, front air dam and rear spoiler; plus satin black accents around window openings, headlamp openings and bezels, parking lamps, taillamps and grille louvers, as well as rocker panel, quarter, rear panel and fender areas. A large 'Spyder' script identification decal appeared on both doors. Dual side stripes came in black or gold, with Spyder lettering outlined in red, white or gold. The $199 package (for 2+2 only) also included black sport mirrors, black Rally II

1977 Monza 2 + 2 hatchback coupe, V-8

wheels and bright trim rings. Spyder's equipment package sold separately at $274. That one included an F41 suspension, console, sport steering wheel, sport mirrors, large Spyder emblem, hood header panel, modified front stabilizer and rear shocks, and BR70 x 13 radial tires. Other Monza options included aluminum wheels, Sport equipment and front-end appearance packages, front/rear spoilers, and an instrument set (including tachometer). Added to the option list: a digital clock over the glove box, angled toward the driver. Fourteen body colors were available, plus three new luxury cloth interior trims and four colors of vinyl trim. Both hatchback and Towne Coupe carried a standard 140 cu. in. (2.3-liter) Dura-Built four-cylinder engine, with four-speed manual transmission. A 305 cu. in. (5.0-liter) V-8 was also available, as were a five-speed manual gearbox and three-speed automatic. The 262 V-8 was gone. The standard 2+2 came with finned wheel covers.

1977 Nova Concours sedan (CH)

NOVA — SERIES 1X — SIX/V-8 — The basic Nova carried over its 1976 styling, offered again as a two-door coupe, two-door hatchback, or four-door sedan. Nova's grille had square holes in a 2 x 12 arrangement, with vertical parking lamps at outer ends. The upscale Concours had a new fine-mesh grille made up of many thin vertical bars, separated into four rows, intended to offer a massive look. Lower-profile parking lamps sat slightly inboard of grille ends. A new chromed center filler panel was meant to give an illusion of depth, in company with the restyled hood molding, grille and bumper. Outer ends of the bumper filler panel were body-colored. Bright headlamp bezels were restyled, as were fender end caps. Concours also sported a stand-up hood ornament, new wide wheel opening moldings, and distinctive 'C' script insignias at front, side and rear, plus new triple rectangular taillamps. Inside, the Concours featured woodgrain appliques on door panels, instrument panel and steering wheel. Powerplant possibilities included 305 and 350 cu. in. V-8s as well as the standard inline six (250 cu. in.). Three- and four-speed manual gearboxes were available, along with three-speed automatic. Of the 14 Nova body colors, nine were new (all metallic): medium green, dark aqua, light blue, buckskin, light buckskin, orange, silver, brown, or dark blue. Antique white, black, red, bright yellow and firethorn metallic were repeated from 1976. A new Nova Rally option for coupe and hatchback was announced for mid-year availability, to replace the Super Sport. It consisted of a new chrome-plated, diamond-pattern grille with inset horizontal parking lamps and five-color 'Nova Rally' nameplate in the center. The name was repeated on fenders and decklid (above right taillamp). Rally models also had black headlamp bezels with bright edges plus white, black or gold tri-band striping along lower bodysides and rear end panel. Rally wheels were color-keyed to the stripes (but argent-finished when ordered with black striping).

1977 Camaro Type LT coupe (CH)

CAMARO — SERIES 1F — SIX/V-8 — Camaro changed little for 1977. The lineup included the standard Sport Coupe and luxury Type LT. A Rally Sport option came in three new contrasting accent colors for the satin black trim: medium gray, dark blue metallic, and buckskin metallic. Satin black treatment was found on Rally hood, front end, grille, headlamp bezels, forward roof section, rear end panel, and rocker panels. Otherwise, body color selection was the same as Nova: nine new colors and five carryovers. Inside was new cloth in the base interior. Type LT had new knit cloth and puffed-texture vinyl materials. The familiar inline 250 cu. in. (4.1-liter) six became the standard powerplant for Type LT this year. Optional were two V-8s: a 305 cu. in. (5.0-liter) and 350 (5.7-liter). Transmissions included the standard three-speed manual, four- speed manual, or three-speed automatic. Standard axle ratio for the V-8 with automatic changed from 2.73:1 to 2.56:1, to help boost gas mileage. The four-speed transmission shift pattern was revised this year. Reverse was now engaged by a rearward (toward the driver) lifting motion, rather than forward as before. A new refillable carbon-dioxide canister replaced the disposable freon-filled unit used to inflate the stowaway spare tire. Intermittent wipers joined the option list, and all Camaro wipers were hidden. Away from the lineup for two years, the high-performance Z28 returned as a 1977½ model, debuting at the Chicago Auto Show. Special wide-profile radial tires were mounted on 15 x 7 in. mag-type wheels. Under the hood was a special 350 cu. in. V-8; atop it, an identifying decal. The chassis held front and rear stablizer bars, special spring rates and quicker steering. This new Z28 had body-color bumpers, spoilers, mirrors and wheels, plus a blackout grille, rear-end panel, rocker panels, moldings, headlamp bezels and taillamp bezels. Rounding out the Z28's appearance were rocker/wheelhouse stripes and emblems, and 'Z28' badge on the driver's side of the grille. Transmission was a Borg-Warner four-speed, and the "open" exhaust used dual resonators.

1977 Chevelle Malibu Classic Landau Coupe ((CH)

CHEVELLE MALIBU — SERIES 1A — SIX/V-8 — Chevelle dropped down to two series for 1977: Malibu and Malibu Classic. Two-door coupe, four-door sedan and station wagon bodies (two or three seat) were offered in both. The Laguna coupe and Malibu Classic Estate wagon were gone. Both series had new grilles and six-section taillamps this year. Malibu Classic's grille showed a vertical theme with many narrow bars. Malibu's was a mesh pattern of many wide rectangles. As before, Classics had stacked rectangular headlamps, regular Malibus single round ones. Script was in the grille's lower corner (driver's side). Small horizontal rectangular parking lamps were again inset in the bumper. The Malibu coupe's rear side windows got "coach" style glass this year. Classic taillamps had fancier brightwork that reached toward the license plate, and rockers wore wide bright moldings. Station wagons had a standard 305 cu. in. (5.0-liter) V-8, and the Malibu Classic wagon held a 350 (5.7-liter) V-8, now with four-barrel carb. The 400 V-8 was gone. Base engine for other bodies was the inline 250 six. Three-speed manual transmission was standard on six-cylinder models except the Malibu Classic sedan, which had Turbo Hydra-matic. Wagons also had automatic plus power brakes and steering. Also standard: heater/defroster, carpeting, lighter, and FR78 x 15/B fiberglass-belted radial tires (HR78 x 15/B steel-belted radials on wagons). The Classic Landau added a vinyl roof, dual horns, sport mirrors (left remote-controlled), deluxe front/rear bumpers, and full wheel covers. Coupes rode a 112-inch wheelbase, sedans and wagons 116- inch. Chevelle's design went all the way back to 1964. Of ten body colors, four were new this year. And of seven vinyl top colors, three were new. Six new trim colors were available for Malibu Classic, five for Malibu.

1977 Monte Carlo Landau Coupe (CH)

MONTE CARLO — SERIES 1A — V-8 — Personal-luxury Montes entered another year with a restyled, bold grille texture: still three separate rows, but eight holes across each one. Stacked rectangular headlamps continued, but horizontal rectangular parking lamps below the headlamps had a more square look. New wider taillamps had horizontal divider bars. End caps were also new. A new hood ornament on "flip-flop" pedestal carried the Monte Carlo crest surrounded by a bright ring. Fourteen body colors (nine new) were offered, plus seven interior trim fabrics (two new) and seven vinyl tops (two new). Monte's chassis had new front springs for a softer ride, plus improved corrosion protection. A radiator pressure relief cap improved cooling.

Wheelbase was still 116 inches, length 212.7 inches. Again, the 305 cu. in. (5.0-liter) V-8 was the base engine. The 400 cu. in. V-8 was no longer available, but the 350 cu. in. (5.7-liter) V-8 with four- barrel was optional. Turbo Hydra-matic was standard with both engines. Standard equipment also included power steering and brakes, electric clock, hide-away wipers, deluxe wheel covers, heater/defroster, carpeting, lighter, inside hood release, wheel opening moldings, and GR70 x 15 steel-belted radial tires. The Landau coupe added a vinyl roof, dual body- color sport mirrors (left one remote-controlled), pinstriping, and Turbine II wheels.

1977 Impala Custom Coupe (CH)

IMPALA/CAPRICE CLASSIC — SERIES 1B — SIX /V-8 — Downsized full-size Chevrolet sedans were 5.5 inches shorter in wheelbase, 10.6 inches shorter overall and 4 inches narrower but 2.5 inches taller. Both Impala and Caprice kept their "big car" look and ample interior dimensions, but lost some 700 pounds. Impala's silhouette was more angular than before, with flatter side panels and a blunt front and rear look. Now they came with a base six- cylinder engine (the familiar inline 250 cu. in.) and smaller (305 cu. in.) base V-8 for better mileage. Wagons had the 305 as standard. All models could also get a 350 cu. in. (5.7- liter) V-8 with four-barrel carburetor. A new diagnostic connector under the hood allowed up to 35 engine tests. Coupe/sedan fuel tanks shrunk from 26 to 21 gallons. The big 400 and 454 engines were gone, but full-size models could have an optional sport or heavy-duty suspension. Impala's 'S' model was dropped. So were sport sedans. All models now had pillars; the true hardtop had become a relic of the past. The rear-facing third seat for wagons was offered as a regular production option. The Landau coupe option emerged during the year. Of ten full-size body colors, four were new. Three new two-tone combinations were offered, along with seven vinyl top colors (three new). New interior trim came in six colors. Impalas had an 8 x 3 hole "eggcrate" grille pattern with center bowtie emblem, plus quad rectangular headlamps over quad park/signal lamps. Caprice's grille had a finer mesh pattern. Caprice also had wraparound marker lamps and small parking lamps inset down in the bumper. Back ends were similar, with taillamps in three side-by-side sections (outer one slightly angled). Caprice's version put backup lamps alongside the license plate. Caprice also displayed a stand- up hood ornament. Impala's new Custom coupe model had a distinctive back window treatment. Caprice wagons got a new two-way tailgate that opened either downward or to the side. Standard Impala/Caprice equipment included Turbo Hydra- matic transmission, power steering and brakes, heater/defroster, carpeting, cigarette lighter, hide-away windshield wipers, and FR78 x 15/B fiberglass-belted radial tires. Wagons had HR78 x 15/B steel-belted tires and a power tailgate. Caprice Estate added an electric clock, dual horns, and quiet sound group.

I.D. DATA: Chevrolets again had a 13-symbol Vehicle Identification Number (VIN) on the upper left surface of the instrument panel, visible through the windshield. Coding was similar to 1976. Body type codes '45' (three-seat station wagon) and '39' (full-size sport sedan) were dropped. Model year code changed to '7' for 1977. Engine codes 'N' (L4110), 'O' (L4122 EFI), 'G' (V8262), 'A' (L4140 1Bbl.) and 'S' (V8454) were dropped. The code for V8305 changed from 'Q' to 'U'.

CHEVETTE (FOUR)

Model Number	Body/Style Number	Body Type & Seating	Factory Price	Shipping Weight	Production Total
1T	B08	2-dr. Hatch-4P	3225	1958	120,278

CHEVETTE SCOOTER (FOUR)

Model Number	Body/Style Number	Body Type & Seating	Factory Price	Shipping Weight	Production Total
1T	J08	2-dr. Hatch-4P	2999	1898	13,191

VEGA (FOUR)

Model Number	Body/Style Number	Body Type & Seating	Factory Price	Shipping Weight	Production Total
1H	V11	2-dr. Coupe-4P	3249	2459	12,365
1H	V77	2-dr. Hatch-4P	3359	2522	37,395
1H	V15	2-dr. Sta Wag-4P	3522	2571	25,181
1H	V15	2-dr. Est Wag-4P	3745	N/A	3,461

1977 Monza 2-dr Town Coupe, 4-cyl

MONZA (FOUR/V-8)

Model Number	Body/Style Number	Body Type & Seating	Factory Price	Shipping Weight	Production Total
1H	M27	2-dr Twne Cpe-4P	3560/3765	2580	34,133
1H	R07	2-dr. Hatch 2+2-4P	3840/4045	2671	39,215

NOVA (SIX/V-8)

Model Number	Body/Style Number	Body Type & Seating	Factory Price	Shipping Weight	Production Total
1X	X27	2-dr. Cpe-6P	3482/3602	3139/3257	132,833
1X	X17	2-dr. Hatch-6P	3646/3766	3214/3335	18,048
1X	X69	4-dr. Sedan-6P	3532/3652	3174/3292	141,028

NOVA CONCOURS (SIX/V-8)

Model Number	Body/Style Number	Body Type & Seating	Factory Price	Shipping Weight	Production Total
1X	Y27	2-dr. Cpe-6P	3991/4111	3285/3391	28,602
1X	Y17	2-dr. Hatch-6P	4154/4274	3378/3486	5,481
1X	Y69	4-dr. Sedan-6P	4066/4186	3329/3437	39,272

CAMARO (SIX/V-8)

Model Number	Body/Style Number	Body Type & Seating	Factory Price	Shipping Weight	Production Total
1F	Q87	2-dr. Spt Cpe-4P	4113/4223	3369/3476	131,717
1F	S87	2-dr. LT Cpe-4P	4478/4598	3422/3529	72,787
1F	Q87	2-dr. Z28 Cpe-4P	-- /5170	-- / N/A	14,349

CHEVELLE MALIBU (SIX/V-8)

Model Number	Body/Style Number	Body Type & Seating	Factory Price	Shipping Weight	Production Total
1A	C37	2-dr. Cpe-6P	3885/4005	3551/3650	28,793
1A	C29	4-dr. Sed-6P	3935/4055	3628/3727	39,064
1A	C35	4-dr. Sta Wag-6P	-- /4734	-- /4139	18,023
1A	C35	4-dr. 3S Wag-9P	-- /4877	-- / N/A	4,014

CHEVELLE MALIBU CLASSIC (SIX/V-8)

Model Number	Body/Style Number	Body Type & Seating	Factory Price	Shipping Weight	Production Total
1A	D37	2-dr. Cpe-6P	4125/4245	3599/3698	73,739
1A	D37	2-dr. Lan Cpe-6P	4353/4473	N/A	37,215
1A	D29	4-dr. Sed-6P	4475/4595	3725/3824	76,776
1A	D35	4-dr. Sta Wag-6P	-- /5065	-- /4233	31,539
1A	D35	4-dr. 3S Wag-9P	-- /5208	-- / N/A	19,053

MONTE CARLO (V-8)

Model Number	Body/Style Number	Body Type & Seating	Factory Price	Shipping Weight	Production Total
1A	H57	2-dr. 'S' Cpe-6P	4968	3852	224,327
1A	H57	2-dr. Lan Cpe-6P	5298	N/A	186,711

FULL-SIZE CHEVROLETS IMPALA (SIX/V-8)

Model Number	Body/Style Number	Body Type & Seating	Factory Price	Shipping Weight	Production Total
1B	L47	2-dr. Cust Cpe-6P	4876/4996	3533/3628	55,347
1B	L47	2-dr. Lan Cpe-6P	N/A	N/A	2,745
1B	L69	4-dr. Sedan-6P	4901/5021	3564/3659	196,824
1B	L35	4-dr. Sta Wag-6P	-- /5289	-- /4042	37,108
1B	L35	4-dr. 3S Wag-9P	-- /5406	-- / N/A	28,255

CAPRICE CLASSIC (SIX/V-8)

Model Number	Body/Style Number	Body Type & Seating	Factory Price	Shipping Weight	Production Total
1B	N47	2-dr. Coupe-6P	5187/5307	3571/3666	62,366
1B	N47	2-dr. Lan Cpe-6P	N/A	N/A	9,607
1B	N69	4-dr. Sedan-6P	5237/5357	3606/3701	212,840
1B	N35	4-dr. Est Wag-6P	-- /5617	-- /4088	22,930
1B	N35	4-dr. 3S Est-6P	-- /5734	-- / N/A	33,639

FACTORY PRICE AND WEIGHT NOTE: Where two prices and weights are shown, the figure to the left of the slash is for six-cylinder model, to right of slash for V-8 (except Monza, four-cylinder and V-8).

ENGINE DATA: BASE FOUR (Chevette): Inline. Overhead cam. Four-cylinder. Cast iron block and head. Displacement: 85.0 cu. in. (1.4 liters). Bore & stroke: 3.23 x 2.61 in. Compression ratio: 8.5:1. Brake horsepower: 57 at 5200 R.P.M. Torque: 71 lbs.-ft. at 3600 R.P.M. Five main bearings. Hydraulic valve lifters. Carburetor: 1Bbl. Rochester 1ME. VIN Code: 1. OPTIONAL FOUR (Chevette): Inline. Overhead cam. Four-cylinder. Cast iron block and head. Displacement: 97.6 cu. in. (1.6 liters). Bore & stroke: 3.23 x 2.98 in. Compression ratio: 8.5:1. Brake horsepower: 63 at 4800 R.P.M. Torque: 82 lbs.-ft. at 3200 R.P.M. Five main bearings. Hydraulic valve lifters. Carburetor: 1Bbl. Roch. 1ME. VIN Code: E. BASE FOUR (Vega, Monza): Inline. Overhead cam. Four-cylinder. Aluminum block and cast iron head. Displacement: 140 cu. in. (2.3 liters). Bore & stroke: 3.50 x 3.63 in. Compression ratio: 8.0:1. Brake horsepower: 84 at 4400 R.P.M. Torque: 117 lbs.-ft. at 2400 R.P.M. Five main bearings. Hydraulic valve lifters. Carburetor: 2Bbl. Holley 5210C. VIN Code: B. BASE SIX (Nova, Chevelle, Camaro, Impala, Caprice): Inline. OHV. Six-cylinder. Cast iron block and head. Displacement: 250 cu. in. (4.1 liters). Bore & stroke: 3.88 x 3.53 in. Compression ratio: 8.3:1. Brake horsepower: 110 at 3800 R.P.M. Torque: 195 lbs.-ft. at 1600 R.P.M. Seven main bearings. Hydraulic valve lifters. Carburetor: 1Bbl. Roch. 1ME. VIN Code: D. BASE V-8 (Monte Carlo, Malibu wagon, Impala/Caprice wagon); OPTIONAL (Monza, Nova, Chevelle, Camaro, Impala, Caprice): 90-degree, overhead valve V-8. Cast iron block and head. Displacement: 305 cu. in. (5.0 liters). Bore & stroke: 3.74 x 3.48 in. Compression ratio: 8.5:1. Brake horsepower: 145 at 3800 R.P.M. Torque: 245 lbs.-ft. at 2400 R.P.M. Five main bearings. Hydraulic valve lifters. Carburetor: 2Bbl. Roch. 2GC. VIN Code: U. BASE V-8 (Malibu Classic wagon); OPTIONAL (Nova, Camaro, Chevelle, Monte Carlo, Impala, Caprice): 90-degree, overhead valve V-8. Cast iron block and head. Displacement: 350 cu. in. (5.7 liters). Bore & stroke: 4.00 x 3.48 in. Compression ratio: 8.5:1. Brake horsepower: 170 at 3800 R.P.M. Torque: 270 lbs.-ft. at 2400 R.P.M. Five main bearings. Hydraulic valve lifters. Carburetor: 4Bbl. Roch. M4MC. VIN Code: L.

1977 Caprice Classic 4-dr sedan, V-8

CHASSIS DATA: Wheelbase: (Chevette) 94.3 in.' (Vega/Monza) 97.0 in.; (Camaro) 108.0 in.; (Nova) 111.0 in.; (Chevelle cpe) 112.0 in.; (Chevelle sed/wag, Monte, Imp/Capr) 116.0 in. Overall length: (Chevette) 158.7 in.; (Vega) 175.4 in.; (Monza Twne cpe) 177.8 in.; (Monza hatch) 179.3 in.; (Nova) 196.7 in.; (Nova Concours) 197.7 in.; (Camaro) 195.4 in.; (Chevelle cpe) 205.7 in.; (Chevelle sed) 209.7 in.; (Chevelle wag) 215.4 in.; (Monte) 213.3 in.; (Imp/Capr) 212.1 in.; (Imp/Capr wag) 214.7 in. Height: (Chevette) 52.3 in.; (Vega spt cpe/wag) 51.8 in.; (Vega hatch) 50.0 in.; (Monza Twne cpe) 49.8 in.; (Monza hatch) 50.2 in.; (Nova) 53.6 in.; (Camaro) 49.2 in.; (Chevelle cpe) 53.4 in.; (Chevelle sed) 54.1 in.; (Chevelle wag) 55.8 in.; (Monte) 52.8 in.; (Imp/Capr cpe) 55.3 in.; (Imp/Capr sed) 56.0 in.; (Imp/Capr wag) 58.0 in. Width: (Chevette) 61.8 in.; (Vega/Monza) 65.4 in.; (Nova) 72.2 in.; (Camaro) 74.4 in.; (Chevelle) 76.9 in.; (Chevelle wag) 76.8 in.; (Monte) 77.6 in.; (Imp/Capr) 75.5 in.; (Imp/Capr wag) 79.1 in. Front Tread: Chevette) 51.2 in.; (Vega/Monza) 54.8 in.; (Nova/Camaro) 61.3 in.; (Camaro LT) 61.6 in.; (Chevelle) 61.5 in.; (Monte) 61.9 in.; (Imp/Capr) 61.8 in.; (Imp/Capr wag) 62.2 in. Rear Tread: (Chevette) 51.2 in.; (Vega/Monza 53.6 in.; (Nova) 59.0 in.; (Camaro) 60.0 in.; (Camaro LT) 60.3 in.; (Chevelle/Monte) 60.7 in.; (Imp/Capr) 60.8 in.; (Imp/Capr wag) 64.1 in. Standard Tires: (Chevette) 155/80 x 13/B; (Vega/Monza) A78 x 13/B; (Nova) E78 x 14/B; (Nova Concours, Camaro) FR78 x 14/B SBR; (Chevelle/Imp/Capr) FR78 x 15/B GBR; (Chevelle/Imp/Capr wag) HR78 x 15/B SBR; (Monte) GR70 x 15.

TECHNICAL: Transmission: Three-speed manual transmission (column shift) standard on Chevelle; floor shift on Camaro. Gear ratios: (1st) 3.11:1; (2nd) 1.84:1; (3rd) 1.00:1; (Rev) 3.22:1. Four- speed floor shift standard on Chevette: (1st) 3.75:1; (2nd) 2.16:1; (3rd) 1.38:1; (4th) 1.00:1; (Rev) 3.82:1. Four-speed floor shift standard on Vega, Monza four: (1st) 3.11:1; (2nd) 2.20:1; (3rd) 1.47:1; (4th) 1.00:1; (Rev) 3.11:1. Four-speed floor shift standard on Monza V-8, optional on Nova/Camaro V8350: (1st) 2.85:1; (2nd) 2.02:1; (3rd) 1.35:1; (4th) 1.00:1; (Rev) 2.85:1. Five-speed floor shift available on Vega, Monza four: (1st) 3.40:1; (2nd) 2.08:1; (3rd) 1.39:1; (4th) 1.00:1; (5th) 0.80:1; (Rev) 3.36:1. Three-speed Turbo Hydra-matic standard on some Malibus, Monte Carlo and Caprice/Impala, optional on others. Automatic gear ratios: (1st) 2.52:1; (2nd) 1.52:1; (3rd) 1.00:1; (Rev) 1.94:1 except standard Caprice/Impala, Monza V-8, Chevette and Nova (V8305) ratios: (1st) 2.74:1; (2nd) 1.57:1; (3rd) 1.00:1; (Rev) 2.07:1. Standard final drive ratio: (Chevette) 3.70:1 exc. w/1.4- liter engine and automatic, 4.11:1; (Vega) 2.92:1; (Monza four) 3.42:1; (Monza V-8) 2.73:1; (Nova) 2.73:1; (Camaro) 2.73:1 exc. 2.56:1 w/V-8 and automatic; (Z28) 3.73:1; (Chevelle six) 2.73:1; (Chevelle V-8) 2.56:1; (Monte) 2.56:1; (Imp/Capr six) 2.73:1; (Imp/Capr V-8) 2.56:1. Steering: (Chevette) rack and pinion; (others) recirculating ball. Suspension/Body: same as 1976. Brakes: front disc, rear drum. Ignition: Electronic. Fuel tank: (Chevette) 13 gal.; (Vega) 16 gal.; (Monza) 18.5 gal.; (Nova/Camaro) 21 gal.; (Chevelle/Monte) 22 gal.; (Imp/Capr) 21 gal.; (Imp/Capr wag) 22 gal.

DRIVETRAIN OPTIONS: Engines: 1.6-liter four: Chevette ($55). 305 cu. in., 2Bbl. V-8: Monza ($205); Nova/Camaro, Chevelle/Imp/Caprice cpe/sed ($120). 350 cu. in., 4Bbl. V-8: Nova/Camaro/Chevelle ($210); Chevelle/Imp/Capr wag, Monte ($90); Imp/Capr cpe/sed ($210). Transmission/Differential: Four-speed manual shift: Nova/Camaro ($252). Five-speed manual shift: Vega/Monza ($248). Turbo Hydra-matic transmission: Chevette/Vega/Monza ($248); Nova/Camaro, Chevelle cpe/sed ($282). Sport shifter w/console: Chevette ($43). Floor shift lever: Nova ($31). Positraction axle: Vega/Monza ($50); Nova/Camaro/Chevelle/Monte ($54); Imp/Capr ($58). Highway axle ratio: Monza ($13). Performance axle ratio ($13-$14). Power Accessories: Power brakes: Chvt/Vega/Monza ($58); Nova, Camaro, Chevelle cpe/sed ($61). Power steering: Vega/Monza ($129); Nova, Chevelle cpe/sed ($146). Suspension: F40 H.D. suspension: Nova ($8-$31); Chevelle/Monte/Imp/Capr ($19). F41 sport susp.: Vega ($149); Monza ($28); Nova, Camaro, Chevelle/Imp/Capr cpe/sed ($36). Superlift rear shock absorbers: Imp/Capr ($47). Rear stabilizer bar: Chevette ($28). Other: Heavy-duty radiator ($27-$37). H.D. alternator (61- amp): Chevelle/Monte/Imp/Capr ($29). H.D. battery ($16- $17). California emission system ($70). High altitude emission system ($22).

CHEVETTE/VEGA/MONZA CONVENIENCE/APPEARANCE OPTIONS: Option Packages: Sandpiper pkg.: Chevette (N/A). Rally sport equipment: Chevette ($295-$321). GT pkg.: Vega hatch ($401); Vega wagon ($373). Sport equipment: Monza ($134). Sport front-end appearance pkg.: Monza ($118). Spyder equipment pkg.: Monza ($274). Spyder appearance pkg.: Monza ($199). Quiet sound group: Chvt ($31-$42); Vega ($34-$46). Comfort/Convenience: Air conditioning ($442). Rear defogger ($71). Tinted glass ($48). Sport steering wheel ($16). Comfortilt steering wheel: Vega/Monza ($50). Special instrumentation: Chvt ($60); Vega ($77); Monza ($60-$77). Econominder gauge: Monza ($28). Electric clock: Chvt/Monza ($17). Digital clock: Monza ($43). Cigarette lighter: Chvt ($5). Glove compartment lock: Chvt ($3). Intermittent wipers: Chvt/Vega ($28). Lighting, Horns and Mirrors: Aux. lighting: Chvt ($33- $38); Vega ($16-$31); Monza ($16-$20). Sport mirrors, left remote: Vega/Monza ($28). Twin remote sport mirrors: Chevette ($46). Driver's remote sport mirror: Chvt ($20). Day/night mirror ($8). Entertainment: AM radio ($67). AM/FM radio ($129). AM/FM stereo radio: Vega/Monza ($212). Stereo tape player w/AM radio: Vega/Monza ($196). Stereo tape player with AM/FM stereo radio: Vega/Monza ($304). Rear speaker ($22). Windshield antenna: Vega/Monza ($16); incl. w/radios. Exterior Trim: Sky roof: Vega/Monza ($210). Vinyl roof: Monza ($145) incl. opera windows. Spoilers, front/rear: Monza ($87). Swing-out windows: Chvt ($48); Vega cpe ($33-$39). Custom exterior: Chvt ($86); Vega ($62-$92). Decor group: Vega ($6-$36). Sport stripes: Vega ($80). Bodyside moldings ($38). Wheel opening moldings: Vega/Monza ($20). Side window reveal moldings: Chvt ($63). Door edge guards ($8). Roof carrier: Chvt/Vega ($56). Rear air deflector: Vega ($24). Deluxe bumpers, front/rear: Chvt ($29). Deluxe bumpers w/guards: Monza ($65). Deluxe front bumper guards: Vega ($18). Deluxe bumper guards, front/rear: Chvt ($36-$65); Monza ($36). Bumper rub strips, front/rear: Vega ($47). Interior Trim/Upholstery: Custom interior trim: Chevette ($151-$199); Vega ($139-$188). Console: Chvt ($17); Vega/Monza ($77). Bucket seats (plaid cloth): Chvt ($9-$18); Vega ($18). Knit cloth bucket seats: Monza ($18). Custom knit cloth bucket seats: Monza ($135-$151). Leather bucket seats: Monza ($213). Adjustable driver's seatback: Vega/Monza ($17). Folding rear seat: Monza ($87). Rear seat delete: Chvt ($56 credit). Load floor carpet: Chvt ($43). Color-keyed floor mats ($15). Front mats: Chvt ($9). Deluxe seatbelts ($17). Wheels and Tires: Aluminum wheels: Monza ($186-$209). Rally II wheels: Vega ($74-$104). Wheel covers: Vega ($30). Deluxe wheel covers: Monza ($33). Sport wheel covers: Chevette ($71). Wheel trim rings: Chvt ($32); Vega ($2-$32). 155/8013/B WSW: Chvt ($38). 155/8013/B SBR: Chvt ($99). 155/8013/B SBR WSW: Chvt ($137). 155/8013/B SBR WLT: Chvt ($151). A78 x 13/B WSW: Vega ($38); Monza ($30-$38). BR78 x 13/B SBR: Vega ($35-$151); Monza ($94-$151). BR78 x 13/B SBR WSW: Vega ($73-$188); Monza ($124-$188). BR70 x 13/C SBR BSW: Monza (NC to $190). BR70 x 13/C SBR WSW: Monza ($30-$227). BR70 x 13/C SBR WLT: Vega ($126-$241); Monza ($42-$241). Conventional spare: Monza (NC).

NOVA/CAMARO/CHEVELLE/MONTE CARLO CONVENIENCE/APPEARANCE OPTIONS: Option Packages: Rally Sport equipment: base Camaro ($281); Camaro LT ($186). Estate equipment: Chevelle wag ($185). Interior decor/quiet sound group: base Camaro ($57). Comfort/Convenience: Air conditioning ($478-$507). Rear defogger, forced-air ($48). Rear defogger (electric): Monte ($82). Cruise-master speed control ($80). Tinted glass: Nova/Camaro ($50); Chevelle ($54); Monte ($58). Comfortilt steering wheel ($57). Six-way power seat: Chevelle/Monte ($137). Power windows ($108-$151). Power door locks: Nova/Chevelle ($68-$96); Camaro/Monte ($68). Power trunk release: Chevelle/Monte ($18). Power tailgate release: Chevelle 2S wag ($22). Electric clock: Nova, base Camaro ($19); Chevelle ($20). Special instrumentation (incl. tach and clock): Nova/Camaro ($99). Econominder gauge pkg.: Nova/Chevelle/Monte ($47). Intermittent wipers ($30). Lighting, Horns and Mirrors: Aux. lighting ($22-$44). Dual horns: Nova, base Camaro, Chevelle ($6). Remote-control driver's mirror: Nova/Chevelle/Monte ($15). Twin sport mirrors (left remote): Nova, base Camaro, Chevelle/Monte ($30). Twin remote sport mirrors: Chevelle/Monte ($21-$51). Day/night mirror: base Nova ($8). Visor vanity mirror: Chevelle/Monte ($4). Lighted visor mirror: Chevelle ($28); Monte ($24-$28). Entertainment: AM radio ($72). AM/FM radio: Nova/Camaro/Chevelle ($137); Monte ($146). AM/FM stereo radio ($226). Stereo tape player w/AM radio: Nova/Camaro/Chevelle ($209); Monte ($225). Stereo tape player with AM/FM stereo radio ($324). Rear speaker ($23). Windshield antenna ($17); incl. w/radios. Exterior Trim: Electric sky roof: Monte ($394). Vinyl roof: Nova/Camaro ($96); Chevelle ($111); Monte ($131). Cabriolet roof: Nova ($162). Spoilers, front/rear: Camaro ($87). Exterior decor pkg.: base Nova ($78); Chevelle ($20-$54). Custom appearance group: Nova Concours ($70-$81). Exterior style trim pkg.: Camaro ($61). Fashion-tone paint: Monte ($112). Two-tone paint: Nova, Chevelle cpe/sed ($43). Swing- out rear side windows: Nova ($52). Swing-out rear window: Chevelle 2S wag ($52). Bodyside moldings: Nova/Camaro/Chevelle ($40). Deluxe bodyside moldings: Nova Concours, Monte ($51). Door edge guards ($8-$12). Wheel opening moldings: base Nova ($20). Roof drip moldings: base Nova, Camaro ($17). Bodyside pinstriping: Nova ($28). Rear window air deflector: Chevelle wag ($26). Roof carrier: Chevelle wag ($71). Bumper rub strips: Chevelle/Monte ($32). Bumper rub strips and guards, front/rear: base Nova ($68). Bumper guards, front/rear: Camaro/Chevelle/Monte ($39); Chevelle wag ($20). Interior Trim/Upholstery: Interior decor pkg.: Nova ($27). Console: base Nova, Camaro/Chevelle/Monte ($75). Knit or plaid cloth bench seat: Nova ($20). Custom cloth interior: base Nova ($211). Custom vinyl interior: base Nova ($191). Vinyl bench seat: Monte ($20). Bench or notchback bench seat (sport cloth or vinyl): Chevelle ($20). Vinyl bucket seats: base Nova ($272); Chevelle ($109-$129); Monte ($169). Bucket seats (knit cloth): Nova Concours ($143-218). Sport cloth bucket seats: Camaro ($20). Monte custom 50/50 seating (reclining passenger): cloth ($293); vinyl ($313). Adj. driver's seatback: Camaro ($20). Litter container: Chevelle/Monte ($6). Load-floor carpeting: Chevelle wag ($45). Color-keyed mats ($16). Deluxe seatbelts ($16-$22). Deluxe trunk trim: Monte ($38). Wheels and Tires: Custom wheels: Camaro ($85-$125). Rally wheels: base Nova/Camaro ($65); Nova Concours ($42); Chevelle ($38-$65); Monte ($50). Wire wheel covers: base Nova ($108); Nova Concours ($75). Full wheel covers: base Nova, Camaro/Chevelle ($33). Deluxe wheel covers: Monte ($20). Sport wheel covers: Chevelle ($48-$81); Monte ($66). E78 x 14/B BSW: Camaro ($87-$107 credit). E78 x 14/B WSW: base Nova ($31-$39); Camaro ($56-$63 credit). FR78 x 14/B SBR: base Nova ($86-$107). FR78 x 14/B SBR WSW: base Nova ($119-$148); Nova Concours, Camaro ($33-$41). FR78 x 14/B SBR WLT: base Nova ($129-$161); Nova Concours, Camaro ($44-$55). FR78 x 15/B GBR WSW: Chevelle ($33-$41). FR78 x 15/B SBR BSW: Chevelle ($35-$45). FR78 x 15/B SBR WSW: Chevelle ($68-$86). GR78 x 15/B SBR BSW: Chevelle ($56-$71). GR78 x 15/B SBR WSW: Chevelle ($90-$114). HR78 x 15/B SBR BSW: Chevelle ($110). HR78 x 15/B SBR WSW: Chevelle ($157); Chevelle wag ($47). GR70 x 15/B SBR BSW: Chevelle ($74-$93). GR70 x 15/B SBR WSW: Chevelle ($108-$136); Monte ($34-$43). GR70 x 15/B SBR WLT: Chevelle ($119-$150). Stowaway spare: Nova w/o radials ($15); Camaro/Chevelle/Monte (NC).

1977 Caprice Classic Estate Wagon (CH)

IMPALA/CAPRICE CONVENIENCE/APPEARANCE OPTIONS: Option Packages: Estate equipment: wag ($210). Value appearance group: bodyside and wheel opening moldings, full wheel covers ($69). Comfort/Convenience: Four season air cond. ($527). Comfortron auto-temp air cond. ($607). Rear defogger, forced-air: cpe/sed ($48). Rear defogger, electric ($83). Cruise-Master speed control ($84). Tinted glass ($69). Comfortilt steering wheel ($58). Power door locks ($70-$98). Six-way power driver's seat ($139). Power windows ($114-$171). Power trunk release ($18). Power tailgate lock: wag ($37). Electric clock: Imp ($20). Digital clock: Imp ($42); Caprice ($23). Econominder gauge pkg. ($47). Intermittent wipers ($30). Quiet sound group: Imp ($41). Lighting, Horns and Mirrors: Aux. lighting ($23-$38). Dome reading light ($15). Dual horns: Imp ($6). Driver's remote mirror ($15). Dual remote mirrors ($45). Dual sport mirrors, left remote ($30). Dual remote body-color sport mirrors ($51). Visor vanity mirror ($4). Lighted visor mirror ($28). Entertainment: AM radio ($73). AM/FM radio ($148). AM/FM stereo radio ($229). Stereo tape player w/AM radio ($228); with AM/FM stereo radio ($328). Rear speaker ($23). Power antenna ($57); w/radio ($40). Windshield antenna ($17); incl. w/radios. Exterior Trim: Vinyl roof ($135). Two-tone paint ($44). Custom two-tone ($99). Pinstriping ($31). Roof carrier: wag ($104). Bodyside moldings ($41). Door edge guards ($8-$12). Wheel opening moldings ($20). Roof drip moldings: Imp ($17). Bumper rub strips, front/rear ($45). Bumper guards ($46). Interior Trim/Upholstery: Vinyl bench seat: cpe/sed ($20). Knit or sport cloth bench seat: wag ($20). Knit cloth 50/50 seat: cpe/sed ($153). Knit or sport cloth 50/50 seat: wag ($173). Vinyl 50/50 seat ($153-$173). Special custom cloth 50/50 seat: cpe/sed ($285). Deluxe load-floor carpet: wag ($66). Deluxe cargo area carpet: wag ($95). Color-keyed mats ($16). Litter container ($6). Deluxe seatbelts ($19-$22). Deluxe trunk trim ($38). Wheel Covers: Full wheel covers ($34). Sport wheel covers: Imp ($82); Capr ($48). Coupe/Sedan Tires: FR78 x 15/B GBR WSW ($41). FR78 x 15/B SBR BSW ($45). FR78 x 15/B SBR WSW ($86). GR78 x 15/B SBR BSW ($71). GR78 x 15/B SBR WSW ($114). GR70 x 15/B SBR WSW ($136). Wagon Tires: HR78 x 15/B SBR WSW ($47).

HISTORY: Introduced: Sept. 30, 1976. Model year production (U.S.): 2,079,798 (incl. Corvettes but not incl. 3,299 Acadians). Of the total North American production for U.S. market, 263,829 had four-cylinder engines, 283,874 sixes, and 1,872,643 V-8s. Calendar year production: 2,135,942 (including 36,605 Sportvans, 46,345 Corvettes and 4,678 Acadians). Calendar year sales by U.S. dealers: 2,280,439 (incl. 36,609 Sportvans and 42,571 Corvettes) for a 25.1 percent market share. Full- size Chevrolets sold the best. Model year sales by U.S. dealers: 2,239,538 (incl. 39,640 Sportvans and 40,764 Corvettes).

Historical Footnotes: Caprice Classic, in its new downsized form, was voted *Motor Trend* "Car-of-the-Year" for 1977. That magazine considered Caprice "the most car you can get for your dollar" and applauded its "understated elegance." Model year sales rose by 8 percent over 1976, due largely to popular acceptance of the smaller full-sized models. Full-size sales rose by a healthy 38 percent, giving Chevrolet back the title of best selling passenger car in the industry (formerly held by Olds Cutlass). Calendar year production gained 4.5 percent. Only the discontinued Vega and soon-to-be-shrunk Malibu posted a loss for the calendar year. For the first time, Chevrolet began to supply other GM divisions with its 350 cu. in. V-8. Unfortunately, the installation of that V-8 in Oldsmobiles led eventually to class-action lawsuits and ultimate rebates to customers who felt they'd been cheated by not receiving a "real" Olds powerplant. In the four-cylinder engine marketplace, Pontiac's new cast iron "Iron Duke" powerplant was expected to tempt some customers away from Chevrolet with its all- aluminum 140 cu. in. four. But Chevrolet would soon obtain the Pontiac powerplant for its Monza. Chevette was the first serious attempt by a domestic automaker to compete against the smallest imports. That market began to fall, but Chevette remained a strong competitor. "It'll drive you happy" was Chevette's theme, and the rear-drive subcompact would hang around for another decade before being overrun by front-drive models. Monza's Spyder was thought by some observers to show revived Detroit interest in "muscle cars," though a Monza hardly seemed in the same league with some of the truly muscular beasts of the past.

1978 CHEVROLET

After downsizing of full-size models for 1977, the mid- size A body Malibu and Monte Carlo got the same treatment this year. Each was a foot shorter and 500-800 pounds lighter than equivalent 1977 models. Vega was dropped, but that line's hatchback and wagon continued under the Monza name. Chevrolet offered two new V-6 engines: a 200 cu. in. that was now standard on the downsized Malibu, and a 231 (supplied by Buick) for the Monte Carlo. Monza's new small V-8 (196 cu. in.) also originated at Buick. A new four, dubbed the "Iron Duke," came from Pontiac.

1978 Chevette hatchback sedan (CH)

CHEVETTE — SERIES 1T — FOUR — After two seasons as a two-door, Chevette added a six- window four-door hatchback sedan on a three-inch longer wheelbase. Rear legroom stretched five inches over the two- door's. Rear door glass in the sedan retracted only partly; side quarter glass was fixed. This year's grille used new molding treatments around each air inlet louver, plus single horizontal and double vertical bars through each opening. The result: a dozen large, boxy holes arranged in 3 x 2 pattern on each half of the angled panel. Grille moldings were argent on the Scooter coupe, bright chrome on other models. Small amber rectangular parking lamps were below the bumper rub strip; similar amber side marker lenses on front fenders. 'Chevette' script was on the front fender, just ahead of the door. Standard engine was now the 98 cu. in. (1.6-liter) overhead-cam four, rated 63 horsepower, replacing the smaller 1.4-liter of 1977. A high- output version (not available in California) had a bigger carburetor, revised manifolds, reduced exhaust back pressure, and higher-speed camshaft. Even though Chevette's price rose only modestly, 18 items that had been optional now became standard. Standard equipment (except on Scooter) now included a front spoiler, AM radio, center console with coin pocket, whitewall tires, wheel trim rings, bumper rub strips, bodyside and sill moldings, sport steering wheel, and cigarette lighter. The coupe had a swing-out rear window. Also standard: fully synchronized four-speed manual transmission, glove box lock, color-keyed dash, and carpeting. New options included tri-tone sport stripes (five color choices), and seven-position comfortilt steering wheel. Most automatic transmissions were produced at Strasbourg, identical to those used on European Chevettes. Body acoustics were revised for quieter road operation. Zincro-metal inner fender skirts and galvanized fender reinforcements joined the list of special corrosion-protection treatments. All-vinyl interiors came in black, blue, carmine, green or camel. Cloth/vinyl upholstery came in black, carmine or camel. Scooters were upholstered with all-vinyl or Sport cloth/vinyl, in black or camel. Optional Custom interiors were "Rattan" all-vinyl or "Darby" woven cloth/vinyl. Of the 14 body colors, ten were new this year.

MONZA — SERIES 1H — FOUR/V-6/V-8 — With the departure of Vega, the subcompact Monza line grew to seven two-door models in two groups. Monza took over two carryover Vega body styles: the hatchback and wagon. That gave the standard lineup an 'S' hatchback, 2+2 hatchback, coupe, and two station wagons. Monza's Sport series, repeating the soft fascia of 1977, came in two body types: sport coupe and 2+2 hatchback. Standard models had single round headlamps with restyled housings, black-accented bright grille and moldings with single crossbars and center bowtie emblem, new header panel, and bright steel bumpers. A new

1978 Monza S hatchback coupe (CH)

body-colored filler strip at the rear closed the gap between bumper and body. Rear end of the wagon and hatchback coupe looked the same as their Vega predecessors, except for the steel bumper. Monza Sport displayed quad rectangular headlamps and the Euro-look soft fascia, restyled with new front cover and headlamp bezels. Bumper guards and strips (front and rear) switched to body color this year. Upper air intake slots were gone this year, replaced by a single wide opening over the bumper, with round emblem above. Separate 'Monza' block letters stood at the center of the thin, full-width grille opening. Engine choices were the new base 151 cu. in. (2.5-liter) four; new optional 196 cu. in. (3.2-liter) V-6; and optional 305 cu. in. (5.0-liter) V-8. All three had two-barrel carburetors. Both new engines came from other GM divisions. California Monzas carried a 231 cu. in. V-6 rather than the 196, and the four came only with automatic shift. Fours and the V6196 weren't available in high-altitude areas. The V-8 was available only in notchback or 2+2 models. The new base engine replaced the former aluminum 140 cu. in. four, which had its share of troubles. The 151 had a cast iron head, block and manifolds, with two-barrel two- stage carburetor. The new 196 V-6 also used cast iron construction. The California V-6 was similar but with larger bore. Transmissions were the standard four-speed manual or optional five-speed (available for four or V-6 engine). Turbo Hydra-matic was available for all engines. The acoustical package was upgraded this year, with full hood insulation. Front disc brakes had ventilated rotors. New GT coupe equipment packages featured 'GT' striping and BR70 x 13/C tires. Spyder performance equipment for the Sport 2+2 hatchback included special-handling suspension and BR70 x 13/C tires. V-8 versions had dual exhaust outlets. A 'Spyder' nameplate went on front fender; emblems on hood header and rear keylock cover. A companion Spyder appearance package could again be ordered separately. A new Estate package was offered for station wagons.

1978 Nova Custom sedan (CH)

NOVA — SERIES 1X — SIX/V-8 — A new Nova Custom series combined the 1977 Concours body trim with the custom interior option. Otherwise, appearance was unchanged except for new colors, trims, emblems, and steering wheel. A two-door coupe and four-door sedan came in both levels, plus a two-door hatchback coupe in basic Nova dress only. The list of optional body moldings was expanded. A new front seatbelt retractor system provided greater rear seat comfort and more convenient operation. The "Nova Rally" coupe appearance option package for the Custom coupe was similar to the 1977 version, but the grille nameplate was deleted. Custom models were identified by a modified block-letter 'Nova Custom' emblem on front fender. Styling features included a massive-look grille made of thin vertical bars, inset low-profile vertical parking lamps, chromed headlamp bezels, bright wide hood edge moldings, and tri-section taillamps. The former Concours' stand-up hood ornament did not continue. Small horizontal side marker lenses were again near the front of front fenders. New colors this year were silver, light camel, bright blue metallic, camel or dark camel metallic, saffron metallic, and carmine metallic. Carried over: black, white, light blue or green metallic, dark blue-green metallic, bright yellow, and light red. Standard engine was the inline 250 cu. in. (4.1-liter) six with three-speed manual transmission. Optional: 305 cu. in. (5.0-liter) and 350 (5.7-liter) V-8s. Four-speed manual transmission was required with the 305 V-8, while automatic was mandatory with the 350 V-8. California Novas came only with automatic. Novas could even be ordered with a police package, offering handling that some compared to a Camaro Z28. Nova's Rally Equipment package included striping at lower bodyside, rear end panel and over wheel openings; a chromed diamond-pattern grille; black headlamp bezels; Rally nameplates; and 14 x 6 in. (or 14 x 7 in.) Rally wheels.

CAMARO — SERIES 1F — SIX/V-8 — Though unchanged in basic design, Camaros managed a fresh look with a new body-colored soft nose section and rear bumper. The new design used the same cellular urethane as Corvette, to replace the former aluminum face bar and spring bumper system. Camaro's grille was similar to 1977, but with fewer horizontal bars and larger holes (ten rows across), and a deeper repeated lower section below the narrow bumper. At the rear were wedge-shaped wraparound taillamps with inboard amber directional signal lamps and clear backup lamps. Rally Sport became a model this year rather than an option, with new paint striping. Both standard and Type LT Rally Sport coupe models had a bold contrasting paint scheme.

1978 Camaro Sport Coupe (CH)

The forward roof section, hood surface and front header (to below the grille opening) were black metallic. Tri-color striping separated those black surfaces from the basic body color. 'Rally Sport' decals were on front fenders and decklid. Standard engine was the 250 cu. in. inline six, now rated 110 horsepower, with three-speed manual transmission. Optional: 305 and 350 V-8s, now with base four-speed manual gearbox. California Camaros only came with automatic, while high-altitude buyers could get only the 350 V-8 and automatic. The six had improved exhaust system isolation this year. An aluminum intake manifold helped cut the 305 V-8's weight by 35 pounds. Chassis had improved front frame reinforcements. And the brake-pressure differential switch was now made of nylon. All axle ratios were lowered in an attempt to boost gas mileage. Body colors this year were white, silver, black, light or bright blue, orange-yellow, bright yellow, dark blue- green, camel, dark camel, saffron, light red, and carmine. New Rally wheels came in all body colors. Camaros had new standard cloth seat trim, a new door trim design, and could have new optional aluminum wheels. Also joining the option list: a T-bar twin hatch roof with tinted glass lift-out roof panels, operated by a single latch on each panel. A total of 9,875 T-roofs were installed this year. The high-performance Z28 added a new pointed hood panel air scoop with black throat, functional slanted front-fender air louvers, body-color rear spoiler, modified body striping, and simulated string-wrapped steering wheel. Powerplant was the 350 (5.7-liter) V-8 with four-barrel and dual exhaust outlets, putting out 170 or 185 horsepower. Z28s had a 3.42:1 or 3.73:1 axle ratio, special handling suspension, and GR70 x 15/B white-letter tires. Suspension revisions this year increased front-end rigidity and limited transverse movement of the rear axle. A 'Z28' decal was below the air louvers.

1978 Malibu Classic Landau Coupe (CH)

MALIBU — SERIES 1A — V-6/V-8 — New-size Malibus rode a 108 inch wheelbase and averaged 193 inches. Over all that was 12½ to 22 inches shorter than 1977 equivalents. This year's editions were narrower, too, but as tall as before. Slimmer doors and reduced bodyside curvature helped keep interior space ample. Broad glass area improved visibility. Rear armrests in sedans and wagons were now recessed into back door trim panels, so door glass was fixed rather than movable. Somehow, the newly shrunken Malibus managed to offer more interior and luggage space. Shell-type seats helped add head/leg room. Coupes lost 550 pounds, wagons closer to half a ton. Models included a two-door coupe, four-door sedan, and four-door (two-seat) station wagon, in both Malibu and Malibu Classic series. A Malibu Classic Landau coupe was available. So was an Estate option for the Malibu Classic wagon. The old Chevelle name faded away this year. Both Malibus had a new wide, chrome-plated plastic grille in horizontally-oriented lattice style, with 'Chevrolet' block lettering in the upper molding. Vertical rectangular parking lamps sat between the grille and single chrome-bezel rectangular headlamps. Bright steel bumpers had horizontal sculpture lines. Tapered, angled amber side marker lamps stood at front fender tips. 'Malibu' or 'Malibu Classic' identification was at the rear of quarter panels. Both models had bright roof drip moldings and wheel covers. Six-window sedans had large pivoting quarter vent windows. At the rear were large tri-section taillamps, level with the license plate, with outboard lenses wrapping around to form side markers. (Wagon taillamps sat in the back bumper.) A 'Chevrolet' block-letter nameplate was on the lower right of the decklid. Malibu Classic added extra rear moldings and bright taillamp trim, plus wheel opening moldings (also on Malibu wagon). Standard powerplant was a new Chevrolet 200 cu. in. (3.3-liter) V-6, derived from the popular small-block V-8. The new engine had a cast iron block and cylinder heads, new "Dualjet" carburetor, and lightweight aluminum intake manifold. New dynamic balancing was supposed to ensure smooth running. California models, though, required a 231 V-6. Standard transmission was the three-speed manual, except in California where the otherwise optional Turbo Hydra-matic was mandatory. An optional 305 cu. in. (5.0-liter) V-8 could have either four-speed manual or automatic. Wagons in high- altitude areas had to have the four-barrel 350 cu. in. V-8. A new vertical-style instrument panel, mounted well forward, helped to enhance the spacious feeling. A separate module held radio/heater controls and instruments. Plug-in components and a swing-down glove compartment made behind- dash servicing easier. The dimmer switch moved to the turn- signal lever. A new ventilation system delivered outside air under all driving conditions, whether power assited or ram vented. Sedans and wagons had standard swing-out rear vent windows. Drivers had a delta-spoke soft vinyl steering wheel. Wagons had a much wider cargo opening than before, plus a split tailgate instead of the previous swing-up version. As in full-size wagons, storage compartments were in the rear quarter trim panels, just inside the tailgate. The new Malibus used a full perimeter frame to keep their "big car" ride. The chassis featured coil springs all around, a single-piece propeller shaft, lower rear axle ratios, relay-type steering, and front disc (rear drum) brakes. The new fuel tank held 17.5 gallons. Malibus rode radial-ply tires on 14 inch wheels. All had a modular mini-enersorber bumper system. A new temporary spare tire saved 15 pounds and allowed greater trunk space. Fourteen tuned rubber body mounts helped keep road noise down. In addition to 14 solid colors, five custom two-tone combinations were optional: dark blue and light blue metallic; gold and light camel; carmine and dark carmine metallic; green and light green metallic; and silver with medium gray accent. Standard equipment included heater/defroster, carpeting, bright windshield and back window reveal moldings, bright belt side moldings, front stabilizer bar, Freedom battery, and P185/75R14 fiberglass- belted radial tires (wagons had P195/75R14). Malibu Classic added dual horns. Malibu Classic Landau had a vinyl roof, bodyside striping, rally wheels, and sport wheel covers. Power brakes and steering, V-8 engines and Turbo Hydra-matic were optional.

1978 Monte Carlo Sport Coupe (CH)

MONTE CARLO — SERIES 1A — V-6/V-8 — The third-generation Monte, according to Chevrolet, was "reengineered to meet the need for modern levels of vehicle efficiency" to provide "a new dimension in affordable luxury." Weight was cut by over 800 pounds. Overall length shrunk by 12.9 inches, wheelbase by nearly 8 inches (down to 108.1), while height rose slightly. Even so, interior dimensions managed to grow instead of shrink. The downsized version displayed a more formal roofline with sweeping fender and body lines (but lacking the former body bulges), much larger quarter windows, and frameless door glass. Single bright-bezeled rectangular headlamps sat between large parking lamps (which wrapped around to amber marker lamps) and the bright, fine-mesh grid-pattern grille. At the rear were distinctive five-segment taillamps. Lower body contours retained the look of former Montes. Large, soft bumper impact areas held bright impact strips. Up front was a standup header emblem and 'Monte Carlo' script nameplate. Nameplates were also on front fenders; nameplate with bowtie emblem on decklid; Monte crest on the sail panel. Basic mechanical (and bodily) changes were similar to Malibu. The new standard 231 cu. in. (3.8-liter) V-6 engine with two-barrel carburetor was claimed to deliver 24 percent better gas mileage than the former base V-8. Sole V-8 option this year was the 305 cu. in. (5.0-liter). Base transmission was three-speed manual, with four-speed manual and automatic available. The V-8 came with automatic, but could have four-speed manual. Automatics were required in California. For improved handling, Monte got a special frame, front and rear stabilizer bars, and P205/70R14 steel-belted radial tires. The new body used aluminum inner and outer decklid panels to save weight. Rear brake drums were finned aluminum. Improved corrosion protection included zincro-metal, aluminum, galvanized metal, zinc priming, anti-corrosion dip, plus special sealers and coatings. Front and rear bumper reinforcement bars were aluminum. The new integrated-look outer covering was injection-molded and pliable, finished in body color. Monte's standard interior used a bench seat with split back, in vinyl or woven cloth. Optional: a 55/45 split bench seat (velour or vinyl), or vinyl buckets with individual adjustments. Standard equipment included the 231 V-6, three- speed manual transmission, manual front disc brakes, electric clock, day/night mirror, dual horns, bright wheel opening and roof drip moldings, bumper impact strips, front and rear stabilizer bars, heater/defroster, and carpeting. Body colors this year were white, silver, black, light blue, light camel, or nine metallics: light or dark blue, light or medium green, camel, dark camel, saffron, carmine, or dark carmine. A new Landau model had a vinyl half-roof with unique white-metalized rear quarter window treatment, sport mirrors, special wheel covers, wide sill moldings, lower body applique, upper body pinstriping, and 'Landau' nameplates with decorative crest. As before, Landaus came with standard automatic transmission, power brakes and steering. Added to the option list; a twin hatch sunroof with removable tinted glass panels. Still available was the power-operated steel sunroof.

1978 Impala Sport Coupe (CH)

IMPALA/CAPRICE CLASSIC — SERIES 1B — SIX/V-8 — Apart from revised front and rear styling treatments, the full-size Chevrolets were carryovers from their 1977 downsizing. Impalas carried a new horizontal-bar grille, with bowtie above rather than on the grille itself. Caprice's version had a lattice crosshatch pattern (with fewer divider bars than before). Taillamps and moldings were also restyled. Both Caprice and Impala were again available in two-door coupe, four-door sedan and four-door station wagon (two- or three-seat) body styles. Powertrains were the same as 1977, except for reduced axle ratios to achieve greater economy. Standard engine was again the 250 cu. in. (4.1-liter) inline six, with both 305 and 350 V-8s available. The six now had an integral distributor cap and coil, while the 305 V-8 lost 35 pounds as a result of a new aluminum intake manifold. A larger power brake booster reduced pedal effort. Of the 14 standard body colors, ten were new this year. In addition to styling differences, Caprice added a few items of standard equipment absent on Impalas. They included a

1978 Caprice Classic sedan (CH)

dual-note horn, full wheel covers, wheel opening moldings, clock, interior lighting, and fold-down center armrest on sedans. The Caprice Classic Landau coupe, introduced during the 1977 model year, was continued this year. That appearance package included an elk-grain forward vinyl top with bright rear-edge molding, sport mirrors, wire wheel covers with Landau hub identification, accent striping, and belt moldings painted to match the vinyl top. Roof panels held a Landau nameplate. New options this year: new wheel trim covers for Impala, an electrically-powered sliding steel sunroof for coupes and sedans, and 40-channel CB built into AM/FM radio.

I.D. DATA: As before, Chevrolet used a 13-symbol Vehicle Identification Number (VIN) displayed on the upper left surface of the instrument panel, visible through the windshield. The first digit ('1') indicates Chevrolet division. Next is a letter identifying the series (car line): 'B' Chevette; 'J' Chevette Scooter; 'M' Monza; 'R' Monza Sport; 'X' Nova; 'Y' Nova Custom; 'Q' Camaro; 'S' Camaro Type LT; 'Y' Nova Concours; 'T' Malibu; 'W' Malibu Classic; 'Z' Monte Carlo; 'L' Impala; 'N' Caprice Classic. Symbols 34 indicate body type: '08' 2-dr. (4-pass.) hatchback coupe; '07' 2-dr. (2+2) hatchback coupe; '77' 2-dr. hatchback coupe; '17' Nova 2-dr. (6- pass.) hatchback coupe; '27' 2-dr. coupe or notchback coupe; '87' 2-dr. (4-pass.) sport coupe; '37' 2-dr. (6- pass.) sport coupe; '47' 2-dr. (6-pass.) coupe; '19' 4- dr. (6-pass.) sedan; '68' 4-dr. (4-pass.) hatchback sedan; '69' 4-dr. (6-pass.) sedan; '15' 2-dr. (4-pass.) station wagon; '35' 4-dr. station wagon. Symbol five is the engine code: 'E' L497.6 1Bbl.; 'J' L497.6 H.O.; 'V' L4151 2Bbl.; 'C' V6196 2Bbl.; 'M' V6200 2Bbl.; 'A' V6231 2Bbl.; 'D' L6250 1Bbl.; 'U' V8305 2Bbl.; 'L' V8350 4Bbl. Next is a code for model year ('8' 1978). Symbol seven denotes assembly plant: 'B' Baltimore, MD; 'C' South Gate, CA; 'D' Doraville, GA; 'J' Janesville, WI; 'K' Leeds, MO; 'U' Lordstown, OH; 'L' Van Nuys, CA; 'N' Norwood, OH; 'R' Arlington, TX; 'S' St. Louis, MO; 'T' Tarrytown, NY; 'W' Willow Run, MI; 'Y' Wilmington, DE; 'Z' Fremont, CA; '1' Oshawa, Ontario. The last six digits are the sequential serial number. A Body Number Plate on the upper horizontal surface of the shroud (except X-bodies, on the vertical surface) identifies model year, car division, series, style, body assembly plant, body number, trim combination, modular seat code, paint code, and date build code. A two- or three-symbol code (combined with a serial number) identifies each engine. Chevette engine numbers are on a pad at right of block, below No. 1 spark plug. Pontiac (151) fours have a number pad at the right side of the block, by distributor shaft hole. On sixes, the pad is at the right side of the block, to rear of distributor. On V-8s, that pad is just forward of the right cylinder head.

CHEVETTE (FOUR)

Model Number	Body/Style Number	Body Type & Seating	Factory Price	Shipping Weight	Production Total
1T	B08	2-dr. Hatch Cpe-4P	3354	1965	118,375
1T	B68	4-dr. Hatch Sed-4P	3764	2035	167,769

CHEVETTE SCOOTER (FOUR)

1T	J08	2-dr. Hatch Cpe-4P	2999	1932	12,829

Chevette Production Note: 11,316 Chevettes were built for sale in Canada as Acadians.

MONZA (FOUR/V-6/V-8)

1H	M07	2-dr. Hatch 2+2-4P	3609	2732	36,227
1H	M77	2-dr. 'S' Hatch-4P	3527	2643	2,326
1H	M27	2-dr. Cpe-4P	3462	2688	37,878
1H	M15	2-dr. Sta Wag-4P	3698	2723	24,255
1H	M15/YC6	2-dr. Est Wag-4P	3932	N/A	2,478

1978 Monza Sport Coupe (CH)

MONZA SPORT (FOUR/V-6/V-8)

Model Number	Body/Style Number	Body Type & Seating	Factory Price	Shipping Weight	Production Total
1H	R27	2-dr. Spt Cpe-4P	3930	2730	6,823
1H	R07	2-dr. Hatch 2+2-4P	4077	2777	28,845

Monza Engine Note: Prices shown are for four-cylinder engine. The 196 cu. in. V-6 cost $130 extra; a 231 V-6, $170. Monza could also have a 305 V-8 for $320 over the four-cylinder price. A total of 41,995 Monzas had a V6-196 installed, and 16,254 a 231 V-6. Only 9,478 had a V-8 engine.

NOVA (SIX/V-8)

1X	X27	2-dr. Cpe-6P	3702/3887	3132/3277	101,858
1X	X17	2-dr. Hatch-6P	3866/4051	3258/3403	12,665
1X	X69	4-dr. Sedan-6P	3777/3962	3173/3318	123,158

NOVA CUSTOM (SIX/V-8)

1X	Y27	2-dr. Cpe-6P	3960/4145	3261/3396	23,953
1X	Y69	4-dr. Sedan-6P	4035/4220	3298/3443	26,475

CAMARO (SIX/V-8)

1F	Q87	2-dr. Spt Cpe-4P	4414/4599	3300/3425	134,491
1F	Q87/Z85	2-dr. Rally Cpe-4P	4784/4969	N/A	11,902

CAMARO TYPE LT (SIX/V-8)

1F	S87	2-dr. Spt Cpe-4P	4814/4999	3352/3477	65,635
1F	S87/Z85	2-dr. Rally Cpe-4P	5065/5250	N/A	5,696

CAMARO Z28 (V-8)

1F	Q87	2-dr. Spt Cpe-4P	-- /5604	-- / N/A	54,907

MALIBU (V-6/V-8)

1A	T27	2-dr. Spt Cpe-6P	4204/4394	3001/3138	27,089
1A	T19	4-dr. Sed-6P	4279/4469	3006/3143	44,426
1A	T35	4-dr. Sta Wag-6P	4516/4706	3169/3350	30,850

MALIBU CLASSIC (V-6/V-8)

1A	W27	2-dr. Spt Cpe-6P	4461/4651	3031/3167	60,992
1A	W27/Z03	2-dr. Lan Cpe-6P	4684/4874	N/A	29,160
1A	W19	4-dr. Sed-6P	4561/4651	3039/3175	102,967
1A	W35	4-dr. Sta Wag-6P	4714/4904	3196/3377	63,152

Malibu Engine Note: Only 8,930 Malibus had the 231 V-6 engine, and only 802 had the 350 V-8 (code (LM1).

MONTE CARLO (V-6/V-8)

1A	Z37	2-dr. Spt Cpe-6P	4785/4935	3040/3175	216,730
1A	Z37/Z03	2-dr. Lan Cpe-6P	5678/5838	N/A	141,461

IMPALA (SIX/V-8)

1B	L47	2-dr. Spt Cpe-6P	5208/5393	3511/3619	33,990
1B	L47/Z03	2-dr. Lan Cpe-6P	5598/5783	N/A	4,652
1B	L69	4-dr. Sedan-6P	5283/5468	3530/3638	183,161
1B	L35	4-dr. Sta Wag-6P	-- /5777	-- /4037	40,423
1B	L35/AQ4	4-dr. 3S Wag-8P	-- /5904	-- /4071	28,518

CAPRICE CLASSIC (SIX/V-8)

1B	N47	2-dr. Spt Cpe-6P	5526/5711	3548/3656	37,301
1B	N47/Z03	2-dr. Lan Cpe-6P	5830/6015	N/A	22,771
1B	N69	4-dr. Sedan-6P	5626/5811	3578/3686	203,837
1B	N35	4-dr. Sta Wag-6P	-- /6012	-- /4079	24,792
1B	N35/AQ4	4-dr. 3S Wag-8P	-- /6151	-- /4109	32,952

FACTORY PRICE AND WEIGHT NOTE: Where two prices and weights are shown, the figure to the left of the slash is for six-cylinder model, to right of slash for V-8. **BODY/STYLE NO. NOTE:** Some models are actually option packages. Figure after the slash (e.g., Z03) is the number of the option package that comes with the model listed.

ENGINE DATA: BASE FOUR (Chevette): Inline. Overhead cam. Four-cylinder. Cast iron block and head. Displacement: 97.6 cu. in. (1.6 liters). Bore & stroke: 3.23 x 2.98 in. Compression ratio: 8.6:1. Brake horsepower: 63 at 4800 R.P.M. Torque: 82 lbs.-ft. at 3200 R.P.M. Five main bearings. Hydraulic valve lifters. Carburetor: 1Bbl. Rochester 1ME. VIN Code: E. OPTIONAL FOUR (Chevette): Same as above except Brake H.P.: 68 at 5000 R.P.M. Torque: 84 lbs.-ft. at 3200 R.P.M. VIN Code: J. BASE FOUR (Monza): Inline. Overhead valve. Four-cylinder. Cast iron block. Displacement: 151 cu. in. (2.5 liters). Bore & stroke: 4.00 x 3.00 in. Compression ratio: 8.3:1. Brake horsepower: 85 at 4400 R.P.M. Torque: 123 lbs.-ft. at 2800 R.P.M. Five main bearings. Hydraulic valve lifters. Carburetor: 2Bbl. Holley 5210C. VIN Code: V. OPTIONAL V-6 (Monza): 90-degree, overhead-valve V-6. Cast iron block and head. Displacement: 196 cu. in. (3.2 liters). Bore & stroke: 3.50 x 3.40 in. Compression ratio: 8.0:1. Brake horsepower: 90 at 3600 R.P.M. Torque: 165 lbs.-ft. at 2000 R.P.M. Four main bearings. Hydraulic valve lifters. Carburetor: 2Bbl. Rochester 2GE. VIN Code: C. BASE V-6 (Malibu): 90-degree, overhead-valve V-6. Cast iron block and head. Displacement: 200 cu. in. (3.3 liters). Bore & stroke: 3.50 x 3.48 in. Compression ratio: 8.2:1. Brake horsepower: 95 at 3800 R.P.M. Torque: 160 lbs.-ft. at 2000 R.P.M. Four main bearings. Hydraulic valve lifters. Carburetor: 2Bbl. Rochester 2GC. VIN Code: M. BASE V-6 (Monte Carlo); OPTIONAL (Monza, Malibu): 90-degree, overhead-valve V-6. Cast iron block and head. Displacement: 231 cu. in. (3.8 liters). Bore & stroke: 3.80 x 3.40 in. Compression ratio: 8.0:1. Brake horsepower: 105 at 3400 R.P.M. Torque: 185 lbs.-ft. at 2000 R.P.M. Four main bearings. Hydraulic valve lifters. Carburetor: 2Bbl. Rochester 2GE. VIN Code: A. BASE SIX (Nova, Camaro, Impala, Caprice): Inline. OHV. Six-cylinder. Cast iron block and head. Displacement: 250 cu. in. (4.1 liters). Bore & stroke: 3.88 x 3.53 in. Compression ratio: 8.1:1. Brake horsepower: 110 at 3800 R.P.M. Torque: 190 lbs.-ft. at 1600 R.P.M. Seven main bearings. Hydraulic valve lifters. Carburetor: 1Bbl. Rochester 1ME. VIN Code: D. BASE V-8 (Impala/Caprice wagon); OPTIONAL (Monza, Nova, Camaro, Malibu, Monte Carlo, Impala, Caprice): 90-degree, overhead valve V-8. Cast iron block and head. Displacement: 305 cu. in. (5.0 liters). Bore & stroke: 3.74 x 3.48 in. Compression ratio: 8.4:1. Brake horsepower: 145 at 3800 R.P.M. Torque: 245 lbs.-ft. at 2400 R.P.M. Five main bearings. Hydraulic valve lifters. Carburetor: 2Bbl. Rochester 2GC. VIN Code: U. BASE V-8 (Camaro Z28); OPTIONAL (Nova, Camaro, Malibu wagon, Impala, Caprice): 90-degree, overhead valve V-8. Cast iron block and head. Displacement: 350 cu. in. (5.7 liters). Bore & stroke: 4.00 x 3.48 in. Compression ratio: 8.2:1. Brake horsepower: 170 at 3800 R.P.M. Torque: 270 lbs.-ft. at 2400 R.P.M. Five main bearings. Hydraulic valve lifters. Carburetor: 4Bbl. Rochester M4MC. VIN Code: L. OPTIONAL V-8 (Camaro Z28): Same as 350 V-8 above but Brake H.P.: 185 at 4000 R.P.M. Torque: 280 lbs.-ft. at 2400 R.P.M.

CHASSIS DATA: Wheelbase: (Chevette 2-dr.) 94.3 in.; (Chvt 4-dr.) 97.3 in.; (Monza) 97.0 in.; (Camaro) 108.0 in.; (Nova) 111.0 in.; (Malibu/Monte) 108.1 in.; (Caprice/Imp) 116.0 in. Overall length: (Chevette 2-dr.) 159.7 in.; (Chvt 4-dr.) 162.6 in.; (Monza) 178.0-179.3 in.; (Nova) 196.7 in.; (Camaro) 197.6 in.; (Malibu) 192.7 in.; (Malibu wag) 193.4 in.; (Monte) 200.4 in.; (Capr/Imp) 212.1 in.; (Capr/Imp wag) 214.7 in. Height: (Chevette 2-dr.) 52.3 in.; (Chvt 4-dr.) 53.3 in.; (Monza cpe) 49.8 in.; (Monza hatch) 50.2 in.; (Monza wag) 51.8 in.; (Nova 2-dr.) 52.7 in.; (Nova 4dr.) 53.6 in.; (Camaro) 49.2 in.; (Malibu cpe) 53.3 in.; (Malibu sed) 54.2 in.; (Malibu wag) 54.5 in.; (Monte) 53.9 in.; (Capr/Imp cpe) 55.3 in.; (Capr/Imp sed) 56.0 in.; (Capr/Imp wag) 58.0 in. Width: (Chevette) 61.8 in.; (Monza) 65.4 in.; (Nova) 72.2 in.; (Camaro) 74.5 in.; (Malibu/Monte) 71.5 in.; (Malibu wag) 71.2 in.; (Capr/Imp) 76.0 in.; (Capr/Imp wag) 79.1 in. Front Tread: (Chevette) 51.2 in.; (Monza) 54.8 in.; (Nova/Camaro) 61.3 in.; (Camaro LT) 61.6 in.; (Malibu/Monte) 58.5 in.; (Capr/Imp) 61.8 in.; (Capr/Imp wag) 62.2 in. Rear Tread: (Chevette) 51.2 in.; (Monza) 53.6 in.; (Nova) 59.0 in.; (Camaro) 60.0 in.; (Camaro LT) 60.3 in.; (Malibu/Monte) 57.8 in.; (Capr/Imp) 60.8 in.; (Capr/Imp wag) 64.1 in. Standard Tires: (Chevette) P155/80 x 13; (Monza) A78 x 13; (Monza wag) B78 x 13; (Nova) E78 x 14; (Camaro) FR78 x 14/B SBR; (Malibu) P185/75R14 GBR; (Malibu wag) P195/75R14 GBR; (Imp/Capr) FR78 x 15 GBR; (Imp/Capr wag) HR78 x 15 SBR; (Monte) P205/70R14 SBR.

1978 Camaro Z28 Sport Coupe (CP)

TECHNICAL: Transmission: Three-speed manual transmission (floor shift) standard on Camaro, Nova and Monte Carlo six. Gear ratios: (1st) 3.50:1; (2nd) 1.81:1; (3rd) 1.00:1; (Rev) 3.62:1. Four- speed floor shift standard on Chevette: (1st) 3.75:1; (2nd) 2.16:1; (3rd) 1.38:1; (4th) 1.00:1; (Rev) 3.82:1. Four-speed floor shift optional on Monza four and Monte V-6: (1st) 3.50:1; (2nd) 2.48:1; (3rd) 1.66:1; (4th) 1.00:1; (Rev) 3.50:1. Four-speed floor shift standard on Nova (V8350) and Camaro V-8, optional on Chevette, Monza, Monte: (1st) 2.85:1; (2nd) 2.02:1; (3rd) 1.35:1; (4th) 1.00:1; (Rev) 2.85:1. Camaro Z28 four-speed floor shift: (1st) 2.64:1; (2nd) 1.75:1; (3rd) 1.34:1; (4th) 1.00:1; (Rev) 2.55:1. Five-speed floor shift available on Monza V-6: (1st) 3.40:1; (2nd) 2.08:1; (3rd) 1.39:1; (4th) 1.00:1; (5th) 0.80:1; (Rev) 3.36:1. Three-speed Turbo Hydra-matic standard on Caprice/Impala, optional on others. Gear ratios: (1st) 2.52:1; (2nd) 1.52:1; (3rd) 1.00:1; (Rev) 1.94:1 except standard Caprice/Impala V-8, Monza V-6, Malibu six and Monte (V8305) ratios: (1st) 2.74:1; (2nd) 1.57:1; (3rd) 1.00:1; (Rev) 2.07:1. Chevette/Monza four automatic trans.: (1st) 2.40:1; (2nd) 1.48:1; (3rd) 1.00:1; (Rev) 1.92:1. Standard final drive ratio: (Chevette) 3.70:1; (Monza four) 2.73:1 exc. 3.23:1 w/5spd; (Monza V-6) 2.56:1 exc. 2.73:1 w/5spd or auto.; (Monza V-8) 3.08:1 w/4spd, 2.29:1 w/auto.; (Nova) 2.73:1 exc. 3.08:1 w/V-8 or 2.41:1 w/V8305 and auto.; (Camaro six) 2.73:1; (Camaro V-8) 3.08:1; (Camaro Z28) 3.42:1 or 3.73:1; (Malibu) 2.73:1 exc. 2.29:1 w/V-8; (Malibu wag) 2.41:1; (Monte V-6) 2.93:1 w/3spd, 2.56:1 w/auto.; (Monte V-8) 2.73:1 w/4spd, 2.29:1 w/auto.; (Capr/Imp six) 2.73:1; (Capr/Imp V-8) 2.41:1; (Capr/Imp wag) 2.56:1. Steering/Suspension/Body: same as 1976-77. Brakes: front disc, rear drum. Fuel tank: (Chevette) 12.5 gal.; (Monza cpe) 18.5 gal.; (Monza hatch/wag) 15 gal.; (Nova/Camaro) 21 gal.; (Malibu/Monte) 17.5 gal.; Malibu wag) 18 gal.; (Capr/Imp) 21 gal.; (Capr/Imp wag) 22 gal.

DRIVETRAIN OPTIONS: Engines: 1.6-liter H.O. four: Chevette ($55). 196 cu. in. V-6: Monza ($130). 231 cu. in. V-6: Monza ($170); Malibu ($40). 305 cu. in., 2Bbl. V-8: Monza ($320); Nova/Camaro ($185); Malibu ($190); Monte ($150); Imp/Caprice cpe/sed ($185). 350 cu. in., 4Bbl. V-8: Nova/Camaro ($300); Malibu wag ($305); Imp/Capr cpe/sed ($300); Imp/Capr wag ($115). Transmission/Differential: Four-speed manual shift: Nova/Camaro/Malibu/Monte ($125). Close-ratio four-speed manual shift: Camaro (NC). Five-speed manual shift: Monza ($175). Turbo Hydra-matic: Chevette/Monza ($270); Nova/Camaro/Malibu/Monte ($307); Camaro Z28 ($45). Sport shifter: Chvt ($28). Positraction axle: Monza ($55); Nova/Camaro ($59); Malibu/Monte ($60); Imp/Capr ($63). Performance axle ratio ($14-$17). Power Accessories: Power brakes: Chvt/Monza ($66); Nova/Camaro/Monte, Malibu cpe/sed ($69). Power steering: Monza ($134); Nova/Malibu/Monte ($152). Suspension: F40 H.D. suspension: Nova ($9-$33); Malibu cpe/sed, Monte/Imp/Capr ($20). F41 sport suspension: Monza ($30); Nova ($41); Camaro, Malibu/Imp/Capr cpe/sed ($38). Superlift rear shock absorbers: Imp/Capr ($50). Rear stabilizer bar: Chvt ($30). Other: Heavy-duty radiator ($29-$31) exc. Imp/Capr ($40). H.D. alternator (61-amp): Malibu/Monte/Imp/Capr ($31). H.D. battery ($17-$18). California emission system ($75) exc. Monza four ($100). High altitude emission system ($33).

1978 Monza Estate 2-dr station wagon, 4-cyl

CHEVETTE/MONZA CONVENIENCE/APPEARANCE OPTIONS: Option Packages: Spyder equipment pkg.: Monza ($252). Spyder appearance pkg.: Monza ($216). Quiet sound group: Chvt ($33-$45); Monza ($24-$34). Comfort/Convenience: Air conditioning ($470). Rear defogger, electric ($79). Tinted glass ($54). Sport steering wheel: Monza ($17). Comfortilt steering wheel: Monza ($62). Special instrumentation: Chvt ($64); Monza ($64-$82). Electric clock ($18). Digital clock: Monza ($45). Cigarette lighter: Scooter ($5). Intermittent wipers ($30). Lighting, Horns and Mirrors: Aux. lighting: Chvt ($34-$35); Monza ($17-$33). Twin sport mirrors, left remote: Monza ($31). Driver's remote sport mirror: Chvt ($22). Twin remote sport mirrors: Chvt ($49). Day/night mirror ($9). Entertainment: AM radio ($71); std. on base Chevette. AM/FM radio: Chvt ($68); Scooter/Monza ($139). AM/FM stereo radio: Monza ($215). Stereo tape player w/AM radio: Monza ($216). Stereo tape player with AM/FM stereo radio: Monza ($308). Rear speaker ($23). Windshield antenna: Monza ($24); incl. w/radios. Exterior Trim: Sky roof ($215). Cabriolet vinyl roof: Monza ($153) incl. opera windows. Spoilers, front/rear: Monza ($93). Swing-out windows: Chvt ($51) but std. on base; Monza ($42). Custom exterior (wheel opening, side window and rocker panel moldings): Chvt ($99). Tri-tone sport stripes: Chvt ($67); w/o bodyside moldings ($27). Bodyside moldings ($40); std. on base Chevette. Wheel opening moldings: Monza ($21). Side window reveal moldings: Chvt ($67). Door edge guards ($11-$18). Roof carrier: Chvt ($60). Rear air deflector: Monza ($26). Deluxe bumpers, front/rear: Scooter ($33). Bumper guards, front/rear: Chvt ($38-$71); Monza ($38). Interior Trim/Upholstery: Console: Monza ($77). Bucket seats (sport cloth): Chvt ($10-$19); Monza ($19). Custom Chevette bucket seats: cloth ($170); vinyl ($151). Custom vinyl bucket seats: Monza (NC to $192). Custom sport cloth bucket seats: Monza ($19-$211). Adjustable driver's seatback: Monza ($19). Folding rear seat: Monza ($93) but std. on 2+2. Rear seat delete: Chvt ($56 credit). Load floor carpet: Chvt ($46). Color-keyed floor mats ($18). Deluxe seatbelts ($19). Wheels and Tires: Aluminum wheels: Monza ($178-$258). Rally II wheels: Monza ($43-$80). Styled gold wheels: Monza ($101- $181). Deluxe wheel covers: Monza ($37). Sport wheel covers: Chvt ($42). Wheel trim rings: Scooter ($34). 155/8013/B WSW: Scooter ($43). 155/8013/B SBR: Chvt ($62); Scooter ($105). 155/8013/B SBR WSW: Chvt ($105); Scooter ($148). 155/8013/B SBR WLT: Chvt ($120); Scooter ($163). B78 x 13 WSW: Monza (NC to $19). BR78 x 13 SBR BSW: Monza ($65-$117). BR78 x 13 SBR WSW: Monza ($125-$160). BR70 x 13 SBR BSW: Monza (NC to $157). BR70 x 13 SBR WSW: Monza ($132-$200). BR70 x 13 SBR WLT: Monza ($47-$215). Conventional spare: Monza (NC).

NOVA/CAMARO/MALIBU/MONTE CARLO CONVENIENCE/APPEARANCE OPTIONS: Option Packages: Rally equipment: Nova cpe ($199). Estate equipment: Malibu wag ($235). Interior decor/quiet sound group: Camaro ($61); std. on LT. Quiet sound group: Malibu ($46). Security pkg.: Malibu wag ($35). Comfort/Convenience: Air conditioning: Nova/Camaro ($508- $539); Malibu/Monte ($544). Rear defogger, forced-air ($51). Rear defogger (electric): Malibu/Monte ($92). Cruise-master speed control ($90). Tinted glass: Nova/Camaro ($56); Malibu/Monte ($62). Comfortilt steering wheel ($69). Six-way power seat: Malibu/Monte ($151). Power windows: Nova ($118- $164); Camaro/Monte ($124); Malibu ($124-$172). Power door locks: Nova/Malibu ($74-$112); Camaro/Monte ($80). Power trunk release: Malibu/Monte ($21). Electric clock: Nova, base Camaro ($20); Malibu ($21). Special instrumentation: Nova, base Camaro ($106); Malibu ($118); Monte ($97). Econominder gauge pkg.: Nova ($50). Gauge pkg.: Malibu ($53); Monte ($32). Intermittent wipers ($32). Lighting, Horns and Mirrors: Aux. lighting ($28-$52). Dome reading light: Malibu/Monte ($16). Dual horns: Nova, base Camaro, Z28, base Malibu ($7). Remote-control driver's mirror: Nova/Malibu/Monte ($16). Twin sport mirrors (left remote): Nova, base Camaro, Malibu/Monte ($33). Twin remote sport mirrors: Malibu/Monte ($57); Monte Lan ($24). Day/night mirror: Nova ($9). Visor vanity mirror: Malibu/Monte ($4). Lighted visor mirror: Malibu ($37); Monte ($33-$37). Entertainment: AM radio ($77-$79). AM/FM radio: Nova/Camaro/Malibu ($149); Monte ($154). AM/FM stereo radio ($229). Stereo tape player w/AM radio: Nova/Camaro ($229); Malibu/Monte ($233). Stereo tape player with AM/FM stereo radio ($328). Rear speaker ($24). Dual front speakers: Malibu/Monte ($20). Windshield antenna ($25); incl. w/radios. Power antenna: Malibu/Monte ($45). Exterior Trim: Removable glass roof panels: Camaro/Monte ($625). Power sky roof: Malibu cpe/sed, Monte ($499). Vinyl roof: Nova ($97); Camaro ($102); Malibu ($116); Monte ($131). Cabriolet roof: Nova ($179). Rear spoiler: Camaro/LT ($55). Style trim pkg.: Camaro ($70). Two-tone paint: Nova ($46); Malibu ($62-$110). Swing-out rear side windows: Nova ($56). Bodyside moldings: Nova/Camaro ($42). Deluxe bodyside moldings: Nova/Malibu/Monte ($53). Door edge guards ($11- $18). Bright rocker moldings and extensions: Nova ($37). Bright sill moldings: Monte ($44). Wheel opening moldings: Nova/Malibu ($21). Wide wheel opening moldings: Nova ($39). Side window sill moldings: Monte ($31). Side window reveal moldings: Nova/Malibu ($41). Roof drip moldings: Nova ($18); Camaro ($23). Bodyside pinstriping: Nova ($30); Malibu ($48); Monte ($33). Rear window air deflector: Malibu wag ($28). Roof carrier: Malibu wag ($85). Bumper rub strips: Malibu/Monte ($36). Bumper rub strips and guards, front/rear: Nova ($73). Bumper guards, front/rear: Malibu ($40). Interior Trim/Upholstery: Interior decor pkg.: base Nova ($29). Console ($80). Vinyl bench seat: Malibu cpe/sed, Monte ($24). Sport cloth bench seat: Nova ($21). Custom vinyl bench seat: Nova (NC). Custom vinyl bucket seats: Nova ($110). Vinyl bucket seats: Malibu cpe/sed, Monte ($110). Custom vinyl bucket seats: Camaro Z28 ($294). Sport cloth bucket seats: Camaro ($21). Custom cloth or sport cloth bucket seats: Camaro LT ($21); Z28 ($315). Knit cloth 50/50 seating: Malibu cpe/sed ($164). Vinyl 50/50 seating: Malibu cpe/sed ($188); Malibu wag ($164). Monte custom 55/45 seating: cloth ($340); vinyl ($364). Adj. driver's seatback: Camaro ($21). Litter container: Malibu/Monte ($6). Color-keyed mats ($20). Deluxe seatbelts ($19-$21). Deluxe trunk trim: Malibu/Monte ($41). Wheels and Tires: Aluminum wheels: Camaro ($180-$265). Custom styled wheels: Camaro ($91-$133). Rally wheels: Nova ($69); Camaro ($85) but std. on LT; Malibu ($41-$78); Malibu Lan (NC); Monte ($41). Color-keyed Rally wheels: Nova ($82). Full wheel covers: Nova, Camaro, Malibu cpe/sed ($37). Sport wheel covers (silver or gold): Malibu ($49-$86). Wire wheel covers: Nova ($120); Malibu ($60-$146); Monte ($109); Monte Landau ($60). E78 x 14/B BSW: Camaro ($90-$113 credit). E78 x 14/B WSW: Nova ($36-$44); Camaro ($55-$69 credit). FR78 x 14/B SBR: Nova ($91-$113). FR78 x 14/B SBR WSW: Nova ($128-$159); Camaro ($37-$46). FR78 x 14/B SBR WLT: Nova ($140-$174); Camaro ($49-$61). P185/75R14 GBR WSW: Malibu cpe/sed ($37). P195/75R14 SBR WSW: Malibu cpe/sed ($96); Malibu wag ($78). P205/75R14 SBR WSW: Malibu cpe/sed ($148). P195/75R14 GBR WSW: Malibu wag ($39). P205/75R14 SBR WLT: Malibu cpe/sed ($160). P205/70R14 SBR WSW: Monte ($42). Stowaway spare: Nova ($17); Camaro (NC).

1978 Impala 2-dr Sport Coupe, V-8

IMPALA/CAPRICE CONVENIENCE/APPEARANCE OPTIONS: Option Packages: Estate equipment: wag ($235). Value appearance group: bodyside and wheel opening moldings, full wheel covers ($73). Comfort/Convenience: Four season air cond. ($569). Comfortron auto-temp air cond. ($655). Rear defogger, forced-air: wag ($51). Rear defogger, electric ($94). Cruise-Master speed control ($95). Tinted glass ($76). Comfortilt steering wheel ($70). Power door locks ($82-$114). Six-way power driver's seat ($151). Power windows ($130-$190). Power trunk release ($21). Power tailgate lock: wag ($40). Electric clock: Imp ($21). Digital clock: Imp ($49); Caprice ($28). Econominder gauge pkg. ($50). Intermittent wipers ($32). Quiet sound group: Imp ($51-$55). Lighting, Horns and Mirrors: Aux. lighting ($32-$46). Dual horns: Imp ($7). Driver's remote mirror ($16). Dual remote mirrors ($48). Dual sport mirrors, left remote ($33). Dual remote body-color sport mirrors ($57) exc. Lan ($24). Visor vanity mirror ($4). Lighted visor mirror ($37). Entertainment: AM radio ($80). AM/FM radio ($160). AM/FM stereo radio ($232). Stereo tape player with AM/FM radio ($250); with AM/FM stereo radio ($332). AM/FM/CB radio and power antenna ($498). Rear speakers ($24). Dual front speakers ($20). Power antenna ($45). Windshield antenna ($25); incl. w/radios. Exterior Trim: Power sky roof: cpe/sed ($595). Vinyl roof: cpe/sed ($142). Two-tone paint ($47). Custom two-tone ($115). Pinstriping ($33). Roof carrier ($110). Color-keyed bodyside moldings ($43). Door edge guards ($11-$18). Wheel opening moldings: Imp ($21). Bumper rub strips, front/rear ($50). Bumper guards ($46). Interior Trim/Upholstery: Vinyl bench seat: cpe/sed ($24). Knit cloth 50/50 seat: cpe/sed ($224). Sport cloth 50/50 seat: wag ($248). Vinyl 50/50 seat ($224-$248). Special custom cloth 50/50 seat: cpe/sed ($365). Deluxe load-floor carpet: wag ($71). Deluxe cargo area carpet: wag ($102). Color-keyed mats ($20). Litter container ($6). Color-keyed seatbelts ($21-$24). Deluxe trunk trim ($44). Wheel Covers: Full wheel covers ($38). Sport wheel covers: Imp ($88); Caprice ($50). Coupe/Sedan Tires: FR78 x 15/B GBR WSW ($46). FR78 x 15/B SBR BSW ($48). FR78 x 15/B SBR WSW ($94). GR78 x 15/B SBR WSW ($124). GR70 x 15/B SBR WSW ($147). Wagon Tires: HR78 x 15/B SBR WSW ($52).

HISTORY: Introduced: Oct. 6, 1977. Model year production (U.S.): 2,197,861 (incl. Corvettes but not incl. 11,316 Acadians). The North American total of 2,474,547 units for the U.S. market included 381,394 four-cylinder engines, 521,162 sixes and 1,571,991 V-8s. Chevrolet reported a total of 2,252,111 passenger cars shipped. Calendar year production: 2,347,327 (including 30,150 Sportvans, 48,522 Corvettes and 13,585 Acadians). Calendar year sales by U.S. dealers: 2,349,781 (incl. 43,582 Sportvans and 42,247 Corvettes) for a 25.3 percent market share. Model year sales by U.S. dealers: 2,342,035 (incl. 43,594 Sportvans and 43,106 Corvettes).

Historical Footnotes: Model year sales rose by 4.6 percent (from 2,239,538 to 2,342,035), making 1977 the third highest year in Chevrolet history. After two sluggish years, Chevette seemed to finally catch on, showing a whopping 71 percent sales gain. The freshly downsized Malibu and Monte Carlo took a while to get moving in sales. But the full-size (downsized in '77) Caprice and Impala continued to move well, taking 22.5 percent of the company's sales. In recent years, other GM divisions had been using more shared components and body style offerings. Chevrolet continued to retain more individuality, at least for the time being. The new 200 cu. in. V-6 was built at Chevrolet's Tonawanda, New York plant. However, the 231 cu. in V-6 came from Buick, as did the 196 V-8. And 151 cu. in. four-cylinder engines were supplied by Pontiac. Late in the model year, a handful of Chevettes came off the line with a passive restraint system, the first examples on a domestic automobile.

1979 CHEVROLET

This was primarily a carryover year, with some engine changes, horsepower boosts (and losses) and appearance restyles, but nothing drastic. The 305 cu. in. V-8 managed to lose 15 horsepower, down to 130. Biggest news would actually be the mid-year introduction of the new Citation X- car as an early 1980 model—the first front-drive Chevrolet— which replaced the Nova.

1979 Chevette hatchback coupe (CP)

CHEVETTE — SERIES 1T — FOUR — Chevrolet's subcompact got a new front-end look including a "real" separate brightwork crosshatch grille insert with bright/black bowtie emblem in the center, rather than the previous slots in a body-colored panel. Also new: a shorter hood and single recessed rectangular headlamps with bright bezels. Parking lamps remained down below the bumper rub strips. Bumpers, rub strips and valance panel were the same as in 1978. A driver's side lower duct increased air flow to the interior. The low-budget Scooter carried no bodyside trim. Standard tires were now glass-belted radials. A new two-stage carburetor, tuned intake manifold, valve port refinements, heavier pistons and improved EGR valve added to the driveability and gas mileage of the standard 7.6 cu. in. (1.6-liter) four. A trapped vacuum spark system gave it better cold-start qualities. Axle ratio was again 3.70:1 with either the standard or high-output engine, coupled to standard four-speed manual or optional three-speed automatic transmission. The formerly optional 4.11:1 ratio was dropped. A new F41 Sport Suspension option replaced the previous rear stabilizer bar option. It included a larger front stabilizer bar and bushings, plus a new and bigger eyeless- type rear stabilizer with new bushings and linkage. Steel- belted radial tires were required with the package. Other new options included ah AM/FM stereo radio with three speakers, and a pair of sport mirrors (left one remote-controlled and the right one convex). The twin-remote sport mirror option was dropped. Chevettes kept their full coil suspension with torque tube drive. All Chevettes had a front stabilizer bar, Delco Freedom battery, heater/defroster, front bucket seats, and courtesy dome light. All but the Scooter also had an AM radio, fold-down back seat, color-keyed instrument panel, sport steering wheel, mini console, bumper impact strips, and cigarette lighter. Standard models had whitewall 155/80R13 glass-belted radial tires; Scooters wore blackwalls. Coupes (except Scooter) had swing-out rear windows.

1979 Monza Spyder 2-dr hatchback coupe, V-8

MONZA — SERIES 1H — FOUR/V-6/V-8 — Though unchanged in appearance, Monza added a few horsepower to the base 151 cu. in. (2.5-liter) four-cylinder engine, supplied by Pontiac. That engine had a redesigned cross-flow cylinder head and new Varajet two-stage, two- barrel carburetor. That meant a triple-venturi first stage and air valve secondary for power-on-demand. A new aluminum intake manifold cut weight. The engine was now all-metric design, with a new replaceable-element air cleaner. Optional engines: a 196 cu. in. (3.2-liter) V-6 on all models, a 231 cu. in. (3.8-liter) V-6, plus a 305 cu. in. (5.0-liter) V-8 available on all except the 'S' hatchback coupe and wagon. Four-cylinder and V-6 models could have standard four- speed manual, optional five-speed manual, or automatic transmission. The V-8, which had a new Dualjet carburetor, came with four-speed manual or optional three-speed automatic. Monza interiors sported new front seats and a sport steering wheel. The Value Series got a new interior look with new seat design and upgraded vinyl and cloth fabrics. Corrosion protection was improved on rear compartment pan and door panels (inner/outer). Bodyside moldings were standard. New radio choices were available. As in 1978, the Sport 2+2's grille was just one wide, squat opening stretching to fender tips, while the standard coupe carried a crossbar grille. All Monzas had energy-absorbing bumpers, standard A78 x 13 whitewall tires and full wheel covers, high-back bucket seats, heater/defroster, carpeting, AM radio, color-keyed instrument panel, tinted glass, center dome light, and cigarette lighter. All except the standard coupe held an interior console. Only 225 Monzas had a performance axle ratio installed this year, while 5,004 carried a five-speed transmission and 683 came with aluminum wheels. The Monza Spyder appearance package included front/rear spoilers; lower striping with Spyder name; black headlamp, parking light and belt moldings; black taillamp openings, sport mirrors and rear end panel; black lower body treatment from front to rear wheel openings; black windshield, back window, door and quarter-window moldings; and Rally II wheels. To add a bit of performance to looks, the separate Spyder equipment package included an F41 suspension, BR70 x 13/C radial tires and modified front stabilizer and rear shocks, as well as a day/night mirror. Spyder emblems went on the hood header panel and rear keylock cover. A total of 9,679 Spyder equipment packages were produced, and 8,670 appearance packages.

1979 Nova coupe (AA)

NOVA — SERIES 1X — SIX/V-8 — For its final year in the lineup, the compact Nova carried a new horizontally-ribbed grille, with single rectangular headlamps and inset clear vertical rectangular park/signal lamps with chrome bezels. The 'Chevrolet' insignia was on the heavy top bar of the grille. Separate 'Nova' letters stood on fender sides, somewhat forward of the door, in line with bodyside moldings. Two-door coupe and four-door bodies were again available in base or Custom series, along with the Nova hatchback coupe. Base engine continued to be the 250 cu. in. (4.1-liter) inline six, with optional 305 V-8. That V-8 actually lost 15 horsepower this year. Again, the three-speed manual transmission was standard with the six, four-speed with V-8 Novas. Turbo Hydra-matic was optional on both. Only in California or high altitude was the 350 four-barrel V-8 offered. A new steering column lock was supposed to thwart thieves. Rally wheels had a smaller center hub area with new Chevrolet bowtie emblem and chrome-accented vents. They were available separately, or as part of the Nova Rally option. A total of 2,299 Rally Novas were produced this year. Only 616 Novas came with a four-speed gearbox, 792 with the F41 sport suspension, and 303 with a performance axle ratio. Nova standard equipment included a built-in windshield radio antenna, heater/defroster, carpeting, locking glove compartment, manual steering and brakes, Freedom battery, and E78 x 14 blackwall tires. Nova Custom added a set of interior extras: cigarette lighter, glove box light, bright instrument cluster accents, right front door courtesy light switch, and day/night mirror. Nova's Rally Sport Equipment package included lower bodyside and wheel opening stripes, a chrome diamond-pattern grille, black headlamp bezels, parking lamp accents, Rally wheels with trim rings and bright center hubs, and Rally nameplates.

1979 Camaro Rally Sport coupe (CP)

CAMARO — SERIES 1F — SIX/V-8 — A new Berlinetta version, promoted as the "new way to take your pulse," took the place of the former Type LT Camaro. Berlinettas had body pinstriping, a bright grille, and black rocker panels. Camaros got a new instrument panel and anti-theft steering column. The performance Z28 had new flared front wheel openings as well as a three-piece front air dam that wrapped around the sides, up into wheel openings. Z28 also had a blackout front end with center grille emblem. Its identifying decal moved from the front fender to the door. Both Z28 and Rally Camaros had a standard rear spoiler (but 81 examples were produced without one). The spoiler was a common option on other models. New radio options included a CB, cassette player or clock built into an AM/FM stereo. Both mast and windshield antennas were available. The base 250 cu. in. (4.1-liter) inline six had a lower axle ratio this year to raise gas mileage. Both 305 and 350 cu. in. V-8s were available. Only

1979 Camaro Berlinetta Sport Coupe (CH)

2,438 Camaros were produced with a performance axle ratio, while 33,584 had the optional removable glass roof panels. Camaro standard equipment included power steering, Delco Freedom battery, front stabilizer bar, concealed two-speed windshield wipers, carpeting, heater/defroster, front bucket seats, center dome light, four-spoke sport steering wheel, day/night mirror, and FR78 x 14 steel-belted radial tires. The Berlinetta added whitewall tires on color-keyed custom styled wheels, body-color sport mirrors (left one remote- controlled), dual pinstripes, chrome headlamp bezels, soft fascia bumper systems (front and rear), bright windshield and back window moldings, and argent rear-panel applique. Camaro Z28 came with a standard 350 cu. in. four-barrel V-8; four-speed close-ratio manual gearbox; simulated hood air scoop (bolt-on, with black throat); black windshield and back window moldings; plus two-tone striping on front fenders and flares, air dam, door panels and rear deck panel. Also on Z28: front fender air louvers; body-color spoilers (front and rear); black grille, headlamp/taillamp bezels, rear end panel, and license mount; body-color sport mirrors, door handle inserts and back bumper; and white-letter P225/70R15 steel-belted tires on body-color 7 in. wheels.

1979 Malibu Classic 2-dr Sport Coupe, V-8

1979 Malibu Classic Landau Coupe (CP)

MALIBU — SERIES 1A — V-6/V-8 — Buyers may have been promised "a fresh new slice of apple pie," but mid-size Chevrolets didn't change much this year. Both Malibu and Malibu Classic had a new checkered-look horizontally-divided grille, along with new taillamps, for their second season in downsized form. The grille was actually in four horizontal sections, each one divided into two rows. Parking lamps and single rectangular headlamps were structured as in 1978. Base engine was again the 200 cu. in. (3.3-liter) V-6, with an optional 305 cu. in. (5.0-liter) V-8. But one other option was added: a small-block 267 cu. in. (4.4-liter) V-8. Like other Chevrolet engines, Malibu's gained improvements in the EGR system and cold-trapped spark control system. Malibus came in Landau and sport coupe form, as well as sedans, Classic and Estate wagons. There was also a Special Equipment Order police car this year, succeeding the popular Nova police vehicle that had come into existence during the 1973-74 energy crisis. A total of 849 Malibus were built with the optional power sky roof, while 8,300 had the F41 sport suspension and 1,903 carried the MM4 four-speed transmission. Standard equipment included the 200 cu. in. V-6, three- speed manual shift, High Energy ignition, front stabilizer bar, heater/defroster, concealed wipers, inside day/night mirror, inside hood release, and locking glove compartment. Malibu Classic and Landau added dual horns and a special acoustical package. Malibu Classic models now carried an identifying script on the dashboard. Malibu Landau had a vinyl roof and silver sport wheel covers. Wagons had power brakes, wheel opening moldings, and full wheel covers.

1979 Monte Carlo Sport Coupe (CH)

MONTE CARLO — SERIES 1A — V-6/V-8 — Monte had a new grille with tight crosshatch pattern this year. Restyled wraparound angular side marker lamps and park/signal lamps were housed in a single bright bezel with horizontal divider bars. Taillamps were divided into three sections by vertical bars, with backup lenses in the section nearest the center. Body changes also included wide, bright lower body molding extensions. Landau models showed a new canopy-type roof with bright moldings behind the rear quarter windows. Seats had new cloth and vinyl fabrics. Like Malibu, Monte added a new engine possibility: the small-block 267 cu. in. (4.4-liter) V-8. Base engine was still the 200 cu. in. (3.3-liter) V-6. Also optional: a 231 V-6 and 305 V-8. All Montes came with standard front/rear stabilizer bars, heater/defroster, concealed wipers, electric clock, day/night mirror, locking glove compartment, dual horns, and P205/70R14 steel-belted radial tires. The 200 cu. in. V-6 and three-speed manual shift were standard, with manual brakes and steering. Monte Landaus had an automatic transmission, power brakes and steering, vinyl canopy roof, bodyside and rear striping, bright body sill moldings, visor vanity mirror (right side), and twin sport mirrors (left remote- controlled). A total of 7,830 Montes came with the optional power sky roof; 10,764 with removable glass roof panels.

1979 Caprice Classic sedan (CH)

IMPALA/CAPRICE CLASSIC — SERIES 1B — SIX/V-8 — Full-size appearance changes for 1979 included front and rear refinements plus more subtle differences in side view. Impalas, as usual, had several styling differences to separate them from the costlier Caprice: a new "ladder" style grille with wide, squat holes; restyled park/signal lamps (inset in the bumper); narrow side marker lamps with horizontal dividers; and front fender end caps. Otherwise, the two full-size models remained similar, available in the same body styles: Sport coupe, Landau coupe, four-door sedan, and two- or three-seat wagon. Impala cost about $300 less than Caprice. Caprice's new grille, with wide-hole crosshatch pattern, was separated into ten side-by-side segments by dominant vertical bars. As before, the pattern repeated in slots below the bumper rub strip. Front fender extensions were reinforced fiberglass, molded continuously with the grille header for a full-width, flowing appearance. Front side marker lamps now had horizontal strip dividers. At the rear, Caprice had wider three-section taillamp clusters with a central Caprice crest. Backup lenses sat below each taillamp cluster. Both Impala and Caprice rear side marker lamps were restyled, with horizontal grid detailing. Both continued their quad rectangular headlamps. Base engine remained the 250 cu. in. (4.1-liter) inline six, which added five horsepower this year and ran a lower axle ratio than before. Wagons carried a standard 305 cu. in. (5.0-liter) V-8, which dropped from 145 to 130 horsepower. New, paler body colors were offered this year, including soft blues, greens and browns. Radios could have built-in tape players or CB transceivers. All full-size Chevrolets came with automatic transmission, power steering and brakes, Freedom battery, front stabilizer bar, heater/defroster, concealed two-speed wipers, carpeting, inside hood release, day/night mirror, locking glove compartment, and FR78 x 15 fiberglass-belted blackwall radial tires. Coupes had automatic front seatback locks. Caprice Classic added dual horns and wheel opening moldings. Caprice Classic Landau coupe added twin sport mirrors (left remote-controlled), a vinyl roof, and bodyside pinstriping. Impala's Landau coupe added a vinyl roof, wheel opening moldings, and bodyside pinstriping.

I.D. DATA: Chevrolet again used a 13-symbol Vehicle Identification Number (VIN), on a pad atop the dashboard, visible through the windshield. Coding was similar to 1978. Under Series, code 'S' now indicated Camaro Berlinetta rather than LT. Code '77' under body/style was dropped. Model year code changed to '9' for 1979. Engine codes were as follows: 'E' L4-97.6 2Bbl.; 'O' L4-97.6 H.O.; 'V' L4-151 2Bbl.; 'C' V6196 2Bbl.; 'M' V6200 2Bbl.; 'A' V6231 2Bbl.; 'D' L6250 1Bbl.; 'J' V8267 2Bbl.; 'G' V8305 2Bbl.; 'H' V8305 4Bbl.; 'L' V8350 4Bbl. Under assembly plants, code '2' for St. Therese, Quebec was dropped; code 'A' for Lakewood, GA added.

1979 Chevette 2-dr hatchback coupe (w/turbo-injection)

CHEVETTE (FOUR)

Model Number	Body/Style Number	Body Type & Seating	Factory Price	Shipping Weight	Production Total
1T	B08	2-dr. Hatch Cpe-4P	3794	1978	136,145
1T	B68	4-dr. Hatch Sed-4P	3914	2057	208,865

CHEVETTE SCOOTER (FOUR)

1T	J08	2-dr. Hatch Cpe-4P	3299	1929	24,099

1979 Monza coupe (CH)

MONZA (FOUR/V-6/V-8)

1H	M07	2-dr. Hatch 2+2-4P	3844	2630	56,871
1H	M27	2-dr. Cpe-4P	3617	2577	61,110
1H	M15	2-dr. Sta Wag-4P	3974	2631	15,190

MONZA SPORT (FOUR/V-6/V-8)

1H	R07	2-dr. Hatch 2+2-4P	4291	2676	30,662

Monza Engine Note: Prices shown are for four-cylinder engine. The 196 cu. in. V-6 cost $160 extra; the 305 V-8 cost $395. Only 8,180 Monzas had a V-8 engine.

NOVA (SIX/V-8)

1X	X27	2-dr. Cpe-6P	3955/4190	3135/3265	36,800
1X	X17	2-dr. Hatch-6P	4118/4353	3264/3394	4,819
1X	X69	4-dr. Sedan-6P	4055/4290	3179/3309	40,883

NOVA CUSTOM (SIX/V-8)

1X	Y27	2-dr. Cpe-6P	4164/4399	3194/3324	7,529
1X	Y69	4-dr. Sedan-6P	4264/4499	3228/3358	7,690

CAMARO (SIX/V-8)

Model Number	Body/Style Number	Body Type & Seating	Factory Price	Shipping Weight	Production Total
1F	Q87	2-dr. Spt Cpe-4P	4677/4912	3305/3435	111,357
1F	Q87/Z85	2-dr. Rally Cpe-4P	5073/5308	N/A	19,101

CAMARO BERLINETTA (SIX/V-8)

1F	S87	2-dr. Spt Cpe-4P	5396/5631	3358/3488	67,236

CAMARO Z28 (V-8)

1F	Q87/Z28	2-dr. Spt Cpe-4P	-- /6115	-- / N/A	84,877

MALIBU (V-6/V-8)

1A	T27	2-dr. Spt Cpe-6P	4398/4588	2983/3111	41,848
1A	T19	4-dr. Sed-6P	4498/4688	2988/3116	59,674
1A	T35	4-dr. Sta Wag-6P	4745/4935	3155/3297	50,344

MALIBU CLASSIC (V-6/V-8)

1A	W27	2-dr. Spt Cpe-6P	4676/4866	3017/3145	60,751
1A	W27/Z03	2-dr. Lan Cpe-6P	4915/5105	N/A	25,213
1A	W19	4-dr. Sed-6P	4801/4991	3024/3152	104,222
1A	W35	4-dr. Sta Wag-6P	4955/5145	3183/3325	70,095

MONTE CARLO (V-6/V-8)

1A	Z37	2-dr. Spt Cpe-6P	4995/5185	3039/3169	225,073
1A	Z37/Z03	2-dr. Lan Cpe-6P	5907/6097	N/A	91,850

Malibu/Monte Carlo Engine Note: V-8 prices are for the small-block 267; the 305 V-8 cost $105 more. Only 3,812 Malibus had the 350 V-8 (code LM1).

1979 Impala Sport Coupe (CP)

IMPALA (SIX/V-8)

1B	L47	2-dr. Spt Cpe-6P	5497/5732	3495/3606	26,589
1B	L47/Z03	2-dr. Lan Cpe-6P	5961/6196	N/A	3,247
1B	L69	4-dr. Sedan-6P	5597/5832	3513/3624	172,717
1B	L35	4-dr. Sta Wag-6P	-- /6109	-- /4013	39,644
1B	L35/AQ4	4-dr. 3S Wag-8P	-- /6239	-- /4045	28,710

CAPRICE CLASSIC (SIX/V-8)

1B	N47	2-dr. Spt Cpe-6P	5837/6072	3535/3649	36,629
1B	N47/Z03	2-dr. Lan Cpe-6P	6234/6469	N/A	21,824
1B	N69	4-dr. Sedan-6P	5962/6197	3564/3675	203,017
1B	N35	4-dr. Sta Wag-6P	-- /6389	-- /4056	23,568
1B	N35/AQ4	4-dr. 3S Wag-8P	-- /6544	-- /4088	32,693

FACTORY PRICE AND WEIGHT NOTE: Where two prices and weights are shown, the figure to the left of the slash is for six-cylinder model, to right of slash for V-8. Body/Style No. Note: Some models are actually option packages. Figure after the slash (e.g., Z03) is the number of the option package that comes with the model listed.

ENGINE DATA: BASE FOUR (Chevette): Inline. Overhead cam. Four-cylinder. Cast iron block and head. Displacement: 97.6 cu. in. (1.6 liters). Bore & stroke: 3.23 x 2.98 in. Compression ratio: 8.6:1. Brake horsepower: 70 at 5200 R.P.M. Torque: 82 lbs.-ft. at 2400 R.P.M. Five main bearings. Hydraulic valve lifters. Carburetor: 2Bbl. Holley 5210C. VIN Code: E. OPTIONAL HIGH-OUTPUT FOUR (Chevette): Same as above except Brake H.P.: 74 at 5200 R.P.M. Torque: 88 lbs.-ft. at 2800 R.P.M. VIN Code: O. BASE FOUR (Monza): Inline. Overhead valve. Four-cylinder. Cast iron block. Displacement: 151 cu. in. (2.5 liters). Bore & stroke: 4.00 x 3.00 in. Compression ratio: 8.3:1. Brake horsepower: 90 at 4000 R.P.M. Torque: 128 lbs.-ft. at 2400 R.P.M. Five main bearings. Hydraulic valve lifters. Carburetor: 2Bbl. Rochester 2SE. VIN Code: V. OPTIONAL V-6 (Monza): 90-degree, overhead-valve V-6. Cast iron block and head. Displacement: 196 cu. in. (3.2 liters). Bore & stroke: 3.50 x 3.40 in. Compression ratio: 8.0:1. Brake horsepower: 105 at 4000 R.P.M. Torque: 160 lbs.-ft. at 2000 R.P.M. Four main bearings. Hydraulic valve lifters. Carburetor: 2Bbl. Rochester M2ME. VIN Code: C. BASE V-6 (Malibu, Monte Carlo): 90-degree, overhead-valve V-6. Cast iron block and head. Displacement: 200 cu. in. (3.3 liters). Bore & stroke: 3.50 x 3.48 in. Compression ratio: 8.2:1. Brake horsepower: 94 at 4000 R.P.M. Torque: 154 lbs.-ft. at 2000 R.P.M. Four main bearings. Hydraulic valve lifters. Carburetor: 2Bbl. Rochester M2ME. VIN Code: M. OPTIONAL V-6 (Monza, Malibu, Monte Carlo): 90-degree, overhead-valve V-6. Cast iron block and head. Displacement: 231 cu. in. (3.8 liters). Bore & stroke: 3.80 x 3.40 in. Compression ratio: 8.0:1. Brake horsepower: 115 at 3800 R.P.M. Torque: 190 lbs.-ft. at 2000 R.P.M. Four main bearings. Hydraulic valve lifters. Carburetor: 2Bbl. Rochester M2ME. VIN Code: A. BASE SIX (Nova, Camaro, Impala, Caprice): Inline. OHV. Six-cylinder. Cast iron block and head. Displacement: 250 cu. in. (4.1 liters). Bore & stroke: 3.88 x 3.53 in. Compression ratio: 8.0:1. Brake horsepower: 115 at 3800 R.P.M. Torque: 200 lbs.-ft. at 1600 R.P.M. Seven main bearings. Hydraulic valve lifters. Carburetor: 1Bbl. Rochester 1ME. VIN Code D. OPTIONAL V-8 (Malibu, Monte Carlo); 90-degree, overhead valve V-8. Cast iron block and head. Displacement: 267 cu. in. (4.4 liters). Bore & stroke: 3.50 x 3.48 in. Compression ratio: 8.2:1. Brake horsepower: 125 at 3800 R.P.M. Torque: 215 lbs.-ft. at 2400 R.P.M. Five main bearings. Hydraulic valve lifters. Carburetor: 2Bbl. Rochester M2MC. VIN Code: J. BASE V-8 (Impala/Caprice wagon); OPTIONAL (Monza, Nova, Camaro, Impala, Caprice): 90-degree, overhead valve V-8. Cast iron block and head. Displacement: 305 cu. in. (5.0 liters). Bore & stroke: 3.74 x 3.48 in. Compression ratio: 8.4:1. Brake horsepower: 130 at 3200 R.P.M. Torque: 245 lbs.-ft. at 2000 R.P.M. Five main bearings. Hydraulic valve lifters. Carburetor: 2Bbl. Rochester M2MC. VIN Code: G. OPTIONAL V-8 (Malibu, Monte Carlo): 90-degree, overhead valve V-8. Cast iron block and head. Displacement: 305 cu. in. (5.0 liters). Bore & stroke: 3.74 x 3.48 in. Compression ratio: 8.4:1. Brake horsepower: 160 at 4000 R.P.M. Torque: 235 lbs.-ft. at 2400 R.P.M. Five main bearings. Hydraulic valve lifters. Carburetor: 4Bbl. Rochester M4MC. VIN Code: H. OPTIONAL V-8 (Nova, Malibu wagon, Impala, Caprice): 90-degree, overhead valve V-8. Cast iron block and head. Displacement: 350 cu. in. (5.7 liters). Bore & stroke: 4.00 x 3.48 in. Compression ratio: 8.2:1. Brake horsepower: 165-170 at 3800 R.P.M. Torque: 260-270 lbs.-ft. at 2400 R.P.M. Five main bearings. Hydraulic valve lifters. Carburetor: 4Bbl. Rochester M4MC. VIN Code: L. BASE V-8 (Camaro Z28); OPTIONAL (Camaro): Same as 350 V-8 above but Brake H.P.: 175 at 4000 R.P.M. Torque: 270 lbs.-ft. at 2400 R.P.M.

CHASSIS DATA: Dimensions same as 1978, except Chevette Scooter overall length, 158.8 in. New Camaro Berlinetta had same dimensions as prior Type LT. Chevette tires were now 155/80R13 GBR.

TECHNICAL: Transmission: Three-speed manual transmission standard on Camaro, Nova, and Malibu/Monte six. Gear ratios: (1st) 3.50:1; (2nd) 1.89:1; (3rd) 1.00:1; (Rev) 3.62:1. Four-speed floor shift standard on Chevette: (1st) 3.75:1; (2nd) 2.16:1; (3rd) 1.38:1; (4th) 1.00:1; (Rev) 3.82:1. Four-speed floor shift standard on Monza four and V-6: (1st) 3.50:1; (2nd) 2.48:1; (3rd) 1.66:1; (4th) 1.00:1; (Rev) 3.50:1. Four-speed floor shift standard on Monza/Camaro/Nova (V8305) and Camaro 350, optional on Malibu/Monza/Monte: (1st) 2.85:1; (2nd) 2.02:1; (3rd) 1.35:1; (4th) 1.00:1; (Rev) 2.85:1. Four-speed on Malibu V8267: (1st) 3.11:1; (2nd) 2.20:1; (3rd) 1.47:1; (4th) 1.00:1; (Rev) 3.11:1. Camaro Z28 four-speed floor shift: (1st) 2.64:1; (2nd) 1.75:1; (3rd) 1.34:1; (4th) 1.00:1; (Rev) 2.55:1. Five-speed floor shift available on Monza: (1st) 3.40:1; (2nd) 2.08:1; (3rd) 1.39:1; (4th) 1.00:1; (5th) 0.80:1; (Rev) 3.36:1. Three-speed Turbo Hydra- matic standard on Monte Carlo Landau and Caprice/Impala, optional on others. Gear ratios: (1st) 2.52:1; (2nd) 1.52:1; (3rd) 1.00:1; (Rev) 1.93:1 except Caprice/Impala V8305, Monza four and some Malibu six ratios: (1st) 2.74:1; (2nd) 1.57:1; (3rd) 1.00:1; (Rev) 2.07:1. Chevette four automatic trans.: (1st) 2.40:1; (2nd) 1.48:1; (3rd) 1.00:1; (Rev) 1.92:1. Standard final drive ratio: (Chevette) 3.70:1; (Monza four) 2.73:1 or 2.93:1 w/4-spd, 3.08:1 w/5-spd, 2.73:1 w/auto.; (Monza V-6) 2.73:1 exc. 2.93:1 w/5-spd; (Monza V-8) 3.08:1 w/4-spd, 2.29:1 w/auto.; (Nova) 2.56:1 w/six, 3.08:1 w/V-8 and 4-spd, 2.41:1 w/V-8 and auto.; (Camaro six) 2.56:1; (Camaro V-8) 3.08:1 w/4spd, 2.41:1 or 3.08:1 w/auto.; (Z28) 3.73:1 w/4spd, 3.42:1 w/auto.; (Malibu six) 2.73:1; (Malibu V-8) 2.29:1 exc. 2.73:1 w/auto.; (Malibu V-8 wag) 2.56:1 or 2.41:1; (Monte V-6) 2.73:1 or 2.41:1; (Monte V-8) 2.29:1; (Capr/Imp six) 2.56:1; (Capr/Imp V-8) 2.41:1 exc. Steering: (Chevette) rack and pinion; (others) recirculating ball. Suspension/Body: same as 1976-78. Brakes: front disc, rear drum. Fuel tank: (Chevette) 12.5 gal.; (Monza) 18.5 gal.; (Monza wag) 15 gal.; (Nova/Camaro) 21 gal.; (Malibu/Monte) 18.1 gal.; (Caprice/Imp) 20.7 gal.; (Caprice/Imp wag) 22 gal.

DRIVETRAIN OPTIONS: Engines: 1.6-liter H.O. four: Chevette ($60). 196 cu. in., 2Bbl. V-6: Monza ($160). 231 cu. in., 2Bbl. V-6: Monza ($200); Malibu ($40); Monte ($30). 267 cu. in., 2Bbl. V-8: Malibu/Monte ($190). 305 cu. in., 2Bbl. V-8: Monza ($395); Nova/Camaro ($235); Imp/Caprice cpe/sed ($235). 305 cu. in., 4Bbl. V-8: Malibu/Monte ($295). 350 cu. in., 4Bbl. V-8: Nova/Camaro ($360); Malibu wag ($360); Imp/Capr cpe/sed ($360); Imp/Capr wag ($125). Transmission/Differential: Four-speed manual shift: Nova (NC); Camaro/Malibu ($135). Close-ratio four-speed manual: Camaro (NC). Five-speed manual shift: Monza ($175). Turbo Hydra-matic: Chvt/Monza ($295); Nova/Camaro/Malibu/Monte ($335); Camaro Z28 ($59). Sport shifter: Chvt ($30). Positraction axle: Monza ($60); Nova/Camaro ($64); Malibu/Monte ($65); Imp/Capr ($68). Performance axle ratio: Monza ($17); Nova/Camaro/Malibu/Monte ($18); Imp/Capr ($19). Power Accessories: Power brakes: Chvt/Monza ($71); Nova/Camaro/Monte, Malibu cpe/sed ($76). Power steering: Monza ($146); Nova/Malibu/Monte ($163). Suspension: F40 H.D. susp.: Nova ($11-$36); Malibu cpe/sed, Monte ($22); Imp/Capr ($23). F41 sport susp.: Chvt ($33); Monza ($31); Nova ($45); Camaro, Malibu cpe/sed ($41); Imp/Capr cpe/sed ($42). Superlift rear shock absorbers: Imp/Capr ($56). Front stabilizer bar: Monza ($27). Other: Heavy-duty radiator ($31-$33) exc. Imp/Capr ($42). H.D. alternator (63-amp): Malibu/Monte ($5-$33); Imp/Capr ($34). H.D. battery ($19-$21). California emission system ($83) exc. Monza four ($150). High altitude emission ($35).

1979 Monza Sport Spyder 2+2 hatchback (CH)

CHEVETTE/MONZA CONVENIENCE/APPEARANCE OPTIONS: Option Packages: Spyder equipment pkg.: Monza ($164). Spyder appearance pkg.: Monza ($231). Quiet sound group: Chvt ($35-$47); Monza ($29-$39). Auto. shoulder belt convenience group: Chvt ($144-$166). Deluxe appointment group (quiet sound, aux. lighting, clock): Chvt ($94-$137). Comfort/Convenience: Air conditioning ($496). Rear defogger, electric ($87). Tinted glass: Chvt ($60). Comfortilt steering wheel ($68). Special instrumentation (incl. tach): Chvt ($67); Monza ($50-$88). Electric clock ($21). Digital clock: Monza ($49). Cigarette lighter: Scooter ($7). Intermittent wipers ($35). Lighting and Mirrors: Aux. lighting: Chvt ($37-$44); Monza ($20-$37). Driver's remote sport mirror: Chvt ($25). Twin sport mirrors, left remote ($40). Day/night mirror ($10). Entertainment: AM radio: Scooter ($74). AM/FM radio: Chvt/Monza ($74); Scooter ($148). AM/FM stereo radio ($148). AM/FM stereo radio w/digital clock: Monza ($299). Stereo tape player w/AM radio: Monza ($159). Cassette or 8track player with AM/FM stereo radio: Monza ($242). Rear speaker ($23). Exterior Trim: Removable sunroof: Monza ($180). Cabriolet vinyl roof: Monza ($156) incl. opera windows. Spoilers, front/rear: Monza ($97). Deluxe exterior (wheel opening, side window and rocker panel moldings): Chvt ($104). Tri-tone sport stripes: Chvt ($70). Sport striping: Monza wag ($84). Bodyside moldings: Scooter ($40). Wheel opening moldings: Monza ($21). Side window reveal moldings: Chvt ($67). Door edge guards ($12-$19). Roof carrier ($65). Rear air deflector: Monza ($28). Deluxe bumpers, front/rear: Scooter ($37). Bumper guards, front/rear: Chvt ($41-$78); Monza ($42); std. on wag. Interior Trim/Upholstery: Console: Monza cpe ($75). Bucket seats (sport cloth): Chvt ($11-$21). Knit cloth bucket seats: Monza ($21). Custom Chevette interior pkg. w/bucket seats: cloth ($181); vinyl ($160). Custom vinyl bucket seats: Monza ($159) exc. Sport (NC). Custom cloth bucket seats: Monza ($180) exc. Sport ($21). Folding rear seat: Monza ($97) but std. on 2+2. Rear seat delete: Chvt ($51 credit). Load floor carpet: Chvt ($21). Color-keyed floor mats ($21). Automatic shoulder belts: Chvt ($50). Deluxe seatbelts ($21). Wheels and Tires: Rally II wheels: Monza ($45-$88). Color- keyed deluxe wheel covers: Monza ($13-$43). Sport wheel covers: Chvt ($45). Wheel trim rings: Scooter ($37). 155/8013 GBR WSW: Scooter ($37). 155/8013 SBR BSW: Chvt ($11); Scooter ($42). 155/8013 SBR WSW: Chvt ($42); Scooter ($79). 155/8013 SBR WLT: Chvt ($55); Scooter ($92). B78 x 13 WSW: Monza ($19) exc. wag. (NC). BR70 x 13 SBR BSW: Monza ($137) exc. Spyder/wag (NC). BR70 x 13 SBR WSW: Monza ($138- $189). BR70 x 13 SBR WLT: Monza ($50-$205).

1979 Camaro Z28 Sport Coupe (CH)

NOVA/CAMARO/MALIBU/MONTE CARLO CONVENIENCE/APPEARANCE OPTIONS: Option Packages: Rally equipment: Nova ($211). Estate equipment: Malibu wag ($258). Interior decor/quiet sound group: Camaro ($64); std. on Berlinetta. Quiet sound group: Malibu ($51). Value appearance group (roof drip, side window and wheel opening moldings): Nova ($79). Security pkg.: Malibu wag ($37). Comfort/Convenience: Air conditioning: Nova/Camaro ($529- $562); Malibu/Monte ($562). Rear defogger (forced-air): Nova/Malibu ($55). Rear defogger (electric): Camaro/Malibu/Monte ($99). Cruise-master speed control ($103). Tinted glass: Camaro ($64); Malibu/Monte ($70). Comfortilt steering wheel ($75). Six-way power driver's seat: Malibu/Monte ($163). Power windows: Nova ($126-$178); Camaro/Monte ($132); Malibu ($132-$187). Power door locks: Nova/Malibu ($80-$120); Camaro/Monte ($86). Power trunk release: Malibu/Monte ($24). Power tailgate release: Malibu wag ($25). Electric clock: Nova, base Camaro ($23); Malibu ($23). Special instrumentation: Nova, base Camaro ($112); Malibu ($125); Monte ($102). Econominder gauge pkg.: Nova ($53). Gauge pkg.: Malibu ($57); Monte ($34). Intermittent wipers ($38). Lighting, Horns and Mirrors: Aux. lighting ($31-$56). Dome reading light: Malibu/Monte ($20). Dual horns: Nova/Camaro, base Malibu ($9). Remote-control driver's mirror: Nova/Malibu/Monte ($18). Twin sport mirrors (left remote): Nova, base Camaro, Malibu/Monte ($43). Twin remote sport mirrors: Malibu/Monte ($68); Monte Lan ($25). Day/night mirror: Nova ($11). Visor vanity mirror: Malibu/Monte ($5). Lighted visor mirror: Malibu ($40); Monte ($35-$40). Entertainment: AM radio ($82-$85). AM/FM radio ($158). AM/FM stereo radio ($232). AM/FM stereo radio w/digital clock: Nova/Malibu ($395); Camaro ($372-$395). Stereo tape player w/AM radio ($244-$248). Stereo 8track tape player with AM/FM stereo radio ($335). Cassette player with AM/FM stereo radio ($341). AM/FM/CB radio: Camaro/Malibu/Monte ($489). AM/FM stereo radio w/CB: Camaro/Malibu/Monte ($570). Rear speaker ($25). Dual front speakers: Malibu/Monte ($21). Windshield antenna ($27); incl. w/radios. Power antenna: Camaro/Malibu/Monte ($47). Exterior Trim: Removable glass roof panels: Camaro/Monte ($655). Power sky roof: Malibu cpe/sed, Monte ($529). Vinyl roof: Nova ($99); Camaro ($112); Malibu ($116); Monte ($131). Cabriolet roof: Nova ($190). Rear spoiler: Camaro Berlinetta ($58). Style trim pkg.: Camaro ($73). Two-tone paint: Nova ($55); Malibu ($67-$115); Monte ($120-$160). Swing-out rear side windows: Nova ($59). Bodyside moldings: Nova/Camaro ($43). Deluxe bodyside

1979 Malibu Classic Estate station wagon, V-8

moldings: Nova/Malibu/Monte ($53). Door edge guards ($13-$21). Bright rocker moldings and extensions: Nova ($15-$37). Bright sill moldings: Monte ($44). Wheel opening moldings: Nova, Malibu cpe/sed ($23). Wide wheel opening moldings: Nova ($39). Side window sill moldings: Monte ($33). Side window reveal moldings: Nova/Malibu ($41). Roof drip moldings: Nova ($20); Camaro ($24). Bodyside pinstriping: Nova ($30); Malibu ($48); Monte ($40). Rear window air deflector: Malibu wag ($30). Roof carrier: Malibu wag ($90). Bumper rub strips: Malibu ($41). Bumper rub strips and guards, front/rear: Nova ($79). Bumper guards, front/rear: Malibu ($46). Interior Trim/Upholstery: Interior decor pkg.: base Nova ($31). Console ($80). Vinyl bench seat: Malibu cpe/sed, Monte ($26). Sport cloth bench seat: Nova ($23); Malibu (NC). Knit cloth bench seat: Malibu wag ($28). Custom vinyl bench seat: Nova (NC). Custom vinyl bucket seats: Nova ($85); Camaro ($307). Vinyl bucket seats: Malibu cpe/sed, Monte ($85). Cloth bucket seats: Monte ($85). Sport cloth bucket seats: Camaro ($23). Custom knit cloth bucket seats: Camaro Berlinetta ($23); base Camaro ($330). Knit cloth 50/50 seating: Malibu cpe/sed ($172); Malibu wag ($198). Vinyl 50/50 seating: Malibu cpe/sed ($198); Malibu wag ($172). Custom cloth 55/45 seating: Monte ($368). Adj. driver's seatback: Camaro ($23). Litter container: Malibu/Monte ($8). Color-keyed mats ($23). Deluxe load-floor carpet: Malibu ($70). Deluxe seatbelts ($21-$23). Deluxe trunk trim: Malibu/Monte ($43). Wheels and Tires: Aluminum wheels: Camaro ($172-$315). Custom styled wheels: Camaro ($100-$143). Rally wheels: Nova ($88); Camaro ($93), but std. on Rally; Malibu ($47-$90); Monte ($47). Wire wheel covers: Nova ($130); Malibu ($65-$160); Monte ($117); Monte Landau ($65). Full wheel covers: Nova/Camaro/Malibu ($43). Sport wheel covers (silver or gold): Malibu ($52-$95). E78 x 14 BSW: Camaro ($95-$119 credit). E78 x 14 WSW: Nova ($38-$47); Camaro ($58-$72 credit). FR78 x 14 SBR: Nova ($96-$119). FR78 x 14 SBR WSW: Nova ($135-$168); Camaro ($40-$49). FR78 x 14 SBR WLT: Nova ($148-$184); Camaro ($52-$65); Berlinetta ($13-$16). P185/75R14 GBR WSW: Malibu cpe/sed ($40). P195/75R14 GBR WSW: Malibu wag ($41). P195/75R14 SBR WSW: Malibu cpe/sed ($102); Malibu wag ($83). P205/70R14 SBR WSW: Monte ($44); Malibu cpe/sed ($149). Stowaway spare: Nova ($19); Camaro (NC).

IMPALA/CAPRICE CONVENIENCE/APPEARANCE OPTIONS: Option Packages: Estate equipment: wag ($262). Value appearance group: bodyside and wheel opening moldings, full wheel covers ($87). Comfort/Convenience: Four season air cond. ($605). Comfortron auto-temp air cond. ($688). Rear defogger, forced-air: cpe/sed ($57). Rear defogger, electric ($101). Cruise-Master speed control ($108). Tinted glass ($84). Comfortilt steering wheel ($77). Power door locks ($88-$122). Six-way power driver's seat ($166). Power windows ($122-$205). Power trunk release ($25). Power tailgate lock: wag ($40). Electric clock: Imp ($24). Digital clock: Imp ($55); Caprice ($31). Gauge pkg. ($54). Intermittent wipers ($39). Quiet sound group: Imp ($56). Lighting, Horns and Mirrors: Aux. lighting ($35-$50). Dual horns: Imp ($10). Driver's remote mirror ($19). Dual remote mirrors ($56). Dual sport mirrors, left remote ($44). Dual remote sport mirrors, body-color ($69) exc. Lan ($25). Visor vanity mirror ($6). Lighted visor mirror ($41). Entertainment: AM radio ($87). AM/FM radio ($161). AM/FM stereo radio ($236); w/digital clock, Imp ($401). Stereo tape player with AM radio ($265); with AM/FM stereo radio ($340). Cassette player with AM/FM stereo ($346). AM/FM/CB radio and power antenna ($503). AM/FM stereo with CB and power antenna ($578). Rear speaker ($26). Dual front speakers ($22). Power antenna ($48). Windshield antenna ($28); incl. w/radios. Exterior Trim: Power sky roof: cpe/sed ($625). Vinyl roof: cpe/sed ($145). Two-tone paint ($56). Custom two-tone ($87- $120). Pinstriping ($33). Color-keyed bodyside moldings ($44). Door edge guards ($14-$21). Wheel opening moldings: Imp ($23). Bumper rub strips ($56). Bumper guards ($52). Interior Trim/Upholstery: Vinyl bench seat: cpe/sed ($27). Sport or knit cloth bench seat: wag ($27). Vinyl 50/50 seat ($240-$267). Knit cloth 50/50 seat: cpe/sed ($240); wag ($267). Special custom cloth 50/50 seat: cpe/sed ($397). Deluxe load-floor carpet: wag ($75). Deluxe cargo area carpet: wag ($107). Color-keyed mats ($24). Litter container ($8). Color-keyed seatbelts ($24-$27). Deluxe trunk trim ($46). Wheel Covers: Full wheel covers ($44). Sport wheel covers: Imp ($98); Caprice ($54). Wire wheel covers ($120). Coupe/Sedan Tires: FR78 x 15 GBR WSW ($49). FR78 x 15 SBR BSW ($52). FR78 x 15 SBR WSW ($101). GR78 x 15 SBR WSW ($131). GR70 x 15 SBR WSW ($155). Wagon Tires: HR78 x 15 SBR WSW ($55).

HISTORY: Introduced: Sept. 28, 1978. Model year production (U.S.): 2,153,036 (incl. Corvettes but not incl. 44,927 Acadians and early 1980 Citations). Calendar year production: 2,238,226 (including 22,056 Sportvans, 48,568 Corvettes and 17,133 Acadians). Calendar year sales by U.S. dealers: 2,158,839 (incl. 30,630 Sportvans and 38,631 Corvettes) for a 25.9 percent market share. Model year sales by U.S. dealers: 2,257,751 (incl. 33,819 Sportvans and 39,816 Corvettes, plus 273,720 early 1980 Citations.)

Historical Footnotes: Chevrolet fared rather well this year, despite a general slowdown in the auto industry. Chevettes sold particularly well. Sales of small cars were mandatory if the Division expected to reach the CAFE limit of 19 mile-per-gallon fuel economy. Chevrolet built a non-production version of a 1979 turbo injected Chevette, to study optimal performance, economy and driveability.

1980 CHEVROLET

Chevettes had a new rear-end look for 1980. An aero restyling cut the weight of full-size models. Otherwise, apart from the new front-wheel drive Citation, this was a carryover year, devoted more to technical improvements than appearance changes. The old reliable inline six-cylinder engine was gone, replaced by a V-6. Lockup torque converter clutches arrived on automatic transmissions. Over the past few years, the entire Chevrolet line had been downsized, signaling the beginning of a new era of smaller, lighter, fuel-efficient automobiles. This year also marked the first appearance of a diesel V-8, produced by Oldsmobile and installed (for an extra $915) in full-size station wagons.

CHEVETTE — SERIES 1T — FOUR — Chevette gained a new aero-styled rear end this year. Restyled rear quarters held four-lens wraparound taillamps with larger, square backup lenses. Instead of the straight angled hatch of prior years, this year's version bent several inches above the taillamps to create a more vertical rear-end look. A Chevrolet badge was on the hatch, just above the right taillamp. The grille had a new Chevrolet emblem and rectangular headlamps. Also new: a round fuel filler door, revised license plate light, improved pressure-proportioning brake system, and new passive restraint system (a two-piece lap/shoulder belt setup). Once again, Chevette came with either a standard or high-output 1.6-liter engine, both with four-speed fully-synchronized manual transmission (or optional automatic). The standard overhead-cam four had a staged two-barrel carburetor, "tuned" aluminum intake manifold, and special valve porting. The high-output version had a high-speed camshaft and dual-takedown exhaust manifold. Chevettes came in 13 body colors this year: black, gray, red, red orange, white, bright yellow, and a selection of metallics: bright blue, dark blue, light blue, light camel, dark claret, dark green, or silver. Five two-tone combinations were available (except on the stripped-down Scooter). New to Chevette's option list: improved-wear steel- belted radial tires. Interiors held body-contoured, full foam front bucket seats that reclined (except Scooter's).

1980 Chevette hatchback coupe (AA)

Standard vinyl bucket seats came in black, camel, blue or carmine color (Scooter only in black or camel). Cloth bucket seats were available, as was a Custom interior in five two-tone combinations. All Chevettes had a built-in diagnostic connector, standard 155/80R13 glass-belted radial tires (whitewall except Scooter), "smart switch" on the steering column, Freedom battery, rack-and-pinion steering, and full coil suspension. Front disc brakes had audible wear sensors. Improved automatic-transmission driveshaft balancing this year was meant to reduce noise. Chevette's flow-through ventilation system was redesigned for increased defroster airflow. Ball joints had a visible wear indicator. Bolt-on front fenders had plastic inner shields. Standard equipment (except on Scooters) also included an AM radio, center console, wheel trim rings, bodyside and sill moldings, brushed aluminum instrument panel moldings, lighter, glove box lock, sport steering wheel, color-keyed seat/shoulder belts, and right door jamb dome light switch. All models had vinyl-coated headliner, courtesy dome light, day/night mirror, cut-pile carpeting, front stabilizer bar, bumper guards and rub strips, high-pressure compact spare tire, and removable load floor carpet.

1980 Monza Sport Spyder 2+2 hatchback coupe (CH)

MONZA — SERIES 1H — FOUR/V-6 — Apart from new black taillamp bezels and black grille center bars, Monza changed little this year. A restyled front air dam was integrated with wheel openings. Bumper guards were now standard. Emblems had a new finish. Bodyside moldings were sliced off at an angle to allow for new striping. The Spyder option included new hood decals and body stripes. Models included the 2+2 Sport hatchback, regular hatchback coupe, and notchback sedan. The station wagon was dropped, along with the V-8 option and green body color availability. Engine choices this year were the base 151 cu. in. (2.5-liter) four, or optional Buick 231 cu. in. (3.8- liter) V-6. Standard equipment included four-speed floor shift, manual front disc/rear drum brakes, A78 x 13 whitewall tires, front bucket seats, bumper guards (front/rear), vinyl bodyside moldings, AM radio, tinted glass, sport steering wheel, lighter, day/night mirror, carpeting, and Freedom battery. Monza's 2+2 hatchback added bumper rub strips, bright door frame and belt moldings, console, folding back seat, and bright/black rear quarter window moldings. The Monza Sport hatchback 2+2 with slope-back soft front end and bright-bezeled rectangular headlamps came

1980 Monza 2 + 2 hatchback coupe

with all the basic equipment, plus a black front air dam; bright/black windshield reveal molding; black wiper arms/blades; console; folding back seat; soft door trim panels with driver's side map pocket and armrest; bright door frame and belt moldings; body-color bumper rub strips and guards; bright/black rear quarter window and back window moldings; full wheel covers; bright-trimmed wraparound taillamps; and body-color rear end panel. This year's Spyder equipment package, priced at $521, included Rally II wheels, front/rear spoilers, stripes with Spyder inserts, F41 suspension, BR70 x 13/C blackwall tires, modified front stabilizer bar and rear shock absorbers, and a Spyder emblem on the hood header panel. Black accents went on headlamps, parking lamps and belt moldings; taillamp openings; lower rocker panel, quarter panel and front fenders; plus windshield, rear window, quarter window and door moldings. The package also included sport mirrors. A total of 7,589 Spyder packages were installed.

1980 Citation hatchback sedan (CP)

CITATION — SERIES 1X — FOUR/V-6 — Long before the model year began, in spring 1979, Chevrolet introduced the all-new front-drive Citation, described as "the most thoroughly tested new car in Chevy history." Chevrolet's General Manager Robert D. Lund called it "an affordable, functional family-size vehicle which is space efficient, economical to operate, comfortable and serviceable." Citation was claimed to offer "the exterior dimensions of a subcompact, the operating economy of a compact with a V-8, the interior room of a mid-size car and as much luggage capacity as many full-size sedans." Weighing about 2,500 pounds, it was 20 inches shorter and 800 pounds lighter than the compact Nova it replaced. Coupe, hatchback coupe and hatchback sedan models were offered, plus a sporty X11 option on both two-door models. Citation's front-drive chassis held a MacPherson strut front suspension with transverse-mounted engine and transmission, computer-selected coil springs, front

1980 Citation Club Coupe (CP)

and rear stabilizer bars, and rack-and-pinion steering. The variable-rate rear suspension used rubber jounce bumpers as load-carrying springs. Citation's mini-frame construction mounted the powertrain on a separate, bolt-on "cradle" that also served as a mount for the front suspension. In addition to producing a quieter ride, this design allowed easy servicing by replacing the entire engine/powertrain module. Standard engine was a cast iron 151 cu. in. (2.5-liter) four, rated 90 horsepower, supplied by Pontiac. Chevrolet produced the optional powerplant: the industry's first transverse-mounted V-6, a compact 60-degree 173 cu. in. (2.8- liter) design made of cast iron. That engine could fit into the same underhood area as a four. Both engines used two- stage Varajet carburetors that metered fuel into the combustion chambers according to driving needs, increasing flow when passing. Citation had single rectangular headlamps, wraparound amber marker lamps, and vertical parking lamps behind the honeycomb grille with center Chevrolet emblem. On two-tone models, bodyside moldings separated the upper and lower colors, with pinstriping on upper bodysides and fenders. A Citation nameplate was on the forward end of front fenders. Wide three-section taillamps included backup lamps in the center sections. Bodies came in 14 standard colors: beige, black, cinnabar, gray, red, silver, white, and yellow; plus six metallics (dark or light blue, light or medium camel, dark claret, or dark green). Thirteen two-tone combinations were also available. Six interior color trims were available in two trim levels. Standard vinyl bench seats came in black, camel, carmine or green. Custom vinyl and Sport and knit cloths were available, on

1980 Citation X11 hatchback coupe (CP)

bench or bucket seats. Citation was designed with easy servicing in mind. The cylinder head, oil pan, water pump, rear main bearing seal and engine front cover could all be removed without taking the engine out of the car. And even if it did have to come out, the mini-frame "cradle" made that job easier. Only eight bolts had to be removed, and suspension components loosened, to gain clearance for extracting the engine/transaxle unit. Both the engine and transaxle were removable separately too: the engine upward, transaxle downward. Since clutch repair on front-drives could be a problem, manual shift Citations had a constant-tension clutch cable to minimize the risk of early failure. Ball bearings at front and rear wheels were lifetime lubricated. Servicing of other components was also simplified, including the instrument panel cluster, taillamps, heater, and starter. Front fenders bolted onto the unitized body. Standard equipment included a four-speed manual transaxle with overdrive fourth gear, front disc/rear drum brakes (diagonal dual-braking), P185/80R13 glass-belted radial tires, front/rear stabilizer bars, compact spare tire, steel bumpers, concealed hatchback luggage compartment, dome light, and column-mounted turn signal/dimmer/wiper/washer control. Also standard: an inside hood release; locking glove box; inertia seatback latches; color-coded sliding door locks; and glass-belted radial tires. All except the base H11 coupe also had bright rocker panel, wheel opening and drip moldings; a cigarette lighter and ashtray; and pushbutton AM radio. Options included side window reveal moldings, tinted glass, remote swing-out side windows, bodyside pinstriping, full wheel covers, intermittent wipers, roof rack, tilt steering, electric rear defogger, reclining passenger seat, removable pop-up sunroof, plus bumper guards and rub strips. The X11 sport package for hatchback and club coupe included a black-accented grille; black accents on headlamp bezels, taillamps, rocker panels, door lock pillars and rear license plate pocket; decal stripes; rear spoiler; pinstriping; bright side window moldings; body-color sport mirrors; rally wheel trim; sport steering wheel; sport suspension; bumper rub strips; and white-letter P205/70R13 steel-belted radial tires. Large X11 identification was behind the door and on rear panel. X11 models could also have bucket seats, console, and special instrumentation (including tachometer, voltmeter, temp and oil pressure gauges). A total of 24,852 X11 equipment packages were installed this year.

1980 Camaro Z28 Sport Coupe (CP)

CAMARO — SERIES 1F — V-6/V-8 — Camaro entered 1980 wearing a new grille with tighter crosshatch pattern and offering a revised engine selection. A lighter, more economical 229 cu. in. (3.8-liter) V-6 rated 115 horsepower replaced the old familiar 250 cu. in. inline six as standard powerplant. (California Camaros carried a 231 V-6.) There was also a new 267 cu. in. (4.4-liter) optional V-8 rated 120 horsepower, plus a 305 V-8 and the Z28 350 V-8 (not available in California). Automatic transmissions had a new torque converter clutch to eliminate slippage. Rally Sport Camaros came with an all-black "thin-line" grille, while Berlinetta carried a bright grille in the same style. The standard Sport Coupe grille had an emblem in the upper corner; Berlinetta had one in the center. Berlinettas had new standard wire wheel covers. Z28 grilles had a pattern of horizontal bars, with large 'Z28' emblem in the upper corner. Z28, billed as "the maximum Camaro," also had a new (functional) hood air-intake scoop facing to the rear, with an electrically-activated flap that opened when stepping hard on the gas. A side fender port let out hot engine air, and boosted pickup at the same time. Also new to Z28: rear fender flares. Body colors this year were white, black, silver, gold, red, bright blue, dark blue, bright yellow, lime green, red orange, bronze, charcoal, dark brown, and dark claret. Standard Camaro equipment included the 229 cu. in. V-6 engine, three-speed manual transmission, P205/705R14 SBR tires, body-color front/rear bumper covers, bucket seats, console, day/night mirror, and cigarette lighter. The Berlinetta coupe had whitewall tires; bright headlamp bezels, upper/lower grille, windshield and window reveal moldings; black rocker panels; dual horns; electric clock; special instruments; quiet sound group; sport mirrors; and wire wheel covers. Z28 came with P225/70R15 white-letter tires on body- color 15 x 7 in. wheels; black headlamp bezels, upper/lower grille, and reveal moldings; sport mirrors; body-color front spoiler and front flares; a hood scoop decal; front fender louvers; rear spoiler; plus sport suspension, power brakes and four-speed manual shift. Camaro's Rally Sport package included a rear spoiler, sport suspension, black rocker panels, black grille, black headlamp bezels, bright reveal moldings, sport mirrors, plus color-keyed Rally wheels.

1980 Malibu Sport Coupe (AA)

MALIBU — SERIES 1A — V-6/V-8 — Though similar to the previous edition, Malibu sported a brighter, lightweight grille for 1980, made up of narrow vertical bars and divided by two subdued horizontal bars. Its nameplate was again in the lower corner (driver's side). Headlamps, parking lamps and side marker lamps all grew larger. At the rear were three-section wraparound taillamps with side marker lamps. New base engine was the 229 cu. in. (3.8-liter) V-6, with either a 267 (4.4-liter) or 305 (5.0-liter) V-8 optional. Wagons carried the 305 as standard; the big 350 was out of the lineup. Models included the two-door coupe, four- door sedan and four-door wagon; plus a Classic Landau. An Estate wagon package was optional. Malibus had a new, precisely controlled windshield washer (similar to Corvette's). Joining the option list: Rally wheels. The optional automatic transmission could now have a lock-up torque converter clutch. Only 202 Malibus came with a four- speed manual transmission. Malibu standard equipment included three-speed manual floor shift, front stabilizer bar, P185/75R14 tires, windshield and back window reveal moldings, roof drip moldings, day/night mirror, lighter, concealed wipers, and locking glove box. Wagons had P195/75R14 tires. Malibu Classic models added a standup hood ornament; wide

1980 Malibu Classic 4-dr sedan

wheel opening moldings; bright decklid and end cap moldings; dual horns; and full wheelcovers. The Landau coupe had sport wheel covers as well as bodyside and rear pinstriping.

1980 Monte Carlo Turbo T-top coupe (AA)

MONTE CARLO — SERIES 1A — V-6/V-8 — Monte wore a wider-spaced, heavier looking eggcrate grille this year, with 16 holes across in four rows. Also new were quad rectangular headlamps above wide rectangular parking lamps. Wraparound side marker lamps were replaced by separate horizontal lenses just ahead of the wheel, below 'Monte Carlo' script. New base engine was the Chevrolet-built 229 cu. in. (3.8-liter) V-6. But this year's option list included Buick's turbocharged 231 cu. in. V-6 that delivered 170 horsepower (compared to 115 from the base engine). Also available: 267 cu. in. (4.4-liter) and 305 (5.0-liter) V-8s, rated 120 and 155 horsepower respectively. Three-speed manual shift was dropped, so all Montes now carried three-speed Turbo Hydra- matic as well as power brakes and steering. Turbo models had a special hood with raised center and identifying decal. A total of 13,839 turbo engines were installed for the model year. Standard Monte equipment included dual horns, day/night mirror, lighter, concealed wipers, front/rear stabilizer bars, and P205/70R14 steel-belted radial tires; plus moldings for window reveals, wheel openings, decklid, roof drip, and lower bodyside. New options: high-intensity halogen headlamps and a T-roof.

1980 Impala sedan (AA)

IMPALA/CAPRICE CLASSIC — SERIES 1B — V-6/V-8 — In an attempt to boost gas mileage, both full-size models got a lighter weight standard engine: a 229 cu. in. (3.8-liter) V-6 with Dualjet carburetor and aluminum manifold. That powerplant replaced the old inline six. Wagons came with a standard 267 cu. in. (4.4-liter) V-8, also with Dualjet carburetor, introduced a year earlier on mid-sizes. For the first time, wagons could get an optional 350 cu. in. (5.7-liter) Oldsmobile-built diesel V-8 (except in California). All models could also get a 305 cu. in. (5.0- liter) gas V-8 with four-barrel. Sleek new aerodynamic styling on full-size models showed a lower hood, higher rear deck and restyled sides, along with a 100-pound weight loss. Impala's restyled grille had vertical bars over smaller segments. Caprice gained a new eggcrate grille design and three-lens taillamp assembly (with working center light). The new taillamp rear-end panel was removable. Unlike prior versions, the grille pattern was not repeated down in the bumper area. Landau models gained new roof moldings. Also new were a one-piece door beam, aluminum components in radiators and wagon bumpers, high-pressure easy-rolling tires, side-lift frame jack, and a 25-gallon fuel tank (formerly 21) to boost cruising range. Automatic transmissions added a new lockup torque converter clutch. New options included self-sealing tires, plus cornering lamps that worked with turn signals when headlamps were lit. EPA ratings of 18 MPG city, 26 highway, were the highest ever for a full-size Chevrolet. Reaching a step further, in mid-year an economy Impala emerged: the first full-size gas- engine car to achieve a 20 MPG city estimate. A total of 1,612 cars carried the special economy equipment package, while 13,843 had a diesel engine under the hood. Full-size models came in 14 body colors: beige, black, cinnabar, gray, silver, white, and yellow; plus metallic dark or light blue, light or medium camel, dark claret, or dark green. Ten two-tone combinations were offered, plus seven vinyl top colors. Standard front bench seats had cloth upholstery, but vinyl was available. Caprice could get an optional 50/50 split front seat. Standard equipment included Turbo Hydra-matic, power front disc/rear drum brakes, power steering, easy-roll steel- belted radial tires, acoustical headlining, one-piece carpeting, front stabilizer bar, and new compact spare tire. Full-size models had a built-in engine diagnostics connector, foot parking brake, cigarette lighter, heater/defroster, luggage compartment light, Freedom battery, and column lever for turn signal and dimmer.

1980 Caprice Classic 2-dr Landau Coupe

1980 Caprice Classic sedan (AA)

I.D. DATA: For the last time, Chevrolet used a 13-symbol Vehicle Identification Number (VIN), visible through the windshield on the driver's side. The first digit ('1') indicates Chevrolet division. Next is a letter identifying the series (car line): 'B' Chevette; 'J' Chevette Scooter; 'M' Monza; 'R' Monza Sport; 'H' Citation coupe; 'X' Citation; 'Q' Camaro; 'S' Camaro Berlinetta; 'T' Malibu; 'W' Malibu Classic; 'Z' Monte Carlo; 'L' Impala; 'N' Caprice Classic. Symbols 34 indicate body type: '08' 2-dr. hatchback coupe; '07' 2-dr. (2+2) hatchback coupe; '11' 2-dr. notchback; '27' 2-dr. coupe; '87' 2-dr. (4-pass.) sport coupe; '37' 2-dr. (6-pass.) sport coupe; '47' 2-dr. (6-pass.) coupe; '19' 4-dr. (6- window) notchback sedan; '68' 4-dr. (6-window) hatchback sedan; '69' 4-dr. (4-window) notchback sedan; '35' 4-dr. station wagon. Symbol five is the engine code: '9' L497.6 2Bbl.; 'O' L497.6 H.O.; 'V' L4151 2Bbl.; '5' L4151 2Bbl.; '7' V6173 2Bbl.; 'K' V6229 2Bbl.; 'A' V6231 2Bbl.; '3' Turbo V6231 4Bbl.; 'J' V8267 2Bbl.; 'H' V8305 4Bbl.; 'L' V8350 4Bbl; 'N' V8350 diesel. Next is a code for model year ('A' 1980). Symbol seven denotes assembly plant: 'A' Lakewood, GA; 'B' Baltimore, MD; 'C' South Gate, CA; 'D' Doraville, GA; 'J' Janesville, WI; 'K' Leeds, MO; 'U' Lordstown, OH; 'L' Van Nuys, CA; 'N' Norwood, OH; 'R' Arlington, TX; 'S' St. Louis, MO; 'T' Tarrytown, NY; 'W' Willow Run, MI; 'Y' Wilmington, DE; 'Z' Fremont, CA; '6' Oklahoma City, OK; '1' Oshawa, Ontario. The last six digits are the sequential serial number. A Body Number Plate on the upper horizontal surface of the shroud identifies model year, car division, series, style, body assembly plant, body number, trim combination, modular seat code, paint code, roof option, and build date code. Citations have a body style I.D. plate on the front tie bar, behind the right headlamp. A two- or three-symbol code (combined with a serial number) identifies each engine. Chevette engine numbers are on a pad at right of block, below No. 1 spark plug. Pontiac (151) fours have a number pad at the right side of the block, by distributor shaft hole. On sixes, the pad is at the right side of the block, to rear of distributor. On V-8s, that pad is just forward of the right cylinder head. Citation fours have an engine code on a pad at the left front of cylinder block, below the head; and an engine unit/code number label on timing cover. Citation V-6s have an engine unit/code label at rear (or front) of right rocker cover.

CHEVETTE (FOUR)

Model Number	Body/Style Number	Body Type & Seating	Factory Price	Shipping Weight	Production Total
1T	B08	2-dr. Hatch Cpe-4P	4289	1989	146,686
1T	B68	4-dr. Hatch Sed-4P	4418	2048	261,477

CHEVETTE SCOOTER (FOUR)

1T	J08	2-dr. Hatch Cpe-4P	3782	1985	40,998

MONZA (FOUR/V-6)

1H	M07	2-dr. Hatch 2+2-4P	4497/4722	2672	53,415
1H	M27	2-dr. Cpe-4P	4184/4409	2617	95,469

MONZA SPORT (FOUR/V-6)

1H	R07	2-dr. Hatch 2+2-4P	4921/5146	2729	20,534

Monza Production Note: Figures do not include units built in fall 1980 as part of extended model year.

CITATION (FOUR/V-6)

Model Number	Body/Style Number	Body Type & Seating	Factory Price	Shipping Weight	Production Total
1X	H11	2-dr. Cpe-5P	4491/4716	2391/2428	42,909
1X	X11	2-dr. Club Cpe-5P	4905/5130	2397/2434	100,340
1X	X08	2-dr. Hatch Cpe-5P	5032/5257	2417/2454	210,258
1X	X68	4-dr. Hatch Sed-5P	5153/5378	2437/2474	458,033

Citation Production Note: Figures include 187,229 Citations produced during the 1979 model year as early '80s.

CAMARO (V-6/V-8)

Model Number	Body/Style Number	Body Type & Seating	Factory Price	Shipping Weight	Production Total
1F	P87	2-dr. Spt Cpe-4P	5499/5679	3218/3346	68,174
1F	P87/Z85	2-dr. Rally Cpe-4P	5916/6096	N/A	12,015

1980 Camaro Berlinetta Sport Coupe (AA)

CAMARO BERLINETTA (V-6/V-8)

Model Number	Body/Style Number	Body Type & Seating	Factory Price	Shipping Weight	Production Total
1F	S87	2-dr. Spt Cpe-4P	6262/6442	3253/3381	26,679

CAMARO Z28 (V-8)

Model Number	Body/Style Number	Body Type & Seating	Factory Price	Shipping Weight	Production Total
1F	P87/Z28	2-dr. Spt Cpe-4P	-- /7121	N/A	45,137

MALIBU (V-6/V-8)

Model Number	Body/Style Number	Body Type & Seating	Factory Price	Shipping Weight	Production Total
1A	T27	2-dr. Spt Cpe-6P	5133/5313	2996/3117	28,425
1A	T19	4-dr. Sed-6P	5246/5426	3001/3122	67,696
1A	T35	4-dr. Sta Wag-6P	5402/5582	3141/3261	30,794

MALIBU CLASSIC (V-6/V-8)

Model Number	Body/Style Number	Body Type & Seating	Factory Price	Shipping Weight	Production Total
1A	W27	2-dr. Spt Cpe-6P	5439/5619	3027/3148	28,425
1A	W27/Z03	2-dr. Lan Cpe-6P	5688/5868	N/A	9,342
1A	W19	4-dr. Sed-6P	5567/5747	3031/3152	77,938
1A	W35	4-dr. Sta Wag-6P	5654/5834	3167/3387	35,730

MONTE CARLO (V-6/V-8)

Model Number	Body/Style Number	Body Type & Seating	Factory Price	Shipping Weight	Production Total
1A	Z37	2-dr. Spt Cpe-6P	6163/6343	3104/3219	116,580
1A	Z37/Z03	2-dr. Lan Cpe-6P	6411/6591	N/A	32,262

IMPALA (V-6/V-8)

Model Number	Body/Style Number	Body Type & Seating	Factory Price	Shipping Weight	Production Total
1B	L47	2-dr. Spt Cpe-6P	6180/6360	3344/3452	10,756
1B	L69	4-dr. Sedan-6P	6289/6469	3360/3468	70,801
1B	L35	4-dr. Sta Wag-6P	-- /6780	-- /3892	11,203
1B	L35/AQ4	4-dr. 3S Wag-8P	-- /6925	-- /3924	6,767

CAPRICE CLASSIC (V-6/V-8)

Model Number	Body/Style Number	Body Type & Seating	Factory Price	Shipping Weight	Production Total
1B	N47	2-dr. Spt Cpe-6P	6579/6759	3376/3484	13,919
1B	N47/Z03	2-dr. Lan Cpe-6P	7029/7209	N/A	8,857
1B	N69	4-dr. Sedan-6P	6710/6890	3410/3518	91,208
1B	N35	4-dr. Sta Wag-6P	-- /7099	-- /3930	9,873
1B	N35/AQ4	4-dr. 3S Wag-8P	-- /7266	-- /3962	13,431

FACTORY PRICE AND WEIGHT NOTE: Where two prices and weights are shown, the figure to the left of the slash is for six-cylinder model, to right of slash for the 267 cu. in. V-8 (305 V-8 cost $115 more). For Monza and Citation, prices and weights to left of slash are four-cylinder, to right for V-6 engine. All models had at least two price rises during the model year. The new Citation had an ample increase even before introduction. **BODY/STYLE NO. NOTE:** Some models are actually option packages. Figure after the slash (e.g., Z03) is the number of the option package that comes with the model listed.

ENGINE DATA: BASE FOUR (Chevette): Inline. Overhead cam. Four-cylinder. Cast iron block and head. Displacement: 97.6 cu. in. (1.6 liters). Bore & stroke: 3.23 x 2.98 in. Compression ratio: 8.6:1. Brake horsepower: 70 at 5200 R.P.M. Torque: 82 lbs.-ft. at 2400 R.P.M. Five main bearings. Hydraulic valve lifters. Carburetor: 2Bbl. Holley 5210C. VIN Code: 9. OPTIONAL HIGH-OUTPUT FOUR (Chevette): Same as above except Brake H.P.: 74 at 5200 R.P.M. Torque: 88 lbs.-ft. at 2800 R.P.M. VIN Code: O. BASE FOUR (Monza): Inline. Overhead valve. Four-cylinder. Cast iron block. Displacement: 151 cu. in. (2.5 liters). Bore & stroke: 4.00 x 3.00 in. Compression ratio: 8.2:1. Brake horsepower: 86 at 4000 R.P.M. Torque: 128 lbs.-ft. at 2400 R.P.M. Five main bearings. Hydraulic valve lifters. Carburetor: 2Bbl. Rochester 2SE. VIN Code: V. BASE FOUR (Citation): Same as 151 cu. in. four above except Brake H.P.: 90 at 4000 R.P.M. Torque: 134 lbs.-ft. at 2400 R.P.M. VIN Code: 5. OPTIONAL V-6 (Citation): 60-degree, overhead-valve V-6. Cast iron block and head. Displacement: 173 cu. in. (2.8 liters). Bore & stroke: 3.50 x 3.00 in. Compression ratio: 8.5:1. Brake horsepower: 115 at 4800 R.P.M. Torque: 145 lbs.-ft. at 2400 R.P.M. Four main bearings. Hydraulic valve lifters. Carburetor: 2Bbl. Rochester 2SE. VIN Code: 7. BASE V-6 (Camaro, Malibu, Monte Carlo, Impala, Caprice): 90-degree, overhead-valve V-6. Cast iron block and head. Displacement: 229 cu. in. (3.8 liters). Bore & stroke: 3.74 x 3.48 in. Compression ratio: 8.6:1. Brake horsepower: 115 at 4000 R.P.M. Torque: 175 lbs.-ft. at 2000 R.P.M. Four main bearings. Hydraulic valve lifters. Carburetor: 2Bbl. Rochester M2ME. VIN Code: K. OPTIONAL V-6 (Monza); alternate for models above: 90-degree, overhead-valve V-6. Cast iron block and head. Displacement: 231 cu. in. (3.8 liters). Bore & stroke: 3.80 x 3.40 in. Compression ratio: 8.0:1. Brake horsepower: 110 at 3800 R.P.M. Torque: 190 lbs.-ft. at 2000 R.P.M. Four main bearings. Hydraulic valve lifters. Carburetor: 2Bbl. Rochester M2ME. VIN Code: A. TURBOCHARGED V-6; OPTIONAL (Monte Carlo): Same as 231 cu. in. V-6 above, except 4Bbl. Rochester M4ME carburetor Brake H.P.: 170 at 4000 R.P.M. Torque: 265 lbs.- ft. at 2400 R.P.M. VIN Code: 3. OPTIONAL V-8 (Camaro, Malibu, Monte Carlo, Impala, Caprice): 90-degree, overhead valve V-8. Cast iron block and head. Displacement: 267 cu. in. (4.4 liters). Bore & stroke: 3.50 x 3.48 in. Compression ratio: 8.3:1. Brake horsepower: 120 at 3600 R.P.M. Torque: 215 lbs.-ft. at 2000 R.P.M. Five main bearings. Hydraulic valve lifters. Carburetor: 2Bbl. Rochester M2ME. VIN Code: J. OPTIONAL V-8 (Camaro, Malibu, Monte Carlo, Impala, Caprice): 90-degree, overhead valve V-8. Cast iron block and head. Displacement: 305 cu. in. (5.0 liters). Bore & stroke: 3.74 x 3.48 in. Compression ratio: 8.6:1. Brake horsepower: 155 at 4000 R.P.M. Torque: 240 lbs.-ft. at 1600 R.P.M. Five main bearings. Hydraulic valve lifters. Carburetor: 4Bbl. Rochester M4ME. VIN Code: H. BASE V-8 (Camaro Z28): 90-degree, overhead valve V-8. Cast iron block and head. Displacement: 350 cu. in. (5.7 liters). Bore & stroke: 4.00 x 3.48 in. Compression ratio: 8.2:1. Brake horsepower: 190 at 4200 R.P.M. Torque: 280 lbs.-ft. at 2400 R.P.M. Five main bearings. Hydraulic valve lifters. Carburetor: 4Bbl. Rochester M4ME. VIN Code: L. DIESEL V-8; OPTIONAL (Impala/Caprice wagon): 90-degree, overhead valve V-8. Cast iron block and head. Displacement: 350 cu. in. (5.7 liters). Bore & stroke: 4.06 x 3.39 in. Compression ratio: 22.5:1. Brake horsepower: 105 at 3200 R.P.M. Torque: 205 lbs.-ft. at 1600 R.P.M. Five main bearings. Hydraulic valve lifters. Fuel injection. VIN Code: N.

CHASSIS DATA: Wheelbase: (Chevette 2-dr) 94.3 in.; (Chvt 4-dr.) 97.3 in.; (Monza 97.0 in.; (Citation) 104.9 in.; (Camaro) 108.0 in.; (Malibu/Monte) 108.1 in.; (Capr/Imp) 116.0 in. Overall length: (Chvt 2-dr.) 161.9 in; (Chvt 4-dr.) 164.9 in.; (Monza) 179.9 in.; (Cit) 176.7 in.: (Camaro) 197.6 in.; (Malibu) 197.7 in.; (Malibu wag) 193.4 in.; (Monte) 200.4 in.; (Capr/Imp) 212.1 in.; (Capr/Imp wag) 215.1 in. Height: (Chvt) 52.3 in.; (Monza cpe) 50.1 in.; (Monza hatch 50.2 in.; (Cit) 53.1 in.; (Camaro) 49.2 in.; (Malibu cpe) 53.3 in.; (Malibu sed) 54.2 in.; (Malibu wag) 54.5 in.; (Monte) 53.9 in.; (Capr/Imp cpe) 53.3 in.; (Capr/Imp sed) 55.9 in.; (Capr/Imp wag) 57.7 in. Width: (Chvt) 61.8 in.; (Monza) 65.4 in.; (Cit) 68.3 in.; (Camaro) 74.5 in.; (Malibu/Monte) 71.5 in.; (Malibu wag) 71.2 in.; (Capr/Imp) 75.3 in.; (Capr/Imp wag) 79.3 in. Front Tread: (Chvt) 51.2 in.; (Monza) 54.8 in.; (Cit) 58.7 in.; (Camaro) 61.3 in.; (Berlinetta) 61.6 in.; (Malibu/Monte) 58.5 in.; (Capr/Imp) 61.8 in.; (Capr/Imp wag) 62.2 in. Rear Tread: (Chvt) 51.2 in.; (Monza) 53.6 in.; (Cit) 57.0 in.; (Camaro) 60.0 in.; (Berlinetta) 60.3 in.; (Malibu/Monte) 57.8 in.; (Capr/Imp) 60.8 in.; (Capr/Imp wag) 64.1 in. Standard Tires: (Chvt) P155/80R13 GBR; (Monza) A78 x 13; (Cit) P185/80R13 GBR; (Camaro) P205/75R14 SBR; (Malibu) P185/75R14/B GBR; (Malibu wag) P195/75R14/B GBR; (Imp/Caprice) P205/75R15/B SBR; (Imp/Capr wag) P225/75R15/B SBR; (Monte) P205/70R14/B SBR.

TECHNICAL: Transmission: Three-speed manual transmission standard on Camaro and Malibu V-6. Gear ratios: (1st) 3.50:1; (2nd) 1.89:1; (3rd) 1.00:1; (Rev) 3.62:1. Four-speed floor shift standard on Chevette: (1st) 3.75:1; (2nd) 2.16:1; (3rd) 1.38:1; (4th) 1.00:1; (Rev) 3.82:1. Four-speed floor shift standard on Monza: (1st) 3.50:1; (2nd) 2.48:1; (3rd) 1.66:1; (4th) 1.00:1; (Rev) 3.50:1. Citation four-speed floor shift: (1st) 3.53:1; (2nd) 1.96:1; (3rd) 1.24:1; (4th) 0.81:1; (Rev) 3.42:1. Four-speed floor shift optional on Camaro/Malibu V8305: (1st) 2.85:1; (2nd) 2.02:1; (3rd) 1.35:1; (4th) 1.00:1; (Rev) 2.85:1. Four-speed on Camaro V8350: (1st) 3.42:1; (2nd) 2.28:1; (3rd) 1.45:1; (4th) 1.00:1; (Rev) 3.51:1. Three-speed Turbo Hydra-matic standard on Monte Carlo and Caprice/Impala, optional on others. Automatic gear ratios: (1st) 2.52:1; (2nd) 1.52:1; (3rd) 1.00:1; (Rev) 1.93:1 except Caprice/Impala V6/V8267, Monza four, Malibu V-6 and Monte ratios: (1st) 2.74:1; (2nd) 1.57:1; (3rd) 1.00:1; (Rev) 2.07:1. Chevette automatic trans.: (1st) 2.40:1; (2nd) 1.48:1; (3rd) 1.00:1; (Rev) 1.92:1. Citation auto. trans.: (1st) 2.84:1; (2nd) 1.60:1; (3rd) 1.00:1; (Rev) 2.07:1. Standard final drive ratio: (Chevette) 3.70:1; (Monza four) 2.73:1; (Monza V-6) 2.93:1; (Citation) 3.34:1; (Camaro V-6) 2.73:1; (Camaro V-8) 2.56:1; (Malibu V-6) 2.73:1; (Malibu V8) 2.29:1; (Malibu V-8 wag) 2.41:1; (Monte V-6) 2.41:1; (Monte V-8) 2.29:1; (Caprice/Imp V-6) 2.73 :1; (Caprice/Imp V-8) 2.41:1; (Caprice/Imp wag) 2.56:1. Steering: (Chevette/Citation) rack and pinion; (others) recirculating ball. Front Suspension: (Citation) MacPherson struts and coil springs; (others) control arms, coil springs and stabilizer bar. Rear Suspension: (Corvette) rigid axle, torque tube, longitudinal trailing radius arms, transverse linkage bar, coil springs and stablilizer bar; (Citation) rigid axle, trailing arm, control arms and stabliizer arm (Camaro) rigid axle, semi-elliptic leaf springs and stablizer bar; (others) rigid axle, lower trailing radius arms, upper oblique torque arms and coil springs, plus stablizer bar on Monte and full-size. Brakes: front disc rear drum. Body construction: (Chevette / Citation) unibody (Camaro) unibody with separate partial box frame; (others) separate body and perimeter box frame. Fuel tank: (Chvt) 12.5 gal.; (Monza) 18.5 gal.; (Citation) 14 gal.; (Camaro) 21 gal.; (Malibu/Monte) 18.1 gal.; (Malibu wag) 18.2 gal.; (Capr/Imp) 25 gal.; (Capr/Imp wag) 22 gal.

1980 Malibu Estate 4-dr station wagon

DRIVETRAIN OPTIONS: Engines: 1.6-liter H.O. four: Chevette ($60). 173 cu. in., 2Bbl. V-6: Citation ($225). 231 cu. in., 2Bbl. V-6: Monza ($225). Turbo 231 cu. in., 4Bbl. V-6: Monte ($500). 267 cu. in., 2Bbl. V-8: Camaro/Malibu/Monte/Imp/Caprice ($180). 305 cu. in., 4Bbl. V-8: Camaro/Malibu/Monte/Imp/Capr ($295); Imp/Capr wag ($115); Z28 ($50 credit). Diesel 350 cu. in. V-8: Imp/Capr wag ($915). Transmission/Differential: Four-speed manual shift: Camaro ($144); Malibu (N/A). Turbo Hydra-matic: Chvt/Monza ($320); Citation ($337); Camaro/Malibu ($358); Camaro Z28 ($63). Sport shifter: Chvt ($32). Limited-slip differential: Monza ($64); Camaro ($68); Malibu/Monte ($69); Imp/Capr ($73). Performance axle ratio: Monza ($18); Camaro/Malibu/Monte ($19); Imp/Capr ($20). Power Accessories: Power brakes: Chvt/Monza/Citation ($76); Camaro ($81). Power steering: Monza ($158); Citation/Malibu ($174). Suspension: F40 H.D. susp.: Citation ($21); Monte ($24). F40 H.D. shock absorbers: Imp/Capr ($25). F41 sport susp.: Chvt ($35); Monza ($33); Citation ($27); Camaro ($41); Imp/Capr cpe/sed ($45). Inflatable rear shock absorbers: Imp/Capr ($59). Front-stabilizer bar: Monza ($29). Other: Heavy-duty radiator: Monza ($33). H.D. cooling: Chvt ($31-$58); Cit ($32-$59); Camaro/Malibu/Monte ($36-$63) Imp/Capr ($37-$64). Engine block heater: Imp/Capr wag ($16). H.D. alternator (63-amp): Malibu ($6-$35). H.D. alternator (70-amp): Cit ($11-$43); Monte ($32-$67); Imp/Capr ($33-$68). H.D. battery ($20-$22) exc. diesel ($44). California emission system ($250) exc. diesel ($83).

CHEVETTE/MONZA CONVENIENCE/APPEARANCE OPTIONS: Option Packages: Spyder equipment pkg.: Monza ($521). Quiet sound group: Chvt ($38-$50); Monza ($32-$42). Comfort/Convenience: Air conditioning ($531). Rear defogger, electric ($95). Tinted glass: Chvt ($64). Comfortilt steering wheel ($73). Tachometer: Chvt ($67). Gauge pkg. (incl. tach): Monza ($71-$94). Electric clock ($23). Cigarette lighter: Scooter ($8). Intermittent wipers ($37). Lighting and Mirrors: Aux. lighting: Chvt ($40-$41); Monza ($21-$27). Twin sport mirrors, left remote ($43). Driver's remote sport mirror: Chvt ($27). Entertainment: AM radio: Scooter ($79). AM/FM radio: Chvt/Monza ($64); Scooter ($143). AM/FM stereo radio ($101). AM/FM stereo radio w/digital clock: Monza ($252). Stereo 8track tape player w/AM radio: Monza ($154). 8track player with AM/FM: Monza ($176). Cassette player with AM/FM stereo radio: Monza ($188). Rear speaker ($18). Radio delete: Monza ($52 credit). Exterior Trim: Removable sunroof: Monza ($193). Cabriolet vinyl roof: Monza ($165) incl. opera windows. Spoilers, front/rear: Monza ($124). Deluxe exterior (wheel opening, side window and rocker panel moldings): Chvt ($112-$119). Exterior decor pkg. (wheel opening and side window moldings, wheel covers, luggage carrier): Monza ($139-$154). Two-tone paint: Chvt ($110). Sport stripes ($75). Bodyside moldings: Scooter ($43). Wheel opening moldings: Monza ($22). Side window reveal moldings: Chvt ($70-$77). Door edge guards ($13-$20). Roof carrier: Chvt ($70). Interior Trim/Upholstery: Console: Monza cpe ($80). Cloth bucket seats: Chvt ($12-$23); Monza ($23). Custom Chevette interior pkg. w/bucket seats: cloth ($183); vinyl ($160). Custom vinyl bucket seats: Monza ($170) exc. Sport (NC). Custom cloth bucket seats: Monza ($193) exc. Sport ($23). Folding rear seat: Monza ($104) but std. on 2+2. Rear seat delete: Chvt ($54 credit). Color-keyed floor mats ($22). Automatic seat/shoulder belts: Chvt ($65). Wheels and Tires: Rally II wheels: Monza ($48-$94). Color- keyed deluxe wheel covers: Monza ($14-$46). Sport wheel covers: Chvt ($48). Wheel trim rings: Scooter ($40). P155/8013/B GBR WSW: Scooter ($43). P175/7013/B SBR BSW: Chvt ($53); Scooter ($95). P175/7013/B SBR WSW: Chvt ($95); Scooter ($137). P175/7013/B SBR WLT: Chvt ($109); Scooter ($152). B78 x 13/B WSW: Monza ($18). BR70 x 13/C SBR BSW: Monza ($154) exc. Sport ($116). BR70 x 13/C SBR WSW: Monza ($158-$196). BR70 x 13/C SBR WLT: Monza ($57-$211).

1980 Citation hatchback coupe (CP)

CITATION CONVENIENCE/APPEARANCE OPTIONS: Option Packages: X11 sport equipment pkg. ($501). Deluxe exterior pkg. ($102-$144). Quiet sound group ($52). Quiet sound/rear decor pkg. ($72). Comfort/Convenience: Air cond. ($564). Rear defogger, electric ($101). Cruise control ($105). Tinted glass ($70). Sport steering wheel (NC to $20). Comfortilt steering wheel ($75). Power windows ($133-$189). Power remote swing-out windows ($91). Power door locks ($87-$123). Gauge pkg. w/clock ($70). Special instruments incl. tachometer ($109). Electric clock ($25). Cigarette lighter: cpe ($8). Intermittent wipers ($39). Lighting, Horns and Mirrors: Aux. lighting ($41). Right door light switch: cpe ($8). Dual horns ($9). Driver's remote mirror ($18). Dual sport mirrors, left remote ($43). Entertainment: AM radio: cpe ($79). AM/FM radio: cpe ($143); others ($64). AM/FM stereo radio: cpe ($180); others ($101). 8track player with AM/FM stereo: cpe ($255); others ($176). Cassette player with AM/FM stereo: cpe ($267); others ($188). CB with AM/FM stereo: cpe ($492); others ($413). Rear speaker ($18). Dual front/rear speakers ($40). Windshield antenna ($25); incl. w/radios. Radio delete ($52 credit). Exterior Trim: Removable sunroof ($240). Two-tone paint ($148) incl. pinstriping and bodyside moldings. Bodyside pinstriping ($32). Bodyside moldings ($43-$47). Bright rocker panel moldings: cpe ($20). Wheel opening moldings: cpe ($43). Door edge guards ($13-$20). Side window reveal moldings ($41- $65). Roof carrier ($86). Bumper guards ($45). Bumper rub strips ($40). Interior Trim/Upholstery: Console ($80). Reclining passenger seatback ($42-$70). Sport cloth bench seat ($23). Custom knit cloth bench seat ($189-$239). Custom vinyl bench seat ($166- $216). Custom bucket seats: knit cloth ($278-$328); vinyl ($255-$305). Locking glove compartment ($8). Color-keyed mats ($25). Wheels and Tires: Full wheel covers ($43). Wire wheel covers ($113-$156). Wheel trim rings ($48). Rally wheel trim ($35- $78). P185/80R13/B GBR WSW ($45). P185/80R13/B SBR BSW ($49). P185/80R13/B SBR WSW ($93). P205/70R13/B SBR WSW ($182). P205/70R13/B SBR WLT ($196).

CAMARO/MALIBU/MONTE CARLO CONVENIENCE/APPEARANCE OPTIONS: Option Packages: Estate equipment: Malibu wag ($276). Interior decor/quiet sound group: Camaro ($68); std. on Berlinetta. Quiet sound group: Malibu ($55). Value appearance group: Monte ($120-$129). Security pkg.: Malibu wag ($40). Comfort/Convenience: Air cond.: Camaro ($566); Malibu/Monte ($601). Rear defogger (forced-air): Malibu cpe/sed ($59). Rear defogger, electric ($107). Cruise control ($112). Tinted glass: Camaro ($68); Malibu/Monte ($75). Comfortilt steering wheel ($81). Six-way power

1980 Monte Carlo Sport Coupe (CP)

driver's seat: Malibu/Monte ($175). Power windows: Camaro/Monte ($143); Malibu ($143- $202). Power door locks: Malibu ($93-$132); Camaro/Monte ($93). Power trunk release: Monte ($26). Electric clock: base Camaro, Malibu ($25). Gauge pkg.: Monte ($41). Gauge pkg. w/tach: base Camaro ($120); Malibu ($134); Monte ($109). Gauge pkg. w/clock: Malibu ($66). Intermittent wipers ($41). Lighting, Horns and Mirrors: High-intensity high-beam headlamps: Monte ($26). Aux. lighting: Camaro ($33-$40); Malibu ($33-$60); Monte ($33). Dual horns: Camaro, base Malibu ($10). Remote-control driver's mirror: Malibu/Monte ($19). Twin sport mirrors (left remote): base Camaro, Malibu/Monte ($46). Twin remote sport mirrors: Malibu ($73); Monte ($48-$73). Visor vanity mirror: Monte ($6). Lighted visor mirror: Monte ($37-$43). Entertainment: AM radio ($97). AM/FM radio ($153). AM/FM stereo radio ($192). AM/FM stereo radio w/digital clock: Malibu ($353); Camaro ($328-$353). Stereo 8track tape player w/AM radio ($249). Stereo 8track tape player with AM/FM stereo radio ($272). Cassette player with AM/FM stereo radio ($285). AM/FM/CB radio ($473). AM/FM stereo radio w/CB ($525). Rear speaker ($20). Dual front speakers: Monte ($14). Dual front and rear speakers: Malibu/Monte ($43). Windshield antenna ($27); incl. w/radios. Power antenna ($51). Exterior Trim: Removable glass roof panels: Camaro/Monte ($695). Power sky roof: Monte ($561). Vinyl roof: Malibu ($124); Monte ($140). Rear spoiler: Camaro Berlinetta ($62). Style trim pkg.: Camaro ($78). Two-tone paint: Malibu ($72- $123); Monte ($148-$171). Bodyside moldings:

1980 Malibu Classic Landau Coupe (CP)

Camaro ($46). Deluxe bodyside moldings: Malibu/Monte ($57). Door edge guards ($14-$22). Bright sill moldings: Monte ($47). Wheel opening moldings: Malibu cpe/sed ($25). Side window sill moldings: Monte ($35). Side window reveal moldings: Malibu ($47). Roof drip moldings: Camaro ($26). Bodyside pinstriping: Malibu ($51); Monte ($42). Rear window air deflector: Malibu wag ($32). Roof carrier: Malibu wag ($96). Bumper rub strips: Malibu ($44). Bumper guards, front/rear: Malibu ($49). Interior Trim/Upholstery: Console: Malibu cpe/sed, Monte ($86). Vinyl bench seat: Malibu cpe/sed, Monte ($28). Cloth bench seat: Malibu wag ($244). Custom vinyl bench seat: Malibu wag ($64). Cloth 50/50 seating: Malibu ($184-$244). Vinyl 50/50 seating: Malibu ($212-$244). Vinyl bucket seats: Malibu cpe/sed, Monte ($91). Cloth bucket seats: Camaro ($25); Malibu cpe/sed, Monte ($91). Custom vinyl bucket seats: base Camaro ($328). Custom cloth bucket seats: Berlinetta ($25); base Camaro ($353). Monte custom 55/45 seating: cloth ($366); vinyl ($394). Adj. driver's seatback: Camaro ($25). Litter container: Monte ($9). Color-keyed mats: Camaro/Malibu/Monte ($25). Deluxe load-floor carpet: Malibu wag ($75). Deluxe trunk trim: Monte ($46). Wheels and Tires: Aluminum wheels: Camaro ($184-$337). Custom styled wheels: Camaro ($107-$153). Rally wheels: Camaro ($100); Malibu ($50-$96); Monte ($50); Malibu Classic Landau (NC). Full wheel covers: Camaro/Malibu ($46). Sport wheel covers (silver or gold): Malibu ($56-$102). Wire wheel covers: Malibu ($69-$171); Monte ($69-$125). P185/75R14/B GBR WSW: Malibu cpe/sed ($45). P195/75R14/B GBR WSW: Malibu wag ($48). P195/75R14/B SBR WSW: Malibu cpe/sed ($118); Malibu wag ($96). P205/75R14 SBR WSW: Camaro ($51-$65). P205/75R14 SBR WLT: Camaro ($15-$81). P205/70R14/B SBR WSW: Monte ($51); Malibu cpe/sed ($171). P205/70R14/B SBR WLT: Malibu cpe/sed ($185). Stowaway spare: Camaro (NC).

IMPALA/CAPRICE CONVENIENCE/APPEARANCE OPTIONS: Option Packages: Estate equipment: wag ($280). Value appearance group: Imp ($96). Comfort/Convenience: Four season air cond. ($647). Comfortron auto-temp air cond. ($738). Rear defogger, forced-air: cpe/sed ($61). Rear defogger, electric ($109). Cruise control ($118). Tinted glass ($90). Comfortilt steering wheel ($83). Power door locks ($95-$135). Six-way power driver's seat ($179). Power windows ($149-$221). Power trunk release ($27). Power tailgate lock: wag ($43). Electric clock: Imp ($26). Digital clock: Imp ($59); Caprice ($33). Gauge pkg. ($58). Intermittent wipers ($42). Quiet sound group: Imp ($60). Lighting, Horns and Mirrors: High-intensity high-beam headlamps ($27). Cornering lamps ($50). Aux. lighting ($37- $54). Dual horns: Imp ($11). Driver's remote mirror ($20). Dual remote mirrors ($60). Dual sport mirrors, left remote ($47). Dual remote body-color sport mirrors ($27-$74). Visor vanity mirror ($7). Lighted visor mirror ($44). Entertainment: AM radio ($99). AM/FM radio ($156). AM/FM stereo radio ($195); w/digital clock ($358-$384). Stereo 8track tape player with AM radio ($253); with AM/FM stereo radio ($276). Cassette player with AM/FM stereo ($289). AM/FM/CB radio and power antenna ($480). AM/FM stereo with CB and power antenna ($533). Rear speaker ($21). Dual front/rear speakers ($44). Power antenna ($52). Windshield antenna ($28); incl. w/radios. Exterior Trim: Power sky roof ($670). Vinyl roof: cpe/sed ($155). Roof carrier: wag ($123). Two-tone paint ($60). Custom two-tone ($128). Pinstriping ($35). Bodyside moldings ($48). Door edge guards ($15-$22). Wheel opening moldings: Imp ($25). Bumper rub strips, front/rear ($60). Bumper guards ($56). Interior Trim/Upholstery: Vinyl bench seat: cpe/sed ($29). Cloth 50/50 seat ($229-$276). Vinyl 50/50 seat ($247-$276). Custom cloth 50/50 seat: cpe ($412); sed ($437). Deluxe load- floor carpet: wag ($80). Deluxe cargo area carpet: wag ($114). Color-keyed mats: front ($15); rear ($11). Litter container ($9). Deluxe trunk trim ($49). Wheel Covers: Full wheel covers ($47). Sport covers: Imp ($105); Caprice ($58). Custom covers: Imp ($125); Caprice ($78). Wire covers: Caprice ($128). Coupe/Sedan Tires: P205/75R15 SBR WSW ($51). P215/75R15 SBR WSW ($82). P225/70R15 SBR WSW ($124). Wagon Tires: P225/75R15/B SBR WSW ($55). Puncture-sealant tires ($85).

HISTORY: Introduced: Oct. 11, 1979 except Citation, April 19, 1979 and Corvette, Oct. 25, 1979. Model year production (U.S.): 2,017,054 (incl. Corvettes and early 1980 Citations, but not incl. 19,631 Acadians). Calendar year production: 1,737,336 (including 44,190 Corvettes and 18,958 Acadians). Calendar year sales by U.S. dealers: 1,747,534 for a 26.6 percent market share. Model year sales by U.S. dealers: 1,831,953 (incl. 37,471 Corvettes, but not incl. 273,720 early 1980 Citations).

Historical Footnotes: While auto sales fell overall this year, Chevrolet remained GM's top seller (hardly a surprise). Model year sales dropped 20 percent, however. Chevette sales went up a bit, but other models declined. Camaro fell by nearly 44 percent, Monte and full-size models by about 40 percent. Full-size Chevrolet production fell by a whopping 66.3 percent. Only Chevette fared notably better than in 1979. The decline in full-size sales caused production to halt at South Gate, California and St. Louis plants. Only the Janesville, Wisconsin facility continued to build full-size models. South Gate would be the site for production of the 1982 J-cars. Monzas, which still sold fairly well, continued to roll out of the plant at Lordstown, Ohio. Although Citation would soon be plagued by complaints and recalls, it was popular from the start. Chevrolet hoped the new front-drive would appeal to "a whole new generation of car buyers with values and attitudes far different from their parents and even their older brothers and sisters," declared General Manager Robert Lund. Those "new values" buyers for whom a car was "a functional part of their lives" would soon "revolutionize the marketplace." Citation had first been conceived in 1974, when fuel economy was uppermost in engineers' minds. Instead of being evolutionary, as was nearly always the case in earlier periods, it was designed from the ground up. The Chevrolet 60-degree V-6 engine built for Citation at Tonawanda, New York was also distributed to the other GM division builders of X-bodied vehicles.

1981 CHEVROLET

Monza left the lineup this year, but the vacancy would soon be filled by the new (1982) front-drive Cavalier. Opening prices for 1981 were even higher compared to 1980 than 1980 was to '79—up by as much as $1500. Monte Carlo got an aerodynamic restyle, while other models changed their front-end look. For the first time, a four-speed overdrive automatic transmission was installed on full-size Chevrolets with the 5.0-liter V-8. All GM automatic transmissions now had the lockup torque converter that had been introduced on some 1980 models. It offered a direct flywheel-to-driveshaft connection in one or two gears. All gas-engine models had GM's new Computer Command Control that adjusted the air/fuel mixture and spark timing to compensate for driving conditions, altitude, temperature and barometric pressure. It also included self-diagnostic features.

1981 Chevette hatchback sedan (AA)

CHEVETTE — SERIES 1T — FOUR — Immodestly billed as "America's most popular subcompact," Chevette wore a new contemporary flush-mounted windshield with black outline molding. Also new: sporty argent-finish styled steel wheels and a bright-accented black grille. Standard powerplant was again the 98 cu. in. (1.6- liter) four, now with Computer Command Control to monitor the engine and reduce emissions. All models except the low-budget Scooter had a sport shifter in the floor console. Standard coupes had swing-out rear quarter windows, but Scooter's were fixed. A Rally trim option was available. For the first time, power steering was available with automatic transmission and air conditioning a lot of work for that little 1.6 engine to perform. Halogen headlamps and a rear wiper/washer were new options. Body colors were beige, black, red, white, bright yellow, and nine metalliics: medium or light brown, champagne, silver, light or dark blue, maroon, dark green, or burnt orange. The custom interior included high contoured bucket seats up front, upholstered in cloth or vinyl. Standard equipment included the 1.6-liter engine, four- speed manual transmission, maintenance-free battery, energy- absorbing bumpers, front stabilizer bar, diagnostic connector, two-speed wipers, bumper guards and rub strips, day/night mirror, mini-console, vinyl interior, dome light, and P155/8013 fiberglass-belted whitewall tires. Scooter had blackwall tires and lacked various pieces of equipment standard on other models: an AM radio, bodyside moldings, color-keyed seat/shoulder belts, color-keyed instrument panel, sport steering wheel, lighter, and reclining front bucket seats.

CITATION — SERIES 1X — FOUR/V-6 — Named *Motor Trend* "Car of the Year" for 1980, Citation was described (ironically, in view of imminent recalls and troubles) as the "most successful new car ever introduced." Following its huge introductory fanfare as an early 1980 model, Citation changed little for its second full year. The notchback coupe was dropped, so only hatchbacks remained: two-door or four-door. Citation had a 'Chevrolet' nameplate on the decklid, and 'Citation' nameplate at forward end of front fenders. Styling features included a body-color front valance panel, bright hood and windshield moldings, bright bumpers with body-color end caps, wide rocker panel moldings, and pinstriping on decklid and quarter panels. The new bright chrome grille was arranged in a looser 8 x 4 hole pattern, with bowtie emblem in the center. Below was a new slotted air dam. Body colors this year were beige, black, red, white, and bright yellow; plus metallic light or dark blue, light or medium brown, champagne, dark green, maroon, burnt orange, or silver. Cloth or vinyl interiors came in beige, black, dark blue, camel or maroon (vinyl also in champagne). Engine choices again were the base 151 cu. in. (2.5- liter) four or 60-degree 173 cu. in. (2.8-liter) V-6, both with new Computer Command Control. The V-6 also added Electric Early Fuel Evaporation to

1981 Citation hatchback sedan (AA)

improve emissions, by supplying electric current to a heater grid in the carburetor bore for better cold starts and warmup. (1980 carburetor bases were heated by exhaust.) Engines also had a new Electronic Spark Timing system (ESC), plus a new Freedom II battery. Citation tires now took 30 psi air pressure. Engines offered improved service accessibility. A revised X11 package, which was mostly for looks in 1980, now included a high-output (135 horsepower) version of the V-6 engine. Chevrolet claimed that the X11 Citation package "gives you goose bumps." Carrying a Z09 RPO code and $1498 price tag, it included (for starters) a rear spoiler, body-color bumpers with black rub strips, tachometer, 'X11' decal on doors and rear spoiler, power brakes, and P215/60R14 steel- belted radials on 14 x 6.5 inch aluminum alloy wheels. A special lightweight fiberglass-reinforced, sheet-molded compound hood had a molded-in air inlet and 'High Output 660' emblem to show that the performance V-6 was underneath. Aero drag rated only 0.4. The X11 package also included low-drag, semi-metallic brake linings; a dual-snorkel air cleaner; quick-ratio rack-and-pinion steering; sport steeering wheel; special instruments; twin sport mirrors; and larger-diameter exhaust with dual tailpipes. The high-output V-6 had bigger valves, revised valve timing with higher lift and longer duration for better high-end volumetric efficiency, and an aluminum intake manifold. It produced 135 horsepower at 5400 R.P.M., and 145 lbs.-ft. of torque at 2400. The F41 sport suspension included larger-diameter stabilizer bars, higher- rate springs and firmer bushings, plus a numerically higher axle ratio. X11 also had black window moldings, headlamp bezels, and pillar louvers; black-accented grille and rocker panel moldings; and bucket seats. Also joining the option list were halogen headlamps and an automatic speed control with new "resume" feature, plus a reclining driver's seat backrest. Bucket seats could now be ordered with the standard interior. Citation's standard equipment included four-speed manual transmission, front stabilizer bar, P185/80R13 glass-belted radial tires on styled steel wheels, compact spare tire, two-speed wipers, bright roof drip moldings, pushbutton AM radio, day/night mirror, color-keyed steering wheel and seat/shoulder belts, and cut-pile carpeting.

1981 Camaro Berlinetta Sport Coupe (CP)

CAMARO — SERIES 1F — V-6/V-8 — Rally Sport left the Camaro lineup this year, leaving only the base Sport Coupe, Berlinetta, and performance Z28. Not much changed, beyond the new Computer Command Control on all engines. Power brakes, formerly standard only on the Z28, were now universal. All Camaros got a space-saving compact spare tire (formerly an option) and lighter weight Freedom II battery, plus new low-drag front disc brakes. Optional automatic transmissions added a lockup torque converter clutch in third gear. The Z28's torque converter clutch was computer-controlled in both second and third gears. The basic Camaro coupe had an argent grille split (as before) into upper and lower sections, plus wraparound taillamps. Berlinetta's grille was bright-accented argent. Berlinetta came with a standard Quiet Sound Group including inner roof layer of sound-absorbing materials and inside roof covering of soft foam-backed headlining. Special paint and striping emphasized its "sculptured lines." Stripes came in silver, black, blue, beige, gold or red. Berlinetta identification was on the grille header panel, side pillars, and deck lid. Body sills were black (bright on the basic sport coupe). Base engine for both the standard sport coupe and posher Berlinetta remained the 229 cu. in. (3.8-liter) V-6 with three-speed manual transmission. Both 267 cu. in. (4.4-liter) and 305 cu. in. (5.0-liter) V-8s were optional, but required either four-speed or automatic. Z28 had a standard four- barrel 305 V-8 engine, with new wide-ratio four-speed manual transmission (optional on others). That gearbox's 3.42:1 low- gear ratio delivered both economy and low-end performance, hooked to 3.42:1 axle ratio. Z28 Camaros could also get a 350 cu. in. (5.7-liter) V-8 at no charge, but with automatic only. Even California Camaro fans could now get the 5.7-liter V-8 in their Z28s again. Camaro Z28 included a front air dam, front fender flares and air louvers, hood scoop with decal, rear spoiler, P225/70R15 raised white-letter tires on body-color 15 x 7 in. sport wheels, and contour bucket seats. Z28's distinctive grille was body-colored with horizontal bars. There was 'Z28' identification on the driver's side of the grille, and a decal on doors. Other Z28 features included black headlamp/taillamp bezels, rear end panel, license plate opening, parking light bezels, sill moldings, window and windshield moldings; plus tri-tone striping on the rear spoiler and lower bodyside, as well as on front air dam and fender flares. Front and rear bumper covers were body-color urethane. Z28's solenoid-activated hood air intake actually drew in air. So did its fender air scoops. Seven Z28 striping colors were available: silver, charcoal, blue, dark gold, gold, red and orange. Base Camaro sport coupes had the 229 V-6, three-speed manual transmission, power steering and brakes, P205/75R14 steel-belted radial tires, front stabilizer bar, multi-leaf rear springs, concealed two-speed wipers, front bucket seats with console, dome light, four-spoke sport steering wheel, day/night mirror, and body-colored bumpers. Berlinetta added whitewall tires and wire wheel covers, a gauge package (including tachometer), dual horns, sport mirrors (left-hand remote), and electric clock; plus moldings for door pillar, upper fender, hood panel, belt and roof drip. Z28 also included heavy-duty cooling, clock, gauge package, and sport mirrors. Standard colors were black, red, white, and bright yellow; plus metallic bright blue, light or dark blue, dark brown, charcoal, gold, maroon, orange or silver. Cloth or vinyl interiors came in beige, black, dark blue, camel, red or silver. Halogen headlamps were a new option. Camaro's basic body dated back to 1970, but downsizing would come for 1982.

1981 Malibu Classic sedan (AA)

MALIBU — SERIES 1A — V-6/V-8 — Although the mid-size Malibu didn't change drastically this year, it got several appearance alterations. The four- door sedan (now marketed as a "sport sedan") got a dramatically restyled, squarish formal roofline and back window section. (The profile looked similar to that of the 1980 Buick Century.) The new grille with prominent horizontal bars had bright upper and lower moldings that extended the full width of the front end. Malibu also had new headlamp bezels, triple-unit taillamps, and side marker lenses. Argent taillamp bezels had black accents. Full wheel covers were restyled, while the revised dash had a new glossy-black applique. Also new: high-pressure easy-roll tires, Delco maintenance-free Freedom II battery, and a jack that lifted the car from the side. Front ends held single rectangular headlamps. 'Chevrolet' nameplates were on the lower part of the grille (driver's side), as well as on the decklid (passenger side). 'Malibu' nameplates adorned the rear of quarter panels. Classic Landau coupes had a 'Landau' emblem on the 'B' pillar. Malibus had an ornament with Chevrolet crest. Malibu Classic had a stand-up hood ornament and front door pull straps. Body colors were beige, black, cream and white; plus metallic light or dark blue, light or medium brown, jade green, light jade green, maroon, light maroon, silver, or champagne. Cloth and vinyl interiors came in camel, champagne, dark blue, jade or maroon; custom interiors could also have beige. Power steering was now standard. As before, Malibu came in coupe, sedan or station wagon form, plus a Landau coupe. Halogen headlamps were now optional. Standard engine again was the 229 cu. in. (3.8-liter) V-6, with three-speed manual or optional automatic transmission. Both optional V-8s (267 and 305 cu. in.) came only with automatic. The bigger one was available only in wagons (and in California Malibus). Basic Malibu equipment included power brakes, compact spare tire, front stabilizer bar, concealed two-speed wipers, day/night mirror, and locking glove compartment. Malibu Classic models had dual horns and side window reveal moldings (except coupe). The Malibu Classic Landau coupe added a vinyl roof and body pinstriping, plus silver wheel covers. Wagons had wheel opening moldings. Cloth upholstery was standard except for wagons, which used vinyl.

1981 Monte Carlo Sport Coupe

MONTE CARLO — SERIES 1A — V-6/V-8 — Monte's A-Special body got a major aerodynamic restyle this year, including a lowered hood and slightly higher rear deck. The new "subtle wedge shape" was claimed to cut wind drag by 10 percent. High-pressure radial tires helped boost gas mileage. The standard automatic transmission had a torque converter clutch controlled by the CCC system, for lockup in third gear. High-pressure (35 psi) tires cut rolling resistance. Also new: Freedom II battery and side-lift frame jack. Coil springs were computer selected to match a specific car's weight and equipment (but softer to compensate for the higher-pressure tires). New cast aluminum wheels were available. Wide rectangular parking lamps moved to the outer ends of the bumper, well below the quad rectangular headlamps and in line with the license plate. Body-color front/rear bumpers blended into fender sides. Wide lower bodyside moldings ran the full car length. Side marker lamps were recessed into lower moldings (front and rear). Cornering lamps were optional this year. A 'Monte Carlo' nameplate was on the front of the front fender. The crosshatch grille with bright chrome bars was arranged in a 6 x 3 pattern of large holes. 'Monte Carlo' script was on the 'B' pillar (or 'Landau' nameplate and crest for Landau coupes). Monte body colors were the same as Malibu. As before, base engine was the 229 cu. in. (3.8-liter) V-6, with optional turbocharged 231 cu. in. V-6 or a 267 cu. in. (4.4-liter) V-8. The 305 V-8 was now sold only in California. Standard equipment was similar to 1980, including automatic transmission, power steering and brakes, P195/75R14 steel-belted radial tires, compact spare tire, dual horns, concealed two-speed wipers, electric clock, locking glove compartment, body-color bumpers, and lighter. Also standard: wide lower bodyside, roof drip, rear quarter window and wheel opening moldings. Monte's Landau coupe added a vinyl roof, dual sport mirrors (driver's remote-controlled), a passenger visor mirror, side window sill moldings, 55/45 front seat, and body pinstriping.

1981 Impala Sport Coupe (CP)

IMPALA/CAPRICE CLASSIC — SERIES 1B — V-6/V-8 — Impala's three-section argent-finished grille this year had strong horizontal bars and recessed vertical divider bars, forming large holes in an 8 x 3 pattern, with bowtie emblem in the center. Parking/turn signal lights were in the bumper. At the rear were three-unit bright-accented taillamps, plus 'Chevrolet' nameplate on deck lid. An 'Impala' nameplate stood on the pillar behind the rear door. Caprice had a plain crosshatch grille this year, plus new side marker lamps, header moldings and headlamp bezels. Otherwise, the two looked much the same, though Caprice differed from Impala also in interior trim and option choices. Priced higher, however, Caprice (according to Chevrolet) "speaks of success. But not of excess." Both had tri-section taillamps, but Caprice's were bigger and added narrow vertical backup lamps alongside the license plate. Impala's small square backup lenses sat in each center taillamp section.

1981 Caprice Classic Landau Coupe (CP)

Fourteen solid body colors were offered: beige, black, cream and white, plus 10 metallics (light and dark blue, light and medium brown, champagne, light jade green, jade green, light maroon, maroon, and silver). Nine two-tone combinations and seven vinyl top colors were available. Cloth interior colors were beige, dark blue, camel, champagne, jade and maroon. Vinyl came in all except beige. Caprice offered "richly elegant" velour upholstery. Full-size models with an optional 305 cu. in. (5.0- liter) V-8 got the new four-speed overdrive automatic transmission this year. The three-speed automatic continued with V-6 powerplants: standard 229 cu. in. (3.8-liter) in coupes and sedans. Wagons carried a standard 267 cu. in. (4.4-liter) V-8. Both transmissions had a computer-controlled torque converter clutch, which substituted a mechanical link for the customary fluid coupling in both third and fourth gears. A 350 cu. in. (5.7-liter) Oldsmobile diesel was offered again in wagons. Other changes included an easy-to-check plastic master cylinder reservoir, reduced-drag front disc brakes, Freedom II battery, new side-lift frame jack, and a "resume speed memory" for the optional cruise control. Corrosion protection at the underbody and fenders was improved, including durable Elpo dip plus frame assemblies immersed in hot-melt wax. A new compact spare was mounted on a 16 in. wheel. Easy-roll tires were standard, puncture-sealant tires available. Both Impala and Caprice had standard 229 V-6 engine (267 V-8 in wagons) and automatic transmission, plus power brakes and steering, concealed two-speed wipers, color-keyed steering wheel and carpeting, day/night mirror, and locking glove compartment. Impala lacked standard dual horns, an electric clock, wheel opening moldings, stand-up hood ornament, and quiet sound group. The Caprice Classic Landau coupe had wire wheel covers, a vinyl roof, body pinstriping, and dual sport mirrors (driver's remote-controlled). Wagons had vinyl upholstery; sedans and coupes cloth.

I.D. DATA: Chevrolet, like all GM passenger cars, got a new 17- symbol Vehicle Identification Number (VIN) this year. As before, it was on the upper left surface of the instrument panel, visible through the windshield. The first symbol indicates country ('1', U.S.A.; '2' Canada). The second symbol denotes manufacturer ('G' General Motors). Symbol three indicates car make ('1' Chevrolet; '7' GM of Canada. Symbol four is restraint system ('A' non-passive; 'B' automatic belts; 'C' inflatable restraint). Symbol five is the car line/series: 'B' Chevette; 'J' Chevette Scooter; 'X' Citation; 'P' Camaro; 'S' Camaro Berlinetta; 'T' Malibu; 'W' Malibu Classic; 'Z' Monte Carlo; 'L' Impala; 'N' Caprice Classic. Symbols six and seven indicate body type: '08' 2-dr. hatchback coupe; '27' 2-dr. notchback coupe; '37' 2-dr. hardtop coupe; '47' 2-dr. hardtop coupe; '87' 2-dr. sport coupe; '68' 4-dr. hatchback sedan; '69' 4-dr. notchback sedan; '35' 4-dr. station wagon. Symbol eight is the engine code: '9' L4-98 2Bbl.; '5' L4-151 2Bbl.; 'X' V6173 2Bbl.; 'Z' V6173 H.O.; 'K' V6229 2Bbl.; 'A' V6231 2Bbl.; '3' Turbo V6231 4Bbl.; 'J' V8267 2Bbl.; 'H' V8305 4Bbl.; 'L' V8350 4Bbl.; 'N' Diesel V8350. Next comes a check digit. Symbol ten indicates model year ('B' 1981). Symbol eleven is assembly plant: 'A' Lakewood; 'B' Baltimore; 'D' Doraville, GA; 'J' Janesville, WI; 'K' Leeds, MO; 'L' Van Nuys, CA; 'N' Norwood, OH; 'R' Arlington, TX; 'S' St. Louis; 'T' Tarrytown, NY; 'W' Willow Run, MI; 'Y' Wilmington, DE; 'Z' Fremont, CA; '1' Oshawa, Ontario; '6' Oklahoma City. The final six digits make up the sequential serial number for output from each assembly plant. Body Number Plates and engine identification code locations were simlar to 1980.

CHEVETTE (FOUR)

Model Number	Body/Style Number	Body Type & Seating	Factory Price	Shipping Weight	Production Total
1T	B08	2-dr. Hatch Cpe-4P	5255	2000	114,621
1T	B68	4-dr. Hatch Sed-4P	5394	2063	250,616

CHEVETTE SCOOTER (FOUR)

Model Number	Body/Style Number	Body Type & Seating	Factory Price	Shipping Weight	Production Total
1T	J08	2-dr. Hatch Cpe-4P	4695	1945	55,211

CITATION (FOUR/V-6)

Model Number	Body/Style Number	Body Type & Seating	Factory Price	Shipping Weight	Production Total
1X	X08	2-dr. Hatch Cpe-5P	6270/6395	2404/2459	113,983
1X	X68	4-dr. Hatch Sed-5P	6404/6529	2432/2487	299,396

CAMARO (V-6/V-8)

Model Number	Body/Style Number	Body Type & Seating	Factory Price	Shipping Weight	Production Total
1F	P87	2-dr. Spt Cpe-4P	6780/6830	3222/3392	62,614

CAMARO BERLINETTA (V-6/V-8)

Model Number	Body/Style Number	Body Type & Seating	Factory Price	Shipping Weight	Production Total
1F	S87	2-dr. Spt Cpe-4P	7576/7626	3275/3445	20,253

CAMARO Z28 (V-8)

Model Number	Body/Style Number	Body Type & Seating	Factory Price	Shipping Weight	Production Total
1F	P87	2-dr. Spt Cpe-4P	-- /8263	N/A	43,272

MALIBU (V-6/V-8)

Model Number	Body/Style Number	Body Type & Seating	Factory Price	Shipping Weight	Production Total
1A	T27	2-dr. Spt Cpe-6P	6498/6548	3037/3199	15,834
1A	T69	4-dr. Sed-6P	6614/6664	3028/3194	60,643
1A	T35	4-dr. Sta Wag-6P	6792/6842	3201/3369	29,387

MALIBU CLASSIC (V-6/V-8)

Model Number	Body/Style Number	Body Type & Seating	Factory Price	Shipping Weight	Production Total
1A	W27	2-dr. Spt Cpe-6P	6828/6878	3065/3227	14,255
1A	W27/Z03	2-dr. Lan Cpe-6P	7092/7142	N/A	4,622
1A	W69	4-dr. Sed-6P	6961/7011	3059/3225	80,908
1A	W35	4-dr. Sta Wag-6P	7069/7119	3222/3390	36,798

1981 Monte Carlo Sport Coupe (CP)

MONTE CARLO (V-6/V-8)

Model Number	Body/Style Number	Body Type & Seating	Factory Price	Shipping Weight	Production Total
1A	Z37	2-dr. Spt Cpe-6P	7299/7349	3102/3228	149,659
1A	Z37/Z03	2-dr. Lan Cpe-6P	8006/8056	N/A	38,191

IMPALA (V-6/V-8)

Model Number	Body/Style Number	Body Type & Seating	Factory Price	Shipping Weight	Production Total
1B	L47	2-dr. Spt Cpe-6P	7129/7179	3326/3458	6,067
1B	L69	4-dr. Sedan-6P	7241/7291	3354/3486	60,090
1B	L35	4-dr. Sta Wag-6P	-- /7624	-- /3897	11,345
1B	L35/AQ4	4-dr. 3S Wag-8P	-- /7765	-- / N/A	8,462

CAPRICE CLASSIC (V-6/V-8)

Model Number	Body/Style Number	Body Type & Seating	Factory Price	Shipping Weight	Production Total
1B	N47	2-dr. Spt Cpe-6P	7534/7584	3363/3495	9,741
1B	N47/Z03	2-dr. Lan Cpe-6P	7990/8040	N/A	6,615
1B	N69	4-dr. Sedan-6P	7667/7717	3400/3532	89,573
1B	N35	4-dr. Sta Wag-6P	-- /7948	-- /3940	11,184
1B	N35/AQ4	4-dr. 3S Wag-8P	-- /8112	-- / N/A	16,348

FACTORY PRICE AND WEIGHT NOTE: Where two prices and weights are shown, the figure to the left of the slash is for six-cylinder model, to right of slash for V-8 (267 and 305 V-8 were each $50 extra). For Citation, prices and weights to left of slash are four-cylinder, to right for V-6 engine. All models had at least one price rise during the model year, except Chevette, which enjoyed a $100 price cut. **BODY/STYLE NO. NOTE:** Some models were actually option packages. Code after slash (e.g., Z03) is the number of the option package that comes with the model listed.

ENGINE DATA: BASE FOUR (Chevette): Inline. Overhead cam. Four-cylinder. Cast iron block and head. Displacement: 97.6 cu. in. (1.6 liters). Bore & stroke: 3.23 x 2.98 in. Compression ratio: 8.6:1. Brake horsepower: 70 at 5200 R.P.M. Torque: 82 lbs.-ft. at 2400 R.P.M. Five main bearings. Hydraulic valve lifters. Carburetor: 2Bbl. Holley 5210C. VIN Code: 9. BASE FOUR (Citation): Inline. Overhead valve. Four-cylinder. Cast iron block. Displacement: 151 cu. in. (2.5 liters). Bore & stroke: 4.00 x 3.00 in. Compression ratio: 8.2:1. Brake horsepower: 84 at 4000 R.P.M. Torque: 125 lbs.-ft. at 2400 R.P.M. Five main bearings. Hydraulic valve lifters. Carburetor: 2Bbl. Rochester 2SE. Pontiac-built. VIN Code: 5. OPTIONAL V-6 (Citation): 60-degree, overhead-valve V-6. Cast iron block and head. Displacement: 173 cu. in. (2.8 liters). Bore & stroke: 3.50 x 2.99 in. Compression ratio: 8.5:1. Brake horsepower: 110 at 4800 R.P.M. Torque: 145 lbs.-ft. at 2400 R.P.M. Four main bearings. Hydraulic valve lifters. Carburetor: 2Bbl. Rochester 2SE. VIN Code: X. HIGH-OUTPUT V-6 (Citation): Same as 173 cu. in. V-6 above except C.R.: 8.9:1. Brake H.P.: 135 at 5400 R.P.M. Torque: 145 lbs.-ft. at 2400 R.P.M. VIN Code: Z. BASE V-6 (Camaro, Malibu, Monte Carlo, Impala, Caprice): 90-degree, overhead-valve V-6. Cast iron block and head. Displacement: 229 cu. in. (3.8 liters). Bore & stroke: 3.74 x 3.48 in. Compression ratio: 8.6:1. Brake horsepower: 110 at 4200 R.P.M. Torque: 170 lbs.-ft. at 2000 R.P.M. Four main bearings. Hydraulic valve lifters. Carburetor: 2Bbl. Rochester 2ME. VIN Code: K. CALIFORNIA V-6 (for models above): 90-degree, overhead-valve V-6. Cast iron block and head. Displacement: 231 cu. in. (3.8 liters). Bore & stroke: 3.80 x 3.40 in. Compression ratio: 8.0:1. Brake horsepower: 110 at 3800 R.P.M. Torque: 190 lbs.-ft. at 1600 R.P.M. Four main bearings. Hydraulic valve lifters. Carburetor: 2Bbl. Rochester E2ME. Buick-built. VIN Code: A. TURBOCHARGED V-6; OPTIONAL (Monte Carlo): Same as 231 cu. in. V-6 above, except 4Bbl. Rochester E4ME carburetor Brake H.P.: 170 at 4000 R.P.M. Torque: 275 lbs.- ft. at 2400 R.P.M. VIN Code: 3. BASE V-8 (Caprice/Impala wagon); OPTIONAL (Camaro, Malibu, Monte Carlo, Impala, Caprice): 90-degree, overhead valve V-8. Cast iron block and head. Displacement: 267 cu. in. (4.4 liters). Bore & stroke: 3.50 x 3.48 in. Compression ratio: 8.3:1. Brake horsepower: 115 at 4000 R.P.M. Torque: 200 lbs.-ft. at 2400 R.P.M. Five main bearings. Hydraulic valve lifters. Carburetor: 2Bbl. Rochester 2ME. VIN Code: J. OPTIONAL V-8 (Camaro, Malibu, Monte Carlo, Impala, Caprice): 90-degree, overhead valve V-8. Cast iron block and head. Displacement: 305 cu. in. (5.0 liters). Bore & stroke: 3.74 x 3.48 in. Compression ratio: 8.6:1. Brake horsepower: 150 at 3800 R.P.M. Torque: 240 lbs.-ft. at 2400 R.P.M. Five main bearings. Hydraulic valve lifters. Carburetor: 4Bbl. Rochester 4ME. VIN Code: H. BASE V-8 (Camaro Z28): Same as 305 cu. in. V-8 above except Brake H.P.: 165 at 4000 R.P.M. Torque: 245 lbs.-ft. at 2400 R.P.M. M4ME carburetor. OPTIONAL V-8 (Camaro Z28): 90-degree, overhead valve V-8. Cast iron block and head. Displacement: 350 cu. in. (5.7 liters). Bore & stroke: 4.00 x 3.48 in. Compression ratio: 8.2:1. Brake horsepower: 175 at 4000 R.P.M. Torque: 275 lbs.-ft. at 2400 R.P.M. Five main bearings. Hydraulic valve lifters. Carburetor: 4Bbl. Rochester 4ME. VIN Code: L. DIESEL V-8; OPTIONAL (Impala/Caprice): 90-degree, overhead valve V-8. Cast iron block and head. Displacement: 350 cu. in. (5.7 liters). Bore & stroke: 4.057 x 3.385 in. Compression ratio: 22.5:1. Brake horsepower: 105 at 3200 R.P.M. Torque: 200 lbs.-ft. at 1600 R.P.M. Five main bearings. Hydraulic valve lifters. Fuel injection. Olds- built. VIN Code: N.

CHASSIS DATA: Wheelbase: (Chevette 2-dr) 94.3 in.; (Chvt 4-dr.) 97.3 in.; (Citation) 104.9 in.; (Camaro) 108.0 in.; (Malibu/Monte Carlo) 108.1 in.; (Caprice/Imp) 116.0 in. Overall length: (Chvt 2-dr.) 161.9 in; (Chvt 4-dr.) 164.9 in.; (Cit) 176.7 in.; (Camaro) 197.6 in.; (Malibu) 192.7 in.; (Malibu wag) 193.4 in.; (Monte) 200.4 in.; (Capr/Imp) 212.1 in.; (Capr/Imp wag) 215.1 in. Height: (Chvt) 52.9 in.; (Cit) 53.1 in.; (Camaro) 49.2 in.; (Malibu) 55.7 in.; (Malibu wag) 55.8 in.; (Monte) 53.9 in.; (Capr/Imp cpe) 54.6 in.; (Capr/Imp sed) 55.2 in.; (Capr/Imp wag) 57.1 in. Width: (Chvt) 61.8 in.; (Cit) 68.3 in.; (Camaro) 74.5 in.; (Malibu) 72.3 in.; (Malibu wag) 71.9 in.; (Monte) 71.8 in.; (Capr/Imp) 75.3 in.; (Capr/Imp wag) 79.3 in. Front Tread: (Chvt) 51.2 in.; (Cit) 58.7 in.; (Camaro) 61.3 in.; (Camaro Berlinetta) 61.6 in.; (Malibu/Monte) 58.5 in.; (Capr/Imp) 61.8 in.; (Capr/Imp wag) 62.2 in. Rear Tread: (Chvt) 51.2 in.; (Cit) 57.0 in.; (Camaro) 60.0 in.; (Camaro Berlinetta) 60.3 in.; (Malibu/Monte) 57.8 in.; (Capr/Imp) 60.8 in.; (Capr/Imp wag) 64.1 in. Standard Tires: (Chvt) P155/80R13 GBR; (Cit) P185/80R13 GBR; (Camaro) P205/75R14 SBR; (Camaro Z28) P225/70R15 WLT; (Malibu) P185/75R14 GBR; (Malibu wag) P195/75R14 GBR; (Monte) P195/75R14 SBR; (Imp/Capr) P205/75R15 SBR; (Imp/Capr wag) P225/75R15 SBR.

TECHNICAL: Transmission: Three-speed manual transmission standard on Camaro V-6. Gear ratios: (1st) 3.50:1; (2nd) 1.89:1; (3rd) 1.00:1; (Rev) 3.62:1. Four-speed floor shift standard on Chevette: (1st) 3.75:1; (2nd) 2.16:1; (3rd) 1.38:1; (4th) 1.00:1; (Rev) 3.82:1. Citation four-speed floor shift: (1st) 3.53:1; (2nd) 1.95:1; (3rd) 1.24:1; (4th) 0.81:1; (Rev) 3.42:1. Four-speed on Camaro V8305: (1st) 3.42:1; (2nd) 2.28:1; (3rd) 1.45:1; (4th) 1.00:1; (Rev) 3.51:1. Three-speed Turbo Hydra-matic standard on Monte Carlo and Caprice/Impala, optional on others. Gear ratios: (1st) 2.52:1; (2nd) 1.52:1; (3rd) 1.00:1; (Rev) 1.93:1 except Caprice/Impala V6231/V8305, Camaro V6229 and Monte V6231 ratios: (1st) 2.74:1; (2nd) 1.57:1; (3rd) 1.00:1; (Rev) 2.07:1. Base Chevette automatic trans.: (1st) 2.40:1; (2nd) 1.48:1; (3rd) 1.00:1; (Rev) 1.92:1. Citation auto. trans.: (1st) 2.84:1; (2nd) 1.60:1; (3rd) 1.00:1; (Rev) 2.07:1. Standard final drive ratio: (Chevette) 3.70:1; (Scooter) 3.36:1; (Citation) 3.32:1 w/manual, 2.84:1 w/auto.; (Camaro V-6) 2.73:1; (Camaro V-8) 2.56:1; (Camaro V8350) 3.08:1; (Z28) 3.42:1 w/4spd; (Malibu) 2.73:1 w/manual and V-6, 2.41:1 w/auto. and V-6, 2.29:1 w/V-8; (Monte V-6) 2.41:1; (Monte V8267) 2.73:1; (Monte V8305) 2.29:1; (Caprice/Imp V-6) 2.73:1; (Caprice/Imp V-8) 2.41:1. Steering: (Chevette/Citation) rack and pinion; (others) recirculating ball. Suspension/Body: same as 1980. Brakes: front disc, rear drum. Fuel tank: (Chvt) 12.5 gal.; (Cit) 14 gal.; (Camaro) 21 gal.; (Malibu) 18.1 gal.; (Monte) 18.1 gal.; (Capr/Imp) 25 gal.; (Capr/Imp wag) 22 gal.

DRIVETRAIN OPTIONS: Engines: 173 cu. in., 2Bbl. V-6: Citation ($125). Turbo 231 cu. in., 4Bbl. V-6: Monte ($750). 267 cu. in., 2Bbl. V-8: Camaro/Malibu/Monte/Imp/Caprice ($50). 305 cu. in., 4Bbl. V-8: Camaro/Malibu/Monte/Imp/Capr ($50); Imp/Capr wag (NC). 350 cu. in., 4Bbl. V-8: Z28 (NC). Diesel 350 cu. in. V-8: Imp/Capr wag ($695). Transmission/Differential: Four-speed manual shift: Camaro ($141). Three-speed automatic: Chevette ($335); Citation/Camaro/Malibu ($349); Camaro Z28 ($61). Four-speed overdrive automatic trans.: Imp/Capr ($162). Limited-slip differential: Camaro/Malibu/Monte ($67); Imp/Capr ($71). Performance axle ratio: Camaro/Malibu/Monte ($19). Power Accessories: Power brakes: Chvt/Cit ($79). Power steering: Chvt ($164); Cit ($168). Suspension: F40 H.D. susp.: Cit/Malibu/Monte/Imp/Capr ($23). F41 sport susp.: Chvt ($37); Cit ($39); Camaro ($33); Malibu/Monte/Imp/Capr cpe/sed ($43). Inflatable rear shock absorbers: Imp/Capr ($57). Other: H.D. cooling ($34-$61). Engine block heater: Imp/Capr wag ($16). H.D. alternator (63-amp): Malibu ($6-$34). H.D. alternator (70-amp): Cit ($11-$45); Monte/Imp/Capr ($32-$66). H.D. battery ($20) exc. diesel ($40). California emission system ($46).

CHEVETTE CONVENIENCE/APPEARANCE OPTIONS: Comfort/Convenience: Air conditioning ($531). Rear defogger, electric ($102). Tinted glass ($70). Comfortilt steering wheel ($78). Tachometer ($70). Electric clock ($23). Cigarette lighter: Scooter ($8). Intermittent wipers ($41). Rear wiper/washer ($100). Quiet sound group ($40-$52). Lighting and Mirrors: Halogen headlamps ($36). Aux. lighting: Chvt ($42-$43). Twin sport mirrors, left remote ($43). Driver's remote sport mirror ($29). Entertainment: AM radio: Scooter ($78). AM/FM radio ($64); Scooter ($142). AM/FM stereo radio ($100). Rear speaker ($19). Exterior Trim: Deluxe exterior: wheel opening, side window and rocker panel moldings ($118-$125). Two-tone paint ($116). Sport stripes ($78). Bodyside moldings: Scooter ($42). Side window reveal moldings ($69-$76). Door edge guards ($13-$21). Roof carrier ($74). Interior Trim/Upholstery: Cloth bucket seats ($16-$28). Custom bucket seats: cloth ($249); vinyl ($221). Rear **seat delete ($50 credit). Color-keyed floor mates ($23). Wheels and Tires: Rally wheel trim ($52). P175/7013 SBR BSW: Chvt ($60); Scooter ($108). P175/7013 SBR WSW: Chvt ($108); Scooter ($155). P175/7013 SBR WLTL: Chvt ($124); Scooter ($172).**

CITATION CONVENIENCE/APPEARANCE OPTIONS: Option Packages: X11 sport equipment pkg. ($1498). Deluxe exterior pkg. ($117-$151). Quiet sound/rear decor pkg. ($75). Comfort/Convenience: Air cond. ($585). Rear defogger, electric ($107). Cruise control w/resume ($123). Tinted glass ($75). Sport steering wheel (NC to $21). Comfortilt steering wheel ($81). Power windows ($140-$195). Remote swing-out windows ($95). Power door locks ($93-$132). Gauge pkg. w/clock ($73). Special instruments incl. tachometer ($114). Electric clock ($23). Intermittent wipers ($41). Lighting, Horns and Mirrors: Halogen headlamps ($34). Aux. lighting ($43). Dual horns ($10). Driver's remote mirror ($19). Dual sport mirrors, left remote ($47).

Entertainment: AM/FM radio ($64). AM/FM stereo radio ($100). Rear speaker ($19). Dual rear speakers ($28); incl. w/stereo radio. Windshield antenna ($10). Power antenna ($47). Radio delete ($51 credit). Exterior Trim: Removable sunroof ($246). Two-tone paint ($155) incl. pinstriping and bodyside moldings. Bodyside pinstriping ($34). Roof carrier ($90). Bodyside moldings ($44). Door edge guards ($13-$21). Side window reveal moldings ($41-$50). Bumper guards ($48). Bumper rub strips ($43). Interior Trim/Upholstery: Console ($86). Reclining driver or passenger seatback ($41-$69). Sport cloth bench seat ($28). Custom cloth or vinyl bench seat ($391). Vinyl bucket seats ($91-$116). Sport cloth bucket seats ($119-$144). Custom cloth or vinyl bucket seats ($482-$507). Color-keyed mats ($25). **Wheels and Tires:** Full wheel covers ($46). Wire wheel covers ($117-163). Wheel trim rings ($50). Rally wheel trim ($36-82). P185/80R13 GBR WSW ($51). P185/80R13 SBR BSW ($54). P185/80R13 SBR WSW ($105). P205/70R13 SBR WSW ($206). P205/70R13 SBR WLT ($222).

CAMARO/MALIBU/MONTE CARLO CONVENIENCE/APPEARANCE OPTIONS: Option Packages: Estate equipment: Malibu wag ($271). Interior decor/quiet sound group: Camaro ($67). Quiet sound group: Malibu ($54). Security pkg.: Malibu wag ($39). Comfort/Convenience: Air cond.: Camaro ($560); Malibu/Monte ($585). Rear defogger, electric ($107). Cruise control w/resume ($132). Tinted glass ($75). Comfortilt steering wheel ($81). Six-way power driver's seat: Malibu/Monte ($173). Power windows: Camaro/Monte ($140); Malibu ($140- $195). Power door locks: Malibu ($93-$132); Camaro/Monte ($93). Power trunk release: Monte ($27). Electric clock: base Camaro, Malibu ($23). Gauge pkg. w/tach: base Camaro ($118). Gauge pkg. w/clock and trip odometer: Malibu ($80). Gauge pkg. w/trip odometer: Monte ($55). Intermittent wipers ($41). Lighting, Horns and Mirrors: Halogen headlamps: Camaro/Malibu ($36). Halogen high-beams: Monte ($27). Cornering lamps: Monte ($48). Aux. lighting: Camaro ($33-$39); Malibu ($33- $59); Monte ($33). Dual horns: Camaro, base Malibu ($10). Remote-control driver's mirror: Malibu/Monte ($19). Twin sport mirrors (left remote): base Camaro, Malibu/Monte ($47). Twin remote sport mirrors: Malibu ($73); Monte ($26-$73). Visor vanity mirror: Monte ($6). Lighted visor mirror: Monte ($36-$42). Entertainment: AM radio ($90). AM/FM radio ($142). AM/FM stereo radio ($178). Stereo 8track tape player with AM/FM stereo radio ($252). Cassette player with AM/FM stereo radio ($264). AM/FM stereo radio w/CB ($487). Rear speaker ($19). Dual rear speakers: Malibu/Monte ($28). Windshield antenna ($25); incl. w/radios. Power antenna ($47). Exterior Trim: Removable glass roof panels: Camaro/Monte ($695). Power sky roof: Monte ($561). Vinyl roof: Malibu cpe ($115); Malibu sed ($124); Monte ($130). Cabriolet vinyl roof: Malibu ($171). Padded opera roof: Monte ($232). Rear spoiler: Camaro ($60). Style trim pkg.: Camaro ($76). Two- tone paint: Malibu ($71-$121); Monte ($134-$188). Bodyside moldings: Camaro ($44). Deluxe bodyside moldings: Malibu/Monte ($53). Door edge guards: Camaro/Malibu ($13- $21). Wheel opening moldings: Malibu cpe/sed ($25). Side window sill moldings: Monte ($34). Side window reveal moldings: Malibu ($44). Roof drip moldings: Camaro ($25). Bodyside pinstriping: Malibu ($50); Monte ($54). Rear window air deflector: Malibu wag ($32). Roof carrier: Malibu ($96). Bumper rub strips: Malibu ($43). Bumper guards, front/rear: Malibu ($48). Interior Trim/Upholstery: Custom interior (55/45 seating, center armrest, custom door panels and seats): Monte ($201- $387). Custom door/quarter trim panels: Monte ($27). Console: Malibu cpe/sed, Monte ($86). Vinyl bench seat: Malibu cpe/sed, Monte ($28). Cloth bench seat: Malibu wag ($28). Custom vinyl bench seat: Malibu wag ($63). Cloth 55/45 seating: Malibu ($181-$241); Monte ($208). Vinyl 55/45 seating: Malibu ($209-$241); Monte ($236); Monte Landau ($28). Vinyl bucket seats: Malibu cpe/sed ($91); Monte ($118). Cloth bucket seats: Camaro ($28); Malibu cpe/sed ($91); Monte ($118). Custom vinyl bucket seats: base Camaro ($322). Custom cloth bucket seats: Berlinetta ($28); base Camaro ($350). Adj. driver's seatback: Camaro ($23). Color-keyed mats ($25). Deluxe load-floor carpet; Malibu wag ($74). Deluxe trunk trim: Monte ($44). **Wheels and Tires:** Aluminum wheels: Camaro ($180-$331); Monte ($264-$319). Custom styled 14x7 wheels: Camaro ($151). Rally wheels: Camaro ($99); Malibu ($49-$95); Monte ($49); Malibu Classic Landau (NC). Full wheel covers: Camaro/Malibu ($46). Sport wheel covers (silver or gold): Malibu ($55- $101). Wire wheel covers: Malibu ($80-$181); Monte ($80- $135). Wheel cover locks: Berlinetta/Malibu/Monte ($34). P185/75R14 GBR WSW: Malibu cpe/sed ($48). P195/75R14 GBR WSW: Malibu wag ($51). P195/75R14 SBR WSW: Malibu cpe/sed ($125); Malibu wag ($102); Monte ($51). P205/75R14 SBR WSW: Camaro ($54). P205/75R14 SBR WLT: Camaro ($69); Berlinetta ($15). P205/70R14 SBR WSW: Monte ($107); Malibu cpe/sed ($183). P205/70R14 SBR WLT: Malibu cpe/sed ($198).

IMPALA/CAPRICE CONVENIENCE/APPEARANCE OPTIONS: Option Packages: Estate equipment: wag ($271). Value appearance group: bodyside and wheel opening moldings, full wheel covers ($93). Comfort/Convenience: Air cond. ($625). Comfortron auto-temp air cond. ($708). Rear defogger, blower: cpe/sed ($59). Rear defogger, electric ($107). Cruise control w/resume ($135). Tinted glass ($87). Comfortilt steering wheel ($81). Power door locks ($93-$132). Six-way power driver's seat ($173). Power windows ($143-$211). Power trunk release ($27). Power tailgate lock: wag ($43). Electric clock: Imp ($25). Digital clock: Imp ($59); Caprice ($36). Gauge pkg. w/trip odometer ($56). Intermittent wipers ($41). Quiet sound group: Imp ($58). Lighting, Horns and Mirrors: Halogen high-beam headlamps ($27). Cornering lamps ($48). Aux. lighting ($36-$57). Dual horns: Imp ($10). Driver's remote mirror ($19). Dual remote mirrors ($58). Dual sport mirrors, left remote ($47). Dual remote body-color sport mirrors ($26-$73). Visor vanity mirror ($6). Lighted visor mirror ($42). Entertainment: AM radio ($90). AM/FM radio ($142). AM/FM stereo radio ($178). Stereo 8track tape player with AM/FM stereo radio ($252). Cassette player with AM/FM stereo ($264). AM/FM stereo with CB and power antenna ($487). Rear speaker ($19). Dual rear speakers ($28). Power antenna ($47). Windshield antenna ($25); incl. w/radios. Exterior Trim: Power sky roof: cpe/sed ($650). Vinyl roof ($142). Roof carrier: wag ($119). Two-tone paint ($58). Custom two-tone ($124). Pinstriping ($34). Color-keyed bodyside moldings ($44). Door edge guards ($13-$21). Wheel opening moldings: Imp ($25). Bumper rub strips, front/rear ($58). Bumper guards ($54). Interior Trim/Upholstery: Vinyl bench seat: cpe/sed ($28). Cloth bench seat: wag ($28). Cloth 50/50 seat ($222-$268). Vinyl 50/50 seat ($240-$268). Custom cloth 50/50 seat: cpe ($400); sed ($424). Deluxe load-floor carpet: wag ($77). Deluxe cargo area carpet: wag ($114). Color-keyed mats: front ($15); rear ($10). Deluxe trunk trim ($55). **Wheel Covers:** Full wheel covers ($46). Sport wheel covers: Imp ($102); Caprice ($56). Custom wheel covers: Imp ($121); Capr ($75) Wire wheel covers: Capr ($135). Wire wheel cover locks ($34). Coupe/Sedan Tires: P205/75R15 SBR WSW ($54). P215/75R15 SBR WSW ($86). P225/70R15 SBR WSW ($132). Wagon Tires: P225/75R15 SBR WSW ($58). Puncture-sealant tires ($85-$105).

HISTORY: Introduced: Sept. 25, 1980. Model year production (U.S.): 1,582,575 (incl. Corvettes but not incl. 20,363 Acadians or early '82 Cavaliers). Of total production for U.S. market, 744,977 were four-cylinder, 590,984 sixes, and 392,632 V-8s. A total of 49,791 diesels and 3,027 turbos were installed. Calendar year production: 1,307,526 (including 27,990 Corvettes and 18,098 Acadians, but not incl. 139,837 early '82 Cavaliers). Calendar year sales by U.S. dealers: 1,442,281, for a 23.3 percent market share. Model year sales by U.S. dealers: 1,522,536 (incl. 33,414 Corvettes but not incl. 43,855 early 1982 Cavaliers).

Historical Footnotes: Sales had been expected to take an upturn for 1981, but fell far short of expectations, dropping by about 265,000 for the model year (even including early '82 Cavaliers). And 1980 had hardly been a big year either. Only Chevette sold better in 1981 than 1980 (but only slightly). Citation had been the company's best seller for 1980, setting a first-year sales record for General Motors. But second-year sales slipped along with the other models. Full-size Chevrolets sold so poorly that there was speculation they would soon be dropped. Even with sagging sales, prices were raised at mid-year. Incentives (including rebates and reduced finance rates) were announced, but failed to bring in enough customers.

1982 CHEVROLET

Two all-new models (subcompact Cavalier and compact Celebrity) and a major restyle highlighted 1982. Biggest news was the downsized Camaro, even racier than before, which debuted with the family-size Celebrity in January 1982. Some hefty price increases arrived this year too. Opening prices for the restyled Camaros were $976 to $1810 higher than 1981 equivalents. The remaining Malibu models rose by well over a thousand dollars. Unlike some years in this era, though, Chevrolets endured only a $15 price hike during the model year. On the mechanical front, Pontiac's four-cylinder engine (used in Citation, Camaro and Celebrity) added fuel injection. The fact that Malibu now wore a grille similar to full-size models helped fuel rumors that the big Chevrolets were doomed. But reports of their imminent demise proved premature.

1982 Chevette hatchback sedan (AA)

CHEVETTE — SERIES 1T — FOUR — Both gas and diesel engines were offered on the subcompact Chevette this year. The 1.8-liter four-cylinder diesel, coupled to a new five-speed manual transmission, rated 40 MPG city and 55 MPG highway in EPA estimates. It was offered under both coupe and sedan hoods (but not Scooter), priced as a separate model rather than an option. The overhead-cam, 51-horsepower diesel had actually became available late in the 1981 model year, in limited numbers. Built by Isuzu, it had a cross-flow cylinder head and lightweight Bosch distributor-type fuel pump/injection system. The low-budget Scooter came in four-door hatchback form this year, as well as the carryover two-door (priced just under $5000). The four-door cost $241 more. Standard gasoline engine was the 1.6-liter four, with four-speed manual transmission. A new five-speed gearbox was also available, as well as automatic. The five-speed had been added as a late '81 option. Compression ratio of the gas engine rose from 8.6:1 in 1981 to 9.2:1 this year, as a redesigned cylinder head forced the air/fuel mixture into the combustion chamber with a more efficient swirling motion. Standard equipment (except on Scooters) included an AM radio, color-keyed instrument panel, reclining front bucket seats, transmission floor control, and sport steering wheel. Chevettes did not change in appearance.

1982 Cavalier hatchback coupe (CP)

CAVALIER — SERIES 1J — FOUR Introduced on May 21, 1981 as an early '82 model, the new front-drive four-passenger Chevrolet was described as subcompact on the outside, with compact roominess inside. It was also called a "high-content vehicle" with an ample load of standard equipment, including radio, power brakes, reclining bucket seats, stabilizer bar, and remote trunk/hatch/tailgate release. Four models were offered: two- door and four-door sedans, two-door hatchback, and four-door wagon. Cavaliers came in three series: low-budget Cadet, base, and CL. Sole engine at first was a transverse-mounted 112 cu. in. (1.8-liter) four, rated 88 horsepower, with four- speed (overdrive) manual transmission. EPA ratings reached 30 MPG (city). A 2.0-liter four was announced, but arrived later. Cavaliers had a low, horizontal-style grille with bowtie emblem in the solid panel above. Single recessed rectangular headlamps flanked vertical park/signal lamps. Taillamps were split into two sections by a horizontal divider. Base Cavaliers had integrated bright bumper systems with black/argent rub strips; PlastisolR lower body stone chip protection; black wipers; amber rear turn signal lamps; bright hood molding and grille bars; a styled black outside mirror; body-color wraparound bumper end caps; and bodyside moldings. Rally wheels held trim rings. 'Cavalier' nameplates were on front fenders. Hatchbacks came with a flush-mount back window, soft-fascia front-end panel, wide-base Rally wheels, and flush-mount windshield; plus black grille, headlamp and parking lamp bezels. Body colors were white, black, light yellow, beige and red; plus metallic silver, light or dark blue, bright blue, light or dark jade, gold, maroon, or charcoal. After its first half-season, Cavalier got several powertrain changes (mainly in axle ratios and electronic control module) by the time the 1982 model year began. Carburetion and ignition calibration for models with air condtioning was revised to improve cold startups and low- speed response, using a new microchip. Models with air conditioning and automatic transmission got a 3.18:1 final drive ratio, while manual-shift Cavaliers switched from 2.96:1 to 3.32:1 after the start of the full model year. Automatic transmissions were modified too. As the model year began, Cavalier also got a full-width, three-passenger back seat (with optional split folding back), becoming a five- passenger vehicle rather than four. A bigger (2.0-liter), 90- horsepower four was

1982 Cavalier Cadet sedan (CH)

announced, but arrived later. Cavalier's standard equipment included four-speed manual transaxle, P175/80R13 GBR tires on rally steel wheels, AM radio, electric side/rear window defoggers, lighter, digital clock, reclining front bucket seats, trip odometer, console, day/night mirror, color-keyed carpeting, locking glove compartment, front stabilizer bar, bodyside moldings, and bumper rub strips. Hatchbacks also had a gauge package and fold-down rear seat; wagons the fold-down seat and air deflector. Cavalier CL added power steering, AM/FM radio, whitewall tires, sport wheel covers, sport mirrors (left remote), tinted glass, rear stabilizer bar, gauges, intermittent wipers, leather-wrapped steering wheel, and halogen headlamps. CL hatchbacks had a tachometer and rear wiper/washer.

1982 Citation coupe (CH)

CITATION — SERIES 1X — FOUR/V-6 — Electronic fuel injection became standard this year on the base 151 cu. in. (2.5-liter) four, supplied by Pontiac. This produced an estimated 4 MPG mileage increase. Also new were high-pressure (35 psi) easy-roll tires, geometry-tuned suspension, and a relocated rack-and-pinion steering mount. Citation again came in two-door and four-door hatchback form, along with an H11 five-passenger coupe. The high-performance two-door X11 package was offered again, including the HO 600 engine (a 135-horsepower version of the 2.8-liter V-6) and modified suspension components. Citation had a new horizontal grille for 1982, shaped similar to the 1981 crosshatch version. Eight body colors were new. New vinyl upholstery went on standard seats. Interiors came in three new trim colors: charcoal, jadestone, and redwood. New options included automatic speed control for use with manual transmission. The automatic transmission got a lockup torque converter clutch for high gear. The X11 sport equipment package included the high-output V-6 engine, power brakes, sport mirrors, rear spoiler, bucket seats, P215/60R14 tires on aluminum wheels, special instruments, sport steering wheel, F41 sport suspension, and bumper rub strips.

1982 Camaro Berlinetta Sport Coupe (CH)

CAMARO — SERIES 1F — FOUR/V-6/V-8 — An all-new Camaro arrived late in the model year, still rear-wheel drive but in a lighter-weight fastback form. In Chevrolet's words, the new version "captures the essence of the contemporary American performance expression." Offered again in three models, but with a contemporary aerodynamic shape and "aircraft-inspired interior," Camaro weighed some 470 pounds less than in 1981, though it was still no lightweight. The new body was nearly 10 inches shorter, riding a 101 inch wheelbase (down from 108). The fuel filler door was now on the quarter panel (driver's side), with a hatch release lock behind the license plate. Camaros had a new lift-up hatch back window. Standard Sport Coupe engine was now Pontiac's 151 cu. in. (2.5-liter), 90-horsepower "Iron Duke" four with electronic fuel injection. Options: a variant of Citation's 173 cu. in. (2.8-liter) V-6 rated

1982 Camaro Z28 Sport Coupe

102 horsepower, or a four- barrel carbureted 305 cu. in. (5.0-liter) V-8 that produced 145 horsepower. The V-6 was standard in Berlinetta; V-8 standard in Z28. But the Z28 could also have an optional Cross-Fire fuel-injected 305 V-8, rated 165 horsepower, for an extra $450. That version was marked by a 'Cross Fire Injection' decal below the 'Z28' identifier (just behind the front wheel housing), plus operating air inlets. Camaro's optional three-speed automatic transmission had a torque converter lockup clutch. A four-speed manual gearbox was now standard on the base Camaro, so the old three-speed was gone for good. Four-wheel disc brakes were now available with V-8 engines. Inside, a new console held glove box, parking brake lever, and controls for heater, optional stereo radio and air conditioning. The instrument panel was black-finished to minimize reflections. Twin speedometer needles showed both MPH and kilometers per hour. Interior space was similar to before, even though outside dimensions had shrunk. The rear seat's backrest folded down, turning the rear section into a cargo area, accessible through the new hatch. For an extra $611, Z28s could have a new "Conteur" seat option from Lear- Siegler, with six adjustments (backrest bolster, thigh support, cushion bolster, lumbar and recliner). A six-way power seat was now optional on all models. Each model had its own styling features, including specific front air dam and rear fascia. All Camaros had deeply recessed quad rectangular headlamps and tri-color wraparound taillamps (not far removed from prior designs). **Camaro's fastback profile included a compound S-shaped glass hatch. The flush-mounted windshields' 62-degree rake helped produce a 0.368 drag coefficient, one of the lowest ever tested by GM. Z28's front end had no upper grille** opening, while its "ground effects" air dams reached lower to the ground. Z28s also rode special five-spoke aluminum wheels. Body colors for 1982 were white, silver, black, red, maroon, charcoal, light or dark blue, light or dark jade, gold, or dark gold. The new Camaro's body was unitized construction, but with bolt-on front sheetmetal. Rear coils replaced the old leaf springs. The rear suspension now consisted of a longitudinal torque tube, short control arms ahead of the solid axle, and lateral track rod. Front suspension used modified MacPherson struts with coil springs and stabilizer bar. Z28s and the F41 sport suspension added a link-type rear stabilizer bar. Base Sport Coupe standard equipment included four-speed manual shift, power brakes and steering, front stabilizer bar, dual black sport mirrors, black windshield molding, concealed wipers, body-color wheels with hubcaps and P195/75R14 GBR tires, reclining front bucket seats, and a day/night mirror. Berlinetta added P205/70R14 SBR tires, body pinstriping, body-color sport mirrors, black-accented lower body (with stripe), gold-accented aluminum spoke wheels, and higher-level acoustic package. **Camaro Z28 equipment included five-spoke aluminum wheels (gold or charcoal accented) with P215/65R15 white-letter tires, a rear stabilizer bar, specially-tuned suspension, dual mufflers and tailpipes, body-color sport mirrors, front air dam, "ground effects" rocker molding area, and rear deck spoiler. Twin air scoops rode the special Z28 hood. A total of 6,360 Indy 500 Commemorative Editions of the Z28 were built this year, marking the use of a Camaro as Indy Pace Car. All the replicas had a silver/blue body. Indy 500 logos, red-accented silver aluminum wheels and Goodyear Eagle GT white-letter tires. Blue cloth/silver vinyl interiors held the Lear-Siegler Conteur driver's seat, along with special instruments, leather-wrapped steering wheel and AM/FM stereo radio. Chevrolet dealers were entitled to order one special edition apiece.**

CELEBRITY — SERIES 1A — FOUR/V-6 — The new front-wheel drive family sedan was designed to combine small-car economy with "big-car ride, comfort and style." When buying a Celebrity, declared Chevrolet General manager, Robert D. Lund, customers wouldn't find that "they sacrificed comfort, space and prestige" for the sake of economy. Though roughly the same size inside as the Malibu it soon would replace, Celebrity weighed some 500 pounds less and stood a foot shorter in overall length. Wheelbase was identical to Citation's, but Celebrity measured almost a foot longer (188.3 inches overall). Celebrity came in two- door and four-door sedan form, with three five-passenger interior trim levels (base, CS and CL). The wedge-shape design (low nose and high deck) resulted from extensive wind- tunnel testing. Celebrity's 0.38 aero drag coefficient was the lowest rating ever for a mass-produced GM sedan. Celebrity wasn't introduced until after the first of the year, on January 14, 1982. Standard powertrain was a fuel- injected 151 cu. in. (2.5-liter) four-cylinder engine with three-speed automatic transaxle, which produced EPA estimates of 25 MPG city and 40 highway. Both gas and diesel V-6 engines were announced: a 173 cu. in. (2.8-liter) gasoline model and 4.3-liter diesel. But the diesel's appearance was delayed for a year. Gasoline models had an on-board computer system that included self-diagnostics. Celebrity's front end was similar to Cavalier, with a solid panel above the low grille; but the 8x4 hole crosshatch grille held a bowtie emblem in its center. Celebrity also carried quad rectangular headlamps over horizontal park/signal lamps. Wide tri-section taillamps stretched from license plate opening to quarter panel, divided by a horizontal bar. Celebrity came in a dozen solid colors plus six two- tones. Solids were white, light and dark blue, light and dark metallic jadestone or sandstone, light and dark metallic redwood, slate gray, silver metallic, and charcoal metallic. Two-tones were slate gray/silver metallic; dark blue/light blue metallic; dark blue/pastel sandstone; light/dark jadestone metallic; pastel sandstone/light redwood metallic; or dark/light redwood metallic. Cloth or vinyl interior trim came in slate gray, dark blue, jadestone, sandstone, doeskin and redwood. Standard equipment included the four-cylinder engine, power brakes, power rack-and-pinion steering, pushbutton AM radio, maintenance-free battery, front stabilizer bar, chrome bumpers with black rub strips and body-color end caps, and P185/80R13 GBR tires with full wheel covers. Also standard: black side window frames, bright drip and bodyside moldings, front bench seat with fixed armrest, side window defoggers, day/night mirror, and locking glove compartment.

MALIBU CLASSIC — SERIES 1A — V-6/V-8 — This year's Malibu had a distinctive crosshatch grille similar to Caprice, flanked by quad rectangular headlamps that stood over horizontal quad park/signal lamps. A dozen body colors were available, with either cloth or vinyl interiors. A four-door sport sedan and four-door wagon were the only models. Base engine was the 229 cu. in. (3.8-liter) V-6. But Malibu could also have either the 267 cu. in. (4.4- liter) or 305 cu. in. (5.0-liter) gas V-6, or a choice of

1982 Malibu Classic 4-dr sedan

diesels: 4.3-liter V-6 or the big 5.7-liter V-8 from Oldsmobile. The small diesel, which arrived later in the model year, was Chevrolet's first V-6 version (actually produced by Oldsmobile). It had roller hydraulic valve lifters, a serpentine belt system, venturi-shaped prechamber, and a torque-pulse compensator for smoother power flow. The diesel had aluminum cylinder heads, intake manifold, water outlet and oil pump body. Base Malibus were gone, leaving only the Classic, in only sedan and station wagon form. Standard equipment included automatic transmission, power brakes and steering, notchback front bench seats with folding armrests, dual horns, front stabilizer bar, full wheel covers, and stand-up hood ornament. Bodies displayed a bright wide upper grille molding, bright back window and windshield reveal moldings, bright sill and roof drip moldings, and wide wheel opening moldings. Circular instrumentation was similar to Monte Carlo's. Inside were a lighter, dome light and day/night mirror. Sedans had bright decklid and end cap moldings, plus black-accented bright taillamp trim.

1982 Monte Carlo Sport Coupe (CH)

MONTE CARLO — SERIES 1A — V-6/V-8 — A finely-textured crosshatch grille set off Monte's front end this year, divided into three sections by two horizontal bars. Quad rectangular headlamps sat alongside the grille, but wide parking lamps were recessed low in the bumper. The body carried on Monte's "subtle wedge shape," now available in a dozen solid body colors and six two-tones. The Landau coupe was dropped, leaving only one coupe model. Interiors could have either cloth or vinyl trim. A passenger- side mirror was now standard, and a fixed-mast radio antenna replaced the former windshield antenna. Monte rode high- pressure (35 psi) tires and stopped with low-drag brakes. Standard engine remained the 229 cu. in. (3.8-liter) V-6. Two gasoline V-8s were also available: 267 and 305 cu. in. So were a pair of diesels: either the new V-6 or the big Oldsmobile V-8. The turbo V-6 was out. Montes had standard automatic transmission, power brakes and steering, plus P195/75R14 SBR tires on 6 in. wheels. Also standard: body- color bumpers, bright roof drip and windshield reveal moldings, twin bright outside mirrors, bright lower bodyside and quarter window reveal moldings, a stand-up hood ornament, full wheel covers, wheel opening moldings, bright decklid and end cap moldings, full-width front seat with folding armrest, dome light, day/night mirror, dual horns, lighter, and trunk mat.

1982 Impala sedan (CP)

IMPALA/CAPRICE CLASSIC — SERIES 1B — V-6/V-8 — Full-size Chevrolets looked about the same for 1982, but came in fewer models. The Caprice Landau coupe and Impala sport coupe were dropped. Only the three-seat Caprice wagon was offered, along with the sport coupe and four-door sedan. Impala's lineup included the sedan and twin wagons. Oldsmobile's 350 cu. in. (5.7-liter) diesel V-8 was now available on all models, not just the station wagon. Standard engine was the 229 cu. in. (3.8-liter) V-6, with three-speed automatic. Wagons had the 267 cu. in. (4.4-liter) V-8, which cost $70 extra on other models. Optional four-speed overdrive automatic boosted gas mileage on the optional 267 cu. in. (4.4-liter) or 305 (5.0-liter) gas engines. Impala had an argent grille, Caprice a chrome-plated grille. Impala lacked a stand-up hood ornament and had thinner rocker moldings. Its front side marker lenses stood slightly back from fender tips, while Caprice's wrapped around. Standard equipment included three-speed automatic transmission, power brakes and steering, two-speed wipers, front stabilizer bar, bright windshield reveal and roof drip moldings, bright window reveal and frame moldings, day/night mirror, lighter, and one-piece carpeting. Caprice also included full wheel covers, wheel opening moldings, carpeted lower door panels, headlamp-on reminder, dual horns, and bright wide sill moldings. Wagons had a power tailgate window and locking side compartment.

I.D. DATA: Chevrolet's 17-symbol Vehicle Identification Number (VIN) was again on the upper left surface of the instrument panel, visible through the windshield. Coding is similar to 1981, but the following codes were added: Under car line/series (symbol five), code 'D' Cavalier; 'E' Cavalier hatch; 'W' both Celebrity and Malibu. Under body type (symbols six and seven), code '19' 4-dr. sedan; code '77' 2-dr. hatchback coupe. Symbol eight is the engine code: 'C' L4-98 2Bbl.; 'D' L4-111 diesel; 'R' or '2' L4-151 FI; 'X' or '1' V6173 2Bbl.; 'Z' V6173 H.O.; 'K' V6229 2Bbl.; 'V' Diesel V6262. 'J' V8267 2Bbl.; 'H' V8305 4Bbl.; '7' V8305 CFI; 'N' Diesel V8350. Model year (symbol ten) changed to 'C' for 1982. Codes combined with a serial number are also stamped on the engine. Chevette codes are on the right side of the block, below No. 1 plug. Cavalier's are on a pad on the right side of the block (facing the car), below the head. Pontiac 151 fours have coding on a pad at the left front of the block, below the head; or on a flange at left rear, above the starter. The V6173 is coded on the block at the front of the right head, or on the left rocker cover. Other V-6s and V-8s have coding stamped on the left side of the bell housing flange.

CHEVETTE (FOUR)

Model Number	Body/Style Number	Body Type & Seating	Factory Price	Shipping Weight	Production Total
1T	B08	2-dr. Hatch Cpe-4P	5513	2002	51,431
1T	B68	4-dr. Hatch Sed-4P	5660	2063	111,661

CHEVETTE SCOOTER (FOUR)

1T	J08	2-dr. Hatch Cpe-4P	4997	1957	31,281
1T	J68	4-dr. Hatch Sed-4P	5238	2004	21,742

CHEVETTE DIESEL (FOUR)

1T	B08/Z90	2-dr. Hatch Cpe-4P	6579	N/A	4,874
1T	B68/Z90	4-dr. Hatch Sed-4P	6727	N/A	11,819

Chevette Production Note: Totals do not include Chevette diesels (4,252 coupes and 8,900 sedans) produced during the 1981 model year.

1J	D27	2-dr. Coupe-5P	6966	2298	30,245
1J	E77	2-dr. Hatch Cpe-5P	7199	2364	22,114
1J	D69	4-dr. Sedan-5P	7137	2345	52,941
1J	D35	4-dr. Sta Wag-5P	7354	2405	30,853

1982 Cavalier station wagon (CP)

CAVALIER CADET (FOUR)

1J	D27/Z11	2-dr. Coupe-5P	6278	N/A	2,281
1J	D69/Z11	4-dr. Sedan-5P	6433	N/A	9,511
1J	D35/Z11	4-dr. Sta Wag-5P	6704	N/A	4,754

CAVALIER CL (FOUR)

1J	D27/Z12	2-dr. Coupe-5P	7944	2315	6,063
1J	E77/Z12	2-dr. Hatch Cpe-5P	8281	2381	12,792
1J	D69/Z12	4-dr. Sedan-5P	8137	2362	15,916
1J	D35/Z12	4-dr. Sta Wag-5P	8452	2422	7,587

CITATION (FOUR/V-6)

1X	H11	2-dr. Coupe-5P	6297/6515	2404/2468	9,102
1X	X08	2-dr. Hatch Cpe-5P	6754/6972	2413/2477	29,613
1X	X68	4-dr. Hatch Sed-5P	6899/7024	2447/2511	126,932

CAMARO (V-6/V-8)

1F	P87	2-dr. Spt Cpe-4P	7755/7925	2846/3025	78,761

CAMARO BERLINETTA (V-6/V-8)

Model Number	Body/Style Number	Body Type & Seating	Factory Price	Shipping Weight	Production Total
1F	S87	2-dr. Spt Cpe-4P	9266/9436	2880/3094	39,744

CAMARO Z28 (V-8)

Model Number	Body/Style Number	Body Type & Seating	Factory Price	Shipping Weight	Production Total
1F	P87	2-dr. Spt Cpe-4P	-- /9700	-- /3005	63,563

Camaro Engine Note: Prices and weights before slash are for V-6 engine, after slash for V-8. Base Camaro Sport Coupes were also available with a four-cylinder engine, priced at $7631 and weighing 2770 pounds. The Z28 could have an optional CFI V-8 for an additional $450. **Z28 Production Note:** A total of 6,360 Indy 500 Commemorative Editions were built, in addition to standard Z28s. Chevrolet figures also show over 1,300 Z28E hatchback models for export.

CELEBRITY (FOUR/V-6)

Model Number	Body/Style Number	Body Type & Seating	Factory Price	Shipping Weight	Production Total
1A	W27	2-dr. Coupe-5P	8313/8438	2609/2669	19,629
1A	W19	4-dr. Sedan-5P	8463/8588	2651/2711	72,701

MALIBU CLASSIC (V-6/V-8)

Model Number	Body/Style Number	Body Type & Seating	Factory Price	Shipping Weight	Production Total
1A	W69	4-dr. Spt Sed-6P	8137/8207	3097/3228	70,793
1A	W35	4-dr. Sta Wag-6P	8265/8335	3247/3387	45,332

MONTE CARLO (V-6/V-8)

Model Number	Body/Style Number	Body Type & Seating	Factory Price	Shipping Weight	Production Total
1A	Z37	2-dr. Spt Cpe-6P	8177/8247	3116/3245	92,392

IMPALA (V-6/V-8)

Model Number	Body/Style Number	Body Type & Seating	Factory Price	Shipping Weight	Production Total
1B	L69	4-dr. Sedan-6P	7918/7988	3368/3492	47,780
1B	L35	4-dr. Sta Wag-6P	-- /8516	-- /3938	10,654
1B	L35/AQ4	4-dr. 3S Wag-8P	-- /8670	-- / N/A	6,245

CAPRICE CLASSIC (V-6/V-8)

Model Number	Body/Style Number	Body Type & Seating	Factory Price	Shipping Weight	Production Total
1B	N47	2-dr. Spt Cpe-6P	8221/8291	3380/3500	11,999
1B	N69	4-dr. Sedan-6P	8367/8437	3417/3541	86,126
1B	N35/AQ4	4-dr. 3S Wag-9P	-- /9051	-- /4019	25,385

FACTORY PRICE AND WEIGHT NOTE: For Citation and Celebrity, prices and weights to left of slash are for four-cylinder, to right for V-6 engine. For Camaro, Malibu, Monte Carlo and full-size models, figures to left of slash are for six-cylinder model, to right of slash for V-8 (267 and 305 V-8 were each $70 extra). Diesel engines cost considerably more (see option prices). **BODY/STYLE NO. NOTE:** Some models were actually option packages. Code after the slash (e.g., AQ4) is the number of the option package that comes with the model listed.

1982 Malibu Classic station wagon (CH)

ENGINE DATA: BASE FOUR (Chevette): Inline. Overhead cam. Four-cylinder. Cast iron block and head. Displacement: 98 cu. in. (1.6 liters). Bore & stroke: 3.23 x 2.98 in. Compression ratio: 9.2:1. Brake horsepower: 65 at 5200 R.P.M. Torque: 80 lbs.-ft. at 3200 R.P.M. Five main bearings. Hydraulic valve lifters. Carburetor: 2Bbl. Holley 6510C. VIN Code: C. DIESEL FOUR (Chevette): Inline. Overhead cam. Four-cylinder. Cast iron block and head. Displacement: 111 cu. in. (1.8 liters). Bore & stroke: 3.31 x 3.23 in. Compression ratio: 22.0:1. Brake horsepower: 51 at 5200 R.P.M. Torque: 72 lbs.-ft. at 2000 R.P.M. Five main bearings. Solid valve lifters. Fuel injection. VIN Code: D. BASE FOUR (Cavalier): Inline. Overhead valve. Four-cylinder. Cast iron block and head. Displacement: 112 cu. in. (1.8 liters). Bore & stroke: 3.50 x 2.91 in. Compression ratio: 9.0:1. Brake horsepower: 88 at 5100 R.P.M. Torque: 100 lbs.-ft. at 2800 R.P.M. Five main bearings. Hydraulic valve lifters. Carburetor: 2Bbl. Rochester E2SE. VIN Code: G. BASE FOUR (Citation, Celebrity, Camaro): Inline. Overhead valve. Four-cylinder. Cast iron block and head. Displacement: 151 cu. in. (2.5 liters). Bore & stroke: 4.00 x 3.00 in. Compression ratio: 8.2:1. Brake horsepower: 90 at 4000 R.P.M. Torque: 132 lbs.-ft. at 2800 R.P.M. Five main bearings. Hydraulic valve lifters. Throttle-body fuel injection. Pontiac-built. VIN Code: R or 2. BASE V-6 (Camaro Berlinetta); OPTIONAL (Citation, Celebrity, Camaro): 60-degree, overhead-valve V-6. Cast iron block and head. Displacement: 173 cu. in. (2.8 liters). Bore & stroke: 3.50 x 2.99 in. Compression ratio: 8.5:1. Brake horsepower: 102-112 at 4800 R.P.M. (Camaro, 102). Torque: 142-145 lbs.-ft. at 2400 R.P.M. (Camaro, 142). Four main bearings. Hydraulic valve lifters. Carburetor: 2Bbl. Rochester E2SE. VIN Code: X or 1. HIGH-OUTPUT V-6 (Citation): Same as 173 cu. in. V-6 above except C.R.: 8.9:1. Brake H.P.: 135 at 5400 R.P.M. Torque: 145 lbs.- ft. at 2400 R.P.M. VIN Code: Z. BASE V-6 (Malibu, Monte Carlo, Impala, Caprice): 90-degree, overhead-valve V-6. Cast iron block and head. Displacement: 229 cu. in. (3.8 liters). Bore & stroke: 3.74 x 3.48 in. Compression ratio: 8.6:1. Brake horsepower: 110 at 4200 R.P.M. Torque: 170 lbs.-ft. at 2000 R.P.M. Four main bearings. Hydraulic valve lifters. Carburetor: 2Bbl. Rochester E2ME. VIN Code: K. DIESEL V-6 (Malibu, Monte Carlo): 90-degree, overhead-valve V-6. Cast iron block and aluminum head. Displacement: 262 cu. in. (4.3 liters). Bore & stroke: 4.057 x 3.385 in. Compression ratio: 22.5:1. Brake horsepower: 85 at 3600 R.P.M. Torque: 165 lbs.-ft. at 1600 R.P.M. Four main bearings. Hydraulic valve lifters. Fuel injection. VIN Code: V. BASE V-8 (Caprice/Impala wagon); OPTIONAL (Malibu, Monte Carlo, Impala, Caprice): 90-degree, overhead valve V-8. Cast iron block and head. Displacement: 267 cu. in. (4.4 liters). Bore & stroke: 3.50 x 3.48 in. Compression ratio: 8.3:1. Brake horsepower: 115 at 4000 R.P.M. Torque: 205 lbs.-ft. at 2400 R.P.M. Five main bearings. Hydraulic valve lifters. Carburetor: 2Bbl. Rochester E2ME. VIN Code: J. BASE V-8 (Camaro Z28); OPTIONAL (Camaro, Malibu, Monte Carlo, Impala, Caprice): 90-degree, overhead valve V-8. Cast iron block and head. Displacement: 305 cu. in. (5.0 liters). Bore & stroke: 3.74 x 3.48 in. Compression ratio: 8.6:1. Brake horsepower: 145 at 4000 R.P.M. Torque: 240 lbs.-ft. at 2000 R.P.M. Five main bearings. Hydraulic valve lifters. Carburetor: 4Bbl. Rochester E4ME. VIN Code: H. OPTIONAL V-8 (Camaro Z28): Same as 305 cu. in. V-8 above with dual CFI Brake H.P.: 165 at 4200 R.P.M. Torque: 240 lbs.-ft. at 2400 R.P.M. VIN Code: 7. DIESEL V-8; OPTIONAL (Impala/Caprice): 90-degree, overhead valve V-8. Cast iron block and head. Displacement: 350 cu. in. (5.7 liters). Bore & stroke: 4.057 x 3.385 in. Compression ratio: 22.5:1. Brake horsepower: 105 at 3200 R.P.M. Torque: 200 lbs.-ft. at 1600 R.P.M. Five main bearings. Hydraulic valve lifters. Fuel injection. Olds- built. VIN Code: N.

CHASSIS DATA: Wheelbase: (Chevette 2-dr) 94.3 in.; (Chvt) 97.3 in.; (Cavalier) 101.2 in.; (Citation/Celebrity) 104.9 in.; (Camaro) 101.0 in.; (Malibu/Monte Carlo) 108.1 in.; (Capr/Imp) 116.0 in. Overall length: (Chvt 2-dr.) 161.9 in; (Chvt 4-dr.) 164.9 in.; (Cav cpe) 170.4 in.; (Cav hatch) 173.5 in.; (Cav sed) 172.4 in.; (Cav wag) 173.0 in.; (Cit) 176.7 in.: (Camaro) 187.8 in.; (Celeb) 188.3 in.; (Malibu) 192.7 in.; (Malibu wag) 193.3 in.; (Monte) 200.4 in.; (Imp/Capr) 212.1 in.; (Imp/Capr wag) 215.1 in. Height: (Chvt) 52.9 in.; (Cav cpe) 52.0.; (Cav sed) 53.9 in.; (Cav wag) 54.4 in.; (Cit) 53.9 in.; (Camaro) 50.0 in.; (Celeb) 53.7 in.; (Malibu) 55.7 in.; (Malibu wag) 55.8 in.; (Monte) 54.3 in.; (Imp/Capr cpe) 56.4 in.; (Imp/Capr wag) 58.1 in. Width: (Chvt) 61.8 in.; (Cav cpe) 66.0 in.; (Cav sed/wag) 66.3 in.; (Cit) 68.3 in.; (Camaro) 72.8 in.; (Celeb cpe) 69.3 in.; (Celeb sed) 68.8 in.; (Malibu) 72.3 in.; (Malibu wag) 71.9 in.; (Monte) 71.8 in.; (Imp/Capr) 75.3 in.; (Imp/Capr wag) 79.3 in. Front Tread: (Chvt) 51.2 in.; (Cav) 55.4 in.; (Cit/Celeb) 58.7 in.; (Camaro) 60.7 in.; (Malibu/Monte) 58.5 in.; (Imp/Capr) 61.8 in.; (Imp/Capr wag) 62.2 in. Rear Tread: (Chvt) 51.2 in.; (Cav) 55.2 in.; (Cit/Celeb) 57.0 in.; (Camaro) 61.6 in.; (Malibu/Monte) 57.8 in.; (Imp/Capr 60.8 in.; (Imp/Capr wag) 64.1 in. Standard Tires: (Chvt) P155/80R13 GBR; (Cav) P175/80R13 GBR; (Cit/Celeb) P185/80R13 GBR; (Camaro) P195/75R14 GBR; (Camaro Berlinetta) P205/70R14 SBR; (Camaro Z28) P215/65R15 SBR; (Malibu) P185/75R14 GBR; (Malibu wag) P195/75R14 GBR; (Monte) P195/75R14 SBR; **(Imp/Capr) P205/75R15 SBR; (Imp/Capr wag) P225/75R15 SBR. Wheel size: (Camaro) 14 x 5 in.; (Berlinetta) 14 x 7 in.; (Z28) 15 x 7 in.**

TECHNICAL: Transmission: Four-speed floor shift standard on Chevette: Gear ratios (1st) 3.75:1; (2nd) 2.16:1; (3rd) 1.38:1; (4th) 1.00:1; (Rev) 3.82:1. Four-speed floor shift on four-cylinder Cavalier/Citation: (1st) 3.53:1; (2nd) 1.95:1; (3rd) 1.24:1; (4th) 0.81:1 or 0.73:1; (Rev) 3.42:1. Citation H.O. V-6 four- speed manual trans.: (1st) 3.31:1; (2nd) 1.95:1; (3rd) 1.24:1; (4th) 0.81:1; (Rev) 3.42:1. Camaro four/V-6 four-speed manual trans.: (1st) 3.50:1; (2nd) 2.48:1; (3rd) 1.66:1; (4th) 1.00:1; (Rev) 3.50:1. Four-speed on Camaro V8305: (1st) 3.42:1; (2nd) 2.28:1; (3rd) 1.45:1; (4th) 1.00:1; (Rev) 3.51:1. Camaro V8305 TBI four-speed manual trans.: (1st) 2.88:1; (2nd) 1.91:1; (3rd) 1.33:1; (4th) 1.00:1; (Rev) 2.78:1. Chevette five-speed manual shift: (1st) 3.76:1; (2nd) 2.18:1; (3rd) 1.36:1; (4th) 1.00:1; (5th) 0.86:1; (Rev) 3.76:1. Three-speed Turbo Hydra-matic standard on Monte Carlo and Caprice/Impala, optional on others. Automatic gear ratios: (1st) 2.52:1; (2nd) 1.52:1; (3rd) 1.00:1; (Rev) 1.93:1 except Caprice/Impala V6231/V8305, Camaro and Malibu/Monte diesel V-6: (1st) 2.74:1; (2nd) 1.57:1; (3rd) 1.00:1; (Rev) 2.07:1. Chevette automatic trans.: (1st) 2.40:1; (2nd) 1.48:1; (3rd) 1.00:1; (Rev) 1.92:1. Cav/Cit/Celebrity auto. trans.: (1st) 2.84:1; (2nd) 1.60:1; (3rd) 1.00:1; (Rev) 2.07:1. Four-speed overdrive automatic transmission on Caprice/Impala: (1st) 2.74:1; (2nd) 1.57:1; (3rd) 1.00:1; (4th) 0.67:1; (Rev) 2.07:1. Four-speed overdrive automatic on Capr/Imp w/V-6: (1st) 3.06:1; (2nd) 1.63:1; (3rd) 1.00:1; (4th) 0.70:1; (Rev) 2.29:1. Standard final drive ratio: (Chevette) 3.36:1; (Cavalier) 3.32:1 w/manual, 2.84:1 w/auto.; (Cav wag) 3.65:1; (Citation) 3.32:1 w/4-speed, 2.84:1 w/auto. exc. H.O. V-6, 3.65:1 w/4- spd, 3.33:1 w/auto.; (Camaro four) 3.42:1 w/4-spd, 3.08:1 w/auto.; (Camaro V-6) 3.23:1 w/4spd, 3.08:1 w/auto.; (Camaro V-8) 2.73:1; (Camaro "Cross-Fire" V-8) 3.23:1 w/4spd, 2.23:1 w/auto. exc. (Z28) 2.93:1. (Celebrity) 2.84:1; (Malibu V-6) 2.41:1; (Malibu V-8) 2.29:1; (Malibu wag) 2.73:1 w/V-6, 2.56:1 w/V8267, 2.41:1 or 2.73:1 w/V8305; (Monte V-6) 2.41:1; (Monte V-8) 2.29:1; (Capr/Imp V-6) 2.73:1; (Capr/Imp V-8) 2.41:1 or 2.73:1 exc. 3.08:1 w/4-spd and V8305. Steering: (Cavalier/Chevette/Citation/Celebrity) rack and pinion; (others) recirculating ball. Front suspension: (Chevette/Cavalier/Citation/Celeb) MacPherson struts, lower control arms, coil springs, stabilizer bar; (Camaro) modified MacPherson struts, control arms, coil springs, stabilizer bar; (Malibu/Monte/Capr/Imp) upper and lower control arms, coil springs, stabilizer bar. Rear suspension: (Chevette) rigid axle, coil springs, trailing links; (Cavalier) beam axle, trailing arms, variable-rate coil springs; (Citation) beam "twist" axle, trailing arms, control arms, stabilizer bar; (Celeb) beam "twist" axle, trailing arms, coil springs, Panhard rod, stabilizer bar; (Camaro) torque arm, solid axle, lower control arms, track bar and coil springs, plus link-type rear stabilizer bar for F41 sport suspension and Z28; (Malibu/Monte/Capr/Imp) coil springs, four-link live axle, lower trailing radius arms and upper oblique torque arms, plus stabilizer bar on some models. Brakes: front disc, rear drum. Four-wheel discs available with Camaro V-8. Body construction: (Chvt/Cav/Cit/Celeb) unit; (Camaro) unitized with partial front frame and bolt-on front sheetmetal; (Malibu/Monte/Capr/Imp) separate body and frame. Fuel tank: (Chvt) 12.5 gal.; (Cav) 14 gal.; (Cit) 15.9 gal.; (Camaro) 16 gal.; (Celeb) 15.7 gal.; (Celeb V-6) 16.4 gal.; (Malibu) 18.1 gal.; (Malibu wag) 18.2 gal.; (Monte) 18.1 gal.; (Capr/Imp) 25 gal.; (Capr/Imp wag) 22 gal.

DRIVETRAIN OPTIONS: Engines: 173 cu. in., 2Bbl. V-6: Citation, base Camaro, Celeb ($125). 267 cu. in., 2Bbl. V-8: Malibu/Monte/Imp/Caprice ($70). 305 cu. in., 4Bbl. V-8: Camaro ($295); Berlinetta ($170); Malibu wag, Monte/Imp/Capr ($70); Imp/Capr wag (NC). 305 cu. in., dual CFI V-8: Camaro ($450). Diesel 260 cu. in. V-6: Celeb ($775). Diesel 350 cu. in. V-8: Malibu/Monte/Imp/Capr ($825); Imp/Capr wag ($653). Transmission/Differential: Three-speed automatic trans.: Chevette ($380); Cavalier ($370); Citation/Camaro ($396); Camaro Z28 ($72). Four-speed overdrive automatic trans.: Imp/Capr ($172). Limited-slip differential: Camaro/Malibu/Monte ($76); Imp/Capr ($80). Special final drive ratio (2.84:1 or 3.18:1): Cavalier ($20). Performance axle ratio: Camaro, Malibu/Imp/Capr wag ($21). Power Accessories: Power brakes: Chvt/Cit ($93). Power four- wheel disc brakes: Camaro ($179). Power steering: Chvt ($190); Cav ($180); Cit ($195). Suspension: F40 H.D. suspension: Cit/Celeb/Monte/Imp/Capr ($26). F41 sport suspension: Cav ($10-$46); Cit/Celeb ($33); Camaro/Monte/Imp/Capr cpe/sed ($49). Rear stabilizer bar: Cavalier ($36). Inflatable rear shock absorbers: Imp/Capr wag ($64). Other: H.D. radiator: Cavalier ($37-$65). H.D. cooling: Chvt/Cit/Camaro/Celeb/Malibu/Monte/Imp/Capr ($40-$70). Cold climate pkg.: Malibu/Monte/Imp/Capr diesel ($99). Diesel engine and fuel line heater: Celeb ($49). H.D. battery: Cav ($22); others ($25) exc. diesel ($50). California emission system: Chvt/Cit/Malibu/Monte/Imp/Capr (N/A); Cav ($46); Camaro/Celeb($65); Celeb diesel ($205).

CHEVETTE CONVENIENCE/APPEARANCE OPTIONS: Comfort/Convenience: Air conditioning ($595). Rear defogger, electric ($120). Tinted glass ($82). Comfortilt steering wheel ($95). Quartz electric clock ($32). Cigarette lighter: Scooter ($10). Rear wiper/washer ($117). Quiet sound group ($48-$60). Lighting and Mirrors: Halogen headlamps ($10). Aux. lighting ($41-$42). Twin sport mirrors, left remote ($50). Driver's remote sport mirror ($33). Entertainment: AM radio: Scooter ($78). AM/FM radio ($75); Scooter ($153). AM/FM stereo radio ($106). Rear speaker ($20). Radio delete ($51 credit). Exterior Trim: Deluxe exterior ($131-$138). Two-tone paint ($133). Sport stripes ($89). Bodyside moldings: Scooter ($45). Door edge guards ($15-$25). Roof carrier ($87). Interior Trim/Upholstery: Cloth bucket seats ($16-$28). Custom cloth bucket seats ($160). Rear seat delete ($50 credit). Color-keyed floor mats ($25). Wheels and Tires: Rally wheel trim ($59). P155/80R13 SBR WSW ($51). P175/70R13 SBR WSW ($122) exc. Scooter ($173).

CAVALIER CONVENIENCE/APPEARANCE OPTIONS: Comfort/Convenience: Air cond. ($625). Cruise control w/resume ($145-$155). Tinted glass: base ($82). Six-way power driver's seat ($183). Comfortilt steering wheel ($88). Power windows ($152-$216). Power door locks ($99-$142). Remote swing-out side windows ($55). **Gauge pkg. ($46). Special instruments ($78-$124). Intermittent wipers ($44). Rear wiper/washer ($109). Lighting, horns and mirros: Halogen headlamps: base ($38). Aux. lighting ($72-$81). Dual sport mirrors, left remote ($51). Dual electric remote** sport mirrors ($79-$130). Right visor mirror ($7). Lighted visor mirror ($38-$45). Entertainment: AM/FM radio: base ($64). AM/FM stereo radio ($100) exc. CL ($36). AM/FM stereo radio w/8track player ($179) exc. CL ($115). AM/FM stereo radio w/cassette ($217) exc. CL ($153). Rear speaker ($20-$32); dual ($30-$42). Radio delete ($71-$138 credit). Exterior Trim: Removable sunroof ($261). Two-tone paint ($164). Pinstriping ($53). Sport striping ($95). Wheel opening moldings ($26). Door edge guards ($14-$22). Roof carrier ($98). Bumper guards ($51). Interior Trim/Upholstery: Cloth bucket seats ($28). Color- keyed mats: front ($15); rear **($10). Cargo area cover ($60). Wheels and Tires: Aluminum wheels ($272-$317) P175/80R13 GBR WSW ($55). P195/70R13 SBR BSW ($133) exc. CL ($78). P195/70R13 SBR WSW ($188) exc. CL ($133). P195/70R13 SBR WLT ($205) exc. CL ($150). Puncture-sealant tires ($94).**

CITATION/CELEBRITY CONVENIENCE/APPEARANCE OPTIONS: Option Packages: X11 sport equipment pkg.: Citation ($1744). Deluxe exterior pkg.: Citation ($118-$169). Exterior molding pkg. (rocker panel and wheel opening moldings): Celeb ($53). Max. efficiency pkg. (rear spoiler and decals): Cit ($42). Quiet sound/rear decor pkg.: Cit ($87). Comfort/Convenience: Air cond. ($675). Rear defogger, electric ($125). Cruise control ($155-$165). Tinted glass ($88). Comfortilt steering wheel ($95). Six-way power driver's seat: Celeb ($197). Power windows ($165-$235). Remote swing-out side windows: Cit ($108). Power door locks ($106-$152). Gauge pkg. w/clock: Cit ($104). Gauge pkg. w/trip odometer: Celeb ($64). Electric clock: Cit ($32). Digital clock: Celeb ($60). Intermittent wipers ($47). Lighting, Horns and Mirrors: Halogen high-beam headlamps: Celeb ($10). Aux. lighting: Cit ($50). Dual horns: Cit ($12). Driver's remote mirror ($22). Dual sport mirrors, left remote ($55). Dual remote mirrors: Celeb ($86). Entertainment: AM/FM radio ($75-$82). AM/FM stereo radio ($106-$118). AM/FM stereo w/8track: Celeb ($282). AM/FM stereo w/cassette: Celeb ($277). Dual rear speakers ($30); incl. w/stereo radio. Windshield antenna: Cit ($12). Power antenna: Cit ($55). Radio delete ($56 credit). Exterior Trim: Removable sunroof: Cit ($275). Vinyl roof: Celeb ($140). Two-tone paint: Cit ($176) incl. pinstriping and bodyside moldings; Celeb ($148). Bodyside pinstriping: Cit ($39); Celeb ($57). Bodyside moldings: Cit ($47). Door edge guards ($15-$25). Bumper guards ($56-$60). Bumper rub strips: Cit ($50). Interior Trim/Upholstery: Console ($100). Reclining driver and passenger seatbacks ($96). Sport cloth bench seat: Cit ($28). Custom cloth or vinyl bench seat: Cit ($418). Sport cloth bucket seats: Citation ($131-$160) exc. w/X11 (NC). Custom cloth bucket seats: Cit ($397-$534). Vinyl bench seat: Celeb ($28). Celebrity custom bench seat: cloth ($109-$179); vinyl ($137-$207). Celebrity 45/45 seating: cloth ($133); vinyl ($161). Special custom cloth 45/45 seat: Celeb ($399- $459). Color-keyed mats: front ($16); rear ($11). **Wheels and Tires: Full wheel covers: Cit ($52). Sport wheel covers; Celeb ($62). Wire wheel covers; Celeb ($153). Wheel cover locks; Celeb ($39). Rally wheels; Cit ($41-$93); Celeb ($153). P185/80R13 GBR WSW ($58). P185/80R13 SBR BSW** ($64). P185/80R13 SBR WSW ($122). P205/70R13 SBR BSW: Celeb ($179). P205/70R13 SBR WSW: Celeb ($245). P205/70R13 SBR WLT: Cit ($267). P185/75R14 SBR WSW: Celeb ($157). P215/60R14 SBR WLT: Citation X11 ($92). Puncture-sealant tires ($106).

CAMARO/MALIBU/MONTE CARLO CONVENIENCE/APPEARANCE OPTIONS: Option Packages: Estate equipment: Malibu wag ($307). Quiet sound group: Camaro ($72-$82). Security pkg.: Malibu wag ($44). Comfort/Convenience: Air cond. ($675). Rear defogger, electric ($125). Cruise control ($155-$165). Tinted glass ($88). Comfortilt steering wheel ($95). Six-way power driver's seat: Camaro/Monte ($197). Power windows: Camaro/Monte ($165); Malibu ($235). Power door locks: Malibu ($152); Camaro/Monte ($106). Power trunk release: Monte ($32). Power hatch release: Camaro ($32). Power tailgate window release: Malibu wag ($33). Electric clock: base Camaro, Malibu/Monte ($32). Digital clock: Berlinetta/Z28 ($28). Gauge pkg. w/trip odometer: Malibu/Monte ($95). Special instruments: base Camaro ($149). Intermittent wipers ($47). Rear wiper/washer: Camaro ($117). Lighting, Horns and Mirrors: Halogen high-beam headlamps ($10). Cornering lamps: Monte ($55). Aux. lighting: Camaro ($52); Malibu/Monte ($38). Dual horns: Camaro ($12). Remote- control driver's mirror: Malibu ($22). Twin sport mirrors (left remote): base Camaro, Monte ($48); Malibu ($55). Twin remote sport mirrors: Monte ($79). Twin electric remote sport mirrors: Camaro ($89-$137). Lighted visor mirror: Monte ($48). Entertainment: AM radio: Camaro/Monte ($111). AM/FM radio: ($165-$172). AM/FM stereo radio: Camaro ($258-$282); Malibu/Monte ($196). Stereo 8track tape player with AM/FM stereo radio: Camaro ($390-$446); Malibu/Monte ($282). Cassette player with AM/FM stereo radio: Camaro ($385-$441); Malibu/Monte ($283). Dual rear speakers: Camaro ($30-$54); Malibu/Monte ($30). Fixed mast antenna ($41); incl. w/radios. Power antenna ($55). Exterior Trim: Removable glass roof panels: Camaro/Monte ($790). Landau vinyl roof: Monte ($232). Rear spoiler: Camaro ($69). Two-tone paint: Malibu ($138); Monte ($214). Bodyside moldings: Camaro ($47). Deluxe bodyside moldings: Malibu/Monte ($57). Door edge guards ($15-$25). Side window sill and rear hood moldings: Monte ($45). Roof drip moldings: Camaro ($29). Bodyside pinstriping: Malibu ($57); Monte ($61). Rear window air deflector: Malibu wag ($36). Roof carrier: Malibu wag ($115). Bumper rub strips: Malibu ($50). Bumper guards, front/rear: Malibu ($56). Interior Trim/Upholstery: Vinyl bench seat: Malibu cpe/sed, Monte ($28). Cloth bench seat: Malibu wag ($28). Custom cloth bench seat: Malibu sed, Monte ($358). Cloth or vinyl 55/45 seating: Malibu/Monte ($133-$161). Cloth bucket seats: Camaro ($28). Custom cloth or vinyl bucket seats: base Camaro/Z28 ($299). Cloth LS contour bucket seats: Camaro ($312). Custom cloth LS contour bucket seats: Camaro ($611). Color-keyed mats: **Malibu/Monte ($27); Camaro front ($16); Camaro rear ($11). Deluxe load-floor carpet: Malibu wag ($84). Deluxe trunk trim: Camaro ($164); Monte ($47). Wheels and Tires: Aluminum wheels: Monte ($362). Rally wheels: Camaro ($112); Malibu/Monte** ($56). Full wheel covers: Camaro ($52). Sport wheel covers (silver or gold): Malibu ($62). Wire wheel covers: Malibu/Monte ($153). Wheel cover locks: Malibu/Monte ($39). P185/75R14 GBR WSW: Malibu cpe/sed ($58). P195/75R14 GBR WSW: Camaro, Malibu wag ($62). P195/75R14 SBR BSW: Camaro ($65). P195/75R14 SBR WSW: Camaro ($127); Malibu cpe/sed ($151); Malibu wag ($123); Monte ($62). P205/70R14 SBR BSW: base Camaro ($123). P205/70R14 SBR WSW: Camaro ($189); Berlinetta ($66); Monte ($124). P205/70R14 SBR WLT: Camaro ($211). Puncture-sealant tires: Malibu/Monte ($105).

1982 Caprice Classic Estate Wagon (CP)

IMPALA/CAPRICE CONVENIENCE/APPEARANCE OPTIONS: Option Packages: Estate equipment: wag ($307). Value appearance group: bodyside and wheel opening moldings, full wheel covers ($113). Comfort/Convenience: Air cond. ($695). Rear defogger, electric ($125). Cruise control ($155). Tinted glass ($102). Comfortilt steering wheel ($95). Power door locks ($106- $152). Six-way power driver's seat ($197). Power windows ($165-$240). Power trunk release ($32). Power tailgate lock: wag ($49). Electric clock: Imp ($32). Digital clock: Imp ($66); Caprice ($34). Gauge pkg. w/trip odometer ($64). Intermittent wipers ($47). Quiet sound group: Imp ($66-$72). Lighting and Mirrors: Halogen high-beam headlamps ($10). Cornering lamps ($55). Aux. lighting ($42-$64). Driver's remote mirror ($22). Dual remote mirrors ($65). Dual sport mirrors, left remote ($55). Dual remote body-color sport mirrors ($86). Lighted visor mirror ($48). Entertainment: AM radio ($99). AM/FM radio ($153). AM/FM stereo radio ($184). Stereo 8track tape player with AM/FM stereo radio ($270). Cassette player with AM/FM stereo ($271). Dual rear speakers ($30). Power antenna ($55). Windshield antenna ($29); incl. w/radios. Exterior Trim: Vinyl roof: cpe/sed ($165). Roof carrier: wag ($140). Two-tone paint ($65). Custom two-tone ($141). Pinstriping ($39). Color-keyed bodyside moldings ($51). Door edge guards ($15-$25). Bumper rub strips, front/rear ($66). Bumper guards ($62). Interior Trim/Upholstery: Vinyl bench seat: cpe/sed ($28). Cloth bench seat: wag ($28). Cloth 50/50 seat ($238-$285). Custom cloth 50/50 seat: cpe ($428); sed ($452). Deluxe load- floor carpet: wag ($89). Deluxe cargo area carpet: wag ($129). **Color-keyed mats: front ($16); rear ($11). Deluxe trunk trim ($59). Wheels and Tires: Full wheel covers ($52). Sport wheel covers: Imp ($115); Caprice ($63). Wire wheel covers ($153). Wire wheel cover locks ($39). P205/75R15 SBR WSW: cpe/sed ($66). P225/70R15 SBR WSW: cpe/sed ($159). P225/75R15 SBR WSW: wag ($71). Puncture-sealant tires ($106-$131).**

HISTORY: General introduction was Sept. 24, 1981 but Cavalier debuted May 21, 1981; Chevette/Citation/Corvette on Dec. 12, 1981; and Camaro/Celebrity not until Jan. 14, 1982. Model year production (U.S.): 1,131,748 (incl. Corvettes and early '82 Cavaliers but not incl. 10,655 Acadians). Total production for the U.S. market was made up of 524,694 four-cylinder, 356,314 sixes, and 351,518 V-8s. A total of 48,654 diesels were installed. Calendar year production (U.S.): 1,004,244 (including 22,838 Corvettes plus Acadians, but not incl. 139,837 early '82 Cavaliers). Calendar year sales by U.S. dealers: 1,260,620, for a 21.8 percent market share. Model year sales by U.S. dealers: 1,234,988 (incl. 22,086 Corvettes but not incl. 43,855 early 1982 Cavaliers), for a 22.3 percent share.

Historical Footnotes: Cavalier debuted in a national media preview in Washington, DC, amid sales predictions of 345,000 for 1982. Production began slowly and sales proved disappointing, even after early delivery shortages were remedied. Additional assembly plants (at Leeds and Janesville) were prepared to begin Cavalier production in spring 1982. Chevrolet called 1982 the "year of the diesel." Diesel power was now available on Chevettes, Caprice/Impalas, Malibus and Monte Carlos, and soon would arrive on **the new Celebrity. Of the 14 engine sizes available this year in cars and light trucks, five were diesels. General Manager Robert D. Lund estimated that over 300,000 Chevrolet vehicles built in 1982 might have diesel engines. That prediction turned out** to be overly optimistic. Within a couple of years the highly- touted diesel powerplant would begin to fade away, victim of driveability problems, stable gasoline prices, and general lack of customer interest. In one illuminating survey that held portents of the future, Chevrolet discovered that nearly 37 percent of Camaros purchased in 1980 were bought by women. That was higher than any other Chevrolet passenger car, and well above the industry average of 24.5 percent. Twin slogans for the restyled Camaro also suggested what was to come as the decade unrolled. "Excess is out. Efficiency is in" predicted the rising emphasis on fuel-efficiency and modest size. "Brute power is out. Precision is in" seemed to toll the death knell for the big V-8, but it would be around for some time yet.

1983 CHEVROLET

After the three major new product introductions for 1982, this year focused on powertrain refinements for performance and economy. Changes included new five-speed manual gearboxes available for Camaro, Chevette and Cavalier, plus a bigger Cavalier engine. All Citations could get the high-output (135 horsepower) V-6 this year. Mid-year arrivals included a Cavalier convertible, notchback Citation X11, and available four-speed manual transaxle in Celebrity. But the most notable news of all was probably the reworked 1984 Corvette, which debuted in spring and missed the '83 model year completely.

CHEVETTE — SERIES 1T — FOUR — Chevette enjoyed a rather dramatic restyling this year, gaining a deep front air dam that flowed into flared wheel housings, body-color bumpers (but black on Scooters), and a number of blackout body trim pieces. Even so, apart from a higher position of front side marker lamps and front fender script, basic appearance was quite similar to before. Scooters, priced as low as $4997, gained reclining front bucket seats as standard. Chevette's crosshatch grille sported a familiar bowtie emblem in its center. A new 'Chevette S' sport decor package included black and red accents, special wheel trim rings, black grille, black headlamp bezels, and black wheels. Red accents went on bodyside moldings and nameplates. The sport package came in five body colors, others in ten. Four interior colors were offered. Two four-cylinder engine choices were available (1.6- liter gas and 1.8-liter diesel), plus three transmissions: four- and five-speed manual, and three-speed automatic. Five- speed was standard with the diesel, and offered for the first time with the gas engine (though it had been announced earlier). Scooter equipment included a color-keyed front air dam, black steel bumpers with end caps and guards, black grille, dome lamp, day/night mirror, black moldings (windshield, hatch window reveal, roof drip), vinyl reclining front bucket seats, front stabilizer, and styled steel wheels. Standard models added color-keyed bumpers, lighter, mini

1983 Chevette S hatchback coupe (AA)

console, locking glove box, black grille with argent accent, color- keyed dash, black bodyside and rocker moldings, and an AM radio. Diesel Chevettes had standard power brakes.

1983 Cavalier coupe (JG)

CAVALIER — SERIES 1J — FOUR — Appearance was similar to 1982, but a modified standard equipment list allowed significant price cuts to the subcompact Cavalier. The new base prices ($5888 to $6633) were $389 to $1868 lower than equivalent 1982 values. But quite a few items that had been standard now joined the option list. Seven models and three trim levels were available. Top- of-the-line was now the CS, while CL became an option package (priced at $577 to $696), containing many of the former CL series items. The budget-priced Cadet series was dropped, along with the base hatchback coupe. All Cavaliers had beige/charcoal instrument panels and consoles, replacing the former brushed aluminum/woodgrain. Two-door CS models got a new easy-entry passenger seat that slid forward automatically when folded down for access to the back. Standard equipment remaining in the list included radial tires, power brakes, front stabilizer bar, vinyl reclining front bucket seats, and side window defoggers. Cavaliers came in ten body colors and five interior colors. On the

1983 Cavalier 2-dr hatchback coupe

mechanical side, Cavalier became Chevrolet's first front-drive with a five-speed manual transaxle available. It offered two overdrive ratios (0.92:1 in fourth and 0.75:1 in fifth gear), plus a 3.91:1 first gear ratio. Four-speed overdrive manual remained standard, with three- speed automatic optional. Also new was a bigger (2.0-liter) fuel-injected engine with higher compression and torque. A "cyclonic" cylinder head gave faster fuel burning. New, "more aggressive" axle ratios boosted performance. A new convertible arrived later in the model year (January), built by American Sunroof in Lansing, Michigan. Produced in limited numbers, it was the first Chevrolet ragtop since 1975. Cavalier's new standard equipment list included bright bumpers with black/argent rub srips, black grille, black left-hand outside mirror, day/night inside mirror, console with rear ashtray and coin tray, four-spoke charcoal steering wheel, styled steel wheels with P175/80R13 GBR tires, compact spare tire, two-speed wiper/washers, and black moldings (glass and drip). CS models added a lighter, locking glove compartment, halogen headlamps, color-keyed dash, AM radio, three-spoke color-keyed steering wheel, black/argent bodyside moldings, and bright side window moldings. CS hatchbacks also had color-keyed bumpers, fold-down rear seat and special instruments; all but hatchbacks had a bright grille rather than the standard black. The new Cavalier convertible carried tinted glass, power steering, power windows, and twin sport mirrors (left remote). Added to the option list were an electric rear defogger, power hatch or trunk release, electronic-tuning radios, split folding rear seatback, and black/argent bodyside moldings.

1983 Citation hatchback coupe (JG)

CITATION — SERIES 1X — FOUR/V-6 — Little changed on Citation except for upgraded front seats and a restyled instrument panel. Interiors held new low-back front seats with adjustable headrests. Of the five interior colors, maroon and dark brown were new. Maroon was also a new addition to the body color selection. Base engine was still the fuel-injected 151 cu. in. (2.5-liter) four. The high-output V-6 was now optional on all models, not just as part of the X11 option package. Citation was still offered as a two-door hatchback, two-door notchback, or four-door hatchback. Joining the option list this year was a Sport Decor package that included exterior graphics, rear spoiler, rally wheels, color-keyed bumpers, and sport mirrors. The X11 package was again offered for the two-door hatchback and, later in the model year, for the notchback as well. It included special graphics, a bubble hood with nameplates, and high-output V-6 engine. Because of equipment changes, the package cost about $700 less than in 1982. The revised X11 also included bucket seats, sport mirrors, rear spoiler, P215/60R14 SBR tires on 14 in. aluminum alloy wheels, black grille, nameplates, sport steering wheel, power brakes, F41 sport suspension, modified exhaust, color-keyed bumpers with rub strips, sport decal, and black moldings (windshield, window and drip). Price tag was now $998, and 1,934 were installed.

1983 Camaro Z28 T-top Sport Coupe (JG)

CAMARO — SERIES 1F — V-6/V-8 — Camaro's looks changed little this year after the 1982 aero restyle, but more powertrain combinations were available. Engine choices were as before: base 151 cu. in. (2.5-liter) fuel-injected four on the Sport Coupe, Berlinetta's standard 173 cu. in. (2.8-liter) V-6, and two 305 cu. in. (5.0-liter) V-8s. Standard V-8 was carbureted, but Z28 could have the Cross-Fire fuel-injected version. Camaros with the CFI engine had functional dual air intake hood scoops. Five-speed overdrive manual was now optional on the base Sport Coupe, standard on others. New four-speed overdrive automatic (with lockup torque converter) was also available. A new high-output 305 V-8 engine with revised cam and four-barrel carburetor arrived late in the model year, developing 190 horsepower. A total of 3,223 H.O. V-8s were installed in Camaros this year. Optional "Conteur" multi-adjustment driver's seats got matching passenger seats. Stereo radios offered electronic tuning. Z28 had new three-tone upholstery featuring multiple Camaro logos. Body colors this year were white, black and red, plus seven metallics: silver, light or dark blue, light or dark brown, charcoal, and dark gold. Maroon was dropped from the body color list, and brown replaced maroon as an interior choice; but colors otherwise remained the same as before. Camaros again had a rear glass hatch, reclining front bucket seats, and standard power steering. Joining the option list: a rear compartment cover to hide cargo. Optional mats now were carpeted instead of plain rubber.

1983 Celebrity CL sedan (AA)

CELEBRITY — SERIES 1A — FOUR/V-6 — Arriving late this year, the luxury aerodynamic five- passenger family car got the diesel V-6 option (announced earlier) for the first time. A new four-speed overdrive automatic transmission also joined the mid-year option list. Chevrolet's biggest front-drive kept its standard 151 cu. in. (2.5-liter) fuel-injected four, with optional 2.8-liter gas V-6 as well as the diesel. Standard equipment included automatic transmission, power brakes and steering. Interiors came in five colors and two CL trim levels, one with 45/45 seating. A center console was optional. Ten body colors were offered. All radio options now had electronic tuning and the eight-track tape players were dropped, but little else changed.

MALIBU — SERIES 1A — V-6/V-8 — This would be the final season for the rear-drive six- passenger Malibu, whose family-carrying duties were being taken over by the front-drive Celebrity. Base engine was the 229 cu. in. (3.8-liter) V-6, with V-6 and V-8 diesels available as well as the 305 gas V-8. Only two bodies were offered: four-door sedan and four-door wagon. The Malibu Classic nameplate was dropped (replaced by the luxury CL option), so only one series remained this year, stressing economy. Notchback bench or 55/45 split front seats with fold-down armrests came in cloth or vinyl. Several trim items were added to the option list, including rocker panel and wheel opening moldings. Malibu's standard equipment included power brakes and steering, automatic transmission, locking glove compartment, lighter, dome light, compact spare tire, front stabilizer bar, and two-speed wiper/washers. Bodies held bright sill, rear window and windshield reveal, roof drip and belt moldings.

1983 Monte Carlo CL Sport Coupe (AA)

MONTE CARLO — SERIES 1A — V-6/V-8 — Monte's front end gained a bolder, more aggressive look with its new large-segmented (bigger holes) crosshatch grille. Both gas and diesel V-6 and V-8 engines were available, but the small-block 267 cu. in. gas V-8 was dropped, replaced by the 305 cu. in. (5.0-liter) V-8. For the first time in three years, the 305 V-8 was available under both Malibu and Monte Carlo hoods. Standard engine was the 229 cu. in. (3.8-liter) V-6. Monte came in ten body colors and five interior colors, in two trim levels (including a luxury CL option). A revived interest in rear-drive mid-sizes kept Monte in the lineup, offering six-passenger coupe roominess. Standard equipment included power brakes and steering, full wheel covers, front stabilizer bar, body-color bumpers, bright windshield and quarter-window reveal moldings, twin bright mirrors, chromed headlamp bezels, bright lower bodyside moldings, wheel opening and roof drip moldings, dual horns, and a stand-up hood ornament. Montes rode P195/75R14 SBR tires and carried a compact spare. Inside was a full- width front seat with folding armrest, door pull straps, leather-like dash applique, day/night mirror, color-keyed steering wheel, locking glove compartment, lighter, and courtesy lights. In addition to the base model, a new Monte Carlo SS coupe joined the lineup late in the season, powered by a high-output version of the carbureted 305 cu. in. V-8.

1983 Caprice Classic sedan (JG)

IMPALA/CAPRICE CLASSIC — SERIES 1B — V-6/V-8 — Continuing demand kept the twin full-size Chevrolets around, but they lost a number of models this year. All that remained of the Impala name was a four-door sedan, while Caprice fielded a sedan and nine-passenger (three-seat) station wagon. No two-door models were left. Base sedan engine remained the 229 cu. in. (3.8-liter) V-6. The Caprice wagon continued with the 305 cu. in. (5.0- liter) V-8. Options included the 305 gas V-8, 350 diesel V-8, new four-speed overdrive automatic transmission with 0.79:1 top gear, and a higher-number (3.08:1) axle ratio. The 267 cu. in. V-8 was gone. Black was again offered as one of the ten possible body colors, after being unavailable in 1982. Interior trims came in five colors: dark blue, light green, silver, maroon, and dark brown. Caprice sedans cold have a CL luxury interior package. Impala standard equipment included three-speed automatic transmission, power brakes and steering, cloth bench seat, day/night mirror, two-speed wiper/washers, front stabilizer bar, trunk mat, **lighter, and lights for dome, trunk and glove compartment. Impala also wore bright roof drip, windshield and back window reveal, window frame, door frame and lower body side moldings. Caprice added overdrive automatic transmission, a quartz electric** clock, dual horns, full wheel covers, wheel opening moldings, bright wide lower bodyside moldings, dash and ashtray lights, and a headlamps-on warning buzzer. Wagons had a power tailgate window. Caprice sedans had cloth seats, wagons vinyl.

I.D. DATA: Chevrolets again had a 17-symbol Vehicle Identification Number (VIN) on the upper left surface of the instrument panel, visible through the windshield. Symbol one indicates country: '1' U.S.A.; '2' Canada. Next is a manufacturer code: 'G' General Motors. Symbol three is car make: '1' Chevrolet; '2' GM of Canada. Symbol four denotes restraint system: 'A' non-passive (standard); 'B' passive (automatic belts); 'C' passive (inflatable). Symbol five is car line/series: 'B' Chevette; 'J' Chevette Scooter; 'D' Cavalier; 'E' Cavalier hatchback; 'H' Citation coupe; 'X' Citation; 'P' Camaro; 'S' Camaro Berlinetta; 'W' Celebrity or Malibu; 'Z' Monte Carlo; 'L' Impala; 'N' Caprice. Symbols six-seven reveal body type: '08' 2-dr. hatch coupe; '11' 2-dr. notchback coupe; '27' 2-dr. notchback coupe (or convertible); '37' special 2-dr. notch coupe; '77' 2-dr. hatch coupe; '87' 2-dr. sport coupe; '19' 4-dr. 6-window notchback sedan; '68' 4-dr. hatch sedan; '69' 4-dr. 4-window notchback sedan; '35' 4-dr. station wagon. Next is the engine code: 'C' L498 2Bbl.; 'D' L4111 diesel; 'P' L4121 FI; 'R' or '2' L4151 FI; 'X' or '1' V6173 2Bbl.; 'Z' H.O. V6173; 'K' or '9' V6229 2Bbl.; 'T' or 'V' V6262 diesel; 'H' V8305 4Bbl.; 'S' V8305 FI; 'N' V8350 diesel. Next is a check digit, followed by 'D' for model year 1983. Symbol eleven indicates assembly plant: 'B' Baltimore; 'J' Janesville, WI; 'L' Van Nuys, CA; 'N' Norwood, OH; 'R' Arlington, TX; 'T' Tarrytown, NY; 'X' Fairfax, KS; 'Y' Wilmington, DE; '1' Oshawa, Ontario; '6' Oklahoma City, OK; '7' Lordstown, OH. The final six digits are the sequential serial number. Engine number coding is similar to 1982.

CHEVETTE (FOUR)

Model Number	Body/Style Number	Body Type & Seating	Factory Price	Shipping Weight	Production Total
1T	B08	2-dr. Hatch Cpe-4P	5469	2029	37,537
1T	B68	4-dr. Hatch Sed-4P	5616	2090	81,297

CHEVETTE SCOOTER (FOUR)

Model Number	Body/Style Number	Body Type & Seating	Factory Price	Shipping Weight	Production Total
1T	J08	2-dr. Hatch Cpe-4P	4997	1971	33,488
1T	J68	4-dr. Hatch Sed-4P	5333	2040	15,303

CHEVETTE DIESEL (FOUR)

Model Number	Body/Style Number	Body Type & Seating	Factory Price	Shipping Weight	Production Total
1T	B08/Z90	2-dr. Hatch Cpe-4P	6535	N/A	439
1T	B68/Z90	4-dr. Hatch Sed-4P	6683	N/A	1,501

CAVALIER (FOUR)

Model Number	Body/Style Number	Body Type & Seating	Factory Price	Shipping Weight	Production Total
1J	C27	2-dr. Coupe-5P	5888	2315	23,028
1J	C69	4-dr. Sedan-5P	5999	2335	33,333
1J	C35	4-dr. Sta Wag-5P	6141	2395	27,922

CAVALIER CS (FOUR)

Model Number	Body/Style Number	Body Type & Seating	Factory Price	Shipping Weight	Production Total
1J	D27	2-dr. Coupe-5P	6363	2305	22,172
1J	E77	2-dr. Hatch Cpe-5P	6549	2370	25,869
1J	D69	4-dr. Sedan-5P	6484	2357	52,802
1J	D35	4-dr. Sta Wag-5P	6633	2417	32,834
1J	D27/Z08	2-dr. Conv. Cpe-5P	10990	N/A	627

CITATION (FOUR/V-6)

Model Number	Body/Style Number	Body Type & Seating	Factory Price	Shipping Weight	Production Total
1X	H11	2-dr. Coupe-5P	6333/6483	2394/2457	6,456
1X	X08	2-dr. Hatch Cpe-5P	6788/6938	2403/2466	14,323
1X	X68	4-dr. Hatch Sed-5P	6934/7084	2442/2505	71,405

CAMARO (V-6/V-8)

Model Number	Body/Style Number	Body Type & Seating	Factory Price	Shipping Weight	Production Total
1F	P87	2-dr. Spt Cpe-4P	8186/8386	2878/3035	63,806

CAMARO BERLINETTA (V-6/V-8)

Model Number	Body/Style Number	Body Type & Seating	Factory Price	Shipping Weight	Production Total
1F	S87	2-dr. Spt Cpe-4P	9881/10106	2864/3056	27,925

CAMARO Z28 (V-8)

Model Number	Body/Style Number	Body Type & Seating	Factory Price	Shipping Weight	Production Total
1F	P87	2-dr. Spt Cpe-4P	-- /10336	-- /3061	62,100

Camaro Engine Note: Prices and weights before slash are for V-6 engine, after slash for V-8. Base Camaro Sport Coupes were also available with a four-cylinder engine, priced at $8036 and weighing 2803 pounds. The Z28 could have an optional CFI V-8 for an additional $450. **Z28 Production Note:** Chevrolet production figures also show 550 Z28E hatchback sport coupes built for export.

CELEBRITY (FOUR/V-6)

Model Number	Body/Style Number	Body Type & Seating	Factory Price	Shipping Weight	Production Total
1A	W27	2-dr. Coupe-5P	8059/8209	2629/2689	19,221
1A	W19	4-dr. Sedan-5P	8209/8359	2649/2709	120,608

MALIBU CLASSIC (V-6/V-8)

Model Number	Body/Style Number	Body Type & Seating	Factory Price	Shipping Weight	Production Total
1A	W69	4-dr. Spt Sed-6P	8084/8309	3106/3214	61,534
1A	W35	4-dr. Sta Wag-6P	8217/8442	3249/3376	55,892

MONTE CARLO (V-6/V-8)

Model Number	Body/Style Number	Body Type & Seating	Factory Price	Shipping Weight	Production Total
1A	Z37	2-dr. Spt Cpe-6P	8552/8777	3128/3236	91,605

MONTE CARLO 'SS' (V-8)

Model Number	Body/Style Number	Body Type & Seating	Factory Price	Shipping Weight	Production Total
1A	Z37/Z65	2-dr. Spt Cpe-6P	-- /10249	-- /3242	4,714

IMPALA (V-6/V-8)

Model Number	Body/Style Number	Body Type & Seating	Factory Price	Shipping Weight	Production Total
1B	L69	4-dr. Sedan-6P	8331/8556	3356/3460	45,154

CAPRICE CLASSIC (V-6/V-8)

Model Number	Body/Style Number	Body Type & Seating	Factory Price	Shipping Weight	Production Total
1B	N69	4-dr. Sedan-6P	8802/9027	3402/3506	122,613
1B	N35	4-dr. 3S Wag-9P	-- /9518	-- /3975	53,028

FACTORY PRICE AND WEIGHT NOTE: For Citation and Celebrity, prices and weights to left of slash are for four-cylinder, to right for V-6 engine. For Camaro, Malibu, Monte Carlo and full-size models, figures to left of slash are for six-cylinder model, to right of slash for 305 cu. in. V-8. Diesel V-6 and V-8 engines cost considerably more (see option prices). **BODY/STYLE NO. NOTE:** Some models were actually option packages. Code after the slash (e.g., Z65) is the number of the option package that comes with the model listed.

ENGINE DATA: BASE FOUR (Chevette): Inline. Overhead cam. Four-cylinder. Cast iron block and head. Displacement: 98 cu. in. (1.6 liters). Bore & stroke: 3.23 x 2.98 in. Compression ratio: 9.0:1. Brake horsepower: 65 at 5200 R.P.M. Torque: 80 lbs.-ft. at 3200 R.P.M. Five main bearings. Hydraulic valve lifters. Carburetor: 2Bbl. VIN Code: C. DIESEL FOUR (Chevette): Inline. Overhead cam. Four-cylinder. Cast iron block and head. Displacement: 111 cu. in. (1.8 liters). Bore & stroke: 3.31 x 3.23 in. Compression ratio: 22.0:1. Brake horsepower: 51 at 5200 R.P.M. Torque: 72 lbs.-ft. at 2000 R.P.M. Five main bearings. Solid valve lifters. Fuel injection. VIN Code: D. BASE FOUR (Cavalier): Inline. Overhead valve. Four-cylinder. Cast iron block and head. Displacement: 121 cu. in. (2.0 liters). Bore & stroke: 3.50 x 3.15 in. Compression ratio: 9.3:1. Brake horsepower: 88 at 4800 R.P.M. Torque: 110 lbs.-ft. at 2400 R.P.M. Five main bearings. Hydraulic valve lifters. Throttle-body fuel injection. VIN Code: P. BASE FOUR (Citation, Celebrity, Camaro): Inline. Overhead valve. Four-cylinder. Cast iron block and head. Displacement: 151 cu. in. (2.5 liters). Bore & stroke: 4.00 x 3.00 in. Compression ratio: 8.2:1. Brake horsepower: 92 at 4000 R.P.M. Torque: 134 lbs.-ft. at 2800 R.P.M. Five main bearings. Hydraulic valve lifters. Throttle-body fuel injection. Pontiac-built. VIN Code: R exc. (Camaro) 2. BASE V-6 (Camaro Berlinetta); OPTIONAL (Citation, Celebrity, Camaro): 60-degree, overhead-valve V-6. Cast iron block and head. Displacement: 173 cu. in. (2.8 liters). Bore & stroke: 3.50 x 2.99 in. Compression ratio: 8.5:1. Brake horsepower: 112 at 4800 R.P.M. (Camaro, 107 at 4800). Torque: 145 lbs.-ft. at 2100 R.P.M. Four main bearings. Hydraulic valve lifters. Carburetor: 2Bbl. Rochester E2SE. VIN Code: X exc. (Camaro) 1. HIGH-OUTPUT V-6 (Citation): Same as 173 cu. in. V-6 above except C.R.: 8.9:1. Brake H.P.: 135 at 5400 R.P.M. Torque: 145 lbs.- ft. at 2400 R.P.M. VIN Code: Z. BASE V-6 (Malibu, Monte Carlo, Impala, Caprice): 90-degree, overhead-valve V-6. Cast iron block and head. Displacement: 229 cu. in. (3.8 liters). Bore & stroke: 3.74 x 3.48 in. Compression ratio: 8.6:1. Brake horsepower: 110 at 4000 R.P.M. Torque: 190 lbs.-ft. at 1600 R.P.M. Four main bearings. Hydraulic valve lifters. Carburetor: 2Bbl. Rochester E2ME. VIN Code: K or 9. (NOTE: California models used a Buick 231 V-6.) DIESEL V-6 (Malibu, Celebrity, Monte Carlo): 90-degree, overhead-valve V-6. Cast iron block and head. Displacement: 262 cu. in. (4.3 liters). Bore & stroke: 4.057 x 3.385 in. Compression ratio: 22.8:1. Brake horsepower: 85 at 3600 R.P.M. Torque: 165 lbs.-ft. at 1600 R.P.M. Four main bearings. Hydraulic valve lifters. Fuel injection. VIN Code: T or V. BASE V-8 (Camaro Z28, Impala/Caprice wagon): OPTIONAL (Camaro, Malibu, Monte Carlo, Impala, Caprice): 90-degree, overhead valve V-8. Cast iron block and head. Displacement: 305 cu. in. (5.0 liters). Bore & stroke: 3.74 x 3.48 in. Compression ratio: 8.6:1. Brake horsepower: 150 at 4000 R.P.M. Torque: 240 lbs.-ft. at 2400 R.P.M. Five main bearings. Hydraulic valve lifters. Carburetor: 4Bbl. Rochester E4ME. VIN Code: H. HIGH-OUTPUT V-8 (Monte Carlo SS); OPTIONAL (Camaro): Same as 305 cu. in. V-8 above, except Brake H.P.: 175 at 4800 R.P.M. Torque: 235 lbs.-ft. at 3200 R.P.M. OPTIONAL FUEL-INJECTED V-8 (Camaro Z28): Same as 305 cu. in. V-8 above, with dual CFI Brake H.P.: 175 at 4200 R.P.M. Torque: 250 lbs.-ft. at 2800 R.P.M. VIN Code: S. DIESEL V-8; OPTIONAL (Malibu, Monte Carlo, Impala/Caprice): 90-degree, overhead valve V-8. Cast iron block and head. Displacment: 350 cu. in (5.7 liters). Bore & stroke: 4.057 x 3.385 in. Compression ratio: 22.5:1. Brake horsepower: 105 at 3200 R.P.M. Torque: 200 lbs.-ft. at 1600 R.P.M. Five main bearings. Hydraulic valve lifters. Fuel injection. Olds-built. VIN Code: N.

CHASSIS DATA: Dimensions and tires were virtually identical to 1982, except for slight growth in overall length of Cavalier coupe to 170.9 in.

TECHNICAL: Transmission: Four-speed floor shift standard on Chevette: Gear ratios (1st) 3.75:1; (2nd) 2.16:1; (3rd) 1.38:1; (4th) 1.00:1; (Rev) 3.82:1. Four-speed floor shift on Cavalier/Citation: (1st) 3.53:1; (2nd) 1.95:1; (3rd) 1.24:1; (4th) 0.81:1 or 0.73:1; (Rev) 3.42:1. Citation H.O. V-6 four- speed manual trans.: (1st) 3.31:1; (2nd) 1.95:1; (3rd) 1.24:1; (4th) 0.81:1; (Rev) 3.42:1. Camaro four/V-6 four- speed manual trans.: (1st) 3.50:1; (2nd) 2.48:1; (3rd) 1.66:1; (4th) 1.00:1; (Rev) 3.50:1. Cavalier five-speed manual: (1st) 3.91:1; (2nd) 2.04:1; (3rd) 1.33:1; (4th) 0.92:1; (5th) 0.75:1; (Rev) 3.50:1. Camaro four/V-6 five- speed manual: (1st) 3.50:1; (2nd) 2.14:1; (3rd) 1.36:1; (4th) 1.00:1; (5th) 0.78:1; (Rev) 3.39:1. Camaro V8305 five-speed manual: (1st) 2.95:1; (2nd) 1.94:1; (3rd) 1.34:1; (4th) 1.00:1; (5th) 0.73:1; (Rev) 2.76:1. Chevette five-speed manual shift: (1st) 3.76:1; (2nd) 2.18:1; (3rd) 1.36:1; (4th) 1.00:1; (5th) 0.86:1; (Rev) 3.76:1. Three-speed Turbo Hydra- matic standard on Celebrity, Malibu, Monte Carlo and Caprice/Impala. Malibu/Monte/Caprice/Imp gear ratios: (1st) 2.52:1; (2nd) 1.52:1; (3rd) 1.00:1; (Rev) 1.93:1. Camaro four/V-6 and Malibu/Monte diesel V-6: (1st) 2.74:1; (2nd) 1.57:1; (3rd) 1.00:1; (Rev) 2.07:1. Chevette automatic trans.: (1st) 2.40:1; (2nd) 1.48:1; (3rd) 1.00:1; (Rev) 1.92:1. Cavalier/Citation/Celebrity auto. trans.: (1st) 2.84:1; (2nd) 1.84:1; (3rd) 1.00:1; (Rev) 2.07:1. Four-speed overdrive automatic transmission on Caprice/Impala: (1st) 2.74:1; (2nd) 1.57:1; (3rd) 1.00:1; (4th) 0.67:1; (Rev) 2.07:1. Four-speed overdrive automatic on Camaro V8305, Caprice/Imp diesel: (1st) 3.06:1; (2nd) 1.63:1; (3rd) 1.00:1; (4th) 0.70:1; (Rev) 2.29:1. Standard final drive ratio: (Chevette) 3.36:1; (Cavalier) 3.32:1 exc. 2.83:1 w/5spd and 3.18:1 w/auto.; (Citation four) 2.42:1 or 2.39:1; (Cit V-6) 2.69:1 or 2.53:1; (Cit H.O. V-6) 2.96:1 or 3.06:1; (Camaro V-6) 3.42:1 w/5spd, 3.08:1 or 3.23:1 w/auto.; (Camaro V-8) 3.73:1 w/5spd, 3.08:1 or 2.93:1 w/auto.; (Z28) 3.23:1; (Celeb four) 2.39:1; (Celeb V-6) 2.84:1; (Malibu/Monte V-6) 2.41:1; (Malibu/Monte V-8) 2.29:1; (Caprice/Imp V-6) 2.56:1 or 2.73:1; (Caprice/Imp V-8) 2.41:1, 2.73:1 or 2.93:1. Steering: (Cavalier/Chevette/Citation/Celebrity) rack and pinion; (others) recirculating ball. Suspension/Brakes/Body: same as 1982. Fuel tank: (Chvt) 12.5 gal.; (Cav) 14 gal.; (Cit) 15.9 gal.; (Camaro) 16.2 gal. exc. 15.8 with four-cyl. or CFI V-8; (Celeb) 15.7 gal. approx.; (Malibu/Monte) 18.1 gal.; (Capr/Imp) 25 gal.; (Capr/Imp wag) 22 gal.

1983 station wagons, clockwise from right: Caprice, Cavalier and Malibu

DRIVETRAIN OPTIONS: Engines: 173 cu. in., 2Bbl. V-6: Citation, base Camaro, Celeb ($150). H.O. 173 cu. in., 2Bbl. V-6: Citation ($300). 305 cu. in., 4Bbl. V-8: Camaro ($350); Berlinetta ($225); Malibu/Monte, Imp/Caprice sed ($225). H.O. 305 cu. in., 4Bbl. V-8: Camaro ($505). 305 cu. in. CFI V-8: Camaro Z28 ($450). Diesel 260 cu. in. V-6: Celeb/Monte, Malibu sed ($500). Diesel 350 cu. in. V-8: Malibu/Monte/Imp/Caprice ($700); Caprice wag ($525). Transmission/Differential: Three-speed automatic trans.: Chevette/Cavalier ($395); Chvt diesel ($380); Citation/Camaro ($425); Berlinetta ($195). Five-speed manual trans.: Chevette/Cavalier ($75); base Camaro ($125). Four- speed overdrive automatic trans.: base Camaro ($525); Berlinetta/Z28 ($295); Imp/Caprice ($175). Limited-slip differential: Camaro/Malibu/Monte/Imp/Capr ($95). Performance axle ratio Chvt/Cav/Camaro/Malibu/Monte, Imp/Capr wag ($21). Power Accessories: Power brakes: Chevette ($95); Citation ($100). Power four-wheel disc brakes: Camaro V-8 ($179). Power steering: Chvt/Cav ($199); Cit ($210). Suspension: F40 H.D. susp.: Cav/Cit/Celeb/Malibu/Monte/Imp/Capr ($26). F41 sport suspension: Cit/Celeb ($33); Cav/Camaro/Monte, Imp/Capr sed ($49). Rear stabilizer bar: Cavalier ($36). Inflatable rear shock absorbers: Caprice wag ($64). Other: H.D. cooling ($40-$70). Cold climate pkg.: Malibu/Monte/Imp/Capr diesel ($99). Diesel engine and fuel line heater: Celeb ($49). H.D. battery ($25) exc. diesel ($50). California emission system ($75) exc. diesel ($215).

CHEVETTE CONVENIENCE/APPEARANCE OPTIONS: Option Packages: Sport decor pkg.: black grille, headlamp bezels and wheels; bodyside moldings, trim rings and decals ($95). Deluxe exterior: side window reveal moldings, argent wheels and trim rings ($150-$165). Comfort/Convenience: Air conditioning ($625). Rear defogger, electric ($125). Tinted glass ($90). Comfortilt steering wheel ($99). Cigarette lighter: Scooter ($10). Rear wiper/washer ($117). Lighting and Mirrors: Aux. lighting ($41-$42). Twin sport mirrors, left remote ($51). Driver's remote sport mirror ($33). Entertainment: AM radio: Scooter ($83). AM/FM radio ($82); Scooter ($165). AM/FM stereo radio ($109). Radio delete ($51 credit). Exterior Trim: Two-tone paint ($133). Sport stripes ($89). Bodyside moldings: Scooter ($45). Door edge guards ($15-$25). Interior Trim/Upholstery: Cloth bucket seats ($28). Custom cloth bucket seats ($130). Color-keyed floor mats ($25). Wheels and Tires: Wheel trim rings ($52). P155/80R13 GBR WSW ($51). P175/70R13 SBR BSW ($119). P175/70R13 SBR WSW ($173).

CAVALIER CONVENIENCE/APPEARANCE OPTIONS: Option Packages: CL equipment pkg.: custom interior, quiet sound group, visor mirror, leather-wrapped steering wheel, sport mirrors and wheel covers, warning chimes ($577-$696). Comfort/Convenience: Air cond. ($625). Cruise control w/resume ($170). Rear defogger, electric ($125). Tinted glass ($90). Six-way power driver's seat ($210). Comfortilt steering wheel ($99). Power windows ($180-$255). Power door locks ($120-$170). Remote swing-out side windows ($55). Power hatch or trunk release ($40). Power liftgate release ($35). Gauge pkg. w/trip odometer ($69). Special instruments incl. tach ($70-$139). Lighter: base ($14). Intermittent wipers ($49). Rear wiper/washer ($117). Lighting, Horns and Mirrors: Halogen headlamps ($10). Aux. lighting ($72-$95). Dual sport mirrors, left remote ($51). Dual electric remote sport mirrors ($89-$137). Right visor mirror ($7). Entertainment: AM/FM radio: base ($112). AM/FM stereo radio ($171) exc. CS ($82). Electronic-tuning AM/FM stereo radio w/clock ($277) exc. CS ($177). Electronic-tuning AM/FM stereo radio w/cassette ($377) exc. CS ($277). Electronic-tuning AM/FM stereo seek/scan radio w/cassette and clock ($555) exc. CS ($455). Dual rear speakers ($30-$42); premium ($25). Fixed-mast antenna: base ($41) but incl. w/radios. Radio delete ($56 credit). Exterior Trim: Removable sunroof ($295). Two-tone paint ($176). Pinstriping ($53). Sport striping ($95). Bodyside moldings, black/argent ($45). Wheel opening moldings ($30). Door edge guards ($15-$25). Roof carrier ($98). Bumper guards ($56). Interior Trim/Upholstery: Cloth bucket seats ($28). Split-folding rear seatback ($50). Color-keyed mats: front ($15); rear ($10). Cargo area cover ($64). Wheels and Tires: Aluminum wheels ($272-$369). Wheel trim rings ($52). P175/80R13 GBR WSW ($54). P195/70R13 SBR BSW ($169). P195/70R13 SBR WSW ($231). P195/70R13 SBR WLT ($253).

CITATION/CELEBRITY CONVENIENCE/APPEARANCE OPTIONS: Option Packages: X11 sport equipment pkg.: Citation ($998). Sport decor pkg. (rear spoiler, rally wheels, sport mirrors, color-keyed bumpers w/rub strips, decal): Citation ($299). Deluxe exterior pkg.: Cit ($118-$218). Exterior molding pkg. (rocker panel and wheel opening moldings): Celeb ($53). Value appearance group: Cit ($55-$63). Quiet sound group: Cit cpe ($43). Quiet sound/rear decor pkg.: Cit ($92). Comfort/Convenience: Air conditioning ($725). Rear defogger, electric ($135). Cruise control w/resume ($170). Tinted glass ($105). Sport steering wheel: Cit ($22). Comfortilt steering wheel ($105). Six-way power driver's seat: Celeb ($210). Power windows ($180-$255). Remote swing-out side windows: Cit ($108). Power door locks ($120-$170). Gauge pkg. w/clock and trip odometer: Cit ($104). Gauge pkg. w/tachometer: Cit ($149). Gauge pkg. w/trip odometer: Celeb ($64). Electric clock: Cit ($35). Digital clock: Celeb ($39). Lighter: Cit cpe ($10). Intermittent wipers ($49). Lighting, Horns and Mirrors: Halogen high-beam headlamps: Celeb ($10). Aux. lighting ($50). Dual horns: Cit ($12). Driver's remote mirror ($22). Dual sport mirrors, left remote ($59). Dual remote mirrors: Celeb ($89). Entertainment: AM radio: Cit cpe ($83). AM/FM radio: Cit hatch, Celeb ($82); Cit cpe ($165). AM/FM stereo radio: Cit ($109) exc. cpe ($192). AM/FM stereo w/cassette: Cit ($209) exc. cpe ($292). Celebrity electronic-tuning AM/FM stereo radio w/clock ($177); w/cassette ($277); with seek/scan and cassette ($455). Dual rear speakers ($30); incl. w/stereo radio. Premium dual rear speakers: Celeb ($25) but incl. with seek/scan radio. Radio delete ($56 credit). Exterior Trim: Vinyl roof: Celeb ($155). Two-tone paint: Cit ($176-$184) incl. pinstriping and bodyside moldings; Celeb ($148). Bodyside pinstriping: Cit ($39-$47); Celeb ($57). Bodyside moldings: Cit ($55). Door edge guards ($15-$25). Bumper guards ($56). Bumper rub strips: Cit ($50). Interior Trim/Upholstery: Console ($100). Reclining driver and passenger seatbacks: Celeb ($90). Sport cloth bench seat: Cit ($28). Custom trim w/cloth bench seat: Cit ($467). Vinyl bench seat: Celeb ($28). Celebrity custom bench seat: cloth ($179-$250); vinyl ($109-$207). Celebrity 45/45 seating: cloth ($100); custom cloth ($250-$330). Sport cloth bucket seats: Cit ($221-$250). Custom trim w/cloth bucket seats: Cit ($467-$492). Color-keyed mats: front ($17); rear ($12). Deluxe seatbelts: Cit cpe ($26). Wheels and Tires: Full wheel covers: Cit ($52). Sport wheel covers: Celeb ($63). Wire wheel covers: Celeb ($153). Wheel cover locks: Celeb ($39). Rally wheels: Cit ($60-$112); Celeb ($56). P185/80R13 GBR WSW ($58). P185/80R13 SBR BSW ($65). P185/80R13 SBR WSW ($123). P195/74R14 GBR WSW: Celeb ($129). P195/75R14 SBR WSW: Celeb ($194). P205/70R13 SBR WSW: Celeb ($245). P205/70R13 SBR WLT: Cit ($267). P215/60R14 SBR WLT: Citation X11 ($92). Puncture-sealant tires: Celeb ($106).

CAMARO/MALIBU/MONTE CARLO CONVENIENCE/APPEARANCE OPTIONS: Option Packages: Estate equipment: Malibu wag ($307). Quiet sound group: Camaro ($72-$82); Malibu ($66). Security pkg.: Malibu wag ($44). Comfort/Convenience: Air cond. ($725). Rear defogger, electric ($135). Cruise control w/resume ($170). Tinted glass ($105). Comfortilt steering wheel ($105). Six-way power driver's seat: Camaro/Monte ($210). Power windows: Camaro/Monte ($180); Malibu ($255). Power door locks: Malibu ($170); Camaro/Monte ($120). Power trunk opener: Monte ($40). Power hatch release: Camaro ($40). Power tailgate window release: Malibu wag ($40). Electric clock: base Camaro, Malibu/Monte ($35). Digital clock: base Camaro ($39). Gauge pkg. w/trip odometer: Malibu/Monte ($95). Special instruments incl.

1983 Monte Carlo SS Sport Coupe (JG)

tach: base Camaro ($149). Intermittent wipers ($49). Rear wiper/washer: Camaro ($120). Lighting, Horns and Mirrors: Halogen high-beam headlamps ($10). Cornering lamps: Monte ($55). Aux. lighting: Camaro ($52); Malibu ($49-$56); Monte ($28). Dual horns: Camaro/Malibu ($12). Remote-control driver's mirror: Malibu ($22). Twin sport mirrors (left remote): base Camaro, Monte ($51); Malibu ($59). Twin remote sport mirrors: Monte ($81). Twin electric remote sport mirrors: Camaro ($89-$137). Entertainment: AM radio ($112). AM/FM radio ($171). AM/FM stereo radio ($198). Cassette player with AM/FM stereo radio: Malibu/Monte ($298). Camaro electronic-tuning AM/FM stereo radio w/clock ($267-$302); w/cassette and clock ($367-$402); w/cassette and seek/scan ($520-$555). Dual rear speakers ($30). Fixed mast antenna ($41); incl. w/radios. Power antenna: Camaro/Monte ($60). Exterior Trim: Removable glass roof panels: Camaro/Monte ($825). Landau vinyl roof: Monte ($240). Rear spoiler: Camaro ($69). Two-tone paint: Malibu ($138); Monte ($214). Bodyside moldings, black: Camaro ($55). Deluxe bodyside moldings: Malibu/Monte ($57). Rocker panel moldings: Malibu ($25). Wheel opening moldings: Malibu ($30). Side window reveal moldings: Malibu ($44). Door edge guards ($15-$25). Side window sill moldings: Monte ($45). Roof drip moldings: Camaro ($29). Bodyside pinstriping: Malibu ($57); Monte ($61). Rear window air deflector: Malibu wag ($36). Roof carrier: Malibu wag ($125). Bumper rub strips: Malibu ($50). Bumper guards: Malibu ($56). Interior Trim/Upholstery: Vinyl bench seat: Monte ($28). Cloth bench seat: Malibu ($28). Custom cloth bench seat: Malibu ($161); Monte ($358). Custom vinyl bench seat: Malibu ($133). Cloth or vinyl 55/45 seating: Malibu ($233-$261); Monte ($133-$161). Cloth bucket seats: Camaro ($28). Custom cloth or vinyl bucket seats: base Camaro ($299); Z28 ($227). Cloth LS conteur bucket seats: Camaro ($375). Custom cloth LS conteur bucket seats: Camaro ($650). Color-keyed mats: Malibu/Monte ($27); Camaro front ($20); Camaro rear ($15). Cargo area cover: Camaro ($64). Deluxe load-floor carpet: Malibu wag ($84). Deluxe trunk trim: Camaro ($164); Monte ($47). Wheels and Tires: Aluminum wheels: Monte ($362). Rally wheels: Camaro ($112); Malibu ($108); Monte ($56). Full wheel covers: Camaro/Malibu ($52). Sport wheel covers: Malibu ($115). Wire wheel covers: Malibu ($190); Monte ($153). Wheel cover locks: Monte ($39). P185/75R14 GBR WSW: Malibu sed ($58). P195/75R14 GBR WSW: Camaro, Malibu wag ($62). P195/75R14 SBR BSW: Camaro ($64). P195/75R14 SBR WSW: Camaro ($126); Malibu sed ($151); Malibu wag ($122); Monte ($62). P205/70R14 SBR BSW: base Camaro ($123). P205/70R14 SBR WSW: Camaro ($189); Berlinetta ($66); Monte ($124). P205/70R14 SBR WLT: Camaro ($211). P205/75R14 SBR BSW: Malibu ($95). P205/75R14 SBR WSW: Malibu ($151).

IMPALA/CAPRICE CONVENIENCE/APPEARANCE OPTIONS: Option Packages: Estate equipment: wag ($307). Value appearance group: bodyside and wheel opening moldings, full wheel covers ($118). Comfort/Convenience: Air cond. ($725). Rear defogger, electric ($135). Cruise control w/resume ($170). Tinted glass ($105). Comfortilt steering wheel ($105). Power door locks ($170). Six-way power driver's seat ($210). Power windows ($255). Power trunk opener ($40). Power tailgate lock: wag ($49). Electric clock: Imp ($35). Digital clock: Imp ($66); Caprice ($34). Gauge pkg. w/trip odometer ($64). Intermittent wipers ($49). Quiet sound group: Imp ($66). Lighting and Mirrors: Halogen high-beam headlamps ($10). Cornering lamps ($55). Aux. lighting ($32-$42). Driver's remote mirror ($22). Dual remote mirrors ($65). Dual sport mirrors, left remote ($59). Dual remote body-color sport mirrors ($89). Lighted visor mirror ($48). Entertainment: AM radio ($112). AM/FM radio ($171). AM/FM stereo radio ($198). Cassette player with AM/FM stereo ($298). Dual rear speakers ($30). Power antenna ($60). Windshield antenna ($29); incl. w/radios. Exterior Trim: Vinyl roof: sed ($180). Roof carrier: wag ($150). Custom two-tone paint ($141). Pinstriping ($39). Bodyside moldings ($55). Door edge guards ($25). Bumper rub strips ($66). Bumper guards ($62). Interior Trim/Upholstery: Vinyl bench seat: sed ($28). Cloth bench seat: wag ($28). Cloth 50/50 seat ($257-$285). Custom cloth 50/50 seat: sed ($452). Deluxe load-floor carpet: wag ($89). Deluxe cargo area carpet: wag ($129). Color-keyed mats: front ($17); rear ($12). Deluxe trunk trim ($59). Wheels and Tires: Full wheel covers ($52). Sport wheel covers: Imp ($115); Caprice ($63). Wire wheel covers ($153). Wire wheel cover locks ($39). P205/75R15 SBR WSW: sed ($66). P225/70R15 SBR WSW: sed ($159). P225/75R15 SBR WSW: wag ($71). Puncture-sealant tires ($106-$132).

HISTORY: Introduced: Sept. 23, 1982 exc. Camaro Nov. 8, 1982. Model year production (U.S.): 1,012,649 (incl. Corvettes but not incl. 11,640 Acadians). Total production for U.S. market was made up of 500,305 four-cylinder, 350,722 sixes and 374,668 V-8s. A total of 12,480 diesels were installed. Calendar year production (U.S.): 1,294,184 (including 28,174 Corvettes). Calendar year sales by U.S. dealers: 1,347,447 (incl. 28,144 Corvettes), for a 19.8 percent market share. Model year sales by U.S. dealers: 1,306,951 (incl. 25,891 Corvettes) for a 20.2 percent share.

Historical Footnotes: The nation's economic condition may have improved during 1983, but Chevrolet's status remained shaky. Model year sales rose by close to six percent, but domestic cars in general fared far better, up by nearly 17 percent. Both at Chevrolet and in the industry generally, most of that increase came from mid- and full-size models. Robert C. Stempel, Chevrolet's General Manager, promoted a new "pricing strategy which finds more than half of Chevrolet's 1983 passenger car models carrying lower sticker prices than they did in '82." Some of the reduction, though, was due to elimination of formerly standard equipment, a practice that would become common in the years ahead. Citation sales fell sharply, down from a healthy 321,023 in 1981 and so-so 209,545 in 1982 to a piddling 116,460 this year. No doubt, the well-publicized recall of 1980 models contributed to much of the decline. NHTSA had ordered that recall for alleged brake problems as this model year began. That action would soon change popular opinion of the X-car in general and Citation in particular. A week-long sales seminar at the Citation plant at Tarrytown, New York this year couldn't do much for sales if the buying public truly turned against the X-car. The newer Cavalier and Celebrity performed better, showing ample sales gains, partly as a result of marketing Cavalier as a sporty economy car. Far fewer Chevette diesels were sold than in 1982: only 1,940 total. Camaro was named *Motor Trend* "Car of the Year" for 1982. In a GM reshufffling, Chevrolet became part of the new Chevrolet-Pontiac-GM of Canada Group, which was to emphasize small cars. That group was headed by Lloyd E. Reuss, formerly Buick's General Manager; Robert C. Stempel of Chevrolet moved over to the new Buick-Oldsmobile-Cadillac group, which focused on large cars. Robert D. Burger then became Chevrolet's General Manager.

1984 CHEVROLET

This year saw the arrival of only one new body style, the Celebrity station wagon, along with a "re-launching" of the troubled X-car (as Citation II), Malibu was dropped, its role as a mid-size family car having been usurped by the front-drive Celebrity. Scooter was gone too, but Monte Carlo added a high-performance SS model to lure enthusiasts and Celebrity fielded a Eurosport option. Otherwise, 1984 was mainly a year for engineering changes.

1984 Chevette CS hatchback sedan (CP)

CHEVETTE — SERIES 1T — FOUR — Except for a new passenger door map pocket, the rear- drive subcompact showed virtually no change for 1984. Once again, Chevette came with either a 1.6-liter gasoline four or a 1.8-liter diesel, which could (according to Chevrolet) deliver fuel mileage in the 60 MPG neighborhood. Diesels added a fuel-line heater. Both two-door and four-door hatchbacks were again available, in two trim levels. Joining the option list: new chrome bumpers and sport wheel covers. The stripped-down Scooter was abandoned, but Chevettes still came in two series: base and CS. Base Chevettes came with black bumpers (with guards and end caps), vinyl reclining front bucket seats, fold-down rear seat, front stabilizer bar, four-speed manual transmission, two-speed wipers, styled steel wheels, and a passenger map pocket. Chevette CS added color-keyed bumpers, a cigarette lighter, mini-console, AM radio, and black bodyside moldings. Diesels included a five-speed transmission and power brakes. Chevette's CS Sport Decor package (price $95) included a black grille, black headlamps with red accents, bodyside moldings, black bumper with end caps, and black styled wheels with bright trim rings and decals. A Custom Exterior package included black window frames with narrow bright side window moldings, plus argent styled steel wheels with trim rings. CS displayed a 'Chevette' nameplate ahead of front doors; base models did not.

1984 Cavalier sedan (CP)

CAVALIER — SERIES 1J — FOUR — Cavalier's new wind-tunnel-tuned front end got a new grille, quad headlamps and bumper this year. The crosshatch- pattern grille, tapered inward at the base, had a Chevrolet bowtie in the center and occupied the entire opening, with no solid upper panel as before. Wide rectangular park/signal lamps moved down below the rub strips in the body-colored bumpers. Quad rectangular headlamps were recessed. Cavaliers now came in eight body colors and four interior colors. Sedans and wagons came in base or CS trim, but the base/CS two-door coupe and hatchback were dropped. The sporty Type 10, initially offered only in hatchback form, added the convertible and two-door notchback coupe to its body list. Type 10 models carried their special nameplates on bodysides, just ahead of the rear wheels. CS Cavaliers wore an identifier just ahead of the front door. More examples of the convertible, offered in limited number during 1983, were expected to find buyers this year. A total of 5,161 Cavaliers are reported to have come with an Olympic Special Appearance package. Cavalier's standard suspension got larger-diameter stabilizer bars and softer front bushings. The rear stabilizer bar on the optional F41 sport suspension was also larger in diameter. Standard equipment included power brakes, four-speed manual transaxle (with overdrive), argent grille, charcoal instrument panel, bright window moldings, color- keyed bumpers, vinyl front reclining bucket seats, front stabilizer bar, and four-spoke charcoal steering wheel. P175/80R13 GBR tires rode styled steel wheels. Type 10 added a black grille, color-keyed dash with black trim plate, cigarette lighter and ashtray light, AM radio,

1984 Cavalier 2-dr coupe

three-spoke color-keyed steering wheel, glove compartment lock, black window moldings, and bodyside moldings. Cavalier CS models had a bright grille. Convertible equipment was similar to Type 10 but with tinted glass, warning chimes, bright rocker panel moldings, power steering and windows, and dual black sport mirrors (left remote-controlled). An optional CL Custom Interior package included modified door and quarter trim, custom reclining seats with adjustable head restraints, and fender nameplates. On the Type 10 hatchback, it also included a leather steering wheel and split folding seat. This year's options added a leather-wrapped steering wheel and rear window louvers, plus a rear spoiler and sport wheel covers.

1984 Citation II 4-dr hatchback sedan

CITATION II — SERIES 1X — FOUR/V-6 — Chevrolet's X-car got a slightly different name this year, supposedly in response to the many improvements it had received during the preceding three years. But renamed or not, it was still essentially a carryover. All-season steel- belted radial tires were standard on all models. New body badges identified engines. Engine mounts were revised to reduce vibration at idle. The high-performance X11 equipment package, offered on both notchback and hatchback coupes. attempted to capitalize on a good record in SCCA showroom stock racing. Citation again came with a 151 cu. in. (2.5-liter) four- cylinder engine or optional V-6. Standard equipment included bright bumpers and grille, day/night mirror, four-speed manual transmission, styled steel wheels, two-speed wiper/washers, low-back vinyl bench front seat, locking glove box, and bright windshield and fender moldings. Hatchbacks also had a lighter, AM radio, black back window molding, rocker panel and wheel opening moldings. The X11 package included P215/60R14 SBR tires on cast aluminum wheels, hood scoop, sport suspension, color-keyed bumpers with black rub strips, power brakes, AM radio; and on hatchbacks, a cigarette lighter and removable cargo cover. Package price was $981 for an X11 hatchback, or $911 when installed on the coupe.

1984 Camaro Berlinetta Sport Coupe (CP)

CAMARO — SERIES 1F — V-6/V-8 — Berlinetta gained the most attention this year. That model's new "space-age instrumentation" included digital readouts, a pivoting pedestal-mounted radio, and dual adjustable fingertip control pods that could be moved close to the steering wheel. The Corvette-inspired cockpit also sported a roof console, plus adjustable low-back seats. A digital display ahead of the driver showed road speed (miles or kilometers per hour) plus odometer or engine speed. An adjoining vertical-bar tachometer flashed more urgently as engine speed increased, while a monitor farther to the right signaled low fluid levels or other trouble spots. At the left were conventional needle-type gauges. The twin pods contained switches for lights and instrument displays, plus wiper and climate control. Other pushbutton controls were in the floor console, while the overhead console contained a swivel map light and

1984 Camaro Z28 T-top Sport Coupe (CP)

small storage pouch. A remote-controlled, electronically-tuned AM/FM stereo radio with digital clock was standard; tape player and graphic equalizer optional. The radio could swivel for easy operation by either the driver or passenger. Buttons for optional cruise control were on Berlinetta's steering wheel, not the column. Berlinettas could be spotted by their gold-colored body trim. On the mechanical side, Cross-Fire Injection was dropped, but the Z28 could have an optional high-output 5.0- liter engine (RPO code L69) rated 190 horsepower, hooked to either five-speed manual or four-speed automatic transmission. That H.O. V-8 (introduced in spring 1983) was the most powerful carbureted engine offered in a Chevrolet. It had a higher-lift, longer-duration camshaft, retuned valve system, and 9.5:1 compression. The H.O. engine also had a specially-calibrated Rochester Quadrajet carb, dual-snorkel cold-air intake, large-diameter exhaust and tailpipes, and wide-mouth (Corvette-type) catalytic converter. Steel-belted radial tires were now made standard on the Sport Coupe with four-cylinder engine, thus standard on all Camaros. All except Z28 now carried fourth-generation All- Season tires. Once again, 173 cu. in. (2.8-liter) V-6 and 305 cu. in. (5.0-liter) V-8 engines were available. The three- speed automatic transmission was dropped, replaced by a four- speed overdrive unit. A hydraulic clutch was now used with all manual gearboxes. The base Camaro Sport Coupe still came with a choice of four, six or eight cylinder power. Camaro's basic "grille" hardly qualified for that name, consisting of no more than three side-by-side slots in the front panel flanked by rectangular headlamps. The Z28 didn't even have those slots in its upper panel, but displayed subtle '5.0-Liter H.O.' badges on its back bumper and rocker panels (and air cleaner), plus dual tailpipes at the back. Base Sport Coupe equipment was similar to 1983, now with SBR tires and color-keyed front/rear bumpers with black accents. Body colors were the same as 1983, but added Dark Gold. In addition to the electronic instrumentation and roof console, Berlinetta equipment included an AM/FM stereo electronic-tuning radio, digital clock, hood and sail panel decals, lockable fuel filler door, sport aluminum hood, dual horns, five-speed manual gearbox, smooth-ride suspension, intermittent wipers, and custom vinyl reclining front bucket seats with adjustable head restraints. Berlinettas carried color-keyed sport mirrors and lower accent body paint with striping. Their 14 x 7 in. wheels were gold/aluminum finned. Z28 equipment was similar to 1983. Other models could have Berlinetta's roof console for an extra $50, while a locking rear storage cover cost $80.

1984 Celebrity station wagon (AA)

CELEBRITY — SERIES 1A — FOUR/V-6 — Like Cavalier, the mid-size Celebrity boasted a new front-end design this year. The taller grille wore a center bowtie emblem and filled the entire space, lacking the solid upper panel of the prior version. Its top was roughly aligned with the top of the headlamps, and the crosshatch pattern was made up of thin vertical slots with two horizontal divider bars. New police and taxi packages were based on the standard four-door sedan platform. A new four-door station wagon came with either two seats or a rear-facing third seat, and a rear opening wider than the Malibu that it replaced. Eurosport versions of each body style included specially-tuned suspension, unique blackout trim, and special decals. The Eurosport name was on front doors, in block letters. A high-output 173 cu. in.

1984 Celebrity Eurosport sedan (AA)

(2.8-liter) V-6 engine, similar to Citation's but with slightly less horsepower, became optional on coupes and sedans. Only 2,945 of them were installed this year. A four-speed manual gearbox was offered for the first time, standard equipment with the base four (or V-6 diesel). Also new: four-speed overdrive automatic with V-6 engines. Celebrity's standard equipment included chrome bumpers with end caps and black rub strips (with white inserts), side window defoggers, black left mirror, AM radio, front and rear stabilizer bars, power steering, and full wheel covers. Also standard: two-passenger vinyl front bench seat with folding center armrest, black windshield/window moldings, bright headlamp bezels, wide bodyside moldings, and a concealed spare tire. Wagons had a three-passenger vinyl bench front seat, power brakes, tailgate-ajar light, and hidden floor stowage area. The Eurosport package included an F41 sport suspension, sport steering wheel, P195/7514 SBR tires on 6 in. rally wheels, red accent striping, blackout decor, black bodyside moldings, and red-finish nameplates. The price was $226 for coupe or sedan, $191 on wagons. A total of 26,844 Eurosport packages were installed for the year.

1984 Monte Carlo Sport Coupe (CP)

MONTE CARLO — SERIES 1G — V-6/V-8 — Two options returned to Monte Carlo's lineup this year: bucket seats and a console. Also joining the list was the four-speed overdrive automatic transmission. With the loss of Malibu, Monte remained the only rear-drive mid-size Chevrolet. The diesel V-6 engine was dropped, but the V-8 diesel remained available with a $700 price tag. The high-output 305 cu. in. (5.0-liter) V-8 in the high- performance Monte Carlo SS (added to the lineup in spring 1983) got a boost to 180 horsepower to become what Chevrolet called a "street version of current NASCAR point leader." The SS powertrain also consisted of a high-stall-speed automatic transmission, dual exhausts, 3.42:1 axle ratio, and low- profile Goodyear Eagle GT white-letter P215/65R15 tires on 7 in. rally wheels. Cleanly styled SS Montes carried no body brightwork and wore a wind-tunnel-tuned nose plus a rear spoiler, producing a drag coefficient of just .375. The simple, slightly-angled blackout grille was flanked by quad rectangular headlamps. Wide recessed parking/signal lamps sat below the bumper rub strips. Monte SS bodies were painted only in dark metalic blue or white. Large door decals identified the SS, which also displayed an easy-to-spot "ground effects" front panel. Base Monte standard equipment included power brakes and steering, three-speed automatic transmission, cloth- upholstered bench seats with folding armrest, P195/75R14 SBR tires, compact spare tire, full wheel covers, wheel opening and roof drip moldings, dual chrome mirrors, dual horns, two- speed wiper/washers, and courtesy lights. Monte Carlo SS eliminated the wheel opening moldings but added gauges, black roof drip moldings, a rear spoiler, tachometer, sport suspension, and sport mirrors (left remote). A total of 7,281 Montes had the optional removable glass roof panels.

1984 Impala Sport Coupe (CP)

IMPALA/CAPRICE CLASSIC — SERIES 1B — V-6/V-8 — After a year's absence, the Caprice Classic two-door coupe returned for 1984. The coupe and wagon came only in Caprice Classic trim, while sedans were sold under both Caprice and Impala names. Standard engine was again the 229 cu. in. (3.8-liter) V-6, with 305 cu. in. (5.0-liter) gas V-8 or 5.7-liter diesel optional. External appearance was unchanged. The wiper/washer controls moved from the dashboard to the turn signal lever. Optional cruise control gained incremental acceleration/deceleration, which allowed speed changes down to just 1 MPH at a time. Gas-engine wagons had standard heavy-duty suspension, while diesel wagons had standard four-speed overdrive automatic transmission. Impala's standard equipment included the V-6 engine, power brakes and steering, three-speed automatic transmission, front stabilizer bar, full wheel covers, cloth bench seat, padded door trim panels, trunk mat, day/night mirror, and bright moldings (windshield, door frame and roof drip). Also dome, trunk and glove box lights. Caprice equipment was similar, but added a folding center armrest, quartz clock, wheel opening moldings, color-keyed steering wheel with woodgrain insert, headlamps-on warning buzzer, and lower-carpeted door trim panels with pull straps. Caprice sport coupes and sedans had bumper rub strips. Wagons had vinyl bench seating plus the overdrive automatic transmission. A Landau equipment package with vinyl roof cost an extra $306.

I.D. DATA: Coding of the 17-symbol Vehicle Identification Number (VIN) was similar to 1983. Symbol five (car line/series) was now: 'J' base Chevette; 'B' Chevette CS; 'C' Cavalier; 'D' Cavalier CS; 'E' Cavalier Type 10; 'H' Citation coupe; 'X' Citation; 'P' Camaro; 'S' Camaro Berlinetta; 'W' Celebrity ; 'G' Monte Carlo; 'L' Impala; 'N' Caprice. Body type (symbols six-seven) added code '47' for full-size 2-dr. sport coupe. Code 'S' for V8305 FI engine was dropped. Code 'G' for H.O. V8305 4Bbl. was added. The model year code changed to 'E' for 1984.

CHEVETTE (FOUR)

Model Number	Body/Style Number	Body Type & Seating	Factory Price	Shipping Weight	Production Total
1T	J08	2-dr. Hatch Cpe-4P	4997	1988	66,446
1T	J68	4-dr. Hatch Sed-4P	5333	2051	28,466

CHEVETTE CS (FOUR)

1T	B08	2-dr. Hatch Cpe-4P	5489	2032	47,032
1T	B68	4-dr. Hatch Sed-4P	5636	2091	94,897

CHEVETTE DIESEL (FOUR)

1T	J08/Z90	2-dr. Hatch Cpe-4P	5500	N/A	1,495
1T	J68/Z90	4-dr. Hatch Sed-4P	5851	N/A	1,180

CHEVETTE CS DIESEL (FOUR)

1T	B08/Z90	2-dr. Hatch Cpe-4P	5999	N/A	1,000
1T	B68/Z90	4-dr. Hatch Sed-4P	6161	N/A	3,384

CAVALIER (FOUR)

1J	C69	4-dr. Sedan-5P	6222	2320	90,023
1J	C35	4-dr. Sta Wag-5P	6375	2392	50,718

CAVALIER CS (FOUR)

1J	D69	4-dr. Sedan-5P	6666	2334	110,295
1J	D35	4-dr. Sta Wag-5P	6821	2405	58,739

1984 Cavalier Type 10 convertible (AA)

CAVALIER TYPE 10 (FOUR)

1J	E27	2-dr. Coupe-5P	6477	2300	103,204
1J	E77	2-dr. Hatch Cpe-5P	6654	2350	44,146
1J	E27/Z08	2-dr. Conv. Cpe-4P	11299	2515	5,486

CITATION II (FOUR/V-6)

1X	H11	2-dr. Coupe-5P	6445/6695	2382/2454	4,936
1X	X08	2-dr. Hatch Cpe-5P	6900/7150	2399/2471	8,783
1X	X68	4-dr. Hatch Sed-5P	7046/7296	2435/2507	83,486

1984 Camaro Z28 5.0L HO T-top Sport Coupe (CP)

CAMARO (V-6/V-8)

1F	P87	2-dr. Spt Cpe-4P	8245/8545	2907/3091	127,292

CAMARO BERLINETTA (V-6/V-8)

Model Number	Body/Style Number	Body Type & Seating	Factory Price	Shipping Weight	Production Total
1F	S87	2-dr. Spt Cpe-4P	10895/11270	2919/3157	33,400

CAMARO Z28 (V-8)

Model Number	Body/Style Number	Body Type & Seating	Factory Price	Shipping Weight	Production Total
1F	P87	2-dr. Spt Cpe-4P	-- /10620	-- /3107	100,416

Camaro Engine Note: Prices and weights before slash are for V-6 engine, after slash for V-8. Base Camaro Sport Coupes were also available with a four-cylinder engine, priced at $7995 and weighing 2813 pounds. The Z28 could have an optional high-output V-8 for an additional $530. **Z28 Production Note:** Chevrolet production figures also show 478 Z28E hatchback sport coupes.

CELEBRITY (FOUR/V-6)

Model Number	Body/Style Number	Body Type & Seating	Factory Price	Shipping Weight	Production Total
1A	W27	2-dr. Coupe-5P	7711/7961	2587/2719	29,191
1A	W19	4-dr. Sedan-5P	7890/8140	2623/2755	200,259
1A	W35	4-dr. Sta Wag-5P	8214/8464	2771/2894	48,295
1A	W35/AQ4	4-dr. 3S Wag-8P	8429/8679	N/A	31,543

MONTE CARLO (V-6/V-8)

Model Number	Body/Style Number	Body Type & Seating	Factory Price	Shipping Weight	Production Total
1G	Z37	2-dr. Spt Cpe-6P	8936/9311	3085/3200	112,730

MONTE CARLO 'SS' (V-8)

Model Number	Body/Style Number	Body Type & Seating	Factory Price	Shipping Weight	Production Total
1G	Z37/Z65	2-dr. Spt Cpe-6P	-- /10700	-- /3336	24,050

IMPALA (V-6/V-8)

Model Number	Body/Style Number	Body Type & Seating	Factory Price	Shipping Weight	Production Total
1B	L69	4-dr. Sedan-6P	8895/9270	3352/3450	55,296

1984 Caprice Classic sedan (CP)

CAPRICE CLASSIC (V-6/V-8)

Model Number	Body/Style Number	Body Type & Seating	Factory Price	Shipping Weight	Production Total
1B	N47	2-dr. Spt Cpe-6P	9253/9628	3363/3461	19,541
1B	N69	4-dr. Sedan-6P	9399/9774	3396/3494	135,970
1B	N35	4-dr. 3S Wag-8P	-- /10210	-- /3952	65,688

FACTORY PRICE AND WEIGHT NOTE: For Citation and Celebrity, prices and weights to left of slash are for four-cylinder, to right for V-6 engine. For Camaro, Monte Carlo and full-size models, figures to left of slash are for six-cylinder model, to right of slash for 305 cu. in. V-8. Celebrity diesel V-6 cost $250 more than gas V-6. Diesel V-8 was $325 more than gas V-8. **BODY/STYLE NO. NOTE:** Some models were actually option packages. Code after the slash (e.g., Z65) is the number of the option package that comes with the model listed.

ENGINE DATA: BASE FOUR (Chevette): Inline. Overhead cam. Four-cylinder. Cast iron block and head. Displacement: 98 cu. in. (1.6 liters). Bore & stroke: 3.23 x 2.98 in. Compression ratio: 9.0:1. Brake horsepower: 65 at 5200 R.P.M. Torque: 80 lbs.-ft. at 3200 R.P.M. Five main bearings. Hydraulic valve lifters. Carburetor: 2Bbl. VIN Code: C. DIESEL FOUR (Chevette): Inline. Overhead cam. Four-cylinder. Cast iron block and head. Displacement: 111 cu. in. (1.8 liters). Bore & stroke: 3.31 x 3.23 in. Compression ratio: 22.0:1. Brake horsepower: 51 at 5000 R.P.M. Torque: 72 lbs.-ft. at 2000 R.P.M. Five main bearings. Solid valve lifters. Fuel injection. VIN Code: D. BASE FOUR (Cavalier): Inline. Overhead valve. Four-cylinder. Cast iron block and head. Displacement: 121 cu. in. (2.0 liters). Bore & stroke: 3.50 x 3.15 in. Compression ratio: 9.3:1. Brake horsepower: 88 at 4800 R.P.M. Torque: 110 lbs.-ft. at 2400 R.P.M. Five main bearings. Hydraulic valve lifters. Throttle-body fuel injection. VIN Code: P. BASE FOUR (Citation, Celebrity, Camaro): Inline. Overhead valve. Four-cylinder. Cast iron block and head. Displacement: 151 cu. in. (2.5 liters). Bore & stroke: 4.00 x 3.00 in. Compression ratio: 9.0:1. Brake horsepower: 92 at 4000 R.P.M. Torque: 132 lbs.-ft. at 2800 R.P.M. Five main bearings. Hydraulic valve lifters. Throttle-body fuel injection. Pontiac-built. VIN Code: R exc. (Camaro) 2. BASE V-6 (Camaro Berlinetta); OPTIONAL (Citation, Celebrity, Camaro): 60-degree, overhead-valve V-6. Cast iron block and head. Displacement: 173 cu. in. (2.8 liters). Bore & stroke: 3.50 x 2.99 in. Compression ratio: 8.5:1. Brake horsepower: 112 at 4800 R.P.M. (Camaro, 107 at 4800). Torque: 145 lbs.-ft. at 2100 R.P.M. Four main bearings. Hydraulic valve lifters. Carburetor: 2Bbl. VIN Code: X exc. (Camaro) 1. HIGH-OUTPUT V-6; OPTIONAL (Citation, Celebrity): Same as 173 cu. in. V-6 above except C.R.: 8.9:1. Brake H.P.: 135 at 5400 R.P.M. (Celebrity, 130 H.P.). Torque: 145 lbs.-ft. at 2400 R.P.M. VIN Code: Z. BASE V-6 (Monte Carlo, Impala, Caprice): 90-degree, overhead-valve V-6. Cast iron block and head. Displacement: 229 cu. in. (3.8 liters). Bore & stroke: 3.74 x 3.48 in. Compression ratio: 8.6:1. Brake horsepower: 110 at 4000 R.P.M. Torque: 190 lbs.-ft. at 1600 R.P.M. Four main bearings. Hydraulic valve lifters. Carburetor: 2Bbl. VIN Code: 9. (NOTE: California models used a Buick 231 V-6.) DIESEL V-6 (Celebrity): 90-degree, overhead-valve V-6. Cast iron block and head. Displacement: 262 cu. in. (4.3 liters). Bore & stroke: 4.057 x 3.385 in Compression ratio: 22.8:1. Brake horsepower: 85 at 3600 R.P.M. Torque: 165 lbs.-ft. at 1600 R.P.M. Four main bearings. Hydraulic valve lifters. Fuel injection. VIN Code: T. BASE V-8 (Camaro Z28, Caprice wagon); OPTIONAL (Camaro, Monte Carlo, Impala, Caprice): 90-degree, overhead valve V-8. Cast iron block and head. Displacement: 305 cu. in. (5.0 liters). Bore & stroke: 3.74 x 3.48 in. Compression ratio: 8.6:1. Brake horsepower: 150 at 4000 R.P.M. Torque: 240 lbs.-ft. at 2400 R.P.M. Five main bearings. Hydraulic valve lifters. Carburetor: 4Bbl. VIN Code: H. HIGH-OUTPUT V-8 (Monte Carlo SS): Same as 305 cu. in. V-8 above, except Brake H.P.: 180 at 4800 R.P.M. Torque: 235 lbs.-ft. at 3200 R.P.M. VIN Code: G. HIGH-OUTPUT V-8; OPTIONAL (Camaro Z28): Same as 305 cu. in V-8 above, except C.R.: 9.5:1. Brake H.P.: 190 at 4800 R.P.M. Torque: 240 lbs.-ft. at 3200 R.P.M. VIN Code: G. DIESEL V-8; OPTIONAL (Monte Carlo, Impala/Caprice): 90-degree, overhead valve V-8. Cast iron block and head. Displacement: 350 cu. in (5.7 liters). Bore & stroke: 4.057 x 3.385 in. Compression ratio: 22.1:1. Brake horsepower: 105 at 3200 R.P.M. Torque: 200 lbs.-ft. at 1600 R.P.M. Five main bearings. Hydraulic valve lifters. Fuel injection. Olds-built. VIN Code: N.

1984 Cavalier CS station wagon (CP)

CHASSIS DATA: Wheelbase: (Chevette 2-dr.) 94.3 in.; (Chvt 4-dr.) 97.3 in.; (Cavalier) 101.2 in.; (Citation/Celebrity) 104.9 in.; (Camaro) 101.0 in.; (Monte Carlo) 108.0 in.; (Imp/Caprice) 116.0 in. Overall length: (Chvt 2-dr.) 161.9 in.; (Chvt 4-dr.) 164.9 in.; (Cav cpe/conv) 172.4 in.; (Cav sed) 174.3 in.; (Cav wag) 174.5 in.; (Cit) 176.7 in.; (Camaro) 187.8 in.; (Celeb) 188.3 in.; (Celeb wag) 190.8 in.; (Monte) 200.4 in.; (Monte SS) 202.4 in.; (Impala) 212.2 in.; (Caprice sed) 212.8 in.; (Capr wag) 215.1 in. Height: (Chvt) 52.8 in.; (Cav cpe) 51.9 in.; (Cav hatch) 51.7 in.; (Cav conv) 52.7 in.; (Cav sed) 53.8 in.; (Cav wag) 54.3 in.; (Cit) 53.9 in.; (Camaro) 50.0 in.; (Camaro Z28) 50.3 in.; (Celeb) 53.9 in.; (Celeb wag) 54.3 in.; (Monte) 54.4 in.; (Monte SS) 55.0 in.; (Imp/Capr sed) 56.4 in.; (Capr wag) 58.1 in. Width: (Chvt) 61.8 in.; (Cav cpe/conv) 66.0 in.; (Cav sed/wag) 66.3 in.; (Cit) 68.3 in.; (Camaro) 72.8 in.; (Celeb) 69.3 in.; (Monte) 71.8 in.; (Imp/Capr) 75.4 in.; (Capr wag) 79.3 in. Front Tread: (Chvt) 51.2 in.; (Cav) 55.4 in.; (Cit/Celeb) 58.7 in.; (Camaro) 60.7 in.; (Monte) 58.5 in.; (Imp/Capr) 61.7 in.; (Caprice wag) 62.2 in. Rear Tread: (Chvt) 51.2 in.; (Cav) 55.2 in.; (Cit/Celeb) 57.0 in.; (Camaro) 61.6 in.; (Monte) 57.8 in.; (Imp/Capr) 60.7 in.; (Caprice wag) 64.1 in. Standard Tires: (Chvt) P155/80R13 GBR; (Cav) P175/80R13 GBR; (Cit/Celeb) P185/80R13 SBR; (Celeb wag) P185/75R14 SBR; (Camaro) P195/75R14 SBR; (Camaro Berlinetta) P205/70R14 SBR; (Camaro Z28) P215/65R15 WLT SBR; (Monte) P195/75R14 SBR; (Monte SS) P215/65R15; (Imp/Capr) P205/75R15 SBR; (Caprice wag) P225/75R15 SBR.

TECHNICAL: Transmission: Four-speed floor shift standard on Chevette. Gear ratios (1st) 3.75:1; (2nd) 2.16:1; (3rd) 1.38:1; (4th) 1.00:1; (Rev) 3.82:1. Four-speed floor shift on Cavalier/Citation/Celebrity: (1st) 3.53:1; (2nd) 1.95:1; (3rd) 1.24:1; (4th) 0.81:1 or 0.73:1; (Rev) 3.42:1. Citation H.O. V-6 four-speed manual trans.: (1st) 3.31:1; (2nd) 1.95:1; (3rd) 1.24:1; (4th) 0.81:1; (Rev) 3.42:1. Camaro four four-speed manual trans.: (1st) 3.50:1; (2nd) 2.48:1; (3rd) 1.66:1; (4th) 1.00:1; (Rev) 3.50:1. Cavalier five-speed manual: (1st) 3.91:1; (2nd) 2.15:1; (3rd) 1.33:1; (4th) 0.92:1; (5th) 0.74:1; (Rev) 3.50:1. Camaro four five-speed manual: (1st) 3.76:1; (2nd) 2.18:1; (3rd) 1.42:1; (4th) 1.00:1; (5th) 0.86:1; (Rev) 3.76:1. Camaro V-6 five-speed manual: (1st) 3.50:1; (2nd) 2.14:1; (3rd) 1.36:1; (4th) 1.00:1; (5th) 0.78:1; (Rev) 3.39:1. Camaro V8305 five-speed manual.: (1st) 2.95:1; (2nd) 1.94:1; (3rd) 1.34:1; (4th) 1.00:1; (5th) 0.73:1; (Rev) 2.76:1. Chevette five-speed manual shift: (1st) 3.76:1; (2nd) 2.18:1; (3rd) 1.36:1; (4th) 1.00:1; (5th) 0.86:1; (Rev) 3.76:1. Three-speed Turbo Hydra- matic standard on Monte Carlo and Imp/Caprice: (1st) 2.74:1; (2nd) 1.57:1; (3rd) 1.00:1; (Rev) 2.07:1. Monte/Imp/Caprice w/V6229: (1st) 2.52:1; (2nd) 1.52:1; (3rd) 1.00:1; (Rev) 1.93:1. Chevette auto. trans.: (1st) 2.40:1; (2nd) 1.48:1; (3rd) 1.00:1; (Rev) 1.92:1. Cav/Cit/Celeb auto. trans.: (1st) 2.84:1; (2nd) 1.60:1; (3rd) 1.00:1; (Rev) 2.07:1. Four-speed overdrive automatic on Imp/Caprice: (1st) 2.74:1; (2nd) 1.57:1; (3rd) 1.00:1; (4th) 0.67:1; (Rev) 2.07:1. Four-speed overdrive automatic on Celebrity: (1st) 2.92:1; (2nd) 1.57:1; (3rd) 1.00:1; (4th) 0.70:1; (Rev) 2.38:1. Four-speed overdrive automatic on Camaro: (1st) 3.06:1; (2nd) 1.63:1; (3rd) 1.00:1; (4th) 0.70:1; (Rev) 2.29:1. Standard final drive ratio: (Chevette) 3.36:1 or 3.62:1; (Cavalier) 3.32:1 or 4.10:1 w/4spd, 3.83:1 w/5spd or 3.73:1 w/auto.; (Citation four) 3.32:1 or 3.65:1 exc. 2.39:1 or 2.84:1 w/auto.; (Cit V-6) 3.32:1 exc. 2.53:1 w/auto.; (Cit H.O. V-6) 3.65:1 exc. 3.33:1 w/auto.; (Camaro four) 3.42:1 exc. 3.73:1 w/auto. or 5spd; (Camaro V-6) 3.42:1 w/5spd, 3.20:1 w/auto.; (Camaro V-8) 3.20:1 or 3.78:1 w/5spd, 3.08:1 or 3.73:1 w/auto.; (Z28) 3.20:1 w/auto.; (Celebrity four) 3.65:1 exc. 2.39:1 w/auto.; (Celeb V-6) 2.84:1 or 3.06:1; (Celeb H.O. V-6) 3.33:1; (Monte V-6) 2.41:1 or 2.73:1; (Monte V-8) 3.42:1 or 3.73:1; (Monte H.O. V-8) 3.42:1 or 3.73:1; (Monte SS) 3.42:1; (Imp/Caprice V-6) 2.73:1 or 3.23:1; (Imp/Capr V-8) 2.73:1 or 3.08:1. Steering, Suspension, Brakes and Body: same as 1982-83. Fuel tank: (Chvt) 12.2 gal.; (Cav) 13.6 gal.; (Cit four) 14.6 gal.; (Cit V-6) 15.1 gal.; (Camaro four) 15.5 gal.; (Camaro V-6) 16.2 gal.; (Celeb four) 15.7 gal.; (Celeb V-6) 16.4 gal.; (Monte) 18.1 gal.; (Imp/Capr) 25 gal.; (Caprice wag) 22 gal.

DRIVETRAIN OPTIONS: Engines: 173 cu. in., 2Bbl. V-6: Citation, base Camaro, Celeb ($250). H.O. 173 cu. in., 2Bbl. V-6: Citation ($400). 305 cu. in., 4Bbl. V-8: Camaro ($550); Berlinetta ($375); Monte, Imp/Caprice cpe/sed ($375). H.O. 305 cu. in., 4Bbl. V-8: Camaro Z28 ($530). Diesel 260 cu. in. V-6: Celeb ($500). Diesel 350 cu. in. V-8: Monte/Imp/Caprice ($700). Transmission/Differential: Five-speed manual trans.: Chevette/Cavalier ($75); base Camaro ($125). Three-speed automatic trans.: Chevette/Cavalier ($395); Chvt diesel ($380); Citation/Celeb ($425). Four-speed overdrive automatic trans.: base Camaro ($525); Berlinetta/Z28 ($295); Celeb (N/A); Monte, Imp/Capr cpe/sed ($175). Limited-slip differential: Camaro/Monte/Imp/Capr ($95). Performance axle ratio ($21). Power Accessories: Power brakes: Chevette ($95); Citation, Celeb cpe/sed ($100). Power four-wheel disc brakes: Camaro V-8 ($179). Power steering: Chvt/Cav ($204); Cit ($215). Suspension: F40 H.D. susp.: Cav/Cit/Celeb/Monte/Imp/Capr ($26). F41 sport suspension: Cit/Celeb ($33); Cav ($44-$49); Camaro/Monte, Imp/Capr cpe/sed ($49). Inflatable rear shock absorbers: Celeb/Caprice wag ($64). Other: H.D. cooling ($40-$70). Engine block heater ($20). Cold climate pkg.: Monte/Imp/Caprice diesel ($99). Diesel engine and fuel line heater: Celeb ($49). H.D. battery ($26) exc. diesel ($52). California emission system ($99).

CHEVETTE CONVENIENCE/APPEARANCE OPTIONS: Option Packages: Sport decor pkg.: black grille, headlamp bezels and wheels; bodyside moldings, trim rings and decals ($95). Deluxe exterior: side window reveal moldings, argent wheels and trim rings ($152-$167). Comfort/Convenience: Air conditioning ($630). Rear defogger, electric ($130). Tinted glass ($95). Comfortilt steering wheel ($104). Cigarette lighter: Scooter ($10). Lighting and Mirrors: Twin sport mirrors, left remote ($53). Driver's remote sport mirror ($34). Entertainment: AM radio: Scooter ($83). AM/FM radio ($82); Scooter ($165). AM/FM stereo radio ($109). Radio delete ($51 credit). Exterior Trim: Two-tone paint ($133). Rear spoiler ($69). Bodyside moldings: Scooter ($45). Door edge guards ($15-$25). Chrome bumpers ($25). Interior Trim/Upholstery: Cloth bucket seats ($28). Custom cloth bucket seats ($130). Color-keyed floor mats ($25). Wheels and Tires: Sport wheel covers ($97). Wheel trim rings ($52). P155/80R13 GBR WSW ($51). P175/70R13 SBR BSW ($119). P175/70R13 SBR WSW ($173).

CAVALIER CONVENIENCE/APPEARANCE OPTIONS: Option Packages: CL equipment pkg.: custom interior w/reclining seats, quiet sound group, three-spoke leather-wrapped steering wheel, custom door/quarter trim ($275-$375); incl. split folding rear seat on hatch/wagon. Comfort/Convenience: Air cond. ($630). Cruise control ($175). Rear defogger, electric ($130). Tinted glass ($95). Six-way power driver's seat ($215). Leather-wrapped steering wheel ($74-$95). Comfortilt steering wheel ($99). Power windows ($185-$260). Power door locks ($125-$175). Power hatch or trunk release ($40). Power liftgate release ($35). Gauge pkg. w/trip odometer ($69). Special instruments incl. tach ($139). Lighter: base ($14). Intermittent wipers ($50). Rear wiper/washer ($120). Lighting and Mirrors: Halogen headlamps ($10). Aux. lighting ($72-$95). Dual sport mirrors, left remote ($53). Right visor mirror ($7). Entertainment: AM radio: base ($112). AM/FM radio ($171) exc. CS/10 ($82). Electronic-tuning AM/FM stereo radio: CS/10 ($177). Elect.-tuning AM/FM stereo radio w/clock ($277) exc. CS/10 ($177). Elect.-tuning AM/FM stereo radio w/cassette ($377) exc. CS/10 ($277). Elect.-tuning AM/FM stereo seek/scan radio w/cassette, equalizer and clock ($605) exc. CS/10 ($505). Dual rear speakers ($30-$42); premium ($25). Fixed-mast antenna: base ($41) but incl. w/radios. Radio delete ($56 credit). Exterior Trim: Removable sunroof ($300). Rear spoiler ($69). Rear window louvers ($199). Pinstriping ($53). Sport striping ($95). Bodyside moldings, black/argent ($45). Wheel opening moldings ($30). Wheel opening and rocker panel moldings ($55). Door edge guards ($15-$25). Roof carrier ($105). Bumper guards ($56). Interior Trim/Upholstery: Cloth or CS bucket seats ($28). Split-folding rear seatback ($50). Color-keyed mats: front ($15); rear ($10). Cargo area cover ($69). Wheels and Tires: Aluminum wheels ($369). Sport wheel covers w/black wheels ($97). Wheel trim rings ($52). P175/80R13 GBR WSW ($54). P195/70R13 SBR BSW ($169). P195/70R13 SBR WSW ($231). P195/70R13 SBR WLT ($253).

1984 Citation II X11 hatchback coupe (AA)

CITATION/CELEBRITY CONVENIENCE/APPEARANCE OPTIONS: Option Packages: X11 sport equipment pkg.: Citation ($919- $981). Eurosport pkg.: Celeb cpe/sed ($226); wag ($191). Sport decor pkg. (rear spoiler, rally wheels, sport mirrors, color-keyed bumpers w/rub strips, decal): Citation ($249). Deluxe exterior pkg.: Cit ($68-$168). Exterior molding pkg. (black rocker panel and wheel opening moldings): Celeb ($55). Value appearance group: Cit ($55-$63). Quiet sound group: Cit cpe ($43). Quiet sound/rear decor pkg.: Cit ($92). Security pkg.: Celeb wag ($44). Comfort/Convenience: Air cond. ($725-$730). Rear defogger, electric ($140). Cruise control ($175). Tinted glass ($110). Sport steering wheel: Cit ($22). Comfortilt steering wheel ($110). Six-way power driver's seat: Celeb ($215). Power windows ($185-$260). Remote swing-out side windows: Cit ($108). Power door locks ($125-$175). Citation gauge pkg. w/clock and trip odometer ($104); w/tachometer ($149). Gauge pkg. w/trip odometer: Celeb ($64). Electric clock: Cit ($35). Digital clock: Celeb ($39). Lighter: Cit cpe ($10). Intermittent wipers ($50). Rear wiper/washer: Celeb ($120). Lighting, Horns and Mirrors: Halogen high-beam headlamps: Celeb ($10). Aux. lighting: Cit ($50); Celeb ($43-$57). Dome reading lamp: Celeb ($24). Dual horns: Cit ($12). Driver's remote mirror ($23). Dual sport mirrors, left remote ($61). Dual remote mirrors: Celeb ($91). Entertainment: AM radio: Cit cpe ($83). AM/FM radio: Cit hatch, Celeb ($82); Cit cpe ($165). AM/FM stereo radio: Cit ($109) exc. cpe ($192). AM/FM stereo w/cassette: Cit ($209) exc. cpe ($292). Celebrity electronic-tuning AM/FM stereo radio w/clock ($177); w/cassette ($277); with seek/scan, equalizer and cassette ($505). Dual rear speakers ($30); incl. w/stereo radio. Premium dual rear speakers: Celeb ($25) but incl. with elect. tuning radio. Radio delete ($56 credit). Exterior Trim: Vinyl roof: Celeb ($160). Two-tone paint: Cit ($176-$184) incl. pinstriping and bodyside moldings; Celeb ($148). Bodyside pinstriping: Cit ($39-$47); Celeb ($57). Bodyside moldings: Cit ($55). Door edge guards ($15-$25). Rear window air deflector: Celeb wag ($40). Swing-out quarter vent windows: Celeb ($75). Swing-out tailgate: Celeb ($105). Roof carrier: Celeb wag ($105). Bumper guards ($56). Bumper rub strips: Cit ($50). Citation Interior Trim/Upholstery: Console ($105). Sport cloth bench seat ($28). Custom trim w/cloth bench seat ($195); w/custom cloth bucket seats ($367-$392). Sport cloth bucket seats ($221-$250). Color-keyed mats: front ($17); rear ($12). Deluxe seatbelts: cpe ($26). Celebrity Interior Trim/Upholstery: Console ($105). Reclining driver and passenger seatbacks ($90). Two-pass. vinyl front bench seat: cpe/sed ($28). Three-pass. vinyl front bench seat: sed ($78). Three-pass. cloth front bench seat ($28-$50). CL custom cloth 45/45 seat ($250-$330). CL three-pass. custom bench seating: vinyl ($229); cloth ($257). CL two- pass. custom cloth bench seating ($109-$179). 45/45 cloth seating ($100). Cloth bucket seats ($147). Color-keyed mats: front ($17); rear ($12). Deluxe luggage area trim: wag ($40). Citation Wheels/Tires: Rally wheels ($56). P185/80R13 SBR WSW ($58). P205/70R13 SBR WLT ($202). P215/60R14 SBR WLT: X11 ($92). Celebrity Wheels/Tires: Aluminum wheels ($306-$362). Sport wheel covers ($65). Wire wheel covers ($159). Wheel cover locks ($39). Rally wheels ($56). P185/80R13 SBR WSW ($58). P185/75R14 SBR BSW ($36). P185/75R14 SBR WSW ($58-$94). P195/70R14 SBR BSW ($28). P195/75R14 SBR BSW ($31-$67). P195/75R14 SBR WSW ($93-$129). P205/70R13 SBR WSW ($180).

1984 Monte Carlo SS Sport Coupe (CP)

CAMARO/MONTE CARLO CONVENIENCE/APPEARANCE OPTIONS: Comfort/Convenience: Air conditioning ($730). Rear defogger, electric ($140). Cruise control ($175-$185). Tinted glass ($110). Comfortilt steering wheel ($110). Six-way power driver's seat ($215). Power windows ($185). Power door locks ($125). Power trunk opener: Monte ($40). Power hatch release: Camaro ($40). Electric clock ($35). Gauge pkg. w/trip odometer: Monte ($95). Gauge pkg. incl. tach: Camaro ($149). Intermittent wipers ($50). Rear wiper/washer: Camaro ($120). Quiet sound group: Camaro ($72-$82). Lighting, Horns and Mirrors: Halogen high-beam headlamps ($10). Cornering lamps: Monte ($55). Aux. lighting: Camaro ($37-$72); Monte ($28). Dual horns: Camaro ($12). Twin sport mirrors (left remote): base Camaro, Monte ($53). Twin remote sport mirrors: Monte ($83); SS ($30). Twin electric remote sport mirrors: Camaro ($91-$139). Entertainment: AM radio ($112). AM/FM radio ($171). AM/FM stereo radio: Monte ($198). Cassette player with AM/FM stereo radio: Monte ($298). Camaro electronic-tuning AM/FM stereo radio ($263); w/clock ($267-$302); w/cassette and clock ($367-$402); w/cassette, clock and seek/scan ($570-$605). Dual rear speakers ($30). Fixed mast antenna ($41); incl. w/radios. Power antenna ($60). Exterior Trim: Removable glass roof panels ($825). Landau vinyl roof: Monte ($245). Rear spoiler: Camaro ($69). Two- tone paint: Monte ($214). Bodyside moldings, black: Camaro ($55). Deluxe bodyside moldings: Monte ($57). Door edge guards ($15). Side window sill moldings: Monte ($45). Roof drip moldings: Camaro ($29). Bodyside pinstriping: Monte ($61). Interior Trim/Upholstery: Console: Camaro ($50); Monte ($105). Vinyl bench seat: base Monte ($28). Cloth 55/45 seating: base Monte ($133). Cloth bucket seats: Camaro ($28); Monte ($147). Custom cloth or vinyl bucket seats: base Camaro ($359); Z28 ($287). Custom cloth CL 55/45 seating: base Monte ($385). Cloth LS contour bucket seats: Camaro ($375). Custom cloth LS contour bucket seats: Camaro ($650). Mats w/carpeted inserts: Camaro front ($20); Camaro rear ($15). Color-keyed mats: Monte ($27). Cargo area cover: Camaro ($69). Deluxe trunk trim: Camaro ($164); Z28 ($84). Locking rear storage cover: Camaro ($80). Wheels and Tires: Aluminum wheels: Monte ($362). Rally wheels: Camaro ($112); Monte ($56). Full wheel covers: Camaro ($52). Wire wheel covers: Monte ($159). Wheel cover locks: Monte ($39). P195/75R14 GBR WSW: Camaro ($62). P195/75R14 SBR WSW: Monte ($62). P205/70R14 SBR BSW: base Camaro ($58). P205/70R14 SBR WSW: Camaro ($124); Berlinetta ($66); Monte ($124). P205/70R14 SBR WLT: Camaro ($146). P215/65R15 SBR BSW: Z28 ($92 credit).

IMPALA/CAPRICE CONVENIENCE/APPEARANCE OPTIONS: Option Packages: Estate equipment: wag ($307). Landau equipment pkg.: vinyl roof, sport mirrors and reveal moldings ($306). Comfort/Convenience: Air cond. ($730). Rear defogger, electric ($140). Cruise control ($175). Tinted glass ($110). Comfortilt steering wheel ($110). Power door locks ($125- $175). Six-way power driver's seat ($215). Power windows ($185-$260). Power trunk opener ($40). Power tailgate lock: wag ($50). Electric clock: Imp ($35). Digital clock: Imp ($66); Caprice ($34). Gauge pkg. w/trip odometer ($64). Intermittent wipers ($50). Quiet sound group: Imp ($66). Lighting and Mirrors: Halogen high-beam headlamps ($10). Cornering lamps ($55). Aux. lighting ($32-$42). Driver's remote mirror ($23). Dual remote mirrors ($67). Dual sport mirrors, left remote ($61). Dual remote body-color sport mirrors ($91) exc. Landau ($30). Lighted visor mirror ($48). Entertainment: Same as 1983. AM radio ($112). AM/FM radio ($171). AM/FM stereo radio ($198). Cassette player with AM/FM stereo ($298). Dual rear speakers ($30). Power antenna ($60). Windshield antenna ($29); incl. w/radios. Exterior Trim: Vinyl roof: sed ($185). Roof carrier: wag ($110). Custom two-tone paint ($141). Pinstriping ($39). Bodyside moldings ($55). Door edge guards ($15-$25). Rear window air deflector: wag ($40). Bumper rub strips ($66). Bumper guards ($62). Interior Trim/Upholstery: Reclining passenger seatback ($45). Vinyl bench seat: Imp sed ($28). Cloth bench seat: wag ($28). Cloth 50/50 seating: Caprice ($195-$225). Deluxe load-floor carpet: wag ($89). Deluxe cargo area carpet: wag ($129). Color-keyed mats: front ($17); rear ($12). Deluxe trunk trim ($59). Wheels and Tires: Sport wheel covers ($65). Wire wheel covers ($159). Wire wheel cover locks ($39). P205/75R15 SBR WSW: cpe/sed ($66). P225/70R15 SBR WSW: cpe/sed ($159). P225/75R15 SBR WSW: wag ($71). Puncture-sealant tires ($106-$132).

1984 Camaro Z28 5.0L HO T-top Sport Coupe (CP)

HISTORY: Introduced: Sept. 22, 1983. Model year production (U.S.): 1,658,868 (incl. Corvettes but not incl. 18,314 Acadians). Total production for the U.S. market included 871,578 four- cylinder, 466,797 sixes and 507,774 V-8s. A total of 11,452 diesels were installed. Calendar year production (U.S.): 1,471,462 (including 35,661 Corvettes). Calendar year sales by U.S. dealers: 1,565,143 (incl. 30,424 Corvettes) for a 19.7 percent market share. Model year sales by U.S. dealers: 1,585,902 (incl. 27,986 Corvettes) for a 20.1 percent share.

Historical Footnotes: Model year sales finished nearly 23 percent higher than the 1983 result, with all lines (except Citation) performing well. Sales of that forlorn X-car fell by more than half. As demand for Citations slowed, production was halted at the Oklahoma plant and cut to one shift at Tarrytown, New York. Cavalier continued as America's best selling car, with Celebrity not far behind. Two new imports, Sprint (built by Suzuki) and Spectrum (by Isuzu) would soon give Chevrolet another toehold on the rising small-car market. Sprint went on sale late in the 1984 model year, Spectrum later, both as '85 models. To help plan for the enthusiast's market, surveys revealed that nearly two-thirds of Camaro buyers were under age 35. *Road & Track* magazine called the '84 Camaro one of the dozen top enthusiast cars, and it tied with Trans Am for best Sports GT in its price league. The International Race of Champions returned to the racing circuit during 1984, after a three-year absence. Co- sponsored by Chevrolet, Anheuser-Busch, Goodyear and True Value Hardware, the races would put a dozen of the world's top drivers behind the wheel of identically-prepared Camaro Z28s. That IROC racing series had begun in 1974 using Porsches, then switched to Camaros. With heavy TV coverage, this year's races would draw considerable attention to Camaro and perhaps help pave the way for the soon-to-come IROCZ production models. On another level, Chevrolet hosted a traveling Chevy Sports Hall of Fame show in urban shopping malls this year, as part of greatly increased advertising and promotional expenditures.

1985 CHEVROLET

Chevrolet claimed this year to offer "America's highest- mileage car, America's fastest car...America's most popular full-size car and America's most popular car, regardless of size." Still, 1985 was a year of refinement and evolution rather than revolution. But several intriguing models and engines were announced, including the new IROCZ Camaro, performance Z24 Cavalier, and 4.3-liter V-6 engine with fuel injection. That 130-horsepower powerplant was the standard eight in Caprice and Monte Carlo, intended to tempt V-8 fans who might appreciate a bit better gas mileage. Also new was a multi-port fuel-injected version of the 2.8-liter V-6, identified by 'MFI' logo when installed in a Cavalier, Celebrity, Citation II or Camaro. Unfortunately, the Z24 Cavalier didn't actually arrive until the 1986 model year, nearly a year later than scheduled. The old reliable 305 cu. in. (5.0-liter) V-8 got a boost in compression ratio and new Electronic Spark Control.

1985 Chevette CS hatchback sedan (CP)

CHEVETTE — SERIES 1T — FOUR — In the face of a flurry of front-drive subcompacts, Chevette hung on with rear-wheel drive. Little changed this year, except that the base Chevette was dropped, leaving only the CS version, again in two- or four-door hatchback form. Base powertrain remained the 1.6-liter gas four with four-speed manual transmission. The diesel four was still available, but only a handful were sold. A five-speed manual gearbox was now available on all models (formerly only on two-doors without air conditioning). Diesels could no longer get automatic. Of the 10 body colors, eight were new this year. Also new: Custom two-tone combinations. Four-doors now had standard Custom Cloth front bucket seats. New bodyside moldings had argent inserts. Returning to the option list was a Z13 Sport Decor graphic package, including black grille, bumpers and wheels, plus black bodyside moldings with red inserts.

1985 Cavalier sedan (AA)

CAVALIER — SERIES 1J — FOUR/V-6 — Two-door Cavaliers got new taillamps, wheels and hubcaps, plus a new steering wheel. An upshift light was added to manual-gearbox models. Base models had upgraded seats. The lineup again included two-door notchbacks and hatchbacks, four-door sedans and wagons, plus the convertible. The convertible officially became a separate line this year, rather than an option package. Both Type 10 and convertible models got a "cockpit" styled instrument panel, with switches in control pods at the sides of the cluster. Cavaliers also got new interior trim colors and "Star Wars" instrumentation. Of the dozen body colors, ten were new this year. Cavaliers again had a crosshatch-pattern grille, angled inward at the base with bowtie emblem in the middle, and flanked by recessed quad rectangular headlamps. Parking lights were below the bumper rub strips. The base 121 cu. in. (2.0-liter) four, rated 85 horsepower, got refinements to improve durability and economy. But the biggest news for Cavalier was the availability of a 2.8-liter V-6 with multi-port fuel injection. Arriving later in the season, the V-6 was rated 125 horsepower, standard with the announced Z24 sports package but available in all models. That Z24 package, scheduled for spring 1985 arrival, was to include flared rocker panels, specific fascia, rally wheels, and digital instruments. But it didn't actually appear until the 1986 model year. Cavalier standard equipment included four-speed manual (overdrive) transmission, power brakes, front/rear ashtrays, color-keyed bumpers with black/argent rub strips, side window defogger, argent grille, day/night mirror, front stabilizer bar, styled steel wheels, fixed quarter windows, black windshield and back window moldings, and vinyl reclining bucket seats. Type 10 Cavaliers included black/red bumper rub strips, lighter, black grille, AM radio, color-keyed sport steering wheel, black/red bodyside moldings, plus black window and belt moldings. CS equipment, though similar to Type 10, included black/argent bodyside moldings and a bright grille. Convertibles came with a power top, power windows (drop-down rear quarter), black/argent bumper rub strips, tinted glass, black sport mirrors, and bright rocker panel moldings. Convertible interiors held cloth or vinyl custom reclining bucket seats.

1985 Citation II X11 hatchback coupe (AA)

CITATION II — SERIES 1X — FOUR/V-6 — All the final Citations were hatchbacks, as the notchback coupe was dropped this year X-cars had been plagued by problems, including court battles, largely for alleged brake flaws on the 1980 models. A new dashboard included a horizontal-style radio. Electronic-tuning models were now available, with or without a cassette tape player. A dozen body colors were offered (nine new this year). Citation's X11 package now included a 130-horsepower 173 cu. in. (2.8-liter) V-6 with multi-port fuel injection. That powerplant was also available separately, in all models. The base 151 cu. in. (2.5-liter) four added hydraulic roller valve lifters this year, while the carbureted 2.8 V-6 continued in its prior form. The X11 package also included power brakes, sport steering wheel, sport cloth bucket seats, domed hood with air inlet, body-color bumpers, X11 decals, rear deck spoiler, F41 sport suspension, and P215/60R14 SBR tires on newly-styled Rally wheels. Black headlamp bezels, grille, B-pillar/window frames and taillamp frames completed the package. Aluminum wheels were optional.

1985 Camaro IROC-Z (Z28) Sport Coupe

CAMARO — SERIES 1F — FOUR/V-6/V-8 — Most appealing to connoisseurs was the new IROCZ, styled along the lines of the racing models that performed in the International Race of Champions and with a nod to Corvette. IROCZ was packaged as a Z28 option. In appearance, it could be spotted by twin foglamps inset in the grille opening (alongside the license plate mount), a low front air dam, ornamental hood louvers, and striping at rocker panel level. IROCZ had a solid angled front panel between deeply recessed quad headlamps, with parking lamps just below the crease line. Deep body-color "ground effects" skirting encircled the entire car. Special 16 x 8 in. aluminum wheels held Corvette-inspired P245/50VR16 Goodyear Eagle GT unidirectional tires. Near the base of each door were large 'IROCZ' decals. The IROCZ chassis featured Delco/Bilstein rear shock absorbers, special struts and springs, special rear stabilizer, and reinforced front frame rails. The IROCZ could have any of three 305 cu. in. (5.0- liter) V-8s: standard four-barrel with five-speed manual gearbox (four-speed overdrive automatic available), a high- output L69 carbureted V-8 with five-speed, or the new LB9 tuned-port fuel injection (TPI) version. The TPI came only with four-speed automatic. Individually-tuned runners channeled incoming air to each cylinder in the TPI V-8, while computer-controlled port injectors delivered precisely-metered fuel. In limited-production IROCZ dress, the factory claimed a 060 MPH time in the seven-second area, and 15- second quarter-mile acceleration times. "Ordinary" Z28s could have only the standard or TPI versions, not the carbureted H.O. Z28s in general had a selection of changes in appearance details, including grille and parking lamps, deeper ground- effects rocker panels, hood louvers, deeper chin spoiler, three-element taillamps, larger rear bumper fascia, and new body nameplates. Inside were new speedometer graphics and tachometer. Berlinetta got a new standard 173 cu. in. (2.8-liter) V-6 with multi-port fuel injection and only one option: the carbureted 5.0-liter V-8. Also new were body graphics and subtly-patterned interior fabrics. The base Sport Coupe again came with either a four, V-6 or V-8 engine under the hood. Like the Z28, it had new body styling, a wider selection of optional sound systems with electronic-tuning radios, and revised optional instrument cluster graphics. All Camaros had new "wet arm" windshield wipers, with washer outlets mounted on the blades. The double-needle speedometer was abandoned. Split rear seatbacks were a new option, and cast aluminum wheels (standard on Z28) were available on the base Camaro. Body colors this year were white, silver, copper, red maroon, black, medium gray, dark or bright blue, yellow or light yellow, and light brown.

1985 Celebrity 2-dr coupe

CELEBRITY — SERIES 1F — FOUR/V-6 — Like other models, Celebrity got a new optional 173 cu. in. (2.8-liter) V-6 with multi-port fuel injection, available on all models. Also optional: a carbureted 2.8 and a 4.3- liter V-6 diesel, plus the standard 151 cu. in. (2.5-liter) four. All models now had 14 in. wheels and standard power brakes. Gas engines had new hydraulic mounts, plus the availability of four-speed overdrive automatic transmission. The Eurosport option package added gas-charged shock absorbers. Of the dozen body colors, nine were new this year. Station wagons could get a new woodgrain Estate Package. Coupes and sedans could be ordered with a new Celebrity Classic padded vinyl roof. Interior trim styles and colors were also new. The lineup continued as a two-door coupe, four-door sedan, and two- or three-seat wagons. The Eurosport package included black-finish body hardware with red accents, specific nameplates (inside and out), Rally wheels, red-accented bodyside molding rub strips, sport steering wheel, special F41 sport suspension, and gas-charged front struts and rear shocks. 'Eurosport' block lettering was at the forward edge of front doors; a '2.8FI' engine identifier on the decklid.

1985 Monte Carlo SS Sport Coupe

MONTE CARLO — SERIES 1G — V-6/V-8 — Under the hood of standard Montes was a new base 262 cu. in. (4.3-liter) V-6. Chevrolet claimed that the new 4.3 V-6 would be as economical as the prior carbureted 3.8, and nearly as "frisky" as a V-8. Standard Sport Coupes got new cloth interior trim and five new interior colors, plus new standard wheel covers. Still, the Monte Carlo SS, "cousin to the Grand National stock cars" on the NASCAR circuit, received the strongest promotion. Formerly offered only in white or blue body colors, this year's SS came in silver, maroon, white or black.

1985 Monte Carlo Sport Coupe (CP)

Interiors could be gray or maroon, either bench or bucket style. This street version of the NASCAR racing car had special instruments, sport suspension, rear spoiler, sport mirrors and steering wheel, plus P215/65R15 white- letter radial tires on special rally wheels. Apart from 'Monte Carlo SS' lettering on the doors and decklid, the body was nearly devoid of ornamentation. The blackout grille was a simple crosshatch pattern, flanked by recessed quad rectangular headlamps with deeply inset park/signal lamps below the forward crease line. Taillamp lenses sat nearly flush with the decklid panel. Monte SS again carried a high-output (RPO code L69) version of the familiar 305 cu. in. (5.0-liter) V-8, now with four-speed overdrive automatic transmission. SS mufflers grew in capacity; axles got larger ring gears. Removable black roof panels were to become available on SS later in the model year.

1985 Caprice Classic Landau Sport Coupe (AA)

IMPALA/CAPRICE CLASSIC — SERIES 1B — V-6/V-8 — Full-size Chevrolets had some changes to produce a more controlled ride, plus an economical new 262 cu. in. (4.3- liter) V-6 engine rated 130 horsepower. That new base engine was described as "a standard V-6 that acts like a V-8." All full-size models now wore fourth-generation All-Season tires. Four-speed overdrive automatic was available across the board. For the last time, the 5.7-liter diesel V-8 was optional (except in California). The lineup again included Caprice Classic two-door, four-door and station wagon, plus the four-door Impala sedan. Interiors received their most extensive reworking since 1977, all presumably to give a more contemporary, less stodgy look and feel. Wagons again came with a standard 305 cu. in. (5.0-liter) V-8, which was optional in other models. This year, it got a boost in compression (and horsepower), plus a new exhaust system. Caprice had a bold crosshatch grille, parking lamps inset into the bumper, wraparound cornering lamps, and quad rectangular headlamps. A 'Caprice Classic' script was at the forward end of front fenders. Impalas had standard AM radio, folding front center armrest, power brakes and steering, three-speed automatic transmission, lighter, padded door panels, argent grille, day/night mirror, cloth bench seats, full wheel covers, two- speed wiper/washers, and bright moldings. Caprice added a quartz clock, dual horns, wheel opening and lower bodyside moldings, headlamps-on buzzer, and bumper rub strips (except wagons). Wagons included vinyl bench seating, a locking side compartment, heavy-duty front/rear suspension, power liftgate window, and overdrive automatic transmission, along with the V-8 engine.

I.D. DATA: Chevrolets again had a 17-symbol Vehicle Identification Number (VIN) on the upper left surface of the instrument panel, visible through the windshield. Symbol one indicates country: '1' U.S.A.; '2' Canada. Next is a manufacturer code: 'G' General Motors. Symbol three is car make: '1' Chevrolet; '7' GM of Canada. Symbol four denotes restraint system: 'A' non-passive (standard); 'B' passive (automatic belts); 'C' passive (inflatable). Symbol five is car line/series: 'B' Chevette; 'C' Cavalier; 'D' Cavalier CS; 'E' Cavalier Type 10; 'X' Citation; 'P' Camaro; 'S' Camaro Berlinetta; 'W' Celebrity; 'Z' Monte Carlo; 'L' Impala; 'N' Caprice. Symbols six-seven reveal body type: '08' 2-dr. hatch coupe; '27' 2-dr. notchback coupe (or convertible); '37' special 2-dr. notch coupe; '47' full-size 2-dr. sport coupe; '77' 2-dr. hatch coupe; '87' 2-dr. sport coupe; '19' 4-dr. 6-window notchback sedan; '68' 4-dr. 6-window hatch sedan; '69' 4-dr. 4- window notchback sedan; '35' 4-dr. station wagon. Next is the engine code: 'C' L498 2Bbl.; 'D' L4111 diesel; 'P' L4121 FI; 'R' or 'Z' L4151 FI; 'X' V6173 2Bbl.; 'S' or 'W' V6173 MFI; 'Z' V6262 FI; 'T' V6262 diesel; 'H' V8305 4Bbl.; 'G' H.O. V8305 4Bbl.; 'F' V8305 TPI; 'N' V8350 diesel. Next is a check digit, followed by 'F' for model year 1985. Symbol eleven indicates assembly plant: 'B' Baltimore; 'J' Janesville, WI; 'L' Van Nuys, CA; 'N' Norwood, OH; 'R' Arlington, TX; 'T' Tarrytown, NY; 'X' Fairfax, KS; 'Y' Wilmington, DE; '1' Oshawa, Ontario; '6' Oklahoma City, OK; '7' Lordstown, OH. The final six digits are the sequential serial number. Engine number coding is similar to 1981-84.

CHEVETTE CS (FOUR)

Model Number	Body/Style Number	Body Type & Seating	Factory Price	Shipping Weight	Production Total
1T	B08	2-dr. Hatch Cpe-4P	5340	2032	57,706
1T	B68	4-dr. Hatch Sed-4P	5690	2091	65,128

CHEVETTE CS DIESEL (FOUR)

Model Number	Body/Style Number	Body Type & Seating	Factory Price	Shipping Weight	Production Total
1T	B08/Z90	2-dr. Hatch Cpe-4P	5850	N/A	203
1T	B68/Z90	4-dr. Hatch Sed-4P	6215	N/A	462

CAVALIER (FOUR)

Model Number	Body/Style Number	Body Type & Seating	Factory Price	Shipping Weight	Production Total
1J	C69	4-dr. Sedan-5P	6477	2320	86,597
1J	C35	4-dr. Sta Wag-5P	6633	2392	34,581

CAVALIER CS (FOUR)

Model Number	Body/Style Number	Body Type & Seating	Factory Price	Shipping Weight	Production Total
1J	D69	4-dr. Sedan-5P	6900	2334	93,386
1J	D35	4-dr. Sta Wag-5P	7066	2405	33,551

CAVALIER TYPE 10 (FOUR)

Model Number	Body/Style Number	Body Type & Seating	Factory Price	Shipping Weight	Production Total
1J	E27	2-dr. Coupe-5P	6737	2300	106,021
1J	E77	2-dr. Hatch Cpe-5P	6919	2350	25,508
1J	E27/Z08	2-dr. Conv. Cpe-4P	11693	2515	4,108

Cavalier Engine Note: A V-6 engine became available during the model year, priced at $560.

CITATION II (FOUR/V-6)

Model Number	Body/Style Number	Body Type & Seating	Factory Price	Shipping Weight	Production Total
1X	X08	2-dr. Hatch Cpe-5P	6940/7200	2399/2471	7,443
1X	X68	4-dr. Hatch Sed-5P	7090/7350	2435/2507	55,279

CAMARO (V-6/V-8)

Model Number	Body/Style Number	Body Type & Seating	Factory Price	Shipping Weight	Production Total
1F	P87	2-dr. Spt Cpe-4P	8698/8998	2907/3091	97,966

CAMARO BERLINETTA (V-6/V-8)

Model Number	Body/Style Number	Body Type & Seating	Factory Price	Shipping Weight	Production Total
1F	S87	2-dr. Spt Cpe-4P	11060/11360	2919/3157	13,649

CAMARO Z28 (V-8)

Model Number	Body/Style Number	Body Type & Seating	Factory Price	Shipping Weight	Production Total
1F	P87	2-dr. Spt Cpe-4P	-- /11060	-- /3107	68,199

Camaro Engine Note: Prices and weights before slash are for V-6 engine, after slash for V-8. Base Camaro Sport Coupes were also available with a four-cylinder engine, priced at $8363 and weighing 2813 pounds. The Z28 could have an optional fuel-injected or carbureted (IROCZ) high-output V-8 for an additional $695. **Z28 IROCZ Production Note:** A total of 21,177 Z28s had the IROCZ performance package (RPO Code B4Z). Chevrolet production figures also show 204 Z28E hatchback sport coupes.

1985 Celebrity Eurosport sedan (AA)

CELEBRITY (FOUR/V-6)

Model Number	Body/Style Number	Body Type & Seating	Factory Price	Shipping Weight	Production Total
1A	W27	2-dr. Coupe-5P	8102/8362	2587/2719	29,010
1A	W19	4-dr. Sedan-5P	8288/8548	2623/2755	239,763
1A	W35	4-dr. Sta Wag-5P	8479/8739	2771/2894	45,602
1A	W35/AQ4	4-dr. 3S Wag-8P	8699/8959	N/A	40,547

MONTE CARLO (V-6/V-8)

Model Number	Body/Style Number	Body Type & Seating	Factory Price	Shipping Weight	Production Total
1G	Z37	2-dr. Spt Cpe-6P	9540/9780	3085/3093	83,573

MONTE CARLO 'SS' (V-8)

Model Number	Body/Style Number	Body Type & Seating	Factory Price	Shipping Weight	Production Total
1G	Z37/Z65	2-dr. Spt Cpe-6P	-- /11380	-- /3336	35,484

IMPALA (V-6/V-8)

Model Number	Body/Style Number	Body Type & Seating	Factory Price	Shipping Weight	Production Total
1B	L69	4-dr. Sedan-6P	9519/9759	3352/3366	53,438

CAPRICE CLASSIC (V-6/V-8)

Model Number	Body/Style Number	Body Type & Seating	Factory Price	Shipping Weight	Production Total
1B	N47	2-dr. Spt Cpe-6P	9888/10128	3363/3377	16,229
1B	N69	4-dr. Sedan-6P	10038/10278	3396/3410	139,240
1B	N35	4-dr. 3S Wag-8P	-- /10714	-- /3952	55,886

FACTORY PRICE AND WEIGHT NOTE: For Citation and Celebrity, prices and weights to left of slash are for four-cylinder, to right for V-6 engine. For Camaro, Monte Carlo and full-size models, figures to left of slash are for six-cylinder model, to right of slash for 305 cu. in. V-8. Celebrity diesel V-6 cost the same as gas V-6. Diesel V-8 for Caprice/Impala was also priced the same as gas V-8. Optional engine prices rose during the model year. **BODY/STYLE NO. NOTE:** Some models were actually option packages. Code after the slash (e.g., Z65) is the number of the option package that comes with the model listed.

1985 station wagons, clockwise from right: Celebrity, Cavalier and Caprice Classic

ENGINE DATA: BASE FOUR (Chevette): Inline. Overhead cam. Four-cylinder. Cast iron block and head. Displacement: 98 cu. in. (1.6 liters). Bore & stroke: 3.23 x 2.98 in. Compression ratio: 9.0:1. Brake horsepower: 65 at 5200 R.P.M. Torque: 80 lbs.-ft. at 3200 R.P.M. Five main bearings. Hydraulic valve lifters. Carburetor: 2Bbl. VIN Code: A. DIESEL FOUR (Chevette): Inline. Overhead cam. Four-cylinder. Cast iron block and head. Displacement: 111 cu. in. (1.8 liters). Bore & stroke: 3.31 x 3.23 in. Compression ratio: 22.0:1. Brake horsepower: 51 at 5000 R.P.M. Torque: 72 lbs.-ft. at 2000 R.P.M. Five main bearings. Fuel injection. VIN Code: B. BASE FOUR (Cavalier): Inline. Overhead valve. Four-cylinder. Cast iron block and head. Displacement: 121 cu. in. (2.0 liters). Bore & stroke: 3.50 x 3.15 in. Compression ratio: 9.0:1. Brake horsepower: 85 at 4800 R.P.M. Torque: 110 lbs.-ft. at 2400 R.P.M. Five main bearings. Hydraulic valve lifters. Throttle-body fuel injection. VIN Code: P. BASE FOUR (Citation, Celebrity, Camaro): Inline. Overhead valve. Four-cylinder. Cast iron block and head. Displacement: 151 cu. in. (2.5 liters). Bore & stroke: 4.00 x 3.00 in. Compression ratio: 9.0:1. Brake horsepower: 92 at 4400 R.P.M. (Camaro, 88 at 4400). Torque: 134 lbs.-ft. at 2800 R.P.M. (Camaro, 132 at 2800). Five main bearings. Hydraulic valve lifters. Throttle-body fuel injection. Pontiac-built. VIN Code: R exc. (Camaro) 2. OPTIONAL V-6 (Citation, Celebrity): 60-degree, overhead-valve V-6. Cast iron block and head. Displacement: 173 cu. in. (2.8 liters). Bore & stroke: 3.50 x 2.99 in. Compression ratio: 8.5:1. Brake horsepower: 112 at 4800 R.P.M. Torque: 145 lbs.-ft. at 2100 R.P.M. Four main bearings. Hydraulic valve lifters. Carburetor: 2Bbl. VIN Code: X. HIGH-OUTPUT V-6 (Camaro Berlinetta); OPTIONAL (Cavalier, Citation, Camaro, Celebrity): Same as 173 cu. in. V-6 above except with multi-port fuel injection C.R.: 8.9:1. Brake H.P.: 135 at 5100 R.P.M. (Cavalier, 125 at 4800; Citation/Celebrity, 130 at 4800). Torque: 165 lbs.-ft. at 3600 R.P.M. (Cavalier/Citation/Celeb, 155 at 3600). VIN Code: W exc. (Camaro) S. BASE V-6 (Monte Carlo, Impala, Caprice): 90-degree, overhead-valve V-6. Cast iron block and head. Displacement: 262 cu. in. (4.3 liters). Bore & stroke: 4.00 x 3.48 in. Compression ratio: 9.3:1. Brake horsepower: 130 at 3600 R.P.M. Torque: 210 lbs.-ft. at 2000 R.P.M. Four main bearings. Hydraulic valve lifters. Fuel injection. VIN Code: Z. DIESEL V-6 (Celebrity): 90-degree, overhead-valve V-6. Cast iron block and head. Displacement: 262 cu. in. (4.3 liters). Bore & stroke: 4.057 x 3.385 in. Compression ratio: 22.8:1. Brake horsepower: 85 at 3600 R.P.M. Torque: 165 lbs.-ft. at 1600 R.P.M. Four main bearings. Hydraulic valve lifters. Fuel injection. VIN Code: T. BASE V-8 (Camaro Z28, Caprice wagon): OPTIONAL (Camaro, Monte Carlo, Impala, Caprice): 90-degree, overhead valve V-8. Cast iron block and head. Displacement: 305 cu. in. (5.0 liters). Bore & stroke: 3.74 x 3.48 in. Compression ratio: 9.5:1. Brake horsepower: 155 at 4200 R.P.M. (Monte, 150 at 4000; Caprice/Imp, 165 at 4200). Torque: 245 lbs.-ft. at 2000 R.P.M. (Monte, 240 at 2000; Caprice/Imp, 245 at 2400). Five main bearings. Hydraulic valve lifters. Carburetor: 4Bbl. VIN Code: H. HIGH-OUTPUT V-8 (Monte Carlo SS): Same as 305 cu. in. V-8 above, except Brake H.P.: 180 at 4800 R.P.M. Torque: 235 lbs.-ft. at 3200 R.P.M. VIN Code: G. OPTIONAL HIGH-OUTPUT V-8 (Camaro Z28/IROC-Z): Same as 305 cu. in. V-8 above, except Brake H.P.: 190 at 4800 R.P.M. Torque: 240 lbs.-ft. at 3200 R.P.M. RPO Code: L69. VIN Code: G. OPTIONAL HIGH-OUTPUT V-8 (Camaro Z28/IROC-Z): Same as 305 cu. in. V-8 above, but with tuned port fuel injection Brake H.P.: 215 at 4400 R.P.M. Torque: 275 lbs.-ft. at 3200 R.P.M. RPO Code: LB9. VIN Code: F. DIESEL V-8; OPTIONAL (Impala/Caprice): 90-degree, overhead valve V-8. Cast iron block and head. Displacement: 350 cu. in. (5.7 liters). Bore & stroke: 4.057 x 3.385 in. Compression ratio: 22.1:1. Brake horsepower: 105 at 3200 R.P.M. Torque: 200 lbs.-ft. at 1600 R.P.M. Five main bearings. Hydraulic valve lifters. Fuel injection. Olds- built. VIN Code: N.

CHASSIS DATA: Wheelbase: (Chevette 2-dr.) 94.3 in.; (Chvt 4-dr.) 97.3 in.; (Cavalier) 101.2 in.; (Citation/Celeb) 104.9 in.; (Camaro) 101.0 in.; (Monte Carlo) 108.0 in.; (Imp/Caprice) 116.0 in. Overall length: (Chvt 2-dr.) 161.9 in.; (Chvt 4-dr.) 164.9 in.; (Cav cpe/conv) 172.4 in.; (Cav sed) 174.3 in.; (Cav wag) 174.5 in.; (Cit) 176.7 in.; (Camaro) 188.0 in.; (Camaro Z28) 192.0 in.; (Celeb) 188.3 in.; (Celeb wag) 190.8 in.; (Monte) 200.4 in.; (Monte SS) 202.4 in.; (Imp/Capr sed) 212.8 in.; (Caprice wag) 215.1 in. Height: (Chvt) 52.8 in.; (Cav cpe) 50.2 in.; (Cav conv) 52.7 in.; (Cav sed) 52.1 in.; (Cav wag) 52.8 in.; (Cit) 53.9 in.; (Camaro) 50.0 in.; (Camaro Z28) 50.3 in.; (Celeb) 54.1 in.; (Celeb wag) 54.3 in.; (Monte) 54.4 in.; (Monte SS) 54.9 in.; (Imp/Capr sed) 56.4 in.; (Caprice wag) 58.2 in. Width: (Chvt) 61.8 in.; (Cav cpe/conv) 66.0 in.; (Cav sed/wag) 66.3 in.; (Cit) 68.3 in.; (Camaro) 72.8 in.; (Celeb) 69.3 in.; (Monte) 71.8 in.; (Imp/Capr) 75.4 in.; (Caprice wag) 79.3 in. Front Tread: (Chvt) 51.2 in.; (Cav) 55.4 in.; (Cit/Celeb) 58.7 in.; (Camaro) 60.7 in.; (Camaro Berlinetta/Z28) 60.0 in.; (Monte) 58.5 in.; (Imp/Capr) 61.7 in.; (Caprice wag) 62.2 in. Rear Tread: (Chvt) 51.2 in.; (Cav) 55.2 in.; (Cit/Celeb) 57.0 in.; (Camaro) 61.6 in.; (Camaro Berlinetta/Z28): 60.9 in.; (Monte) 57.8 in.; (Imp/Capr) 60.7 in.; (Caprice wag) 64.1 in. Standard Tires: (Chvt) P155/80R13 GBR; (Cav) P175/80R13 GBR; (Cav Type 10) P215/60R14 SBR; (Cit) P185/80R13 SBR; (Celeb) P185/75R14 SBR; (Camaro) P195/75R14 SBR; (Camaro Berlinetta) P205/70R14 SBR; (Camaro Z28) P215/65R15 WLT SBR; (Monte) P195/75R14 SBR; (Monte SS) P215/65R15 SBR; (Imp/Capr) P205/75R15 SBR; (Caprice wag) P225/75R15 SBR.

TECHNICAL: Transmission: Four-speed floor shift standard on Chevette: Gear ratios (1st) 3.75:1; (2nd) 2.16:1; (3rd) 1.38:1; (4th) 1.00:1; (Rev) 3.82:1. Four-speed floor shift on Cavalier/Citation/Celebrity: (1st) 3.53:1; (2nd) 1.95:1; (3rd) 1.24:1; (4th) 0.81:1 or 0.73:1; (Rev) 3.42:1. Citation V-6 FI and Cavalier V-6 four-speed manual trans.: (1st) 3.31:1; (2nd) 1.95:1; (3rd) 1.24:1; (4th) 0.90:1; (Rev) 3.42:1. Camaro four four-speed manual trans.: (1st) 3.50:1; (2nd) 2.48:1; (3rd) 1.66:1; (4th) 1.00:1; (Rev) 3.50:1. Cavalier five-speed manual: (1st) 3.73:1; (2nd) 2.15:1; (3rd) 1.33:1; (4th) 0.92:1; (5th) 0.74:1; (Rev) 3.50:1. Camaro four five-speed manual: (1st) 3.76:1; (2nd) 2.18:1; (3rd) 1.42:1; (4th) 1.00:1; (5th) 0.86:1; (Rev) 3.76:1. Camaro V-6 five-speed manual: (1st) 3.50:1; (2nd) 2.14:1; (3rd) 1.36:1; (4th) 1.00:1; (5th) 0.78:1;

(Rev) 3.39:1. Camaro V-8 five-speed manual.: (1st) 2.95:1; (2nd) 1.94:1; (3rd) 1.34:1; (4th) 1.00:1; (5th) 0.73:1; (Rev) 2.76:1. Chevette five-speed manual shift: (1st) 3.76:1; (2nd) 2.18:1; (3rd) 1.36:1; (4th) 1.00:1; (5th) 0.86:1; (Rev) 3.76:1. Three-speed Turbo Hydra- matic standard on Monte Carlo and Imp/Caprice: (1st) 2.74:1; (2nd) 1.57:1; (3rd) 1.00:1; (Rev) 2.07:1. Chevette automatic trans.: (1st) 2.40:1; (2nd) 1.48:1; (3rd) 1.00:1; (Rev) 1.92:1. Cavalier/Citation/Celebrity auto. trans.: (1st) 2.84:1; (2nd) 1.60:1; (3rd) 1.00:1; (Rev) 2.07:1. Four-speed overdrive automatic transmission on Monte Carlo: (1st) 2.74:1; (2nd) 1.57:1; (3rd) 1.00:1; (4th) 0.67:1; (Rev) 2.07:1. Four-speed overdrive automatic on Celebrity: (1st) 2.92:1; (2nd) 1.57:1; (3rd) 1.00:1; (4th) 0.70:1; (Rev) 2.38:1. Four-speed overdrive automatic on Camaro/Capr/Imp: (1st) 3.06:1; (2nd) 1.63:1; (3rd) 1.00:1; (4th) 0.70:1; (Rev) 2.29:1. Standard final drive ratio: (Chevette) 3.36:1 or 3.62:1; (Cavalier) 3.32:1 on notchback, 3.65:1 on others exc. 3.83:1 w/5-spd, 3.18:1 or 3.43:1 w/auto., 3.65:1 w/V-6 and 4-spd; (Citation) 3.32:1 w/4spd, 2.39:1 or 2.53:1 w/auto.; (Cit H.O. V-6) 3.65:1 w/4spd, 2.84:1 or 3.18:1 w/auto.; (Camaro four) 3.73:1; (Camaro V-6) 3.42:1; (Camaro V-8) 3.23:1 exc. 3.08:1 w/auto.; (Camaro TPI V-8) 3.23:1; (Camaro H.O. V-8) 3.73:1; (Celebrity four) 3.65:1 w/4spd, 2.39:1 w/auto.; (Celeb V-6) 2.84:1 or 3.06:1; (Monte) 2.29:1 or 2.41:1; (Monte H.O. V-8) 3.73:1; (Imp/Caprice V-6) 2.56:1 or 3.08:1; (Imp/Capr V-8) 2.73:1 or 3.08:1. Steering/Suspension/Brakes/Body: same as 1982-84. Fuel tank: (Chvt) 12.2 gal.; (Cav) 13.6 gal.; (Cit) 14.6 or 15.1 gal.; (Camaro) 15.5 or 16.2 gal.; (Celeb) 15.7 or 16.4 gal.; (Monte) 17.6 or 18.1 gal.; (Imp/Capr) 25 gal.; (Caprice wag) 22 gal.

DRIVETRAIN OPTIONS: (Note: Prices of many options rose soon after the model year began.) Engines: 173 cu. in., 2Bbl. V-6: Cavalier ($560); Citation ($260); base Camaro ($335) Celeb ($260). H.O. 173 cu. in., 2Bbl. V-6: Citation/Celeb ($435). 305 cu. in., 4Bbl. V-8: Camaro ($635); Berlinetta ($300); Monte, Imp/Caprice cpe/sed ($240). H.O. 305 cu. in., 4Bbl. V-8: Camaro IROCZ ($680). 350 cu. in., TPI V-8: Camaro Z28 ($680). Diesel 260 cu. in. V-6: Celeb ($260). Diesel 350 cu. in. V-8: Imp/Caprice ($240) exc. wag (NC). Transmission/Differential: Five-speed manual trans.: **Chevette/Cavalier ($75); Camaro (NC). Three-speed automatic trans.; Chevette/ Cavalier ($425); Citation/Celeb ($425). Four-speed overdrive automatic trans.: Camaro ($395); Celeb ($600) base Monte, Imp/Caprice cpe/sed ($175). Limited-slip** differential: Camaro/Monte/Imp/Capr ($95). Performance axle ratio ($21). Power Accessories: Power brakes: Chevette ($100); Citation ($100). Power four-wheel disc brakes: Camaro V-8 ($179). Power steering: Chevette/Cavalier ($215); Citation ($215). Suspension: F40 H.D. susp.: Cav/Cit/Celeb/Imp/Capr ($26). F41 sport susp.: Cit ($33); Cav ($44-$49); Camaro/Monte, Imp/Capr cpe/sed ($49). Inflatable rear shock absorbers: Celeb/Caprice wag ($64). Other: H.D. cooling ($40-$70). Engine block heater ($20). Cold climate pkg.: Imp/Capr diesel ($99). Diesel engine and fuel line heater: Celeb ($49). H.D. battery ($26) exc. diesel ($52). California emission system ($99).

CHEVETTE CONVENIENCE/APPEARANCE OPTIONS: Option Packages: Sport decor pkg.: black grille, wheels, bodyside moldings, bumpers; black trim w/red accents ($95). Custom exterior: black window moldings, styled argent wheels and bright trim rings ($152-$167). Comfort/Convenience: Air conditioning ($645). Rear defogger, electric ($135). Tinted glass ($99). Comfortilt steering wheel ($115). Lighting and Mirrors: Twin sport mirrors, left remote ($53). Driver's remote sport mirror ($34). Entertainment: AM/FM radio ($82). AM/FM stereo radio ($109). Radio delete ($51 credit). Exterior Trim: Two-tone paint ($133). Rear spoiler (N/A). Door edge guards ($15-$25). Chrome bumpers ($25). Interior Trim/Upholstery: Cloth bucket seats: cpe ($28). Custom cloth bucket seats: cpe ($130). Color-keyed floor mats ($25). Wheels and Tires: Sport wheel covers ($45-$97). Wheel trim rings ($52). P155/80R13 GBR WSW ($51). P175/70R13 SBR BSW ($118). P175/70R13 SBR WSW ($172).

1985 Cavalier Type 10 convertible (CP)

CAVALIER CONVENIENCE/APPEARANCE OPTIONS: Option Packages: CL custom interior pkg.: reclining seats w/adj. head restraints, quiet sound group, sport steering wheel, console (for manual shift), custom door/quarter trim ($251-$325); incl. split folding rear seat on hatch/wagon. Comfort/Convenience: Air cond. ($645). Cruise control w/resume ($175). Rear defogger, electric ($135). Tinted glass ($99). Six-way power driver's seat ($225). Black sport steering wheel ($22-$40). Comfortilt steering wheel ($115). Power windows ($195-$270). Power door locks ($130-$180). Power hatch or trunk release ($40). Power liftgate release ($40). Electronic instrument cluster ($295). Gauge pkg. w/trip odometer ($69); incl. tach ($139). Digital clock: 10/conv. ($39). Lighter: base ($14). Intermittent wipers ($50). Rear wiper/washer ($125). Lighting and Mirrors: Halogen headlamps ($25). Aux. lighting ($43-$95). Dual black sport mirrors, left remote ($53). Right visor mirror ($7). Entertainment: AM radio: base ($112). AM/FM radio ($82) exc. base ($171). Electronic-tuning AM/FM stereo radio ($138) exc. base ($238); w/clock ($177) exc. base ($277); with seek/scan (N/A). Electronic-tuning AM/FM stereo seek/scan radio w/cassette ($319) exc. base ($419). Electronic-tuning AM stereo/FM seek/scan radio w/cassette, equalizer and clock ($494-$504) exc. base ($594). Dual rear speakers ($30-$42); premium ($25). Extended-range sound system: 10/Z24/conv. ($35). Fixed-mast antenna: base ($41) but incl. w/radios. Radio delete ($56 credit). Exterior Trim: Removable sunroof ($310). Rear spoiler: Type 10 ($69). Rear window louvers: Type 10 hatch ($199). Custom two-tone paint: CS ($176); Type 10 ($123). Pinstriping ($53). Bodyside moldings, black ($45). Wheel opening moldings: conv. ($30). Wheel opening and rocker panel moldings ($55). Door edge guards ($15-$25). Wagon roof carrier ($105). Bumper guards ($56). Interior Trim/Upholstery: Cloth or sport cloth reclining bucket seats ($28). Custom CL reclining bucket seats: CS/10/conv. (NC). Split-folding rear seatback: wag/hatch ($50). Color-keyed mats: front ($18); rear ($15). Cargo area cover: wag/hatch ($69). Wheels and Tires: Aluminum wheels, 13 x 5.5 in. ($285); 14 x 6 in. (N/A). Styled 14 in. wheels: 10/conv. ($52). Sport wheel covers ($97). Wheel trim rings ($52). P175/80R13 SBR WSW ($54). P195/70R13 SBR BSW ($104). P195/70R13 SBR WSW ($166). P195/70R13 SBR RWL ($188). P215/60R14 SBR BSW: 10/conv. ($246). P215/60R14 SBR RWL: 10/conv. ($338); Z24 ($92).

CITATION/CELEBRITY CONVENIENCE/APPEARANCE OPTIONS: Option Packages: X11 sport equipment pkg.: Citation ($941). Eurosport pkg.: Celeb ($199). Sport decor pkg. (rear spoiler, rally wheels, sport mirrors, color-keyed bumpers w/rub strips, black grille and moldings, black-accent trim, decal): Citation cpe ($249). Exterior molding **pkg. (rocker panel and wheel opening moldings): Celeb ($55). CL custom interior (Deluxe door trim w/cloth insert, custom cloth seats, rear ashtray, custom steering wheel): Citation cpe. reclining bucket seats ($392); Citation sed, bench seat ($195).** Quiet sound/rear decor pkg.: Cit ($92). Security pkg.: Celeb wag ($44). Comfort/Convenience: Air conditioning ($730). Rear defogger, electric ($140). Cruise control ($175). Tinted glass ($110). Sport steering wheel: Cit ($22). Comfortilt steering wheel ($110). Six-way power driver's seat: Celeb ($215). Power windows ($185-$260). Power door locks ($125-$175). Power trunk or liftgate release: Celeb ($40). Gauge pkg. w/trip odometer: Cit ($69); Celeb ($64). Gauge pkg. w/tachometer: Cit ($149). Digital clock: Celeb ($39). Intermittent wipers ($50). Rear wiper/washer: Celeb ($120). Lighting, Horns and Mirrors: Halogen headlamps: Celeb ($22). Aux. lighting: Cit ($50); Celeb ($43-$57). Dome reading lamp: Celeb ($24). Dual horns ($12). Driver's remote mirror ($23). Dual sport mirrors, left remote ($61). Dual remote sport mirrors: Celeb ($91). Entertainment: AM/FM radio ($82). Electronic-tuning AM/FM stereo radio ($138); w/clock ($177); w/cassette, clock and seek/scan ($319). Electronic-tuning AM stereo/FM radio w/clock, seek/scan, equalizer and cassette: Celeb ($504). Dual rear speakers ($30). Extended-range rear speakers: Celeb ($35). Radio delete ($56 credit). Exterior Trim: Removable sunroof: Celeb ($300). Padded vinyl roof: Celeb ($270). Two-tone paint: Cit ($176) incl. pinstriping and bodyside moldings; Celeb ($148). Bodyside pinstriping: Cit ($39); Celeb ($57). Bodyside moldings, black: Cit ($55). Side window reveal moldings: Cit ($45-$55). Door edge guards ($15-$25). Rear window air deflector: Celeb wag ($40). Rear quarter vent windows: Celeb ($75). Swing-out tailgate: Celeb wag ($105). Decklid or roof (wagon) luggage carrier: Celeb ($100-$105). Bumper guards ($56). Bumper rub strips: Cit ($50). Interior Trim/Upholstery: Console ($105). Reclining driver and passenger seatbacks: Celeb ($90). Cloth bench seat: Cit ($28). Reclining cloth bucket seats: Cit ($243). Celebrity cpe/sed vinyl front bench seat: two-pass. ($28). Celebrity sed vinyl front bench seat: three-pass. ($78). Celebrity three-pass. cloth front bench seat ($28-$50). Celebrity CL three-pass. custom bench seating: vinyl ($229); cloth ($229- $257). Celebrity CL two-pass. custom cloth bench seating ($109-$179). Celebrity 45/45 cloth seating ($100). Celebrity CL custom cloth 45/45 seat ($250-$330). Cloth bucket seats: Celeb ($147). Color-keyed mats: front ($17); rear ($12). Deluxe trunk or wagon luggage area trim: Celeb ($40-$47). Wheels and Tires: Aluminum wheels: Cit ($306); Celeb ($306- $362). Sport wheel covers: Celeb ($65). Locking wire wheel covers: Celeb ($190). Rally wheels ($56). P185/80R13 SBR WSW: Cit ($58). P185/75R14 SBR WSW: Celeb ($58). P195/70R14 Eagle GT SBR BSW: Celeb ($60). P195/75R14 SBR BSW: Celeb ($30). P195/75R14 SBR WSW: Celeb ($92). P205/70R13 SBR WLT: Cit ($202). P215/60R14 SBR WLT: Cit ($92).

1985 Camaro Z28 Sport Coupe (CP)

CAMARO/MONTE CARLO CONVENIENCE/APPEARANCE OPTIONS: Option Packages: IROC-Z sport equipment pkg.: Camaro Z28 ($659). Comfort/Convenience: Air conditioning ($730). Rear defogger ($140). Cruise control w/resume ($175-$185). Tinted glass ($110). Comfortilt steering wheel ($110). Six-way power driver's seat ($215). Power windows ($185). Power door locks ($125). Power trunk opener: Monte ($40). Power hatch release: Camaro ($40). Electric clock ($35). Gauge pkg. w/trip odometer: Monte ($95). Gauge pkg. incl. tach: base Camaro ($149). Intermittent wipers ($50). Rear wiper/washer: Camaro ($120). Quiet sound group: Camaro ($72-$82). Lighting, Horns and Mirrors: Halogen headlamps ($22). Cornering lamps: Monte ($55). Aux. lighting: Camaro ($37- $72); Monte ($28). Dual horns: Camaro ($12). Twin sport mirrors (left remote): base Camaro, Monte ($53). Twin remote sport mirrors: Monte ($83); SS ($30). Twin electric remote sport mirrors: Camaro ($91-$139). Entertainment: AM/FM radio ($82). AM/FM stereo radio: Monte ($109). Cassette player with AM/FM stereo radio: Monte ($198). Electronic-tuning AM/FM stereo radio: base Camaro/Z28 ($173); w/clock ($177-$212); w/cassette, clock and seek/scan ($319-$354). Camaro seek/scan AM stereo/FM w/cassette, equalizer and clock ($469-$504). Seek/scan AM/FM stereo w/remote control: Berlinetta ($242). Dual rear speakers ($30). Power antenna ($60). Radio delete: Camaro ($56 credit); Berlinetta ($256 credit). Exterior Trim: Removable glass roof panels ($825). Landau vinyl roof: Monte ($245). Rear spoiler: Camaro ($69). Two- tone paint: Monte ($214). Bodyside moldings, black: Camaro ($55). Deluxe vinyl bodyside moldings: Monte ($57). Door edge guards ($15). Side window sill moldings: Monte ($45). Bodyside pinstriping: Monte ($61). Interior Trim/Upholstery: Console: Monte ($105). Roof console: Camaro/Z28 ($50). Vinyl bench seat: base Monte ($28). Cloth 55/45 seating: base Monte ($133). Cloth bucket seats: Camaro ($28); Monte ($147). Custom cloth bucket seats: base Camaro/Z28 ($359). Custom cloth CL 55/45 seating: base Monte ($385). Custom cloth LS conteur bucket seats: Camaro Z28 ($650). Split folding back seat: Camaro ($50). Mats w/carpeted inserts: Camaro front ($20); rear ($15). Color- keyed mats: Monte front ($17); rear ($12). Cargo area cover: Camaro ($69). Deluxe trunk trim: Camaro ($164); Z28 ($84). Locking rear storage cover: base Camaro ($80). Wheels and Tires: Aluminum wheels: Monte ($362); Camaro ($225); std. Z28. Rally wheels: base Camaro ($112); Monte ($56). Full wheel covers: base Camaro ($52). Locking wire wheel covers: Monte ($159). P195/75R14 SBR WSW: base Camaro ($62). P195/75R14 SBR WSW: Monte ($62). P205/70R14 SBR BSW: base Camaro ($58). P205/70R14 SBR WSW: Camaro ($124); Berlinetta ($66); Monte ($124). P205/70R14 SBR WLT: base Camaro ($146). P235/60VR15 SBR BSW: Z28 ($85).

IMPALA/CAPRICE CONVENIENCE/APPEARANCE OPTIONS: Option Packages: Estate equipment: wag ($307). Landau equipment pkg.: vinyl roof, sport mirrors and reveal moldings ($306). Comfort/Convenience: Air cond. ($730). Rear defogger, electric ($140). Cruise control ($175). Tinted glass ($110). Comfortilt steering wheel ($110). Power door locks ($125- $175). Six-way power driver's seat ($215). Power windows ($185-$260). Power trunk opener ($40). Power tailgate lock: wag ($50). Electric clock: Imp ($35). Gauge pkg. w/trip odometer ($64). Intermittent wipers ($50). Quiet sound group: Imp ($66). Lighting and Mirrors: Halogen headlamps ($22). Cornering lamps ($55). Aux. lighting ($32-$42). Driver's remote mirror ($23). Dual remote mirrors ($67). Dual sport mirrors, left remote ($61). Dual remote color-keyed sport mirrors ($91) exc. Landau ($30). Lighted right visor mirror ($48). Entertainment: AM/FM radio ($82). Electronic-tuning AM/FM stereo radio ($138); w/clock ($142-$177); w/cassette and seek/scan ($264-$319); w/cassette, seek/scan, equalizer and clock ($394-$464). Dual rear speakers ($30); extended-range ($35). Power antenna ($60). Radio delete ($56 credit). Exterior Trim: Vinyl roof: sed ($185). Roof carrier: wag ($110). Custom two-tone paint ($141). Pinstriping ($39). Bodyside moldings ($55). Wheel opening moldings: Imp ($30). Door edge guards ($15-$25). Rear window air deflector: wag ($40). Bumper rub strips ($66). Bumper guards ($62). Interior Trim/Upholstery: Reclining passenger seatback ($45). Vinyl bench seat: Imp sed ($28). Cloth bench seat: wag ($28). Cloth 50/50 seating: Caprice ($195-$225). Deluxe load-floor carpet: wag ($89). Deluxe cargo area carpet: wag ($129). Color-keyed mats: front ($17); rear ($12). Mats w/carpet insert: front ($25); rear ($20). Deluxe trunk trim ($59). Wheels and Tires: Sport wheel covers ($65). Wire wheel covers: Caprice ($159). Wire wheel cover locks ($39). P205/75R15 SBR WSW: cpe/sed ($66). P225/70R15 SBR WSW: cpe/sed ($157). P225/75R15 SBR WSW: wag ($71). Puncture- sealant tires ($105-$130).

HISTORY: General introduction was Oct. 2, 1984 but Camaro/Cavalier debuted on November 8 and Chevette on Nov. 21. The new imported subcompact Sprint was introduced on May 30, 1984 and the Spectrum on November 15. Model year production (U.S.): 1,415,097 (incl. Corvettes but not incl. early '86 Novas and 8,992 Acadians). Of total production for sale in U.S. 695,893 were four-cylinder, 449,156 six, and 420,410 V-8. A total of 2,167 diesels were installed. Calendar year production (U.S.): 1,708,970 (including 46,304 Corvettes). Calendar year sales by U.S. dealers: 1,600,200 (incl. 37,956 Corvettes), for a 19.5 percent market share. Model year sales by U.S. dealers: 1,595,504 (incl. 37,878 Corvettes), for a 19.0 percent share.

Historical Footnotes: Model year sales rose only slightly over 1984, due mainly to the popularity of Cavalier and Celebrity, which ranked 1st and 3rd in the national ranking. Even so, Chevrolet's market share dropped a a full percentage point, down to 19 percent. Only 5,485 Cavalier convertibles had been built in the 1984 model year, but production was even lower in 1985. Prices rose a fairly modest 2.3 percent for 1985. (Chevette was cut in price, by $121 to $183.) Chevettes and Cavaliers arrived a bit late as the 1984 model year was extended to take advantage of their stronger CAFE fuel economy ratings. Chevrolet was the only GM division not receiving either a new C-body or N-body car this year. This year's ad theme was "Today's Chevrolet" and focused on the new IROC-Z and awaited Cavalier Z24, as well as the multi-port fuel-injection V-6 engine. The new subcompact Japanese imports, Spectrum and Sprint, arrived to give Chevrolet a stronger grasp on the small-car market. The three-cylinder Sprint (from Suzuki) debuted on the west coast in May 1984. Spectrum (built by Isuzu) arrived in November 1984, first sold only on the east coast. The new California-built Nova, a joint venture by Chevrolet and Toyota, would arrive as an early '86 model. Its initial sales looked good, requiring the addition of a second shift to the plant in Fremont, California by winter 1985. Also contributing to Chevrolet's versatility in the marketplace was the new Astro passenger van, intended to compete with the twin Chrysler mini-vans. A prototype "Customer Communications Systems" began test operation at selected Chevrolet dealerships. Prospects could view the benefits of Chevrolet ownership via touch-screen computer videodisc with bold graphics. A "Commitment to Excellence" program provided enhanced pre-delivery inspection of each new car sold by a dealer, an orientation drive by the saleperson, and customer benefit package mailed to the owner after purchase.

1986 CHEVROLET

Chevrolet's ill-fated Citation X-car finally bit the dust, but its place in the lineup was taken up by the new subcompact Nova, produced in a joint venture between Chevrolet and Toyota. The rear-drive Chevette was still hanging on, but its days were numbered. Front-drive had become the rule for small cars and quite a few large ones as well. On the sporty front, Cavalier's Z24 package finally arrived, creating an obvious small-scale rival to the Camaro Z28. And for peak performance, the IROCZ package returned for the Z28. Monte Carlo added a new luxury model, but the Impala name dropped out of the Chevrolet list after nearly three decades of service. Diesel engines left the lineup, except for a handful installed in Chevettes.

CHEVETTE — SERIES 1T — FOUR — A new bowtie emblem went on Chevette's grille this year and one new body color (yellow beige) was offered. New Custom seat cloth became standard on the four-door, optional on the two-door. All-season P155/80R13 SBR blackwall tires were made standard. As before, the 1.6-liter four and four-speed manual gearbox were standard, with diesel four and three-speed automatic available. Diesels were no longer available in California. A $95 Sport Decor package included a black grille and bumpers, black bodyside moldings with red inserts, and black wheels; plus red 'Chevette S' and 'Chevrolet' decals on front fender and hatch. Though antiquated in mechanical design, the rear-drive Chevette was promoted not only as an entry-level car, but as a vehicle for fleets and light delivery.

1986 Nova hatchback sedan (CH)

NOVA — SERIES 1S — FOUR — Produced in a joint venture between Chevrolet and Toyota, the five-passenger front-drive subcompact Nova went on sale in June 1985 in half the states. For the full 1986 model year, it was made available nationwide, and a four-door hatchback joined the original four-door notchback sedan. Riding a 95.7 inch wheelbase, Nova weighed about 200 pounds less than an equivalent Cavalier. Hatchbacks had split- folding rear seats, for carrying both passengers and cargo. Nova wore a black crosshatch grille with three horizontal divider bars and seven vertical divider bars, with center bowtie emblem. Wraparound cornering lamps flanked quad rectangular headlamps, with parking lamps inset low in the bumper. The original 97 cu. in. (1.6-liter) four-cylinder engine rated 70 horsepower, while the full-year version added four more. New engine mounts were meant to reduce idle shake, and the optional air conditioner got a larger compressor. A five-speed manual (overdrive) transaxle was standard, with three-speed automatic available. Standard equipment included power brakes, rack-and- pinion steering, AM radio, black bumpers with silver stripe, side window defoggers, cloth door panels with map pockets, full console, and a locking fuel filler door. Also standard: tinted glass, temperature gauge, locking glove box, day/night mirror, black left mirror (remote-controlled), temporary spare tire, trip odometer, cloth/vinyl low-back reclining front bucket seats, and an audible warning system. Argent styled wheels held P155/80R13 SBR blackwall tires. Wiper/washers had a mist cycle. Bodies carried narrow black bodyside, roof drip and windshield moldings. Hatchbacks had a black rear spoiler. Nova's option list was unusually small: just a series of packages rather than individual items. Step-up CL option packages each included a set of extras, in addition to the items indicated in the option lists. Those extra features included a custom cloth interior, wide bodyside moldings, bright belt and roof drip moldings, black door frames and rocker panels, console with storage box, trunk carpet and light, tilt steering column, remote trunk and fuel filler door openers, right visor vanity mirror, soft steering wheel, driver's seat with vertical adjustment and lumbar support, and passenger assist grips.

1986 Cavalier Z24 coupe (CP)

CAVALIER — SERIES 1J — FOUR/V-6 — After nearly a year's delay, Cavalier's new Z24 performance package (obviously inspired by Camaro's Z28) finally arrived to become a highlight of 1986. Offered in either two-door coupe or two-door hatchback form, it carried a 173 cu. in. (2.8-liter) V-6 with multi-port fuel injection, four-speed manual transaxle, 14 in. Eagle GT radial tires on Rally wheels, and sports package with all-around ground- effects skirting similar to Z28. A cockpit-style instrument panel displayed "Star Wars" electronic instrumentation. Control pods sat on each side of the steering wheel. The simple Z24 grille had four horizontal bars, with bowtie emblem at the center. Park/signal lamps sat at bumper level, below the quad rectangular headlamps. Also new this year was the sporty RS series (replacing the former Type 10). This one had standard F41 sport suspension, power steering, All-Season radial tires, and a distinctive exterior look. 'Cavalier RS' and engine identifier badges were red. Five different RS bodies were offered: four-door sedan and wagon, two-door coupe and hatchback, and the convertible. Base and CS Cavaliers came in four-door sedan or wagon form, as well as two-door bodies. A new Electronic Control Module reduced current drain when the car was idle, and included improved self-diagnostic features. New options this year were a decklid rack (for notchback coupes and sedans), plus new seat cloth and door panel trim for the CL custom interior. Base Cavaliers had standard power brakes, color-keyed bumpers with rub strips, full console with storage, side window defoggers, an argent grille, black left-hand mirror, day/night mirror, compact spare tire, two-speed wiper/washer, vinyl reclining bucket seats, and front stabilizer bar. Styled steel argent wheels held P175/80R13 SBR tires. Cavaliers had bright belt, drip, door and window moldings; plus black windshield and back window moldings. Cavalier CS added an AM radio and fixed-mast antenna, lighter, locking glove box, bright grille, and black bodyside moldings. RS models had black bumper rub strips with red accents, a cockpit-style console, power steering, black sport steering wheel, sport suspension, wheel trim rings, red- accented black bodyside moldings, and a set of black moldings (drip, rocker panel, belt, door, window). Convertibles lacked some of those moldings but included a boot cover, tinted glass, and front/rear courtesy lights. Z24 added an air dam, electronic instrument cluster, tachometer and trip odometer, dual black sport mirrors, and black bodyside and drip moldings.

1986 Camaro Sport Coupe (CP)

CAMARO — SERIES 1F — V-6/V-8 — Base Camaro Sport Coupes could take on the tone of the famed Z28 this year. When ordered with either optional engine (2.8-liter V-6 or 5.0-liter V-8), the base coupe also came equipped with a sport suspension, P215/65R15 blackwall tires on 15 x 7 in. styled steel wheels, and sport-tone exhaust. Even four-cylinder Camaros got the sport suspension and 14 in. styled wheels. With V-6 power, a five-speed manual gearbox was included (four-speed automatic optional). With a V-8 option, the four-speed automatic was installed. Appearance changes this year included black accents on headlamps and front fascia vents, lower body stripes (with black or charcoal finish below), black sport mirrors, and Rally wheels. Sport Coupe taillamps had a new black accent band. New 'Chevrolet' lettering replaced the Camaro name on rear fascia. New Sport Coupe standard equipment included styled wheels with trim rings, raised-letter SBR tires, retuned exhaust system with dual tailpipes, black sport mirrors, blackout rockers and fascia, and special stripes. An upshift indicator was added to manual-gearbox models. All Camaros got an air conditioning cutout switch, for use when full power was needed. The full-opening rear hatch had a new automatic closure. All Camaros had wet-arm windshield wipers. New standard items included an automatic rear hatch pulldown latch, plus softer-feel leather for steering wheel, shift lever and parking brake lever. Five engines were available: the "Iron Duke" four (from Pontiac), MFI 173 cu. in. (2.8-liter) V-6, standard 305 cu. in. (5.0-liter) V-8, high-output carbureted 5.0 V-8, and Tuned-port injection 5.0 V-8. Bodyside moldings now came in eight colors or black (black only on Sport Coupe). All 12 body colors (eight of them new) were applied using a new basecoat/clearcoat process. New to the option list were halogen foglamps (as on the IROCZ), available on all models; an automatic day/night mirror; color-keyed bodyside moldings; and an AM radio with digital clock. The top-performance IROC-Z, introduced a year earlier, was virtually unchanged except for new colors. Same with Z28 in general, except for new colors on lower panels and accent stripes. IROCZ had no grille opening at all in the front, but two foglamps alongside the license plate opening and parking lamps farther outboard. Quad rectangular headlamps were deeply recessed, flanking a solid angled body panel with tiny emblem in the center. Base Sport Coupe standard equipment included an AM radio, power steering and brakes, five-speed manual transmission, front/rear stabilizer bars, cockpit-style instrument panel, center console with stowage, side window defoggers, remote-controlled left mirror, day/night inside mirror, vinyl reclining front bucket seats, and tape stripes. P205/70R14 SBR all-season tires (P215/65R15 with V-6 or V-8) rode Rally steel wheels with trim rings. Bodies had black lower body accent, plus black windshield and drip moldings and color-keyed bumpers. Berlinetta added an electronic-tuning AM/FM stereo radio with digital clock, dual horns, electronic instruments, locking rear storage cover, dome and

1986 Camaro IROC-Z Sport Coupe (CH)

map lights, color-keyed sport mirrors (left remote), intermittent wipers, roof console, full wheel covers, and a tachometer. Bodies showed color-keyed lower accent paint with striping; interiors held custom cloth reclining front bucket seats. Standard Berlinetta tires were P205/70R14 SBR. Berlinetta lacked rocker panel moldings and a rear stabilizer bar. Z28 added an air dam, gauge package, color-keyed sport mirrors, visor vanity mirror (passenger), AM radio with digital clock, rear spoiler, leather-wrapped steering wheel, tachometer, and P215/65R15 tires on color-keyed aluminum wheels. The IROCZ Sport Equipment package (RPO code B4Z, for Z28) included P245/50VR16 Goodyear Eagle GT tires on 16 in. aluminum wheels, halogen foglamps, and special suspension components: special front struts and springs, rear springs, larger-diameter stabilizer bar, and Delco/Bilstein gas-filled shock absorbers. IROCZ also had front frame reinforcement and specific steering gear valving. All that plus body-color lower ground-effect panels, door panel decals, and lower-body accent stripes.

1986 Celebrity sedan (CH)

CELEBRITY — SERIES 1A — FOUR/V-6 — Celebrity wore a new finely-louvered grille with center bowtie emblem for a new front-end look, the most notable styling revision since the family mid-size was introduced in 1982. New wraparound side marker lamps flowed past the quad rectangular headlamps, with prominent bright bezels surrounding the entire assembly. New full wheel covers were standard. 'Celebrity' lettering was on the front door, engine identification at the forward end of front fenders, small parking lamps below the bumper rub strip. The new rear-end look consisted of three rectangular lamps, with side marker lamps included in the outboard unit. A new three-passenger front seat gave Celebrity six-passenger capacity rather than the previous five. At mid-year, a landau roof coupe option became available. Diesel engines were gone, and Celebrity's base prices were up by over $600. Standard engine was the 151 cu. in. (2.5-liter) four, with either carbureted or multi-port fuel injected 173 cu. in. (2.8-liter) V-6 optional. A new valve cover and gaskets improved oil sealing in all engines. Modified exhaust systems improved noise isolation. A fully galvanized floor pan was added at mid-year. A new variable- displacement air conditioning compressor for four-cylinder models was designed for quieter, more economical operation. New options included 55/45 front seating, a tachometer, AM radio with digital clock, and passenger visor mirror (standard or illuminated). Wagons could have an Estate package for $325. Both coupes and sedans could have a padded vinyl roof for $270. Celebrity Eurosports came in three new solid colors: silver metallic, light brown metallic, and black. Grilles, wheels and moldings matched the body color. The $225 Eurosport package included a sport suspension, sport steering wheel, P195/75R14 SBR tires on Rally wheels with trim rings, bodyside moldings with red accent stripes, color-accented bumper rub strips, and gas shock absorbers. Red 'Eurosport' nameplates on the doors made the model easy to identify.

1986 Monte Carlo SS Sport Coupe (CP)

MONTE CARLO — SERIES 1G — V-6/V-8 — Monte was moderately restyled for 1986, and a new luxury LS model joined the base and SS coupes after the start of the model year. Standard Montes kept their 1985-style grilles and quad rectangular headlamps, but the LS was different. An aerodynamic LS front end held wide flush-mount composite headlamps and a wide-look finely-crosshatched grille with 11 vertical dividers and distinctive center crest emblem. Parking lamps (also wide) sat below the bumper rub strips. Engine identification was on the forward end of the front fender. The LS had wide and bright bodyside moldings, semi- wraparound taillamps, and restyled standard wheels. All Montes got new aerodynamic sport mirrors (black on base model, body-color optional). Sport Coupe and LS Montes got new wheel covers. Retuned suspensions used harder bushings and stiffer shock valving. Inside was a new color- keyed two-spoke steering wheel. P205/70R14 tires with improved rolling resistance were optional on the Sport Coupe. Delco 2000 Series electronically-tuned radios were on the option list. Also optional: a tachometer and passenger visor vanity mirror (plain or illuminated). Monte Carlo SS had new aluminum wheels, plus gas-pressure shock absorbers (front and rear). Engine choices were the same as 1985: 262 cu. in. (4.3-liter) V-6 or 305 cu. in. (5.0-liter) V-8, with a high-output, 180-horsepower 305 under SS hoods. All Monte Carlos had standard power brakes and steering, three-speed overdrive automatic (four-speed on SS), AM radio with digital clock, cloth bench seats, dual black mirrors, dual-note horn, full wheel covers, color-keyed bumpers, and front stabilizer bar. Bodies held bright wheel opening, belt, window/windshield reveal, lower bodyside and roof drip moldings. Monte Carlo SS had a rear spoiler, black sport steering wheel, tachometer, black grille and moldings, sport mirrors (left remote-controlled), gauge package, and **P215/65R15 white-letter tires. Rarest of the SS Montes is the strking Aerocoupe fast-back. Only 200 were built, a tiny fraction of Monte Carlo output.**

1986 Caprice Classic sedan (CP)

CAPRICE CLASSIC — SERIES 1B — V-6/V-8 — With a history dating back to 1958, the Impala name departed this year, but a new Caprice Classic Brougham Sedan joined the full-size lineup (at the top). Three other Classic models were offered (two-door sport coupe, four-door sedan and four-door wagon), plus a basic lower-priced four-door Caprice sedan. All models had the same, somewhat rounded front-end look this year. That included a new grille and bumper filler panel, flush-mounted crest, and new bezels for headlamps and marker lamps. Coupes and sedans also had restyled tri-section tailamps in a full-width end panel, plus a new filler panel and bumper rub strip. Each taillamp section was split horizontally. Base prices were $700-$800 higher than in 1985. Four-speed overdrive automatic was now optional with the base 262 cu. in. (4.3-liter) V-6 engine. The diesel V-8 was dropped, **but the 305 cu. in. (5.0-liter) gasoline V-8 remained optional (standard on wagons). Engines used a new poly V alternator drive belt. Power window and seat controls moved to the top of new front door armrest extensions. The new Brougham Sedan** package included a full vinyl roof, cloth 55/45 pillow-style front seats with center armrest, front- door dome/map and warning lights, bright brushed metal center pillar applique, and 'Brougham' identification. Standard equipment on the basic Caprice sedan included an AM radio, power brakes and steering, three-speed automatic transmission, full wheel covers, folding front center armrest, cloth bench seats, day/night mirror, front stabilizer bar, two-speed wiper/washers, bright moldings (roof drip, windshield, belt and sill), and lower carpet door trim panels. Caprice Classic added a quartz clock, cloth- insert door trim panels, dual-note horn, wheel opening and bright wide lower bodyside moldings, and headlamps-on buzzer. Coupes and sedans had bumper rub strips. Wagons had a power tailgate window, heavy-duty suspension, and overdrive automatic transmission. Caprice and Pontiac's Parisienne were the last traditional rear-drive full-size family sedans left in the GM lineup, regularly threatened with extinction but continuing to find quite a few buyers.

I.D. DATA: Chevrolets again had a 17-symbol Vehicle Identification Number (VIN) on the upper left surface of the instrument panel, visible through the windshield. Symbol one indicates country: '1' U.S.A.; '2' Canada. Next is a manufacturer code: 'G' General Motors. Symbol three is car make: '1' Chevrolet; '7' GM of Canada. Symbol four denotes restraint system: 'A' non-passive (standard); 'B' passive (automatic belts); 'C' passive (inflatable). Symbol five is car line/series: 'B' Chevette; 'K' Nova; 'C' Cavalier; 'D' Cavalier CS; 'E' Cavalier RS; 'F' Cavalier Z24; 'P' Camaro; 'S' Camaro Berlinetta; 'W' Celebrity; 'Z' Monte Carlo; 'L' Impala; 'N' Caprice. Symbols six-seven reveal body type: '08' 2-dr. hatch coupe; '27' 2-dr. notchback coupe; '37' special 2-dr. notch coupe; '47' full-size 2-dr. sport coupe; '67' 2-dr. convertible coupe; '77' 2-dr. hatch coupe; '87' 2-dr. sport coupe; '19' 4- dr. 6-window notchback sedan; '68' 4-dr. 6-window hatch sedan; '69' 4-dr. 4-window notchback sedan; '35' 4-dr. station wagon. Next is the engine code: 'C' L498 2Bbl.; '4' L497 2Bbl.; 'D' L4111 diesel; 'P' L4121 FI; 'R' or '2' L4151 FI; 'X' V6173 2Bbl.; 'S' or 'W' V6173 MFI; 'Z' V6262 FI; 'H' or 'Y' V8305 4Bbl.; 'G' H.O. V8305 4Bbl.; 'F' V8305 TPI. Next is a check digit, followed by 'G' for model year 1986. Symbol eleven indicates assembly plant: 'B' Baltimore; 'J' Janesville, WI; 'L' Van Nuys, CA; 'N' Norwood, OH; 'R' Arlington, TX; 'T' Tarrytown, NY; 'X' Fairfax, KS; 'Y' Wilmington, DE; '1' Oshawa, Ontario; '6' Oklahoma City, OK; '7' Lordstown, OH. The final six digits are the sequential serial number. Engine number coding is similar to 1981-85.

CHEVETTE CS (FOUR)

Model Number	Body/Style Number	Body Type & Seating	Factory Price	Shipping Weight	Production Total
1T	B08	2-dr. Hatch Cpe-4P	5645	2022	48,756
1T	B68	4-dr. Hatch Sed-4P	5959	2083	54,164

CHEVETTE CS DIESEL (FOUR)

1T	B08/Z90	2-dr. Hatch Cpe-4P	6152	2194	124
1T	B68/Z90	4-dr. Hatch Sed-4P	6487	2255	200

NOVA (FOUR)

Model Number	Body/Style Number	Body Type & Seating	Factory Price	Shipping Weight	Production Total
1S	K19	4-dr. Sedan-4P	7435	2016	124,961
1S	K68	4-dr. Hatch Sed-4P	7669	2057	42,788

Nova Production Note: An additional 27,943 Nova sedans were built late in the 1985 model year, placed on sale in June 1986.

CAVALIER (FOUR/V-6)

1J	C27	2-dr. Coupe-5P	6706/7316	2231/2351	57,370
1J	C69	4-dr. Sedan-5P	6888/7498	2274/2394	86,492
1J	C35	4-dr. Sta Wag-5P	7047/7657	2344/2464	30,490

CAVALIER CS (FOUR/V-6)

1J	D77	2-dr. Hatch Cpe-5P	7373/7983	2287/2407	8,046
1J	D69	4-dr. Sedan-5P	7350/7960	2306/2426	89,168
1J	D35	4-dr. Sta Wag-5P	7525/8135	2355/2475	23,101

CAVALIER RS (FOUR/V-6)

1J	E27	2-dr. Coupe-5P	7640/8250	2257/2377	53,941
1J	E77	2-dr. Hatch Cpe-5P	7830/8440	2319/2439	7,504
1J	E69	4-dr. Sedan-5P	7811/8451	2299/2419	17,361
1J	E35	4-dr. Sta Wag-5P	7979/8589	2371/2491	6,252
1J	E67	2-dr. Conv. Cpe-4P	12530/13140	-- /2376	5,785

CAVALIER Z24 (V-6)

1J	F27	2-dr. Spt Cpe-5P	-- /8878	-- /2451	36,365
1J	F77	2-dr. Hatch Cpe-5P	-- /9068	-- /2513	10,226

CAMARO (V-6/V-8)

1F	P87	2-dr. Spt Cpe-4P	9285/9685	2912/3071	99,517

CAMARO BERLINETTA (V-6/V-8)

1F	S87	2dr. Spt Cpe-4P	11902/12302	2983/3162	4,479

CAMARO Z28 (V-8)

1F	P87/Z28	2-dr. Spt Cpe-4P	-- /11902	-- /3121	38,547

CAMARO IROC-Z (V-8)

1F	P87/B4Z	2-dr. Spt Cpe-4P	-- /12561	N/A	49,585

Camaro Engine Note: Prices and weights before slash are for V-6 engine, after slash for V-8. Base Camaro Sport Coupes were also available with a four-cylinder engine, priced at $8935 and weighing 2781 pounds. **Z28 Production Note:** Chevrolet production figures also show 91 Z28E hatchback sport coupes built for export. IROC-Z was actually a $659 option package for the Z28, not a separate model.

CELEBRITY (FOUR/V-6)

1A	W27	2-dr. Coupe-6P	8735/9170	2609/2720	29,223
1A	W19	4-dr. Sedan-6P	8931/9366	2638/2749	291,760
1A	W35	4-dr. Sta Wag-6P	9081/9516	2790/2881	36,655
1A	W35/AQ4	4-dr. 3S Wag-8P	9313/9748	N/A	47,245

MONTE CARLO (V-6/V-8)

1G	Z37	2-dr. Spt Cpe-6P	10241/10631	3046/3120	50,418
1G	Z37/Z09	2-dr. LS Cpe-6P	10451/10841	3046/3170	27,428

MONTE CARLO 'SS' (V-8)

1G	Z37/Z65	2-dr. Spt Cpe-6P	—/12466	—/3293	41,164
1G	Z37/Z65	2-dr. Aerocpe-6P	—/14191	—/3440	200

CAPRICE (V-6/V-8)

1B	L69	4-dr. Sedan-6P	10243/10633	3399/3499	50,751

CAPRICE CLASSIC (V-6/V-8)

1B	N47	2-dr. Spt Cpe-6P	10635/11025	3411/3511	9,869
1B	N69	4-dr. Sedan-6P	10795/11185	3428/3528	67,772
1B	N69/B45	4-dr. Brghm-6P	11429/11819	N/A	69,320
1B	N69/B45	4-dr. LS Brghm-6P	N/A	N/A	2,117
1B	N35	4-dr. 3S Wag-8P	-- /11511	-- /3977	45,183

FACTORY PRICE AND WEIGHT NOTE: For Cavalier and Celebrity, prices and weights to left of slash are for four-cylinder, to right for V-6 engine. For Camaro, Monte Carlo and Caprice, figures to left of slash are for six-cylinder model, to right of slash for 305 cu. in. V-8. **BODY/STYLE NO. NOTE:** Some models were actually option packages. Code after the slash (e.g., B45) is the number of the option package that comes with the model listed.

ENGINE DATA: BASE FOUR (Chevette): Inline. Overhead cam. Four-cylinder. Cast iron block and head. Displacement: 98 cu. in. (1.6 liters). Bore & stroke: 3.23 x 2.98 in. Compression ratio: 9.0:1. Brake horsepower: 65 at 5200 R.P.M. Torque: 80 lbs.-ft. at 3200 R.P.M. Five main bearings. Hydraulic valve lifters. Carburetor: 2Bbl. VIN Code: C. DIESEL FOUR (Chevette): Inline. Overhead cam. Four-cylinder. Cast iron block and head. Displacement: 111 cu. in. (1.8 liters). Bore & stroke: 3.31 x 3.23 in. Compression ratio: 22.0:1. Brake horsepower: 51 at 5000 R.P.M. Torque: 72 lbs.-ft. at 2000 R.P.M. Five main bearings. Solid valve lifters. Fuel injection. VIN Code: D. BASE FOUR (Nova): Inline. Overhead cam. Four-cylinder. Cast iron block and head. Displacement: 97 cu. in. (1.6 liters). Bore & stroke: 3.19 x 3.03 in. Compression ratio: 9.0:1. Brake horsepower: 74 at 5200 R.P.M. Torque: 86 lbs.-ft. at 2800 R.P.M. Solid valve lifters. Carburetor: Aisan 2Bbl. VIN Code: 4. BASE FOUR (Cavalier): Inline. Overhead valve. Four-cylinder. Cast iron block and head. Displacement: 121 cu. in. (2.0 liters). Bore & stroke: 3.50 x 3.15 in. Compression ratio: 9.0:1. Brake horsepower: 85 at 4800 R.P.M. Torque: 110 lbs.-ft. at 2400 R.P.M. Five main bearings. Hydraulic valve lifters. Throttle-body fuel injection. VIN Code: P. BASE FOUR (Celebrity, Camaro): Inline. Overhead valve. Four-cylinder. Cast iron block and head. Displacement: 151 cu. in. (2.5 liters). Bore & stroke: 4.00 x 3.00 in. Compression ratio: 9.0:1. Brake horsepower: 92 at 4400 R.P.M. (Camaro, 88 at 4400). Torque: 134 lbs.-ft. at 2800 R.P.M. (Camaro, 130 at 2800). Five main bearings. Hydraulic valve lifters. Throttle-body fuel injection. Pontiac-built. VIN Code: R or 2. OPTIONAL V-6 (Celebrity) 60-degree, overhead-valve V-6. Cast iron block and head. Displacement: 173 cu. in (2.8 liters). Bore & stroke: 3.50 x 2.99 in. Compression ratio: 8.0:1. Brake horsepower: 112 at 4800 R.P.M. Torque: 145 lbs.-ft. at 2100 R.P.M. Four main bearings. Hydraulic valve lifters. Carburetor: 2Bbl. VIN CODE: X. HIGH-OUTPUT V-6 (Camaro Berlinetta, Cavalier Z24): OPTIONAL (Cavalier, Camaro, Celebrity): Same as 173 cu. in. V-6 above except multi-port fuel injection C.R.: 8.5:1 (Camaro 8.9:1). Brake H.P.: 135 at 5100 R.P.M. (Cavalier, 120 at 4800; Celebrity, 125 at 4800). Torque: 160 lbs.-ft. at 3900 R.P.M. (Cavalier, 155 at 3600; Celeb. 160 at 3600). VIN Code: W or S. BASE V-6 (Monte Carlo, Caprice): 90-degree, overhead-valve V-6. Cast iron block and head. Displacement: 262 cu. in. (4.3 liters). Bore & stroke: 4:00 x 3.48 in. Compression ratio: 9.3:1. Brake horsepower: 140 at 4000 R.P.M. Torque: 225 lbs.-ft. at 2000 R.P.M. Four main bearings. Hydraulic valve lifters. Fuel injection. VIN CODE: Z. BASE V-8 (Camaro Z28. Caprice wagon): OPTIONAL (Camaro, Monte Carlo, Caprice): 90-degree, overhead valve V-8. Cast iron block and head. Displacement: 305 cu. in. (5.0 liters). Bore & stroke: 3.74 x 3.48 in. Compression ratio: 9.5:1. Brake horsepower: 155 at 4200 R.P.M. (Monte, 150 at 4000; Caprice, 165 at 4200, Z28, 165 at 4400). Torque: 245 lbs.-ft. at 2000 R.P.M. (Monte, 240 at 2000; Caprice, 245 at 2400; Z28, 250 at 2000). Five main bearings. Hydraulic valve lifters. Carburetor: 4Bbl. VIN Code: H exc. (Caprice) Y. HIGH-OUTPUT V-8 (Monte Carlo SS): Same as 305 cu. in. V-8 above, except Brake H.P.: 180 at 4800 R.P.M. Torque: 225 lbs.-ft. at 3200 R.P.M. VIN Code: G. OPTIONAL HIGH-OUTPUT V-8 (Camaro Z28/IROC-Z): Same as 305 cu. in V-8 above, except Brake H.P.: 190 at 4800 R.P.M. Torque: 240 lbs.-ft. at 3200 R.P.M. VIN Code: G. OPTIONAL HIGH-OUTPUT V-8 (Camaro Z28/IROC-Z): Same as 305 cu. in V-8 above, but with tuned port fuel injection Brake H.P.: 190 at 4000 R.P.M. Torque: 285 lbs.-ft. at 2800 R.P.M. VIN Code: F.

CHASSIS DATA: Wheelbase: (Chevette cpe) 94.3 in.; (Chvt sed) 97.3 in.; (Nova) 95.7 in.; (Cavalier) 101.2 in.; (Celebrity) 104.9 in.; (Camaro) 101.0 in.; (Monte Carlo) 108.0 in.; (Caprice) 116.0 in. Overall length: (Chvt cpe) 161.9 in.; (Chvt sed) 164.9 in.; (Nova) 166.3 in.; (Cav cpe/conv) 172.4 in.; (Cav sed) 174.3 in.; (Cav wag) 174.5 in.; (Camaro) 188.0 in.; (Camaro Z28) 192.0 in.; (Celeb) 188.3 in.; (Celeb wag) 190.8 in.; (Monte) 200.4 in.; (Monte SS) 202.4 in.; (Monte LS) 203.3 in.; (Caprice cpe) 212.8 in.; (Capr sed) 212.2 in.; (Capr wag) 215.1 in. Height: (Chvt) 52.8 in.; (Nova) 52.7 in.; (Cav cpe) 50.2 in.; (Cav conv) 52.7 in.; (Cav sed) 52.1 in.; (Cav wag) 52.8 in.; (Camaro) 50.0 in.; (Camaro Z28) 50.3 in.; (Celeb) 54.1 in.; (Celeb wag) 54.3 in.; (Monte) 54.4 in.; (Monte SS) 54.9 in.; (Caprice) 56.4 in.; (Caprice wag) 58.2 in. Width: (Chvt) 61.8 in.; (Nova) 64.4 in.; (Cav cpe/conv) 66.0 in.; (Cav sed/wag) 66.3 in.; (Camaro) 72.8 in.; (Celeb) 69.3 in.; (Monte) 71.8 in.; (Caprice) 75.4 in.; (Capr wag) 79.3 in. Front Tread: (Chvt) 51.2 in.; (Nova) 56.1 in.; (Cav) 55.4 in.; (Celeb) 58.7 in.; (Camaro) 60.7 in.; (Camaro Z28) 60.0 in.; (Monte) 58.5 in.; (Caprice) 61.7 in.; (Capr wag) 2.2 in. Rear Tread: (Chvt) 51.2 in.; (Nova) 55.3 in.; (Cav) 55.2 in.; (Celeb) 57.0 in.; (Camaro) 61.6 in.; (Camaro Z28): 60.9 in.; (Monte) 57.8 in.; (Caprice) 60.7 in.; (Capr wag) 64.1 in. Standard Tires: (Chvt/Nova) P155/80R13 SBR; (Cav) P175/80R13 SBR; (Cav RS) P195/70R13 SBR; (Cav Z24) P215/60R14 SBR; (Celeb) P185/75R14 SBR; (Celeb Eurosport) P195/75R14 SBR; (Camaro) P205/70R14 SBR; (Camaro Z28) P215/65R15 SBR; (Camaro IROCZ) P245/50VR16 SBR; (Monte) P195/75R14 SBR; (Monte SS) P215/65R15 SBR; (Caprice) P205/75R15 SBR; (Caprice wag) P225/75R15 SBR.

TECHNICAL: Transmission: Four-speed manual shift standard on Chevette and Celebrity. Four-speed overdrive manual shift standard on Cavalier. Five-speed manual shift standard on Chevette diesel, Nova, Camaro. Three-speed Turbo Hydra-matic standard on Monte Carlo and Caprice: (1st) 2.74:1; (2nd) 1.57:1; (3rd) 1.00:1; (Rev) 2.07:1. Chevette automatic trans.: (1st) 2.40:1; (2nd) 1.48:1; (3rd) 1.00:1; (Rev) 1.92:1. Nova auto. trans.: (1st) 2.30:1; (2nd) 1.55:1; (3rd) 1.00:1; (Rev) 2.81:1. Cavalier/Celebrity auto. trans.: (1st) 2.84:1; (2nd) 1.60:1; (3rd) 1.00:1; (Rev) 2.07:1. Four-speed overdrive automatic transmission on Monte Carlo: (1st) 2.74:1; (2nd) 1.57:1; (3rd) 1.00:1; (4th) 0.67:1; (Rev) 2.07:1. Four-speed overdrive automatic on Celebrity: (1st) 2.92:1; (2nd) 1.56:1; (3rd) 1.00:1; (4th) 0.70:1; (Rev) 2.38:1. Four-speed overdrive automatic on Camaro/Caprice: (1st) 3.06:1; (2nd) 1.63:1; (3rd) 1.00:1; (4th) 0.70:1; (Rev) 2.29:1. Standard final drive ratio: (Chevette) 3.36:1; (Nova) 3.72:1 w/5spd, 3.42:1 w/auto.; (Cavalier four) 3.32:1 w/4spd, 3.83:1 w/5spd, 3.18:1 w/auto.; (Cavalier V-6) 3.65:1 w/4spd, 3.18:1 w/auto.; (Camaro four) 3.73:1; (Camaro V-6) 3.42:1; (Camaro V-8) 2.73:1 or 3.23:1; (Celebrity four) 3.65:1 w/4spd, 2.39:1 w/auto.; (Celeb V-6) 2.84:1 or 3.06:1; (Celeb wag) 2.84:1; (Monte V-6) 2.29:1 or 2.41:1; (Monte V-8) 2.41:1 or 3.73:1; (Caprice V-6) 2.56:1; (Capr V-8) 2.73:1. Steering: (Cavalier/Chevette/Nova/Celebrity) rack and pinion; (others) recirculating ball. Front Suspension: (Chevette/Monte/Caprice) unequal-length control arms, coil springs, stabilizer bar; (Nova) MacPherson struts w/coil springs and lower control arms; (Cavalier/Camaro/Celeb) MacPherson struts with coil springs, lower control arms and stabilizer. Rear Suspension: (Chevette) rigid axle and torque tube w/four links and track bar, coil springs, stabilizer; (Nova) fully independent MacPherson struts, dual links, coil springs and stabilizer bar; (Cavalier) semi-independent with beam axle, trailing arms, coil springs, stabilizer available; (Camaro) rigid axle and torque tube with longitudinal control arms, Panhard rod, coil springs and stabilizer; (Celeb) beam twist axle with integral stabilizer, trailing arms, Panhard rod and coil springs; (Monte/Caprice) rigid axle with four links, control arms, coil springs, stabilizer available. Brakes: front disc, rear drum; four-wheel discs available on Camaro V-8. Body construction: unibody except (Camaro) unibody with partial frame; (Monte/Caprice) separate body and frame. Fuel tank: (Chvt) 13.2 gal.; (Cav) 13.6 gal.; (Camaro) 15.5 gal.; (Camaro V-8) 16.2 gal.; (Celeb) 15.7 or 16.4 gal.; (Monte) 17.6 or 18.1 gal.; (Capr) 24.5 gal.; (Capr wag) 22 gal.

DRIVETRAIN OPTIONS: Engines: 173 cu. in., 2Bbl. V-6: Cavalier ($670); base Camaro ($350); Celeb ($435). 173 cu. in., MFI V-6: Celeb ($560). 305 cu. in., 4Bbl. V-8: base Camaro ($750); Berlinetta ($400); base Monte, Caprice cpe/sed ($390). H.O. 305 cu. in., 4Bbl. V-8: Camaro Z28 ($695). 350 cu. in., TPI V-8: Camaro Z28 ($695). Transmission/Differential: Five-speed manual trans.: Chevette/Cavalier ($75). Three-speed automatic trans.: Chevette ($425); Cavalier ($465); Celeb ($490). Four-speed overdrive auto. trans.: Camaro ($465); Celeb ($665); base Monte, Caprice cpe/sed ($175). Limited-slip differential: Camaro/Monte/Caprice ($100).

Performance axle ratio ($21). Power Accessories: Power brakes: Chevette ($100). Power four- wheel disc brakes: Camaro V-8 ($179). Power steering: Chvt/Cav ($215). Suspension: F40 H.D. susp.: Cav/Celeb/Caprice ($26). F41 sport susp.: Cav ($44-$49); Monte, Caprice cpe/sed ($49). Inflatable rear shock absorbers: Celeb/Caprice wag ($64). Other: H.D. cooling ($40-$70). Engine block heater ($20). H.D. battery ($26). California emission system ($99).

CHEVETTE CONVENIENCE/APPEARANCE OPTIONS: Option Packages: Sport Decor pkg.: black grille, headlamps bezels, bodyside moldings w/red accents; black bumpers; black wheels w/bright trim rings and red decals ($95). Custom exterior: black window moldings, styled argent wheels and bright trim rings ($152-$167). Comfort/Convenience: Air conditioning ($645). Rear defogger, electric ($135). Tinted glass ($99). Comfortilt steering wheel ($115). Lighting and Mirrors: Twin sport mirrors, left remote ($53). Driver's remote sport mirror ($34). Entertainment: AM/FM radio ($82). AM/FM stereo radio ($109). Radio delete ($51 credit). Exterior Trim: Two-tone paint ($133). Door edge guards ($15- $25). Chrome bumpers ($25). Interior Trim/Upholstery: Cloth bucket seats: cpe ($28). Custom cloth bucket seats: cpe ($130). Color-keyed floor mats ($25). Wheels and Tires: Sport wheel covers ($45-$97). Wheel trim rings ($52). P155/80R13 SBR WSW ($51).

NOVA CONVENIENCE/APPEARANCE OPTIONS: Nova had only one individual option: two-tone paint ($176). All other options came in packages, as follows. Pkg. 1: Five-speed trans., AM radio, P155/80R13 BSW tires (NC). Pkg. 2: Pkg. 1 plus power steering and automatic trans. ($610). Pkg. 3: Pkg. 1 plus air conditioning, electronic-tuning AM/FM stereo seek/scan radio w/digital clock, dual mirrors (left remote), power steering, electric rear defogger and halogen headlamps ($1180). Pkg. 4: Same as pkg. 3 plus automatic trans. ($1575). Pkg. 5: Automatic trans., P155/80R13 tires, AM/FM with clock, power steering and air cond. ($1525). CL Pkg. 1: Five-speed trans., air cond., P155/80R13 BSW tires, seek/scan AM/FM stereo radio with digital clock, dual mirrors (left remote), power steering, rear defogger, halogen headlamps and Custom CL features ($1730). CL Pkg. 2: Same as CL 1 plus automatic trans. ($2125). CL Pkg. 3: Same as CL 1 plus AM/FM stereo radio w/cassette player and clock, aluminum wheels, P175/70R13 SBR BSW tires, intermittent wipers, cruise control and (on hatchback) rear wiper/washer ($2515-$2640). CL Pkg. 4: Same as CL 3, but with automatic trans. and P155/80R13 tires, plus power door locks ($2620-$2745).

1986 Cavalier RS convertible (CH)

CAVALIER CONVENIENCE/APPEARANCE OPTIONS: Option Packages: CL custom interior pkg.: reclining bucket seats, quiet sound group, sport steering wheel, console, custom door/quarter trim w/carpet inserts, fender nameplates ($251-$325); incl. split folding rear seat on hatch/wagon. Comfort/Convenience: Air cond. ($645). Cruise control w/resume ($175). Rear defogger, electric ($135). Tinted glass ($99). Six-way power driver's seat ($225). Black sport steering wheel ($22-$40). Comfortilt steering wheel ($115). Power windows ($195-$270). Power door locks ($130-$180). Power hatch or trunk release ($40). Power liftgate release ($40). Electronic instrument cluster ($295). Gauge pkg. w/trip odometer ($69); incl. tach ($139). Digital clock: RS/Z24. ($39). Lighter: base ($14). Intermittent wipers ($50). Rear wiper/washer ($125). Lighting and Mirrors: Halogen headlamps ($25). Aux. lighting ($43-$95). Dual black sport mirrors, left remote ($53). Entertainment: AM radio: base ($112). Electronic-tuning seek/scan AM/FM stereo radio ($158) exc. base ($258); w/clock ($197) exc. base ($297); w/cassette ($319) exc. base ($419). Electronic-tuning AM stereo/FM seek/scan radio w/cassette, equalizer and clock ($494-$504) exc. base ($594). Premium dual rear speakers ($25). Extended-range sound system: RS/Z24/conv. ($35). Fixed-mast antenna: base ($41) but incl. w/radios. Radio delete ($56 credit). Exterior Trim: Removable sunroof ($310). Rear spoiler: RS/Z24 ($69). Rear window louvers ($199). Custom two-tone paint: CS ($176); RS ($123). Pinstriping ($53). Bodyside moldings, black: base ($45). Wheel opening moldings, black: conv. ($30). Wheel opening and rocker panel moldings ($55). Door edge guards ($15-$25). Wagon roof carrier ($105). Decklid luggage rack ($100). Bumper guards ($56). Interior Trim/Upholstery: Cloth reclining bucket seats: base/CS ($28). Sport cloth reclining bucket seats: Z24 (NC). Custom CL cloth bucket seats: CS/RS/Z24 (NC). Custom CL vinyl bucket seats: RS/Z24 (NC). Split-folding rear seatback: wag/hatch ($50). Color-keyed mats: front ($18); rear ($15). Cargo area cover: wag/hatch ($69). Deluxe seat/shoulder belts: base ($26). Wheels and Tires: Aluminum wheels, 13 in. ($233-$285); 14 in., Z24 ($173). Rally 14 in. wheels: conv. ($56). Sport wheel covers ($45-$97). Wheel trim rings: base/CS ($52). P175/80R13 SBR WSW: base/CS ($54). P195/70R13 SBR BSW: base/CS ($104). P195/70R13 SBR WSW: base/CS ($166). P195/70R13 SBR RWL: base/CS ($188); RS ($84). P215/60R14 SBR BSW: RS ($142). P215/60R14 SBR RWL: RS ($234); Z24 ($92).

CELEBRITY/CAPRICE CONVENIENCE/APPEARANCE OPTIONS: Option Packages: Eurosport pkg.: Celeb ($225). Estate equipment: Capr wag ($307). Landau equipment (vinyl roof, sport mirrors and reveal moldings): Capr ($306). Exterior molding pkg. (rocker panel and wheel opening moldings): Celeb ($55). Security pkg.: Celeb wag ($44). Quiet sound group: base Capr ($66). Comfort/Convenience: Air cond. ($750). Rear defogger, electric ($145-$150). Cruise control ($175). Tinted glass ($115). Comfortilt steering wheel ($115). Six-way power driver's seat ($215-$225). Power windows ($195-$270). Power door locks ($130-$180). Power trunk or liftgate release ($40). Power tailgate lock: Capr wag ($50). Gauge pkg. w/trip odometer ($64). Tachometer: Celeb ($90). Quartz clock: base Capr ($39). Intermittent wipers ($50). Rear wiper/washer: Celeb ($125). Lighting, Horns and Mirrors: Halogen headlamps ($25). Cornering lamps: Capr ($55). Aux. lighting: Celeb ($51-$67); Capr ($32-$42). Dome reading lamp: Celeb ($24). Dual horns: Celeb ($12). Driver's remote mirror ($23). Dual sport mirrors, left remote ($61). Dual remote sport mirrors ($91) exc. Capr Lan ($30). Right visor mirror: Celeb ($7). Lighted visor mirror ($50). Entertainment: AM radio w/digital clock: Celeb ($39). Electronic-tuning seek/scan AM/FM stereo radio ($158); w/clock ($162-$197); w/cassette, clock and seek/scan ($284- $319). Seek/scan AM/FM stereo radio w/casssette, equalizer and clock: Capr ($394-$464). Seek/scan AM stereo/FM radio w/clock, equalizer and cassette: Celeb ($504). Extended-range rear speakers ($35). Power antenna: Capr ($65). Radio delete ($56 credit). Exterior Trim: Removable sunroof: Celeb ($310). Padded vinyl roof: Celeb ($270). Vinyl roof: Capr sed ($185). Two-tone paint ($141-$148). Bodyside pinstriping ($39-$57). Bodyside moldings: Capr ($55). Wheel opening moldings: base Capr ($30). Door edge guards ($15-$25). Rear window air deflector: wag ($40). Rear quarter vent windows: Celeb ($75). Swing-out tailgate: Celeb wag ($105). Decklid luggage carrier: Celeb ($100). Roof carrier: wag ($105-$110). Bumper rub strips: Capr ($66). Bumper guards ($56-$62). Celebrity Interior: Console ($110). Reclining passenger seatback ($45); both ($90). Cloth bench seat: wag ($28). Vinyl bench seat: cpe/sed ($28). Cloth 55/45 seat ($133). CL custom cloth 45/45 seat ($200-$330). CL custom cloth 55/45 seating ($305-$435). Cloth reclining bucket seats ($147). Color-keyed rubber mats: front ($17); rear ($12). Carpeted mats: front ($25); rear ($20). Deluxe trunk or wagon luggage area trim ($40-$47). Caprice Interior: Reclining passenger seatback: Classic ($45). Vinyl bench seat: base sed ($28). Cloth bench seat: wag ($28). Cloth 50/50 seating: Classic ($195-$225). Vinyl 50/50 seating ($195). Deluxe load-floor carpet: wag ($89). Deluxe cargo area trim: wag ($129). Mats w/carpet insert: front ($25); rear ($20). Deluxe trunk trim ($59). Celebrity Wheels/Tires: Aluminum wheels ($306-$362). Sport wheel covers ($65). Locking wire wheel covers ($199). Rally wheels ($56). P185/75R14 SBR WSW ($58). P195/70R14 Eagle GT SBR BSW: Eurosport ($80). P195/75R14 SBR BSW ($30). P195/75R14 SBR WSW ($92). Caprice Wheels/Tires: Sport wheel covers ($65). Wire wheel covers w/locks ($199). P205/75R15 SBR WSW: cpe/sed ($66). P225/70R15 SBR WSW: cpe/sed ($157). P225/75R15 SBR WSW: wag ($71). Puncture-sealant tires ($115-$140).

1986½ Monte Carlo Aerocoupe SS

CAMARO/MONTE CARLO CONVENIENCE/APPEARANCE OPTIONS: Option Packages: IROCZ sport equipment pkg.: Camaro Z28 ($659). Comfort/Convenience: Air cond. ($750). Rear defogger (electric) ($145). Cruise control w/resume ($175-$185). Tinted glass ($115). Comfortilt steering wheel ($115). Six- way power driver's seat ($225). Power windows ($195). Power door locks ($130). Power trunk opener: Monte ($40). Power hatch release: Camaro ($40). Tachometer: Monte ($90). Gauge pkg. w/trip odometer: Monte ($69). Gauge pkg. incl. tach: base Camaro ($149). Intermittent wipers ($50). Rear wiper/washer: Camaro ($125). Quiet sound group: Camaro ($82). Lighting, Horns and Mirrors: Halogen headlamps ($25). Halogen foglamps: Camaro ($60). Aux. lighting: Camaro ($37-$72); Monte ($28). Dual horns: Camaro ($12). Twin sport mirrors (left remote): Monte ($53). Twin remote sport mirrors: Monte ($83); SS ($30). Twin electric remote sport mirrors: Camaro ($91). Automatic day/night mirror: Camaro ($80). Right visor mirror: Monte ($7); lighted ($50). Entertainment: AM radio w/digital clock: base ($39). Electronic-tuning seek/scan AM/FM stereo radio: base Camaro ($193); Electronic-tuning seek/scan AM/FM stereo radio w/clock: Camaro ($197-$232); w/cassette and clock ($319-$354); w/AM stereo and cassette ($469-$504). Seek/scan AM/FM stereo w/remote control and cassette: Berlinetta ($242). Monte seek/scan electronic-tuning AM/FM stereo radio ($158); w/clock ($197); w/cassette ($319); with AM stereo and cassette ($494). Premium rear speakers: Monte ($25). Power antenna: Camaro ($60). Radio delete ($56 credit) exc. Berlinetta ($256 credit); Z28 ($95 credit). Exterior Trim: Removable glass roof panels: Camaro ($846); Monte ($875). Landau vinyl roof: Monte ($245). Rear spoiler: Camaro ($69). Rear window louvers: Camaro ($210). Two-tone paint: Monte ($214). Bodyside moldings, black: Camaro ($55). Deluxe vinyl bodyside moldings: Monte ($57). Door edge guards ($15). Side window sill moldings: Monte ($45). Bodyside pinstriping: Monte ($61). Interior Trim/Upholstery: Console: Monte ($110). Roof console: Camaro/Z28 ($50). Vinyl bench seat: Monte ($28). Cloth 55/45 seating: base Monte ($133). Cloth bucket seats: Camaro ($28); Monte ($147). Custom cloth bucket seats: base Camaro/Z28 ($359). Custom cloth CL 55/45 seating: base Monte ($385). Split folding back seat: Camaro ($50). Mats w/carpeted inserts: front ($20); rear ($15). Cargo area cover: Camaro ($69). Deluxe trunk trim: Camaro ($164); Z28 ($84). Locking rear storage cover: Z28 ($80). Wheels and Tires: Aluminum wheels: Monte ($362); Berlinetta ($225). Wheel locks: Berlinetta/Z28 ($16). Rally wheels: Monte ($56). Locking wire wheel covers: Monte ($199). P195/70R14 SBR BSW Eagle GT: Berlinetta ($80). P195/75R14 SBR WSW: Monte ($62). P205/70R14 SBR WSW: Berlinetta ($66); Monte ($124). P215/65R15 SBR BSW: Z28 ($92 credit). P215/65R15 SBR RWL: Camaro four ($92). P235/60VR15 SBR BSW: Z28 ($85).

HISTORY: Introduced: Oct. 3, 1985. Model year production (U.S.): 1,564,303 (incl. Corvettes but not incl. 21,643 Acadians). Total production for sale in U.S. consisted of 867,823 four-cylinder, 433,461 sixes, and 448,221 V-8s. Only 588 leftover diesels were installed. Calendar year production (U.S.): 1,518,794 (including 28,410 Corvettes). Calendar year sales by U.S. dealers: 1,558,476, for a 19.5 percent market share. Model year sales by U.S. dealers: 1,587,024 (incl. 35,969 Corvettes) for a 19.7 percent share.

Historical Footnotes: The new joint-venture Nova, produced by Chevrolet and Toyota, helped Chevrolet sales come close to the 1985 figure. Total sales still dropped a bit for the model year. Even so, Chevrolet's domestic market share managed to grow somewhat. A total of 170,661 Novas were sold during the full model year, but Cavalier and Celebrity were still the top sellers. Actually, Celebrity pulled ahead and made No. 1 this year. As Nova production increased, the outmoded rear-drive Chevette's days were numbered, especially when Chevrolet announced in late 1985 that the Lakewood, Georgia plant that assembled Chevettes would be converted to rear-drive production. Chevettes sales shrunk to 75,761, prompting a price cut for 1987 and abandonment early in tht model year. With the new Nova (based on Toyota's Corolla) and the twin Japanese imports sold under the Chevrolet banner (Spectrum and Sprint), Chevrolet offered a total of five small cars. Chevrolet's General Manager Robert D. Burger predicted that subcompacts and smaller would account for nearly 40 percent of total car sales in this country in 1986. The company was especially interested in attracting first-time, younger buyers, who might later want to move up to a "better" Chevrolet model. In addition to the small-car lineup. Chevrolet claimed to have America's fastest car (Corvette), most popular car (Cavalier), most popular mid- and full-size cars (Celebrity and Caprice), and favorite sporty 2+2 (Camaro). Low-interest loans (7.7 percent) were offered by GM late in the 1985 model year, and 8.8 percent rates arrived for 1986. One Illinois dealer opened experimental operations in a shopping mall, in an attempt to lure buyers who might otherwise be missed. A Women's Marketing Committee was formed to develop approaches to attract female buyers, whose role in auto purchasing was gaining steadily by the mid-1980s. Among other innovations was a pre-approved credit plan for women customers, through General Motors Acceptance Corporation. Dealers also held "Car Care Clinics" for women. Nova's manufacturing facility was called New United Motor Manufacturing, Inc. (NUMMI), located at Fremont, California.

STANDARD CATALOG OF CHEVROLET 1987-1990

Chevrolet celebrated three-quarters of a century of automaking in 1987.

"Today's Chevrolet is keeping a commitment we made 75 years ago," said one advertisement. "To give you the kind of cars you want."

Filling every niche in the market was more than a goal; it was a necessity for a company which had dropped more than five percent in market share since 1980. With American buyers flocking to Japanese cars, Chevy's patriotic "baseball, hot dogs and apple pie" appeal was waning. After 1,200 workers lost their jobs in a $311 million shut-down and modernization of the 40-year-old Wilmington, Del. plant in Feb. 1986, it became clear that the company's future was dependent upon success of the new Nova — coming out of its New United Motor Manufacturing joint-venture with Toyota, in Fremont, Calif. — and its Corsica/Beretta "world class" models.

The importance of these new product plans was even greater by mid-year, by which time Chevrolet deliveries were running 133,500 units below the previous season and Ford was threatening to take over the number one sales slot. Unfortunately, the introduction of Corsica and Beretta (as 1988 models) was delayed until March, 1987, to allow a test of 17,000 cars by rental car companies and shipping of 45,000 to dealer showrooms nationwide. Hailed as "the slowest new car launch in history," this sluggish promotion induced, Chevy General Manager Bob Burger, to lower sales goods by some 50,000 units.

During 1987 model announcements, Chevrolet promised "cars with the latest technology and most advanced engineering available at affordable prices". The model lineup started with the Sprint, which was actually an import built by Suzuki, and therefore outside the scope of this catalog. Next came the entry-level Chevette, in its 11th year and now lacking a diesel. It was followed by the smaller, but pricier Spectrum, a badge-engineered Isuzu built stateside. It had a re-calibrated suspension and optional turbo-charged 1.5 liter four good for 0-to-60 in less than nine seconds. America's best selling car, the Cavalier, was back again in five models, including a convertible. A new Getrag five-speed was available with the optional V-6.

Chevy's 1987 family fleet included the two Nova four-doors, three Celebritys and the full-sized Caprice. All Celebritys with the Eurosport package or optional V-6 could be had with a Getrag-like five-speed. Caprice buyers had a choice of a 4.3 liter V-6 or 5.0 liter V-8 and many picked the fancier Brougham trim level to emphasis old-fashioned splendor.

Possibly qualifying as future collectibles were the Camaro (especially IROCs with the hot 190 hp Vette V-8) and the Monte Carlo, which could still be had in limited-production Aero Coupe SS format boasting 80 hp.

At the 1987 Daytona 500, Benny Parsons drove a Monte Carlo SS to a second place win. Two of the Monte Carlos cars placed in the top 10 finishers. In May, at Indianapolis Motor Speedway, Mario Andretti drove a Lola IMSA racing car with an Indy V-8 Indy V-8 to ninth place at the "Brickyard" in a hint of things to come.

With the 1988 Corsica/Beretta selling at over 30,000 units per month by June, 1987, Chevrolet entered model-year 1988 with Bob Burger predicting sales of 1.7 million cars. This projection equated to nearly 17 percent of the year's anticipated 10.3 million industry output and eventually matched the company's domestic and imported car production of 1,709,742 units in the model year. Retail sales of U.S. built Chevys, in the calendar year, stood at 1,363,187.

Gone for 1988 was the Chevette, which left a niche for the Spectrum to fill completely. The good looks of this 13-foot-long replacement were now enchanced with alloy wheels and a spoiler, if the 110 hp Turbo package was ordered. Other Turbo goodies included the five-speed gearbox, F41 sport suspension, P185/GOR14 tires, full instrumentation and fog lamps.

Another new "special-interest" '88 was the Twin Cam Nova, featuring a potent 110 hp, 16-valve, twin cam engine, stiff suspension, aluminum rims and four-wheel disc brakes. It came with a 120-mph speedometer and found favor with about 10 percent of Nova buyers.

New for the Cavalier was an Aero package with spoilers, flares and a 130 hp Z24 V-6. The convertible remained available for enthusiasts, too. In fact, it was upgraded to Z24 status and a $15,000-plus price tag.

Subtle refinements graced the 1988 Celebritys, along with a re-tuned Eurosport suspension and better anti-corrosion protection. The Monte Carlo returned, 99 and 44/100 percent unchanged, but now offering a third engine option — the 5.0 liter HO with 200 horses at 4800 rpm.

Big news for Camaro collectors was the release of a convertible, available in both Sport Coupe and IROC-Z trim levels. LT and Z28 models were discontinued. Four engines were offered: 130 hp, 165 hp, 190 hp and 220 hp. As Motor Trend said, "You can still play kick-the-Porsche with one of the best performing American anachronisms on the street."

A Chevy V-8 powered Penske racing car driven by Rick Mears won the 1988 Indy 500, with second and third places also going to Chevrolet engined cars. At the Daytona 500, a Monte Carlo SS driven by Terry Labonte and Ken Schrader placed fifth and sixth.

An interesting new development for Chevrolet, in 1989, was the GEO Metro, replacing the Sprint with two-door hatch and four-door sedan versions of this Suzuki-built, Honda Civic competitor. There was a choice of three throttle-body injected three-cylinder engines with 48, 70 and 80 hp, respectively, plus a LSi trim level. However, these import cars are not covered by our catalog of American Chevrolets. Neither is the renamed GEO Spectrum, which came as an economical Express and a hatch-backed Sport.

Maintaining its sporty image was the '89 Cavalier, with base, RS, Z24 and VL trim levels. Only the coupe and rag-top came with the 130 hp Z24 option and the VL — an entry-level variation — was available for just the coupe.

The Corsica and Beretta line — now housing the best-selling Chevys since 1980, — reflected ongoing change for 1989. A hatchback Corsica sedan had been added, as well as the four-door LTZ with a sport suspension and stick shift and V-6. Most collectable was the GTU package with Aero body mods, 16 inch wheels and 205/55 VR tires.

Celebritys had a revamped cylinder head for the base

2.5 liter balance-shaft four, with the three speed automatic. When the V-6 was added, buyers could select a four-speed automatic or a five-speed manual gear box. Larger families, desiring more room, could opt for a Caprice or Caprice Classic wagon with 5.0 liter V-8. The wagon's engine used a four-barrel carburetor and generated 140 hp. Thirty additional horses were produced by a 5.0 liter EFI V-8.

Last, but not least, came the two Camaros (RS and IROC-Z) in two body styles (coupe/convertible), now with a Pass-Key anti-theft system. The RS looked a bit more like the discontinued Z-28, while top output for the IROC was bumped to 225 hp at 4200 rpm.

1987 CHEVROLET

Late in the model year, two new Chevrolet models arrived: the front-drive Corsica and Beretta. Rather than heading straight for new-car dealers, they first had a tryout as rental vehicles. In addition to all the domestic models, Chevrolet marketed the subcompact Sprint (built by Suzuki) and slightly larger Spectrum (from Isuzu).

CHEVETTE — SERIES 1T — FOUR —
Chevette's diesel engine option was dropped this year, but few other changes were evident for the subcompact's final season. Sole powerplant was the 1.6-liter gasoline four, with standard four-speed manual gearbox, optional five-speed, or optional three-speed automatic.

NOVA — SERIES 1S — FOUR —
Taillamps were a little wider this year, and bumpers turned to body color. Otherwise, little changed in the front-drive Nova, built in California as a joint venture between GM and Toyota. New standard equipment included a rear-window defogger. Notchback and hatchback four-door sedans were offered, powered by a 1.6-liter four that produced 74 horsepower and standard five-speed gearbox. An automatic transmission was available only as part of an option package.

1987 Cavalier RS 4-dr sedan

CAVALIER — SERIES 1J — FOUR/V-6 —
Customers for Chevrolet's popular J-body subcompact had quite a variety to choose from this year: five body styles and four trim levels. Both the 2.0-liter four-cylinder and 2.8-liter V-6 engines went into Generation II versions, and added the option of a five-speed Getrag-designed manual gearbox. With a new Computer Controlled Coil Ignition sending power to its spark plugs, the four-cylinder engine no longer had need for a distributor. Standard in the performance-oriented Z24 and optional in the RS convertible, the V-6 added a new aluminum cylinder head, new fuel injectors, and electronic spark control for a rating of 125 or 130 horsepower. One belt now drove all the accessories under V-6 hoods. Modifications to the Z24 included a fresh-air induction hood, low-restriction exhaust system, and the installation of new 14-inch aluminum wheels.

1987 Camaro IROC-Z 2-dr convertible

CAMARO — SERIES 1F — V-6/V-8 —
Biggest news for performance fans was the arrival of the 350 cu. in. (5.7-liter) V-8 with roller lifters as an option for the IROC-Z. Both the four-cylinder engine and the high-output carbureted 5.0-liter V-8 were dropped this year, giving the 173 cu. in. (2.8-liter) Generation II V-6 new duty as Camaro's base powerplant. A new LT model (actually a set of option packages) replaced the former Berlinetta. A 165-horsepower carbureted 5.0-liter V-8 was optional in the base and LT Camaros, and standard under Z28 hoods. But the Z28 could also be ordered with a tuned-port injection version of that V-8, delivering 215 horsepower. All Camaros could have either a five-speed manual gearbox or four-speed overdrive automatic, except the IROC-Z with 5.7-liter V-8, which came only with automatic. Otherwise, Camaros changed little in appearance apart from new wet-arm wipers and the mounting of the required center high-mount stoplight on the rear spoiler (if installed).

CORSICA/BERETTA — SERIES 1L — FOUR/V-6 —
Intended to replace the ill-starred Citation, which was dropped after 1985, the new compact Corsica sedan and Beretta coupe rode a 103.4 inch wheelbase and carried either a 121 cu. in. (2.0-liter) four or optional 2.8-liter V-6. A five-speed gearbox was standard. Though both appeared late in the 1987 model year they were actually early '88 models. See 1988 listing for further details.

CELEBRITY — SERIES 1A — FOUR/V-6 —
During 1986, Chevrolet's front-drive A-body mid-size took over Cavalier's role as most popular American automobile. This year's front end held composite aerodynamic headlamps with integral side marker lamps, while engine compartments contained Generation II engines: either a 2.5-liter four or 2.8-liter V-6. The four-cylinder engine added six horsepower as a result of reworked fuel metering, a restyled intake manifold and lighter pistons. New aluminum cylinder heads helped knock a few pounds off the V-6 weight, while horsepower rose to 135. For the first time, a Getrag-designed five-speed gearbox was offered with the V-6, which formerly came only with automatic. Standard transmission was a three-speed automatic, with four-speed automatic available (V-6 only).

MONTE CARLO — SERIES 1G — V-6/V-8 —
Both LS and SS rear-drive Montes were offered this year in the mid-size coupe body. Also available again was the stylish fastback Aerocoupe, only 200 of which had appeared in 1986. Base powerplant for the LS was the 262 cu. in. (4.3-liter) V-6 with throttle-body fuel injection and new roller valve lifters. Optional again was the carbureted 305 cu. in (5.0-liter) V-8, producing 150 horsepower. The SS had a high-output version of the V-8, rated 180 horsepower. Six-cylinder Montes came with a standard three-speed automatic, while V-8s sent their power through a four-speed. Aerodynamic composite headlamps, introduced for 1986 on the LS, also went on the SS this time around. Otherwise, apart from a few design revisions in the back end, little change was evident.

1987 Caprice Classic 4-dr sedan

CAPRICE — SERIES 1B — V-6/V-8 —
On the outside, full-size Chevrolet coupes, sedans and wagons got new stand-up hood ornaments this year, plus composite headlamps that combined high and low beams into a single unit. Joining the upscale Classic Brougham was a new Brougham LS sedan, aiming even further upscale with its formal Landau vinyl roof. A new base station wagon joined the former Classic wagon, both carrying a standard 307 cu. in. (5.0-liter) V-8 engine. Coupes and sedans came with a standard 262 cu. in. (4.3 liter) V-6, with a 305 cu. in. V-8 optional. All three engines added roller lifters this year, and both V-8s used four-barrel carburetors.

I.D. DATA: Chevrolets again had a 17-symbol Vehicle Identification Number (VIN) on the upper left surface of the instrument panel, visible through the windshield. Symbol one indicates country: '1' - U.S.A.; '2' - Canada. Next is a manufacturer code: 'G' - General Motors. Symbol three is car make: '1' - Chevrolet; '7' - GM of Canada. Symbol four denotes restraint system: 'A' - non-passive (standard); 'B' - passive (automatic belts); 'C' - passive (inflatable). Symbol five is car line/series. Symbols six-seven reveal body type. Next is the engine code, followed by a check digit, then 'H' for model year 1987. Symbol eleven indicates assembly plant. The final six digits are the sequential serial number. Engine number coding is similar to 1981-86.

CHEVETTE CS (FOUR)

Model Number	Body/Style Number	Body Type & Seating	Factory Price	Shipping Weight	Production Total
1T	B08	2-dr. Hatch Cpe-4P	4995	2078	26,135
1T	B68	4-dr. Hatch Sed-4P	5495	2137	20,073
NOVA (FOUR)					
1S	K19	4-dr. Sedan-4P	8258	2206	123,782
1S	K68	4-dr. Hatch Sed-4P	8510	2253	26,224
CAVALIER (FOUR/V-6)					
1J	C27	2-dr. Coupe-5P	7255/7915	2300/—	53,678
1J	C69	4-dr. Sedan-5P	7449/8109	2345/—	84,445
1J	C35	4-dr. Sta Wag-5P	7615/8275	2401/—	25,542
CAVALIER CS (FOUR/V-6)					
1J	D77	2-dr. Hatch Cpe-5P	7978/8638	2359/—	3,480
1J	D69	4-dr. Sedan-5P	7953/8613	2355/—	50,625
1J	D35	4-dr. Sta Wag-5P	8140/8800	2411/—	15,023
CAVALIER RS (FOUR/V-6)					
1J	E27	2-dr. Coupe-5P	8318/8978	2360/—	36,353
1J	E77	2-dr. Hatch Cpe-5P	8520/9180	2408/—	2,818
1J	E69	4-dr. Sedan-5P	8499/9159	2397/—	15,482
1J	E35	4-dr. Sta Wag-5P	8677/9337	2460/—	5,575
1J	E67	2-dr. Conv. Cpe-4P	13446/14106	2519/—	5,826
CAVALIER Z24 (V-6)					
1J	F27	2-dr. Spt Cpe-5P	—/9913	—/2511	42,890
1J	F77	2-dr. Hatch Cpe-5P	—/10115	—/2560	4,517
CAMARO (V-6/V-8)					
1F	P87	2-dr. Spt Cpe-4P	9995/10395	3062/3181	83,890
1F	P67	2-dr. Conv Cpe-4P	—/14794	N/A	263
CAMARO Z28 (V-8)					
1F	P87/Z28	2-dr. Spt Cpe-4P	12819	3228	52,863
1F	P67/Z28	2-dr. Conv Cpe-4P	17218	N/A	744
CAMARO IROC-Z (V-8)					
1F	P87/Z28	2-dr. Spt Cpe-4P	13488	N/A	Note 1
1F	P67/Z28	2-dr. Conv Cpe-4P	17917	N/A	Note 1
CORSICA (FOUR/V-6)					
1L	T69	4-dr. Sedan-5P	8995/9655	2491/2609	8,973
BERETTA (FOUR/V-6)					
1L	V37	2-dr. Coupe-5P	9555/10215	2550/2648	8,072
CELEBRITY (FOUR/V-6)					
1A	W27	2-dr. Coupe-5P	9995/10605	2685/2769	18,198
1A	W19	4-dr. Sedan-5P	10265/10875	2715/2799	273,864
1A	W35	4-dr. Sta Wag-6P	10425/11035	2847/2931	33,894
1A	W35/AQ4	4-dr. 3S Wag-8P	10672/11382	N/A	36,568
MONTE CARLO (V-6/V-8)					
1G	Z37	2-dr. LS Cpe-6P	11306/11746	3283/3389	72,993
MONTE CARLO 'SS' (V-8)					
1G	Z37/Z65	2-dr. Spt Cpe-6P	13463	3473	Note 2
1G	Z37/Z16	2-dr. Aerocpe-6P	14838	3526	6,052

CAPRICE (V-6/V-8)

Model Number	Body/Style Number	Body Type & Seating	Factory Price	Shipping Weight	Production Total
1B	L69	4-dr. Sedan-6P	10995/11435	3510/3603	56,266
1B	L35	4-dr. 3S Wag-8P	—/11995	—/4114	11,953
CAPRICE CLASSIC (V-6/V-8)					
1B	N47	2-dr. Coupe-6P	11392/11802	3512/3605	3,110
1B	N69	4-dr. Sedan-6P	11560/12000	3527/3620	53,802
1B	U69	4-dr. Brghm-6P	12549/12989	3576/3669	51,341
1B	U69/B6N	4-dr. LS Brghm-6P	13805/14245	N/A	23,641
1B	N35	4-dr. 3S Wag-8P	—/12586	—/4125	28,387

Note 1: IROC-Z production included in Z28 total.
Note 2: Monte Carlo SS sport coupe production included in LS total.

FACTORY PRICE AND WEIGHT NOTE: For Cavalier, Corsica, Beretta and Celebrity, prices and weights to left of slash are for four-cylinder, to right for V-6 engine. For Camaro, Monte Carlo and Caprice, figures to left of slash are for six-cylinder model, to right of slash for least expensive V-8.

BODY/STYLE NO. NOTE: Some models were actually option packages. Code after the slash (e.g., Z28) is the number of the option package that comes with the model listed.

ENGINE DATA: BASE FOUR (Chevette): Inline. Overhead cam. Four-cylinder. Cast iron block and head. Displacement: 98 cu. in. (1.6 liters). Bore & stroke: 3.23 x 2.98 in. Compression ratio: 9.0:1. Brake horsepower: 65 at 5600 RPM. Torque: 80 lbs.-ft. at 3200 RPM. Five main bearings. Hydraulic valve lifters. Carburetor: 2Bbl. BASE FOUR (Nova): Inline. Overhead cam. Four-cylinder. Cast iron block and head. Displacement: 97 cu. in. (1.6 liters). Bore & stroke: 3.19 x 3.03 in. Compression ratio: 9.0:1. Brake horsepower: 74 at 5200 RPM. Torque: 86 lbs.-ft. at 2800 RPM. Solid valve lifters. Carburetor: Aisan 2Bbl. BASE FOUR (Cavalier, Corsica/Beretta): Inline. Overhead valve. Four-cylinder. Cast iron block and aluminum head. Displacement: 121 cu. in. (2.0 liters). Bore & stroke: 3.50 x 3.15 in. Compression ratio: 9.0:1. Brake horsepower: 90 at 5600 RPM. Torque: 108 lbs.-ft. at 3200 RPM. Five main bearings. Hydraulic valve lifters. Throttle-body fuel injection. BASE FOUR (Celebrity): Inline. Overhead valve. Four-cylinder. Cast iron block and head. Displacement: 151 cu. in (2.5 liters). Bore & stroke: 4.00 x 3.00 in. Compression ratio: 9.0:1. Brake horsepower: 98 at 4400 RPM. Torque: 135 lbs.-ft. at 3200 RPM. Five main bearings. Hydraulic valve lifters. Throttle-body fuel injection. BASE V-6 (Camaro, Cavalier Z24); OPTIONAL (Cavalier RS conv. Celebrity): 60-degree, overhead-valve V-6. Cast iron block and head. Displacement: 173 cu. in. (2.8 liters). Bore & stroke: 3.50 x 2.99 in. Compression ratio: 8.9:1. Brake horsepower: (Cavalier) 125/130 at 4500; (Corsica/Beretta) 125 at 4500; (Camaro) 135 at 4900; (Celebrity) 125 at 4500. Torque: (Cavalier) 160/165 at 3600; (Corsica/Beretta) N/A; (Camaro) 160 at 3900; (Celeb) 160 at 3600. Multi-port fuel injection. BASE V-6 (Monte Carlo, Caprice); 90-degree, overhead-valve V-6. Cast iron block and head. Displacement: 262 cu. in. (4.3 liters). Bore & stroke: 4.00 x 3.48 in. Compression ratio: 9.3:1. Brake horsepower: (Caprice) 140 at 3200 RPM; (Monte) 145 at 4200. Torque: 225 lbs.-ft. at 2000 RPM. Four main bearings. Hydraulic valve lifters. Throttle-body fuel injection. BASE V-8 (Camaro Z28, Caprice wagon); OPTIONAL (Camaro, Monte Carlo, Caprice): 90-degree, overhead valve V-8. Cast iron block and head. Displacement: 305 cu. in. (5.0 liters). Bore & stroke: 3.74 x 3.48 in. Compression ratio: (Camaro) 9.3:1; (Monte/Caprice) 9.5:1. Brake horsepower: (Camaro) 165 at 4400 RPM; (Monte) 150 at 4000; (Caprice) 170 at 4400. Torque: (Camaro) 245/250 lbs.-ft. at 2800 RPM (Monte) 240 at 2000; (Caprice) 250 at 2800. Five main bearings. Hydraulic valve lifters. Carburetor: 4Bbl. HIGH-OUTPUT V-8 (Monte Carlo SS): Same as 305 cu. in. V-8 above, except — BHP: 180 at 4800 RPM. Torque: 225 lbs.-ft. at 3200 RPM. OPTIONAL HIGH-OUTPUT V-8 (Camaro Z28): Same as 305 cu. in. V-8 above, but with turned port fuel injection — BHP: 215 at 4400 RPM (190 at 4000 with automatic). Torque: 250 lbs.-ft. at 3200 RPM (295 at 2800 with automatic). OPTIONAL V-8 (Caprice wagon): 90-degree, overhead valve V-8. Cast iron block and head. Displacement: 307 cu. in. (5.0 liters). Bore & stroke: 3.80 x 3.38 in. Compression ratio: 8.0:1 Brake horsepower: 140 at 3200 RPM. Torque: 225 lbs.-ft. at 2000 RPM. Five main bearings. Hydraulic roller valve lifters. Carburetor: 4Bbl. OPTIONAL V-8 (Camaro IROC-Z): 90-degree, overhead valve V-8. Cast iron block and head. Displacement: 350 cu. in. (5.7 liters). Bore & stroke; 4.00 x 3.48 in. Compression ratio: 9.0:1. Brake horsepower: 225 at 4400 RPM. Torque: 330 lbs.-ft. at 2800 RPM.

1987 Monte Carlo Aerocoupe SS

CHASSIS DATA: Wheelbase: (Chevette cpe) 94.3 in.; (Chvt sed) 97.3 in.; (Nova) 95.7 in.; (Cavalier) 101.2 in.; (Camaro) 101.0 in.; (Corsica/Beretta) 103.4 in.; (Celebrity) 104.9 in.; (Monte Carlo) 108.0 in.; (Caprice) 116.0 in.
Overall length: (Chvt cpe) 161.9 in.; (Chvt sed) 164.9 in.; (Nova) 166.3 in.; (Cav cpe/conv) 172.4 in.; (Cav sed) 174.3 in.; (Cav wag) 174.5 in.; (Camaro) 188.0 in.; (Camaro Z28/IROC-Z) 192.0 in.; (Corsica) 183.4 in.; (Beretta) 187.2 in.; (Celeb) 188.3. in.; (Celeb wag) 190.8 in.; (Monte) 200.4 in.; (Caprice cpe) 212.8 in.; (Capr sed) 212.2 in.; (Capr w)ag) 215.1 in.
Height: (Chvt) 52.8 in.; (Nova sed) 53.0 in.; (Nova hatch) 52.8 in.; (Cav cpe) 50.2 in.; (Cav conv) 52.7 in.; (Cav sed) 52.1 in.; (Cav wag) 52.8 in.; (Camaro) 50.0 in.; (Corsica) 52.7 in.; (Beretta) 52.6 in.; (Celeb) 54.1 in.; (Celeb Wag) 54.3 in.; (Monte) 54.4 in.; (Caprice) 56.4 in.; (Caprice wag) 58.2 in.
Width: (Chvt) 61.8 in.; (Nova) 64.4 in.; (Cap cpe/conv) 66.0 in.; (Cav sed/wag) 66.3 in.; (Camaro 72.8 in.; (Corsica) 68.2 in.; (Beretta) 68.0 in.; (Celeb) 69.3 in.; (Monte) 71.8 in.; (Caprice) 75.4 in.; (Capr wag) 79.3 in.
Front Tread: (Chvt) 51.2 in.; (Nova) 56.1 in.; (Cav) 55.4 in.; (Camaro) 60.7 in.; (Corsica/Beretta) 55.6 in.; (Celeb) 58.7 in.; (Monte) 58.5 in.; (Caprice 61.7 in.; (Capr wag) 62.2 in.
Rear Tread: (Chvt) 51.2 in.; (Nova) 55.3 in.; (Cav) 55.2 in.; (Camaro) 61.6 in.; (Corsica) 55.1 in.; (Beretta) 56.5 in.; (Celeb) 57.0 in.; (Monte) 57.8 in.; (Caprice) 60.7 in.; (Capr wag) 64.1 in.

Standard Tires: (Chvt/Nova) P155/80R13; (Cav) P185/80R13; (Cav RS) P195/70R13; (Cav Z24) P215/60R14; (Camaro) P205/70R14; (Camaro Z28) P215/65R15; (Corsica/Beretta) P185/80R13; (Celeb) P185/75R14; (Celeb Eurosport) P195/75R14; (Monte) P195/75R14; (Monte SS) P215/65R15; (Caprice) P205/75R15; (Caprice wag) P225/75R15.

TECHNICAL: Transmission: Four-speed manual shift standard on Chevette. Four-speed overdrive manual shift standard on Cavalier. Five-speed manual shift standard on Nova, Cavalier Z24, Corsica/Beretta and Camaro. Three-speed automatic standard on Celebrity, Monte Carlo and Caprice.
Steering: (Cavalier/Chevette/Nova/Corsica/Beretta/Celebrity) rack and pinion; (others) recirculating ball.
Front Suspension: (Chevette/Monte/Caprice) unequal-length control arms, coil springs, stabilizer bar; (Nova) MacPherson struts w/coil springs and lower control arms; (Corsica/Beretta) MacPherson struts with coil springs; (Cavalier/Camaro/Celeb) MacPherson struts with coil springs, lower control arms and stabilizer bar.
Rear Suspension: (Chevette) rigid axle and torque tube w/four links and track bar, coil springs; (Nova) fully independent MacPherson struts, dual links, coil springs and stabilizer bar; (Cavalier) semi-independent with beam axle, trailing arms, coil springs, stabilizer bar available; (Camaro) rigid axle and torque tube with longitudinal control arms, Panhard rod, coil springs and stabilizer bar; (Corsica/Beretta) trailing twist axle with coil springs; (Celeb) beam twist axle with integral stabilizer, trailing arms, Panhard rod and coil springs; (Monte/Caprice) rigid axle with four links, coil springs, stabilizer available.
Brakes: front disc, rear drum; four-wheel discs available on Camaro.
Body construction: unibody except (Monte/Caprice) separate body and frame.
Fuel tank: (Chvt) 12.2 gal.; (Nova) 13.2 gal.; (Cav) 13.6 gal.; (Camaro) 15.5 gal.; (Corsica/Beretta) 13.6 gal.; (Celeb) 15.7 gal.; (Monte V-6) 17.6 gal.; (Monte V-8) 18.1 gal.; (Capr) 24.5 gal.; (Capr wag) 22 gal.

DRIVETRAIN OPTIONS: Engines: 173 cu. in. V-6: Cavalier RS conv ($660); Celeb ($610). 305 cu. in., 4Bbl. V-8: Camaro ($400); Monte Carlo LS, Caprice cpe/sed ($440). 305 cu. in., TPI V-8: Camaro Z28 ($745). 350 cu. in., TPI V-8: Camaro IROC-Z ($1045).
Transmission/Differential: Five-speed manual trans.: Chevette/Cavalier ($75); Celeb ($440 credit). Three-speed automatic trans.: Chevette ($450); Cavalier ($490); Cavalier Z24 ($415). Four-speed overdrive auto. trans.: Camaro ($490); Celeb V-6 ($175); Monte LS, Caprice cpe/sed ($175). Limited-slip differential: Camaro/Monte/Caprice ($100). Performance axle ratio: Chevette/Camaro/Celeb/Monte/Caprice ($21).
Power Accessories: Power brakes: Chevette ($105). Power four-wheel disc brakes: Camaro ($179). Power steering: Chvt/Cav ($225).
Suspension: F40 H.D. susp.: Cav/Celeb.Caprice ($26). F41 sport susp.: Cav ($44-$49); Monte LS, Caprice ($49). Inflatable rear shock absorbers: Celeb/Caprice ($64).

CHEVETTE CONVENIENCE/APPEARANCE OPTIONS: Air conditioning ($675). Heavy-duty battery ($26). Chromed bumpers ($25). Heavy-duty cooling system, w/o air conditioning ($70), w/air conditioning ($40). Custom exterior pkg. 3-door ($139). 5-door ($154). Rear defogger ($145). California emissions pkg. ($99). Tinted glass ($105). Engine block heater ($20). Left remote & right manual mirrors ($53). Left remote mirror ($34). Bodyside moldings ($50). AM/FM radio ($92). AM/FM stereo ($119). AM delete ($51 credit). Exterior sport decor ($132). Tilt steering column ($125). Cloth bucket seats ($28). Custom cloth bucket seats ($130). Custom two-tone paint ($183).

NOVA CONVENIENCE/APPEARANCE OPTIONS: Custom two-tone paint ($176). Option Package 2 ($630). Automatic transmission, power steering. Option Package 3 ($1120), Pkg. 2 plus 5-speed, air conditioning, AM/FM stereo (electronic-tune). Option Package 4 ($1530), Pkg. 3 plus automatic transmission, Option Package 5 ($1480), Pkg. 4 but without rear defogger. CL Option Package 1, 4-door ($2405). 5-door ($2710). Automatic transmission, AM/FM stereo, left remote and right manual mirrors, power steering, air conditioning, Halogen headlamps, P175/70R13 tires. CL Option Package 2, 4-door ($2625). 5-door ($2450). CL pkg 1 plus 5-speed, cassette stereo, intermittent wipers, cruise control, rear wiper/washer (5-door). CL Option Package 3, 4-door ($3200). 5-door ($3630). CL pkg. 2 plus automatic transmission, power windows and door locks, full wheel covers (4-door), aluminum wheels (5-door).
NOTE: All CL Option Packages include windshield tint band wide black bodyside molding, bodyside stripes, remote decklid and fuel filler releases, luggage compartment trim and lamp, driver's seat height and lumbar support adjustments, velour seat trim, console storage box and armrest, right visor mirror, passenger assist grips and tilt steering column.

CAVALIER CONVENIENCE/APPEARANCE OPTIONS: Air conditioning ($675). Heavy-duty battery ($26). Deluxe seatbelts, base ($26). Roof rack, wagons ($115). Decklid rack, 2- & 4-doors ($115). CL Custom Interior, 3-doors ($271). Wagons ($295). RS & Z24 2-doors ($221). CS & RS 4-doors ($245). Cargo area cover ($69). Rear defogger ($145). Power door locks, 2- and 3-doors ($145). 4- & 5-doors ($195). California emissions system ($99). Gauge package ($69). Tinted glass (std. on conv) ($105). Halogen headlamps ($25). Engine block heater ($20). Electronic instrument cluster (std. on Z24) ($295). Auxiliary lighting, All exc. wagons & convertible ($52). Wagon ($58). RS conv. ($35). Left remote & right manual mirrors ($53). Bodyside moldings, base ($50). AM radio, base ($122). AM/FM stereo (electronic-tuning), base ($307). Others ($207). Above w/cassette, base ($429). Others ($329). Above w/equalizer, RS & Z24 ($479). AM delete all exc. base ($56 credit). Fixed-mast antenna w/o factory radio ($41). Power liftgate release ($50). Split folding rear seat (NA 2- & 4-doors) ($50). Cruise control ($175). Rear spoiler ($200). Tilt steering column ($125). Removable glass sunroof ($350). Remote trunk/liftgate release ($50). Cast aluminum wheels ($212). Power windows, 2- & 3-doors ($210). 4-doors, wagons ($285). Intermittent wipers ($55). Rear wiper/washer, 3-doors & wagons ($125). Cloth bucket seats, base & CS ($28). Two tone paint, CS ($176). RS ($123).

CAMARO CONVENIENCE/APPEARANCE OPTIONS: Air conditioning ($775). Heavy-duty battery ($26). Engine oil cooler ($110). Locking rear storage cover ($80). Rear defogger ($145). Power door locks ($145). California emissions pkg. ($99). Gauge pkg., Sport Coupe ($149). Tinted glass ($120). Rear window louvers ($210). Deluxe luggage compartment trim, Sport Coupe ($164). Z28 ($84). Bodyside moldings ($60). Power antenna ($70). T-top roof ($866). Split folding rear seatback ($50). Rear spoiler, Sport Coupe ($69). Cast aluminum wheels w/locks ($215). Sound systems, Sport Coupe, AM/FM stereo cassette ($364). AM/FM stereo ET, EQ ($242). AM/FM stereo ET w/cassette & EQ ($514). Delco-GM/Bose music system ($1127). AM mono radio ($39). Sport Coupe Option Pkg. 2 ($1212). Tinted glass, air conditioning, tilt steering column, AM/FM stereo. Sound systems w/Sport Coupe Pkg. 2, AM/FM stereo cassette ($122). AM/FM stereo w/cassette & EQ ($272). Delco-GM/Bose music system ($885). AM/FM stereo delete ($298 credit). Sport Coupe Option Pkg. 3 ($1628). Pkg. 2 plus four floor mats, bodyside moldings, intermittent wipers, rear spoiler, cruise control, AM/FM stereo w/cassette and extended range speakers. Sport Coupe Option Pkg. 4 ($2126). Pkg. 3 plus power windows and door locks, power hatch release, cargo cover, Halogen headlamps, auxiliary lighting. Sound systems w/Sport Coupe Option Pkgs. 3 or 4. AM/FM stereo w/cassettes & EQ ($150). Delco-GM/Bose music system ($763). AM/FM stereo delete ($420 credit). LT Option Pkg. 1. ($1522). Tinted glass, air conditioning, tilt steering column, AM-FM stereo, full wheel covers, bodyside stripes, custom interior, quiet sound group. Sound systems w/LT Option Pkg. 1. AM/FM cassette ($122). AM/FM w/cassette & EQ ($272). Delco-GM/Bose music system ($885). AM/FM delete ($298 credit). LT Option Pkg. 2 ($1938). Pkg. 1 plus floormats, bodyside moldings, intermittent wipers, rear spoiler, cruise control, AM/FM ST ET cassette w/extended range speakers. LP Option Pkg. 3 ($2387). Pkg. 2 plus power windows and door locks, power hatch release, cargo cover Halogen headlamps. LT Option Pkg. 4 ($2858). Pkg. 3 plus power seat, interior roof console, automatic day/night mirror, power remote mirrors, Halogen fog lamps. Sound Systems w/LT Option Pkg. 2, 3 or 4. AM/FM stereo ET w/cassette & EQ ($150). Delco-

GM/Bose music system ($763). AM/FM stereo ET cassette delete ($420 credit). Sound Systems, Z28. AM/FM ET cassette ($325). AM/FM stereo ET ($203). AM/FM w/cassette & EQ ($475). Delco-GM/Bose music system ($1088). Z28 Option Pkg. 2 ($1999). Sport equipment, tinted glass, air conditioning, tilt steering wheel, floormats, bodyside moldings, intermittent wipers, cruise control. AM/FM stereo ET cassette with extended range speakers. Z28 Option Pkg. 3, w/o cargo cover ($2470). w/cargo cover ($2539). Pkg. 2 plus power windows and door locks, power hatch release, auxiliary lighting, Halogen headlamps, cargo cover, power mirrors, power seat, automatic day/night mirror, interior roof console, Halogen fog lamps. Sound system w/Z28 Option Pkg. 2 or 3. AM/FM stereo ET w/cassette & EQ ($150). Delco-GM/Bose music system ($763). AM/FM ET w/cassette, deleted ($381 credit). IROC Option Pkg. 1 ($669). Halogen fog lamps, uprated suspension, P245-50VR16 tires on aluminum wheels. Sound systems w/IROC Pkg. 1. AM/FM stereo ET cassette ($325). AM/FM stereo ET ($203). AM-FM stereo ET w/cassette & EQ ($475). Delco-GM/Bose music system ($1088). IROC Option Pkg. 2 ($2409). Pkg. 1 plus sport equipment, tinted glass, air conditioning, tilt steering column, floor mats, intermittent wipers, AM/FM stereo ET cassette with extended range speakers, power windows and door locks, power hatch release. Sound Systems w/IROC Pkg. 2. AM/FM stereo ET w/cassette & EQ ($150). Delco-GM/Bose music system ($763). AM/FM stereo ET cassette, deleted ($381 credit). IROC Option Pkg. 3 ($3273). W/o cargo cover ($3204). Pkg. 2 plus power mirrors, cruise control, bodyside moldings, cargo cover, auxiliary lighting, automatic day/night mirror, power seat, interior roof console, AM/FM stereo ET with cassette and equalizer, extended range speakers. Sound systems w/IROC Pkg. 3. Delco-GM/Bose music system ($613). AM/FM stereo ET w/cassette & EQ delete ($531 credit).

CORSICA/BERETTA CONVENIENCE/APPEARANCE OPTIONS: See 1988 listing

CELEBRITY CONVENIENCE/APPEARANCE OPTIONS: Air conditioning ($775). Rear window air deflector, wagon ($40). Heavy-duty battery ($26). Bumper guards ($56). Roof carrier (wagon) or decklid rack (others) ($115). Center console w/shift lever ($110). Heavy-duty cooling system. W/air conditioning ($40). W/o air conditioning ($70). Rear defogger ($145). Power door locks. Coupe ($145). Sedans, wagons ($195). California emissions pkg. ($99). Estate equipment wagon ($325). Eurosport Package ($240). (Sport suspension, sport steering wheel, P195/75R14 all season tires, rally wheels, side moldings and rub strips w/specific color treatment and blackout decor.) Gauge Package (incl. trip odometer) ($64). Tinted glass ($120). Engine block heater ($20). Auxiliary lighting. Coupe ($52). Sedan ($64). 2-seat wagon ($70). 3-seat wagon ($56). Coupe w/sunroof ($28). Sedan w/sunroof ($40). 2-seat wagon w/sunroof ($46). 3-seat wagon w/sunroof ($32). Deluxe luggage compartment trim ($47). Left remote mirror ($23). Left remote & right manual mirrors ($61). Dual remote mirrors ($91). Right visor mirror ($7). Illuminated right visor mirror ($50). Exterior molding pkg. ($55). Sound systems. AM radio ($39). AM/FM stereo ET ($168). Above w/cassette ($329). Above w/graphic equalizer ($514). Extended range speakers ($35). Deluxe rear compartment decor ($40). Power driver's seat ($240). Reclining front seatbacks (each) ($45). Cargo area security pkg., wagon ($44). Cruise control ($175). Tilt steering column ($125). Removable glass sunroof ($350). Tachometer ($90). Power trunk or liftgate release ($50). Locking wire wheel covers ($199). Cast aluminum wheels, w/o Eurosport ($199). W/Eurosport ($143). Rally wheels ($56). Swing-out rear vent windows, wagon ($75). Swing-out tailgate window, wagon ($105). Power windows, coupe ($210). Sedan & wagon ($285). Intermittent wipers ($55). Rear wiper/washer, wagon ($125).

MONTE CARLO CONVENIENCE/APPEARANCE OPTIONS: Air conditioning ($775). Heavy-duty battery ($26). Console ($110). Heavy-duty cooling, w/o A/C ($70). W/A/C ($40). Rear defogger ($145). Power door locks ($145). California emissions system ($99). Gauge package, LS ($69). Tinted glass ($120). Halogen headlamps, SS ($25). Engine block heater ($20). Auxiliary lighting. W/o T-top roof ($33). W/T-top roof ($15). Left remote & right manual mirrors, LS ($53). Dual remote mirrors, LS ($83). SS ($30). Sound systems. AM/FM stereo ET ($168). W/cassette & equalizer ($329). AM radio delete ($56 credit). Power antenna ($70). Premium rear speakers ($25). T-top roof ($895). 6-way power driver's seat (55/45 seat req.) ($240). Cruise control ($175). Tilt steering column ($125). Tachometer LS ($90). Power trunk lid release ($50). Locking wire wheel covers ($199). Styled rally wheels ($56). Cast aluminum wheels ($230). Power windows ($210). Intermittent wipers ($55). Custom two-tone paint ($214). Padded vinyl Landau roof ($260). Cloth 55/45 seat ($133). Cloth bucket seats ($147). Vinyl bench seat ($28). Custom cloth CL 55/45 seat ($385).

CAPRICE CONVENIENCE/APPEARANCE OPTIONS: Air conditioning ($775). Rear air deflector, wagons ($65). Heavy-duty battery ($26). Bumper rub strips, base ($66). Bumper guards ($62). Roof luggage rack ($115). Heavy-duty cooling, w/o A/C ($70). W/A/C ($40). Rear defogger ($145). Power door locks, 2-doors ($145). 4-doors, wagons ($195). California emissions system ($99). Estate equipment ($307). Deluxe load floor carpeting, wagons ($89). Gauge package ($64). Tinted glass ($120). Engine block heater ($20). Cornering lamps ($55). Auxiliary lighting base ($50). Classic ($32). Deluxe luggage compartment trim ($59). Left remote mirror ($23). Dual remote mirrors, w/o Landau roof ($91). W/Landau roof ($30). Left remote & right manual mirros, base ($61). Illuminated passenger visor mirror ($50). Bodyside moldings ($60). Quiet Sound Group, base ($66). Sound Systems. AM/FM stereo ET, Classic & Brougham ($129). Base($168). AM/FM stereo ET cassette, Classic & Brougham ($290). Base ($329). W/equalizer, Classic & Brougham ($435). Classic wagon ($400). Base sedan ($474). Base wagon ($439). AM radio delete base ($56 credit). Classic & Brougham ($95 credit). Power antenna ($70). Extended range speakers ($35). Deluxe rear compartment decor, wagons ($129). Power seats ($240 each). Passenger seat recliner ($45). Cruise control ($175). Tilt steering wheel ($125). Power tailgate lock ($60). Puncture sealant tires, exc. wagon ($125). Wagon ($150). Remote trunk release ($50). Locking wire wheel covers ($199). Power windows, 2-doors ($210). 4-doors, wagons ($285). Intermittent wipers ($55). Custom two-tone paint ($141). Landau roof & sport mirrors (std. on LS) ($321). Full vinyl roof (std. on Brougham) ($200). Cloth bench seat, base wagon ($28). Vinyl bench seat, base sedan ($28). Vinyl 50/50 seat, base sedan ($225). Base wagon ($195). Cloth 50/50 seat, base sedan ($195). Base wagon ($225). Classic ($195).

1987 Sprint Turbo 2-dr hatchback coupe

HISTORY: Introduced: October 9, 1986. Model year production: 1,553,252 (incl. 30,632 Corvettes, 63,570 imported Sprints and 91,708 imported Spectrums). Calendar year production (U.S.): 1,516,449 (including 28,514 Corvettes). Model year sales by U.S. dealers: 1,391,281 (incl. 25,266 Corvettes but not including imports).

1988 CHEVROLET

After introduction as early '88 models, the Corsica sedan and Beretta coupe entered their first full model year. The subcompact Chevette was gone, while the Monte Carlo coupe, favored by stock-car racers, had just one more season before it too would disappear. Cavalier enjoyed a restyle that gave it a rounded, aerodynamic look, not unlike the Corsica/Beretta duo. Also departed: Camaro's Z28, but the IROC-Z took over its spot in the performance lineup.

NOVA — SERIES 1S — FOUR —
Customers for the joint-venture Toyota/Chevrolet subcompact had a second powerplant choice this year: a 16-valve, dual-overhead-cam version of the 97 cu. in. (1.6-liter) four, producing 110 horsepower. This was Chevrolet's first multi-valve engine. The Twin-Cam Nova sedan came in just one color choice: basic black metallic, with gray interior. Standard Twin-Cam equipment included disc brakes all around and P175/70HR13 Goodyear Eagle GT tires on aluminum wheels. Base Nova engine remained the 74-horsepower four, with five-speed gearbox. Twin-Cam buyers could get a four-speed automatic instead of the five-speed manual, but the base four-door sedan and hatchback offered only a three-speed automatic option. All three models now had an AM/FM stereo radio and rear defogger.

1988 Cavalier 2-dr convertible

CAVALIER — SERIES 1J — FOUR/V-6 —
Cavalier's formerly lengthy model list shrunk this year to base, RS and Z24 levels. Fresh sheetmetal gave the subcompact a more aerodynamic appearance, with a new grille and composite headlamps in a rounded front end. Back-end changes included a new decklid, taillamps and bumper. Coupes even got a new roof profile. A 2.8-liter V-6 engine was standard in the sporty Z24, which came in coupe and convertible form, but optional only in the station wagon this year. Other models came only with the 2.0-liter four. The former RS convertible was dropped, as was the hatchback coupe. Analog instruments (including a tachometer) were standard on the Z24, with electronic instruments optional. All models came with a standard five-speed manual gearbox or optional three-speed automatic.

CAMARO — SERIES 1F — V-6/V-8 —
Most noticeable of the Camaro changes this year may have been the absence of a Z28. Only the base sport coupe and IROC-Z were offered, with the latter gaining status as a specific model rather than an option package. With the demise of the Z28, the base coupe added standard equipment including a rear spoiler, aluminum wheels, lower bodyside panels, and body-color mirrors. Base powerplant remained the 2.8-liter V-6, rated 125 horsepower. The optional 5.0-liter V-8 (standard on the IROC-Z) switched from a four-barrel carburetor to throttle-body fuel injection, gaining five horsepower in the process. Two multi-point fuel-injected V-8 options were offered on the IROC-Z: a high-output 5.0-liter rated at 220 horsepower with five-speed manual shift (but 195 horsepowrer with automatic), or the 350- cu. in. (5.7-liter) edition which came only with four-speed automatic. Barely a thousand Camaro convertibles had been produced during the 1987 model year, but for this full season their numbers rose to 5,620.

1988 Corsica 4-dr sedan

CORSICA/BERETTA — SERIES 1L — FOUR/V-6 —
For their first complete year of production, the compact Corsica sedan and Beretta coupe found a sizable share of customers, though little changed from their debut in early 1987. Base remained the 2.0-liter four hooked to five-speed manual gearbox. With a 2.8-liter V-6 and three-speed automatic optional. Models with the V-6 and manual gearbox added an upshift indicator light. A digital clock was included with the standard AM/FM stereo radio. Corsica sedans with the V-6 gained some suspension revisions, including bigger stabilizer bars.

1988 Celebrity Eurosport VR 2-dr coupe

CELEBRITY — SERIES 1A — FOUR/V-6 —
Appearance changed little this year, but Chevrolet's mid-size coupe, sedan and wagon gained a tougher 2.5-liter Tech IV base engine with balance shafts. Low-friction pistons went into the 2.8-liter V-6, optional in each model. Standand transmission was a three-speed automatic, but V-6 Celebs could get either a four-speed automatic or, with the Eurosport option package, a Getrag five-speed manual gearbox. That Eurosport edition included special body trim as well as an F41 sport suspension and bigger (P195/75R14) tires, with the option of even larger P195/70R14 Goodyear Eagle GT+4 rubber. Standard equipment included outside mirrors on both sides.

MONTE CARLO — SERIES 1G — V-6/V-8 —
For its final season in the lineup, the rear-drive mid-size coupe came in LS and SS form, the latter with a standard 305 cu. in. (5.0-liter) V-8 under its hood, rated 180 horsepower. Base powerplant for the LS remained a 262 cu. in. (4.3-liter) V-6, with a less powerful V-8 option available. Both came with a standard four-speed overdrive automatic transmission, replacing the former three-speed. New standard equipment also included tinted glass, twin mirrors, and AM/FM stereo with built-in clock. The fastback SS Aerocoupe faded away this year.

CAPRICE — SERIES 1B — V-6/V-8 —
No more full-size coupes were offered, but the four-door sedan and station wagon carried on (the latter only in Classic form). Caprice Classic sedans could have base, Brougham or Brougham LS trim. Standard equipment now included tinted glass, a remote-control driver's mirror (manual on the passenger side), automatic headlamp on/off, and an AM/FM stereo radio with built-in clock. Base engine for sedans remained the 262 cu. in. (4.3-liter) V-6, with 305 cu. in. (5.0-liter) V-8 optional. Under the Classic wagon hood was a 307 cu. in. (5.0-liter) V-8. Four-speed overdrive automatic was standard on all models.

I.D. DATA: Chevrolets again had a 17-symbol Vehicle Identification Number (VIN) on the upper left surface of the instrument panel, visible through the windshield. Symbol one indicates country: '1' - U.S.A.; '2' - Canada. Next is a manufacturer code: 'G' - General Motors. Symbol three is car make: '1' - Chevrolet; '7' - GM of Canada. Symbol four denotes restraint system: 'A' - non-passive (standard); 'B' - passive (automatic belts); 'C' - passive (inflatable). Symbol five is car line/series. Symbols six-seven reveal body type. Next is the engine code, followed by a check digit, the 'J' for model year 1988. Symbol eleven indicates assembly plant. The final six digits are the sequential serial number. Engine number coding is similar to 1981-87.

Model Number	Body/Style Number	Body Type & Seating	Factory Price	Shipping Weight	Production Total
NOVA (FOUR)					
1S	K19	4-dr. Sedan-4P	8795	2211	87,263
1S	K68	4-dr. Hatch Sed-4P	9050	2257	18,570
1S	L19	4-dr. Twin-Cam Sed-4P	11395	N/A	3,300
CAVALIER (FOUR)					
1J	C37	2-dr. Coupe-5P	8120	2359	34,470
1J	C37/WV9	2-dr. VL Cpe-5P	6995	N/A	43,611
1J	C69	4-dr. Sedan-5P	8195	2363	107,438
1J	C35	4-dr. Sta Wag-5P	8490	2413	29,806

Cavalier Engine Note: A V-6 engine cost $660 additional.

Model Number	Body/Style Number	Body Type & Seating	Factory Price	Shipping Weight	Production Total
CAVALIER RS (FOUR)					
1J	E37	2-dr. Coupe-5P	9175	2371	24,359
1J	E69	4-dr. Sedan-5P	9385	2414	18,852
CAVALIER Z24 (V-6)					
1J	F37	2-dr. Coupe-5P	10725	2558	55,658
1J	F67	2-dr. Conv Cpe-4P	15990	2665	8,745
CAMARO (V-6/V-8)					
1F	P87	2-dr. Spt Cpe-4P	10995/11395	3054/3228	66,605
1F	P87/Z08	2-dr. Conv Cpe-4P	—/16255	—/3350	1,859
CAMARO IROC-Z (V-8)					
1F	P87/Z28	2-dr. Spt Cpe-4P	13490	3229	24,050
1F	P87/Z08	2-dr. Conv Cpe-4P	18015	3352	3,761
CORSICA (FOUR/V-6)					
1L	T69	4-dr. Sedan-5P	9555/10215	2589/2688	291,163
BERETTA (FOUR/V-6)					
1L	V37	2-dr. Coupe-5P	10135/10795	2608/2707	275,098
CELEBRITY (FOUR/V-6)					
1A	W27	2-dr. Coupe-5P	10585/11195	2727/2793	11,909
1A	W19	4-dr. Sedan-5P	11025/11635	2765/2833	195,205
1A	W35/B5E	4-dr. Sta Wag-6P	11350/11960	2903/2970	23,759
1A	W35/AQ4	4-dr. 3S Wag-8P	11590/12200	N/A	27,583
MONTE CARLO (V-6/V-8)					
1G	Z37	2-dr. LS Cpe-6P	12330/12770	3212/3267	13,970
MONTE CARLO 'SS' (V-8)					
1G	Z37/Z65	2-dr. Spt Cpe-6P	14320	3239	16,204
CAPRICE (V-6/V-8)					
1B	L69	4-dr. Sedan-6P	12030/12470	3540/3633	60,900
CAPRICE CLASSIC (V-6/V-8)					
1B	N69	4-dr. Sedan-6P	12575/13015	3556/3649	42,292
1B	U69	4-dr. Brghm-6P	13645/14085	3607/3700	33,685
1B	U69/B6N	4-dr. LS Brghm-6P	14820/15260	N/A	21,586
1B	N35	4-dr. 3S Wag-8P	—/14340	—/4158	30,645

FACTORY PRICE AND WEIGHT NOTE: For Corsica, Beretta and Celebrity, prices and weights to left of slash are for four-cylinder, to right for V-6 engine. For Camaro, Monte Carlo and Caprice, figures to left of slash are for six-cylinder model, to right of slash for least expensive V-8.

BODY/STYLE NO. NOTE: Some models were actually packages. Code after the slash (2.g., Z28) is the number of the option package tht comes with the model listed.

ENGINE DATA: BASE FOUR (Nova): Inline. Overhead cam. Four-cylinder. Cast iron block and head. Displacement: 97 cu. in. (1.6 liters). Bore & stroke: 3.19 x 3.03 in. Compression ratio: 9.0:1 Brake horsepower: 74 at 5200 RPM. Torque: 86 lbs.-ft. at 2800 RPM. Solid valve lifters. Carburetor: Aisan 2Bbl.
BASE FOUR (Twin-Cam Nova): Same as 97 cu. in. four above, but with dual overhead camshafts (16 valves). Compression ratio: 9.4:1. Brake horsepower: 110 at 6600 RPM. Torque: 98 lbs.-ft. at 4800 RPM. BASE FOUR (Cavalier, Corsica/Beretta): Inline. Overhead valve. Four-cylinder. Cast iron block and aluminum head. Displacement: 121 cu. in. (2.0 liters). bore & strike: 3.50 x3.15 in. Compression ratio: 9.0:1. Brake horsepower: 90 at 5600 RPM. Torque: 108 lbs.-ft. at 3200 RPM. Five main bearings. Hydraulic valve lifters. Throttle-body fuel injection. BASE FOUR (Celebrity): Inline. Overhead valve. Four-cylinder. Cast iron block and head. Displacement: 151 cu. in. (2.5 liters). Bore & stroke: 4.00 x 3.00 in. Compression ratio: 8.3:1. Brake horsepower: 98 at 4800 RPM. Torque: 135 lbs.-ft. at 3200 RPM. Five main bearings. Hydraulic valve lifters. Throttle-body fuel injection. BASE V-6 (Camaro, Cavalier Z24); OPTIONAL (Cavalier wagon, Corsica/Beretta, Celebrity): 60-degree, overhead-valve V-6. Cast iron block and head. Displacement: 173 cu. in. (2.8 liters). Bore & stroke: 3.50 x 2.99 in. Compression ratio: 8.9:1. Brake horsepower: (Cavalier/Celeb) 125 at 4500; (Corsica/Beretta) 130 at 4700; (Camaro) 135 at 4900. Torque: (Cavalier/Celeb/Corsica/Beretta) 160 at 3600; (Camaro) 160 at 3900. Multi-port fuel injection. BASE V-6 (Monte Carlo, Caprice): 90-degree, overhead-valve V-6. Cast iron block and head. Displacement: 262 cu. in. (4.3 liters). Bore & stroke: 4.00 x 3.48 in. Compression ratio: 9.3:1. Brake horsepower: (Caprice) 140 at 4200 RPM; (Monte) 145 at 4200. Torque: 225 lbs.-ft. at 2000 RPM. Four main bearings. Hydraulic valve lifters. Throttle-body fuel injection. OPTIONAL V-8 (Monte Carlo, Caprice sedan): 90-degree, overhead valve V-8. Cast iron block and head. Displacement: 305 cu. in. (5.0 liters). Bore & stroke: 3.74 x 3.48 in. Compression ratio: 9.3:1. Brake horsepower: (Monte) 150 at 4000 RPM; (Caprice) 170 at 4400. Torque:(Monte) 240 lbs.-ft. at 2000 RPM; (Caprice) 250 at 2800. Five main bearings. Hydraulic valve lifters. Carburetor: 4Bbl. BASE V-8 (Camaro IROC-Z): OPTIONAL (Camaro): Same as 305 cu. in. V-8 above but with throttle-body fuel injection. Compression ratio: 9.3:1. Brake horsepower: 170 at 4000 RPM. Torque: 255 lbs.-ft. 2400 RPM. OPTIONAL V-8 (Camaro IROC-Z): Same as 305 cu. in. V-8 above, with port fuel injection. Compression ratio: 9.3:1. Brake horsepower: 220 at 4400 RPM (195 hp with automatic). Toruqe: 290 lbs.-ft. at 3200 RPM. HIGH-OUTPUT V-8 (Monte Carlo SS): Same as 305 cu. in. V-8 above, except — BHP: 180 at 4800 RPM. Toruqe: 225 lbs.-ft. at 3200 RPM. BASE V-8 (Caprice wagon): 90-degree, overhead valve V-8. Cast iron block and head. Displacement: 307 cu. in. (5.0 liters). Bore & stroke: 3.80 x 3.38 in. Compression ratio: 8.0:1. Brake horsepower: 140 at 3200 RPM. Torque: 225 lbs.-ft. at 2000 RPM. Five main bearings. Hydraulic roller valve lifters. Carburetor: 4Bbl. OPTIONAL V-8 (Camaro IROC-Z): 90-degree, overhead valve V-8. Cast iron block and head. Displacement: 350 cu. in. (5.7 liters). Bore & stroke: 4.00 x 3.48 in. Compression ratio: 9.3:1. Brake horsepower: 230 at 4400 RPM. Torque: 330 lbs.-ft. at 3200 RPM.

CHASSIS DATA: Wheelbase: (Nova) 95.7 in.; (Cavalier) 101.2 in.; (Camaro) 101.0 in.; (Corsica/Beretta) 103.4 in.; (Celebrity) 104.9 in.; (Monte Carlo) 108.0 in.; (Caprice) 116.0 in.
Overall length: (Nova) 166.3 in.; (Cav cpe/sed) 174.5 in.; (Cav conv) 178.7 in.; (Cav wag) 177.9 in.; (Camaro) 192.0 in.; (Corsica) 183.4 in.; (Beretta) 187.2 in.; (Celeb) 188.3 in.; (Celeb wag) 190.8 in.; (Monte) 200.4 in.; (Caprice sed) 212.2 in.; (Capr wag) 215.1 in.
Height: (Nova sed) 53.0 in.; (Nova hatch) 52.8 in.; (Cav cpe) 50.2 in.; (Cav conv) 52.7 in.; (Cav sed) 52.1 in.; (Cav wag) 52.8 in.; (Camaro) 50.0 in. (Corsica) 52.7 in.; (Beretta) 55.3 in.; (Celeb) 54.1 in.; (Celeb wag) 54.3 in.; (Monte) 54.4 in.; (Caprice) 56.4 in.; (Caprice wag) 58.2 in.
Width: (Nova) 64.4 in.; (Cav cpe/conv) 66.0 in.; (Cav sed/wag) 66.3 in.; (Camaro) 72.8 in.; (Corsica/Beretta) 68.2 in.; (Celeb) 69.3 in.; (Monte) 71.8 in.; (Caprice) 75.4 in.; (Capr wag) 79.3 in.
Front Tread: (Nova) 56.1 in.; (Cav) 55.4 in.; (Camaro) 60.7 in.; (Corsica/Beretta) 55.6 in.; (Celeb) 58.7 in.; (Monte) 58.5 in.; (Caprice) 61.7 in.; (Capr wag) 62.2 in.
Rear Tread: (Nova) 55.3 in.; (Cav) 55.2 in.; (Camaro) 61.6 in.; (Corsica) 55.1 in.; (Beretta) 56.6 in.; (Celeb) 57.0 in.; (Monte) 57.8 in.; (Caprice) 60.7 in.; (Capr wag) 64.1 in.
Standard Tires: (Nova) P155/80R13; (Nova Twin-Cam) P175/70HR13; (Cav) P185/80R13; (Cav Z24) P215/60R14; (Camaro) P215/65R15; (Corsica/Beretta) P185/80R13; (Celeb) P185/75R14; (Celeb Eurosport) P195/75R14; (Monte) P195/75R14; (Monte SS) P215/65R15; (Caprice) P205/75R15; (Caprice wag) P225/75R15.

1988 Beretta 2-dr coupe

TECHNICAL: Transmission: Five-speed manual shift standard on Nova, Cavalier, Corsica/Beretta and Camaro. Three-speed automatic standard on Celebrity. Four-speed overdrive automatic standard on Monte Carlo and Caprice.
Steering: (Cavalier/Nova/Corsica/Beretta/Celebrity) rack and pinion; (others) recirculating ball.
Front Suspension: (Monte/Caprice) unequal-length control arms, coil springs, stabilizer bar; (Nova) MacPherson struts w/coil springs and lower control arms; (Corsica/Beretta) MacPherson struts with coil springs; (Cavalier/Camaro/Celeb) MacPherson struts with coil springs, lower control arms and stabilizer bar.
Rear Suspension: (Nova) fully independent MacPherson struts, dual links, coil springs and stabilizer bar; (Cavalier) semii-independent with beam axle, trailing arms, coil springs, stabilizer bar available; (Camaro) rigid axle and torque tube with longitudinal control arms, Panhard rod, coil springs and stabilizer bar; (Corsica/Beretta) trailing twist axle with coil springs; (Celeb) beam twist axle with inegral stablilizer, trailing arms, Panhard rod and coil springs; (Monte/Caprice) rigid axle with four links, coil springs, stablilizer available.
Brakes: front disc, rear drum; four-wheel discs standard on Twin-Cam Nova and available on Camaro.

Body construction: unibody except (Monte/Caprice) separate body and frame.

Fuel tank: (Nova) 13.2 gal.; (Cav) 13.6 gal.; (Camaro) 15.5 gal.; (Corsica/Beretta) 13.6 gal.; (Celeb) 15.7 gal.; (Monte V-6) 17.6 gal.; (Monte V-8) 18.1 gal.; (Caprice) 24.5 gal.; (Caprice wag) 22 gal.

DRIVETRAIN OPTIONS: Engines: 173 cu. in. V-6: Cavalier wagon ($660); Corsica/Beretta ($660); Celeb ($610). 305 cu. in. V-8: Camaro ($400); Monte Carlo LS, Caprice sed ($440). 305 cu. in., TPI V-8: Camaro IROC-Z ($745). 350 cu. in. V-8: Camaro IROC-Z ($1045).
Transmission/Differential:
Five-speed manual trans.: Celeb ($440 credit). Three-speed automatic trans.: Cavalier ($415); Corsica/Beretta ($490). Four-speed overdrive auto. trans.: Camaro ($490); Celeb V-6 ($175). Limited-slip differential: Camaro/Monte/Caprice ($100). Performance axle ratio: Camaro/Monte/Caprice ($21).
Power Accessories:
Power four-wheel disc brakes: Camaro ($179). Power steering: base Cav ($225).
Suspension: FE2 sport suspension: Cav base/RS ($27). F40 H.D. susp.: Corsica/Beretta/Celeb/Caprice ($26). F41 sport susp.: Corsica/Beretta, Monte LS, Caprice ($49). Inflatable rear shock absorbers: Celeb/Caprice ($64).

NOVA CONVENIENCE/APPEARANCE OPTIONS: Option Pkg. 2, Incl Auto Trans: P155/80R-13 All Seasons Blackwall tires; Elect Tuned AM/FM Stereo w/Seek & Scan & Digital Clock; Pwr Strg ($645). Opt. Pkg. 3, Incl 5 Spd Trans; P155/80R-13 All Seasons Blackwall Tires; Elect Tuned AM/FM Stereo w/Seek & Scan & Digital Clock; Pwr Steering; Air Cond ($900). Opt. Pkg. 4, Incl Auto Trans; P155/80R-13 All Seasons Blackwall Tires; Elect Tuned AM/FM Stereo w/Seek & Scan & Digital Clock; Pwr Steering; Air Cond; Pwr Door Locks ($1515). Nova CL Opt. Pkg. 5 (1SK19 only) Incl. 5-Spd Trans; P175/70R-13 All Seasons Blackwall Tires; Elect Tuned AM/FM Stereo w/Seek & Scan & Digital Clock; Pwr Strg; Air Cond; Custom CL Feature Pkg; Speed Control, w/resume feature; Intermittent Wipers; Pwr. Dr. Locks ($2119). Nova CL Opt. Pkg. 6 (1SK19 only), Incl Auto Trans; P175/70R-13 All Seasons Blackwall Tires; Elect Tuned AM/FM Stereo w/seek & Scan & Digital Clock; Pwr Strg; Air Cond; Custom CL Feature Pkg; Spd Control w/resume feature; Intermittent Wipers; Pwr Dr Locks ($2539). Twin Cam Opt. Pkg. 2, (1SL19 only) Incl Twin Cam Eng; Auto Trans; P175/70HR-13 High Perf Blackwall Tires; Elect Tuned AM/FM Stereo w/Seek & Scan & Digital Clock; Pwr Strg; Tachometer; Alum Wheels ($790). Twin Cam Opt. Pkg. 3, (1SL19 only) Incl Twin Cam Eng; 5-Sped Trans; P175/70HR-13 High Perf Blackwall Tires; Elect Tuned AM/FM Stereo w/Seek & Scan & Digital Clock; Pwr Strg; Tachometer; Alum Wheels; Air Cond ($675). Twin Cam Opt. Pkg. 4, (1SL19 only) Incl Twin Cam Eng; Auto Trans; P175/70HR-13 High perf. Blackwall Tires; Elect Tuned AM/FM Stereo w/Seek & Scan & Digital Clock; Pwr Strg; Tachometer; Alum Wheels; Air Cond ($1465). Twin Cam Opt. Pkg. 5, (1SL19 only) Incl Twin Cam Eng; 5-Spd Trans; P175/70HR-13 High perf. Blackwall tires; Elect. Tuned AM/FM Stereo w/Seek & Scan & Digital Clock; Pwr. Strg; Alum Wheels; Air Cond; Spd Control w/resume feature; Intermittent Wipers; Pwr. Dr. Locks; Pwr Windows & Tachometer ($1370). Twin Cam Opt Plg. 6, (1SL19 only) Incl Twin Cam Eng; Auto Trans; P175/70HR-13 High perf. Blackwall Tires; Elect Tuned AM/FM Stereo w/Seek & Scan & Digital Clock; Pwr Strg; Tachometer, Alum Wheels; Air Cond; Spd Control w/resume; Intermittent Wipers; Pwr Dr. Locks; Pwr. Windows ($2160). Color-Keyed Mats Carpeted, Front only ($25); Rear only ($15).

CAVALIER CONVENIENCE/APPEARANCE OPTIONS: VL Opt. Pkg. (1JC37/WV9 only) Incl Air Cond; Tinted Glass, Spt LH Remote & RH Man Mirrors, Black Body Side moldings, Pwr Strg ($1078). VL Opt. Pkg. 3, (1JC37/WV9 only) Air Cond; Tinted Glass, Spt LH Remote & RH Manual Mirrors, Blk Body Side moldings, Pwr Strg; Carpeted Mats; Aux Lighting, Spd Control. w/resume speed; Comfortilt Strg Wheel; Intermittent Windshied Wiper System ($1488). Cavalier Opt. Pkg. 2, Air Cond; Tinted Glass; Spt, LH Remote & RH Manual Mirrors ($1078). Sta Wgn Opt. Pkg. 3, Air Cond, Tinted Glass, Spt LH Remote & RH Manual Mirrors; Black Body Side Moldings; Pwr Strg, Carpeted Mats F&R; Roof Carrier; Pwr Liftgate Release; Comfortilt Wheel, Intermittent Windshield Wiper System ($1436). Sta Wag Opt. Pkg. 4, Air Cond. Tinted Glass, Spt LH Remote & RH Manual Mirrors; Black Body Side Moldings; Pwr Strg; Carpeted Mats, F&R; Roof Carrier; Pwr Liftgate Release; Comfortilt Strg Wheel; Intermittent Windshield Wiper System, Pwr Door Lock System; Lighting; Spd Control w/resume ($1834). Opt. Pkg. 3 (1JC37-1JC69) Air Cond; Tinted Glass; Spt LH Remote & RH Manual; Black Body Side Moldings, Pwr Strg; Carpeted Mats F&R; Aux Lighting, Spd Control w/resume; Comfortilt Strg Wheel; Intermittent Windshield Wiper System ($1488). RS Opt. Pkg. 2, (1JE37-1JE69) Air Cond; Carpeted Mats F&R; Tinted Glass; Speed Control w/resume; Comfortilt Wheel; Intermittent Windshield Wiper System ($1138). RS Opt. Pkg. 2, (1JE37-1JE69) Air Cond; Carpeted Mats F&R; Tinted Glass; Elect Speed Control w/resume; Comfortilt Strg Wheel; Intermittent Windshield Wiper System; Pwr Dr Lock System; Aux Lighting; AM/FM Stereo w/Seek & San, Stereo Cass. Tape & Digital Clock; Incl ext range sound system; Pwr Trunk Opener, Pwr Windows; RS Coupe ($1677). RS Sedan ($1802). Z24 Opt. Pkg. 2, Air Cond; Carpeted Mats F&R; Tinted Glass; Speed Control w/resume; Comfortilt Strg Wheel; Intermittent Windshield Wiper System ($1138). Z24 Opt. Pkg. 3, Air Cond, Carpeted Mats F&R; Tinted Glass; Speed Control w/resume speed; Comfortilt Strg Wheel; Intermittent Windshield Wiper System;Pwr Door Lock System, Aux Lighting; Elect Tuned AM/FM Stereo w/Seek & Scan, Stereo Cass. Tape & Digital Clock, Incl extd. range sound system, Pwr Trunk Release; Pwr Windows ($1687). Convertible Opt. Pkg. 2, Air Cond; Carpeted Mats F&R; Aux Lighting; AM/FM Stereo w/Seek & Scan, Stereo Cass. Tape & Digital Clock; Incl extd range sound system; Pwr Trunk Release; Spd Control w/resume; Comfortilt Strg. Wheel; Intermittent Windshield Wiper System ($1270). Cloth Bucket Seats ($28). Vinyl Bucket Seats (NC). Sport Cloth Bucket Seats Wgn only (incl Split Folding Rr Seat ($325). Air Conditioning (Incl increased cooling ($675). Arm Rest, Center Console ($58). H.D. Battery ($26). Frt License Plate Bracket (NC). Roof Carrier Bright ($115). Deck Lid Carrier Bright ($115). Black ($115). Rr Window Defogger ($145). Pwr Door Lock System Coupes ($145). Sedans & Wgns ($195). Calif Emission System ($99). Carpeted Color-Keyed Mats F&R ($33). Gauge Pkg. w/o Tachometer, (trip odometer, temp, voltmeter & oil pressure gauges) ($69). Gauge Pkg. w/Tachometer, (trip odometer, temp, voltmeter & oil pressure gauges) ($139). Tinted Glass All windows ($105). Eng. Block Heater ($20). Electronic Instrument Cluster, (Incl convertional tachometer) RS only ($295). Z24 only ($156). Body Side Moldings ($50). Door Edge, Guards, Blk RS Coupe ($15). RS Sedan ($25). VL (332) Elect Tuned AM/FM Stereo w/Seek & Scan & Digital Clock, (Incl extd range sound system) Elect Tuned AM/FM Stereo w/Seek & Scan Stereo Cass. Tape & Digital Clock; (Incl extd. range sound system VL (454); others (122) Elect Tuned Am Stereo & FM Stereo w/Seek & Scan, Stereo Cass Tape w/Search & Repeat, Graphic Equalizer & Digital Clock (Incl Z24/RS (272) or (150) extd range sound system; Pwr. Base Steering ($225). Removable Sun Roof ($350). Tires: P185/80R-13 All Seasons Steel Belted Radial White Stripe ($68). P205/70R-13 All Seasons Steel Belted Radial Blackwall ($124). P205/70R-13 All Seasons Steel Belted Radial White Lettered ($212). P215/60R-14 Steel Belted Radial White Outline Lettered ($102). Wheel Trim rings ($39). Alum Wheels 13x5.5" ($212). Pwr Windows Coupes ($210). Sedans & Wag ($285).

CAMARO CONVENIENCE/APPEARANCE OPTIONS: Spt Coupe Opt. Pkg. 2, Air Cond; Tinted Glass; Body Side Color-Keyed Moldings ($920). Spt Coupe Opt. Pkg. 3, Air Cond; Tinted Glass; Body Side, Color-Keyed Moldings; Carpeted Mats F&R; Pwr Hatch Release; Electronic Speed Control w/resume speed; Comfortilt Strg Wheel; Pwr Windows; Intermittent Windshield Wiper System ($1555). Spt Coupe Opt. Pkg. 4 Air Cond; Tinted Glass; Body Side, Color-Keyed Moldings; Color-Keyed Carpeted Mats F&R; Pwr Hatch Release; Spd Control w/resume speed; Comfortilt Strg Wheel; Pwr Windows; Intermittent Windshield Wiper System; Rr Compartment Cargo Cover; Dome & Reading Lamp; Pwr Dr Lock System; Halogen Headlamps, High & Low Beam; Aux Lighting; Elect Tuned AM/FM Stereo w/Seek & Scan, Stereo Radio w/Seek & Scan, Stereo Cass. Tape & Digital Clock, (Incl extended range sound system) ($1939). IROC-Z Opt. Pkg. 2, IROC-Z Equip; Air Cond; Pwr Dr Lock System; Carpeted Mats F&R; Tinted Glass; Pwr Hatch Release; Aux Lighting; Body Side, Color-Keyed Moldings; Elect Tuned AM/FM Stereo w/Seek & Scan, Stereo Cass. Tape & Digital Clock, (Incl extd range sound system); Elect Spd Control w/resume speed; Comfortilt Steering Wheel; Pwr Windows; Intermittent Windshield Wiper System ($1846). IROC-Z Opt. Pkg. 3 IROC-Z Equip; Air Cond, Pwr Dr Lock System, Color-Keyed Carpeted Mats F&R; Tinted Glass; Pwr Hatch Release; Aux Lighting; Body Side Color-Keyed Moldings; Elect Speed Control w/resume speed; Comfortilt Strg Wheel; Pwr Windows; Intermittent Windshield Wiper System; Rr. Comp. Cargo Cover; Dome & Reading Lamp; Halogen Headlamps High & Low Beam; Spt. Elect Twin Remote mirrors; Pwr Driver Seat; Elect Tuned AM/FM Stereo w/Seek & Scan, Stereo Cass. Tape Graphic Equalizer & Digital Clock extd range sound system ($2410). w/U U8 Radio, Add ($613). Convertible Opt. Pkg. 2, Air Cond; Tinted Glass, Body Side Color-Keyed Moldings ($920). Convertible Opt. Pkg. 3, Air Cond; Tinted Glass; Body Side Color-Keyed Moldings; Color-Keyed Carpeted Mats F&R; Elec Spd Control, w/resume speed; Comfortilt Strg Wheel; Pwr Windows; Intermittent Windshield Wiper System ($1505). Convertible Opt Pkg. 4; Air Cond; Tinted Glass; Body Side Color-Keyed Moldings; Carpeted Mats F&R, Color-Keyed; Elect Spd Control, w/resume speed; Comfortilt Strg Wheel; Pwr Windows; Intermittent Windshield Wiper System; Pwr Dr; Halogen Headlamps (High & Low Beam); Elect. Tuned AM/FM Stereo w/Seek & Scan, Stereo Cass. Tape & Digital Clock, Incl ext range sound system ($1747). IROC-Z Convertible Opt. Pkg. 2, IROC-Z Equip; Air Cond; Pwr Door Lock System; Carpeted Color-Keyed Mats F&R; Tinted Glass; Body Side Color-Keyed Molding; Elect Tuned AM/FM Stereo w/Seek & Scan; Stereo Cass. Tape & Digital Clock, Incl ext range sound system; Elec Spd Control w/resume speed; Comfortilt Strg Wheel; Pwr Windows; Intermittent Windshield Wiper System ($1747). IROC-Z Convertible Opt. Pkg. 3, IROC-Z Equip; Air Cond; Pwr Dr Lock System; Carpeted Mats, F&R, Color-Keyed; Tinted Glass; Body Side, Color-Keyed Moldings; Elect Spd Control w/resume speed; Comfortilt Strg Wheel; Pwr Windows; Intermittent Windshield Wiper System; Halogen headlamps, (High & Low Beam); Twin Remote Spt Mirrors; Pwr Drive Seat; Elect Tuned AM Stereo/FM Stereo w/Seek & Scan, Stereo Cass. Tape, Graphic Equalizer & Digital Clock, Incld Ext Range Sound System ($2218). Custom Cloth Bucket Sets ($277). Custom Leather Bucket Seats ($750). Air Conditioning (Incl increased cooling) ($775). Ltd. Slip Differential ($100). Performance Axle Ratio ($212). H.D. Battery ($26). Frt. License Plate Bracket (NC). Pwr F&D Disc Brakes ($179). Eng Oil Cooler ($110). Locking Rr. Storage Cover ($80). Decal & Stripe delete ($60 credit). Rr. Window Electric Defogger ($145). Pwr Door Lock System ($145). Calif Emission System ($99). Tinted Glass, All Windows ($120). Eng. Block Heater ($20). Rr. Window Louvers ($210). Deluxe Luggage Comp Trim Spt Cpe Incl Lckg Rr Comp Storage Cover ($164). IROC-Z Sport Cpe ($84). Body Side Color-Keyed Molding on IROC-Z Spt Cpe & Blk on Spt Cpe ($60). Blk Dr Edge Guards ($15). Elect Tuned AM Stereo/FM Stereo w/Seek & Scan, Stereo Cass Tape w/Search & Repeat, Graphic Equalizer & Digital Clock (150/272); Elect Tuned AM/FM Stereo w/Seek & Scan, Stereo Cass Tape & Digital Clock (122) Elect Tuned Delco/Bose Music System, Incl AM/FM Stereo w/Seek & Scan, Stereo Cass Tape & Digital Clock, special tone & balance control & 4 spkrs; Pwr Antenna ($70). Removable Roof Panels, Incl locks ($866). Split, Folding Rr Seat Backs ($50). Alum Wheels, 16" Incl Wheels Locks & P245/50 VR16 Blackwall Tires ($468). Pwr. Windows ($210).

CORSICA CONVENIENCE/APPEARANCE OPTIONS: UM6 Radio ($122). UX1 Radio ($272). Option Pkg. 2 Incl. A/C, Tinted Glass ($870). W/UM6 Radio ($122). W/UX1 Radio ($272). Opt. Pkg. 3, Incl A/C, Tinted Glass Carpeted Mats F&R; Dual Horns, Elect Spd Control, w/resume Spd; Comfortilt Strg Wheel; Intermittent Wipers ($1270). W/UM6 Radio ($122). W/UX1 Radio ($272). Opt. Pkg. 4, Incl A/C, Tinted Glass, Carpeted Mats F&R, Dual Horns, Elect Spd Control w/resume; Comfortilt Strg Wheel; Intermitten Wipers, Pwr Dr Lock System; Aux Lighting; Elect Tuned AM/FM Stereo w/Seek & Scan, Stereo Cass. Tape & Digital Clock (incl ext range sound system; Pwr Trunk Opener; Pwr Windows ($1986). W/UX1 Radio ($150). LT Opt. Pkg. 1 ($234). W/UM6 Radio ($122). W/UX1 Radio ($272). LT Opt. Pkg. 2, A/C, Tinted Glass ($1104). W/UM6 Radio ($122). W/UX1 Radio ($272). Lt Opt. Pkg 3, Incl AC, Tinted Glass; Carpeted Mats F&R; Dual Horns; Spd Control w/resume; Comfortilt Strg Wheel; Intermittent Wipers ($1504). W/UM6 Radio ($122). W/UX1 Radio ($272). Lt Opt. Pkg. 4, Incl A/C, Tinted Glass, Carpeted Mats F&R; Dual Horns, Spd Control, w/resume; Comfortilt Strg Wheel; Intermittent Wipers; Pwr Dr Lock System; Aux Lighting; Elect Tuned AM/FM Stereo w/Seek & Scan, Stereo Cass. Tape & Digital Clock (Incl ext range sound system); Pwr Trunk Opener; Pwr Windows ($2220). Vinyl Bucket Seats ($28). Custom Cloth CL Bucket Seats ($275). Custom Two-Tone Paint ($123). Air Cond ($750). H.D. Battery ($26). Frt Lic Plate Brackets (NC). Console ($60). Rr Window Elec Defogger ($145). Pwr Dr Lock System ($195). Calif Emission System ($99). Gauge Pkg. w/Tach, Incl Voltmeter, Oil Pressure, Temp. Gauges & Trip Odometer ($139). Tinted Glass, All Windows ($120). Eng Block Heater ($20). Body Side Striping ($57). **TIRES:** P195/70 R-14 All Seasons SBR Blackwall ($104). 195/70 R-14 All Seasons SBR White Stripe ($166). P185/80 R-13 All Seasons SBR White Stripe ($68). Spt Wheel Covers ($45). Styled Wheels ($56). Alum Wheels Incl Locks ($215). W/Z1 LT Equipment Pkg ($159). Pwr Windows ($285). Intermittent Windshield Wiper System ($55).

1988 Beretta GTU 2-dr sport coupe

BERETTA CONVENIENCE/APPEARANCE OPTIONS: UM6 Radio ($122). UX1 Radio ($272). Opt. Pkg. 2, Incl A/C, Carpeted F&R Mats ($783). W/UM6 Radio ($122). W/UX1 Radio ($272). Opt. Pkg. 3, Incl A/C, Carpeted F&R Mats; Aux Lighting; Elect Spd Control, w/resume; Comfortilt Strg. Wheel, Intermittent Wipers ($1170). W/UM6 Radio ($122). W/UX1 Radio ($272). Opt. Pkg. 4, Incl A/C, Carpeted F&R Mats; Aux Lighting, Elect Spt Control, w/resume; Comfortilt Strg Wheel, Intermittent Wipers; Pwr Dr Lock System; Elect Tuned AM/FM Stereo w/Seek & Scan, Stereo Cass Tape & Digital Clock; (incl extd range sound system), Pwr Trunk Opener; Pwr Windows ($1697). W/UX1 Radio ($150). GT Opt. Pkg. 1, Incl A/C ($1716). W/UM6 Radio ($122). W/UX1 Radio ($272). GT Opt. Pkg. 2, Incl A/C Carpeted Mats F&R, Electronic Spd Control, w/Resume; Comfortilt Intermittent Wipers ($2104) W/UM6 Radio ($122). W/UX1 Radio ($272). GT Opt. Pkg 3, Incl A/C, Carpeted F&R Mats; Elect Spd Control, w/resume; Comfortilt Strg Wheel; Intermittent Wipers; Pwr Dr Lock System, Aux Lighting; Elect Tuned AM/FM Stereo w/Seek & Scan, Stereo Cass Tape & Digital Clock; Pwr Trunk Opener($2663). W/UX1 Radio ($150). Custom Two-Tone ($123). Air Cond ($750). H.D. Battery ($26). Frt Lic Plate Bracket (NC). Elec Rr Window Defogger ($145). Pwr Dr Lock System ($145). Calif Emission System ($99). Eng Block Heater ($20). Elec Instrumentation; Bar Graph Speedometer & Digital Readout, Incl Tach ($156). Z51 Performance Hdlg. Pkg, Incl Spt Suspension; 15'' Styled Wheels; P205/60R-15 Tires & Ext Body Emblems ($153). Removable Sunroof ($350). **TIRES:** P195/70 R-14 All Seasons SBR Ply White Stripe ($72). Styled Wheels ($56). Alum Wheels, Incld Locks ($215). w/Z21 GT Equip Pkg ($159). Pwr Windows ($210). Intermittent Windshield Wiper System ($55).

CELEBRITY CONVENIENCE/APPEARANCE OPTIONS: Opt. Pkg. 2, Incl Air Cond; Color-Keyed Flr Mats F&R; Ext Mldg. Pkg; Speed Control w/resume speed; Comfortilt Steering Wheel; Intermittent Windshield Wiper System ($1164). Opt. Pkg 3, Incl Air Cond; Color-Keyed Flr Mats F&R only; Ext Pkg Molding; Spd Control, w/resume speed; Comfortilt Steering wheel; Intermittent Windshield Wiper System; Bumper Guards; Pwr Dr Lock System; Gauge Pkg w/Trip Odometer; Aux Lighting; Remote Spt Mirrors, Dr Edge Guards, Power Trunk Opener; Pwr Windows; Coupe ($1725). Sedan ($1861). Eurosport Opt Pkg. 1 ($230). Eurosport Opt Pkg. 2 Air Cond; Color-Keyed Floor Mats F&R; Gauge Pkg w/Trip Odometer; Molding Pkg; Elec Spd Control, w/resume Spd; Comfortilt Strg Wheel; Intermittent Windshield Wiper System ($1458). Eurosport Opt. Pkg. 3, Air Cond; Color-Keyed F&R Flt Mats; Gauge Pkg. w/Trip Odometer; Mldg. Pkg; Elect Spd Control, w/resume speed; Comfortilt Strg Wheel; Intermittent Windshield Wiper System; Pwr Dr Lock System; Aux Lighting; Spt Twin Remote Mirrors; Black Dr Edge Guard Moldings; AM/FM Radio w/Seek & Scan, Stereo Cass Tape & Digital Clock (Incl Ext Range Sound System); Pwr Trunk Opener; Pwr Windows; Eurosport Coupe ($2020). Eurosport Sedan ($2157). Wagon Opt. Pkg. 2, Incl Air Cond; Color-Keyed Mats F&R; Pwr Liftgate Release, Ext Pkg Molding; Roof Carrier; Spd Control, w/resume speed; Comfortilt Strg Wheel; Intermittent Windshield Wiper System ($1304). Wagon Opt. Pkg. 3, Incl Air Cond; Color-Keyed Floor Mats F&R; Pwr Liftgate Release, Ext Mldg. Pkg; Roof Carrier; Spd Control, Elec w/resume speed; Comfortilt Strg Wheel; Intermittent Windshield Wiper System; Bumper Guards; Pwr Door Lock System, Gauge Pkg w/trip odometer; Aux Lighting; Spt Twin Remote Mirrors; Black Moldings; Dr Edge Guard; AM/FM Radio Stereo w/Seek & Scan, Stereo Cass Tape & Digital Clock; (Incl ext range sound system); Db Rr Compartment Decor; Cargo Area Security Pkg; Pwr Windows ($2159). Eurosport Wgn Opt. Pkg. 1 ($230). Eurosport Wgn Opt. Pkg. 2, Incl Air Cond; Roof Carrier, Flr Mats F&R; Gauge Pkg w/Trip Odometer; Pwr Liftgate Release; Ext Mdlg Pkg; Spd Control w/resume spd; Comfortilt Strg Wheel; Intermittent Windshield Wiper System ($1598). Eurosport Wgn Opt Pkg 3, Incl Air Cond; Roof Carrier; Flr Mats F&R; Gauge Pkg w/Trip Odometer, Pwr Liftgate Release; Ext Mldg Pkg; Spd Control w/resume spd; Comfortilt Strg Wheel; Intermittent Windshield Wiper System; Pwr Door Locks; Aux Lighting; Spt Twin Remote Mirrors; Black Dr Edge Guard; AM/FM Stereo Radio w/Seek & Scan, Stereo Cass Tape & Digital Clock, Ext Range Sound System; Dix Pwr Rr Compartment Decor; Cargo Area Sec Pkg; Pwr Windows ($2333). Cloth Bench Seat Wagon ($28). Cloth Bucket Seats w/console ($257). Cloth 45/55 Seat ($133). Vinyl Bench Seat Coupe & Sedan ($28). Custom Cloth CL 45/55 (Incl split, individual folding second seat back on wgn) Sedan ($385). Coupe ($305). Wagon ($435). Custom Cloth CL 45/45 w/console, (Incl split, individual folding second seat back on wgn.) Sedan ($335). Coupe ($255). Wagon ($385). Custom Two-Tone Paint; Incl lower body accent & ext. mldg. pkg; w/1SB or 1SC Pkg ($93). W/1SA Pkg ($148). Air Cond ($775). Rr Window Air Deflector ($40). H.D. Battery ($26). Frt. License Plate Bracket (NC). H.D. Cooling; w/o Air Cond ($70). w/Air Cond ($40). Electric Rr Window Defogger ($145). Pwr Door Lock System; Coupe ($145). Sedan & Wagon ($195). Calif Emission System ($99). Eng. Block Heater ($20). Elect Tuned AM/FM Stereo Radio w/Seek & Scan, Stereo Cass Tape & Digital Clock (Incl ext range sound system) ($122). Pwr 6-way Frt Seat ($240). Body Striping ($57). Tachometer ($90). **TIRES;** P185/75R14 All Season Steel Belted Radial White Stripe ($68). P195/75R14 All Seasons Steel Belted Radial Blackwall ($40). P195/75 R14 All Seasons Steel Belted Radial White Stripe ($102). P195/70 R14 All Seasons Steel Belted Radial Black Lettered ($90). Sport Wheel Covers ($65). Wire w/Locks Wheel Covers ($199). Alum Wheels w/o ZV8 Eurosport Equip Pkg ($199). W/ZV8 Eurosport Equip Pkg ($143). Rally Wheels, Incl styled wheels, special hub caps & rim rings ($56). Pwr Windows, coupe ($210). Sedan & Wagon ($285). Rr Window Wiper/Washer ($125).

MONTE CARLO CONVENIENCE/APPEARANCE OPTIONS: LS Opt. Pkg. 2, Air Cond, Color-Keyed Carpeted Mats, F&R; Aux Lighting; Deluxe Body Side Moldings; Spd Control, w/resume speed; Comfortilt Strg Wheel; Intermittent Windshield Wiper System ($1243). LS Opt. Pkg. 3, Air Cond, Color-Keyed Carpeted Mats F&R; Aux Lighting; Deluxe Body Side Molding; Spd Control w/resume spd; Comfortilt Strg Wheel; Intermittent Windshield Wiper System; Power Dr Locks, Gauge Pkg w/Trip Odometer, Spt Twin Remote Mirrors; Dr Edge Guards; Side Window Sill; AM/FM Radio, w/Seek & Scan, Stereo Cass Tape & Digital Clock (Incl ext range sound system) Power Trunk Opener; Pwr Window ($1854). SS Opt. Pkg. 2: Air Cond; Color-Keyed Carpeted Mats F&R; Pwr Dr Lock system; Halogen Headlamps (High & Low Beam); Aux Lighting; Spt Twin Remote Mirrors; AM/FM Radio Stereo, w/Seek & Scan, Stereo Cass Tape & Digital Clock, Incl ext range sound system; Spd Control, w/resume speed; Comfortilt Strg Wheel; Pwr Trunk Opener, Pwr Windows; Intermittent Windshield Wiper System ($1790). Vinyl Bench Seat ($28). Cloth 45/55 Seat ($133). Cloth Bucket Seats ($257). Custom Cloth CL 45/55 Seat ($385). Custom Two-Tone Paint, incl upper body accent & color-keyed strpping ($214). Padded Vinyl Landau Roof ($260). Air Conditioning ($775). Ltd Slip Differential ($100). Performance Axle Ratio ($21). H.D. Battery ($26). Frt License Plate Bracket (NC). H.D. Cooling Air Cond ($70). Air Cond ($40). Rr Window Electric Defogger ($145). Pwr Door Lock system ($145). Calif Emission System ($99). Eng Block Heater ($20). Lighted right visor mirror ($50). Elect Tuned AM/FM Stereo Radio w/Seek & Scan, Stereo Cass Tape & Digital Clock, Incl ext range sound system ($122). Elect Tuned AM Stereo & FM Stereo w/Seek & Scan, Stereo Cass Tape w/Search & Repeat, Graphic Equalizer & Digital Clock, Incl ext range sound system ($150/272). Pwr Antenna ($70). Removable Roof Panels, Incl locks w/o 1SB or 1SC Opt Pkg ($895). W/1SB or 1SC Opt Pkg ($877). Pwr 6-Way Driver's Seat w/45/55 Seat ($240). Body Striping ($61). Tachometer, Spt Cpe ($90). **TIRES:** P195/75 R-14 All Season Steel Belted Radial White Stripe ($72). P205/70 R-14 All Seasons Steel Belted Radial White Stripe ($134). Wire Wheel Covers w/Locks ($199). Rally Wheels. Incl special hub caps & trim rings ($56). Alum Wheels ($230).

CAPRICE CONVENIENCE/APPEARANCE OPTIONS: Caprice Sdn Opt. Pkg. 2, Incl Air Cond; Carpeted Colored-keyed Mats F&R; Body Side Wheel Opening Moldings; Spd Control w/resume spd; Comfortilt Strg Wheel ($1185). Caprice Sdn Opt Pkg. 3, Incl Air Cond; Carpeted Color-Keyed Mats F&R; Body Side Moldings; Wheel Opening Moldings; Spd Control w/resume speed; Comfortilt Strg Wheel; Dr. Lock System; Aux Lighting; Intermittent Windshield Wiper System ($1452). Caprice Classic Sdn Opt. Pkg. 2, Incl Air Cond; Carpeted Color-Keyed Mats F&R; Body Side Moldings, Spd Control w/resume speed; Comfortilt Strg Wheel; Intermittent Windshield Wiper System ($1210). Caprice Classic Sdn Opt. Pkg. 3, Incl Air Cond; Carpeted Color-Keyed Mats F&R; Body Side Moldings; Spd Control w/resume spd; Comfortilt Strg Wheel Intermittent Windshield Wiper System; Bumpers Guards, F&R; Power Dr Lock System, Aux Lighting; Twim Remote Sport Mirrors; Pwr Trunk Opener; Pwr Windows ($1814). Caprice Classic Sdn Opt. Pkg. 4, Incl Air Cond. Carpeted Color-Keyed Mats F&R; Body Side Moldings; Spd Control w/resume speed; Comfortilt Strg Wheel, Intermittent Windshield Wiper System; Bumper Guards F&R; Pwr Dr Lock System; Aux Lighting; Twin Remote Sport Mirrors; Pwr Trunk Opener; Pwr Windows; Gauge Pkg w/trip odometer; Twilight Sentine Headlamps; Cornering Lamps; Deluxe Luggage Compartment Trim' Lighted RH Visor Mirror; Dr. Edge Guard Moldings; Pwr Antenna; AM/FM Radio w/Seek & Scan w/Cass Tape & Digital Clock, Incl dual rear spkrs ($2259). Caprice Classic Wgn Opt. Pkg. 2, Incl Roof Carrier; Color-Keyed Body Side Moldings; exc w/BX3 Estate which is woodgrain moldings; Spd Control; Comfortilt Strg Wheel; Pwr Tailgate Lock; Intermittent Windshield Wiper System ($590). Caprice Classic Wgn Opt Pkg. 3; Incl Roof Carrier; Color-Keyed Body Side Moldings; exc w/BX3 Estate which is woodgrain Moldings; Spd Control w/resume speed; Comfortilt Strg Wheel; Pwr Tailgate Lock; Dix Load Flr Carpeting; Carpeted Color-Keyed Mats F&R; Aux Lighting; Spt Twin Remote Mirrors; Pwr Windows ($1241). (1SD) Caprice Classic Wgn Opt. Pkg. 4, Incl Roof Carrier; Color-Keyed Body Side Moldings; exc w/BX3 Estate which is woodgrain; Spd Control w/resume speed; Comfortilt Strg Wheel; Pwr Tailgate Lock; Intermittent Windshield Wiper System; Pwr Dr Lock System; Dix Load Floor Carpet; Carpeted Mats F&R; Aux Lighting; Spt Twin Remote Mirrors; Pwr Windows; F&R Bumper Guards; Gauge Pkg w/Trip Odometer; Twilight Sentine Headlamps; Cornering Lamps; Dix Rr. Comp Dec; Pwr Antenna; AM/FM Stereo Radio w/Seek & Scan, Stereo Cass Tape & Digital Clock, Incl dual rear spkrs ($1714). Caprice Classic Brghm Opt Pkg. 2, Incl Air Cond; Bumper Guards F&R; Pwr Door Lock System; Carpted Mats F&R; Spt Twin Remote Mirrors; Body Side Moldings; Pwr Seat; Six-Way Drive; Electronic Spd Control w/resume speed; Comfortilt Strg Wheel; Pwr Trunk Opener; Pwr Windows; Intermittent Windshield Wiper System; AM/FM Stereo Radio w/Seek & Scan, Stereo Cass Tape & Digital Clock, Incl rear spkrs ($2219). Caprice Classic Brgh Opt. Pkg 3, Incl Air Cond; bumper Guards F&R; Pwr Dr Lock System; Color-keyed Carpeted Mats F&R; Spt Twin Remote Mirrors; Body Side Moldings; pwr Six-Way Driver Seat; Electronic Spd Control w/resume spd; Comfortilt Trunk Opener; Pwr Windows; Intermittent Windshield Wiper System; Gauge Pkg w/Trip Odometer; Twilight Sentinel Headlamps; Cornering Lamps; Deluxe Luggage Comp Trim; RH Visor Illum Mirror; Dr Edge Guard; Pwr Antennas; Elect Turned AM/FM Stereo Radio w/Seek & Scan, Stereo Cass Tape Graphic Equalizer & Digital Clock, (Incl ext range sound system) ($2697). Vinyl Bench Seat Caprice Sedan ($28). Caprice Classic Wagon delete ($172 credit). Vinyl 50/50 Seat Caprice Sedan ($260). Caprice Classic Wagon ($58). Cloth 50/50 Seat Caprice Sedan ($230). Caprice Classic Wagon ($230). Caprice Classic Wagon ($230). Leather 45/55 Seat ($550). Custom Two-Tone Paint, Incl body accent, color-keyed striping & o/s dr handle inserts ($141). Roof Full Vinyl ($200) Sedan. Air Cond ($775). Rr Window Air Deflector ($65). Ltd Slip Differential ($100). Performance Axle Ratio ($21). H.D. Battery ($26). Frt. License Plate Bracket (NC). W/o Air Cond ($70). W Air Cond ($40). Rr Window Electric Defogger ($145). Pwr Dr Lock System ($195). Calif Emission System ($99). Estate Equipment ($307). Eng. Block Heater ($20). Elect. Tuned AM/FM Stereo Radio w/Seek & Scan, Stereo Cass Tape & Digital Clock, Incl dual Rr spkrs ($122). Elect Tuned AM/FM Stereo w/Seek & Scan, Stereo Cass Tape, Graphic Equalizer & Digital Clock Caprice Sdn, Classic Sdn & Brghm only (Incls ext range sound system) ($145/267). Caprice Classic Wgns only. Incl dual rear spkrs; Ext Range Sound System ($35). Powr 6-Way Seat; Driver's side w/5050 or 45/55 Seat ($240). Pass. side w/50/50 or 45/55 Seat ($240). Body Striping ($61). **TIRES:** P205/75R-15 All Seasons Steel Belted Radial White Stripe ($76). P225/70R-15 Steel Belted Radial White Stripe ($188). P225/75R-15 All Seasons Steel Belted Radial White Stripe (NC). Custom Wheel Covers Std/Brghm ($65). Wire Wheel Cover w/Locks ($134). All exc. Brghm ($199).

HISTORY: Introduced: October 1, 1987. Model year production: 1,709,742 (incl. 22,789 Corvettes, 53,250 imported Sprints and 61,357 imported Spectrums). Model year sales by U.S. dealers: 1,340,840 (incl. 25,425 Corvettes but not including imports).

1989 CHEVROLET

Two familiar names left the Chevrolet lineup: Nova (the short-lived Toyota/Chevy joint venture) and Monte Carlo. Sales were strong for the Corsica and Beretta pair, at least when considered together rather than as separate models. In fact, the pair ranked No. One in sales for part of the calendar year. Chevrolet imports took on the Geo name this year: the former Chevrolet Sprint became Geo Metro, while the Spectrum simply added the Geo designation.

1989 Cavalier Z24 2-dr sport coupe

CAVALIER — SERIES 1J — FOUR/V-6 —
Little was new in Chevrolet's subcompact, apart from a new self-aligning steering wheel with energy-absorbing hub. The RS coupe and sedan models were dropped, but replaced by RS option packages (including sport suspension and 14-inch tires) for the three base Cavaliers. Other models included the Value Leader (VL) coupe and the Z24 coupe and convertible, which added gas-pressurized shock absorbers. A 130-horsepower V-6 continued as standard under Z24 hoods, but others carried the 2.0 liter four. The station wagon was available with either engine. All models had rear shoulder belts this year.

1989 Camaro RS sport coupe

CAMARO — SERIES 1F — V-6/V-8 —
Two versions of the rear-drive Camaro were available again this year, but the cheaper of the pair was now called RS. Both the RS and IROC-Z came in hatchback coupe or convertible form, and both added a "pass-key" theft-deterrent system as standard equipment. That piece of equipment should have been welcome news to customers, since Camaros ranked as the most popular vehicle among car thieves. The RS coupe actually debuted first in California, with a standard 2.8-liter V-6 engine, as a model intended to keep insurance costs down. Both the IROC-Z duo and the RS convertible had a standard 170-horsepower V-8, and the IROC-Z also had a choice of 220-horsepower 5.0-liter V-8 or the big 5.7-liter V-8 with 10 more horses.

1989 Corsica 4-dr hatchback sedan

CORSICA/BERETTA — SERIES 1L — FOUR/V-6 —
A sporty new LTZ edition gave the compact Corsica sedan the appearance of a performance boost, if not the reality. As for the Beretta coupe, its former GT option package became a full-fledged model this year, wearing 15-inch tires on aluminum wheels. Corsica also added a four-door hatchback sedan to its regular notchback version, with a standard rollup cargo cover. Both the GT and LTZ carried the 173 cu. in. (2.8-liter) V-6 engine and sport suspension, while base models had either the standard 2.0-liter four or the V-6 as an option. The LTZ also included a decklid luggage rack. Tires in the base models grew to P185/70R14 size for the Corsica, P195/70R14 for Beretta. Later in the model year, a GTU Beretta arrived as the sportiest of the lot.

CELEBRITY — SERIES 1A — FOUR/V-6 —
Only the four-door sedan and station wagon remained in the mid-size front-drive lineup, as the coupe departed. Both the base 151 cu. in. (2.5-liter) four and the optional 2.8-liter V-6 came with standard three-speed automatic, while V-6 Celebs could have a four-speed overdrive automatic instead. Due to weak sales, the five-speed manual gearbox (formerly a credit option) was abandoned this year.

1989 Caprice Classic 4-dr sedan

CAPRICE — SERIES 1B — V-8 —
All Caprice models now came with a V-8 engine and standard air conditioning, as the base sedan V-6 disappeared. Instead of the former four-barrel carburetor, the 305 cu. in. (5.0-liter) V-8 now had throttle-body fuel injection. Horsepower remained the same as before, while torque got a slight boost. Caprice wagons still had their own carbureted V-8, displacing 307 cubic inches and delivering 140 horsepower (30 less than the sedan's). This version of the full-size Chevrolet had been around since 1977, and a restyle was anticipated soon.

I.D. DATA: Chevrolets again had a 17-symbol Vehicle Identification Number (VIN) on the upper left surface of the instrument panel, visible through the windshield. Symbol one indicates country: '1' - U.S.A.; '2' - Canada. Next is a manufacturer code: 'G' - General Motors. Symbol three is car made: '1' - Chevrolet; '7' - GM of Canada. Symbol four denotes restraint system: 'A' - non-passive (standard); 'B' - passive (automatic belts); 'C' - passive (inflatable). Symbol five is car line/series. Symbols six-seven reveal body type. Next is the engine code, followed by a check digit, then 'K' for model year 1989. Symbol eleven indicates assembly plant. The final six digits are the sequential serial number. Engine number coding is similar to 1981-88.

Model Number	Body/Style Number	Body Type & Seating	Factory Price	Shipping Weight	Production Total
CAVALIER (FOUR)					
1J	C37	2-dr. Coupe-5P	8395	2418	
1J	C37/WV9	2-dr. VL Cpe-5P	7375	N/A	
1J	C69	4-dr. Sedan-5P	8595	2423	
1J	C35	4-dr. Sta Wag-5P	8975	2478	

Cavalier Engine Note: Station wagon could have a V-6 engine for $660 additional.

Model Number	Body/Style Number	Body Type & Seating	Factory Price	Shipping Weight	Production Total
CAVALIER Z24 (V-6)					
1J	F37	2-dr. Coupe-5P	11325	N/A	
1J	F67	2-dr. Conv Cpe-4P	16615	2729	
CAMARO (V-6/V-8)					
1F	P87	2-dr. RS Cpe-4P	11495/11895	3082/3285	
1F	P67	2-dr. RS Cov-4P	—/16995	—/3116	
CAMARO IROC-Z (V-8)					
1F	P87/Z28	2-dr. Spt Cpe-rP	14145	3264	
1F	P67/Z28	2-dr. Conv Cpe-4P	18945	N/A	
CORSICA (FOUR/V-6)					
1L	T69	4-dr. Sedan-5P	9985/10645	2595/2690	
1L	Z69	4-dr. LTZ Sed-5P	—/12825	N/A	
1L	T68	4-dr. Hatch-5P	10375/11035	2648/—	
BERETTA (FOUR/V-6)					
1L	V37	2-dr. Coupe-5P	10575/11235	2631/2727	
1L	W37	2-dr. GT Cpe-5P	—/12685	N/A	
1L	W37	2-dr. GTU Cpe-5P	N/A	N/A	
CELEBRITY (FOUR/V-6)					
1A	W19	4-dr. Sedan-6P	11495/12280	2751/2819	
1A	W35/B5E	4-dr. Sta Wag-6P	11925/12710	2888/2928	
1A	W35/AQ4	4-dr. 3S Wag-8P	12175/12960	N/A	
CAPRICE (V-8)					
1B	L69	4-dr. Sedan-6P	13865	3693	
1B	N69	4-dr. Sedan-6P	14445	N/A	
1B	U69	4-dr. Brghm-6P	15615	N/A	
1B	U69/B6N	4-dr. LS Brghm-6P	16835	N/A	
1B	N35	4-dr. 3S Wag-8P	15025	4192	

FACTORY PRICE AND WEIGHT NOTE: For Corsica, Beretta and Celebrity, prices and weights to left of slash are for four-cylinder, to right for V-6 engine. For Camaro RS, figures to left of slash are for six-cylinder model, to right of slash for V-8.

BODY/STYLE NO. NOTE: Some models were actually option packages. Code after the slash (e.g., B6N) is the number of the option package that comes with the model listed.

ENGINE DATA: BASE FOUR (Cavalier, Corsica/Beretta): Inline. Overhead valve. Four-cylinder. Cast iron block and aluminum head. Displacement: 121 cu. in. (2.0 liters). Bore & stroke: 3.50 x 3.15 in. Compression ratio: 9.0:1 Brake horsepower: 90 at 5600 RPM. Torque: 108 lbs.-ft. at 3200 RPM. Five main bearings. Hydraulic valve lifters. Throttle-body fuel injection. BASE FOUR (Celebrity): Inline. Overhead valve. Four-cylinder. Cast iron block and head. Displacement: 151 cu. in. (2.5 liters). Bore & stroke: 4.00 x3.00 in. Compression ratio: 8.3:1. Brake horsepower: 98 at 4800 RPM (later, 110 horsepower). Torque: 135 lbs.-ft. at 3200 RPM. Five main bearings. Hydraulic valve lifters. Throttle-body fuel injection. BASE V-6 (Camaro RS coupe, Cavalier Z24, Corsica LTZ, Beretta GT); OPTIONAL (Cavalier wagon, Corsica/Beretta, Celebrity): 60-degree, overhead-valve V-6. Cast iron block and head. Displacement: 173 cu. in. (2.8 liters). Bore & stroke: 3.50 x 2.99 in. Compression ratio: 8.9:1. Brake horsepower: (Celeb) 125 at 4500; (Cavalier) 130 at 4500; (Corsica/Beretta) 130 at 4700; (Camaro) 135 at 4900. Torque: (Cavalier/Celeb/Corsica/Beretta) 160 at 3600; (Camaro) 160 at 3900. Multi-port fuel injection. BASE V-8 (Caprice sedan): 90-degree, overhead valve V-8. Cast iron block and head. Displacement: 305 cu. in. (5.0 liters). Bore & stroke: 3.74 x 3.48 in. Compression ratio: 9.3:1. Brake horsepower: 170 at 4000 RPM. Torque: 255 lbs.-ft. at 2400 RPM. Five main bearings. Hydraulic valve lifters. Throttle-body fuel injection. BASE V-8 (Camaro RS convertible, IROC-Z); OPTIONAL (Camaro RS coupe): Same as 305 cu. in. V-8 above but with throttle-body fuel injection. Compression ratio: 9.3:1. Brake horsepower: 170 at 4000 RPM. Torque: 255 lbs.-ft. at 2400 RPM. OPTIONAL (Camaro IROC-Z): Same as 305 cu. in. V-8 above, with port fuel injection. Compression ratio: 9.3:1. Brake horsepower: 220 at 4400 RPM)195 with automatic). Torque: 290 lbs.-ft. 3200 RPM (295 at 2800 with automatic). BASE V-8 (Caprice wagon): 90-degree, overhead valve V-8. Cast iron block and head. Displacement: 307 cu. in. (5.0 liters). Bore & stroke: 3.80 x 3.38 in. Compression ratio: 8.0:1 Brake horsepower: 140 at 3200 RPM. Torque: 255 lbs.-ft. at 2000 RPM. Five main bearings. Hydraulic roller valve lifters. Carburetor: 4Bbl. OPTIONAL V-8 (Camaro IROC-Z): 90-degree, overhead valve V-8. Cast iron block and head. Displacement: 350 cu. in. (5.7 liters). Bore & stroke: 4.00 x 3.48 in. Compression ratio: 9.3:1. Brake horsepower: 230 at 4400 RPM. Torque: 330 lbs.-ft. at 3200 RPM.

CHASSIS DATA: Wheelbase: (Cavalier) 101.2 in.; (Camaro) 101.1 in.; (Corsica/Beretta) 103.4 in.; (Celebrity) 104.9 in.; (Caprice) 116.0 in.
Overall length: (Cav cpe/sed) 178.4 in.; (Cav conv) 178.7 in.; (Cav wag) 174.5 in.; (Camaro) 192.0 in.; (Corsica) 183.4 in.; (Beretta) 187.2 in.; (Celeb) 188.3 in.; (Celeb wag) 190.8 in.; (Caprice sed) 212.2 in.; (Capr wag) 215.7 in.
Height: (Cavalier) 52.0-52.8 in.; (Camaro cpe) 50.0 in.; (Camaro conv) 50.3 in.; (Corsica) 56.2in.; (Beretta) 55.3 in.; (Celeb) 54.1 in.; (Celeb wag) 54.3 in.; (Caprice) 56.4 in.; (Caprice wag) 58.2 in.
Width: (Cav cpe/conv) 66.0 in.; (Cav sed/wag) 66.3 in.; (Camaro) 72.8 in.; (Corsica/Beretta) 68.2 in.; (Celeb) 69.3 in.; (Caprice) 75.4 in.; (Capr wag) 79.3 in.
Front Tread: (Cav) 55.4 in.; (Camaro) 60.7 in.; (Corsica/Beretta) 55.6 in.; (Celeb) 58.7 in.; (Caprice) 61.7 in.; (Capr wag) 62.2 in.
Rear Tread: (Cav) 55.2 in.; (Camaro) 61.6 in.; (Corsica) 55.1 in.; (Beretta) 56.6 in.; (Celeb) 57.0 in.; (Caprice) 60.7 in.; (Capr wag) 64.1 in.
Standard Tires: (Cav) P185/80R13; (Cav Z24) P215/60R14; (Camaro) P215/65R15; (Corsica) P185/75R14; (Beretta) P195/75R14; (Corsica LTZ/Beretta GT) P205/60R15; (Celeb) P185/75R14; (Celeb Eurosport) P195/75R14; (Caprice) P205/75R15; (Caprice wag) P225/75R15.

TECHNICAL: Transmission: Five-speed manual shift standard on Cavalier, Corsica/Beretta and Camaro. Three-speed automatic standard on Celebrity. Four-speed overdrive automatic standard on Caprice.
Steering: (Cavalier/Corsica/Beretta/Celebrity) rack and pinion; (others) recirculating ball.
Front Suspension: (Cavalier/Camaro Celeb) MacPherson struts with coil springs, lower control arms and stabilizer bar; Corsica/Beretta) MacPherson struts with coil springs; (Caprice) unequal-length control arms, coil springs, stabilizer bar.

Rear Suspension: (Cavalier) semi-independent with beam axle, trailing arms, coil springs, stabilizer bar available; (Camaro) rigid axle and torque tube with longitudinal control arms, Panhard rod, coil springs and stabilizer bar; (Corsica/Beretta) trailing twist axle with control arms and coil springs; (Celeb) beam twist axle with integral stabilizer, trailing arms, Panhard rod and coil springs; (Caprice) rigid axle with four links, coil springs, stabilizer available.
Brakes: front disc, rear drum; four-wheel discs available on Camaro.

Body construction: unibody except (Caprice) separate body and frame.

Fuel tank: (Cav) 13.6 gal.; (Camaro) 15.5 gal.; (Corsica/Beretta) 13.6 gal.; (Celeb) 15.7 gal.; (Caprice) 24.5 gal.; (Caprice wag) 22 gal.

DRIVETRAIN OPTIONS: Engines: 173 cu. in. V-6: Cavalier wagon ($660); Corsica/Beretta ($660); Celeb ($610). 305 cu. in. V-8: Camaro RS cpe ($400); Caprice sed ($440). 305 cu. in., TPI V-8: Camaro IROC-Z ($745). 350 cu. in. V-8: Camaro IROC-Z ($1045).
Transmission/Differential:
Five-speed manual trans.: Celeb ($440 credit). Three-speed automatic trans.: Cavalier ($415); Corsica/Beretta ($490). Four-speed overdrive auto. trans.: Camaro ($490); Celeb V-6 ($175). Limited-slip differential: Camaro/Caprice ($100). Performance axle ratio: Caprice ($21).
Power Accessories:
Power four-wheel disc brakes: Camaro ($179). **Suspension:** FE2 sport suspension: Cavalier ($27). F40 H.D. susp.: Celeb/Caprice ($26). F41 sport susp.: Corsica/Beretta, Caprice ($49). Inflatable rear shock absorbers: Celeb/Caprice ($64).

1989 Cavalier Z24 2-dr sport coupe

CAVALIER CONVENIENCE/APPEARANCE OPTIONS: VL Preferred Equip. Grp. 1. Aux Lighting, Pwr Strg;w/5 Spd Trans; H.D. Battery ($303). W/Auto Trans. ($277). VL Preferred Equip. Grp. 2. Incl Color-Keyed Carpeted Mats F&R; Tinted Glass; Aux Lighting; Spt LH Remote & RH Manual Mirrors; Body Side Moldings; Pwr Strg; w/5 Spd Trans; H.D. Battery ($544). W/Auto Trans ($518). VL Preferred Equip. Grp. 3. Incl Air Cond; Color-Keyed Carpeted Mats F&R; Tinted Glass; Aux Lighting; Spt LH Remote & RH Manual Mirrors; Body Side Moldings; Electronic Spd Control; w/resume speed; Pwr Strg; Comfortilt Wheel; Intermittent Windshield Wiper System; W/5 Spd Trans; H.D. Battery ($1604). W/Auto Trans ($1578). Cavalier Preferred Equip. Grp. 1, 1JC35, 1JC37, 1JC69. Incl Aux Lighting, Pwr Strg; w/2.0 Liter Eng & 5 Spd Trans or 2.8 Liter Eng. Coupe & Sedan ($303). Wagon ($309). W/Auto Trans. & 2.0 Liter Eng. Coupe & Sedan ($277). Wagon ($283). Cavalier Preferred Equip. Grp. 2, 1JC35, 1JC37, 1JC69. Color-Keyed Carpeted Mats F&R; Tinted Glass; Aux Lighting; Spt. LH Remote & RH Manual Mirrors; Body Side Moldings; Pwr Strg; H.D. Battery; 2.0 Liter Eng & 5 Spd Trans or 2.8 Liter Eng; Sedan ($544). Wagon ($550). W/Auto Trans & 2.0 Liter Eng Coupe & Sedan ($518). Wagon ($524). Cavalier Preferred Equipment Grp. 3, 1JC37, 1JC69. Air Cond, Color-Keyed Carpeted Mats F&R; Tinted Glass; Aux Lighting; Spt LH Remote & RH Manual Mirrors; Body Side Moldings; Spd Control, Electronic Spd w/resume Spd; Pwr Strg; Comfortilt Wheel; Intermittent Windshield Wiper System; w/5 Spd Trans; H.D. Battery ($1604). W/Auto Trans & LL8 2.0 Liter Eng ($1578). Station Wgn Preferred Equip. Grp. 3. Air Cond; Roof Carrier; Color-Keyed Carpeted Mats F&R; Tinted Glass, Aux Lighting; Spt LH Remote & RH Manual Mirros; Body Side Moldings; Spd Control, w/resume Spd; Comfortilt Strg Wheel; Intermittent Windshield Wiper System, w/LL8 2.0 Liter Eng & 5 Spd Trans. or LB6 2.8 Liter Eng; H.D. Battery ($1725). W/Auto Trans & LL8. 2.0 Liter Eng ($1699). Cavalier Preferred Equip. Grp 4. 1JC37, 1JC69. Air Cond; Pwr Dr Lock System, Color-Keyed Carpeted Mats F&R; Tinted Glass; Aux Lighting; Spt LH Remote & RH Manual Mirrors; Body Side Moldings; Elect. Tuned AM/FM Stereo Radio w/Seek & Scan, Stereo Cass Tape & Digital Clock; Extd range sound system; Spd Control, w/resume; Pwr Strg; Comfortilt Strg Wheel; Pwr Windows; H.D. Battery; Intermittent Windshield Wiper System; Coupe ($2101). Sedan ($2226). W/Auto Trans & 2.0 Liter Eng. Coupe ($2075). Sedan ($2200). RS Equipment Pkg Coupe ($696). Sedan ($705). RS Preferred Equip. Grp. 1, 1JC35, 1JC37, 1JC69, Color-Keyed Carpeted Mats F&R; Tinted Glass; Aux Lighting; H.D. Battery; 2.0 Liter Eng. & 5 Spd Trans. or 2.8 Liter Eng. Coupe ($911). Sedan ($921). Wagon ($927). W/Auto Trans & 2.0 Liter Eng Coupe ($885). Sedan ($895). Wagon ($901). RS Preferred Equip. Grp. 2, 1JC35, 1JC37, 1JC69. Air Cond; Color-Keyed Carpeted Mats F&R; Tinted Glass; Aux Lighting, Spd Control w/resume Spd; Comfortilt Strg Wheel; Intermittent Windshield Wiper System; H.D. Battery; w/2.0 Liter Eng & 5 Spd Trans or 2.8 Liter Eng ($1971). Coupe ($1981). Sedan ($1981). Wagon ($1989). W/Auto Trans & 2.0 Liter Eng Coupe ($1945). Sedan ($1955). Wagon ($1961). RS Preferred Equip. Grp. 3, 1JC37, 1JC69. Air Cond; Decklid Carrier (Cpe only); Pwr Dr Lock System, Color-Keyed Carpeted Mats F&R; Tinted Glass; Aux Lighting; H.D. Battery; AM/FM Stereo w/Seek & Scan; Stereo Cass Tape & Digital CL Clock; Extd range sound system; Elect Spd Control, w/resume Spd; Comfortilt Strg Wheel; Pwr Windows; Intermittent Windshield Wiper System; w/5 Spd Trans. RS Coupe ($2633). RS Sedan ($2653). W/Auto Trans & 2.0 Liter Eng RS Coupe ($2607). RS Sedan ($2627). RS Wagon Preferred Equip. Grp. 3, Air Cond; Roof Carrier; Pwr Dr Lock System; Color-Keyed Carpeted Mats F&R; Tinted Glass, Aux Lighting; AM/FM Stereo Radio, w/Seek & Scan, Stereo Cass Tape & Digital Clock; Extd range sound system; Electonic Spd Control, w/resume Spd; Comfortilt Strg Wheel; Intermittent Windshield Wiper System; 2.0 Liter Eng & 5 Spd Trans. or 2.8 Liter Eng ($2724). W/Auto Trans & 2.0 Liter Eng ($2698). Z24 Cpe Preferred Equip. Grp. 1. Air Cond; H.D. Battery Tinted Glass; Aux Lighting; Z24 Cpe. Preferred Equip. Grp. 2. Air Cond; H.D. Battery Color-Keyed Carpeted Mats F&R; Tinted Glass; Aux Lighting; Elect Tuned AM/FM Stereo Radio w/Seek & Scan, Stereo Cass Tape & Digital Clock, Extd range sound system; Spd Control, w/resume Spd; Comfortilt Strg Wheel; Intermittent Windshield Wiper System ($1390). Z24 Cpe Preferred Equip. Grp. 3. Air Cond; H.D. Battery; Pwr Dr Lock System; Color-Keyed Carpeted Mats F&R; Tinted Glass; Aux Lighting; Elect Tuned AM Stereo/FM Stereo Radio, w/Seek & Scan, Stereo Cass Tape w/Search and Repeat; Graphic Equalizer & Digital Clock; Extd range sound; Elect Spd Control, w/resume Spd; Comfortilt Strg Wheel; Pwr Trunk Opener; Pwr Windows, Intermittent Windshield Wiper System ($1965). Z24 Convertible Preferred Equip. Grp. 1. Air Cond; H.D. Battery; Aux Lighting; AM/FM Stereo Radio w/Seek & Scan Stereo Cass Tape & Digital Clock; Extd range sound system ($858). Z24 Convertible preferred Equip. Grp. 2. Air Cond; H.D. Battery Aux Lighting; Color-Keyed Carpeted Mats F&R; Elec Tuned AM Stereo.FM Stereo Radio, w/Seek & Scan, Stereo Cass Tape w/Search & Repeat; Graphic Equalizer & Digital Clock; Extd range sound system; Pwr Trunk Opener; Spd Control, w/resume Spd; Comfortilt Strg Wheel; Intermittent Windshield Wiper System ($1456). Cloth Bucket Seats ($28). Sport Cloth bucket Seats, Incl arm rest & Split Fldg Rr Seat Coupe ($459). Sedan ($483). Wagon ($383). Air Cond ($695). Frt License Plate Bracket (NC). Roof Carrier Bright or Black ($115). Deck Lid Carrier Black ($115). Electric Rr Window Defogger ($150). Pwr Door Lock System ($155). Sedans & Wagon ($205). Calif Emission System ($100). Color-Keyed Carpeted Mats F&R ($33). Tinted Glass All Windows ($105). Eng Block Heater ($20). Electronic Instrument Cluster, Incl conventional tachometer ($156). Body Side Molding ($50). Radio: VL (332); Elect tuned AM/FM Stereo Radio, w/Seek & Scan, Stereo Cass Tape & Digital Clock, Extd range sound system; VL (454); base/Z24 (122); Elect Tuned AM Stereo & FM Stereo w/Seek & Scan, Stereo Cass Tape w/Search & Repeat, Graphic Equalizer & Digital Clock, Extd range sound system Z24/RS (150/272). Removable Sun Roof ($350). TIRES: P185/80R13 All Seasons SBR White Stripe ($68). P195/70R14 All Seasons SBR Blk Lettered, Incld in RS Equip ($129). P215/60R14 SBR White Outline Lettered ($102). Pwr Trunk Opener ($50). Wheel Trim Rings ($39). Styled Steel 14" Wheels (NC). Alum Wheels 13x5.5" ($265). Pwr Windows ($295).

CAMARO CONVENIENCE/APPEARANCE OPTIONS: RS Cpe Preferred Equip. Grp. 1. H.D. Battery; Tinted Glass, Aux Lighting; Body Side Moldings ($255). RS Cpe Preferred Equip. Grp. 2. Air Cond; Powr Dr Locks; H.D. Battery; Color-Keyed Carpeted Mats F&R; Tinted Glass; Aux Lighting; Body Side Moldings; Elect. Tuned AM/FM Stereo Radio w/Seek & Scan, Stereo Cass Tape & Digital Clock; Extd range sound system; Spd Control, w/resume Spd; Comfortilt Strg Wheel; Intermittent Windshield Wiper System ($1727). RS Cpe Preferred Equip. Grp. 3. Air Cond; H.D. Battery; Cargo Cover; Pwr Dr Lock System; Carpeted Mats F&R; Tinted Glass; Halogen Headlamps, High & Low Beam; Aux Lighting; Mirror w/Dual Reading lamps; Body Side Moldings; Elect Tuned AM/FM Stereo Radio w/Seek & Scan, Stereo Cass Tape & Digital Clock; Extd range sound system; Electronic Spd Cntrl, w/resume Spd; Comfortilt Strg Wheel; Intermittent Windshield Wiper System; IROC-Z Preferred Equip. Grp. 1; Tinted Glass; H.D. Battery; Aux Lighting; Body Side Mldgs; w/o 5.7 Liter Eng. ($255). 5.7 Liter Eng ($229). IROC-Z Preferred Equip. Gr. 2; Air Cond; Pwr Dr Lock System; Carpeted Mats F&R; Tinted Glass; Pwr Hatch Release; Aux Lighting; Body Side Molding; Elect Tuned AM/FM Stereo Radio w/Seek & Scan, Stereo Cass Tape & Digital Clock, extd range sound sys; Spd Control, w/Resume Spd; H.D. Battery; Comfortilt Strg Wheel; Intermittent Windshield Wiper System; w/o 5.7 Liter Eng ($1777). IROC-Z Preferred Equip. Grp 3; Air Cond; Pwr Dr Lock System; Cargo Cover; Color-Keyed Carpeted Mats F&R; Tinted Glas; Halogen Headlamps, High & Low Beam; Pwr Hatch Release; Aux Lighting; Mirror, w/Dual Reading Lamps; Twin Remote Sport Mirrors; Body Side Moldings; Elect. Tuned AM Stereo/FM Stereo Radio w/Seek & Scan Stereo Cass Tape w/Search & Repeat; Graphic Equalizer & Digital Clock, extd range sound system; Pwr Driver's Seat; Electronic Spd Control, w/Resume Spd; H.D. Battery; Comfortilt Strg Wheel; Pwr Windows; Intermittent Windshield Wiper System; w/o 5.7 Liter Eng ($2605). W/B2L 5.7 Liter Eng ($2579). RS Convertible Preferred Equip. Grp. 1. H.D. Battery; Tinted Glass; Body Side Moldings ($206). RS Convertible Preferred Equip. Grp. 2. Air Cond; H.D. Battery; Pwr Dr Lock System; Color-Keyed Carpeted Mats F&R; Tinted Glass; Body Side Moldings; Elect Tuned AM/FM Stereo Radio, w/Seek & Scan, Stereo Cass Tape & Digital Clock; Extd range sound system; Electronic Spd Control, w/resume Spd; Comfortilt Strg Wheel; Intermittent Windshield Wiper System ($1678). RS Convertible Preferred Equip. Grp 3. Air Cond; H.D. Battery; Pwr Dr Lock System; Color-Keyed Carpeted Mats F&R; Tinted Glass; Halogen Headlamps, High & Low Beam; Body Side Moldings; Elect Tuned AM/FM Stereo Radio, w/Seek & Scan, Stereo Cass Tape & Digital Clock; Extd range sound system; Electronic Spd Control, w/resume Spd; Comfortilt Strg Wheel; Pwr Windows; Intermittent Windshield Wiper System ($1923). IROC-Z Convertible Preferred Equip. Grp. 1. H.D. Battery, Tinted Glass; Body Side Moldings ($206). IROC-Z Convertible Preferred Equip. Grp. 2. Air cond; H.D. Battery; Pwr Dr Lock System; Carpeted Mats F&R; Tinted Glass; Body Side Moldings; Elect Tuned AM/FM Stereo Radio, w/Seek & Scan; Stereo Cass Tape & Digital Clock; Extd range sound system; Spd Control, w/resume Spd; Comfortilt Strg Wheel; Intermittent Windshield Wiper System ($1678). IROC-Z Convertible Preferred Equip. Grp. 3. Air Cond; H.D. Battery Pwr Dr Lock System; Carpeted Mats F&R; Tinted Glass, Halogen headlamps, High & Low Beam; Twin Remote Sport Mirrors; Body Side Moldings; Elect Radio Tuned AM Stereo/FM Stereo Radio, w/Seek & Scan, Stereo Cass Tape w/Search & Repeat, Graphic Equalizer & Digital Clock; Extd range sound system; Pwr Seat Driver; Spd Control, w/resume Spd; Comfortilt Strg Wheel;Pwr Windows; Intermittent Windshield Wiper System ($2414). Custom Cloth Bucket Seats ($277). Custom Leather Bucket Seats ($750). Air Cond ($795). Ltd Slip Differential ($100). Performance Axle Ratio; Incl Dual Exhaust ($177). Frt Lic Plate Bracket (NC). Pwr F&D Disc Brakes ($179). Eng Oil Cooler ($110). Lckg Rr Storage Cover ($80). Decal & Stripe Delete ($60 credit). Electric Rr Window Defogger ($150). pwr Door Lock system ($155). Calif Emission System ($100). Pwr Hatch Release ($50). Eng Block Heater ($20). Rr Window Louvers ($210). Deluxe Luggage Comp. Trim RS Cpe only, Incld Lckg Rr Comp Storage Cover ($164). IROC-Z Cpe ($84). Spt Twin Remote Mirrors ($91). Dr. Edge Guards Blk ($15). Elect Tuned AM Stereo/FM Stereo Radio w/Seek & Scan, Stereo Cass Tape w/Search & Repeat, graphic Equalizer & Digital Clock ($150/272). Elect Tuned AM/FM Stereo w/Seek & Scan, Stereo Cass Tape & Digital Clock ($122). Elec Tuned Delco/Bose Music System, Incdl AM/FM Stereo w/Seek & Scan, Stereo Cass Tape & Digital Clock, special tone & balance control & 4 Spkrs ($613/885). Electronically tuned AM/FM Stereo Radio w/Seek & Scan, Compact Disc Player & Digital Clock ($124/396). Pwr Antenna ($70). Removable Roof Panels, Incl Locks ($866). Split Fldg Rr Seat Back ($50). Cast Alum 16" Wheels, Incl Wheel Locks & P245/50 VR16 SBR Blackwall Tires ($520).

CORSICA CONVENIENCE/APPEARANCE OPTIONS: Preferred Equip. Grp. 1. H.D. Battery, Carpeted Mats F&R; Tinted Glass; Aux Lighting, Sedan ($243). Hatchback ($235). Preferred Equip. Grp. 2. Air Cond; H.D. Battery; Tinted Glass, Carpeted Mats F&R; Aux Lighting; Spd Control, w/resume Spd; Comfortilt Strg Wheel; Intermittent Windshield Wiper System ($1378). Hatchback ($1370). Preferred Equip. Grp. 3. Air Cond; H.D. Battery; Power Dr Lock System; Carpeted Mats F&R; Tinted Glass; Aux Lighting; Elect Tuned AM/FM Stereo Radio, w/Seek & Scan, Stereo Cass Tape & Digital Clock, Extd range sound system; Spd Control, w/resume Spd; Comfortilt Strg Wheel; Trunk/Hatch Opener, Pwr Windows; Intermittent Windshield Wiper System; Sedan ($2050). Hatchback ($2042). LT Preferred Equip. Grp. 1. H.D. Battery; Carpeted Mats F&R; Tinted Glass, Aux Lighting; Sedan ($487). Hatchback ($479). LT Preferred Equip. Grp. 2. Air cond; H.D. Battery; Carpeted Mats F&R; Gauge Pkg w/Tachometer; Tinted Glass; Aux Lighting; Spd Control, w/resume Spd; Comfortilt Strg Wheel; Intermittent Windshield Wiper System; Sedan ($1761). Hatchback ($1753). LT Preferred Equip. Grp. 3. Air Cond; H.D. Battery; Pwr Dr Lock System; Carpeted Mats F&R; Gauge Pkg w/Tachometer, Tinted Glass, Aux Lighting, Elect Tuned AM/Fm Stereo Radio w/Seek & Scan, Stereo Cass Tape & Digital Clock; Extd range sound system; Electonic Spd Control, w/resume Spd; Comfortilt Strg Wheel; Pwr Trunk/Hatch Opener; Pwr Windows; Intermittent Windshield Wiper System; Sedan ($2433). Hatchback ($2425). LTZ Preferred Equip. Grp. 1. H.D. Battery; Carpeted Mats F&R; Tinted Glass; Electronic Spd Control, w/resume Spd; Comfortilt Strg Wheel; Intermittent Windshield Wiper System ($544). LTZ Preferred Equip. Grp. 2. H.D. Battery, Pwr Dr Lock System, Carpeted Mats F&R; Tinted Glass; Elect Tune AM/FM Stereo Radio w/Seek & Scan, Stereo Cass Tape & Digital Clock, Extd range sound system; Electronic Spd Control, w/resume Spd; Comfortilt Strg Wheel; Pwr Trunk Opener; Pwr Windows; Intermittent Windshield Wiper System ($1216). Custom Cloth CL Bucket Seats, Sedan ($425). Hatchback ($275). LTZ (NC). Custom Two-Tone Paint ($123). Air Cond Incld w/LTZ ($770). H.D. Battery ($26). Frt License Plate Bracket (NC). Deck Lid Carrier Blk, Incld w/LTZ ($115). Flr Mounted Console ($60). Rr Window Electric Defogger ($150). Pwr Door Lock System ($205). Calif Emission system ($100). Gauge Pkg W/Tachometer, voltmeter, oil pressure, temp. gauges & trip odometer, Incld w/LTZ ($139). Eng. Block Heater ($20). Aux Lighting courtesy, instrument panel eng & dual reading lamp, Incl w/LTZ Sedan ($64). Hatchback only ($56). Elect Tuned Am/FM Stereo Radio w/Seek & Scan, Stereo Cass Tape & Digital Clock, Incld extd sound system ($122). Elect tuned AM Stereo/FM Stereo w/Seek & Scan, Stereo Cass Tape w/Search & Repeat, Graphic Equalizer & Digital Clock, Incl extd range sound system ($150/272). Body Side Striping ($57). TIRES P195/70 R14 All Seasons SBR Blk Lettered, incl w/Lt ($93). P185/75 R14 All Season SBR White Stripe ($68). Styled Wheels, Incl w/LT Equip Pkg ($265). w/LT Equip Pkg ($210). Intermittent Windshield Wiper System ($55).

1989 Beretta GT 2-dr sports coupe

BERETTA CONVENIENCE/APPEARANCE OPTIONS: Preferred Equip. Grp. 1. H.D. Battery; Carpeted F&R Mats; Aux Lighting ($91). Preferred Equip. Grp. 2. Air Cond; H.D. Battery Carpeted Mats F&R; Aux Lighting; Spd Control, w/resume Spd; Elect Comfortilt Strg. Wheel, Intermittent Wipers ($1226). Preferred Equip. Grp. 3. Air Cond; H.D. Battery; Pwr Dr Lock System; Carpeted Mats F&R; Aux Lighting, Elect Tuned AM/FM Stereo w/Seek & Scan, Stereo Cass Tape & Digital Clock; Incl extd range sound system; Spd Control, w/resume Spd; Comfortilt Strg Wheel; Pwr Trunk Opener; Pwr Windows; Intermittent Windshield Wiper System; ($1773). GT Preferred Equip. Grp. 1. H.D. Battery; Color-Keyed Carpeted Mats F&R; Aux Lighting; Electronic Spd Control, w/Resume; Comfortilt Strg Wheel; Intermittent Wipers ($458) GT Preferred Equip. Grp. 2. H.D. Battery; Pwr Dr Lock System; Carpeted Mats F&R; Aux Lighting; elect Tuned AM/FM Stereo Radio w/Seek & Scan, Stereo Cass Tape & Digital Clock; Extd range sound; Electronic Spd Control, w/resume Spd; Comfortilt Strg Wheel; Pwr Trunk Opener; Intermittent Wipers ($1003). Custom Two-Tone Paint ($123). Air Cond Incld w/GT ($770). H.D. Battery ($26). Frt Lic Plate Bracket (NC). Deck lid Carrier Blk ($115). Electric Rr Window Defogger ($150). Pwr Dr Lock System ($155). Calif Emission system ($100). Eng Block Heater ($20). Electronic instrumentation Speedometer Bar Graph & Digital readout, Tachometer ($156). Aux Lighting Incld Eng & dual reading lamps ($32). Elect Tuned AM/FM Stereo Radio w/Seek & Scan, Stereo Cass Tape & Digital Clock, Extd range sound system ($122). Elect Tuned AM Stereo/FM Stereo w/Seek & Scan, Stereo Cass Tape w/Search & Repeat, Graphic Equalizer & Digital Clock, Incld extd range sound system ($150/272). Removable Sun Roof ($350). Alum Wheels w/Locks ($210). Intermittent Windshield Wiper System ($55).

1989 Celebrity Eurosport 4-dr sports sedan

CELEBRITY CONVENIENCE/APPEARANCE OPTIONS: Preferred Equip. Grp. 1. Air Cond; Color-Keyed Flr Mats F&R; Aux Lighting; Ext Molding Pkg; 2.5 Liter Eng ($931). w/LB6 2.8 Liter Eng ($957). Preferred Equip. Grp. 2. Air Cond; Pwr Dr Lock System, Color-Keyed Mats F&R; Gauge Pkg w/Trip odometer; Aux Lighting; Ext Mldg Pkg; Spd Control, w/resume Spd; Comfortilt Strg Wheel; Intermittent Windshield Wiper System;($1565). 2.8 Liter Eng ($1565). 2.8 Liter Eng ($1591). Preferred Equip. Grp. 3. Air Cond. pwer Dr. Lock System; Color-Keyed Mats F&R; Gauge Pkg w/Trip Odometer; Aux Lighting, Spt Twin Remote Mirrors; Ext Pkg Moldings; Elect Tuned AM/FM Stereo Radio w/Seek & Scan, Stereo Cass Tape & Digital Clock; Incl extd range sound system; Spd Control, w/resume Spd; Comfortilt Strg Wheel; Pwr Trunk Opener, Pwr Windows; Intermittent Windshield Wiper System; 2.5 Liter Eng ($2062). 2.8 Liter Eng ($2088). Eurosport Equip Pkg ($230). Eurosport Preferred Equip. Grp. 1. Eurosport Equip; Air Cond; Color-Keyed Mats F&R; Aux Lighting; Ext Molding Pkg; 2.5 Liter Eng ($1161). 2.8 Liter Eng ($1187); Eurosport Preferred Equip. Grp. 2. Eurosport Equip; Air Cond; Pwr Dr Lock System; Color-Keyed Mats F&R; Gauge pkg w/Trip Odometer, Aux Lighting; Exterior Molding Pkg; Spd Control, w/resume Spd; Comfortilt Strg Wheel; Intermittent Windshield Wiper System; 2.5 Liter Eng ($1795). 2.8 Liter Eng ($1821). Eurosport Preferred Equip. Grp. 3. Eurosport Equip; air Cond; Pwr Dr Lock System; Color-Keyed Mats F&R; Gauge Pkg w/Trip Odometer; Aux Lighting; Spt Twin Remote Mirrors; Ext Molding Pkg; AM/FM Stereo Radio w/Seek & Scan, Stereo Cass Tape & Digital Clock, Extd range sound system; Electronic Spd Control, w/resume Spd; Comfortilt Strg Wheel; Pwr Trunk Opener; Pwr Windows; Intermittent Windshield Wiper System 2.5 Liter Eng ($2292). 2.8 Liter Eng ($2318). Wgn Preferred Equip Grp. 1. Air Cond; Color-Keyed Mats F&R; Aux Lighting; Ext Molding Pkg w/2.5 Liter Eng ($923). w/LB6 2.5 Liter Eng ($949). Wgn Preferred Equip Grp. 2. Air Cond; Chrome Roof Carrier; Pwr Dr Lock system; Color-Keyed Mats F&R; Gauge Pkg w/Trip Odometer; Pwr Liftgate Release; Aux Lighting; Ext Molding Pkg; Electronic Spd Control, w/resume Spd; Comfortilt Strg Wheel; Intermittent Windshield Wiper System; 2.5 liter Eng ($1722). 2.8 Liter Eng ($1748). Wgn Preferred Equip. Grp. 3. Air Cond; Chrome Roof Carrier; Pwr Dr Lock System; Color-Keyed Mats F&R; Gauge Pkg w/Trip Odometer; Pwr Liftgate Release; Aux Lighting; Spt Twin Remote Mirrors; Molding Pkg; AM/FM Stereo Radio w/Seek & Scan, Stereo Cass Tape & Digital Clock, Extd range sound system; Deluxe Rr Compartment Decor; Cargo Area Security pkg; Electronic Spd Control, w/resume Spd; Comfortilt Strg Wheel; Pwr Windows; Intermittent Windshield Wiper System; 2.5 Liter Eng ($2253). w/2.8 Liter Eng ($2279). Eurosport Wgn Preferred Equip. Grp. 1. Eurosport Equip. Pkg; Air Cond; Color-Keyed Mats F&R; Aux lighting; Exterior Mldg. Pkg w.2.5 Liter Eng ($1153). 2.8 Liter Eng. Incld H.D. Battery ($1179). Eurosport Wgn Preferred Equip. Grp. 2. Eurosport Equip. Pkg; Air Cond; Roof Carrier; Pwr Dr Lock System; Color-Keyed Mats F&R; Gauge pkg w/Trip Odometer; Pwr Liftgate Release; Aux Lighting; Exterior Mldg. Pkg. Electronic Spd Control, w/resume Spd; Comfortilt Strg Wheel; Intermittent Windshield Wiper System; 2.5 Liter Eng ($1952). 2.8 Liter Eng

1989 Celebrity Eurosport 4-dr sedan

($1978). Eurosport Wgn Preferred Equip. Grp. 3. Eurosport Equip. Pkg; Air Cond; Roof Carrier; Pwr Dr Lock System; Flr Mats F&R; Gauge pkg w/Trip Odometer; Pwer Liftgate Release; Aux Lighting; Spt Twin Remote Mirrors; Ext Mldg Pkg; AM/FM Stereo Radio w/Seek & Scan, stereo Cass Tape & Digital Clock, Extd range sound system, Deluxe Rr Compartment Decor; Cargo Security Pkg; Spd Control, w/resume Spd; Comfortilt Strg Wheel; Pwr Windows; Intermittent Windshield Wiper System; 2.5 Liter Eng ($2483). 2.8 liter Eng ($2509). Cloth Bucket Seats w/console ($257). Cloth 55/45 Seat ($133). Custom Cloth CL 55/45 Sedan ($385). Wagon Incld split individual fldg second seat back Wagon ($435). Custom Cloth CL 45/45 w/console Sedan ($335). Inclds split individual fldg second seat back Wagon ($385). Custom Two-Tone paint, Inclds Lwr body accent & Ext Mldg. Pkg. w/1SB, 1SC or 1SD Pkg ($93). w/1SA Pkg ($148). Air Cond; Incld increased cooling ($795). Rr Window Air Deflector ($40). Frt Lic Plate Bracket (NC). H.D. Cooling w.o Cond ($70). Air Cond ($40). Rr Window Electric Defogger ($150). Pwr Dr Lock System ($205). Calif Emission system ($100). Color-Keyed Mats Front ($17). Rr ($12). Gauge Pkg, Inclds voltmeter, Trip Odometer & Temp Gauges ($64). Eng Block Heater ($20). Exterior Molding Pkg, inclds rocker panel & wheel opening mldgs, Incl wCustom Two-Tone Paint ($55). Elec Tuned AM/FM Stereo Radio w/Seek & Scan, Stereo Cass Tape & Digital Clock, Extd range sound system ($122). Deluxe Rr Compartment Decor ($40). 6-way Pwr Driver's Seat ($250). Reclining Seat Back, Driver & Pass ($90). Cargo Area Security Pkg ($44). TIRES P185/75 R14 All Season SBR White Stripe ($68). P195/70R14 All Seasons SBR Blackwall ($90). Sport Wheel Covers ($656). Wire Wheel Covers, w/Locks ($215). Alum Wheels ($195). Rally Wheels, Incld w/Eurosport Equip., Inclds styled wheels special hub cabs & trim rings ($56). Rr Window Wiper/Washer ($125).

CAPRICE CONVENIENCE/APPEARANCE OPTIONS: Sdn Preferred Equip. Grp. 1; H.D. Battery; Color-Keyed Carpeted Mats F&R; Body Side Moldings; Wheel Opening; Extd Range Spkrs ($196). Sdn Preferred Equip. Grp. 2; H.D. Battery; Pwr Dr Lock System; Carpeted Mats F&R; Aus Lighting; Body Side Mldgs; Wheel Opening Mlds; Extd Range Spkrs; Spd Control, w/resume Spd; Comfortilt Strg Wheel; Intermittent Windshield Wiper System ($816). Classic Sdn Preferred Equip. Grp. 1; H.D. Battery; Carpeted Mats F&R; Aux Lighting, Spt Twin Remote Mirrors; Body Side Mlds; Extd Range Spkrs; Spd Control, w/resume Spd; Comfortilt Strg Wheel; P205/75R15 All Seasons SBR Ply White Stripe; Pwr Trunk Opener; Intermittent Windshield Wiper System ($719). Classic Sdn Preferred Equip Grp 2; H.D. Battery Pwr Dr Lock System; Color-Keyed Carpeted Mats F&R; Aux Lighting; Deluxe Luggage Comp Trim; Spt Twin Remote Mirrors; RH Lighted Visor Mirror; Body Side Moldings, Elect Tuned AM/FM Stereo Radio, w/Seek & Scan, Stereo Cass Tape, Digital Clock & Pwr Antenna; extd range sound system; Elect Spd Control, w/resume Spd; Comfortilt Strg Wheel;Spd Control, w/resume Spd; Comfortilt Strg Wheel; P205/75R15 All Seasons SBR White Stripe Tires; Pwr Trunk Opener; Pwr Windows; Intermittent Windshield Wiper System; w/50/50 Seats, Inclds driver & pass pwr seats ($2020). w/Bench Seat ($1520). Classic Wgn Preferred Equip. Grp. 1; H.D. Battery, Dlx Load Flr Carpeting; Aux lighting; Spt Twin Remote Mirrors; Body Side Mldgs. Color-Keyes exc. Estate which is woodgrain ($237). Caprice Classic Wgn Preferred Equip Grp. 2. H.D. Battery; Roof Carrier; Pwer Dr Lock system; Incl Tailgate Lock; Dlx Load Floor Carpeting F&R; Aux Lighting; Spt Twin Remote Mirrors; body Side Mlds; Color-Keyed exc w/Estate which is woodgrain; Elect Tuned AM/FM Stereo Radio w/Seek & Scan, Stereo Cass Tape Pwr Antenna & Digital Clock, dual Rr spkrs; Electronic Spd Control, w/resume Spd; Comfortilt Strg Wheel; Pwr Windows; Intermittent Windshield Wiper System ($1514). Caprice Classic Wgn Preferred Equip. Grp. 3. H.D. Battery; Roof Carrier; Pwr Dr Lock System; Inclds Tailgate Lock; Color-Keyed Carpeted Mats F&R; Gauge Pkg w/Trip Odometer; Twilight Sentinel Headlamps; Cornering Lamps; Aux Lighting RH Lighted Visor Mirror; Spt Twin Remote Mirrors; Body Side Mldgs; Color-Keyed exc w/Estate which is woodgrain; Elect Tuned AM/FM Stereo Radio w/Seek & Scan, Stereo Cass Tape, Graphic Equalizer, Pwr Antenna & Digital Clock; Dual Rr spkrs. Dlx Rr Comp Decor; Electronic Spd Cntrol, w/resume Spd; Comfortilt Strg Wheel; Pwr Windows; Intermittent Windshield Wiper System; w/50/50 Seats, Inclds Driver & Pass Pwr Seats w/Bench Seat ($2393). w/Bench Seat ($1893). Caprice Classic Brghm Preferred Equip. Grp. 1. H.D. Battery; Carpeted mats F&R; Gauge Pkg w/Trip Odometer; Twilight Sentinel RH Visor Illum Mirror; Spt Twin Remote Mirrors; Body Side Mldgs; Extd Range Spkrs; TIRES P205/75R15 All Seasons SBR White Stripe; Pwr Trunk Opener ($496). Caprice Brghm Preferred Equip Grp 2, H.D. Battery; Pwr Dr Lock System, Carpeted mats F&R; Gauge Pkg w/Trip odometer; Twilight Sentinel Cornering Lamps; Dlx Luggage Comp Trim; Lighted RH Visor Mirror; Spt Twin Remote Mirrors; Body Side Mldgs; Elect Tuned AM/FM Stereo Radio w/Seek & Scan Stereo Cass Tape; Pwr Antenna & Digital Cloc, Extd range sound system; Pwr Six-Way Driver & Pass Seats; Spd Cntrl, w/resume Spd; Comfortilt Strg Wheel; P205/75R15 All Seasons SBR White Stripe Tires; Pwr Trunk Opener; Wire Wheel Covers w/Locks, Pwr Windows; Intermittent Windshield Wiper System ($2317). Caprice Classic Brghm IS Preferred Equip. Grp. 1. H.D. Battery; Pwr Dr Lock System; Color-Keyed Carpeted mats F&R; Gauge Pkg w/Trip Odometer; Twilight Sentinel Headlamps; Lighted RH Visor Mirror; Spt Twin Remote Mirrors; Body Side Mlds; Elect Tuned AM/FM Stereo Radio w/Seek & Scan, Stereo Cass Tape, pwer Antenna & Digital Clock; Extd range sound system; Six-Way Pwr Driver & Pass Seats; Spd Cntrl, w/resume Spd; Comfortilt Strg Wheel; P205/75R15 All Season SBR White Stripe Tires; Pwr Trunk Opener; Wire Wheel Covers w/locks; Pwr Windows; Intermittent Windshield Wiper System ($2203). Caprice Classic Brghm IS Preferred Equip Grp. 2; H.D. Battery; Pwr Dr Lock System; Color-Keyed Carpeted Mats F&R; Gauge pkg w/Trip Odometer; Twilight Sentinel Headlamps; Cornering Lamps; Dlx Luggage Comp Trim; RH Visor Illum Mirror; Spt Twin Remote Mirrors; Body Side Mldgs; Elect Tuned AM/FM Stereo Radio w/Seek & Scan, Stereo Cass Tape, Graphic Equalizer, Pwr Antenna & Digital Clock, Extd range sound system; Pwr 6-Way Driver & Pass Seats; Electronic Spd Control, w/resume Spd; Comfortilt Strg Wheel; P205/75R15 All Season SBR White Stripe Tires; Pwer Trunk; Wire Wheel Covers w/Locks; Pwr Windows; Intermittent Windshield Wiper System ($2427). Vinyl Bench Seat Caprice Sdn ($28). Caprice Classic Wgn ($172). Vinyl 50/50 Seat Caprice Sdn ($305). Caprice Classic Wgn ($103). Cloth 50/50 Seat ($275). Cloth 45/55 Seat (NC). Leather 45/55 Seat ($550). Custom Two-Tone paint, Inclds Lwr body accent color-keyed striping & outside door handle inserts ($141). Full Vinyl Roof Cover ($200). Rr Window Air Deflector ($65). Frt Lic Plate Bracket (NC). Trunk Cargo Net ($30). H.D. Cooling ($40). Rr Window Electric Defogger ($150). Pwr. Dr. Lock System Sedans ($205). Wgn Inclds Tailgate Lock ($265). Calif Emission system ($100). Estate Equip ($307). Eng Block Heater ($20). Elect Tuned AM/FM Stereo w/Seek & Scan, Stereo Cass Tape & Digital Clock ($122/227). Elect Tuned AM/FM Stereo w/Seek & Scan, Stereo Cass Tape, Graphic Equalizer & Digital Clock ($110/337). Pin Striping Color-Keyed ($61). TIRES P205/75 R15 All Seasons SBR White Stripe ($76). P225/70 R15 SBR White Stripe ($188). P225/75R15 All Season SBR White (NC). Custom Wheel Covers Std/Brghm ($65). Wire Wheel Cover w/Locks Brghm ($150). All others ($215).

1990 CHEVROLET

1990 Lumina Euro Coupe

Lumina was the new name for 1990, a front-drive mid-size coupe and sedan to replace the Monte Carlo coupe (dropped after 1988) and the Celebrity sedan, which faded away this year. Its natural rival was the popular Ford Taurus. In addition to the coupe and sedan, a Lumina APV (All Purpose Vehicle) emerged this year, one of three futuristically-styled GM minivans in which composite body panels were bonded to a steel frame. Oldsmobile's Silhouette and Pontiac's Trans Sport were the others in the dramatic front-drive trio, each of which took on a distinct personality.

CAVALIER — SERIES 1J — FOUR/V-6 —
All Cavaliers had a solid top this year, as the convertible faded away. The standard four-cylinder engine grew from 2.0 to 2.2 liters (133 cu. in.) adding five horsepower in the process. At the same time, the V-6, optional under station wagon hoods and standard in the Z24, grew to 190 cu. in. (3.1 liters), for an increase of 10 horsepower. Both the VL (Value Leader) model and the step-up RS option package now were offered in all three body styles: coupe, sedan and station wagon. All except the VL now had standard tinted glass and power steering. Each engine came with a standard five-speed gearbox, but the four-cylinder version was built by Isuzu, the V-6's by Muncie-Getrag. Three-speed automatic remained optional. Exhaust systems were made of stainless steel.

1990 Camaro RS coupe

CAMARO — SERIES 1F — V-6/V-8 —
Only for a short model run did this year's Camaros become available, as the facelifted '91 models were scheduled to arrive in spring 1990. The Camaro RS got a larger base V-6 engine: 190 cu. in. (3.1 liters) versus the former 2.8-liter. Both the RS and IROC-Z added a driver's air bag, for the coupe and convertible. A five-speed manual gearbox remained standard, but Camaros with the optional four-speed overdrive automatic got a modified torque converter with higher lockup points for improved gas mileage. New standard equipment included Halogen headlamps, tinted glass, intermittent wipers and a tilt steering wheel. New 16-inch alloy wheels became standard on the IROC-Z convertible (optional on the coupe). IROC-Z also had a standard limited-slip differential. Leather upholstery joined the interior option list, while the instrument panel switched to new yellow graphics.

1990 Beretta GTZ coupe

CORSICA/BERETTA — SERIES 1L — FOUR/V-6 —
A high-performance GTZ Beretta coupe replaced the former GTU this year, powered by GM's high-output Quad Four dual-overhead-cam engine and rated 180 horsepower. With the demise of Cavalier's convertible came the promise of an open Beretta, arriving late in the season. Instead of being fully open-air, that ragtop featured a structural roof bar, which was not intended to serve as a rollbar but to add integrity to the body and minimize wind drafts to passengers. Corsica added standard equipment this year, with base models carrying the same gear as the prior season's LT series, including black body trim. Corsica LTZ added adjustable lumbar supports, and carried 15-inch tires on alloy wheels as well as stabilizer bars at front and rear. Corsica/Beretta's base four-cylinder engine grew from 2.0 to 2.2 liters, while the V-6 went from 2.8 to 3.1 liters, GTZ had a unique grille and extended rocker panels, plus 16-inch alloy wheels instead of the usual 15-nchers. All Berettas came with a standard five-speed manual gearbox, and all but the GTZ could get the optional three-speed automatic. Corsicas had either an Isuzu-built five-speed or, with V-6 power, a Muncie-Getrag unit, as well as the automatic option. Fuel capacities grew to 15.6 gallons with the adoption of a new molded tank.

1990 Celebrity Eurosport Wagon

CELEBRITY — SERIES 1A — FOUR/V-6 —
After losing its coupe a year earlier, the mid-size front-drive Celebrity also lost the four-door sedan this time. So only the station wagon remained, as the others were replaced by the new Lumina. Both two-seat (six-passenger) and three-seat (eight-passenger) versions were available, in base trim or with the Eurosport package. A dozen more horsepower found their way into the base four-cylinder engine, as a result of modifications in the cylinder walls and heads. Eurosport Celebs carried a new 190 cu. in. (3.1-liter) V-6, rated 135 horsepower, with four-speed overdrive automatic transmission. That V-6 was optional on the base model, which used a standard three-speed automatic. New standard equipment included intermittent wipers, Scotchgard fabric protection, map pockets in front doors, and heavy-duty suspension.

1990 Lumina Euro Sedan

LUMINA — SERIES 1W — FOUR/V-6 —
A sedan led off the front-drive Lumina lineup, arriving in late spring 1989, followed by a coupe in the fall. The mid-size sedan evolved from the coupe design introduced for 1988 as the Buick Regal, Oldsmobile Cutlass Supreme and Pontiac Grand Prix. Base and Eurosport models were offered, with a 151 cu. in. (2.5-liter) four-cylinder engine standard in the base model and a 191 cu. in. (3.1-liter) V-6 in the Euro. Both engines drove a standard three-speed automatic, with four-speed overdrive automatic optional in V-6 models. Standard equipment included disc brakes and independent suspension on all four wheels, plus power steering, tinted glass, intermittent wipers, and an AM/FM radio. The Euro edition was air conditioned, displayed blackout body trim and a decklid spoiler, and contained a sport suspension with larger (15-inch) tires than the base model.

CAPRICE — SERIES 1B — V-8 —
Not much changed in the full-size rear-drive Chevrolet, as a completely different, more rounded Caprice was expected as an early '91 model, to replace the traditional boxy sedan and wagon. This carryover Caprice still was powered by one of two 5.0-liter V-8s: 305 cubic inches and 170 horsepower for the sedan, but 307 cid and 140 horses for

1990 Caprice Classic Brougham LS sedan

the wagon. Both engines had throttle-body fuel injection and hooked to a four-speed overdrive automatic transmission. Under the hood, new quick-connect fuel lines were supposed to speed up servicing. Interiors had new Scotchgard fabric protection. Two new metallic red body colors were offered.

I.D. DATA: Chevrolets again had a 17-symbol Vehicle Identification Number (VIN) on the upper left surface of the instrument panel, visible through the windshield. Symbol one indicates country: '1' = U.S.A.; '2' = Canada. Next is a manufacturer code: 'G' = General Motors. Symbol three is car made: '1' = Chevrolet; '7' = GM of Canada. Symbol four denotes restraint system: 'A' = non-passive (standard); 'B' = passive (automatic belts); 'C' = passive (inflatable). Symbol five is car line/series. Symbols six-seven reveal body type. Next is the engine code, followed by a check digit, then 'L' for model year 1990. Symbol eleven indicates assembly plant. The final six digits are the sequential serial number. Engine number coding is similar to 1981-89.

Model Number	Body/Style Number	Body Type & Seating	Factory Price	Shipping Weight	Production Total
CAVALIER (FOUR/V-6)					
1J	C37	2-dr. Coupe-5P	8620	2291	
1J	C69	4-dr. Sedan-5P	8820	2295	
1J	C35	4-dr. Sta Wag-5P	9195	2295	
CAVALIER VL (FOUR/V-6)					
1J	C37/WV9	2-dr. Coupe-5P	7577	2291	
1J	C69/WV9	4-dr/ Seden-5P	8165	2291	
1J	C35/WV9	4-dr. Sta Wag-5P	8165	2295	
Cavalier Engine Note: A V-6 engine cost $685 additional.					
CAVALIER Z24 (V-6)					
1J	F37	2-dr. Coupe-5P	11505	2489	
CAMARO (V-6/V-8)					
1F	P87	2-dr. RS Cpe-4P	10995/11345	2975/3143	
1F	P67	2-dr. RS Conv-4P	—/16880	—/3270	
CAMARO IROC-Z (V-8)					
1F	P87/Z28	2-dr. Spt Cpe-4P	14555	3149	
1F	P67/Z28	2-dr. Conv Cpe-4P	20195	3272	
CORSICA (FOUR/V-6)					
1L	T69	4-dr. Sedan-5P	9495/10180	2520/2525	
1L	Z69	4-dr. LTZ Sed-5P	—/12795	—/2545	
1L	T68	4-dr. Hatch-5P	9895/10580	2540/2545	
BERETTA (FOUR/V-6)					
1L	V37	2-dr. Coupe-5P	10320/11005	2540/—	
1L	W37	2-dr. GT Cpe-5P	—/12500	—/2676	
1L	W37	2-dr. GTZ Cpe-5P	—/13750	N/A	
CELEBRITY (V-6)					
1A	W35	4-dr. Sta Wag-6P	12395	2809	
1A	W35	4-dr. Sta Wag-8P	12645	N/A	
LUMINA (FOUR/V-6)					
1W	L27	2-dr. Coupe-6P	12140/12800	2953/—	
1W	L69	4-dr. Sedan-6P	12340/13000	3033/—	
LUMINA EUROSPORT (V-6)					
1W	N27	2-dr. Coupe-6P	14040	N/A	
1W	N69	4-dr. Sedan-6P	14340	N/A	
CAPRICE (V-8)					
1B	L69	4-dr. Sedan-6P	14525	3406	
CAPRICE CLASSIC (V-8)					
1B	N69	4-dr. Sedan-6P	15125	3355	
1B	U69	4-dr. Brghm-6P	16325	3470	
1B	U69/B6N	4-dr. LS Brghm-6P	17525	3475	
1B	N35	4-dr. 3S Wag-8P	15725	4041	

FACTORY PRICE AND WEIGHT NOTE: For Corsica and Beretta, prices and weights to left of slash are for four-cylinder, to right for V-6 engine. For Camaro RS, figures to left of slash are for six-cylinder model, to right of slash for V-8.

BODY/STYLE NO. NOTE: Some models were actually option packages. Code after the slash (e.g., B6N) is the number of the option package that comes with the model listed.

ENGINE DATA: BASE FOUR (Cavalier, Corsica/Beretta): Inline. Overhead valve. Four-cylinder. Cast iron block and aluminum head. Displacement: 133 cu. in. (2.2 liters). Bore & stroke: 3.50 x 3.46 in. Compression ratio: 9.0:1 Brake horsepower: 95 at 5200 RPM. Torque: 120 lbs.-ft. at 3200 RPM. Five main bearings. Hydraulic valve lifters. Throttle-body fuel injection. BASE QUAD FOUR (Beretta GTZ): Inline. Dual overhead cam (16-valve). Four-cylinder. Cast iron block and aluminum head. Displacement: 138 cu. in (2.3 liters). Bore & stroke: 3.63 x 3.35 in. Compression ratio: 10.0:1. Brake horsepower: 180 at 6200 RPM. Torque: 160 lbs.-ft. at 5200 RPM. Port fuel injection. BASE FOUR (Celebrity, Lumina): Inline. Overhead valve. Four-cylinder. Case iron block and head. Displacement: 151 cu. in. (2.5 liters). Bore & stroke: 4.00 x 3.00 in. Compression ratio: 8.3:1. Brake horsepower: 110 at 5200 RPM. Torque: 135 lbs.-ft. at 3200 RPM. Five main bearings. Hydraulic valve lifters. Throttle-body fuel injection. BASE V-6 (Camaro RS coupe, Cavalier Z24, Corsica LTZ, Beretta GT/con, Lumina Eurosport); OPTIONAL (Cavalier wagon, Corsica/Beretta, Celebrity, Luminia): Overhead-valve V-6. Cast iron block and head. Displacement: 191 cu. in. (3.1 liters). Bore & stroke: 3.50 x 3.31 in. Compression ratio: 8.8:1. Brake horsepower: (Celeb/Lumina) 135 at 4400 RPM; (Cavalier) 135 at 4500; (Corsica/Beretta) 135 at 4200; (Camaro) 144 at 4400. Torque: (Cavalier/Celeb/Corsica/Beretta/Camaro) 180 at 3600; Multi-port fuel injection. BASE V-8 (Caprice sedan): 90-degree, overhead-valve V-8. Cast iron block and head. Displacement: 305 cu. in. (5.0 liters). Bore & stroke: 3.74 x 3.48 in. Compression ratio: 9.3:1. Brake horsepower: 170 at 4000 RPM; Torque: 225 lbs.-ft. at 2400 RPM. Five main bearings. Hydraulic valve lifters. Throttle-body fuel injection. BASE V-8 (Camaro RS convertible, IROC-Z): OPTIONAL (Camaro RS coupe): Same as 305 cu. in V-8 above but with throttle-body fuel injection. Compression ratio: 9.3:1. Brake horsepower: 170 at 4000 RPM. Torque: 255 lbs.-ft. at 2400 RPM. OPTIONAL V-8 (Camaro IROC-Z): Same as 305 cu. in. V-8 above, with port fuel injection. Compression ratio: 9.3:1. Brake horsepower: 220 at 4400 RPM; Torque: 290 lbs.-ft. at 3200 RPM. BASE V-8 (Caprice wagon): 90-degree, overhead valve V-8. Cast iron block and head. Displacement: 307 cu. in. (5.0 liters). Bore & stroke: 3.80 x 3.38 in. compression ratio: 8.0:1. Brake horsepower: 140 at 3200 RPM. Torque: 255 lbs.-ft. at at 2000 RPM. Five main bearings. Hydraulic roller valve lifters. Carburetor: 4Bbl. OPTIONAL V-8 (Camaro IROC-Z): 90-degree, overhead valve V-8. Cast iron block and head. Displacement: 350 cu. in. (5.7 liters). Bore & stroke: 4.00 x 3.48 in. Compression ratio: 9.3:1. Brake horsepower: 230 at 4400 RPM. Torque: 330 lbs.-ft. at 3200 RPM.

CHASSIS DATA: Wheelbase: (Cavalier) 101.2 in.; (Camaro) 101.0 in.; (Corsica/Beretta) 103.4 in.; (Celebrity) 104.9 in.; (Lumina) 107.5 in.; (Caprice) 116.0 in. **Overall length:** (Cav cpe/sed) 178.4 in.; (Cav wag) 174.5 in.; (Camaro) 192.0 in.; (Corsica) 183.4 in.; (Beretta) 187.2 in.; (Celeb) 190.8 in.; (Lumina cpe) 198.4 in.; (Lumina sed) 197.6 in.; (Caprice sed) 212.2 in.; (Capr wag) 215.7 in. **Height:** (Cavalier) 52.0-52.8 in.; Camaro cpe) 50.0 in.; (Camaro conv) 50.3 in.; (Corsica) 56.2 in.; (Beretta) 52.6 in.; (Celeb) 54.3 in.; (Lumina cpe) 53.3 in.; (Lumina sed) 53.6 in.; (Caprice) 56.4 in.; (Caprice wag) 58.2 in. **Width:** (Cav cpe) 66.0 in.; (Cav sed/wag) 66.3 in.; (Camaro) 72.8 in.; (Corsica) 68.2 in.; (Beretta 68.0 in.; (Celeb) 69.3 in.; (Lumina) 71.0-71.1 in.; (Caprice) 75.4 in.; (Capr wag) 79.3 in. **Front Tread:** (Cav) 55.8 in.; (Camaro) 60.0 in.; (Corsica/Beretta) 55.6 in.; (Celeb) 58.7 in.; (Lumina) 59.5 in.; (Caprice) 61.7 in.; (Capr wag) 62.2 in. **Rear Tread:** (Cav) 55.2 in.; (Camaro) 60.9 in.; (Corsica/Beretta) 55.1 in.; (Beretta) 56.6 in.; (Celeb) 57.0 in.; (Lumina) 58.0 in.; (Caprice) 60.7 in.; (Capr wag) 64.1 in. **Standard Tires:** (Cav) P185/80R13; (Cav Z24) P215/60R14; (Camaro) P215/65R15; (Camaro IROC-Z conv) P245/50ZR16); (Corsica) P185/75R14; (Beretta) P185/70R14; (Corsica LTZ/Beretta GT) P205/60R15; Beretta conv/GTZ) 205/55R16; (Celeb) P185/75R14; (Lumina) P195/75R14; Lumina Euro) P195/70R15; (Caprice) P205/75R15; (Caprice wag) P225/75R15.

TECHNICAL: Transmission: Five-speed manual shift standard on Cavalier, Corsica/Beretta and Camaro. Three-speed automatic standard on Celebrity and Lumina. Four-speed overdrive automatic standard on Caprice. **Steering:** (Camaro/Caprice) recirculating ball; (others) rack and pinion. **Front Suspension:** (Cavalier) MacPherson struts with coil springs, lower control arms and stabilizer bar; (Corsica/Beretta) MacPherson struts with coil springs; (Camaro) modified MacPherson struts with coil springs; (Celeb) MacPherson struts with coil springs, lower control arms; (Lumina) MacPherson struts with coil springs and stabilizer bar; (Caprice) unequal-length control arms, coil springs, stabilizer bar. **Rear Suspension:** (Cavalier) trailing crank arm with twist beam axle and coil springs; (Camaro) Salibury axle and torque arm with ICA, coil springs and track bar; (Corsica/Beretta) trailing twist axle with coil springs; (Celeb) trailing arms with stamped control arms and open section; (Lumina) MacPherson struts with transverse leaf spring and stablilizer bar; (Caprice) rigid axle with four links, coil springs, stablilizer available. **Brakes:** front disc, rear drum; four-wheel discs standard on Lumina.

Body construction: unibody except (Caprice) separate body and frame.

Fuel tank: (Cav) 13.6 gal.; (Camaro) 15.5 gal.; (Corsica/Beretta) 15.6 gal.; (Celeb) 15.7 gal.; (Lumina) 17.1 gal.; (Caprice) 24.5 gal.; (Caprice wag) 22 gal.

DRIVETRAIN OPTIONS: Engines: 3.1-liter V-6: Cavalier wagon ($685); Corsica/Beretta ($685); Celeb/Lumina ($660). 305 cu. in. V-8: Camaro RS cpe ($350); Caprice sed ($440). 350 cu. in., V-8: Camaro IROC-Z ($300). **Transmission/Differential:** Three-speed automatic trans.: Cavalier ($465); Corsica/Beretta ($540). Four-speed overdrive auto. trans.: Camaro ($515); Celeb/Lumina V-6 ($200). Limited-slip differential: Caprice ($100). Performance axle ratio: ($21). Performance axle ratio w/dual exhausts: Camaro ($466). **Suspension:** F40 H.D. susp.: Caprice ($26). F41 sport susp.: Caprice ($49). Inflatable rear shock absorbers: Celeb/Caprice ($64).

1990 Cavalier sedan

CAVALIER CONVENIENCE/APPEARANCE OPTIONS: VL Preferred Equip. Grp 1, Pwr Strg; Body Side Moldings ($275). VL Preferred Equip. Grp 2, Pwr Strg; Tinted Glass; Spt LH Remote & RH Manual Mirrors; Body Side Moldings; Carpeted Mats ($443). Cavalier Preferred Equip. Grp 1; Folding split back rear seat; Intermittent Windshield Wiper System; Spt LH Remote & RH Manual Mirrors; Body Side Molding; Carpeted Mats ($318). Cavalier Preferred Equip Grp 2, 1JC37, 1JC69 only, Air Cond; Electronic Spd Control, w/resume Spd; Comfortilt Strg Wheel; Split Back, Folding Rr Seat; Intermittent Windshield Wiper System; Spt. LH Remote & RH Manual Mirrors; body Side Moldings; Color-Keyed Carpeted Mats ($1368). Cavalier Wgn Preferred Equip. Grp 2, Air Cond; Spd Control, w/resume Spd; Comfortilt Strg Wheel; Roof Carrier; Fldg. Rear Seat Split Back; Intermittent Windshield Wiper System; Spt LH Remote & RH Manual Mirrors; Body Side Moldings; Color-Keyed Carpeted Mats, F&R ($1483). Cavalier Preferred Equip. Grp. 3, 1JC37, 1JC69 only, Air Cond; Electronically Tuned AM/FM Stereo Radio, w/Seek & Scan, Stereo Cass Tape & Digital Clock w/extended range sound system; Pwr Windows; Pwr Dr Lock System; Spd Control; w/resume Spd; Comfortilt Strg Wheel; Folding Rr Seat Split Back; Intermittent Windshield Wiper System; Spt, LH Remote & RH Manual Mirrors; Body Side Moldings; Carpeted Mats Coupe ($1913). Sedan ($2018). Preferred Equip. Grp 3, 1JC35; Air Cond; Electronically Tuned AM/FM Stereo Radio, w/Seek & Scan, Stereo Cass Tape & Digital Clock, extended range sound system; Pwr Windows; Pwr Dr Lock System, Spd Control, w/resume Spd; Comfortilt Strg Wheel; Roof Carrier; Split Back, Fldg, Rear Seat; Intermittent Windshield Wiper System, Spt LH Remote & RH Manual Mirrors; Body Side Moldings, Carpeted Mats; F&R ($2133). Z24 Cpe Preferred Equip Grp 1, Air Cond; Dome Reading Lamp ($744). Z24 Cpe Preferred Equip. Grp. 2; Air Cond; Electronically Tuned AM/FM Stereo Radio, w/Seek & Scan, Stereo Cass Tape & Digital Clock, extended range sound system; Spd Control w/resume Spd; Comfortilt Strg Wheel; Intermittent Windshield Wiper System; Color-Keyed Carpeted Mats F&R; Dome Reading Lamp ($1302). Z24 Cpe Preferred Equip. Grp 3; Air Cond; Electronically tuned AM Stereo/FM Stereo Radio, w/Seek & Scan, Stereo s Tape w/Search & Repeat, Graphic Equalizer & Digital Clock, extended range sound system; Pwr Windows; Pwr Door Lock System; Electronic Spd Control, w/resume Spd; Comfortilt Wheel; Intermittent Windshield Wiper System; Pwr Trunk Opener; Carpeted Mats F&R; Dome Reading Lamp ($1907). Air Cond ($720). Frt License Plate Bracket ($NC). Deck Lid Carrier Black ($115). Roof Carrier ($115). Rr Window Defogger Electric ($160). Pwr Door Lock System Coupes ($175). Sedans & Wgns ($175). Calif Emission System ($100). Tinted Glass, All Windows ($105). Body Side Moldings, Std/Z24 ($50). Electronically Tuned AM/FM Stereo w/Seek & Scan & Digital Clock, extended range sound system VL ($332). Electronically tuned AM/FM Stereo w/Seek & Scan, Stereo Cass Tape & Digital Clock extended range sound system VL ($472); others ($140); Electronically Tuned AM Stereo & FM Stereo w/Seek & Scan, Stereo Cass. Tape w/Search & Repeat, Graphic Equalizer & Digital Clock extended range sound system ($150/290). R/S Sport Pkg ($405). Removable Sun Roof ($350). TIRES P185/80R13 All Seasons Steel Belted Radial White Stripe ($68). P195/70R14 All Seasons Steel Belted Radial Blackwall ($156). P215/60R14 All Seasons Steel Belted Radial White Outline Lettered ($102). Aluminum Painted Wheels ($265). Styled Steel Wheels (NC).

CAMARO CONVENIENCE/APPEARANCE OPTIONS: RS Coupe Preferred Equip. Grp 1, Air Cond; Electronically Tuned. AM/FM Stereo Radio, w/Seek & Scan, Stereo Cass Tape & Digital Clock, extended range sound system; Pwr Dr Lock System; Spd Control, w/resume Spd; Body Side Moldings ($1410). RS Coupe Preferred Equip. Grp. 2, Air Cond; Electronically tuned AM/FM Stereo Radio, w/Seek & Scan, Stereo Cass Tape & Digital Clock, extd range sound system; Pwr Windows; Pwr Dr Lock; Electronic Spd Control w/resume Spd; Pwr Hatch Release; Cargo Cover; Body Side Moldings, Carpeted Mats F&R; Mirror w/Dual Reading Lamps ($1782). IROC-Z Preferred Equip. Grp. 1; Air Cond. Body Side Moldings ($865). IROC-Z Preferred Equip. Grp. 2; Air Cond; Electronically tuned AM/FM Stereo Radio, w/Seek & Scan; Stereo Cass Tape & Digital Clock, extd. range sound system; Pwr Windows; Pwr Dr Lock System; Electronic Spd Control w/resume spd; Pwr Hatch Release; Cargo Cover; Body Side Moldings; Carpeted Mats, F&R ($1759). IROC-Z Preferred Equip. Grp. 3; Air Cond; Electronically Tuned AM/FM Stereo Radio; w/Seek & Scan, Stereo Cass Tape & Digital Clock, ext range sound system; Pwr Windows; Pwr Seat, drivers side only; Pwr Dr Lock System; Electronic Spd Control, w/resume spd; Pwr Hatch Release; Spt Electric Twin Remote Spt Mirrors; Cargo Cover, Body Side Moldings; Carpeted Mats F&R; Mirror, w/Dual Reading Lamps ($2143). RS Convertible Preferred Equip. Grp. 1; Air Cond; Electronically Tuned AM/FM Stereo Radio w/Seek & Scan, Stereo Cass Tape & Digital Clock, extended range sound system; Body Side Moldings; Carpeted Mats, F&R ($1040). RS Convertible Preferred Equip. Grp 2; Air Cond; Electronically Tuned AM/FM Stereo Radio w/Seek & Scan, Stereo Cass Tape & Digital Clock, extended range sound system; Pwr Windows; Pwr Dr Lock System; Spd Control, w/resume spd; Body Side Moldings; Carpeted Mats, FR&R ($1640). IROC-Z Convertible Preferred Equip. Grp 1; Air Cond; Body Side Moldings ($865). IROC-Z Convertible Preferred Equip. Grp. 2; Air Cond; Electronically tuned AM/FM Stereo Radio w/Seek & Scan, Stereo Cass Tape & Digital Clock, extended range sound system; Spd Control, w/resume Spd; Body Side Moldings; Carpeted Mats, F&R ($1640). IROC-Z Convertible Preferred Equip. Grp 3; Air Cond; Electronically Tuned AM/FM Stereo Radio, w/Seek & Scan, Stereo Cass Tape & Digital Clock, extended range sound system; Pwr Windows; Pwr Seat Driver Side only; Pwr Dr Lock System; Electronic Spd Control, w/resume Spd; Spt Electric Twin Remote Mirrors; Body Side Moldings; Carpeted Mats, F&R ($2001). Custom Cloth Bucket Seats ($327). Custom Leather Bucket Seats ($800). Air Cond, Incl increased cooling ($805). Frt License Plate Bracket (NC). Decal & Stripe Delete ($60 credit). Rear Window Defogger ($160). Pwr Door Lock System ($175). Calif Emission System ($100). Pwr Hatch Release ($50). Engine Block Heater ($20). Rr Window Louvers ($210). Spt. Twin Remote Electric Mirrors ($91). Electronically Tuned AM/FM Stereo w/Seek & Scan, Stereo Cass Tape & Digital Clock ($140). Electronically Tuned Delco/Bose Music System, Incl AM/FM Stereo w/Seek & Scan, Stereo Cass Tape & Digital Clock, special tone & balance control & 4 speakers ($875/1015). Removable Glass Roof Panels, Incl locks ($866). Cast Alum Wheels 16", incl wheel locks & P245/50 ZR16 SBR Blackwall Tires ($520).

1990 Corsica LTZ hatchback sedan

CORSICA CONVENIENCE/APPEARANCE OPTIONS: LT Preferred Equip. Grp. 1, Tinted Glass; Intermittent Windshield Wiper System; Carpeted Mats F&R, Map Lamps w/Consolette ($232). LT Preferred Equip. Grp 2; Air Cond; Spd Control, w/resume Spd; Comfortilt Strg Wheel; Tinted Glass; Intermittent Windshield Wipers System; Carpeted Mats F&R; Map Lamps w/Consolette ($1342). LT Preferred Equip. Grp 3; Air Cond. Electronically Tuned AM/FM Stereo Radio, w/Seek & Scan, Stereo Cass Tape & Digital Clock, extended range sound system; Pwr Windows; Pwr Dr Lock System; Electronic Spd Control, w/resume Spd; Comfortilt Strg Wheel; Tinted Glass; Intermittent Windshield Wiper Trunk/Hatch Opener; Carpeted Mats F&R; Map Lamps w/Consolette ($2042). LTZ Preferred Equip. Grp. 1, Electronic Spd Control, w/resume Spd; Comfortilt Strg Wheel; Carpeted Mats F&R ($363). LTZ Preferred Equip. Grp 2; Electronically Tuned AM/FM Stereo Radio, w/Seek & Scan, Stereo Cass Tape & Digital Clcok, extended range sound system; Pwr Windows; Pwr Dr Lock System; Electronic Spd Control, w/resume Spd; Comfortilt Strg Wheel; Pwr Trunk Opener; Carpeted Mats, F&R ($1063). Custom Cloth CL Bucket Seats Sedan ($425). Hatchback ($275). Sport Cloth Bucket, Inc w/LTZ (NC). Custom Two-Tone Paint ($123). Air Cond, Incl increased cooling, Std on LTZ ($780). Frt License Plate Bracket (NC). Deck Lid Carrier, Black ($115). Floor Mounted Console ($60). Rear Window Defogger Electric ($160). Pwr Door Lock System ($215). Calif Emission System ($100). Gauge Pkg w/Tachometer, Incl Voltmeter, Oil Pressure, Temperature Gauges & Trip Odometer, Std on LTZ ($139). Electronically Tuned AM/FM Stereo Radio, w/Seek & Scan, Stereo Cass Tape & Digital Clock Incl extended range sound system ($140). Electronically Tuned AM Stereo/FM Stereo Radio, w/Seek & Scan, Stereo Cass Tape w/Search & Repeat, Graphic Equalizer & Digital Clock Incl extended range sound system ($150/290). TIRES P185/75 R14 All Seasons SBR White Stripe ($68). Styled Wheels ($56).

1990 Corsica LTZ sedan

1990 Beretta coupe

BERETTA CONVENIENCE/APPEARANCE OPTIONS: Preferred Equip. Grp. 1; Intermittent Windshield Wipers System; Carpeted Mats F&R; Map Lamps w/Consolette ($112). Preferred Equip. Grp. 2; Air Cond; Spd Control, w/resume Spd; Comfortilt Strg Wheel; Intermittent Windshield Wiper System; Carpeted Mats, F&R; Map Lamps w/Consolette ($1222). Preferred Equip. Grp. 3; Air Cond; Electronically Tuned AM/FM Stereo Radio, w/Seek & Scan; Stereo Cass Tape & Digital Clock, Extd range sound system, Pwr Windows; Pwr Dr Lock System; Electronic Spd Control, w/resume Spd; Comfortilt Strg Wheel; Intermittent Windshield Wiper System; Pwr Trunk Opener; Carpeted Mats F&R; Map Lamps w/Consolette ($1817). GT Preferred Equip. Grp. 1, Electronic Spd Control, w/resume Spd; Comfortilt Strg Wheel; Intermittent Windshield Wiper System; Carpeted Mats F&R; Map Lamps w/Consolette ($442). GT Preferred Equip. Grp.2, Electronically Tuned AM/FM Stereo Radio, w/Seek & Scan, Stereo Cass Tape & Digital Clock, Extd. range sound system; Pwr Windows; Pwr Dr Lock System, Electronic Spd Control, w/resume Spd; Comfortilt Str Wheel; Intermittent Windshield Wiper System; Pwr Trunk Opener; Carpeted Mats F&R; Map Lamps w/Consolette ($1037). GTZ Preferred Equip. Grp. 1; Electronic Spd Control, w/resume Spd; Comfortilt Strg Wheel; Carpeted Mats F&R ($363). GTZ Preferred Equip. Grp. 2; Electronically Tuned AM/FM Stereo Radio, w/Seek & Scan; Stereo Cass Tape & Digital Clock, Extd range sound system; Pwr Windows; Pwr Dr Lock System, Pwr Spd Control, Electronic w/resume Spd; Comfortilt Strg Wheel; Pwr Trunk Opener, Carpeted Mats F&R ($958). Custom Two-Tone Paint ($123). Air Cond, Incl w/GT & GTZ ($780). Frt License Plate Bracket (NC). Deck Lid Carrier, Black ($115). Rr Window Defogger, Electric ($160). Pwr Door Lock System ($175). Electronic Instrumentation; Speedometer Bar Graph & Digital readout, Incl Tachometer ($156). Electronically Tuned AM/FM Stereo Radio, w/Seek & Scan, Stereo Cass Tape & Digital Clock, Incl extd range sound system ($140). Electronically Tuned AM Stereo/FM Stereo Radio w/Seek & Scan, Stereo Cass Tape w/Search & Repeat, Graphic Equalizer & Digital Clock, Incl extd range sound system ($150/290). Manual Sun roof, Removable ($350). Alum Wheels w/Locks ($210).

CELEBRITY CONVENIENCE/APPEARANCE OPTIONS:
Wgn Preferred Equip. Grp. 1; Air Cond; Molding Pkg; Aux Lighting; Color-Keyed Mats F&R ($921). Wgn Preferred Equip. Grp. 2; Air Cond; Pwr Dr Lock System; Electronic Spd Control, w/resume Spd; Comfortilt Strg Wheel, Roof Carrier (Blk); Gauge Pkg w/Trip Odometer; Ext Molding Pkg; pwr Liftgate Release; Aux Lighting; Color-Keyed, F&R ($1710). Wgn Preferred Equip. Grp. 3, Air Cond; Electronically Tuned AM/FM Stereo Radio, w/Seek & Scan, Stereo Cass Tape & Digital Clock w/ext range sound system; Pwr Windows; Pwr Dr Lock System; Spd Control, w/resume Spd; Comfortilt Strg Wheel; Roof Carrier (blk); Gauge Pkg w/Trip Odometer; Exterior Molding Pkg; Pwr Liftgate Rlease; Cargo Area Security Pkg; Aux Lighting; Deluxe Rr Compartment Decor; Spt Twin Remote Mirrors; Color-keyed Flr Mats F&R ($2269). Eurosport Wgn Base Equip. Grp; Air Cond; 3.1L Eng; 4 Spd Auto Trans ($1895). Eurosport Wgn Preferred Equipment Grp 1; Air Cond; 3.1L Eng; 4 Spd Auto Trans; Molding Pkg; Aux Lighting; Color-keyed Mats F&R ($2011). Eurosport Wgn Preferred Equip. Grp. 2, Air Cond; 3.1L Eng; 4 Spd Auto Trans; Pwr Dr Lock system; Electronic Spd Control, w/resume Spd; Comfortilt Strg Wheel; Roof Carrier (Blk); Gauge Pkg, w/Trip Odometer; Exterior Molding Pkg; Powr Liftgate Release; Aux Lighting; Color-keyed Flr Mats F&R ($2800). Eurosport Wgn Preferred Equip. Grp. 3; Air Cond; 3.1L Eng; 4 Spd Auto Trans; Electronically Tuned Am/FM Stereo Radio, w/Seek & Scan, Stereo Cass Tape & Digital Clock w/extd range sound system; Pwr Windows; Pwr Dr Lock System; Electronic Spd Control, w/resume Spd; Comfortilt Steering Wheel; Roof Carrier (Blk); Gauge Pkg w/Trip Odometer; Molding Pkdg; Pwr Liftgate Release; Cargo Area Security Pkg; Aux Lighting; Deluxe Rr Compartment Decor; Spt Twin Remote Mirrors; Color-keyed Flr Mats F&R ($3349). Cloth 55/45 Seat ($133). Air Cond ($805). Frt License Plate Bracket (NC). Rear Window Defogger Electric ($160). Calif Emission System ($100). Pwr Dr Lock System ($215). 6-Way Pwr Seat, Driver Side ($270). Electronically Tuned AM/FM Stereo Radio, w/Seek & Scan, Stereo Cass Tape & Digital Clock, Incl extd range sound system ($140). Pwr Recling Seat Backs, Driver & Pass ($110). TIRES P185/75R14 All Season Steel Belted Radial White Stripe ($68). Sport Wheel Covers ($65). Cast Alum Wheels ($195). Rear Window Wiper/Washer ($125).

LUMINA CONVENIENCE/APPEARANCE OPTIONS:
Preferred Equip. Grp 1; Air Cond; Electronic Spd Control, w/resume Spd; Comfortilt Strg Wheel; Carpeted Mats F&R ($1180). Lumina Preferred Equip. Grp. 2; Air Cond; Pwr Windows; Pwr Dr Lock System; Spd Control, w/resume Spd; Comfortilt Strg Wheel; Pwr Trunk Opener; Pwr Mirrors, Spt. Twin Remote; Carpeted Mats F&R; Coupe ($1665). Sedan ($1770). Euro Preferred Equip. Grp. 1; Electronic Spd Control, w/resume Spd; Comfortilt Strg Wheel; Gauge Pkg w/Tachometer; Carpeted Mats F&R ($475). Euro Preferred Equip. Grp. 2; Electronically tuned AM/FM Stereo Radio, w/Seek & Scan, Stereo Cass Tape & Digital Clock, extended range sound system; Pwr Windows; Pwr Dr Lock System; Electronic Pwr Spd Control, w/resume Spd; Comfortilt Strg Wheel; Pwr Trunk Opener; Gauge Pkg. w/Tachometer; Spt Twin Remote Mirrors; Carpeted Mats F&R; Coupe ($1100). Sedan ($1205). Custom Cloth Bucket Seats w/console ($299). Custom Cloth 60/40 Seat ($199). Cloth 60/40 Seat ($159). Air Cond, Std.Euro ($805). Frt License Plate Bracket (NC). Rear Window Defogger Electric ($160). Pwr Door Lock System; Coupe ($175). Sedan ($215). Calif Emission System ($100). Electronically Tuned AM/FM Stereo Radio, w/Seek & Scan; Stereo Cass Tape & Digital Clock, Incl extd range sound system ($140). Pwr 6-way Driver's Seat ($270). Rear Spoiler, Delete ($128). TIRES P195/75 R14 All Seasons Steel Belted Radial White Stripe ($72). P215/60 R16 All Seasons Steel Belted Radial Black Wall ($76). Alum Wheels ($250).

CAPRICE CONVENIENCE/APPEARANCE OPTIONS: Caprice Sdn Preferred Equip. Grp. 1; Body Side Moldings; Carpeted Mats F&R; Extended Range Spkrs; Wheel Opening Moldings ($170). Caprice Sdn Preferred Equip. Grp. 2; pwr Dr Lock System; Spd Control, w/resume Spd; Comfortilt Strg Wheel; Body Side Moldings, Intermittent Windshield Wiper System; Aux Lighting; Color-keyed Carpeted Mats F&R; Extd Range Spkrs; Wheel Opening Moldings ($820). Caprice Classic Sdn Preferred Equip. Grp. 1; Spd Control, w/resume Spd; Comfortilt Strg Wheel; P205/75R15 All Seasons SBR White Stripe Tires; Body Side Moldings; Intermittent Windshield Wiper System; Pwr Trunk Opener; Aux Lighting; Color-keyed Carpeted Mats F&R; Extd Range Spkrs; Spt Twin Remote Mirrors ($713). Caprice Classic Sdn Preferred Equip Grp 2; Elect Tuned AM/FM Stereo Radio, w/Seek & Scan, Stereo Cass Tape, Digital Clock & pwr Antenna; extd range sound system; Pwr Windows; Pwr 6-Way Driver & Pass Seats; Pwr Dr Lock System; Spd Control, w/resume Spd; Comfortilt Strg Wheel; P205/75R15 All Seasons SBR White Stripe Tires; Body Side Moldings; Luggage Compartment Trim; Intermittent Windshield Wiper System; Pwr Trunk Opener; Aux Lighting; RH Visor Illum Mirror; Carpeted mats; Spt Twin Remote Mirrors; W50/50 Sets, Incl Driver & Pass Pwr Seats ($1547). Caprice Classic Wgn Preferred Equip. Grp. 1; Body Side Moldings; Aux Lighting; Dlx Load Flr Carpeting; Spt Twin Remote Mirrors ($211). Caprice Classic Wgn Preferred Equip. Grp. 2; Electronically Tuned AM/FM Stereo Radio, w/Seek & Scan, Stereo Cass Tape; pwr Antenna & Digital Clock; Dual Rear Spkrs; Pwr Windows, Pwr Dr Lock System; Incl Tailgate Lock; Spd Control, w/resume Spd; Comfortilt Strg Wheel; Roof Carrier; Body Side Moldings; Aux Lighting; Intermittent Windshield Wiper System; Dlx Load Floor Carpeting; Carpeted mats, Spt Twin-Remote Mirrors ($1556). Caprice Classic Wgn Preferred Equip. Grp. 3; Elect Tuned AM/FM Stereo Radio, w/Seek & Scan; Stereo Cass Tape, Graphic Equalizer, Pwr Antenna & Digital Clock; Dual Rear Spkrs; Pwr Windows; pwr Dr Lock System, Incl Tailgate Lock; Pwr 6-way Drive & Pass Seats; Spd Control, w/resume spd; Deluxe Rear Compartment Decor; Comfortilt Strg Wheel, Roof Carrier; Gauge Pkg w/Trip Odometer; Body Side Moldings; Twilight Sentinel Headlamps; Intermittent Windshield Wiper System; Aux Lighting; Cornering Lamps; RH Visor Illum Mirror; Carpeted Mats; Spt Twin Remote Mirrors; w/50/50 Seats, Incl Driver & Pass Pwr Seats ($2475). W/Bench Seat ($1935). Caprice Classic Brghm Preferred Equip. Grp. 1; P205/75R15 SBR White Stripe Tires; Gauge Pkg W/Trip Odometer; Body Side Moldings; Twilight Sentinel; Pwr Trunk Opener; RH Visor Illum Mirror; Carpeted Mats; Extd Range Spkrs; Spt Twin Remote Mirrors ($470). Caprice Brghm Preferred Equip. Grp. 2; Elect Tuned AM/FM Stereo Radio, w/Seek & Scan, Stereo Cass Tape, Pwr Ant & Digital Clock, Extd Range Sound System; Pwr Windows; Pwr 6-way Driver & Pass Seats; Pwr Dr Lock System, Electronic w/resume Spd; Wire Wheel Covers w/locks; Comfortilt Strg Wheel; P205/75R15 All Seasons SBR White Stripe Tires; Gauge Pkg w/Trip Odometer; Body Side Moldings; Twlight Sentinel Headlamps; Deluxe Luggage Comp Trim; Intermittent Windshield Wiper System; Cornering Lamps, Pwr Trunk Opener; RH Visor Illum Mirror; Carpeted Mats, Spt Twin Remote Mirrors ($2384).

Caprice Classic Brghm LS Preferred Equip Grp 1, Elect Tuned AM/FM Stereo Radio 2/Seek & Scan, Stereo Cass Tape, Pwr Antenna & Digital Clock, Exted Range Sound System, Pwr Windows, Pwr 6-way Driver & Pass Seats; Pwr Dr Lock System; Electronic Spd Control w/resume Spd; Wire Wheel Covers w/Locks; Comfortilt Strg Wheel; P205/75R15 All Season SBR White Stripe Tires; Gauge Pkg w/Trip Odometer; Body Side Moldings; Twilight Sentinel; Intermittent Windshield Wiper System; Pwr Trunk Opener; RH Visor Illum Mirro, Carpeted Mats; Spt Twin Remote Mirrors ($2270). Caprice Classic Brghm LS Preferred Equip. Grp. 2; Elect Tuned AM/FM Stereo Radio w/Seek & Scan, Stereo Cass Tape, Graphic Equalizer, pwr Antenna & Digital Clock; Extd Range Sound System; Pwr Windows; Pwr 6-way Driver & Pass Seats; Pwr Dr Lock System, Electronic Spd Control, w/resume Spd; Wire Wheel Covers w/Locks; Comfortilt Strg Wheel; P205/75R15 All Season SBR White Stripe Tires; Gauge Pkg w/Trip Odometer; Body Side Moldings, Twilight Sentinel Headlights; Deluxe Luggage Compartment Trim; Intermittent Windshield Wiper System; Cornering Lamps; Pwr Trunk Opener; RH Visor Illum Mirror; Carpeted Mats; Spt Twin Remote Mirrors ($2494). Vinyl Bench Seat Caprice Sedan ($28). Caprice Classic Wgn ($172). Vinyl 50/50 Seat Caprice Sedan ($305). Caprice Classic Wgn ($103). Cloth 50/50 Seat ($275). Cloth 45/55 Seat (NC). Leather 45/55 Seat ($550). Custom Two-Tone Paint; Incl lower body accent, color-keyes striping & o/s dr handle inserts ($141). Full Vinyl Roof Cover ($200). Air Deflector, Rr Window ($65). Frt License Plate Bracket (NC). Trunk Cargo Net ($30). H.D. Cooling ($40). Rear Window Defogger Electric ($160). pwr Dr Lock System Electric Sedans ($215). Wgn Incl Tailgate Lock ($290). Calif Emission System ($100). Estate Equipment ($307). Engine Block Heater ($20). Elect Tuned AM/FM Stereo w/Seek & Scan, Stereo Cass Tape & Digital Clock ($140-250). Elect Tuned AM/FM Stereo w/Seek & Scan, Stereo Cass Tape, Graphic Equalizer & Digital Clock ($110-360). Pin Striping Color-keyed ($61). TIRES: P205/75R15 All Seasons SBR White Stripe ($76). P225/79R15 SBR White Stripe ($188). Custom Wheel Covers Std on Brghm ($65). Wire Wheel Cover w/Locks ($150). Brghm ($150). All except Brghm ($215).

CORVAIR

1960-1969

The Chevrolet Corvair, introduced in the fall of 1959 as a 1960 model, is perhaps the most significant automobile of the postwar era. The controversy surrounding the han-

dling qualities of the 1960-1963 Corvairs inspired Ralph Nader to write a best-selling book on "the designed-in dangers of the American automobile." Entitled *Unsafe At Any Speed* that book ushered in a new era of zealous governmental regulation that continues to this day.

By Tony Hossain

The Corvair was a wholly unconventional automobile. It measured a tight 180 inches in overall length and it sat on a compact 108 inch wheelbase. An aluminum, air-cooled, horizontally-opposed six cylinder engine was rear-mounted, as in the popular German Volkswagen. The fully independent suspension system used coil springs all around and swing axles in the rear. An oddly shaped trunk was up front, where the engine was on all other American

cars. The Corvair's primary competition, the Ford Falcon and the Plymouth Valiant, were also introduced in the 1960 model year. But they were, basically, scaled down versions of bigger cars.

Auto enthusiasts loved the new Corvair. *Motor Trend* Magazine proclaimed it 'Car of the Year.' The buff books liked the quick handling qualities, the gutsy sounding rear engine and the European flavor of Chevy's new small car.

Unfortunately the public was unsure. The conventionally engineered Ford Falcon outsold the Corvair by a wide margin in 1960.

It was the Monza Club Coupe, introduced in April, 1960 that saved the day for the Corvair. By 1961 the Monza, with its luxurious appointments and sporty bucket seats, was outselling every other Corvair model. The Corvair had found its niche, not as a small family compact but as an economical sporty car. Monza owners found out that four-speed transmissions and agile handling made driving a lot more fun.

In mid-1962 the station wagon Corvair, never very popular, was phased out. The Monza convertible took its place on the assembly line. Also making its debut in 1962 was the Monza Spyder option, with its handling suspension and turbocharged engine.

An all-new Corvair arrived in 1965. The lines were very smooth and would characterize GM styling for years to come. Once again, the Corvair was one of America's style leaders. A new rear suspension, Corvette-inspired, corrected some of the oversteering tendencies of the original

design and in turbocharged form horsepower ratings went as high as 180. But it was too late. On April 17, 1964 the Ford Motor Company introduced the car that quickly took over the 'Monza market' that Chevy had discovered four years earlier. That car was the Mustang.

With the bad publicity stemming from Ralph Nader's book and the public's preference for the relatively unsophisticated, but brutally powerful V-8 Mustang, Corvair sales plummeted in 1966. Chevy introduced the Camaro

in 1967 but the Corvair limped along as an afterthought in the Division's model line for two more years. The last Corvair built, a gold Monza coupe, left the Willow Run, Michigan assembly line on May 14, 1969.

1960 CORVAIR

1960 Corvair, Series 500 4-dr sedan, 6-cyl

CORVAIRS STANDARD — (SIX) — SERIES 500 — The first Corvair was publicly introduced on October 2, 1959. Its lightweight air-cooled rear engine, unique suspension system and rear mounted transaxle drive setup were a radical departure from other American cars of the day. All of the compact Corvairs were just over four feet high and 15 feet in overall length. All were designed to seat six people. Unitized construction of frame and body was a technical advance for Corvair's maker, Chevrolet. The Series 500 models were the standard line. Equipment features included electric windshield wipers; lefthand sun visor; turn signals and five tubeless black sidewall tires. Other items found in all 1960 Corvairs were friction type ventipane latches; single key locking system; pushbutton outside door handles; dual horizontal headlamps; front ash tray and center dome light with instrument panel switch. The sole model available at introduction time was the four-door sedan, but a standard 500 Series two-door coupe was a running addition to the line in January, 1960.

VEHICLE IDENTIFICATION NUMBERS: The numbering system and code locations were the same as for Chevrolet models. Corvair Serial Numbers were located on the left center body pillar. Twelve numbers appeared. The first symbol designated the model year ('0' = 1960). The second and third symbols designated the series ('05' = 500; '07' = 700; '09' = 900 Monza). The fourth and fifth symbols designated the type of body (See second column of charts below). The sixth symbol designated the assembly plant. The following group of symbols was the sequential unit production number. The Corvair production sequence began at 100001 and went up from there at each factory where Corvair production was quartered. Body Style Numbers were comprised of the two-digit series and body type codes and appeared, on the vehicle, with a two-digit model year prefix (for example: 60-0569, for a 1960 Corvair 500 four-door sedan). In this catalog, the main Body Style Number appears in the second column of charts; the prefix is not shown, but will always correspond to the year. The Engine Number for Corvairs is stamped on top of the block, ahead of the generator/oil filter adapter. It consists of six or seven symbols, the first identifying the point of manufacture; the next two indicating month of manufacture and the final one or two symbols identifying the horsepower and the type of transmission attachment.

STANDARD SERIES 500

Series Number	Body/Style Number	Body Type & Seating	Factory Price	Shipping Weight	Production Total
500	0569	4-dr Sed-6P	2038	2305	47,683
500	0527	2-dr Clb Cpe-6P	1984	2270	14,628

CORVAIR 500 SERIES ENGINE DATA
Horizontally opposed Six. Overhead valves. Aluminum block. Displacement: 140 (139.6) cubic inches. Bore and stroke: 3.375 x 2.60 inches. Compression ratio: 8.0:1. Brake horsepower: 80 at 4400 R.P.M. Four main bearings. Hydraulic valve lifters. Carburetor: Two (2) Rochester one-barrels Model 7015311.

1960 Corvair, Series 700 4-dr sedan, 6-cyl (AA)

CORVAIR DELUXE — (SIX) — SERIES 700 — Corvairs in the Series 700 line were DeLuxe models. Standard equipment included everything found on Corvair 500s, plus righthand sun visor; chrome exterior moldings; front arm rest; cigarette lighter and upgraded upholstery design. There were also dual horns; automatic front door dome light switches; luggage compartment mat; colored-keyed floor mats and a choice of three different interior trims. Like the standard models, the Corvair DeLuxe 700 came only as a four-door sedan at first, but a two-door coupe was added to the line in January, 1960. As opposed to the four-door sedan's flat-top, overhanging roof styling, the two-door edition had a smooth, flowing roofline with large, curved glass backlight.

CORVAIR DELUXE SERIES 700

Series Number	Body/Style Number	Body Type & Seating	Factory Price	Shipping Weight	Production Total
700	0769	4-dr Sed-6P	2103	2315	139,208
700	0727	2-dr Clb Cpe-6P	2049	2290	36,562

CORVAIR 700 SERIES ENGINE
See 1960 Corvair 500 Series engine data.

CORVAIR MONZA — (SIX) — SERIES 900 — The sporty Corvair Monza two-door Club Coupe made its debut at the Chicago Auto Show, in February 1960, as a show car. It was a dressed up DeLuxe 700 coupe with bucket seats and a sun roof. Public response prompted the release of a production model, bearing the same name, in May of the year. Standard equipment included bucket seats with chrome trim; stainless steel rocker sill moldings; special wheel covers; bright metal seat and arm rest moldings; leather-like vinyl upholstery; chrome simulated rear deck air vents; folding rear seat; rear ash trays; dual sun visors and glove box light, plus all other Series 700 features.

MONZA SERIES 900

Series Number	Body/Style Number	Body Type & Seating	Factory Price	Shipping Weight	Production Total
900	0927	2-dr Clb Cpe-5P	2238	2280	11,926

MONZA 900 SERIES ENGINE
See 1960 Corvair 500 Series engine data.

CHASSIS FEATURES: Wheelbase: (all models) 108 inches. Overall length: (all models) 180 inches. Front tread: (all models) 54 inches. Rear tread (all models) 54 inches. Tires: (all models) 6.50 x 13.

POWERTRAIN OPTIONS: Three-speed manual transmission was standard. Automatic transmission ($146). Six-cylinder 140 cubic inch 95 horsepower dual one-barrel engine ($27). Heavy-duty battery ($3). Available rear axle gear ratios: (standard) 3.55:1; (optional) 3.89:1.

CONVENIENCE OPTIONS: Rear axle with 3.89:1 ratio gearing ($2). Heater ($74). Padded dash ($18). Manual radio ($54). Rear folding seat, standard in Monza ($32). Wheel trim rings ($11). Five (5) white sidewall tires, 6.50 x 13, four-ply ($21). Two-tone paint in selected schemes was offered as R.P.O., only. Undergear paint was always black. Wheel paint was determined by color and tire equipment. Comfort and Convenience Group: including left outside rearview mirror, push-button windshield washers; backup lights and glove box light ($32). DeLuxe Body Equipment Group: including cigarette lighter; righthand sun visor; front arm rests, for standard models only ($11).

Historical footnotes: The first Corvairs were introduced October 2, 1959 and the Monza appeared in dealer showrooms during May. Model year production peaked at 250,007 units. Calendar year sales of 250,000 cars were recorded. Ed Cole was the Chief Executive Officer of Chevrolet this year. Automatic transmission (Powerglide) was installed in 63.5 percent of all 1960 Corvairs, 39.8 percent had radios: 90.2 percent had heaters; 55 percent had whitewall tires; 42.6 percent windshield washers; 42.6 percent backup lamps and only 0.6 percent had E-Z-Eye tinted windshields. Series production amounted to 62,300 Standards; 175,800 DeLuxes and 11,900 Monzas.

1961 CORVAIR

1961 Corvair Greenbrier Sports Wagon, 6-cyl

CORVAIR — (SIX) — SERIES 500 — The Corvair line was expanded for 1961. New models included a station wagon, van type Sports Wagon and three half-ton trucks. (See Krause Publication's *Std. Catalog of American Light-Duty Trucks* for information on Chevrolet trucks). On all models, the spare tire was relocated over the rear engine compartment. Corvairs were advertised and promoted as the lowest-priced Chevrolets. New styling features included a convex nose panel; Corvair lettering (replaced Chevrolet lettering) on rear deck and wider Chevrolet insignia housing on front panel. Series nameplates on 500 models were repositioned to a point high on the sides of the front fenders, but below the belt molding, in the cowl region of the body. Standard equipment for the base series was comprised of directional signals: lefthand sun visor; dual electric windshield wipers; folding rear seat (in Lakewood station wagon) and five 6.50 x 13 black sidewall tubeless tires available except on Lakewood models which used 7.00 x 13 blackwall tubeless. Gray, Green or Blue interior trims, of slightly improved quality, were provided. With the rear seat folded, the new Lakewood station wagons provided 58 cubic feet of load space. The 500 Series Lakewood lasted only this one model year.

VEHICLE IDENTIFICATION NUMBERS: The numbering system and code locations were the same as for previous models with the first symbol changed to a '1' to indicate 1961 model year. New Body Style Numbers identified the Lakewood station wagons.

CORVAIR SERIES 500

Series Number	Body/Style Number	Body Type & Seating	Factory Price	Shipping Weight	Production Total
500	0569	4-dr Sed-6P	1974	2355	18,752
500	0527	2-dr Clb Cpe-5P	1920	2320	16,857
500	0535	4-dr Sta Wag-6P	2266	2530	5,591

CORVAIR SERIES 500 ENGINE
Horizontally opposed Six. Overhead valves. Aluminum block. Displacement: 145 (144.8) cubic inches. Bore and stroke: 3.438 x 2.609 inches. Compression ratio: 8.0:1. Brake horsepower: 80 at 4400 R.P.M. Four main bearings. Hydraulic valve lifters. Carburetor: Two (2) Rochester one-barrel Model 7019101.

1961 Corvair, Series 700 2-dr Club Coupe, 6-cyl

CORVAIR — (SIX) — SERIES 700 — Corvair's middle-priced models wore '700' nameplates on the cowl sides of the fenders. They had all equipment included on the base-level cars, plus chrome exterior moldings; interiors with richer trims; dual horns; coat hooks and automatic light switches that were rigged to operate when the front door was opened.

CORVAIR DELUXE SERIES 700

Series Number	Body/Style Number	Body Type & Seating	Factory Price	Shipping Weight	Production Total
700	0769	4-dr Sed-6P	2039	2380	51,948
700	0727	2-dr Clb Cpe-5P	1985	2350	24,786
700	0735	4-dr Sta Wag-6P	2330	2555	20,451

1961 Corvair, Series 700 4-dr Lakewood station wagon, 6-cyl

CORVAIR SERIES 700 ENGINE
See 1961 Corvair 500 Series engine data.

CORVAIR MONZA — (SIX) — SERIES 900 — Behind the front wheel well of Monza models, a special ornament bearing the 900 Series designation could be seen. Wheelcovers were the same as used on 1961 500 and 700 models. Standard were all features of 700 Series Corvairs, plus front bucket seats; carpeting; all-vinyl interior trim; was standard on two-door Monzas only, while the four-door used a vinyl/cloth combination, front arm rests; cigarette lighter; righthand sun visor; backup lights; DeLuxe steering wheel; glove box light; rear arm rests (sedan) and folding rear seat. The Monza sedan was not available at fall introduction time, but became a running addition to the line soon thereafter. Prices for both Monzas were identical. Interestingly, Chevrolet reduced the rated passenger capacity of all 1961 club coupes by one person. Thus, the coupes in the 500 and 700 DeLuxe Series were not rated as five-passenger models, while the Monza coupe — with bucket seats — was classified a four place car.

CORVAIR MONZA SERIES 900

Series Number	Body/Style Number	Body Type & Seating	Factory Price	Shipping Weight	Production Total
900	0969	4-dr Sed-6P	2201	2420	33,745
900	0927	2-dr Clb Cpe-4P	2201	2395	109,945

MONZA 900 SERIES ENGINE
See 1961 Corvair 500 Series engine data.

CHASSIS FEATURES: Wheelbase: (all models) 108 inches. Overall length: (all models) 180 inches. Front tread: (all models) 54 inches. Rear tread: (all models) 54 inches. Tires: (Lakewood) 7.00 x 13; (all other models) 6.50 x 13.

POWERTRAIN OPTIONS: Three-speed manual transmission was standard. Powerglide automatic transmission ($157). Four-speed manual floor shift transmission ($650). Six-cylinder 145 cubic inch 98 horsepower dual one-barrel engine ($27). Heavy-duty battery ($5). Special crankcase vent ($4). Generator, 35-amp ($38). Available rear axle gear ratios: (standard) 3.27:1; (optional) 3.55.1, but standard in wagons; with air conditioning, or with automatic and 98 hp engine. 3.89:1 optional.

CONVENIENCE OPTIONS: Wheel covers, standard on Monza ($11). Rear door arm rests for 500/700 four-door sedan ($10). Comfort and Convenience Group, 500/700 four-door sedan ($39). Comfort and Convenience Group, Monza ($28). DeLuxe body equipment, 500/700 models ($11). Tinted glass, all windows ($27); windshield only ($13). Direct-air heater ($74). Gasoline operated heater ($92). Padded dash, all models ($18). Spare wheel lock ($5). Two-tone paint finish ($11). Manual radio ($54). Pushbutton radio ($62). Folding rear seat 500/700 coupes and sedans ($27). Heavy-duty shock absorbers ($8). Windshield washer ($11). Two-speed windshield wipers ($16).

1961 Corvair, Series 700 4-dr sedan, 6-cyl

Historical footnotes: The 1961 Corvairs were introduced October 8, 1960 and the Monza sedan appeared in dealer showrooms at mid-season. Model year production peaked at 297,881 units. Calendar year sales of 316,028 cars were recorded. Semon E. 'Bunkie' Knudsen was the Chief Executive Officer of the company this year. On a model year basis, 60.1 percent of 1961 Corvairs had automatic transmission installed; 49.2 percent had radios; 95.4 percent had heaters; 42.5 percent bucket seats; 69.6 percent whitewall tires; 48 percent windshield washers; 24.4 percent tinted glass; 50.9 percent backup lights and one percent had a new, mid-year option, air conditioning. An interesting comparison can be made, between the entire 1961 model year and the first few months of 1962 model production, to show how fast the popularity of bucket seats was growing. A total of 132,000 models built to 1961 specifications had this option, but by December of 1961, there had been 70,470 Corvairs (1962 models) already built with bucket seats.

1962 CORVAIR

1962 Corvair, Monza Spyder 2-dr convertible, 6-cyl (AA)

CORVAIR — SIX — SERIES 500 — There were no significant changes in the 1962 Corvair. After a year of strong sales, Chevrolet decided to leave well enough alone. Revision was seen in the front, side and rear trim; redesigned hub caps and plusher interiors. A V-shaped ornament was placed at the center of the front panel. It was flanked by thin, horizontally divided, simulated air vents on either side. Model nameplates were still on the sides of the front fenders. Interior on the 500 Series models were comparable to the previous DeLuxe trims. They came in vinyl and cloth combinations (with a checkered pattern) in colors of Aqua, Red or Fawn (Tan). Standard equipment included directional signals; lefthand sun visor; electric windshield wipers; heater and defroster; rubber floor mats; front foam seat cushions and five 6.50 x 13 black sidewall tubeless tires. The Corvair 500 Lakewood station wagon was no longer on the market and the four-door sedan was gone too.

VEHICLE IDENTIFICATION NUMBERS: The numbering system and code locations were the same as for previous models, with the first symbol changed to a '2' to indicate 1962 model year. A new convertible used Body Style Number '0967' the '09' designating Monza Series and the '67' designating the new body type.

CORVAIR SERIES 500

Model Number	Body/Style Number	Body Type & Seating	Factory Price	Shipping Weight	Production Total
500	0527	2-dr Clb Cpe-5P	1992	2350	16,245

CORVAIR SERIES ENGINE
Horizontally opposed Six. Overhead valves. Aluminum block. Displacement: 145 cubic inches. Bore and stroke: 3.43 x 2.60 inches. Compression ratio: 8.0:1. Brake horsepower: 80 at 4400 R.P.M. Four main bearings. Hydraulic valve lifters. Carburetor: Two (2) Rochester one-barrel Model 702101.

CORVAIR — (SIX) — SERIES 700 — The Corvair 700 DeLuxe Series models had all equipment found on the basic line, plus extra chrome exterior moldings; dual horns; ungraded upholstery and, on station wagons, a folding rear seat and 7.00 x 13 black sidewall tires. The Lakewood was dropped in the middle of the model run, since it was in direct competition with the new Chevy II station wagon. The latter car was cheaper to build and easier to sell, due to its greater conventionality. Model nameplates on 700s were located ahead of the front wheel housing. Another trim change was that the upper belt molding no longer ran entirely around the cars.

CORVAIR SERIES 700

Model Number	Body/Style Number	Body Type & Seating	Factory Price	Shipping Weight	Production Total
700	0769	4-dr Sed-6P	2111	2410	35,368
700	0727	2-dr Clb Cpe-5P	2057	2390	18,474
700	0735	4-dr Sta Wag-6P	2407	2590	3,716

CORVAIR SERIES 700 ENGINE
See 1962 Corvair 500 Series engine data.

1962 Corvair, Series 900 Monza 2-dr Club Coupe, 6-cyl

CORVAIR MONZA — (SIX) — SERIES 900 — The Monza was becoming the true star of the Corvair lineup, as Chevrolet's rear engined wonder caught on with the sports car crowd. These cars included all items found on lower lines, plus all-vinyl interior trims standard in the coupe and convertible, while four-door Monzas and Monza wagons used a cloth-vinyl upholstery as standard, carpets; rear arm rests; cigarette lighter; righthand sun visor; backup lights; DeLuxe steering wheel (with horn ring); glove box light; wheel coves; folding rear seat and, in coupes and convertibles, bucket type front seats. Model nameplates on Monzas were of a special design, located behind the front wheel well. Bright, ribbed metal rocker panel moldings were used along the lower body sills. New models included an extra-sporty mid-year Monza convertible, plus a short-lived Monza station wagon that was introduced in the fall and killed by the spring.

CORVAIR MONZA SERIES 900

Model Number	Body/Style Number	Body Type & Seating	Factory Price	Shipping Weight	Production Total
900	0969	4-dr Sed-6P	2273	2455	48,059
900	0927	2-dr Clb Cpe-4P	2273	2440	151,738
900	0967	2-dr Conv-4P	2483	2625	16,569
900	0935	4-dr Sta Wag-6P	2569	2590	2,362

CORVAIR MONZA SERIES ENGINE
The 84 hp engine at 4400 R.P.M. was used with Powerglide equipped Monzas, only with compression ratio 9.0.

CORVAIR MONZA SPYDER — (SIX) — SERIES 900 — About the same time that the new convertible appeared, a car called the Monza Spyder began receiving attention in the press. One such car was tested in *Popular Science* magazine, April, 1962 and *Motor Trend* magazine got its hands on another. Technically, Spyder equipment was an options package for the Monza convertible and coupe. At least that's the way it was cataloged in 1963, but most people thought of it as a new model. In either case, the package included a special 150 horsepower, turbo-charged version of the Corvair engine, plus cross-flags identification badges on the rear deck and a round "turbo-charged" emblem on the reardeck. (A crossed flags emblem signified the optional 102 hp engine.) It was not available on cars with air conditioning or two-speed Powerglide automatic transmission.

CORVAIR MONZA SPYDER

Model Number	Body/Style Number	Body Type & Seating	Factory Price	Shipping Weight	Production Total
900	0927	2-dr Clb Cpe-4P	2569	2490	(6,894)
900	0967	2-dr Conv-4P	2779	2675	(2,574)

NOTE: Figures in parenthesis indicate the number of each body style equipped with the turbo-charged Six. These figures are *included* in the Monza Series 900 body style production totals of coupes and convertibles.

CORVAIR MONZA SPYDER ENGINE
Horizontally opposed Six. Overhead valves. Aluminum block. Displacement: 145 cubic inches. Bore and stroke: 3.43 x 2.60 inches. Compression ratio: 8.0:1. Brake horsepower: 150 at 4400 R.P.M. Four main bearings. Hydraulic valve lifters. Induction: Carter one-barrel carburetor Model 3817245 with Turbo-charger.

CHASSIS FEATURES: Wheelbase: (all models) 108 inches. Overall length: (all models) 180 inches. Front tread (all models) 54.5 inches. Rear tread: (all models) 54.5 inches. Tires: (station wagons) 7.00 x 13; (passenger) 6.50 x 13.

POWERTRAIN OPTIONS: Three-speed manual transmission was standard. Automatic transmission ($157). Four-speed manual floor shift transmission ($65). Six-cylinder 145 cubic inch 102 horsepower 9.0:1 engine ($27). Six-cylinder 145 cubic inch 84 horsepower Powerglide engine. Generator, 35-amp ($5). Available rear axle gear ratios: (standard) 3.27:1; and the 355 axle ratio was standard in wagons; with air conditioning; with Spyder equipment, and with the 102 hp engine and Powerglide.

CONVENIENCE OPTIONS: Air Conditioning ($350). Pair of front seat belts, all ($20). Comfort and Convenience Equipment in 500/700 ($39). Comfort and Convenience Equipment in 900 ($28). Tinted glass, all windows ($27); windshield only ($13). Padded instrument panel ($16). Two-tone paint, all models ($11). Manual radio ($48). Push-button radio ($57). Folding rear seat, for 500 Series an Styles 0727/0769 ($27). Front bucket seats for Monza Sedan, standard in 0927/0967 ($54). Heavy-duty suspension, all ($22). Whitewall tires, exchange ($29). Full wheel covers, standard on Monzas ($11). Wire wheel design hub caps, 500/700 ($38); Monzas ($27). Two -speed windshield wipers and washers ($16).

Historical footnotes: The 1962 Corvairs were introduced September 29, 1961 and the convertible and Spyder appeared in dealer showrooms around May, 1962. Model year production peaked at 306,023 units. Calendar year sales of 292,531 cars were recorded. S.E. Knudsen was the Chief Executive Officer of the company this year. Series production, expressed in round figures for the model year included 16,300 Corvair 500s; 53,800 Corvair 700s; 216,400 Monza 900s and 19,500 station wagons. of all Corvair passenger cars (and station wagons) built to 1962 model specifications, 48 percent had automatic transmissions; 38 percent four-speed gear boxes; tires; 55.1 percent radios; 64.6 percent bucket seats; 86.7 percent white sidewall tires; 55 percent windshield washers; 2.5 percent air conditioning and 5.9 percent limited-slip differentials.

1963 CORVAIR

CORVAIR (SIX) — SERIES 500 — The pattern of minimum annual change continued for 1963 in the Corvair lineup. The trim on the front panel was changed once again. A strip of chrome was centered between the quad headlamps, running horizontally across the car. Its center section was finished in black paint. Amber colored front parking lamps were a new touch. So was a Corvair nameplate placed in the upper lefthand corner of the hood latch panel. On the side, model identification badges were placed above and ahead of the front wheel opening. Standard equipment included directional signals; electric windshield wipers; heater and defroster; front foam seat cushions; five 6.50 x 13 black sidewall tires and small hub caps. There was little difference, in the interior, from 1962. The model line up was unchanged. Standard power came from the rear-mounted, air-cooled six carried over from the previous season. It gave 80 horsepower with synchromesh transmission. Prices for the Corvair 500 coupe were unchanged from 1962.

VEHICLE IDENTIFICATION NUMBERS: The numbering system and code locations were the same as for previous models with the first symbol changed to a '3' to indicate 1963 model year.

CORVAIR 500 SERIES

Series Number	Body/Style Number	Doors/Style Seating	Factory Price	Shipping Weight	Production Total
500	0527	2-dr Clb Cpe-5P	1992	2300	16,680

CORVAIR 500 SERIES ENGINE
Horizontally-opposed Six. Overhead valves. Aluminum block. Displacement: 145 cubic inches. Bore and stroke: 3.438 x 2.609 inches. Compression ratio: 8.0:1. Brake horsepower: 80 at 4400 R.P.M. Four main bearings. Hydraulic valve lifters. Carburetor: Two (2) Rochester one-barrel Model 7017360.

CORVAIR (DELUXE) — (SIX) — SERIES 700 — The club coupe and the four-door sedan remained available in the Corvair 700 Series. Prices for both models decreased one dollar. Weights were down, too, indicating the deletion of some formerly standard hardware. One way to spot a 700 was to look for an upper belt molding that followed the body feature line from the middle of the front door forward, around the front end and down to the middle of the opposite door. A Corvair 700 nameplate was seen ahead of the front wheel opening. And a rocker panel molding was used. Standard features began with everything found on lower priced models, plus the chrome exterior moldings; fancier interior upholstery; color-keyed vinyl rubber floor mats; dual horns and automatic dome lamp switches. This was last run for the Corvair 700 club coupe.

CORVAIR 700 SERIES

Series Number	Body/Style Number	Doors/Style Seating	Factory Price	Shipping Weight	Production Total
700	0769	4-dr Sed-6P	2110	2385	20,684
700	0727	2-dr Clb Cpe-5P	2056	2355	12,378

CORVAIR 700 ENGINE
See 1963 Corvair 500 Series engine data.

1963 Corvair, Monza 4-dr sedan, 6-cyl (AA)

CORVAIR MONZA — (SIX) — SERIES 900 — The Corvair Monza had all standard equipment found on other models and more. For example, all-vinyl interiors (with new tufted pattern); used on 4-door models and convertibles only; cigarette lighter; backup lights; DeLuxe steering wheel; glove box light; full wheel covers; rocker panel moldings and distinct model identification badges on the lower front fender, in back of the wheel openings. Bucket seats were standard in all models, including the four-door sedan. Spyder equipment was optional on the coupe and convertible at an attractive price. Sintered metallic brakes no longer included. What did come on Spyders was a round turbo-charged emblem on the reardeck; crossed checkered racing flag emblems on the rear deck of other than Spyder models, tachometer; 120 miles per hour speedometer; full instrumentation; special brushed metal dash insert panel and turbo-charged flat Six. This engine included heavy-duty engine bearings; hardened crank; chromed upper piston rings; special valves; heavy-duty clutch. Spyder had Carter YH single barrel sidedraft carburetor.

CORVAIR 900 SERIES

Series Number	Body/Style Number	Doors/Style Seating	Factory Price	Shipping Weight	Production Total
MONZA					
900	0969	4-dr Sed-6P	2326	2450	31,120
900	0927	2-dr Clb Cpe-4P	2272	2415	129,544
900	0967	2-dr Conv-4P	2481	2525	44,165
MONZA WITH SPYDER OPTION					
900	0927	2-dr Clb Cpe-4P	2589	2440	(11,627)
900	0967	2-dr Conv-4P	2798.45	2550	(7472)

NOTE: Spyder equipment was optional at $317.45 this year. The factory prices for Spyders show the combined price of the base model (Monza 900 coupe or convertible) plus the option. The number of each model sold with Spyder equipment is listed (in parenthesis) in column six. Parenthesis are used since these totals are also included in the Monza 900 body style totals shown above.

1963 Corvair, Series 900 Monza 2-dr convertible, 6-cyl

CORVAIR MONZA 900 SERIES ENGINE
See 1963 Corvair 500 Series engine data for base Monza engine specifications. See 1962 Spyder engine data for Spyder engine specifications.

CHASSIS FEATURES: Wheelbase: (all models) 108 inches. Overall length: (all models) 180 inches. Front tread: (all models) 54.5 inches. Rear tread: (all models) 54.5 inches. Tires: (all models) 6.50 x 13.

POWERTRAIN OPTIONS: Three-speed manual transmission was standard. Powerglide automatic transmission includes 84 horsepower 9.0:1 compression Six ($157) in Monza models only. Four-speed manual floor shift transmission ($92). Six-cylinder 145 cubic inch 102 horsepower turbo-charged engine (*). Positive traction rear axle ($38). Heavy-duty air cleaner ($17). Heavy-duty clutch (*). Available rear axle gear ratios: (standard) 3.27:1; (optional) 3.55.1; was standard in Spyder or with air conditioning, or with 102 hp engine and Powerglide, 3.89 optional and 3.08 used on early 102 hp w/4 speed only. Options marked (*) are included in the Spyder equipment package ($317.45).

CONVENIENCE OPTIONS: Air conditioning ($350). Rear arm rest, style 769 only ($10). Pair of front seat belts ($19). Comfort and Convenience equipment, Monza ($28); others ($39). Tinted glass, all windows ($27); windshield only ($13). Padded instrument panel ($16). Spare wheel lock ($5). Two-tone paint ($11). Manual radio ($48). Pushbutton radio ($57). Pushbutton radio and front and rear speaker, except convertible ($70). Folding rear seat, Styles 727, 769 and all 500s ($27). Four-ply white sidewall tires ($29). Power convertible top ($54). Full wheel covers, standard on Monzas ($11). Wire design wheel covers, 500/700 ($38); Monza ($27). Kelsey-Hayes wire wheels with knock-off hubs, all models ($404).

1963 Corvair, Greenbrier Sports Wagon, 6-cyl

Historical footnotes: The 1963 Corvairs were introduced September 28, 1962. Model year production peaked at 254,571 units. Calendar year production of 261,525 cars was recorded. S.E. Knudsen was the Chief Executive Officer of the company this year. Optional equipment installation rates for Corvettes built to 1963 model specifications were as follows; automatic transmission (44.3 percent); four-speed manual gear box (44.3 percent); radio (55.9 percent); heater (99.4 percent); bucket seats (80.5 percent); seat belts (17.6 percent); whitewall tires (77.4 percent); windshield washers (58.6 percent); tinted windshield (39.4 percent); all tinted glass (8.6 percent); air conditioning (2.5 percent); limited-slip differential (7.7 percent) and full wheel covers (92.0 percent). **NOTE:** Percentage are based on a slightly higher model year output figure (266,564) that included Greenbrier trucks. See Krause Publications *Std. Catalog of American Light-Duty Trucks* for information about Chevrolet trucks.

1964 CORVAIR

CORVAIR — (SIX) — SERIES 500 — Seven models in four series comprised Corvair offerings for 1964. Improved brakes and redesigned suspensions were highlights of the year. The base powerplant now gave 95 horsepower with manual transmission attachments. A thicker cross bar stretched between the headlights. Below it was a triangular Chevrolet badge. Corvair block letters trimmed the edge of the hood and deck. The circular taillamp bezels were redone. Standard equipment on the 500 club coupe was comprised of directional signals; electric wipers; heater and defroster; front foam seat cushions; rubber floor mats; locking glove box; dual sun visors; cigarette lighter; front arm rests; small hub caps and five tubeless black sidewall tires. Model nameplates remained in their location ahead of front wheel cut outs. Interiors came in Red, Aqua and Fawn (tan). They were slightly plainer in design this year. Many refinements made the 1964 Corvair truly the best of the early editions. It was a great machine for the money, which was less than $10 higher for most models.

VEHICLE IDENTIFICATION NUMBERS: The numbering system and code locations were the same as for previous models with the first symbol changed to a '4' to indicate 1964 model year.

CORVAIR 500 SERIES

Series Number	Body/Style Number	Doors/Style Seating	Factory Price	Shipping Weight	Production Total
500	0527	2-dr Clb Cpe-5P	2000	2365	22,968

CORVAIR 500 SERIES ENGINE
Horizontally opposed Six. Overhead valves. Aluminum block. Displacement: 164 (163.6) cubic inches. Bore and stroke: 3.438 x 2.938 inches. Compression ratio: 8.25:1. Brake horsepower: 95 at 3600 R.P.M. Four main bearings. Hydraulic valve lifters. Carburetor: Two (2) Rochester one-barrel Model 7024023.

CORVAIR (DELUXE) — (SIX) — SERIES 700 — Only the four-door sedan was available in the Corvair 700 Series this season. It came with all features found on the base-level models, plus front fender model nameplates; chrome exterior moldings; upgraded interior and dual horns. A Blue cloth and vinyl interior trim combination was offered and buyers could also select from these materials in the same colors available for Corvair 500s. The Series 700 club coupe was dropped due to lagging sales. There were three reasons for the dip in deliveries. First, the new Chevy II had more appeal to conservative buyers in the compact car market. Second, the Corvair hadn't changed much in five years and had lost much of its novelty. Its styling was growing too stale for the mass market, although not for the enthusiast buyer. Third, an unearned reputation for unsafe handling traits was beginning to gain publicity. The result of these three factors combined was that Corvair sales tapered off and also became concentrated in the sportier Monza Series. However, the introduction of the Ford Mustang, in mid 1964, began hurting even the enthusiast market sales. Meanwhile, Chevrolet kept reducing the availability of low trim level Corvairs.

CORVAIR 700 SERIES

Series Number	Body/Style Number	Doors/Style Seating	Factory Price	Shipping Weight	Production Total
700	0769	4-dr Sed-6P	2119	2415	16,295

CORVAIR 700 SERIES ENGINE
See 1964 Corvair 500 Series engine data.

1964 Corvair, Series 900 Monza Club Coupe, 6-cyl

CORVAIR MONZA — (SIX) — SERIES 900 — Corvair Monzas could be most easily identified by their wider rocker panel moldings; inverted cross shaped insignias (mounted behind front wheel housing); stylish full wheel covers and trim moldings along the lips of both front and rear wheel cut outs. A new interior feature was map pockets on the front door panels. Standard equipment included everything found on Series 700 models, plus all-vinyl upholstery; used on 4-door and convertible body styles only; rear arm rests; backup lights; DeLuxe steering wheel with chrome horn ring; glove box light and simulated vents below rear window. The Monza Spyder officially became part of a separate series this year. All Monzas also featured bucket seats.

CORVAIR MONZA 900 SERIES

Series Number	Body/Style Number	Doors/Style Seating	Factory Price	Shipping Weight	Production Total
900	0969	4-dr Sed-5P	2335	2470	21,926
900	0927	2-dr Clb Cpe-4P	2281	2445	88,440
900	0967	2-dr Conv-4P	2492	2555	31,045

CORVAIR MONZA 900 SERIES ENGINE
See 1964 Corvair 500 Series engine data.

1964 Corvair, Monza Spyder 2-dr convertible, 6-cyl (AA)

CORVAIR MONZA SPYDER — (SIX) — SERIES 600 — The Monza Spyder looked a great deal like the Series 900 Monza on the outside and inside. There was a Spyder signature below the Monza badges on the lower front fender and a round turbo-charged emblem on the rear deck. Also, the full wheel covers had special Spyder center inserts. While displacement was up 19 cubic inches over the '63 engine, the 150 h.p. rating was the same (though the '64 developed it at 4000 R.P.M. and the '63 did it at 4400 R.P.M.). Like all 1964 Corvair power-plants, this one had redesigned hardware and gaskets to better seal oil leakage around the rocker arm covers, as this had been a common problem in the past. Also new were finned rear brakes and the addition of a transverse leaf spring to the rear suspension. With all these changes, the 1964 Corvairs were significantly improved automobiles and the Spyder was the best of the lot. Sales, however, dropped by nearly 50 percent.

CORVAIR MONZA SPYDER SERIES 600

Series Number	Body/Style Number	Doors/Style Seating	Factory Price	Shipping Weight	Production Total
600	0627	2-dr Cpe-4P	2599	2470	6,480
600	0667	2-dr Conv-4P	2811	2580	4,761

MONZA SPYDER SERIES ENGINE
Horizontally-opposed Six. Overhead valves. Aluminum block. Displacement: 164 cubic inches. Bore and stroke: 3.438 x 2.938 inches. Compression ratio: 8.25:1. Brake horsepower: 150 at 4000 R.P.M. Four main bearings. Hydraulic valve lifters. Carburetor: Rochester three-barrel.

CHASSIS FEATURES: Wheelbase: (all models) 108 inches. Overall length: (all models) 180 inches. Front tread: (all models) 54.5 inches. Rear tread: (all models) 55.1 inches. Tires: (all models) 6.50 x 14.

POWERTRAIN OPTIONS:
Three-speed manual transmission was standard. Powerglide automatic transmission ($157). Four-speed manual floor shift transmission ($92). Six-cylinder 164 cubic inch 110 horsepower 9.25:1 engine ($30). Six-cylinder 164 cubic inch 150 horsepower turbo-charged engine (*). Positive traction rear axle ($38). Heavy-duty air cleaner ($17). Heavy-duty clutch. (*). Available rear axle gear ratios: 3.27:1; 3.55:1. Generator, 35-ampere ($38).

Options marked (*) are available only as standard equipment on the Monza Spyder.

CONVENIENCE OPTIONS: Same as 1964.

Historical footnotes: The 1964 Corvairs were introduced September 26, 1963. Model year production peaked at 199,387 units. Calendar year production of 195,770 cars was recorded. S.E. Knudsen was the Chief Executive Officer of the company this year. Optional equipment installation rates for Corvairs built to 1964 specifications (including Greenbriers) were as follows: automatic transmission (47 percent); four-speed manual transmission (39.5 percent); radio (92.8); heater (100 percent); bucket seats (79.5 percent); whitewall tires (75 percent); windshield washers (64.8 percent); tinted windshield only (40.5 percent); all tinted glass (7.3 percent); backup lights (87.6 percent); air conditioning (3.1 percent); limited slip differential (6.8 percent) and wheel covers (82.4 percent).

1965 CORVAIR

CORVAIR 500 — (SIX) — SERIES 101 — The Corvair had a completely new body for 1965 and it was beautiful. *Car and Driver* magazine said, "It unabashedly borrows from the best of the already established foreign and domestic coach work without losing any of its identity as a Corvair." The new styling was, indeed, a direct adaptation of the Italian school of industrial design and highlighted smooth-flowing, rounded lines; a 'venturi' shaped profile and a pillarless hardtop look on all closed body styles. The Corvair was also two inches wider than before, somewhat lower and about three inches longer end-to-end. Curved side glass was another innovation. The base Corvair 500 Series included sport coupe and sport sedan. Trim consisted of a horizontal front panel molding, red in color, set directly below the feature line, with a Chevrolet badge at its center; Corvair script above the lefthand headlight housing; rectangular parking lamps set into a smooth bumper underpan; roof gutter rails painted roof colors; nameplates above and behind front wheel opening; Corvair script on right side of engine lid and small center hubcaps. Standard equipment included directional signals; electric wipers; heater and defroster; all-vinyl interior; twin sun visors; front seat belts; front arm rests; locking glove box; cigar lighter, coat hooks and interior light.

VEHICLE IDENTIFICATION NUMBERS: The numbering system and code locations were changed as follows: The Serial Number was located on the top face of the lefthand frame side rail, behind the battery bolts. The Engine Number was on top of the block, behind the oil pressure sending unit. The Vehicle Identification Number had 13 symbols. The first symbol '1' designated Chevrolet product. The second and third symbols designated carline, as follows: '01' = Corvair 500; '05' = Corvair Monza and '07' = Corvair Corsa. The fouth and fifth symbols designated Body Style, as follows: '39' = four-door hardtop (sport sedan); '37' = two-door hardtop (sport coupe); '67' = convertible. The sixth symbol designated the model year ('5' = 1965). The seventh symbol designated the Chevrolet assembly plant. The following group of symbols was the sequential unit production number, with series in mixed production at a specific plant. Body Style Numbers (also called model number) were used and correspond to those in second column of the specifications charts below. These numbers were located on the vehicle data plate, on which they were proceeded by a two-digit prefix indicating model year ('65' for 1965). The 1965 Corvair Engine Numbers contained a two letter code indicating equipment features as follows: 'RA' = manual transmission; 'RB' = base engine; 'RD' = high-performance; 'RE' = manual transmission/air conditioning; 'RF' = high-performance w/air conditioning; 'RG' = Powerglide; 'RH' = high-performance w/Powerglide; 'RJ' = Powerglide w/air-conditioning; 'RK' high-performance w/Powerglide. RA manual transmission, 95 hp; RB Corsa manual transmission, 140 hp; RD opt. manual transmissio, 110 hp; RE manual transmission, 95 hp and A/C; RF opt. manual transmission, 110 hp and A/C; RG automatic, 95 hp; RH opt. automatic, 110 hp; RJ automatic, 95 hp and A/C; RK opt automatic, 110 hp and A/C; RL opt. (Corsa only) manual, 180 hp; RM opt. (except Corsa) manual, 140 hp; RN opt. (except Corsa) automatic, 140 hp.

CORVAIR 500

Series Number	Body/Style Number	Doors/Style Seating	Factory Price	Shipping Weight	Production Total
101	10139	4-dr HT Sed-6P	2096	2405	17,560
101	10137	2-dr HT Cpe-4P	2022	2385	36,747

NOTE: The four-door hardtop is also called the Sport Sedan. The two-door hardtop is also called the Sport Coupe.

CORVAIR 500 SERIES ENGINE
Horizontally opposed Six. Overhead valves. Aluminum block. Displacement: 164 cubic inches. Bore and stroke: 3.438 x 2.938 inches. Compression ratio: 8.25. Brake horsepower: 95 at 3600 R.P.M. Four main bearings. Hydraulic valve lifters. Carburetor: Two (2) Rochester one-barrel Model 7025023.

CORVAIR MONZA — (SIX) — SERIES 105 — Monzas now represented the mid-price Corair models, as the Corvair 700 line was dropped. Standard equipment included all items found on the lower priced cars, plus full wheel covers; rocker sill moldings; front bucket seats; carpeting; courtesy and glove box lights; front arm rests; rear arm rests were not standard (nor available) on 2-dr coupe styles; backup lights and folding rear seats on sport coupes and sport sedan. As in the past, a Monza badge, consisting of a vertical bar passing through a V-shaped horizontal ornament, was seen on the lower front fenders behind the wheel opening. Whereas the Corvair 500 had only Red, Aqua or Fawn interior color choices, the Monza had no Aqua, but Blue, Black, Saddle, Slate, White available with Aqua or Black accents depending on exterior color. The rear panel, to which the engine lid latched, was outlined with a chrome molding. A convertible was also provided in this series and came standard with a manual top and top boot. A handsome new feature of all Corvairs was a slantback instrument panel with deep tunnels containing the gauges. On Series 500 and Monza models they housed a speedometer gas gauge, warning-lights and, if ordered, an optional electric clock.

CORVAIR MONZA

Series Number	Body/Style Number	Doors/Style Seating	Factory Price	Shipping Weight	Production Total
105	10539	4-dr HT Sed-5P	2370	2465	37,157
105	10537	2-dr HT Cpe-4P	2297	2440	88,954
105	10567	2-dr Conv-4P	2440	2675	26,466

NOTE: The four-door hardtop is also called the Sport Sedan. The two-door hardtop is also called the Sport Coupe.

CORVAIR MONZA ENGINE
See 1965 Corvair 500 engine data.

1965 Corvair, Corsa 2-dr convertible, 6-cyl (AA)

CORVAIR CORSA — (SIX) — SERIES 107 — The Corvair Corsa models were the top-line models in 1965. They carried Corsa lettering on the front fender cowl sides, below the main feature line (just under the new, square gas filler door). In addition a Corsa badge was place just ahead of the rear wheel opening. It had an oval shaped ornament, with a 'C' in the middle, flanked by vertical bars running up and down. Standard equipment included all items featured with Monzas, plus electric clock; tachometer; oil pressure gauge; temperature gauge; Satin Silver special ornamentation and special interior trim. There was also a difference in base motivation, the Corsa coming standard with a high-compression 164 cubic inch flat six that put out 140 horsepewer and inducted fuel and air through four single-barrel Rochester carburetors. An important advance on all 1965 Corvairs was a new, Corvette-like, fully independent rear suspension with upper axle half-shafts; lower equal length trailing torque arms, rubber-bushed rods and coil springs at each corner, which was complemented by an improved front suspension. Handling, with this system, was much better than in the past.

CORVAIR CORSA

Series Number	Body/Style Number	Doors/Style Seating	Factory Price	Shipping Weight	Production Total
107	10731	2-dr HT Cpe-4P	2465	2475	20,291
107	10767	2-dr Conv-4P	2608	2710	8,353

NOTE: The two-door hardtop is also called the Sport Coupe.

CORVAIR CORSA SERIES ENGINE
Horizontally opposed Six. Overhead valves. Aluminum block. Displacement: 164 cubic inches. Bore and stroke: 3.438 x 2.938 inches. Compression ratio: 9.25:1. Brake horsepower: 140 at 5200 R.P.M. Four main bearings. Hydraulic valve lifters. Carburetor: Four (4) Rochester one-barrel Model 7025023 with progressive linkage.

CHASSIS FEATURES: Wheelbase: (all models) 108 inches. Overall length: (all models) 183.3 inches. Front tread: (all models) 55 inches. Rear tread: (all models) 56.6 inches. Tires: (all models) 6.50 x 13.

POWERTRAIN OPTIONS: Three-speed manual transmission was standard. Powerglide automatic transmission, in 500 and Monza Series ($157). Four-speed manual floor shift transmission ($92). Monza and 500 six-cylinder 164 cubic inch 110 horsepower Turbo-Air engine ($27). Monza and 500 six-cylinder 164 cubic inch 140 horsepower Turbo-Air engine ($81). Corsa Series six-cylinder 164 cubic inch 180 horsepower Turbo-charged engine ($161). Postitive traction rear axle ($38). Heavy-duty air cleaner, 500 or Monza without air conditioning or 140 horsepower six ($32). Available rear axle gear ratios: 3.27:1 and 3.55 to 1. Heavy-duty 70 ampere battery ($8). Delcotron 47-ampere generator, standard with air conditioning; ($16) on others.

CONVENIENCE OPTIONS: All-weather air conditioning, Series 500 or Monza, not with 140 horsepower Six ($350). Rear antenna, in place of front mounted antenna (No Charge). Rear arm rest, Style Number 139 ($10). Tinted glass, all windows ($27); windshield only ($13). Front or rear bumper guards ($10). Padded instrument panels ($16). Spare wheel lock, all ($5). Two-tone paint available on Model 139 only ($11). Manual radio with front antenna ($50). Pushbutton radio with front antenna ($59). AM/FM pushbutton radio with front antenna ($137). Seat belts with retractor ($8). Folding rear seat, as option ($27). Sport style steering wheel ($32). Telescopic steering shaft, includes Sport style wheel ($75). White sidewall tires, size 6.50 x 13, four-ply ($29). Power top for all convertibles ($54). Wheel covers, on 500 series models ($11). Wire design covers, on 500 Series ($70); on Monza/Corsa ($59). Delete options for credit, heater/defroster ($72 credit); seat belts ($11 credit). 500 Series Convenience Group, includes; left OSRV mirror; non-glare inside mirror; two-speed wiper/washer; backup and glove box lights ($39). Monza/Corsa Comfort and Convenience Group, includes; all above, less backup and glove box lights which are standard. Comfort and Convenience Group 'B' includes; all above with left OSRV remote control mirror, 500 Series ($48); others ($38).

Historical footnotes: The 1965 Corvairs were introduced September 24, 1964. Model year production peaked at 235,500 units. Calendar year sales of 204,007 cars were recorded. S. E. Knudsen was the Chief Executive Officer of the company this year. Of all Corvairs built during the 1965 model year, 53.1 percent had automatic tranmission; 33.6 percent four-speed gearboxes; 62.9 percent had radios; 99.2 percent had heaters; 76.9 percent bucket seats; 92.6 percent seat belts; 73.9 white sidewall tires; 69.2 percent windshield washers; 40.2 percent tinted windshields only; 9.6 percent all windows tinted; 86.8 percent backup lights; 4.0 percent air conditioning; 3.7 percent telescopic steering shafts; 6.1 percent limited-slip differential and 80.7 percent wheel covers. The turbo-charged Corsair could move from 0 to 60 miles per hour in under 11 seconds and cover the quarter-mile in around 18 seconds hitting 79 miles per hour in the process. Top speed was over 113 miles per hour.

1966 CORVAIR

CORVAIR 500 — (SIX) — SERIES 101 — Styling refinements, including a new one-piece rear grille and taillights, were featured in the Corvair for 1966. Slimmer moldings were used to accent the wheel openings front and rear. A front spoiler made the scene. The front panel trim bar was widened and had a blue painted center section. The V-shaped Chevrolet ornament in the center was not quite as large end-to-end, but a little fatter. The Corvair signature was moved (from above the headlights) back onto the front panel, where it was positioned, on the lefthand side, at a rakish angle. The 500 models featured an expanded list of standard equipment, such as padded dash-

padded sun visors; backup lights; two-speed wipers; windshield washers; left outside rearview mirror; cigar lighter; coat hooks; locking glovebox; interior lamps and rear seat belts. A more luxurious all-vinyl interior was seen. Technical advances included a fully-synchromesh three-speed transmission (with both manual gear boxes being highly refined); larger 7.00 x 13 standard tires and the spoiler — below the bumper — which improved both handling and gas mileage.

VEHICLE IDENTIFICATION NUMBERS: The numbering system and code locations were the same as for previous models with the sixth symbol changed to a '6' to indicate 1966 model year. Several new Engine Number codes appeared as follows: 'RQ' = Special high-performance with exhaust emissions system; 'RR' = air conditioned; 'RT' = base engine with exhaust emissions system; 'RV' = Powerglide with exhausts emissions system; 'RW' = high-performance with exhaust emissions system and 'RY' = special high-performance with Powerglide and air conditioning. Codes 'RV' and 'RX', as used in 1965, were changed or deleted, while all other 1965 codes were applicable again. RQ opt. 140 hp, manual transmission, Air*; RR Corsa 140 hp, manual transmission, A/C; RS Std. 95 hp, manual transmission, Air*;RV Std. 95 hp, automatic transmission, Air*; RU opt. 110 hp, manual transmission, Air*;RY opt. 140 hp, automatic transmission, A/C; RW opt. 110 hp, automatic transmission, Air*; RT Corsa 140 hp, Air*.
*Air = air injection reactor (Emissions Control)

CORVAIR 500

Series Number	Body/Style Number	Body Type & Seating	Factory Price	Shipping Weight	Production Total
101	10139	4-dr HT Sed-6P	2157	2445	8,779
101	10139	2-dr HT Cpe-5P	2083	2400	24,045

NOTE: The four-door hardtop sedan is also called the Sport Sedan. The two-door hardtop coupe is also called the Sport Coupe.

CORVAIR 500 SERIES ENGINE
Horizontally opposed Six. Overhead valves. Aluminum block. Displacement: 164 cubic inches. Bore and stroke: 3.438 x 2.938 inches. Compression ratio: 8.25:1. Brake horsepower: 95 at 3600 R.P.M. Four main bearings. Hydraulic valve lifters. Carburetor: Two (2) Rochester one-barrel Model 7026023.

1966 Corvair, Monza 2-dr hardtop sports coupe, 6-cyl (PH)

CORVAIR MONZA — (SIX) — SERIES 105 — The Monza was easy to spot. On the lower front fender, behind the wheel opening, was a badge that looked like a stylized airplane with delta wings flying straight downwards. The center of the badge was black-finished and carried the word Monza across its 'wings'. There were chrome outline moldings around the rear deck panel; thin rocker panel moldings; bright metal roof gutter trim and wheel covers with the delta-winged logo in the center. Standard extras included front bucket seats; carpeting; luggage compartment mat; automatic dome and glove box lights; fold-down rear seat on closed styles; front and rear ash trays and rear foam seat cushions. Pleated upholstery with metal buttons was seen.

CORVAIR MONZA

Series Number	Body/Style Number	Body Type & Seating	Factory Price	Shipping Weight	Production Total
105	10539	4-dr HT Sed-5P	2424	2495	12,497
105	10537	2-dr HT Cpe-4P	2350	2445	37,605
105	10567	2-dr Conv-4P	2493	2675	10,345

NOTE: The four-door hardtop is also called the Sport Sedan. The two-door hardtop is also called the Sport Coupe.

CORVAIR MONZA ENGINE
See 1966 Corvair 500 engine data.

CORVAIR CORSA — (SIX) — SERIES 107 — In its last season, the sporty, high-performance Corsa still clung to a few visual distinctions to set it apart from more lowly models. Most evident was Corsa front fender lettering (above and behind wheel opening and below feature line); special Corsa ornaments ahead of rear wheel openings; Satin Silver finished engine lid latch panel and an emblem that reads 140 or Turbo-Charged, depending upon the engine ordered at the very center of the engine lid. The wheel covers had special turbine style center inserts with the Corsa C-inside-oval badge at the middle. This badge was also seen on the special steering wheel hub insert. Standard equipment included everything found with Monzas, plus full instrumentation; tachometer; oil pressure gauge; temperature gauge. For 1966, three special colors — Marina Blue, Lemonwood Yellow and Chateau Slate — came only on Monzas and Corsas.

CORVAIR CORSA

Series Number	Body/Style Number	Body Type & Seating	Factory Price	Shipping Weight	Production Total
107	10737	2-dr HT Cpe-4P	2519	2485	7,330
107	10767	2-dr Conv-4P	2662	2720	3,142

NOTE: The four-door hardtop is also called the Sport Sedan. The two-door hardtop is also called the Sport Coupe.

CORSA SERIES ENGINE DATA
Horizontally opposed Six. overhead valves. Aluminum block. Displacement: 164 cubic inches. Bore and stroke: 3.438 x 2.938 inches. Compression ratio: 9.25.1 Brake horsepower: 140 at 5200 R.P.M. Four main bearings, Hydraulic valve lifters. Carburetor: Four (4) Rochester one-barrel Model 7026023 with progressive linkage.

CHASSIS FEATURES: Wheelbase: (all models) 108 inches. Overall length: (all models) 184 inches. Front tread: (all models) 55 inches. Rear tread: (All models) 56.6 inches. Tires: (all models) 7.00x 14.

POWERTRAIN OPTIONS: Three-speed manual transmission was standard. Four-speed manual floor shift transmission ($92). Monza and 500 six-cylinder 164 cubic inch 140 horsepower Turbo-Air engine ($26). Monza and 500 six-cylinder 164 cubic inch 110 horsepower Turbo-Air engine ($79). Corsa six-cylinder 164 cubic inch 180 horsepower Turbo-charged engine $158). Positive traction rear axle (38). Heavy-duty air cleaner ($32). Heavy-duty battery ($18). Heavy-duty Delcotron ($16). Available rear axle gear ratios; 3.27:1 and 3.55:1.

CONVENIENCE OPTIONS: Same as 1965.

Historical footnotes: The 1966 Corvairs were introduced October 7, 1965. Model year production peaked at 103,743 units. Calendar year production of 73,30 cars was recorded. E.M. Estes was the Chief Executive Officer of the company this year. For the 1966 Corvair model year, optional equipement percentage installation rates were as follows (percentages in parenthesis): automatic transmission (57.2); four-speed manual transmission (26.7); radio (61.4); heater (99); telescopic steering shaft (2.2); bucket seats (68.4); whitewall tires (68); tinted windshield only (39.5); all glass tinted (8.4); air conditioning (4.6); limited-slip axle (6.8); wheel covers (73.6); power antenna (0.4) and non-glare rearview mirror (4.9). At the end of the year Chevrolet announced plans for a major expansion of its Willow Run, Michigan assembly plant.

1967 CORVAIR

CORVAIR 500 — (SIX) — SERIES 101 — The high-priced Corvair Corsa Series was dropped for 1967, leaving only five models in hardtops and convertibles. New Strato bucket seats and oval shaped steering wheels were seen. A wider bezel was used on the taillamps from early 1966 on. Dash padding was heavier; the window handle knobs were color-keyed plastic covered and the Powerglide transmission was no longer operated via a T-handle. Now a more conventional knob was used. Otherwise, appearance aspects were about identical to 1966. An Eight-Track solid state stereo tape player was a brand new option. And 7.00 x 13 tires were used. Standard in Corvair 500 models were all federally mandated safety equipment (called "GM Safety Features"), closed positive crankcase ventilation; all-vinyl interior; cigarette lighter; interior light; foam-cushioned front seat; front door arm rest; three-speed manual full-Synchromesh transmission and 95 horsepower 'Tubo-Air 164' six-cylinder engine.

VEHICLE IDENTIFICATION NUMBERS: The numbering system and code locations were the same as for previous models with the sixth symbol changed to a '7' to indicate 1967 model year. No new 'R' engine codes were used, although several were dropped. There was however, a completely different group of codes, beginning with letter 'Q'. All of these included exhaust emission controls for California sale. They were as follows: 'QM'=manual transmission and air conditioning; 'QO'=Powerglide w/air conditioning; 'QP'=high-performance w/Powerglide and 'QS'=high-performance w/manual transmission and air-conditioning. QM 95 hp manual, A/C and Air; QO 95 hp automatic A/C and Air; QP 110 hp automatic, A/C and Air; QS 110 hp manual, A/C and Air.
*Air = air injection reactor (Emissions Control)

CORVAIR 500

Series Number	Body/Style Number	Doors/Style Seating	Factory Price	Shipping Weight	Production Total
101	10139	4-dr Ht Sed-6P	2194	2470	2,959
101	10137	2-dr HT Cpe-5P	2128	2435	9,257

NOTE: The four-door hardtop is also called the Sport Sedan. The two-door hardtop is also called the Sport Coupe.

CORVAIR 500 SERIES ENGINE
Horizontally opposed Six. Overhead valves. Aluminum block. Displacement: 164 cubic inches. Bore and stroke: 3.438 x 2.938 inches. Compression ratio: 8.25:1. Brake horsepower: 95 at 3600 R.P.M. Four main bearings. Hydraulic valve lifters. Carburetor: Two-(2) Rochester one-barrel Model 7026023.

1967 Corvair, Monza 4-dr hardtop sedan, 6-cyl (AA)

CORVAIR MONZA — (SIX) — SERIES 105 — Appearance distinctions of the 1967 Monza were the same as seen the year before. They included full wheel covers with Monza 'delta-wing' insignia; rocker panel moldings; 'delta-wing' fender side badges, behind front wheel openings; bright metal roof gutter rail moldings; wheel opening moldings and rear panel outline trim. The Monza came with all equipment included on Corvair 500 models, plus dual headlamps; front lockable trunk; bucket seats; carpeting; luggage compartment mat; automatic dome and glove box lights; fold-down rear seat (except convertibles); speedometer, odometer, fuel gauge, generator and temperature warning lights; front and rear ash trays and rear foam seat cushions. The turbo-charged engine was no longer available. The 140 horsepower option was deleted and, then, reinstated. New for this year was General Motor's first engine/drivetrain five-year warranty.

CORVAIR MONZA

Series Number	Body/Style Number	Doors/Style Seating	Factory Price	Shipping Weight	Production Total
105	10539	4-dr HT Sed-5P	2464	2515	3,157
105	10537	2-dr HT Cpe-4P	2398	2465	9,771
105	10567	2-dr Conv-4P	2540	2695	2,109

NOTE: The four-door hardtop is also called the Sport Sedan. The two-door hardtop is also called the Sport Coupe.

MONZA SERIES ENGINE
See 1967 Corvair 500 Series engine data.

CHASSIS FEATURES: Wheelbase: (all models) 108 inches. Overall length: (all models) 183 inches. Front tread: (all models) 55 inches. Rear tread: (all models) 56.6 inches. Tires: (all models) 7.00 x 13.

POWERTRAIN OPTIONS:
Three-speed manual transmission was standard. Four-speed manual floor shift transmission, with 95 horsepower only ($90). Monza and 500 Six-cylinder 164 cubic inch 110 horsepower Turbo-Air engine ($26). Monza Six-cylinder 164 cubic inch 140 horsepower Turbo-Air engine ($79). Postive traction rear axle ($42). Heavy-duty air cleaner ($6). Available rear axle gear ratios: 3.27:1 and 3.55:1. air injection reactor, mandatory California cars ($45). Heavy-Duty 70-ampere battery ($7). Heavy-Duty 47-ampere Delcotron ($16).

CONVENIENCE OPTIONS: All-weather air conditioning ($342). Rear manual antenna, substitution (No Charge). Center rear seat belt ($6). Front and rear Custom DeLuxe seat belts ($6). Center rear seat belt, Custom DeLuxe type ($8). Custom DeLuxe front shoulder belts, with Custom DeLuxe Group ($26). Standard front shoulder belt ($23). Electric clock, all models ($16). Door edge guards, four-door ($6); two door ($3). Tinted glass, all windows ($31); windshield only ($21). Front or rear bumper guards ($10). Two-tone paint ($16). Available on model 139 only. Pushbutton radio, with front antenna ($57). ; and rear speaker ($71). AM/FM pushbutton radio, with front antenna and rear speaker ($133). Eight-Track stereo-tape system, includes quad speakers ($129). White, Black or Blue power convertible top ($53). DeLuxe steering wheel, 500 ($7). Monza ($4). telescoping type ($42). Speed warning indicator ($11). Special purpose (heavy-duty) front and rear suspension ($11). Mag-style wheel covers, 500 ($73). Monza ($63). Simulated wire wheel covers, 500 ($69). Monza ($58). Whitewall tires ($28). Folding rear seat, 500 Series ($26). Appearance Guard Group ($39-42). Auxillary lighting Group ($7-14).

Historical footnotes: The 1967 Corvairs were introduced September 29, 1966. Model year production peaked at 27,253 units. Calendar year production of 18,703 cars was recorded. E.M. Estes was the Chief Executive Officer of the company this year. For the 1967 model year, optional equipment installation rates (percentages in brackets) were as follows: automatic (67.9); four-speed (14.8); AM radio (63.6); air conditioning (5.1); telescoping steering column (1.1); bucket seats (55.2); white sidewall tires (60.8); tinted windshield only (34.7; all tinted glass (7.5); limited-slip axle (4.8); wheel covers (64.2); AM/FM radio (1.3); and electric clock (6.9).

1968 CORVAIR

CORVAIR 500 — (SIX) — SERIES 101 — Model availability for the Corvair dropped from five to three for the 1968 model year. The Monza Sport Sedan and the 500 Sport Sedan were discontinued. This eliminated all four-door styles from the lineup. Side marker lamps on the front and rear fenders are the easy way to spot a 1968 model from past editions. A look inside will reveal a dash with even more stuffings and padded windshield pillar posts. What else was new? A larger floor shift lever knob; restyled, padded arm rests; new vinyl upholstery fabrics and on January 1, 1968, shoulder safety belts became mandatory. The Corvair 500 coupe came with all GM Safety Features; cigarette lighter; heater and defroster (no longer deletable); 7.00 x 13 two-ply, four-ply rated blackwall tires and the 95 horsepwer 'Turbo-Air' Six. The four-carb 'Turbo-Air 140' job was still optional. Hub caps were standard.

VEHICLE IDENTIFICATION NUMBERS: The numbering system and code locations were the same as for previous models with the sixth symbol indicating 1968 model year. Engine/equipment combinations were down to eight choices, coded as follows: 'RS' = manual transmission; 'RM' = high-performance; 'RF' = high-performance with air conditioning; 'RW' = high-performance with Powerglide; 'RJ' = Powerglide with air conditioning' 'RK' = high-performance with Powerglide and air conditioning; 'RE' = air conditioning and 'RV' = Powerglide. **NOTE:** Not explained is why engine codes with air conditioning are listed, although this particular factory option was dropped! RS 95 hp, manual transmission; RU 110 hp, manual transmission; RV 95 hp, automatic transmission; RW 110 hp, automatic transmission; RY 140 hp, manual transmission; RZ 140 hp automatic transmission.

CORVAIR 500

Series Number	Body/Style Number	Body Type & Seating	Factory Price	Shipping Weight	Production Total
101	10137	2-dr HT Cpe-5P	2243	2470	7,206

NOTE: The two-door hardtop coupe was is called the Sport Coupe.

CORVAIR 500
Horizontally opposed Six. Overhead valves. Aluminum block. Displacement: 164 cubic inches. Bore and stroke: 3.438 x 2.938 inches. Compression ratio: 8.25:1. Brake horsepower: 95 at 3600 R.P.M. Four main bearings. Hydraulic valve lifters. Carburetor: Two (2) Rochester one-barrel Model 7028005.

1968 Corvair, Monza 2-dr hardtop sports coupe, 6-cyl (AA)

CORVAIR MONZA — (SIX) — SERIES 105 — The Monza had all features found on the Corvair 500, plus glove box light; dual headlamps; front bucket seats; carpeting; courtesy lights (in convertible) and folding rear seat (in coupe). Appearance extras were full wheel covers; chrome roof gutter strips; rocker panel moldings; rear panel outline trim strips and Monza inverted 'delta wing' badges behind the front wheel opening, plus wheel lip moldings and high-grade interior trimmings in Blue, Black or Gold. The folding rear seat had an improved latching mechanism instead of the old, hard to operate, friction type.

CORVAIR MONZA

Series Number	Body/Style Number	Body Type & Seating	Factory Price	Shipping Weight	Production Total
105	10537	2-dr HT Cpe-4P	2507	2500	6,807
105	10567	2-dr Conv-4P	2626	2725	1,386

NOTE: The two-door hardtop is also called the Sport Coupe.

CORVAIR MONZA SERIES ENGINE
See 1968 Corvair 500 Series engine data.

CHASSIS FEATURES: Wheelbase: (all models) 108 inches. Overall length: (all models) 183 inches. Front tread: (all models) 55 inches. Rear tread: (all models) 56.6 inches. Tires: (all models) 700 x 13.

POWERTRAIN OPTIONS: Three-speed manual transmission was standard. Automatic transmission, all ($153). Four-speed manual floor shift transmission, all ($90).Turbo-Air six-cylinder 164 cubic inch 110 horsepower 9.25:1 engine ($26). Turbo-Air six-cylinder 164 cubic inch 140 horsepower four-carb engine ($79). Heavy-duty 70-ampere battery ($7). Positive traction rear axle ($42). Heavy-duty air cleaner ($6). Available rear axle gear ratios: availability depends on power teams.

CONVENIENCE OPTIONS: Rear manual antenna, except with AM/FM ($10). Front and rear Custom DeLuxe shoulder belts, with bucket seats ($8). Front and rear Custom DeLuxe shoulder belts, with full-width seats ($10). Pair of front shoulder belts, standard type ($23); front and rear ($46). Custom DeLuxe shoulder belts, front pair ($26); front and rear ($53). Electric clock ($16). Rear window defroster, except convertible ($21). Door edge guards, all ($4). Tinted glass, all windows ($31); windshield only ($21). Head restraints, pair, in 500 ($42); in Monza ($52). Spare wheel lock ($5). Twin front and rear floor mats, all ($11). Left OSRV remote control mirror, all ($10). Radios, pushbutton with front antenna ($61); same AM/FM ($134). Rear speaker, except with stereo ($13). Folding rear seat, 500 Series, standard in Monza coupe ($32). Speed warning indicator ($11). Adjustable steering column ($42). DeLuxe steering wheel, 500 coupe ($7); Monzas ($4). Sport style steering wheel, all models ($32). Stereo tape system, includes quadraphonic ($134). Special purpose front and rear suspension ($11). Whitewall tires, 7.00 x 13-4 pr ($28). Power convertible top ($53). Wheel covers: standard in 500 ($21); mag-style, in 500 ($74); mag-style in Monza ($63); wire style in 500 ($69); wire style in Monza ($58). Appearance Guard Group ($34).

Historical footnotes: The 1968 Corvairs were introduced September 21, 1967. Model year production peaked at 15,400 units. Calendar year production 11,490 cars were recorded. John Z. DeLorean was the Chief Executive Officer of the company this year. For the 1968 model year, optional equipment installation rates (percentages in brackets) were as follows: automatic (70); AM radio (66); telescoping steering wheel (1.5); bucket seats (53); whitewalls (58); tinted windshield only (23); all glass tinted (10); limited-slip axle (7); wheel covers (63); AM/FM radio (4) and stereo tape system (0.5).

1969 CORVAIR

CORVAIR 500 — (SIX) — SERIES 101 — Aside from color choices, the 1969 interiors were identical to 1968. Two coupes and one convertible were offered in the last season of Corvair production. Appearance changes were very minor. They included a bigger rearview mirror and amber front side marker lens. The Corviar 500 came with front head rests as a mandatory option; cigarette lighter; heater and defroster; 7.00 x 13 four-ply rated blackwall tires and unchanged 95 horsepwer Turbo-Air engine. Vinyl interiors now came in Black, Blue and medium Green.

VEHICLE IDENTIFICATION NUMBERS: The numbering system and code locations were the same as for previous models with the sixth symbol changed to a '9' to indicate 1969 model year. Engine identification codes were the same as in 1968.

CORVAIR 500

Series Number	Body/Style Number	Body Type & Seating	Factory Price	Shipping Weight	Production Total
101	10137	2-dr HT Cpe-5P	2258	2515	2,762

CORVAIR 500 ENGINE
See 1968 Corvair 500 engine data.

1969 Corvair, Series 105 Monza 2-dr convertible, 6-cyl

CORVAIR MONZA — (SIX) — SERIES 105 — The Monza came with all equipment found on the base-line coupes, plus glove box light; dual headlamps; front bucket seats; courtesy lights (in convertible) and folding rear seat (in coupe). Appearance distinction were identical to those of the 1968 Monza. An Olympic Gold Monza, Serial Number 105379W706000 was the last Corvair built and may be in the possession of General Motors today.

CORVAIR MONZA

Series Number	Body/Style Number	Body Type & Seating	Factory Price	Shipping Weight	Production Total
105	10537	2-dr HT Cpe-4P	2522	2545	2,717
105	10567	2-dr Conv-4P	2641	2770	521

MONZA SERIES ENGINE
See 1968 Corvair 500 engine data.

1969 Corvair, Monza 2-dr hardtop sports coupe, 6-cyl

CHASSIS FEATURES: Wheelbase: Same as 1968.

POWERTRAIN OPTIONS: Same as 1968.

CONVENIENCE OPTIONS: Same as 1958.

Historical footnotes: The 1969 Corvairs were introduced September 26, 1968. Model year production peaked at 6,000 units. Calendar year sales of 3,103 cars were recorded. John Z. DeLorean was the Chief Executive Officer of the company this year. For the 1969 model year, optional equipment installation rates (percentages in brackets) were as follows: Powerglide (72); four-speed gear box (14); AM radio (80); AM/FM radio (3); bucket seats (54); whitewall tires (55); tinted windshield (0.1); all tinted glass (26); posi-traction (8); standard wheel covers (54); optional wheel covers (13); electric clock (11); telescoping steering wheel (2.5); In mid-May, 1969, Chevrolet offered Corvair buyers a $150 discount coupon to use in purchasing any new Chevrolet from then, until 1973. the idea was to compensate for any lost resale value experienced due to the discontinuance of the marque. Today, these cars hold a small premium in the collector market for being last year models.

CORVETTE

1953-1975

The 1953 Corvette was based on the 1952 EX-122 show car. It was one of the few Motorama dream cars to actually go into production with the styling virtually unchanged.

The Corvette was created as an economical sports car for young adults. It was also something that could be used as a performance-image builder while Chevrolet waited for its V-8. The car's fiberglass body was not only novel, but practical. It lowered the cost of production in limited numbers and expedited the Corvette's debut. (Steel-bodied models were originally planned for later model years.)

By Charles Webb

Sports car enthusiast and TV celebrity Dave Garroway heaped a lot of praise on the pretty new Corvette, in the Chevrolet sales promotion film *Halls of Wonder*. Yet, many of the sports car fans it was meant for, snubbed it. They harbored a prejudice that nothing good could come out of Detroit, and certainly not from Chevrolet. (Remember, at that time, a 'Chevy' was the car mothers drove to the A&P to pick up peanut butter and jelly for their children's lunch. The make did not have a hot-car image yet.) The fact that Corvettes used standard 'family car' mechanical components and came with a Powerglide automatic transmission were other points of criticism.

Most of the people who knocked the 'Vette' never drove one. As *ROAD & TRACK* said of the 1954, "The oustanding characteristic of the Corvette is probably its deceptive performance."

The car looked the same in 1955, but the 265 cubic inch V-8 made it much hotter. Unfortunately, like a beautiful debutante with a black belt in karate, its appearance belied its power. Sales were so bad, Chevrolet management was on the verge of killing the Corvette. However, when Ford came out with its two-passenger Thunderbird, the company was forced, for competive reasons, to continue production.

Sales shot up dramatically in 1956. (Although nowhere near T-Bird levels.) One of the main reasons was the Corvette now had looks to match its performance. A manual transmission, roll-up side windows and lockable doors also added to its appeal. And several prestigious racing victories contributed to its performance image.

With the introduction of fuel-injection in 1957, advertising proclaimed, "For the first time in automotive history — one h.p. for every cubic inch." Chrysler 300 fans, of course, knew better, but it did make good copy. And sales once again increased.

The clean, classic styling of 1956 and 1957 was jazzed-up in 1958. Although the basic design was attractive, the chrome-laden 1958 is generally considered the gaudiest Corvette. But, apparently, that's what the public wanted and sales climbed significantly over the previous year's model.

Some of the excess glitter was removed in 1959. In 1961, the Corvette received a new, 'duck tail' rear end treatment. Two years later, in a major restyling, the 1963s were an immediate hit. Demand was so great many customers had to wait two months or more to take delivery of their new Sting Ray coupe or ragtop. By now, Corvette's reputation as a powerful sports car was firmly established on the track and street.

A four-passenger Corvette was considered for 1963. It might have been quite successful. After all, Thunderbird sales soared when it went that route in 1958. However, the T-Bird never really claimed to be a true sports car, rather it was a 'sporty' personal car. Putting a back seat in Corvettes might have hurt its image.

The basic areodynamic styling introduced in 1968 would remain until 1983. Although after the early 1970's, Corvettes became significantly tamer. Still, when you mention performance, the American car that comes first to most people's minds is Corvette.

1953 CORVETTE

1953 Corvette, 2-dr roadster convertible, 6-cyl (AA)

CORVETTE — (6-CYL) — SERIES E2934 — The new 1953 Corvette had a fiberglass body, chrome-framed grille with 13 heavy vertical chrome bars, rounded front fenders with recessed headlights, no side windows or outside door handles, a wraparound windshield and protruding, fender-integrated taillights. The interior featured a floor-mounted shifter, Powerglide automatic and a full array of gauges including a tachometer. Each 1953 Corvette was virtually handbuilt and a lot of minor changes were made during the production run. Buyers could order any color they wanted, so long as it was Polo white with red bucket-seat interior.

VEHICLE IDENTIFICATION NUMBERS: The Corvette used the standard Chevrolet coding system. It consisted of a total of ten symbols, except for V-8s, which in some years utalized eleven symbols. The first symbol was an 'E' for 1953-1957 models and a 'J' for 1958-1959 models. The second and third symbols designated model year, for example '53' = 1953. The fourth symbol designated the manufacturing plant, as follows: F = Flint, Michigan and S = Saint Louis, Missouri. The following group of numbers (usually six digits) was the sequential unit production number. Corvettes, for 1953, were numbered E53F001001 to E53F001300. The Serial Number was located on the left front door hinge pillar post. Engine Numbers were found on the righthand side of the crankcase, behind the distributor. The Engine Numbers for 1953 models used the prefix 'LAY'. Since Corvette bodies were virtually handmade, they did not carry Standard Fisher Body Division Style Numbers, as did other General Motors cars. The Corvette Model Number consisted of four symbols '2934', which also served as the Body Style Number for the early production years.

Model Number	Body/Style Number	Body Type & Seating	Factory Price	Shipping Weight	Production Total
2934	2934	2-dr Conv-2P	3498	2705	300

CORVETTE SERIES ENGINE
Inline six. Overhead valves. Cast iron block. Displacement: 235.5 cubic inches. Bore and stroke: 3.56 x 3.93 inches. Compression ratio: 8.0:1. Brake horsepower: 150 at 4200 R.P.M. Carburetor: Three (3) Carter Type YH one-barrels Model 2066S (early models); Model 2055S (late models).

CHASSIS FEATURES: Wheelbase: 102 inches. Overall length: 167 inches. Front tread: 57 inches. Rear tread: 59 inches. Tires: 6.70 x 15.

POWERTRAIN OPTIONS: Automatic transmission with floor shift was standard.

CONVENIENCE OPTIONS: Signal-seeking AM radio ($145.15). Heater ($91.40). White sidewall tires.

Historical Footnotes: The first Corvette was built on June 30, 1953 at the Flint, Michigan assembly plant. Model year production peaked at 200 units. Calendar year sales of 300 cars were recorded. T.H. Keating was the Chief Executive Officer of Chevrolet this year. By early 1954, Chevrolet announced the 315 Corvettes had been built and that production of the model had been shifted to the assembly plant in St. Louis. Programming, at that point, called for production of 1,000 Corvettes per month, by June, 1954. The company predicted that 10,000 per year could be built and sold.

1954 CORVETTE

CORVETTE SERIES — (6-CYL) — SERIES E2934 — For all practical purposes, the 1953 and 1954 Corvettes were the same. Minor changes were made to the window storage bag, air cleaners, starter and location of the fuel and brake lines. Unlike the previous year's model, 1954s were available in Pennant Blue, Sportsman Red and Black in addition to Polo White. The soft top was now offered only in beige.

VEHICLE IDENTIFICATION NUMBERS: The numbering system and code locations were the same as for previous models. Serial Numbers were E54S001001 to E54S004640. Engine Numbers, for 1954, had the suffix 'YG'.

1954 Corvette, 2-dr roadster convertible, 6-cyl (AA)

CORVETTE

Model Number	Body/Style Number	Body Type & Seating	Factory Price	Shipping Weight	Production Total
2934	2934	2-dr Conv-2P	3523	2705	3,640

CORVETTE SERIES ENGINE
Inline Six. Overhead valves. Cast iron block. Displacement: 235.5 cubic inches. Bore and stroke: 3.56 x 3.93 inches. Compression ratio: 8.00:1. Brake horsepower: 150 at 4200 R.P.M. Four main bearings. Solid valve lifters. Carburetor: Carter, three (3) one-barrel Type YH Model 2066SA.

NOTE: Later in the model year, a new camshaft upped horsepower to 155.

CHASSIS FEATURES: Wheelbase: 102 inches. Overall length: 167 inches. Front tread: 57 inches. Rear tread: 59 inches. Tires: 6.70 x 15.

POWERTRAIN OPTIONS: Automatic transmission with floor shift was standard. Available rear axle gear ratios (various).

CONVENIENCE OPTIONS: Signal-seeking AM radio ($145.15). Heater ($91.40). Windshield washer ($11.85). Parking brake alarm ($5.65).

Historical footnotes: Approximately 80 percent of 1954 Corvettes were painted white. About 16 percent had a blue exterior. A 1954 Corvette could go from 0 to 60 M.P.H. in 11 seconds. From 0 to 100 in 41 seconds.

1955 CORVETTE

1955 Corvette, 2-dr roadster convertible, V-8

CORVETTE SERIES — (6-CYL) — SERIES E2934 — Styling remained the same as last year's model. The big news was the availability of a V-8 engine. An enlarged gold 'V' in the word Chevrolet, on the front fenders, was a quick way to tell V-8 powered (12-volt electrical system) cars from those with a six-cylinder engine (and 6-volt system).

VEHICLE IDENTIFICATION NUMBERS: The numbering system and code locations were the same as for previous models with the number symbols changed as follows: VE55S001001 to VE55S001700. **NOTE:** Cars equipped with a six-cylinder engine did *not* have a 'V' in their vehicle identification number. Motor Number suffixes used were 'YG' (six-cylinder); 'FG' (V-8 and automatic) and 'GR' (V-8 with manual transmission).

Model Number	Body/Style Number	Body Type & Seating	Factory Price	Shipping Weight	Production Total
2934	2934	2-dr Conv-2P	2934	2705	700

CORVETTE SERIES ENGINE
Inline, six. Overhead valves. Cast iron block. Displacement: 235.5 cubic inches. Bore and stroke: 3.56 x 3.93 inches. Compression ratio: 8.00:1. Brake horsepower 155 at 4200 R.P.M. Four main bearings. Solid valve lifters. Carburetor: Three (3) Carter one-barrel Model 3706989.

V-8. Overhead valves. Cast iron block. Displacement: 265 cubic inches. Bore and stroke: 8.00:1. Brake horsepower: 195 at 5000 R.P.M. Five main bearings. Carburetor: Rochester Type solid. Four-barrel Model 7008005.

CHASSIS FEATURES: Wheelbase: 102 inches. Overall length: 167 inches. Front tread: 57 inches. Rear tread: 59 inches. Tires: 6.70 x 15.

POWERTRAIN OPTIONS: Automatic transmission with floor shift was standard. Six-cylinder 235.5 cubic inch 155 horsepower 'Tri-Carb' engine. V-8 265 cubic inch 195 horsepower four-barrel engine ($135).

CONVENIENCE OPTIONS: Parking brake alarm ($5.65). Signal-seeking AM radio ($145.15). Windshield washer ($11.85). Heater ($91.40).

Historical Footnotes: The overwhelming majority of 1955 Corvettes were V-8 powered, but at least a half-dozen six-cylinder models wre reportedly produced. A V-8 powered 1955 Corvette could go from 0 to 60 mph in 8.7 seconds; from 0 to 100 mph in 24.7 seconds. Harvest Gold exterior finish was introduced along with Gypsy Red and Corvette Copper. Tops now came in white, dark green, or beige. Red, yellow, light beige and dark beige Elascofab interiors were available.

1956 CORVETTE

1956 Corvette, 2-dr convertible, V-8 (AA)

CORVETTE SERIES — (V-8) — SERIES E2934 — A lot of people would have been perfectly content if Chevrolet had frozen Corvette styling with the 1956 model. Although the same basic grille was kept, there were new front fenders with chrome rimmed headlights; external door handles; chrome outlined concave side body sculpturing ('cove') and sloping, taillight-integrated rear fenders. The dash layout remained the same as in the past. Upholstery colors were limited to beige or red, but six nitrocellulose lacquer finishes were available. Oxynx Black, Polo White, Venetian Red, Cascade Green, Aztec Copper and Artic Blue.

VEHICLE IDENTIFICATION NUMBERS: were the same as for previous models with the number symbols changed as follows E56S001001 to E56S004467. Starting Engine Numbers were 0001001 and up at each assembly plant, with an 'F' = Flint, Michigan and 'T' = Tonawanda, New York. Suffixes were as follows: 'GV' for 265 cubic inch V-8 with Synchromesh; 'GU' for 265 cubic inch V-8 with two (2) four-barrel carburetors and high-lift camshaft; 'GR' for regular 265 cubic inch dual four-barrel V-8; 'FK' for 265 cubic inch V-8 with Powerglide and 'FG' for latter V-8 combinations with dual four-barrel carburetors.

CORVETTE Model Number	Body/Style Number	Body Type & Seating	Factory Price	Shipping Weight	Production Total
2934	2934	2-dr Conv-2P	3120	2870	3,467

CORVETTE SERIES ENGINE
V-8. Overhead valves. Cast iron block. Displacement: 265 cubic inches. Bore and stroke: 3.75 x 3 inches. Compression ratio: 9.25:1. Brake horsepower: 210 at 5200 R.P.M. Five main bearings. Solid valve lifters. Carburetor: Carter Type WCFB four-barrel Model 2419S.

CHASSIS FEATURES: Wheelbase: 102 inches. Overall length: 168 inches. Front tread: 57 inches. Rear tread: 59 inches. Tires: 6.70 x 15.

POWERTRAIN OPTIONS: A close ratio three-speed manual floor shift transmission was standard. Automatic transmission ($175). V-8 265 cubic inch 225 horsepower dual four-barrel carburetors, high-lift cam engine ($175). V-8 265 cubic inch 240 horsepower dual four-barrel engine ($160). Available rear axle gear ratios: 3.27:1.

CONVENIENCE OPTIONS: Power top ($100). Power windows ($60). Windshield washer ($11). Detachable hardtop ($200). Signal seeking AM radio ($185). Heater ($115).

Historical footnotes: A 225 horsepower 1956 Corvette could go from 0 to 60 M.P.H. in 7.3 seconds; from 0 to 100 M.P.H. in 20.7 seconds.

1957 CORVETTE

CORVETTE SERIES — (V-8) — SERIES E2934 — The 1957 Corvette looked the same as last year's model. The big news was the availability of a 283 horsepower 283 cubic inch fuel-injected V-8. Among the standard features were: dual exhaust; all-vinyl bucket seats; three-spoke competition style steering wheel; carpeting; outside rearview mirror; electric clock and tachometer. It was available in seven colors: Onyx Black; Polo White; Aztec Copper; Artic Blue; Cascade Green; Venetian Red or Silver. White, silver, and beige were optional color choices for the cove.

VEHICLE IDENTIFICATION NUMBERS: The numbering system and code locations were the same as for previous models with the numbers changed as follows: E57S100001 to E57S106339. Engine Number suffixes were: 'EF' four-barrel/synchromesh; 'EG' dual four-barrel high-lift synchromesh; 'EH' dual four-barrel/synchromesh; 'EL' fuel-injection/high-lift; 'EN' fuel-injection/high; 'FG' Powerglide dual four-barrel; 'FH' Powerglide and 'FK' Powerglide/fuel-injection.

1957 Corvette, 2-dr convertible, V-8 (AA)

CORVETTTE Model Number	Body/Style Number	Body Type & Seating	Factory Price	Shipping Weight	Production Total
2934	2934	2-dr Conv-2P	3465	2730	6,339

CORVETTE SERIES ENGINE
V-8. Overhead valves. Cast iron block. Displacement: 283 cubic inches. Bore and stroke: 3.87 x 3 inches. Compression ratio: 9.50:1. Brake horsepower: 220 at 4800 R.P.M. Five main bearings. Valve lifters: (see note). Carburetor: Carter four-barrel Model 3744925. **NOTE:** A solid lifter camshaft was used with 'EL' and 'EG' engines; hydraulic lifters with others.

CHASSIS FEATURES: Wheelbase: 102 inches. Overall length: 168 inches. Front tread: 57 inches. Rear tread: 59 inches. Tires: 6.70 x 15.

POWERTRAIN OPTIONS: Three-speed manual floor shift transmission was standard. Automatic transmission ($175). Four-speed manual floor shift transmission ($188). V-8 283 cubic inch 245 horsepower dual four-barrel carb. engine ($140). V-8 283 cubic inch 270 horspower dual four-barrel carb. engine ($170*). V-8 283 cubic inch 250 horsepower fuel-injection engine ($450). V-8 283 cubic inch 283 horsepower fuel-injection engine ($450*). "RPO 579E" V-8 283 cubic inch 283 horsepower fuel-injection engine ($675**). Positive traction rear axle ($45). Heavy-duty racing suspension ($725). Available rear axle gear ratios 3.70:1, 4.11:1, 4.56:1.

* With competition camshaft
** With cold-air induction system

CONVENIENCE OPTIONS: Special 15 x 5.5 inch wheels ($14). Signal-seeking AM radio ($185). Detachable hardtop ($215). Power top ($130). Courtesy lights ($8). Heater ($118). Windshield washer ($12). Parking brake alarm ($5). Whitewall tires ($32). Dual carbs ($151). Two-tone paint ($19). Motorola radio ($125). Electric windows ($55). Hydraulic power top ($99).

Historical Footnotes: Only 1040 of the 1957 Corvettes were fuel-injected. A 283 horsepower fuel injection 1957 Corvette could go from 0 to 60 miles per hour in 5.7 seconds. From 0 to 100 miles per hour in 16.8 seconds. It had a top speed of 132 miles per hour.

1958 CORVETTE

1958 Corvette, 2-dr convertible, V-8 (AA)

CORVETTE SERIES — (V-8) — SERIES J800 — Styling was jazzed up for 1958. There were now four chrome rimmed headlights with a fender length chrome strip running between each pair of lights. As if that weren't enough glitter, fake louvers were placed on the hood. The grille was similar to last year's, but had four fewer vertical bars. Three horizontal chrome strips were added to the new cove. A couple of vertical chrome bars decorated the trunk. They detracted from an otherwise graceful rear end treatment. The wraparound front and rear bumpers were larger. The interior changed dramatically. The gauges were clustered together, rather than spread across the dash as before. A center console and passenger assist (sissy) bar were added. Upholstery was available in red, charcoal, or blue-green. There were six acrylic lacquer exterior colors offered: Charcoal, White, Yellow, Red, Blue and Turquoise. The cove could be painted silver or white.

VEHICLE IDENTIFICATION NUMBERS: The numbering system and code locations were the same as for previous models with the numbers changed as follows: J58S100001 to J58S109168. Engine codes were: 'CQ' = manual transmission; 'CR' = manual and fuel injection; 'CS' = manual/high-lift cam and fuel injection; 'CT' = manual and dual four-barrels; 'CU' = manual/high-lift and dual four-barrels; 'DG' = Powerglide transmission; 'DH' = Powerglide and fule-injection and 'DJ' = Powerglide and dual four-barrel.

NOTE: Both three and four-speed manual transmissions used same engine code suffixes.

CORVETTE

Series Number	Body/Style Number	Body Type & Seating	Factory Price	Shipping Weight	Production Total
J800	867	2-dr Conv-2P	3631	2781	9,168

CORVETTE SERIES ENGINE
V-8. Overhead valves. Cast iron block. Displacement: 283 cubic inches. Bore and stroke: 3.87 x 3 inches. Compression ratio: 9.50:1. Brake horsepower: 230 at 4800 R.P.M. Five main bearings. Hydraulic valve lifters. Carburetor: Carter Type WCFB four-barrel.

CHASSIS FEATURES: Wheelbase: 102 inches. Overall length: 177.2 inches. Front tread: 57 inches. Rear tread: 59 inches. Tires: 5.70 x 15.

POWERTRAIN OPTIONS: Three-speed manual floor shift transmission was standard. Automatic transmission ($188). Four-speed manual floor shift transmission ($215). V-8 283 cubic inch 245 horsepower dual four-barrel carb engine ($150). V-8 283 cubic inch 270 horsepower dual four-barrel carb engine ($182.95). V-8 283 cubic inch 250 horsepower fuel-injection engine ($484). V-8 283 cubic inch 290 horsepower fuel-injection engine ($484). Positive traction rear axle ($48.45). Heavy-duty brakes and suspension ($780.10). Available rear axle gear ratios: 3.70:1; 4.11:1; 4.56:1.

CONVENIENCE OPTIONS: Heater ($97). Power top ($140). Additional cove color ($16.15). Detachable hardtop ($215). Signal-seeking AM radio ($144). Power windows ($59.20). Special 15 x 5.5 inch wheels (no cost). Windshield washer ($16). Whitewall tires ($31.55). Courtesy lights ($6.50). Parking brake alarm ($5.40).

Historical footnotes: Almost 11 percent of 1958 Corvettes were powered by the 290 horsepower 283 cubic inch fuel-injected V-8. A 1958 Corvette with the standard 230 horsepower V-8 could go from 0 to 60 M.P.H. in 9.2 seconds. One with the 290 horsepower fuel-injected engine took only 6.9 seconds and got slightly better gas mileage.

1959 CORVETTE

1959 Corvette, 2-dr convertible, V-8 (AA)

CORVETTE SERIES — (V-8) — SERIES J800 — The 1959 Corvette was basically a cleaned-up 1958. The fake hood louvers and vertical chrome strips on the trunk were removed. Interior changes included redesigned bucket seats and door panels, a fiberglass package tray under the sissy bar and concave gauge lenses. A tachometer, outside rearview mirror, dual exhausts and electric clock were among the standard features. Seven exterior color choices were offered: Black; White; Cream; Silver; Red; Blue and Crown Sapphire. The cove could be painted either silver or white. Blue, red, turquoise and (for the first time) black interiors were available.

VEHICLE IDENTIFICATION NUMBERS: The numbering system and code locations were the same as for previous models with the numbers changed as follows J59S100001 to J59S109670. Engine Number suffixes were similar to those of 1958.

CORVETTE

Series Number	Body/Style Number	Body Type & Seating	Factory Price	Shipping Weight	Production Total
J800	867	2-dr Conv-2P	3875	2900	9,670

CORVETTE SERIES ENGINE
V-8. Overhead valves. Cast iron block. Displacement: 283 cubic inches. Bore and stroke: 9.50:1. Brake horsepower: 230 at 4800 R.P.M. Five main bearings. Hydraulic valve lifters. Carburetor: Carter Type WCFB four-barrel Model 2816.

CHASSIS FEATURES: Wheelbase: 102 inches. Overall length: 177.2 inches. Front tread: 57 inches. Rear tread: 59 inches. Tires: 6.70 x 15.

POWERTRAIN OPTIONS: Three-speed manual floor shift transmission was standard. Automatic transmission ($199). Four-speed manual floor shift transmission ($188). V-8 283 cubic inch 245 horsepower dual four-barrel carb engine ($150.65). V-8 283 cubic inch 270 horsepower dual four-barrel carb engine ($182.95). V-8 283 cubic inch 250 horsepower fuel-injection engine ($484). V-8 283 cubic inch 290 horsepower fuel-injection engine ($484). Metal brakes ($26.90). Positive traction rear axle ($48.45). Heavy-duty brakes and suspension ($425.05).

CONVENIENCE OPTIONS: Power top ($139.90). Windshield washer ($16.15). Signal-seeking transistor radio ($149.80). DeLuxe heater ($102.25). Two-tone paint ($16.15). Electric windows ($59.20). Courtesy light ($6.50). Parking brake alarm ($5.40). Sunshades ($10.80). Special 15 x 5.5 inch wheels (no cost). Detachable hardtop ($236.75).

Historical footnotes: A 290 horsepower fuel-injected 1959 Corvette could go from 0 to 60 M.P.H. in 6.6 seconds. From 0 to 100 in 15.5 seconds. It had a top speed of 128 miles per hour.

1960 CORVETTE

1960 Corvette, 2-dr convertible, V-8 (AA)

CORVETTE SERIES — (V-8) — SERIES 0800 — The 1960 Corvette looked much the same as last year's model. A new rear suspension sway-bar improved the car's handling. Aluminum heads and radiator were introduced, but later withdrawn. Standard equipment included: tachometer; sun visors; dual exhaust; carpeting; outside rearview mirror and electric clock. Buyers could choose from eight exterior finishes: Black; White; Turquoise; Blue; Silver; Green; Red, and Maroon. The cove was available in silver or white. Three colors of convertible tops: black, white and blue, were offered.

VEHICLE IDENTIFICATION NUMBERS: The numbering system and code locations were the same as for previous models with the numbers changed as follows: 00867S100001 to 00867S110261. The first symbol designated year. The second, third, fourth and fifth symbols designated Model Number ('0800') and Body Style, '67' = convertible; '63' = coupe. The sixth symbol designated manufacturing plant, 'S' = St. Louis. The last six digits were the sequential production numbers.

CORVETTE

Series Number	Body/Style Number	Body Type & Seating	Factory Price	Shipping Weight	Production Total
0800	67	2-dr Conv-2P	3872	2840	10,261

CORVETTE SERIES ENGINE
V-8. Overhead valves. Cast iron block. Displacement: 283 cubic inches. Bore and stroke: 3.87 x 3 inches. Compression ratio: 9.25:1. Brake horsepower: 230 at 4800 R.P.M. Five main bearings. Hydraulic valve lifters. Carburetor: Carter Type WCFB four-barrel Model 3756676.

CHASSIS FEATURES: Wheelbase: 102 inches. Overall length: 177.2 inches. Front tread: 57 inches. Rear tread: 59 inches. Tires: 6.70 x 15.

POWERTRAIN OPTIONS: Three-speed manual floor shift transmission was standard. Automatic transmission ($199.10). Four-speed manual floor shift transmission ($188). V-8 283 cubic inch 245 horsepower dual four-barrel carb. engine ($150.65). V-8 283 cubic inch 270 horsepower dual four-barrel carb. engine ($182.95). V-8 283 cubic inch 275 horsepower fuel-injection engine ($484). V-8 283 cubic inch 315 horsepower fuel-injection engine ($484). Metallic brakes ($26.90). Positive traction rear axle ($43.05). Heavy-duty brakes and suspension ($333.60). Available rear axle gear ratios 3.70:1, 4.11:1, 4.56:1.

CONVENIENCE OPTIONS: Power top ($139.90). Windshield washer ($16.15). Signal-seeking transistor radio ($137.75). DeLuxe heater ($102.25). Detachable hardtop ($236.75). Two-tone paint ($16.15). Electric windows ($59.20). Whitewall tires ($31.55). Courtesy lights ($6.50). Parking brake alarm ($5.40). Sunshades ($10.80). Permanent anti-freeze ($5.00). Special 15 x 5.5 inch wheels (no cost).

Historical Footnotes: The majority of 1960 Corvettes, 50.1 percent, were sold with a detachable hardtop. Most, 51.9 percent, also had a four-speed manual transmission.

1961 CORVETTE

CORVETTE SERIES — (V-8) — SERIES 0800 — A refined, thin vertical and horizontal bar grille and 'duck tail' rear end treatment with four cylindrical taillights quickly set the new 1961 Corvette apart from its predecessor. The exhaust now exited under the car, rather than through bumper ports. Standard equipment included: tachometer; seat belts; sun visors; dual exhaust; carpeting; electric clock and an outside rearview mirror. Seven exterior colors were available: Black; White; Red; Maroon; Beige; Blue and Silver.

VEHICLE IDENTIFICATION NUMBERS: The numbering system and code locations were the same as for previous models with the numbers changed as follows: 10867S100001 to 10867S110939.

CORVETTE

Series Number	Body/Style Number	Body Type & Seating	Factory Price	Shipping Weight	Production Total
0800	67	2-dr Conv-2P	3934	2905	10,939

1961 Corvette, 2-dr convertible, V-8 (AA)

CORVETTE SERIES ENGINE
V-8. Overhead valves. Cast iron block. Displacement: 283 cubic inches. Bore and stroke: 3.87 x 3 inches. Compression ratio: 9.5:1. Brake horsepower: 230 at 4800 R.P.M. Five main bearings. Hydraulic valve lifters. Carburetor: Carter Type WCFB four-barrel Model 3779178.

CHASSIS FEATURES: Wheelbase: 102 inches. Overall length: 177.2 inches. Front tread: 57 inches. Rear tread: 59 inches. Tires: 6.70 x 15.

POWERTRAIN OPTIONS: Three-speed manual floor shift transmission was standard. Automatic transmission ($199). Four-speed manual floor shift transmission ($188). V-8 283 cubic inch 245 horsepower dual four-barrel engine ($150.65). V-8 283 cubic inch 270 horsepower dual four-barrel carb. engine ($182.95). V-8 283 cubic inch 275 horsepower fuel-injection engine ($484). V-8 283 cubic inch 315 horsepower fuel-injection engine ($484). Direct flow exhaust system (no cost). Metallic brakes ($37.70). Positive traction rear axle ($43.05). Heavy-duty brakes and suspension ($333.60).

CONVENIENCE OPTIONS: Power top ($161.40). Windshield washer ($16.15). Signal-seeking transistor radio ($137.75). DeLuxe heater ($102.25). Detachable hardtop ($236.75). Two-tone paint ($16.15). Electric windows ($59.20). Whitewall tires ($31.55). Blackwall Nylon tires ($5.40). Crankcase ventilating system ($5.40). Oversize 24 gallon fuel tank ($161.40). Permanent anti-freeze ($5.00). Special 15 x 5.5 inch wheels (no cost).

Historical Footnotes: Most 1961 Corvettes, 51.9 percent, came with a detachable hardtop and 64.1 percent had a four-speed manual transmission. This was the last year wide whitewall tires were available.

1962 CORVETTE

1962 Corvette, 2-dr convertible, V-8 (AA)

CORVETTE SERIES — (V-8) — SERIES 0800 — The most noticeable changes for 1962 were the removal of the side cove chrome, a blacked-out grille and ribbed chrome rocker panel molding. For the first time since 1955, Corvettes were offered in solid colors only. Standard features included: electric clock; dual exhaust; tach; heater and defroster; seat belts; outside rearview mirror and windshield washer. The wheels were available in black, beige, red, silver or maroon. The last time buyers had a choice of wheel colors was in 1957. In following years, wheels would be offered in only a single color.

VEHICLE IDENTIFICATION NUMBERS: The numbering system and code locations were the same as for previous models with the numbers changed as follows: 20867S100001 to 20867S114531.

CORVETTE

Series Number	Body Style Number	Doors/Style Seating	Factory Price	Shipping Weight	Production Total
0800	67	2-dr Conv-2P	4038	2905	14,531

CORVETTE SERIES ENGINE
V-8. Overhead valves. Cast iron block. Displacement: 327 cubic inches. Bore and stroke: 4 x 3.25 inches. Compression ratio: 10.5:1. Brake horsepower: 250 at 4400 R.P.M. Five main bearings. Hydraulic valve lifters. Carburetor: Carter Type WCFB four-barrel Model 3788246.

CHASSIS FEATURES: Wheelbase: 102 inches. Overall length: 177.2 inches. Front tread: 57 inches. Rear tread: 59 inches. Tires: 6.70 x 15.

POWERTRAIN OPTIONS: Three-speed manual floor shift transmission was standard. Automatic transmission ($199). Four-speed manual floor shift transmission ($188). V-8 326 cubic inch 300 horsepower dual four-barrel carb engine ($53.80). V-8 327 cubic inch 340 horsepower dual four-barrel carb engine ($107.60. V-8 327 cubic inch 360 horsepower fuel injection engine ($484). Direct flow exhaust system (no cost). Metallic brakes ($37.70). Positive traction rear axle ($43.05). Heavy-duty brakes and suspension ($333.60).

CONVENIENCE OPTIONS: Power top ($161.40). Detachable hardtop ($236.75). Signal-seeking transistor radio ($137.75). 24 gallon fuel tank ($118.40). Electric windows ($59.20). Whitewall tires ($31.55). Black wall Nylon tires ($15.70). Crankcase ventilation system ($5.40). Heavy-duty brakes with metallic facings ($37.70). Permanent anti-freeze ($5.00). Special 15 x 5.5 inch wheels (no cost).

Historical footnote: A 360 horsepower fuel-injected 1962 Corvette could go from 0 to 60 miles per hour in 5.9 seconds; from 0 to 100 miles per hour in 14 seconds.

1963 CORVETTE

1963 Corvette, 2-dr Sting Ray coupe, V-8 (AA)

STING RAY SERIES — (V-8) — SERIES 0800 — (The Corvette received major restyling in 1963. Although the rear deck treatment resembled that of the previous year's model, the rest of the car appeared totally new. The headlights were hidden in an electrically operated panel. This was more than a styling gimmick, as it added to the car's basic aerodynamic design. The recessed fake hood louvers were another matter. Front fenders louvers, vents on the roof side panels (of the fastback sport coupe) and ribbed rocker panel molding were styling features used on the sides of the new Corvette. The interior had circular gauges with black faces. There was storage space under the seats of early models. Among the standard equipment was; windshield washer; carpeting; outside rear view mirror; dual exhaust; tachometer; electric clock; heater and defroster; cigarette lighter and safety belts. Seven exterior colors were offered; Black; White; Silver; Silver Blue; Daytona Blue; Red; and Tan. For the first time since 1957, a beige soft top was available.

VEHICLE IDENTIFICATION NUMBERS: The numbering system and code locations were the same as for previous models with the numbers changed as follows: 30867S100001 to 30867S121513, or 30837S100001 to 30837S121513.

STING RAY

Series Number	Body/Style Number	Body Type & Seating	Factory Price	Shipping Weight	Production Total
0800	37	2-dr FsBk Cpe-2P	4257	2859	10,594
0800	67	2-dr Conv-2P	4037	2881	10,919

STING RAY SERIES ENGINE
V-8. Overhead valves. Cast iron block. Displacement: 327 cubic inches. Bore and stroke: 4 x 3.25 inches. Compression ratio: 10:50:1. Brake horsepower: 250 at 4400 R.P.M. Five main bearings. Hydraulic valve lifters. Carburetor: Carter Type WCFB four-barrel Model 3501S.

CHASSIS FEATURES: Wheelbase: 98 inches. Overall length: 175.2 inches. Front tread: 56.8 inches. Rear tread: 57.6 inches. Tires: 6.70 x 15.

POWERTRAIN OPTIONS: Three-speed manual floor-shift transmission was standard. Automatic transmission ($199.10). Four-speed manual floor shift transmission ($188). 'L75' V-8 327 cubic inch 300 horsepower four-barrel carb. engine ($53.80). 'L76' V-8 327 cubic inch 340 horsepower four-barrel carb. engine ($107.60). 'L84' V-8 327 cubic inch 360 horsepower fuel-injection engine ($430.40). Sintered metallic brakes ($37.70). Off-road exhaust system ($37.70). RPO Z06 Special performance package (coupe): metallic power brakes; heavy-duty shocks; stabilizers; knock-off type aluminum wheels; positraction rear axle; four-speed manual gear box; 360 horsepower fuel-injection V-8 ($1,818). Positive traction rear axle ($43.05). Available rear axle gear ratio: 4.11:1, 4.56:1, 3.08:1, 3.36:1, 3.55:1, 3.70:1.

CONVENIENCE OPTIONS: Power brakes ($43.05). Power steering ($73.35). Air conditioning ($421.80). Detachable hardtop ($236.75). Signal-seeking transistor radio ($137.75). Electric windows ($59.20). Whitewall tires ($31.55). Blackwall Nylon tires ($15.70). Heavy-duty brakes with metallic facings ($37.70). Sebring Silver paint ($80.70). Woodgrain plastic steering wheel ($16.15). Aluminum knock-off wheels ($322.80). AM-FM radio ($174). Tinted windshield ($10.80). Tinted glass ($16.15). Leather seat trim ($80.70).

Historical footnotes: A rare option in 1963 Corvettes is air conditioning. Only 1.3 percent were so-equipped. However, 83.5 percent came with four-speed manual transmission. An 'L84' powered Corvette could go from 0 to 60 miles per hour in 5.9 seconds; from 0 to 100 miles per hour in 16.5 seconds. The historic Corvette Grand Sport was constructed in 1963. A total of five were built before the program was canceled. They weighed 1,908 pounds, had 377 cubic inch versions of the small block V-8 equipped with aluminum cylinder block and aluminum hemi-head cylinder heads with twin ignition and port fuel injection.

1964 CORVETTE

1964 Corvette, 2-dr Sting Ray coupe, V-8 (AA)

STING RAY SERIES — (V-8) — SERIES 0800 — Styling was cleaned up a bit for 1964. The distinctive rear window divider was replaced by a solid piece of glass. The fake hood vents were eliminated and the roof vents were restyled. A three-speed fan was available in the coupe to aid in ventilation. Seven exterior colors were offered: Black; White; Tan; Daytona Blue; Silver Blue; Silver and Red.

VEHICLE IDENTIFICATION NUMBERS: The numbering system and code locations were the same as for previous models with the numbers changed as follows 40867S100001 to 40867S122229, or 40837S100001 to 40837S122229.

STING RAY

Series Number	Body/Style Number	Body Type & Seating	Factory Price	Shipping Weight	Production Total
0800	37	2-dr FsBk Cpe-2P	4252	2945	8,304
0800	67	2-dr Conv-2P	4037	2960	13,925

STING RAY SERIES ENGINE
V-8. Overhead valves. Cast iron block. Displacement: 327 cubic inche. Bore and stroke: 4 x 3.25 inches. Compression ratio: 10.50:1. Brake horsepower: 250 at 4400 R.P.M. Carburetor Carter Type WCFB four-barrel Model 3846247.

CHASSIS FEATURES: Wheelbase: 98 inches. Overall length: 174.2 inches. Front tread: 56.8 inches. Rear tread: 57.6 inches. Tires: 6.70 x 15.

POWERTRAIN OPTIONS: Three-speed manual floor shift transmission was standard. Automatic transmission ($199.10). Four-speed manual floor shift transmission ($188). 'L75' V-8 327 cubic inch 300 horsepower four-barrel carb engine ($53.80). 'L76' V-8 327 cubic 365 horsepower four-barrel carb engine ($107.60). 'L84' V-8 327 cubic inch 375 horsepower fuel-injection engine ($538). Positive traction rear axle ($43.50). Off-road exhaust system ($37.70). Special front and rear suspension ($37.70). Transistor ignition system ($73.75). Special Sintered Metallic brakes package ($629.50). Available rear axle gear ratios: 4.11:1; 4.56:1; 3.08:1; 3.36:1; 3.55:1; 3.70:1.

CONVENIENCE OPTIONS: Power brakes ($43.05). Power steering ($73.35). Air conditioning ($421.80). Leather seat trim ($80.70). Soft-ray tinted windows ($16.15). Soft-ray tinted windshield ($10.80). Electric windows ($59.20). Detachable hardtop ($236.75). Sintered metallic power brakes ($53.80). Special 36 gallon fuel tank, coupe only ($202.30). Special cast aluminum knock-off wheels ($322.80). Blackwall Nylon tires ($15.70). Whitewall Rayon tires ($31.85). Backup lights ($10.80). AM/FM radio ($176.50).

Historical footnotes: Only 3.2 percent of 1964 Corvettes were sold with the standard three-speed manual transmission. Most, 85.7 percent were equipped with a four-speed manual transmission. An 'L84' powered 1964 Corvette could go from 0 to 60 miles per hour in 6.3 seconds and from 0 to 100 miles per hour in 14.7 seconds. It had a top speed of 138 miles per hour.

1965 CORVETTE

1965 Corvette, 2-dr Sting Ray coupe, V-8 (AA)

STING RAY SERIES — (V-8) — SERIES 194 — Three functional, vertical front fender louvers; a blacked-out, horizontal bar grille and different rocker panel molding were the main styling changes for 1965. Standard equipment included: tachometer; safety belts; heater and defroster; windshield washer; outside rearview mirror; dual exhaust; electric clock; carpeting; manually operated top (convertible) and sun visors. Eight exterior colors were available; Black; White; Yellow; Red; Blue; Green; Silver and Maroon.

VEHICLE IDENTIFICATION NUMBERS: The numbering system and code locations were the same as on previous models with numbers changed as follows: 194675S00001 to 194675S123562 or 194375S100001 to 194375S123562. The first symbol designated make ('1' = Chevrolet). The second, third, fourth and fifth symbols designated Corvette Series and Body Style ('37' = coupe, '67' = convertible). The sixth symbol designated year. The last six digits were the sequential production numbers and started at 100,001.

STING RAY

Series Number	Body Style Number	Doors/Style Seating	Factory Price	Shipping Weight	Production Total
194	37	2-dr FsBkCpe-2P	2947	3570	8,187
194	67	2-dr Conv-2P	3212	3645	15,377

STING RAY SERIES ENGINE
V-8. Overhead valves. Cast iron block. Displacement: 327 cubic inches. Bore and stroke: 4 x 3.25 inches. Compression ratio: 10.50:1. Brake horsepower: 250 at 4400 R.P.M. Five main bearings. Hydraulic valve lifters. Carburetor: Carter Type WCFB four-barrel Model 3846247.

CHASSIS FEATURES: Wheelbase: 98 inches. Overall length: 175.2 inches. Front tread: 56.8 inches. Rear tread: 57.6 inches. Tires: 7.75 x 15.

POWERTRAIN OPTIONS: Three-speed manual transmission was standard. Automatic transmission ($199.10). Four-speed manual floor shift transmission ($188). Close-ratio four-speed manual transmission with floor shift ($237). 'L75' V-8 327 cubic inch 300 horsepower dual four-barrel carb engine ($53.80). 'L79' V-8 327 cubic inch 350 horsepower dual four-barrel carb engine ($107.60). 'L76' V-8 327 cubic inch 365 horsepower four-barrel carb engine ($129.15). 'L84' V-8 327 cubic inch 375 horse-power fuel-injection engine ($538). 'L78' V-8 396 cubic inch 425 horsepower four-barrel carb engine ($292.70). Special front and rear suspension ($37.70). Off-road exhaust system ($37.70). Side-mount exhaust system ($134.50). Transistor ignition system ($75.35). Positive traction rear axle ($43.05). Available rear axle gear ratios: 4.11:1, 4.56:1, 3.08:1, 3.36:1, 3.55:1, 3.70:1.
CONVENIENCE OPTIONS: Power brakes ($43.05). Power steering ($96.85). Air conditioning ($421.80). Back-up lights and inside rearview mirror ($16.15). Heater and defroster $100.00). Tinted glass ($16.15). Tinted windshield ($10.80). Special 36-gallon fuel tank, coupe only ($202.30). Power windows ($59.20). AM/FM radio with power antenna ($203.00). Teakwood steering wheel ($48.15). Detachable hardtop ($236.75). Whitewall tires ($31.85). Goldwall tires ($51.00). Saddle trim leather seats ($80.70). Special 15 inch knock-off type wheels ($322.80). Telescopic steering column ($43.05).

Production Note: Most 1965 Corvettes (89.6 percent) were sold with a four-speed manual transmission, 8.6 percent had Powerglide automatic transmission; 69.5 percent tinted glass, 10.3 percent air conditioning and 13.7 percent power steering. An 'L78' powered 1965 Corvette could go from 0 to 60 miles per hour in 5.7 seconds: from 0 to 100 miles per hour in 13.4 seconds.

1966 CORVETTE

1966 Corvette, 2-dr Sting Ray coupe, V-8 (AA)

STING RAY SERIES — (V-8) — SERIES 194 — An 'eggcrate' grille; ribbed rocker panel molding; chrome plated exhaust bezels; spoke style wheel covers; vinyl covered headliner and the elimination of roof vents helped set the 1966 Corvette apart from last year's model. Those equipped with the new 427 cubic inch V-8 came with a 'power bulge' hood. The ten lacquer exterior finishes offered: Black; White; Nassau Blue; Laguna Blue; Trophy Blue; Red; Green; Maroon; Yellow and Silver.

VEHICLE IDENTIFICATION NUMBERS: The numbering system and code locations were the same as for previous models with the numbers changed to as follows 194676S100001 to 194676S127720 or 194376S100001 to 194376S127720.

STING RAY

Series Number	Body/Style Number	Body Type & Seating	Factory Price	Shipping Weight	Production Total
194	37	2-dr FsBk Cpe-2P	4295	2985	9,958
194	67	2-dr Conv-2P	4084	3005	17,762

STING RAY SERIES ENGINE
V-8. Overhead valves. Cast iron block. Displacement: 327 cubic inches. Bore and stroke: 4 x 3.25 inches. Compression ratio: 10:5:1. Brake horsepower: 300 at 5000 R.P.M. Five main bearings. Hydraulic valve lifters. Carburetor. Holley four-barrel Model 3884505.

CHASSIS FEATURES: Wheelbase: 98 inches. Overall length: 17.2 inches. Front tread: 56.8 inches. Rear tread: 57.6 inches. Tires: 7.75 x 15.

POWERTRAIN OPTIONS: Three-speed manual transmission was standard. Automatic transmission ($194.85). Four-speed manual floor shift transmission ($184). Close-ratio four-speed manual transmission with floor shift ($184). Heavy-duty close-ratio four-speed manual transmission with floor shift ($237). 'L79' V-8 327 cubic inch 350 horsepower four-barrel carb engine ($105). 'L39' V-8 427 cubic inch 390 horsepower four-barrel carb engine ($181.20). 'L72' V-8 427 cubic inch 425 horsepower four-barrel carb engine ($312). Positive traction rear axle ($42.15). Heavy-duty brakes ($342.30). Special front and rear suspension ($36.90). Transistor ignition system (73.75). Off-road exhaust system ($36.90). Side-mount exhaust system ($131.65). Available rear axle gear ratios: 3.08:1; 3.36:1; 3.55:1; 3.70:1; 4.11:1; 4.56:1.

CONVENIENCE OPTIONS: Power brakes ($43.05). Power steering ($94.80). Air conditioning ($412.90). Leather seats ($79.00). Tinted windows ($15.80). Tinted windshield ($10.55). Electric windows ($59.20). Headrests ($42.15). Shoulder harness ($26.35). Detachable hardtop ($231.75). Special 36-gallon fuel tank ($198.05). Teakwood steering wheel ($48.45). Telescopic steering column ($42.15). Special cast aluminum knock-off wheels ($326.00). Whitewall tires ($31.30). Goldwall tires ($46.55). AM/FM radio ($199.10). Traffic-hazard lamp switch ($11.60).

Historical footnotes: Only two percent of all 1966 Corvettes had a three-speed manual transmission; 89.3 percent came with a four-speed manual gearbox; 13.2 percent had a tilting steering wheel and 20.2 percent had power steering.

1967 CORVETTE

1967 Corvette, 2-dr Sting Ray coupe, V-8 (AA)

STING RAY SERIES — (V-8) — SERIES 194 — Some consider the 1967 the best looking of the early Sting Rays. Its styling, although basically the same, was cleaner and unlike the others, it had five functional front fender louvers. Minor changes were made to the interior. The most noticeable was the relocation of the parking brake from under the dash, to the center console. Standard equipment included: rally wheels; odometer; clock; carpeting; wheel trim rings; tachometer and all-vinyl, foam cushioned bucket seats (available in black, white, teal blue, saddle, bright blue, and green).

VEHICLE IDENTIFICATION NUMBERS: The numbering system and code locations were the same as for previous models with the numbers changed as follows: 194677S100001 to 194677S122940 or 194377S100001 to 194377S122940.

STING RAY

Series Number	Body/Style Number	Body Type & Seating	Factory Price	Shipping Weight	Production Total
194	37	2-dr FsBk Cpe-2P	4353	3000	8,504
194	67	2-dr Conv-2P	4141	3020	14,436

STING RAY SERIES ENGINE
V-8. Overhead valves. Cast iron block. Displacement: 327 cubic inches. Bore and stroke: 4 x 3.25 inches. Compression ratio: 10.00:1. Brake horsepower: 300 at 5000 R.P.M. Five main bearings. Hydraulic valve lifters. Carburetor: Holley four-barrel Model R3810A or R3814A.

CHASSIS FEATURES: Wheelbase: 98 inches. Overall length: 175.2 inches. Front tread: 56.8 inches. Rear tread: 57.6 inches. tires: 7.75 x 15.

POWERTRAIN OPTIONS: Three-speed manual transmission was standard. Automatic transmission ($194.35). Heavy-duty close ratio four-speed manual floor shift transmission ($237). Wide-ratio four-speed manual transmission with floor shift ($184). Close-ratio four-speed manual transmission with floor shift ($184). 'L79' V-8 327 cubic inch 350 horsepower four-barrel carb. engine ($105). 'L36' V-8 427 cubic inch 390 horsepower four-barrel carb. engine ($200.15). 'L68' V-8 427 cubic inch 400 horsepower Tri-carb engine ($305). 'L71' 427 cubic inch 435 horsepower Tri-carb engine ($437). Aluminum cylinder heads for 'L71' V-8 ($368). 'L88' V-8 427 cubic inch with 430 horsepower rating with actual output around 530 hp. Aluminum heads included. Option price $947.90. Single Holley four-barrel. Twenty cars so optioned were produced (no radio, heater, or fan shroud). Special front and rear suspension ($36.90). Heavy-duty brakes ($342.30). Off-road exhaust system ($36.90). Transistor ignition system ($74.75). Side-mount exhaust system ($131.65). Available rear axle gear ratios: 3.08:1, 3.36:1, 3.55:1, 3.70:1, 4.11:1.

CONVENIENCE OPTIONS: Power brakes ($42.15). Power steering ($94.80). Air conditioning ($412.90). Front shoulder belts ($26.35). Special 36-gallon fuel tank ($198.05). Tinted windows ($15.80). Tinted windshield ($10.55). Strato-ease driver and passenger headrests ($42.15). Heater defroster ($97.85). Power windows ($57.95). AM/FM radio with rear antenna ($172.75). Black vinyl roof cover ($52.70). Leather seats ($79). Speed warning indicator ($10.55). Telescope steering shaft ($42.15). Four-ply whitewall tires size 7.75 x 15 ($31.35). Four-ply Red stripe Nylon tires size 7.75 x 15 ($46.55). Detachable hardtop ($231.75). Headrests ($42.15). Cast aluminum bolt-on wheels ($263.30).

Historical footnotes: Eighty-eight percent of 1967 Corvettes came with four-speed manual transmission; 10.1 percent had Powerglide automatic transmission; 20.8 percent had power brakes; 16.5 percent had air-conditioning; 10.5 percent had a tilting steering wheel and 25.1 percent came with power steering. A 300 horsepower 327 cubic inch V-8 powered Corvette of this vintage would go from 0 to 60 miles per hour in 7.8 seconds; from 0 to 100 miles per hour in 23.1 seconds.

1968 CORVETTE

1968 Corvette, 2-dr sports coupe, V-8 (AA)

CORVETTE SERIES — (V-8) — SERIES 194 — The first major restyling since 1963 occurred this year. As the sales brochure said, "Corvette '68 . . . all different all over". The fastback was replaced by a tunneled-roof coupe. It featured a removable back window and a two-piece detachable roof section (i.e. 'T-roof'). The convertible's optional hardtop had a glass rear window. The front end was more aerodynamic than previous Corvettes. As before, the headlights were hidden, but now they were vacuum operated rather than electrically. The wipers also disappeared when not in use. Except for the rocker panels, the sides were devoid of chrome. Conventional door handles were eliminated and in their place were pushbuttons and depression plates. The blunt rear deck contained four round taillights with the word Corvette printed in chrome in the space between them. The wraparound, wing-like rear bumper and license plate holder treatment resembled that used on the 1967. Buyers had their choice of 10 exterior colors.

VEHICLE IDENTIFICATION NUMBERS: The numbering system and code locations were the same as for previous models with the numbers changed as follows: 194678S100001 to 194678S128566 or 194379S100001 to 194378S128566.

CORVETTE

Series Number	Body/Style Number	Body Type & Seating	Factory Price	Shipping Weight	Production Total
194	37	2-dr Spt Cpe-2	4663	3055	9,936
194	67	2-dr Conv-2	4347	3070	18,630

STING RAY SERIES ENGINE DATA
V-8. Overhead valves. Cast iron block. Displacement: 327 cubic inches. Bore and stroke: 4 x 3.25 inches. Compression ratio: 10.00:1. Brake horsepower: 300 at 5000 R.P.M. Five main bearings. Hydraulic valve lifters. Carburetor: Rochester Type 4MV four-barrel Model 7028207.

CHASSIS FEATURES: Wheelbase: 98 inches. Overall length: 182.5 inches. Front tread: 58.7 inches. Rear tread: 59.4 inches. Tires: F70-15.

POWERTRAIN OPTIONS: Three-speed manual transmission was standard. Automatic transmission ($226). Heavy-duty close ratio four-speed manual floor shift transmission ($263). Wide-ratio four-speed manual transmission with floor shift ($184). Close-ratio four-speed manual transmission with floor shift ($184). 'L79' V-8 327 cubic inch 350 horsepower four-barrel carb. engine ($105). 'L36' V-8 427 cubic inch 390 horsepower four-barrel carb engine ($200.15). 'L68' V-8 427 cubic inch 400 horsepower Tri-carb engine ($305). 'L71' V-8 427 cubic inch 435 horsepower Tri-carb engine ($437.10). 'L71/89' V-8 427 cubic inch 435 horsepower Tri-carb engine ($805.75). 'L88' V-8 427 cubic inch 430 horsepower with actual output around 530 hp. Aluminum heads included. Option price $947.90. Single Holley four-barrel. Production of 80 cars. Heater was standard as was a high-rise, freshair, bubble hood. Special front and rear suspension ($36.90). Heavy-duty brakes ($384.45). Off-road exhaust system ($36.90). Transistor ignition system ($73.75). Postitive traction rear axle ($46.35). Available rear axle gear ratios: 2.73:1, 3.08:1, 3.36:1, 3.55:1, 4.11:1.

CONVENIENCE OPTIONS: Power brakes ($42.15). Power steering ($94.80). Air conditioning ($412.90). Custom DeLuxe front shoulder belts ($26.35). Rear window defroster ($31.60). Tinted windows ($15.80). Tinted windshield ($10.55). Driver and passenger head restraints ($42.15). Heavy-duty power brakes ($384.45). Power windows ($57.95). AM/FM radio with fixed height antenna ($172.75). AM/FM stereo radio ($278.10). Black vinyl roof ($52.70). Leather seats ($79). Speed warning indicator ($10.55). Adjustable steering shaft ($42.15). Detachable hardtop ($231.75). Four wheel covers ($57.95). Special red stripe F70-15 tires ($31.30). Special white stripe F70-15 tires ($31.30). Alarm system ($26.35).

Historical footnote: Just over 80 percent of 1968 Corvettes were equipped with four-speed manual transmission; 81 percent had tinted glass; 36.3 percent had power steering; 19.8 percent had air-conditioning and 33.7 percent had power brakes. The 'L-79' powered Corvette of this year could go from 0 to 60 miles per hour in 7.7 seconds and from 0 to 110 miles per hour in 20.7 seconds.

1969 CORVETTE

STINGRAY SERIES — (V-8) — SERIES 194 — After a year's absence, the Stingray name (now spelled as one word) reappeared on the front fenders. The backup lights were integrated into the center taillights. The ignition was now on the steering column and the door depression button used in 1968 was eliminated. (A key lock was put in its place.) Front and rear disc brakes; headlight washers; center console; wheel trim rings; carpeting and all-vinyl upholstery were standard.

1969 Corvette, 2-dr Stingray coupe, V-8 (AA)

VEHICLE IDENTIFICATION NUMBERS: The numbering system and code locations were the same as for previous models with the numbers changed as follows 194679S100001 to 194679S138762 or 194379S100001 to 194379S138762.

STINGRAY

Series Number	Body/Style Number	Body Type & Seating	Factory Price	Shipping Weight	Production Total
194	37	2-dr Spt Cpe-2P	4763	3091	22,129
194	67	2-dr Conv Cpe-2P	4420	3096	16,633

STINGRAY SERIES ENGINE DATA
V-8. Overhead valves. Cast iron block. Displacement: 350 cubic inches. Bore and stroke: 4 x 3.48 inches. Compression ratio: 10.25:1. Brake horsepower: 300 at 4800 R.P.M. Five main bearings. Hydraulic valve lifters. Carburetor: Rochester four-barrel Model 7029203.

CHASSIS FEATURES: Wheelbase: 98 inches. Overall length: 182.5 inches. Front tread: 58.7 inches. Rear tread: 59.4 inches. Tires: F70 x 15.

POWERTRAIN OPTIONS: Three-speed manual transmission was standard. Automatic transmission ($221.80). Heavy-duty close-ratio four-speed manual floor shift transmission ($290). Wide-ratio four-speed manual transmission with floor shift ($184). Close-ratio four-speed manual transmission with floor shift ($184). 'L46' V-8 350 cubic inch 350 horsepower four-barrel engine ($131.65). 'L36' V-8 427 cubic inch 390 horsepower four-barrel engine ($221.20). 'L68' V-8 427 cubic inch 400 horsepower Tri-carb engine ($326). 'L71' V-8 427 cubic inch 435 horsepower Tri-carb engine ($437.10). 'L88' engine option 427 cubic inch, rated at 430 hp with actual output around 530 hp. Aluminum heads included. Option price $1,032.15. Single Holley four-barrel. Production of 116 cars. 'L88' 1967, '68, '69 Corvette engined models were targeted at road racers. The drivetrain was quite different from other 427 equipped Corvettes, with many heavy duty parts and performance assembly techniques. There were no standard visual changes in the body (aside from the '68, '69 hood). A decal on the parking brake console warned of engine damage unless run on 103 octane gasoline. ZL 1 427 cubic inch ($3000). Only two were built. Special front and rear suspension ($36.90). Transistor ignition system ($81.10). Side-mount exhaust system ($147.45). Positive traction rear axle ($46.35). Available rear axle gear ratios: 2.73:1, 3.08:1, 3.36:1, 3.55:1, 3.70:1, 4.11:1, 4.56:1.

CONVENIENCE OPTIONS: Power brakes ($42.15). Power steering ($105.35). Air conditioning ($428.70). Auto alarm system ($26.35). Custom DeLuxe front shoulder belts ($42.15). Rear window defroster ($32.65). Tinted windows ($16.90). Front fender louver trim ($21.10). Heavy-duty power brakes ($384.45). Power windows ($63.20). AM/FM radio with fixed height antenna ($172.75). AM/FM pushbutton stereo radio ($278.10). Black vinyl roof cover ($57.95). Leather seat trim ($79.00). Speed warning indicator ($11.60). Telescopic tilt steering wheel ($84.30). Special red stripe tires ($31.30). Special white stripe tires ($31.30). Detachable hardtop ($252.80). Four wheel covers ($57.95).

Historical footnotes: The majority of 1969 Corvettes, 59.2 percent, came with power steering, 78.4 percent had four-speed manual attachments and one-in-four had power windows. A 300 horsepower 350 cubic inch V-8 was available this season. Cars with this powerplant and automatic transmission were capable of 0 to 60 speeds in the 8.4 second bracket and could move from 0 to 100 miles per hour in approximately 21.7 seconds.

1970 CORVETTE

1970 Corvette, 2-dr Stingray convertible, V-8

STINGRAY SERIES — (V-8) — SERIES 194 — Refinements were made to the basic styling used since 1968. A new 'ice cube tray' design grille and side fender louvers; rectangular, amber front signal lights; fender flares and square exhaust exits were exterior changes. The bucket seats and safety belt retractor containers were also improved. Standard equipment included: front and rear disc brakes; headlight washers; wheel trim rings; carpeting; center console and all-vinyl upholstery (in either black, blue, green, saddle or red).

VEHICLE IDENTIFICATION NUMBERS: The numbering system and code locations were the same as for previous models with the numbers changed as follows: 194670S100001 to 194670S117316 or 194370S100001 to 194370S117316.

STINGRAY

Series Number	Body/Style Number	Body Type & Seating	Factory Price	Shipping Weight	Production Total
194	37	2-dr Spt Cpe-2P	5469	3153	10,668
194	67	2-dr Conv-2P	5129	3167	6,648

STINGRAY SERIES ENGINE
V-8. Overhead valves. Cast iron block. Displacement: 350 cubic inches. Bore and stroke: 4 x 3.48 inches. Compression ratio: 10.25. Brake horsepower: 300 at 4800 R.P.M. Five main bearings. Hydraulic valve lifters. Carburetor: Rochester Type Quadra-jet four-barrel Model 4MV.

CHASSIS FEATURES: Wheelbase: 98 inches. Overall length: 182.5 inches. Front tread: 58.7 inches. Rear tread: 59.4 inches. Tires: F70-15.

POWERTRAIN OPTIONS: Automatic transmission (no cost). A wide-range four-speed manual floor shift transmission was standard. Close-ratio four-speed manual transmission with floor shift (no cost). Heavy-duty close ratio four-speed manual transmission with floor shift ($95). 'L56' V-8 350 cubic inch 350 horsepower four-barrel engine ($158). 'LT1' V-8 350 cubic inch 370 horsepower four-barrel engine ($447.60). 'LS5' V-8 454 cubic inch 390 horsepower four-barrel engine ($289.65). 'LS7' V-8 454 cubic inch 460 horsepower Tri-carb engine ($3,000). Side-mounted exhaust system ($116.65). Full transistor ignition system ($64.16). Special front and rear suspension ($29.20). Positive traction rear axle (standard but optional ratios cost $12). Heavy-duty clutch ($62.50). Available rear axle gear ratios: 2.73:1; 3.08:1; 3.36:1; 3.55:1; 4.11:1; 4.56:1.

CONVENIENCE OPTIONS: Power brakes ($33.55). Power steering ($83.35). Air conditioning ($339.16). Audio alarm system ($20.85). Custom DeLuxe front shoulder belts ($33.35). Rear window defroster ($25.83). Tinted windows ($13.38). Front fender louver trim ($16.70). Heavy-duty power brakes ($304.15). Power windows ($50). AM/FM radio with fixed height antenna ($136.67). AM/FM pushbutton stereo radio ($220.02). Black vinyl roof cover ($45.85). Genuine leather seat trim ($62.50). Speed warning indicator ($9.18). Telescopic tilt steering wheel ($66.70). Detachable hardtop ($200). Wheel covers ($45.85).

Historical footnotes: Most 1970 Corvettes, 70.5 percent, came with four-speed manual transmission; 33.5 percent had tilting steering wheels; 27.9 percent power windows; 38.5 percent air-conditioning and 68.8 percent power steering. An L-70 powered 1970 Corvette would do 0 to 60 in seven seconds and go from 0 to 100 miles per hour in 14 seconds.

1971 CORVETTE

1971 Corvette, 2-dr Stingray convertible with LT-1 package, V-8

STINGRAY SERIES (V-8) — SERIES 194 — If you liked the 1970 Corvette, you'd like the 1971. They were virtually the same car. A new resin process (that supposedly improved the body) and a different interior were the major changes. Under the hood, the compression ratios were dropped a bit to enable Corvette engines to run on lower octane fuel. Standard equipment included: all-vinyl upholstery; dual exhausts; outside rearview mirror; carpeting; center console; wheel trim rings; electric clock; tachometer; heavy-duty battery; front and rear disc brakes with warning light and tinted glass.

VEHICLE IDENTIFICATION NUMBERS: The numbering system and code locations were the same as for previous models with the numbers changed as follows 194671S100001 to 194671S21801 or 194371S100001 to 194371S121801.

STINGRAY

Series Number	Body/Style Number	Body Type & Seating	Factory Price	Shipping Weight	Production Total
194	37	2-dr Spt Cpe-2P	5536	3153	14,680
194	67	2-dr Conv-2P	5299	3167	7,121

STINGRAY SERIES ENGINE
V-8. Overhead valves. Cast iron block. Displacement: 350 cubic inches. Bore and stroke: 4 x 3.48 inches. Compression ratio: 8.50:1. Brake horsepower: 270 at 4800 R.P.M. Five main bearings. Hydraulic valve lifters. Carburetor: Rochester Type Quadra-Jet four-barrel Model 4MV.

CHASSIS FEATURES: Wheelbase: 98 inches. Overall length: 182.5 inches. Front tread: 58.7 inches. Rear tread: 59.4 inches. Tires: F70 x 15.

POWERTRAIN OPTIONS: Automatic transmission (no cost with standard engine, $100 with others). Wide-range four-speed manual floor shift transmission was standard. Close-ratio four-speed manual transmission with floor shift (no cost). Heavy-duty close-ratio four-speed manual transmission with floor shift ($100). 'LT1' V-8 300 cubic inch 350 horsepower four-barrel carb engine ($483). 'LS5' V-8 454 cubic inch 365 horsepower four-barrel carb engine ($295). 'LS6' V-8 454 cubic inch 425 horsepower four-barrel carb engine ($1,221). A 'ZR1' option package included heavy-duty brakes; close-ratio four-speed manual transmission; special front stablilizer bar; special springs and shock absorbers, fully transistorized ignition system and the 'LT-1' engine at a price of $1,010. A 'ZR2' option package included all features listed above, except that the 'LS6' powerplant was substituted, at a price of $1,747. Available rear axle gear ratios: 2.73:1; 3.08:1; 3.36:1; 3.55:1; 4.11:1; 4.56:1.

CONVENIENCE OPTIONS: Power brakes ($47.40). Power steering ($115.90). Air conditioning ($464.50). Audio alarm system ($31.60). Heavy-duty battery ($15.80). Custom DeLuxe shoulder belts ($42.15). Rear window defroster ($42.15). AM/FM pushbutton radio ($178). AM/FM stereo radio ($283.35). Black vinyl roof cover ($63.20). Telescopic tilt steering wheel ($84.30). White stripe tires ($30.35). White letter tires ($43.65). Custom trim ($158). Custom wheel covers ($63.20). Power windows ($85.35).

Historical footnotes: Slightly over one-third of 1971 Corvettes had a tilting steering wheel; 53.9 percent had a four-speed manual; 82.1 percent had power steering: 52.7 percent had air conditioning and 28.4 percent had power windows.

1972 CORVETTE

1972 Corvette, 2-dr Stingray coupe, V-8

STINGRAY SERIES — (V-8) — SERIES Z — The 1972 Corvette was basically the same as the 1971. Among the standard equipment were: a posi-traction rear axle; outside rearview mirror; tinted glass; flo-thru ventilation system; front and rear disc brakes; electric clock; carpeting; wheel trim rings; all-vinyl upholstery and anti-theft alarm system. Ten exterior colors were available. The convertible top could be ordered in white or black.

VEHICLE IDENTIFICATION NUMBERS: The numbering system and code locations were changed as follows 1Z67K2S500001 to 1Z67K2S527004 or 1Z37K2S500001 to 1Z67K2S527004. The first symbol designated make ('1' = Chevrolet). The second symbol designated series ('Z' = Corvette). The third and fourth symbol designated Body Style ('37' = coupe; '67' = convertible) the fifth symbol designated engine ('K' = standard 350 V-8 in 1972; 'J' = standard 350 V-8 in 1973-1976; 'L' = LT-1; 'T' = L-82; 'Y' = 454 V-8). The seventh symbol designated manufacturing-assembly plant ('S' = Saint Louis). The last six digits were the sequential production numbers.

STINGRAY Series Number	Body/Style Number	Body Type & Seating	Factory Price	Shipping Weight	Production Total
Z	37	2-dr Spt Cpe-2P	5472	3215	20,496
Z	67	2-dr Conv-2P	5246	3215	6,508

STINGRAY SERIES ENGINE
V-8. Overhead valves. Cast iron block. Displacement: 350 cubic inches. Bore and stroke: 4 x 3.48 inches. Compression ratio: 8.50:1. Brake horsepower: 200 at 4400 R.P.M. Five main bearings. Hydraulic valve lifters. Carburetor: Rochester Type Quadra-Jet four-barrel Model 4MV.

CHASSIS FEATURES: Wheelbase: 98 inches. Overall length: 182.5 inches. Front tread: 58.7 inches. Rear tread: 59.4 inches. Tires: F70 x 15.

POWERTRAIN OPTIONS: Automatic transmission (no cost with standard engine, $97 with others). Wide range four-speed manual floor shift transmission was standard. Close-ratio four-speed manual transmission with floor shift (no cost). 'LT1' V-8 350 cubic inch 255 horsepower engine ($483.45). 'ZR1' V-8 350 cubic inch 255 horsepower engine ($1,010.05). 'LS5' 454 cubic inch 270 horsepower engine ($294.90). (only 30 ZR1 engine-equipped cars were built)

CONVENIENCE OPTIONS: Power brakes ($47.40). Power steering ($115.90). Air conditioning ($464.50). Custom interior ($158). Electric power windows ($85.35). Custom shoulder belts ($26.35). Detachable hardtop ($273.85). Vinyl roof covering for detachable hardtop ($158). Telescopic tilt steering column ($84.30). Rear window defroster ($42). White stripe Nylon tires ($30.35). White lettered Nylon tires ($42.65). Heavy-duty battery ($15.80). Stereo AM-FM radio ($283). AM-FM radio ($178).

Historical footnotes: Over one-third of 1972 Corvettes came with power windows; 46.1 percent had a four-speed manual; 88.1 percent had power steering; 63.8 percent had air conditioning; 48.1 percent had a tilting steering wheel and one percent were powered by the 'LT1' engine.

1973 CORVETTE

1973 Corvette, 2-dr Stingray coupe, V-8

STINGRAY SERIES — CV-8) — SERIES Z — There were predictions in the automotive press that Chevrolet would introduce a mid-engine Corvette this year. However, nothing as radical as that came to be. Major changes for 1973 were a new domed hood, body-color urethane plastic front bumper and a fixed rear window (which added a little extra trunk space). Radial tires became standard and an effort was made to reduce noise. It was generally effective, but a *ROAD & TRACK* report found the 1973 to be louder than a 1971 in certain circumstances. Buyers who wanted a leather interior could select from black, medium saddle and dark saddle.

STINGRAY Series Number	Body/Style Number	Body Type & Seating	Factory Price	Shipping Weight	Production Total
Z	37	2-dr Spt Cpe-2	5921	3407	25,521
Z	67	2-dr Conv-2P	5685	3407	4,943

STINGRAY SERIES ENGINE
V-8. Overhead valves. Cast iron block. Displacement: 350 cubic inches. Bore and stroke: 4 x 3.48 inches. Compression ratio: 8.50:1. Brake horsepower: 190 at 4400 R.P.M. Five main bearings. Hydraulic valve lifters. Carburetor: Rochester. Type Quadra-Jet four-barrel Model 4MV.

POWERTRAIN OPTIONS: Automatic transmission (no cost). Four-speed manual floor shift transmission (was standard). Close-ratio four-speed manual transmission with floor shift (no cost). 'L82' V-8 350 cubic inch 250 horsepower engine ($299). 'LS4' V-8 454 cubic inch 275 horsepower engine ($250). Off-road suspension and brake package ($369).

CONVENIENCE OPTIONS: Power brakes ($46.00). Power steering ($113.00). Air conditioning ($452). Custom interior ($154). Power windows ($83.00). Custom shoulder belts ($41.00).Detachable hardtop ($267.00). Vinyl roof covering for detachable hardtop ($62.00). Rear window defroster ($42.00). Telescopic tilt steering column ($82.00). Custom wheel covers ($62.00). White stripe radial tires ($32.00) White letter radial tires ($45.00). Heavy-duty battery ($15.00). Stereo AM/FM radio ($276.00). AM/FM radio ($173.00) Cast aluminum wheels ($175.00).

Historical footnotes: The majority of 1973 Corvettes, 70.8 percent were sold with air conditioning; 41.2 percent had a four-speed manual transmission; 91.5 percent power steering; 79.3 percent power brakes and 46 percent power windows. A 1973 'L82' powered Corvette could go from 0 to 60 miles per hour in 7.2 seconds and from 0 to 100 miles per hour in 17.9 seconds.

1974 CORVETTE

1974 Corvette, 2-dr Stingray coupe, V-8

STINGRAY SERIES — (V-8) — SERIES Z — A restyled, sloping rear end and the elimination of the conventional rear bumper with a body-color urethane plastic bumper substitute were two noticeable changes for 1974. The power steering, seat belts and radiator were improved. The alarm system activator was relocated. Buyers once again had their choice of 10 exterior finishes: Medium Blue; Gray; Bright Yellow; Dark Green; Medium Red; Orange; White; Dark Brown; Silver and Mille Miglia Red.

VEHICLE IDENTIFICATION NUMBERS: The numbering system and code locations were the same as for previous models with the numbers changed as follows 1Z67J4S400001 to 1Z67J4S437502 or 1Z37J4S400001 to 1Z37J4S437502.

STINGRAY

Series Number	Body/Style Number	Body Type & Seating	Factory Price	Shipping Weight	Production Total
Z	37	2-dr Spt Cpe-2P	6372	3532	32,028
Z	67	2-dr Conv-2P	6156	3532	5,474

STINGRAY SERIES ENGINE DATA
V-8. Overhead valves. Cast iron block. Displacement: 350 cubic inches. Bore and stroke: 4 x 3.48 inches. Compression ratio: 9.0:1. Brake horsepower: 250 at 5200 R.P.M. Five main bearings. Hydraulic valve lifters. Carburetor: Rochester Type Quadra-Jet four-barrel Model 4MV.

CHASSIS FEATURES: Wheelbase: 98 inches. Overall length: 185.5 inches. Tires: GR70 x 15.

POWERTRAIN OPTIONS: Automatic transmission (no cost with standard engine, $97 with others). Four-speed manual floor shift transmission was standard. Close-ratio four-speed manual transmission with floor shift (no cost). 'L82' V-8 350 cubic inch 250 horsepower engine ($299). 'LS4' V-8 454 cubic inch 270 horsepower engine ($250). Off-road suspension and brake package ($400). Gymkhana suspension ($7).

CONVENIENCE OPTIONS: Power brakes ($49). Power steering ($117). Air conditioning ($467). Custom interior ($154). Power windows ($83). Custom shoulder belts ($41). Detachable hardtop ($267). Vinyl covered detachable hardtop($329). Rear window defogger ($41). Telescopic tilt steering column ($82). White stripe radial tires ($32). White letter radial tires ($45). Dual horns ($4). AM/FM stereo radio ($276). AM/FM radio ($173). Heavy-duty battery ($15). Map light ($5). Cast aluminum wheel trim ($175).

Historical footnotes: Most 1974 Corvettes, 95.6 percent had power steering; 88.3 percent had power brakes; 63.1 percent had power windows; 72.9 percent had tilting steering wheel; 77.7 percent had air-conditioning and 33.7 percent had a four-speed manual transmission.

1975 CORVETTE

STINGRAY SERIES — (V-8) — SERIES Z — Most of the changes for 1975 were hidden. The bumpers were improved (but looked the same). Under the hood were a catalytic converter and a new High Energy ignition. On the inside, the speedometer included kilometers-per-hour for the first time. This was the last year for the Corvette convertible.

1975 Corvette, 2-dr Stingray coupe, V-8

VEHICLE IDENTIFICATION NUMBERS: The numbering system and code locations were the same as for previous models with the numbers changed as follows 1Z67J5S400001 to 1Z67J5S438465 or 1Z37J5S400001 to 1Z37J5S438465.

CORVETTE

Series Number	Body/Style Number	Body Type & Seating	Factory Price	Shipping Weight	Production Total
Z	37	2-dr Spt Cpe-2P	7117	3532	33,836
Z	67	2-dr Conv-2P	6857	3532	4,629

STINGRAY SERIES ENGINE DATA
V-8. Overhead valves. Cast iron block. Displacement: 350 cubic inches. Bore and stroke 4 x 3.48 inches. Compression ratio: 8.50. Brake horsepower: 165 at 3800 R.P.M. Five main bearings. Hydraulic valve lifters. Carburetor: Rochester Type Quadra-Jet four-barrel Model 4MV.

CHASSIS FEATURES: Wheelbase: 98 inches. Overall length: 185.5 inches. Tires: GR70 x 15.

POWERTRAIN OPTIONS: Automatic transmission (no cost). Four-speed manual floor shift transmission was standard. Close-ratio four-speed manual transmission with floor shift (no cost). 'L82' V-8 350 cubic inch 205 horsepower engine ($336). Off-road suspension and brake package ($403). Gymkhana suspension ($7).

CONVENIENCE OPTIONS: Power brakes ($50). Power steering ($129). Air conditioning ($490). Custom interior ($154). Power windows ($93). Custom shoulder belts ($41). Detachable hardtop ($267). Vinyl covered detachable hardtop ($350). Rear window defroster ($46). Telescopic tilt steering column ($82). White stripe tires ($35). White letter tires ($48). Dual horns ($4). AM/FM stereo radio ($284). AM/FM radio ($178). Heavy-duty battery ($15). Map light ($5).

Historical footnotes: The '454' Corvette engine was dropped this year, as was the convertible style. *Car and Driver* tested a 1975 model and covered the quarter-mile in 16.1 seconds. The magazine timed the car at 0 to 60 miles per hour in 7.7 seconds and found it to have a top speed of 129 miles per hour. Robert D. Lund became Chevrolet General Manager, Zora Arkus-Duntov retired as the Division's chief engineer. He was replaced by David R. McLellan.

CORVETTE

1976-1986

By 1976, Corvette's shapely aerodynamic body was eight years old. Yet it would remain in this form for half a dozen more years, attracting performance-minded drivers even though the engine choices were far milder than they had been. After all, what else was there? As Chevrolet proclaimed, Corvette was "America's only true production sports car." Only the Stingray coupe body remained for 1976, as convertible Corvettes became extinct. Removable roof panels would be the closest one could come to open-topped motoring. Corvettes remained fiberglass-bodied, of course; but this year a partial steel underbody was added. Customers had a choice of wide- or close-ratio four-speed gearboxes, and the standard or special (L82) 350 cu. in. V-8 engine. The latter engine, installed in 5,720 cars, had finned aluminum rocker covers and special cylinder heads. Sales hit a record level.

1977 Corvette coupe (CH)

Next year, the Stingray name faded away, but not much else changed. Less than 16 percent of Corvettes came with either the close-ratio or wide-ratio four-speed transmission — a figure typical of this period. Most customers, it seemed, wanted Corvette's performance — but didn't wish to shift for themselves.

1978 Corvette Indy Pace Car (Tom and Cheryl Kell)

An aero restyling of the basic body arrived for Corvette's 25th anniversary year, adding a fastback roofline and large wraparound back window. The high-performance (L82) V-8 added horsepower with a new dual-snorkel air-intake system and lower-restriction exhaust components. Nearly one-third of this year's Corvettes sported optional Silver Anniversary two-tone silver paint. Even more striking were the Indy Pace Car replicas, with black-over-silver paint and a host of extras. They sold for well above retail at the time, and remain among the more desirable Corvettes today.

1979 Turbo Corvette concept car (CP)

Some of those Pace Car features found their way onto standard models for 1979, including bolt-on spoilers and lightweight bucket seats. Both the base and special V-8s now had the dual-snorkel intake. Production slid upward for the model year, but sales slipped a bit. Another modest restyling came in 1980, lowering the hood profile and recessing the grille (and taking off some weight). Lift-off roof panels were made of microscopic glass beads. Front and rear spoilers were now molded into place. Corvette 350 cu. in. V-8s produced as much as 230 horsepower, but speedometers now peaked at 85 MPH.

In another weight-cutting move, a fiberglass-reinforced Monoleaf rear spring was installed on automatic-transmission models in 1981. A new-190 horsepower, 350 cu. in. (5.7-liter) engine had cast magnesium rocker covers and stainless steel exhaust manifolds. In an attempt to keep up with a rising problem, the theft alarm added a starter interrupt.

A new Corvette was in the works, but the 1982 version had some strong points of its own: essentially, a strong new drivetrain in the last of the old bodies. The "Cross Fire" fuel-injected V-8 used throttle-body injectors, but produced only 10 more horsepower (200) than the former version. For the first time since 1955, all Corvettes had automatic shift. A built-to-order Collector Edition featured silver-beige metallic paint and a frameless glass hatch. That was the first Corvette to carry a price tag above $20,000. Sales sagged dramatically, perhaps because customers were waiting for the next (sixth) generation.

1984 Corvette coupe (OCW)

No Corvettes at all were built for the 1983 model year, but the aerodynamic '84 edition (debuting in spring 1983) was worth the wait. The buff books fawned over it with superlatives. Technical changes included an aluminum driveshaft and fiberglass springs. A new transmission was offered—four-speed manual with automatic overdrive in top three gears—but only one in eight Corvettes carried it. The overdrive was locked out during hard acceleration. This year's dual-injector V-8 produced 205 horsepower. One other little change: Corvette's price tag soared past the $23,000 mark.

1986 Corvette coupe (CMD)

Horsepower jumped by 25 for 1985, with a new tuned-port fuel-injected 350 V-8. Next year, a convertible

1986 Corvette Indy Pace Car convertible (CH)

arrived— first open Corvette since 1975. Anti-lock braking also became standard, as did a new VATS anti-theft system. Four-speed overdrive automatic was standard, but a four-speed manual (overdrive in top three gears) cost no more. A switch to aluminum heads for the TPI engine produced a few problems, so early models kept the old cast iron heads. All convertibles (roadsters) were sold as Indy Pace Cars. It can easily be said that all Corvettes are collectible, yet some more so than others. The 1978 Pace Car Replica is one; the '82 Collector Edition another. Neither qualifies as rare, though, as quite a few were produced. No doubt, strong demand will keep the '86 convertible on the desirable list.

1976 CORVETTE

1976 Corvette coupe (CP)

STINGRAY — SERIES Y — V-8 — Unlike some advertisers, Chevrolet was correct in billing the fiberglass-bodied Corvette as "America's only true production sports car." The big-block V-8 had disappeared after 1974, leaving a 350 cu. in. (5.7-liter) small-block as the powerplant for all Corvettes in the next decade. Two V-8s were offered this year, both with four-barrel carburetor. The base L48 version now developed 180 horsepower (15 more than in 1975). An optional L82 V-8 produced 210. That one had special heads with larger valves, impact-extruded pistons, and finned aluminum rocker covers. The standard V-8 drove a new, slightly lighter weight automatic transmission: the Turbo Hydra-matic 350, which was supposed to improve shifting at wide-open throttle. Optional engines kept the prior Turbo Hydra-matic 400, but with a revised torque converter. A wide-range four-speed manual gearbox (with 2.64:1 first gear ratio) was standard; close-ratio version available at no extra cost. A new Carburetor Outside Air Induction system moved intake from the cowl to above the radiator. The convertible was dropped this year, so only the Stingray coupe remained, with twin removable roof panels. A partial steel underbody replaced the customary fiberglass, to add strength and improve shielding from exhaust system heat. A new one-piece bar Corvette nameplate was on the rear, between twin-unit taillights (which were inset in the bumper cover). Of the ten body colors, eight were Corvette exclusives. This year's colors were red, silver, classic white, bright yellow, bright blue, dark green, buckskin, dark brown, mahogany, and orange flame. Corvettes had side marker lights with reflectors, parking lamps that went on with headlamps, lane-change turn signals, and two-speed wiper/washers. Inside was a new, smaller-diameter four-spoke sports steering wheel with crossed-flags medallion, which came from Vega. Not everyone appreciated its lowly origin, so it lasted only this year. A grained vinyl trimmed instrument panel (with stitched seams) held a 160 MPH speedometer with trip odometer, and 7000 R.P.M. electronic tachometer. A key lock in left front fender set the anti-theft alarm. Corvettes had fully independent suspension and four-wheel disc brakes. Wide GR70 SBR tires rode 15 x 8 in. wheels. A total of 5,368 Corvettes had the FE7 Gymkhana suspension installed; 5,720 came with the L82 V-8; and 2,088 had the M21 four-speed close-ratio manual gearbox. Cast aluminum wheels were a new option, installed on 6,253 cars. Standard equipment included bumper guards, flush retracting headlamps, Soft-Ray tinted glass, Hide-A-Way wipers, wide-view day/night mirror, and center console with lighter and ashtray. Behind the seatbacks were three carpeted storage compartments. Bucket seats had textured-vinyl upholstery and deep-pleated saddle-stitched seat panels (black, dark firethorn, light buckskin or white). Interior leather trim was now available in seven colors. Like other GM vehicles, Corvette had a 13-symbol Vehicle identification Number (VIN) atop the dashboard, visible through the windshield on the driver's side. The VIN appears in the form: 1Z37()6S4()()()()(). The '1' indicates Chevrolet Division; 'Z' is Corvette series; '37' body type (2-dr. sport coupe). Fifth symbol is an engine code: 'L' base L48 V-8 and 'X' optional L82 V-8. Next is model year: '6' 1976. The letter 'S' indicates assembly plant (St. Louis). Finally comes a six-digit sequential serial number, starting with 400001. That sequential serial number is repeated on the engine block itself, stamped on a pad just ahead of the cylinder head on the right (passenger) side, combined with a three-letter identification suffix. Cast into the top rear (right side) of the block is a date built code. The first letter of that four-symbol code shows the month the block was cast. The next number (or numbers) reveals the day of the month, while the final digit indicates year.

CORVETTE

Model Number	Body/Style Number	Body Type & Seating	Factory Price	Shipping Weight	Production Total
1Y	Z37	2-dr. Cpe-2P	7605	3445	46,558

ENGINE DATA: BASE V-8: 90-degree, overhead valve V-8. Cast iron block and head. Displacement: 350 cu. in. (5.7 liters). Bore & stroke: 4.00 x 3.48 in. Compression ratio: 8.5:1. Brake horsepower: 180 at 4000 R.P.M. Torque: 270 lbs.-ft. at 2400 R.P.M. Five main bearings. Hydraulic valve lifters. Carburetor: 4Bbl. Rochester M4MC. RPO Code: L48. VIN Code: L. OPTIONAL V-8: Same as above, except Compression ratio: 9.0:1. Brake horsepower: 210 at 5200 R.P.M. Torque: 255 lbs.-ft. at 3600 R.P.M. RPO Code: L82. VIN Code: X.

CHASSIS DATA: Wheelbase: 98.0 in. Overall length: 185.2 in. Height: 48.0 in. Width: 69.0 in. Front Tread: 58.7 in. Rear Tread: 59.5 in. Wheel Size: 15 x 8 in. Standard Tires: GR70 x 15.

TECHNICAL: Transmission: Four-speed fully synchronized manual transmission (floor shift) standard. Gear ratios: (1st) 2.64:1; (2nd) 1.75:1; (3rd) 1.34:1; (4th) 1.00:1; (Rev) 2.55:1. Close-ratio four-speed fully synchronized manual trans. optional: (1st) 2.43:1; (2nd) 1.61:1; (3rd) 1.23:1; (4th) 1.00:1; (Rev) 2.35:1. Three-speed automatic optional: (1st) 2.52:1; (2nd) 1.52:1; (3rd) 1.00:1; (Rev) 1.94:1. Three-speed automatic ratios with L82 engine: (1st) 2.48:1; (2nd) 1.48:1; (3rd) 1.00:1; (Rev) 2.08:1. Standard final drive ratio: 3.36:1 w/4spd, 3.08:1 w/auto. exc. with optional L82 engine 3.55:1 w/4spd, 3.55:1 or 3.70:1 with close-ratio four-speed, or 3.36:1 w/auto. Positraction standard. Steering: recirculating ball. Front Suspension: unequal-length control arms with ball joints, coil springs and stabilizer bar. Rear Suspension: independent with trailing-link, transverse semi-elliptic leaf spring. Brakes: Four-wheel disc (11.75 in. disc dia.). Ignition: HEI electronic. Body construction: Separate fiberglass body and box-type ladder frame with cross-members. Fuel tank: 18 gal.

CORVETTE OPTIONS: Special L82 350 cu. in., 4Bbl. V-8 engine ($481). Close-ratio four-speed manual transmission (NC). Turbo Hydra-matic (NC); but ($134) w/L82 V-8. High-altitude or highway axle ratio ($13). Gymkhana suspension ($35). Power brakes ($59). Power steering ($151). Heavy-duty battery ($16). California emissions system ($50). Four Season air cond. ($523). Rear defogger ($78). Tilt/telescopic steering wheel ($95). Power windows ($107). Map light ($10). Pushbutton AM/FM radio ($187). AM/FM stereo radio ($281). Vinyl interior (NC). Custom interior ($164). Aluminum wheels ($299). GR70 x 15/B SBR WSW tires ($37). GR70 x 15/B SBR WLT ($51).

HISTORY: Introduced: Oct. 2, 1975. Model year production: 46,558. Calendar year production: 47,425. Calendar year sales by U.S. dealers: 41,673. Model year sales by U.S. dealers: 41,027.

Historical Footnotes: Though largely a carryover from 1975, Corvette set a new sales record. Basic design dated back to 1968.

1977 CORVETTE

1977 Corvette coupe (OCW)

SERIES Y — V-8 — Since the Stingray front-fender nameplate departed this year, Chevrolet's sports car no longer had a secondary title. Changes were fairly modest this year, mainly hidden (such as steel hood reinforcement) or inside. New crossed-flags emblems stood between the headlamps, and on the fuel filler door. A thinner blacked-out pillar gave windshield and side glass a more integrated look. Corvette's console was restyled in an aircraft-type cluster design, with individual-look gauges. A voltmeter replaced the former ammeter. "Door ajar" and "headlamp up" warning lights were abandoned. New heater/air conditioning controls, ashtray and lighter were on the horizontal surface. A recessed pocket was now behind the shift lever. Power window switches moved to the new console. The manual shift lever was almost an inch higher, with shorter travel. Automatic transmission levers added a pointer, and both added a new black leather boot. A shorter steering column held a multi-function control lever. This year's steering wheel had a leather-wrapped rim. Of the ten body colors, seven were new and eight exclusive to Corvette. Colors were: Classic white, black, medium red and silver, plus Corvette dark or light blue, orange, dark red, tan or yellow. The Custom interior, formerly an extra-cost option, was now standard. "Dynasty" horizontal-ribbed cloth upholstery was framed with leather (the first cloth trim offered on Corvette), or buyers could have the customary all-leather seat panels. Leather came in ten colors, cloth in six. Two new trim colors were available: red and blue. Door panel inserts were satin finish black instead of the prior woodgrain. Both instrument panel and door trim lost their embossed stitch lines. New padded sunshades could swivel to side windows. Passenger-side roof pillars held a soft vinyl coat hook. Powertrains were the same as in 1976, but power brakes and steering were now standard. A total of 6,148 Corvettes came with the special L82 V-8 engine under the hood, while 7,269 had optional Gymkhana suspension. Only 5,743 Corvettes had the M20 four-speed manual gearbox, and 2,060 the M26 close-ratio four-speed. And just 289 came with trailering equipment. New options included AM/FM stereo radio with tape player, cruise control (for automatic only), and a luggage carrier that could hold the roof panels. Glass roof panels were announced, but delayed for another year.

1977 Corvette coupe (CP)

I.D. DATA: Coding of the 13-symbol Vehicle Identification Number (VIN) was the same as 1976, but it moved to the windshield side pillar (still visible through the windshield). Model year code changed to '7' for 1977.

CORVETTE

Model Number	Body/Style Number	Body Type & Seating	Factory Price	Shipping Weight	Production Total
1Y	Z37	2-dr. Cpe-2P	8648	3448	49,213

ENGINE DATA: BASE V-8: 90-degree, overhead valve V-8. Cast iron block and head. Displacement: 350 cu. in. (5.7 liters). Bore & stroke: 4.00 x 3.48 in. Compression ratio: 8.5:1. Brake horsepower: 180 at 4000 R.P.M. Torque: 270 lbs.-ft. at 2400 R.P.M. Five main bearings. Hydraulic valve lifters. Carburetor: 4Bbl. Rochester M4MC. RPO Code: L48. VIN Code: L. OPTIONAL V-8: Same as above, except C.R.: 9.0:1. B.H.P.: 210 at 5200 R.P.M. Torque: 255 lbs.-ft. at 3600 R.P.M. bearings. RPO Code: L82. VIN Code: X.

CHASSIS DATA: Wheelbase: 98.0 in. Overall length: 185.2 in. Height: 48.0 in. Width: 69.0 in. Front Tread: 58.7 in. Rear Tread: 59.5 in. Standard Tires: GR70x15.

TECHNICAL: Transmission: Four-speed manual transmission (floor shift) standard. Gear ratios: (1st) 2.64:1; (2nd) 1.75:1; (3rd) 1.34:1; (4th) 1.00:1; (Rev) 2.55:1. Close-ratio four-speed manual trans. optional: (1st) 2.43:1; (2nd) 1.61:1; (3rd) 1.23:1; (4th) 1.00:1; (Rev) 2.35:1. Three-speed automatic optional: (1st) 2.48:1; (2nd) 1.48:1; (3rd) 1.00:1; (Rev) 2.08:1. Standard final drive ratio: 3.36:1. Steering/Suspension-/Body: same as 1976. Brakes: Four-wheel disc. Ignition: Electronic. Fuel tank: 17 gal.

CORVETTE OPTIONS: L82 350 cu. in., 4Bbl. V 8 engine ($495). Close-ratio four- speed manual transmission (NC). Turbo Hydra-matic (NC); but ($146) w/L82 V-8. Highway axle ratio ($14). Gymkhana suspension ($38). Heavy-duty battery ($17). Trailer towing equipment ($83). California emissions system ($70). High- altitude emissions ($22). Air conditioning ($553). Rear defogger ($84). Cruise-master speed control ($88). Tilt/telescopic leather steering wheel ($165). Power windows ($116). Convenience group ($22). Sport mirrors, left remote ($36). AM/FM radio ($187). AM/FM stereo radio ($281); with stereo tape player ($414). Luggage carrier/roof panel ($73). Color-keyed floor mats ($22). Aluminum wheels ($321). GR70 x 15/B SBR WL tires ($57).

HISTORY: Introduced: Sept. 30, 1976. Model year production: 49,213 (Chevrolet inititially reported 49,034 units). Calendar year production: 46,345. Calendar year sales by U.S. dealers: 42,571. Model year sales by U.S. dealers: 40,764.

1978 CORVETTE

1978 Corvette Silver Anniversary coupe (CH)

SERIES Y — V-8 — To mark Corvette's 25th anniversary, the 1978 model got a major aerodynamic restyling with large wraparound back window and a fastback roofline. This was the first restyle since 1968. Two special editions were produced, one well known and the other little more than an optional paint job. New tinted glass lift-out roof panels were wired into the standard anti-theft system. A 24-gallon "fuel cell" replaced the former 17-gallon tank, filling space made available by a new temporary spare tire. Six of the ten body colors were new this year. Seven interiors were available (four new). Inside was a a restyled, padded instrument panel with face-mounted round instruments and a new locking glove box (to replace the former map pocket). The restyled interior had more accessible rear storage area, with a roll shade to hide luggage. The wiper/washer control moved from the steering column back to the instrument panel, but turn signal and dimmer controls remained on the column. Door trim was now cut-and-sew design with soft expanded vinyl (or cloth). As in 1977, seats had leather side bolsters, with either leather or cloth seating area in a fine rib pattern. Corvette's optional L82 high-performance 350 V-8 reached 220 horsepower, as a result of a new dual-snorkel cold-air intake system, larger-diameter exhaust and tailpipes, and lower-restriction mufflers. The automatic transmission used with the option V-8 lost weight and had a low-inertia, high-stall torque converter. Base engines used a Muncie four-speed manual gearbox with higher first/second gear ratios than before; the performance V-8 used a close-ratio Borg- Warner. Axle ratios in California and at high altitude switched from 3.08:1 to 3.55:1. A total of 12,739 optional L82 engines were installed, while 3,385 Corvettes had the M21 four-speed close-ratio gearbox and 38,614 had automatic. Glass roof panels, promised earlier, actually became available this year. What Chevrolet described as "aggressive" 60-series white-letter tires also joined the option list for the first time. An optional AM/FM/CB stereo radio used a tri- band power antenna on the rear deck. Each of this year's Corvettes could have Silver Anniversary emblems on the nose and rear deck. A total of 15,283 displayed the $399 special two-tone silver paint option: silver metallic on top, with charcoal silver on the lower body. Pinstripes accentuated fender upper profiles, wheel openings, front fender vents, hood, and rear license cavity. Interiors were also silver. Various other options were required, including aluminum wheels. For a considerably higher price, buyers could have the Limited Edition replica of the Indy Pace Car with distinctive black-over-silver paint and red accent striping. Equipment in this "Indy Package" (RPO code Z78) included a special silver interior with new lightweight highback seats, special front/rear spoilers, P255/60R15 white-letter tires on alloy wheels, and lift-off glass canopy roof panels. It contained nearly all Corvette options, plus special decals (unless the customer specified that they be omitted). Upholstery was silver leather, or leather with smoke (gray) cloth inserts.

I.D. DATA: Corvette's 13-symbol Vehicle Identification Number (VIN), visible through the windshield altered its coding a bit this year. The VIN appears in the form: 1Z87() 8S()()()()()(). The '1' indicates Chevrolet Division, 'Z' is Corvette series; '87' body type (2-dr. sport coupe). Fifth symbol is an engine code; 'L' base L48 V-8 and 'H' optional L82 V-8. Next is model year: '8' 1978. The letter 'S' indicates assembly plant (St. Louis). Finally comes a six-digit sequential serial number, starting with 400001 for standard model but 900001 for Pace Car replicas. This step was taken to make it more difficult to produce counterfeit Pace Cars. As before, the serial number is repeated on the engine block itself, stamped on a pad just ahead of the cylinder head on the right side. A date built code is also cast into the top rear (right side) of the block. The first letter of that four-symbol code shows the month the block was cast. The next number(s) reveal the day of the month, while the final digit indicates year.

1978 Corvette Limited Edition Indy Pace Car (IMSC)

CORVETTE

Model Number	Body/Style Number	Body Type & Seating	Factory Price	Shipping Weight	Production Total
1Y	Z87	2-dr. Cpe-2P	9446	3401	40,275

CORVETTE LIMITED EDITION (PACE CAR REPLICA)

Model Number	Body/Style Number	Body Type & Seating	Factory Price	Shipping Weight	Production Total
1Y	Z87/Z78	2-dr. Cpe-2P	13653	N/A	6,501

ENGINE DATA: BASE V-8: 90-degree, overhead valve V-8. Cast iron block and head. Displacement: 350 cu. in. (5.7 liters). Bore & stroke: 4.00 x 3.48 in. Compression ratio: 8.2:1. Brake horsepower: 185 at 4000 R.P.M. Torque: 280 lbs.-ft. at 2400 R.P.M. Five main bearings. Hydraulic valve lifters. Carburetor: 4Bbl. RPO Code: L48. VIN Code: L. OPTIONAL V-8: Same as above, except C.R.: 8.9:1. B.H.P.: 220 at 5200 R.P.M. Torque: 260 lbs.-ft. at 3600 R.P.M. RPO Code: L82. VIN Code: H.

CHASSIS DATA: Wheelbase: 98.0 in. Overall length: 185.2 in. Height: 48.0 in. Width: 69.0 in. Front Tread: 58.7 in. Rear Tread: 59.5 in. Wheel size: 15 x 8 in. Standard Tires: P225/70R15 SBR. Optional Tires: P225/60R15.

TECHNICAL: Transmission: Four-speed manual transmission (floor shift) standard. Gear ratios: (1st) 2.85:1; (2nd) 2.02:1; (3rd) 1.35:1; (4th) 1.00:1; (Rev) 2.85:1. Close-ratio four-speed manual available at no extra charge: (1st) 2.43:1; (2nd) 1.61:1; (3rd) 1.23:1; (4th) 1.00:1; (Rev) 2.35:1. Three-speed automatic optional: (1st) 2.52:1; (2nd) 1.52:1; (3rd) 1.00:1; (Rev) 1.94:1. Standard final drive ratio: 3.36:1 w/4spd, 3.08:1 w/auto. exc. L82 V-8, 3.70:1 w/4spd and 3.55:1 w/auto. Steering/Suspension/Body: same as 1976-77. Brakes: four-wheel disc (11.75 in. disc dia.). Ignition: Electronic. Fuel tank: 24 gal.

CORVETTE OPTIONS: L82 350 cu. in., 4Bbl. V-8 engine ($525). Close-ratio four- speed manual transmission (NC). Turbo Hydra-matic (NC). Highway axle ratio ($15). Gymkhana suspension ($41). Heavy- duty battery ($18). Trailer towing equipment inc. H.D. radiator and Gymkhana pkg. ($89). California emissions system ($75). High-altitude emissions ($33). Air conditioning ($605). Rear defogger, electric ($95). Cruise-master speed control ($99). Tilt/telescopic leather steering wheel ($175). Power windows ($130). Convenience group ($84). Sport mirrors, left remote ($40). AM/FM radio ($199). AM/FM stereo radio ($286); with stereo tape player ($419). AM/FM stereo radio w/CB and power antenna ($638). Power antenna ($49). 25th anniversary paint ($399). Aluminum wheels ($340). P225/70R15/B SBR WL tires ($51). P225/60R15/B SBR WL tires ($216).

HISTORY: Introduced: Oct. 6, 1977. Model year production: 46,772 (but some industry sources have reported a total of 47,667). Calendar year production: 48,522. Calendar year sales by U.S. dealers: 42,247. Model year sales by U.S. dealers: 43,106.

Historical Footnotes: The limited-edition Pace Car replica was created to commemorate the selection of Corvette as Pace Car for the 62nd Indy 500 race on May 28, 1978. A production run of 2,500 was planned. But so many potential buyers who saw it at the New York Auto Show in February wanted one that the goal quickly expanded to 6,500 roughly one for every Chevrolet dealer. Buyers also had to endure a selection of "Forced RPOs," meaning items installed at the factory whether wanted or not. Those mandatory extras included power windows, air conditioning, sport mirrors, tilt/telescope steering, rear defogger, AM/FM stereo with either an 8-track tape player or CB radio, plus power door locks and a heavy-duty battery. Before long, the original $13,653 list price meant little, as speculators eagerly paid double that amount and more. A year later, as is usually the case, the price retreated to around original list. Even though so many were built, it's still a desirable model. Dave McLellan was now head of engineering for Corvettes, working on the next generation.

1979 CORVETTE

1979 Corvette coupe (CP)

SERIES Y — V-8 — "The Corvette evolution continues," declared this year's catalog. Not much of that evolution was visible, however, after the prior year's massive restyle. Under the hood, the base engine got the dual-snorkel air intake introduced in 1978 for the optional L82 V-8. That added 10 horsepower. The L82 V-8 had a higher-lift cam, special heads with larger valves and higher compression, impact-extruded pistons, forged steel crankshaft, and finned aluminum rocker covers. The "Y" pipe exhaust system had new open-flow mufflers, while the automatic transmission got a higher numerical (3.55:1) rear axle ratio. All Corvettes now had the highback bucket seats introduced on the 1978 limited-edition Indy Pace Car. A high pivot point let the seat backrest fold flat on the passenger side, level with the luggage area floor. An AM/FM radio was now standard. Of ten body colors, only one (dark green metallic) was new this year. The others were Classic white, black and silver, plus Corvette dark or light blue, yellow, light beige, red, and dark brown. Interiors came in black, red, light beige, dark blue, dark brown, oyster, or dark green. Corvettes had black roof panel and window moldings. Bolt-on front and rear spoilers (also from the Pace Car) became available. Buyers who didn't want the full Gymkhana suspension could now order heavy-duty shocks alone. Standard equipment included the L48 V-8 with four-barrel carb, either automatic transmission or four-speed manual gearbox (close-ratio version available), power four-wheel disc brakes, and limited-slip differential. Other standards; tinted glass; front stabilizer bar; concealed wipers/washers; day/night inside mirror; wide outside mirror; anti-theft alarm system; four-spoke sport steering wheel; electric clock; trip odometer; heater/defroster; bumper guards; and luggage security shade. Tires were P225/70R15 steel-belted radial blackwalls on 15 x 8 in. wheels. Corvettes had four-wheel independent suspension. Bucket seats came with cloth/leather or all-leather trim. The aircraft-type console held a 7000 R.P.M. tachometer, voltmeter, oil pressure, temp and fuel gauges. Seat inserts could have either leather or cloth trim.

I.D. DATA: Coding of the 13-symbol Vehicle Identification Number (VIN) was similar to 1978. Engine codes changed to '8' base L48 and '4' optional L82. Model year code changed to '9' for 1979. Serial numbers began with 400001.

1979 Corvette coupe (CP)

CORVETTE

Model Number	Body/Style Number	Body Type & Seating	Factory Price	Shipping Weight	Production Total
1Y	Z87	2-dr. Spt Cpe-2P	10220	3372	53,807

ENGINE DATA: BASE V-8: 90-degree, overhead valve V-8. Cast iron block and head. Displacement: 350 cu. in. (5.7 liters). Bore & stroke: 4.00 x 3.48 in. Compression ratio: 8.2:1. Brake horsepower: 195 at 4000 R.P.M. Torque: 285 lbs.-ft. at 3200 R.P.M. Five main bearings. Hydraulic valve lifters. Carburetor: 4Bbl. RPO Code: L48. VIN Code: 8. OPTIONAL V-8: Same as above, except C.R.: 8.9:1. B.H.P.: 225 at 5200 R.P.M. Torque: 270 lbs.-ft. at 3600 R.P.M. RPO Code: L82. VIN Code: 4.

CHASSIS DATA: Wheelbase: 98.0 in. Overall length: 185.2 in. Height: 48.0 in. Width: 69.0 in. Front Tread: 58.7 in. Rear Tread: 59.5 in. Wheel Size: 15 x 8 in. Standard Tires: P225/70R15 SBR. Optional Tires: P225/60R15.

1979 Corvette coupe (CH)

TECHNICAL: Transmission: Four-speed manual transmission (floor shift) standard. Gear ratios: (1st) 2.85:1; (2nd) 2.02:1; (3rd) 1.35:1; (4th) 1.00:1; (Rev) 2.85:1. Close-ratio four-speed manual trans. optional: (1st) 2.43:1; (2nd) 1.61:1; (3rd) 1.23:1; (4th) 1.00:1; (Rev) 2.35:1. Three-speed automatic optional: (1st) 2.52:1; (2nd) 1.52:1; (3rd) 1.00:1; (Rev) 1.93:1. Standard final drive ratio: 3.36:1 w/4spd, 3.55:1 w/auto. Steering: Recirculating ball. Front Suspension: Control arms, coil springs and stabilizer bar. Rear Suspension: Independent with single transverse leaf spring and lateral struts. Brakes: Four-wheel disc (11.75 in. disc dia). Ignition: Electronic. Body construction: Fiberglass, on separate frame. Fuel tank: 24 gal.

CORVETTE OPTIONS: L82 350 cu. in., 4Bbl. V-8 engine ($565). Close-ratio four- speed manual transmission (NC). Turbo Hydra-matic (NC). Highway axle ratio ($19). Gymkhana suspension ($49). H.D. shock absorbers ($33). Heavy-duty battery ($21). Trailer towing equipment inc. H.D. radiator and Gymkhana suspension ($98). California emissions system (N/A). High-altitude emissions (N/A). Four season air cond. ($635). Rear defogger, electric ($102). Cruise-master speed control ($113). Tilt/telescopic leather-wrapped steering wheel ($190). Power windows ($141). Power windows and door locks ($272). Convenience group ($94). Sport mirrors, left remote ($45). AM/FM stereo radio ($90); with 8track or cassette player ($228-$234). AM/FM stereo radio w/CB and power antenna ($439). Dual rear speakers ($52). Power antenna ($52). Removable glass roof panels ($365). Aluminum wheels ($380). P225/70R15 SBR WL tires ($54). P225/60R15 Aramid-belted radial WL tires ($226).

HISTORY: Introduced: Sept. 25, 1978. Model year production: 53,807 (Chevrolet initially reported a total of 49,901 units.) Calendar year production: 48,568. Calendar year sales by U.S. dealers: 38,631. Model year sales by U.S. dealers: 39,816.

Historical Footnotes: For what it's worth, 7,949 Corvettes this year were painted in Classic White, while 6,960 carried silver paint. Only 4,385 Corvettes had the MM4 four-speed manual gearbox, while 4,062 ran with the close-ratio M21 version.

1980 CORVETTE

1980 Corvette coupe (CP)

SERIES Y — V-8 — Corvette lost close to 250 pounds in a more streamlined restyle. Hood and doors were lighter, glass thinner. Bodies held new fiberglass bumper structures. Lift-off roof panels were made of lightweight, low-density microscopic glass beads. Body panels were urethane-coated. Weight cuts also hit the powertrain. The differential housing and supports were made of aluminum. The 350 cu. in. (5.7-liter) V-8 had a new aluminum intake manifold, while California 305 (5.0- liter) V-8s had a stainless exhaust manifold. Hoods showed a new low profile. The front bumper had an integrated lower air dam, and the bumper cover now extended to wheel openings. Two-piece front cornering lamps worked whenever the lights were switched on. A deeply recessed split grille held integral parking lamps. Front fender air vents contained functional black louvers. New front/rear spoilers were molded in, integrated with bumper caps, no longer the bolt-on type. New emblems included an engine identifier for the optional L82 V-8. Turbo Hydra-matic transmissions added a lockup torque converter that engaged at about 30 MPH, while the four-speed manual got new gear ratios. California Corvettes could only have a 305 V-8 and automatic this year. The base V-8 lost five horsepower, while the optional version gained five. New standard equipment this year included the formerly optional power windows, tilt/telescopic steering wheel, and Four Season air conditioner. Rally wheels held P225/70R15/B blackwall SBR tires with trim rings and center caps. Body colors were: black, silver, red, yellow, white, dark green, dark blue, dark claret, dark brown, or frost beige. Interiors came in black, red, oyster, claret, dark blue, or doeskin. Dashes held a new 85 MPH speedometer. Only two storage bins stood behind the seat, where three used to be.

1980 Corvette coupe (CP)

I.D. DATA: Coding of the 13-symbol Vehicle Identification Number (VIN) was similar to 1978-79. Engine codes were '8' base L48 V-8, '6' optional L82 V-8, and 'H' California V-8. Model year code changed to 'A' for 1980. Serial numbers began with 400001.

CORVETTE

Model Number	Body/Style Number	Body Type & Seating	Factory Price	Shipping Weight	Production Total
1Y	Z87	2-dr. Cpe-2P	13140	3206	40,614

ENGINE DATA: BASE V-8: 90-degree, overhead valve V-8. Cast iron block and head. Displacement: 350 cu. in. (5.7 liters). Bore & stroke: 4.00 x 3.48 in. Compression ratio: 8.2:1. Brake horsepower: 190 at 4200 R.P.M. Torque: 280 lbs.-ft. at 2400 R.P.M. Five main bearings. Hydraulic valve lifters. Carburetor: 4Bbl. RPO Code: L48. VIN Code: 8. OPTIONAL V-8: Same as above, except C.R.: 9.0:1. B.H.P.: 230 at 5200 R.P.M. Torque: 275 lbs.-ft. at 3600 R.P.M. RPO Code: L82. VIN Code: 6. CALIFORNIA V-8: 90-degree, overhead valve V-8. Cast iron block and head. Displacement: 305 cu. in. (5.0 liters). Bore & stroke: 3.74 x 3.48 in. Compression ratio: 8.5:1. Brake horsepower: 180 at 4200 R.P.M. Torque: 255 lbs.-ft. at 2000 R.P.M. Five main bearings. Hydraulic valve lifters. Carburetor: 4Bbl. Roch. M4ME. RPO Code: LG4. VIN Code: H.

CHASSIS DATA: Wheelbase: 98.0 in. Overall length: 185.3 in. Height: 48.1 in. Width: 69.0 in. Front Tread: 58.7 in. Rear Tread: 59.5 in. Wheel size: 15 x 8 in. Standard Tires: P225/70R15/B SBR. Optional Tires: P255/60R15/B.

TECHNICAL: Transmission: Four-speed manual transmission (floor shift) standard. Gear ratios: (1st) 2.88:1; (2nd) 1.91:1; (3rd) 1.33:1; (4th) 1.00:1; (Rev) 2.78:1. Three-speed Turbo Hydra- matic optional: (1st) 2.52:1; (2nd) 1.52:1; (3rd) 1.00:1; (Rev) 1.93:1. Standard final drive ratio: 3.07:1 w/4spd, 3.55:1 w/auto.. Steering/Suspension/Body/Brakes: same as 1979. Fuel tank: 24 gal.

1980 Corvette coupe (CP)

CORVETTE OPTIONS: L82 350 cu. in., 4Bbl. V-8 engine ($595). 305 cu. in., 4Bbl. V-8 ($50 credit). Turbo Hydra-matic (NC). Gymkhana suspension ($55). H.D. shock absorbers ($35). Heavy-duty battery ($22). Trailer towing equipment incl. H.D. radiator and Gymkhana suspension ($105). California emissions system ($250). Rear defogger, electric ($109). Cruise-master speed control ($123). Power door locks ($140). AM/FM stereo radio ($46); with 8track ($155); w/cassette player ($168). AM/FM stereo radio w/CB and power antenna ($391). Dual rear speakers ($31). Power antenna ($56). Radio delete ($126 credit). Removable glass roof panels ($391). Roof panel carrier ($125). Aluminum wheels ($407). P225/70R15/B SBR WL tires ($62). P255/60R15/B SBR WL tires ($426).

HISTORY: Introduced: Oct. 25, 1979. Model year production: 40,614 (but Chevrolet reported a total of 40,564 units). Calendar year production: 44,190. Model year sales by U.S. dealers: 37,471.

Historical Footnotes: Production continued at the St. Louis plant, but a new GMAD operation at Bowling Green, Kentucky was planned to begin production of the next-generation Corvettes. Chevrolet engineers released a TurboVette that used a Garrette AiResearch turbocharger and fuel injection, but press people who drove it discovered performance more sluggish than a regular L82 V-8 could dish out. Only 5,726 Corvettes had the MM4 four-speed manual gearbox. And only 5,069 carried the special L82 engine. A total of 9,907 had the Gymkhana suspension.

1981 CORVETTE

1981 Corvette coupe (JAG)

SERIES Y — V-8 — Probably the most significant change this year was hidden from view. Corvettes with Turbo Hydra-matic had a new fiberglass-reinforced Monoleaf rear spring that weighed just eight pounds (33 pounds less than the multi-leaf steel spring it replaced). Obviously, it also eliminated interleaf friction. Manual-shift models kept the old spring, as did those with optional Gymkhana suspension. Side glass was thinner, in a further attempt to cut weight. A new L81 version of the 350 cu. in. V-8 arrived this year, rated 190 horsepower, with lightweight magnesium rocker covers. New stainless steel free-flow exhaust manifolds weighed 14 pounds less than the previous cast iron. A new thermostatically-controlled auxiliary electric fan boosted cooling, and allowed use of a smaller main fan. Air cleaners had a new chromed cover. Computer Command Control controlled fuel metering as well as the torque converter lockup clutch, which operated in second and third gears. Manual transmission was available in all 50 states, the first time in several years that Californians could have a stick shift. A quartz crystal clock was now standard. Corvette's standard anti-theft alarm added a starter interrupt device. Joining the option list: a six-way power seat. Electronic- tuning radios could have built-in cassette or 8track tape players, or a CB transceiver. Body colors this year were black, white, red, yellow, beige, and five metallics: silver, dark or bright blue, maroon, or charcoal. Four two-tone combinations were available. Interiors came in black, red, silver, rust, camel or blue. Corvette's ample standard equipment list included either four-speed manual or automatic transmission (same price), four-wheel power disc brakes, limited-slip differential, power steering, tinted glass, twin remote-control sport mirrors, and concealed two-speed wipers. Also standard: halogen high-beam retractable headlamps, air conditioning, power windows, tilt/telescope leather-wrapped steering wheel, tachometer, AM/FM radio, trip odometer, courtesy lights, and a luggage compartment security shade. Buyers had a choice of cloth/vinyl or leather/vinyl upholstery. Corvettes rode P225/70R15 steel-belted radial blackwall tires on 15 x 8 in. wheels. The optional Gymkhana suspension (price $54) was also included with the trailer towing package.

1981 Corvette coupe (OCW)

I.D. DATA: Corvettes had a new 17-symbol Vehicle Identification Number (VIN), again visible through the windshield on the driver's side. The VIN took the form: 1G1AY8764B()()()()()(). The '1G1A' portion indicates U.S.A., General Motors, Chevrolet Division, and non-passive restraint system. 'Y' denotes Corvette series. '87' indicates 2-door sport coupe body style. '6' is the engine code. '4' is a check digit. Model year 1981 is revealed by the 'B'. Next is a code for assembly plant: either 'S' for St. Louis or '5' for Bowling Green. The last six digits are the sequential serial number, starting with 400001 for St. Louis models and 100001 for Corvettes built at Bowling Green, Kentucky. As before, the serial number is repeated on the engine block, stamped on a pad just ahead of the cylinder head on the right side. A date built code is also cast into the top rear (right side) of the block. The first letter of that four-symbol code shows the month the block was cast. The next number(s) reveal the day of the month, while the final digit indicates year.

CORVETTE

Model Number	Body/Style Number	Body Type & Seating	Factory Price	Shipping Weight	Production Total
1Y	Y87	2-dr. Cpe-2P	15248	3179	40,606

ENGINE DATA: BASE V-8: 90-degree, overhead valve V-8. Cast iron block and head. Displacement: 350 cu. in. (5.7 liters). Bore & stroke: 4.00 x 3.48 in. Compression ratio: 8.2:1. Brake horsepower: 190 at 4200 R.P.M. Torque: 280 lbs.-ft. at 1600 R.P.M. Five main bearings. Hydraulic valve lifters. Carburetor: 4Bbl. RPO Code: L81. VIN Code: 6.

CHASSIS DATA: Wheelbase: 98.0 in. Overall length: 185.3 in. Height: 48.1 in. Width: 69.0 in. Front Tread: 58.7 in. Rear Tread: 59.5 in. Wheel Size: 15 x 8 in. Standard Tires: P225/70R15 SBR. Optional Tires: P225/60R15.

TECHNICAL: Transmission: Four-speed manual trans. (floor shift) standard. Gear ratios: (1st) 2.88:1; (2nd) 1.91:1; (3rd) 1.33:1; (4th) 1.00:1; (Rev) 2.78:1. Three-speed Turbo Hydra- matic optional: (1st) 2.52:1; (2nd) 1.52:1; (3rd) 1.00:1; (Rev) 1.93:1. Standard final drive ratio: 2.72:1 w/4spd, 2.87:1 w/auto. Steering/Suspension/Body/Brakes: same as 1979-80. Fuel tank: 24 gal.

CORVETTE OPTIONS: Turbo Hydra-matic (NC). Performance axle ratio ($19). Gymkhana suspension ($54). H.D. shock absorbers ($35). Trailer towing equipment incl. H.D. radiator and Gymkhana suspension ($104). California emissions system ($48). Rear defogger, electric ($109). Cruise-master speed control w/resume ($141). Six-way power driver's seat ($173). Power door locks ($135). AM/FM stereo radio ($95). Electronic- tuning AM/FM stereo radio with 8track ($385); w/cassette player ($423); w/8track and CB ($709); w/cassette and CB ($747). Power antenna ($52). Radio delete ($118 credit). Removable glass roof panels ($391). Roof panel carrier ($124). Aluminum wheels ($404). P225/70R15 SBR WL tires ($67). P255/60R15 SBR WL tires ($460).

HISTORY: Introduced: Sept. 25, 1980. Model year production: 40,606 (but Chevrolet first reported a total of 40,593 units). Calendar year production: 27,990. Model year sales by U.S. dealers: 33,414.

Historical Footnotes: Of the total output this model year, 8,995 Corvettes came out of the new plant at Bowling Green, Kentucky, which began production in June 1981. Despite some weak years in the industry, Corvette sales remained strong through this period.

1982 CORVETTE

1982 Corvette coupe (CH)

SERIES Y — V-8 — For the first time since 1955, no stick shift Corvettes were produced. Every one had four-speed automatic, now with lockup in every gear except first. Under the hood, though, was a new kind of 350 cu. in. V-8 with Cross-Fire fuel injection. Twin throttle-body injectors with computerized metering helped boost horsepower to 200 (10 more than 1982), and cut emissions at the same time. This was the first fuel-injected Corvette in nearly two decades, and a much different breed now that mini-computerization had arrived. In the gas tank was a new electric fuel pump. Externally, this final version of the big Corvettes changed little. But this year's Collector Edition displayed quite a few special features, highlighted by a frameless glass liftup hatch instead of the customary fixed backlight. Unique silver-beige metallic paint was accented by pinstripes and fading shadow treatment on hood, fenders and doors, plus distinctive cloisonne emblems. Special finned wheels were similar to the cast aluminum wheels dating back to 1967 (finale for the last prior Corvette era). Removable glass roof panels had special bronze color and solar screening. Crossed-flags emblems read "Corvette Collector Edition" around the rim. Inside was a matching silver-beige metallic interior with multi-tone leather seats and door trim. Even the hand-sewn leather-wrapped steering wheel kept the theme color, and its leather-covered horn button had a cloisonne emblem. Tires were P255/60R15 Goodyear SBR WLT Eagle GT. Back to non-collector models, standard body colors were white, red and black, plus metallic charcoal, silver, silver blue, silver green, dark blue, bright blue, gold, or dark claret. Four two-tones were available. Interiors came in dark red, charcoal, dark blue, camel, silver grey, silver beige, or silver green. Standard equipment included power brakes and steering, P225/70R15/B SBR tires on steel wheels with center hub and trim rings, cornering lamps, front fender louvers, halogen high-beam retractable headlamps, dual remote sport mirrors, and tinted glass. The body-color front bumper had a built-in air dam. Also standard: luggage security shade, air conditioning, pushbutton AM/FM radio, concealed wipers, power windows, time-delay dome/courtesy lamps, headlamp-on reminder, lighted visor vanity mirror, tilt/telescoping leather-wrapped steering wheel, 7000 R.P.M. tachometer, analog clock with sweep second hand, day/night mirror, lighter, and trip odometer. Bucket seats could be all cloth or leather-trimmed.

I.D. DATA: Coding of the 17-symbol Vehicle Identification Number (VIN) was similar to 1981, but several of the codes changed. The VIN took the form: 1G1AY()()8()C51()()()()(). For symbols 67 (body type), '87' standard model and '07' Collector Edition. The next symbol ('8') is the engine code. Next is a check digit: '6' for standard model, '1' for Collector. Model year code 'C' 1982, and '5' indicates the new Bowling Green assembly plant. Six-digit sequential serial numbers began with 100001.

CORVETTE

Model Number	Body/Style Number	Body Type & Seating	Factory Price	Shipping Weight	Production Total
1Y	Y87	2-dr. Spt Cpe-2P	18290	3213	18,648

1982 Corvette Collector Edition coupe (JAG)

CORVETTE COLLECTOR EDITION

1Y	Y07	2-dr. Hatch Cpe-2P	22537	3222	6,759

ENGINE DATA: BASE V-8: 90-degree, overhead valve V-8. Cast iron block and head. Displacement: 350 cu. in. (5.7 liters). Bore & stroke: 4.00 x 3.48 in. Compression ratio: 9.0:1. Brake horsepower: 200 at 4200 R.P.M. Torque: 285 lbs.-ft. at 2800 R.P.M. Five main bearings. Hydraulic valve lifters. Cross-fire fuel injection (twin TBI). RPO Code: L83. VIN Code: 8.

CHASSIS DATA: Wheelbase: 98.0 in. Overall length: 185.3 in. Height: 48.4 in. Width: 69.0 in. Front Tread: 58.7 in. Rear Tread: 59.5 in. Wheel Size: 15 x 8 in. Standard Tires: P225/70R15 SBR (Collector Edition, P255/60R15).

TECHNICAL: Transmission: THM 700R4 four-speed overdrive automatic (floor shift). Gear ratios: (1st) 3.06:1; (2nd) 1.63:1; (3rd) 1.00:1; (4th) 0.70:1; (Rev) 2.29:1. Standard final drive ratio: 2.72:1 exc. 2.87:1 w/aluminum wheels. Steering: Recirculating ball (power assisted). Front Suspension: Upper/lower Aarms, coil springs, stabilizer bar. Rear Suspension: Fully independent with half-shafts, lateral struts, control arms, and transverse leaf spring. Brakes: Power four-wheel discs (11.75 in. dia.). Ignition: Electronic. Body construction: Separate fiberglass body and ladder-type steel frame. Fuel tank: 24 gal.

CORVETTE OPTIONS: Four-speed manual trans. (NC). Gymkhana suspension ($61). H.D. cooling ($57). California emissions system (N/A). Rear defogger, electric ($129). Cruise control w/resume ($165). Six-way power driver's seat ($197). Power door locks ($155). Twin electric remote-control sport mirrors ($125). AM/FM stereo radio ($101). Electronic-tuning AM/FM stereo radio with 8track ($386); w/cassette player ($423); w/cassette and CB ($755) exc. ($458) on Collector Edition. Power antenna ($60). Radio delete ($124 credit). Removable glass roof panels ($443). Roof panel carrier ($144). Custom two-tone paint ($428) w/lower body accents and multi-color striping. Aluminum wheels ($458). P225/70R15 SBR WL tires ($80).

HISTORY: Introduced: Dec. 12, 1981. Model year production: 25,407. Calendar year production: 22,838. Model year sales by U.S. dealers: 22,086.

Historical Footnotes: All Corvettes now came from the factory at Bowling Green, Kentucky. Production fell dramatically this year, reaching the lowest total since 1967. No doubt, some buyers preferred to wait for the next generation to arrive. Still, this was the end of the big Corvette era: "An enthusiast's kind of Corvette. A most civilized one," according to the factory catalog. *Road & Track* called it "truly the last of its series," though one with an all-new drivetrain. The Collector Edition earned the dubious distinction of being the first Corvette into cost more than $20,000. They were built to order, rather than according to a predetermined schedule. Special VIN plates were used, to prevent swindlers from turning an ordinary Corvette into a special edition (which had happened all too often with the Pace Car replicas of 1978).

1983 CORVETTE

1983 Corvettes were not EPA certified; those produced were used for tests and then destroyed.

1984 CORVETTE

SERIES Y — V-8 — The eagerly-awaited sixth-generation Corvette for the eighties missed the 1983 model year completely, but arrived in spring 1983 in an all-new form. An aerodynamic exterior featuring an "acute" windshield rake (64 degrees) covered a series of engineering improvements. A one-piece, full width fiberglass roof (no Tbar) was removable; transparent acrylic lift-off panel with solar screen optional. At the rear was a frameless glass back window/hatch, above four round taillamps. Hidden headlamps were joined by clear, integrated halogen foglamps and front cornering lamps. Dual sport mirrors were electrically remote-controlled. The unit body (with partial front frame) used a front-hinged "clamshell" hood with integral twin-duct air intake. Sole engine was again the L83 350 cu. in. (5.7-liter) V-8 with Cross-Fire fuel injection.

1984 Corvette coupe (CP)

Stainless steel headers led into its exhaust system. Air cleaner and valve train had cast magnesium covers. After being unavailable in the 1982 model, a four-speed manual gearbox returned as the standard transmission (though not until January 1984). A four-plus-three speed automatic, with computer-activated overdrive in every gear except first was offered at no extra cost. It used a hydraulic clutch. Overdrive was locked out during rigorous acceleration above specified speeds, and when a console switch was activated. Under the chassis were an aluminum driveshaft, forged aluminum suspension arms, and fiberglass transverse leaf springs. Power rack-and-pinion steering and power four-wheel disc brakes were standard. Optional Goodyear 50-series "uni-directional" tires were designed for mounting on a specific wheel. Inside, an electronic instrument panel featured both analog and digital LCD readouts, in either English or metric measure. A Driver Information System between speedometer and tach gave a selection of switch-chosen readings. At the driver's left was the parking brake. Body colors were red, black, white, and seven metallics; gold, light or medium blue, light bronze, dark bronze, silver or gray. Two-tone options were light/medium blue, silver/gray, and light/dark bronze. Standard interiors came in graphite, blue, bronze, saddle or gray cloth; optional leather in graphite, saddle, bronze, dark red or gray. Corvette's ample standard equipment list included an advanced (and very necessary) theft-prevention system with starter-interrupt. Other standard equipment: air conditioning, power windows, electronic-tuning seek/scan AM/FM stereo radio with digital clock, reclining bucket seats, leather-wrapped tilt/telescope steering wheel, luggage security shade, and side window defoggers.

1984 Corvette coupe (OCW)

I.D. DATA: Coding of the 17-symbol Vehicle Identification Number (VIN), visible through the windshield, was similar to prior models. The VIN took the form: 1G1AY078()E5100001. The '1G1A' portion indicates U.S.A., General Motors, Chevrolet Division, and non-passive restraint system (standard seatbelts). 'Y' denotes Corvette series. '07' indicates 2door hatchback coupe body style. '8' is the engine code. Next is a check digit, followed by 'E' for the 1984 model year and '5' for the Bowling Green, KY assembly plant. Finally comes the six- digit sequential serial number, starting with 100001. Engine identification numbers again were stamped on a pad on the block, at the front of the right cylinder head. That number reveals assembly plant, date built, and a three- letter engine code.

CORVETTE

Model Number	Body/Style Number	Body Type & Seating	Factory Price	Shipping Weight	Production Total
1Y	Y07	2-dr. Hatch Cpe-2P	23360	3088	51,547

Note: Of the total production, 240 Corvettes were modified for use with leaded gasoline (for export).

ENGINE DATA: BASE V-8: 90-degree, overhead valve V-8. Cast iron block and head. Displacement: 350 cu. in. (5.7 liters). Bore & stroke: 4.00 x 3.48 in. Compression ratio: 9.0:1. Brake horsepower: 205 at 4200 R.P.M. Torque: 290 lbs.-ft. at 2800 R.P.M. Five main bearings. Hydraulic valve lifters. Dual TBI (CFI). RPO Code: L83. VIN Code: 8.

CHASSIS DATA: Wheelbase: 96.2 in. Overall length: 176.5 in. Height: 46.7 in. Width: 71.0 in. Front Tread: 59.6 in. Rear Tread: 60.4 in. Wheel Size: 15 x 7 in. Standard Tires: P215/65R15. Optional Tires: Eagle P255/50VR16 on 16 x 8 in. wheels.

TECHNICAL: Transmission: THM 700-R4 four-speed overdrive automatic (floor shift) standard. Gear ratios: (1st) 3.06:1; (2nd) 1.63:1; (3rd) 1.00:1; (4th) 0.70:1; (Rev) 2.29:1. Four-speed manual transmission optional: (1st) 2.88:1; (2nd) 1.91:1; (3rd) 1.33:1; (4th) 1.00:1; (overdrive) 0.67:1; (Rev) 2.78:1. Standard final drive ratio: 2.73:1 w/auto., 3.07:1 w/4spd (3.31:1 optional). Steering: Rack and pinion (power-assisted). Front Suspension: Single fiberglass composite monoleaf transverse spring with unequal-length aluminum control arms and stabilizer bar. Rear Suspension: Fully independent five-link system with trransverse fiberglass single-leaf spring, aluminum upper/lower trailing links, and strut/tie rod assembly. Brakes: Four-wheel power disc. Body construction: Unibody with partial front frame. Fuel tank: 20 gal.

CORVETTE OPTIONS: Four-speed overdrive manual trans. (NC). California emission system ($75). Performance axle ratio ($22). Performance handling pkg.: H.D. springs/shocks, front/rear stabilizers, special bushings and P255/50VR16 tires on 16 x 91/2 in. wheels ($600). Delco/Bilstein shock absorbers ($189). Engine oil cooler ($158). H.D. cooling ($57). Rear defogger system incl. mirrors ($160). Electronic cruise control w/resume ($185). Six-way power driver's seat ($210). Power door locks ($165). Electronic-tuning AM/FM stereo radio with seek/scan, clock and cassette player ($153). DelcoGM/Bose music system: AM/FM seek/scan stereo radio w/clock, cassette and four speakers ($895). CB radio ($215). Radio delete ($276 credit). Lift-off transparent roof panels ($595). Custom two-tone paint ($428) w/lower body accents. Custom adj. sport cloth bucket seats ($625). Leather bucket seats ($400). P255/50VR16 SBR BSW tires on 16 in. aluminum wheels ($561).

HISTORY: Introduced: March 25, 1984. Model year production: 51,547 (in extended model year). Calendar year production: 35,661. Calendar year sales by U.S. dealers: 30,424. Model year sales by U.S. dealers: 53,877 (including 25,891 sold during the 1983 model year).

Historical Footnotes: Car and Driver called the new Corvette "the most advanced production car on the planet." *Motor Trend* described it as "the best-handling production car in the world, regardless of price." Heady praise indeed. During its year-and-a-half model run, orders poured in well ahead of schedule, even though the new edition cost over $5000 more than the 1982 version. The body offered the lowest drag coefficient of any Corvette: just 0.341. Testing at GM's Proving Grounds revealed 0.95G lateral acceleration—the highest ever for a production car. Only 6,443 Corvettes had a four-speed manual transmission, and only 410 came with a performance axle ratio, but 3,729 had Delco/Bilstein shocks installed.

1985 CORVETTE

1985 Corvette coupe (CP)

SERIES Y — V-8 — Two details marked the 1985 Corvette as different from its newly-restyled 1984 predecessor: a 'Tuned Port Injection' nameplate on fender molding, and straight tailpipes at the rear. That nameplate identified a new 350 cu. in. (5.7-liter) V-8 under the hood, with port fuel injection and a 230- horsepower rating. Peak torque reached 330 lbs.ft, compared to 290 from the prior Cross-Fire V-8. City fuel economy ratings went up too. Otherwise, the only evident change was a slight strengthening in the intensity of the red and silver body colors. Corvette's smoothly sloped nose, adorned by nothing other than the circular emblem, held retracting halogen headlamps. Wide parking/signal lamps nearly filled the space between license plate and outer edge. Wide horizontal side marker lenses were just ahead of the front wheels. The large air cleaner of '82 was replaced by an elongated plenum chamber with eight curved aluminum runners. Mounted ahead of the radiator, it ducted incoming air into the plenum through a Bosch hot-wire mass airflow sensor. Those tuned runners were meant to boost power at low to medium R.P.M., following a principle similar to that used for the tall intake stacks in racing engines. Electronic Spark Control sensed knocking and adjusted timing to fit fuel octane. Under the chassis, the '85 carried a reworked suspension (both standard and optional Z51) to

1985 Corvette coupe (CP)

soften the ride without losing control. The Z51 handling package now included 9.5-inch wheels all around, along with Delco-Bilstein gas-charged shock absorbers and heavy-duty cooling. Stabilizer bars on the Z51 were thicker. Spring rates on both suspensions were reduced. Cast aluminum wheels held P255/50VR16 Eagle GT tires. Master cylinders used a new large-capacity plastic booster. Manual gearboxes drove rear axles with 8.5-inch ring gears. Instrument cluster graphics had a bolder look. Roof panels added more solar screening. An optional leather- trimmed sport seat arrived at mid-year. Corvette standard equipment included an electronic information center, air conditioning, limited-slip differential, power four-wheel disc brakes, power steering, cornering lamps, and seek/scan AM/FM stereo radio with four speakers and automatic power antenna. Also standard: a lighter, digital clock, tachometer, intermittent wipers, halogen foglamps, and side window defoggers. Corvettes had contour high-back cloth bucket seats, power windows, a trip odometer, theft-deterrent system with starter interrupt, compact spare tire, dual electric remote-control sport mirrors, and tinted glass. Bodies held black belt, windshield and bodyside moldings, plus color-keyed rocker panel moldings. Four-speed overdrive automatic transmission was standard, with four-speed manual (overdrive in three gears) available at no extra cost.

1985 Corvette coupe (CP)

I.D. DATA: Coding of the 17-symbol Vehicle Identification Number (VIN) was similar to 1984. Model year code changed to 'F' for 1985.

CORVETTE

Model Number	Body/Style Number	Body Type & Seating	Factory Price	Shipping Weight	Production Total
1Y	Y07	2-dr. Hatch Cpe-2P	24873	3088	39,729

ENGINE DATA: BASE V-8: 90-degree, overhead valve V-8. Cast iron block and head. Displacement: 350 cu. in. (5.7 liters). Bore & stroke: 4.00 x 3.48 in. Compression ratio: 9.0:1. Brake horsepower: 230 at 4000 R.P.M. Torque: 330 lbs.-ft. at 3200 R.P.M. Five main bearings. Hydraulic valve lifters. Tuned-port fuel injection. RPO Code: L98. VIN Code: 8.

CHASSIS DATA: Wheelbase: 96.2 in. Overall length: 176.5 in. Height: 46.4 in. Width: 71.0 in. Front Tread: 59.6 in. Rear Tread: 60.4 in. Wheel Size: 16 x 8.5 in. Standard Tires: P255/50VR16 SBR.

TECHNICAL: Transmission: THM 700R4 four-speed overdrive automatic standard. Gear ratios: (1st) 3.06:1; (2nd) 1.63:1; (3rd) 1.00:1; (4th) 0.70:1; (Rev) 2.29:1. Four-speed overdrive manual transmission available at no extra charge: (1st) 2.88:1; (2nd) 1.91:1; (3rd) 1.33:1; (4th) 1.00:1; (Rev) 2.78:1; planetary overdrive ratios: (2nd) 1.28:1; (3rd) 0.89:1; (4th) 0.67:1. Standard final drive ratio: 3.07:1 or 2.73:1. Steering/Suspension/BrakesBody: same as 1984. Fuel tank: 20.0 gal.

CORVETTE OPTIONS: Four-speed overdrive manual trans. (NC). California emission system ($99). Performance axle ratio ($22). Delco/Bilstein shock absorbers ($189). H.D. cooling ($225). Performance handling pkg. (Z51): H.D. springs and front/rear stabilizers, Delco/Bilstein shocks and H.D. cooling ($470). Rear defogger system incl. mirrors ($160). Electronic cruise control w/resume ($185). Six-way power driver's seat ($215). Power door locks ($170). Electronic-tuning AM/FM stereo radio with seek/scan, clock and cassette player ($122). DelcoGM/Bose music system: AM/FM seek/scan stereo radio w/clock, cassette and four speakers ($895). Radio delete ($256 credit). Lift- off transparent roof panels ($595). Custom two-tone paint ($428) w/lower body accents. Custom adj. sport cloth bucket seats ($625). Leather bucket seats ($400).

HISTORY: Introduced: October 2, 1984. Model year production: 39,729. Calendar year production: 46,304. Calendar year sales by U.S. dealers: 37,956. Model year sales by U.S. dealers: 37,878.

Historical Footnotes: Chevrolet claimed a 17 percent reduction in 0-60 MPH times with the TPI powerplant. To save weight, Corvettes used not only the fiberglass leaf springs front and rear, but over 400 pounds of aluminum parts (including steering/suspension components and frame members). A total of 14,802 Corvettes had the Z51 performance handling package installed, 9,333 had Delco/Bilstein shocks ordered separately, and only 9,576 had a four-speed manual transmission. Only 16 Corvettes are listed as having a CB radio, and only 82 with an economy rear axle ratio.

1986 CORVETTE

SERIES Y — V-8 — One new body style and an engineering development were the highlights of 1986. Corvette added a convertible during the model year, the first since 1975. And computerized anti- lock braking system (ABS) was made standard. During hard braking, the system (based on a Bosch ABS II design) detected any wheel that was about to lock, then altered braking pressure in a pulsating action to prevent lockup from happening. Drivers could feel the pulses in the pedal. This safety innovation helped the driver to maintain traction and keep the car under directional control, without skidding, even on slick and slippery surfaces. Corvette's engine was the same

1986 Corvette Indy Pace Car convertible (CH)

350 cu. in (5.7-liter) 230-horsepower, tuned-port fuel-injected V-8 as 1985, but with centrally-positioned copper-core spark plugs this year. New aluminum cylinder heads had sintered metal valve seats and increased intake port flow, plus higher (9.5:1) compression. The engine had an aluminum intake manifold with tuned runners, magnesium rocker covers, and outside-air induction system. Both four-plus-three manual and four-speed overdrive automatic transmissions were available, now with an upshift indicator light on the instrument cluster. Three monolith catalytic converters in a new dual exhaust system kept emissions down during warmup. Cast alloy wheels gained a new raised hub emblem and a brushed-aluminum look. The instrument cluster was tilted to cut glare. The sport seat from 1985 was made standard this year, with leather optional. Electronic air conditioning, announced earlier, arrived as a late option. Otherwise, standard equipment was similar to a 1985. A new electronic Vehicle Anti-Theft System (VATS) was also made standard. A small electrically-coded pellet was embedded in the ignition key, while a decoder was hidden in the car. When the key was placed in the ignition, its resistance code was "read." Unless that code was compatible, the starter relay wouldn't close and the Electronic Control Module wouldn't activate the fuel injectors. Corvettes came in one new solid color this year (yellow), plus a white/silver metallic two-tone. Carryover body colors were white, black, bright red, silver metallic, medium gray metallic, and gold metallic. New this year were five metallics: medium blue, silver beige, copper, medium brown, and dark red. Corvette's back end held four round recessed lenses, with 'Corvette' block letters in the center. The license plate sat in a recessed housing. Cloth seats had lateral support and back-angle adjustments. Roadsters (convertibles) had a manual top with velour inner liner. The yellow console button that ordinarily controlled Corvette's hatch release opened a fiberglass panel behind the seats to reveal the top storage area. Cast alloy 16 x 8½ in. aluminum alloy wheels held undirectional P255/50VR16 Goodyear Eagle GT SBR tires.

I.D. DATA: Coding of the 17-symbol Vehicle Identification Number (VIN) was similar to 1984-85, but body type codes were now either '07' for hatchback coupe or '67' for the new convertible. Model year code changed to 'G' for 1986.

CORVETTE

Model Number	Body/Style Number	Body Type & Seating	Factory Price	Shipping Weight	Production Total
1Y	Y07	2-dr. Hatch Cpe-2P	27027	3086	27,794
1Y	Y67	2-dr. Conv. Cpe-2P	32032	N/A	7,315

ENGINE DATA: BASE V-8: 90-degree, overhead valve V-8. Cast iron block and head. Displacement: 350 cu. in. (5.7 liters). Bore & stroke: 4.00 x 3.48 in. Compression ratio: 9.5:1. Brake horsepower: 230 at 4000 R.P.M. Torque: 330 lbs.-ft. at 3200 R.P.M. Five main bearings. Hydraulic valve lifters. Tuned-port fuel injection. RPO Code: L98. VIN Code: 8.

CHASSIS DATA: Wheelbase: 96.2 in. Overall length: 176.5 in. Height: 46.4 in. Width: 71.0 in. Front Tread: 59.6 in. Rear Tread: 60.4 in. Wheel Size: 16 x 8.5 in. (9.5 in. wide with optional Z51 suspension). Standard Tires: P245/50VR16 or P255/50VR16 SBR.

TECHNICAL: Transmission: THM 700R4 four-speed overdrive automatic transmission standard. Gear ratios: (1st) 3.06:1; (2nd) 1.63:1; (3rd) 1.00:1; (4th) 0.70:1; (Rev) 2.29:1. Four-speed manual overdrive transmission available at no extra charge. Standard final drive ratio: 3.07:1 w/manual, 2.59:1 or 3.07:1 w/auto. Steering/Suspension: same as 1984-85. Brakes: Anti-lock; power four-wheel disc. Ignition: Electronic. Body construction: Fiberglass; separate ladder frame with cross-members. Fuel tank: 20.0 gal.

CORVETTE OPTIONS: Four-speed overdrive manual trans. with upshift indicator (NC). California emission system ($99). Performance axle ratio ($22). Performance handling pkg. (Z51): H.D. springs and front/rear stabilizers, Delco/Bilstein shocks, H.D. radiator and boost fan, engine cooler and P255/50VR16 Eagle BSW tires ($470). Delco/Bilstein shock absorbers ($189). H.D. radiator ($40). Radiator boost cooling fan ($75). Engine oil cooler ($110). Custom feature pkg.: rear defogger, dual heated electric remote mirrors, map lights, console lighting ($195). Electronic air cond. ($150). Rear defogger system incl. mirrors ($165). Electronic cruise control w/resume ($185). Six-way power driver's seat ($225). Power door locks ($175). Electronic-tuning AM/FM stereo radio with seek/scan, clock and cassette player ($122). DelcoGM/Bose music system: AM/FM seek/scan stereo radio w/clock, cassette and four speakers ($895). Radio delete ($256 credit). Removable roof panel ($595); dual panels ($895) incl. blue or bronze transparent panel. Custom two-tone paint ($428) w/lower body accents. Leather bucket seats ($400). Leather adj. sport bucket seats ($1025).

HISTORY: Introduced: October 3, 1985. Model year production: 35,109. Calendar year production (U.S.): 28,410. Model year sales by U.S. dealers: 35,969.

Historical Footnotes: Styled like the Corvette roadster that would serve as '86 Indy Pace Car, the new convertible went on sale late in the model year. The actual Pace Car was bright yellow, differing from showroom models only in its special track lights. Chevrolet considered "Pace Car" to be synonymous with "open top," so all convertibles were considered Pace Car models. Special decals were packed in the car, but not mounted. Corvette's was the only street legal vehicle to pace the Indy race since 1978 (also a Corvette). Instead of a conversion by an outside company, as had become the practice for most 1980s ragtops, Corvette's roadster was built by Chevrolet, right alongside the coupe. Problems with cracking of the new aluminum cylinder heads meant first '86 models had old cast iron heads. Those difficulties soon were remedied. It was estimated that the new anti-theft system would require half an hour's work to overcome, which would dissuade thieves who are typically in a hurry. A total of 6,242 Corvettes had removable roof panels installed, and 12,821 came with the Z51 performance handling package. Only 6,835 Corvettes carried the MM4 four-speed manual transmission.

CORVETTE

1987-1990

Though little changed from the previous model, the 1987 Corvette Y-body coupe and convertible highlighted state-of-the-art technology throughout. From an electronic instrument panel with eight possible gauge readouts in four locations to aluminum cylinder heads and a high-performance stereo speaker system, the Chevrolet luxury sports car was aimed at buyers who wanted the latest in automotive features, regardless of cost.

Some early 1987 Corvettes experienced problems with cracking of their new aluminum cylinder heads. The problem was ultimately solved, but did have a negative affect on production operations. The 5.7-liter Corvette V-8 was also fitted with new roller lifters which reduced friction and bumped horsepower to 240.

Also new for the year was an optional Z-52 suspension setup, a low-tire-pressure indicating system and Bosch four-wheel anti-lock braking. In the works was a change to recently developed Goodyear 17-inch tires with a racing-style 45 percent aspect ratio, plus a much-desired gearbox change. At a plant in Brewer, Me., the North American branch of Germany's Zahnrad Fabrik Friedrichshafen AG (better known to car buffs as ZF) was busy developing a new six-speed manual transmission for the Corvette. Unfortunately, the new transmission was not ready in 1987, when 86 percent of Corvettes came with Turbo Hydramatic and 14 percent with four-speeds.

Corvette production continued to be housed in Chevrolet's Bowling Green, Ken. factory. Model year production totaled 30,632 (including 10,625 convertibles) although model year sales of 25,266 units fell short of the 35,969 sold in 1986.

For 1988, the Corvette remained available as a hatchback coupe or a roadster, with prices starting just below $30,000. Increased excitement was generated by a new 5.7-liter V-8 that jumped from 235 hp to 245 hp. The 17-inch tires were now made available for cars with the Z-52 option. However, the ZF six-speed remained on the Vette owners' "wish list" and 81.2 percent of the cars had a four-speed automatic. The balance featured the four-speed manual with lock-up overdrive.

Production of 1988 Corvettes began on Aug. 24, 1987 and stopped on July 28, 1988. During that period, Vettes were built on a single shift at the Bowling Green factory, with workers cranking out an average of 11 cars per hour. Output totaled 22,789 units, of which 7,407 were ragtops. Model year sales of 25,425 units again accounted for an .03 percent share of the domestic car market.

A reaction injected molded (RIM) structural composite front bumper beam was new for all 1989 Corvettes and all could also be had with the long-awaited ZF gearbox. Corvette was one of the few American cars to start offering air bags this season. Both coupes and roadsters were powered by a 5.7-liter tuned port injected V-8 which was rated 245 nhp @ 4300 rpm for coupes and 240 nhp @ 4000 rpm for convertibles. A much-heralded ZR-1 "King-of-the-Hill" Corvette was scheduled for mid-1989 release, but its due date was ultimately delayed.

Model year output went in the right direction, rising to 26,412 units, of which 9,749 were open cars. Transmission attachments ran a bit higher for automatics (84.4 percent) despite the availability of the six-speed. Nearly all 1989 Corvettes came 100 percent loaded with options, with some exceptions being a Bose sound system used in 91.4 percent, a rear window defogger in 63.1 percent and power seats in 96.9 percent.

1990 Corvette coupe

An exciting addition to the 1990 Corvette lineup was the ZR-1 coupe, which was engineered in conjunction with Lotus of England and the Mercury Marine Div. of Brunswick Corp., in Stillwater, Okla. It bowed in Sept. 1989, as a 1990 model, and production of 3,000 copies was scheduled for Bowling Green.

The ZR-1's prime attraction was a special high-performance 5.7-liter aluminum double overhead cam V-8 (RPO LT5) which featured four valves per cylinder and 375 horses, mated to the ZF transmission. The car's body also had a wider rear roof bow and quarter panel section made of traditional SMC plastic materials produced by GenCorp at its Reinforced Plastics Div. plant in Marion, Ind. A price tag of $59,495 made the ZR-1 America's most expensive production car.

To go along with the ZR-1 performance image, power on standard L98-powered coupes and convertibles was made 245 nhp (or 250 nhp with sport mufflers). The basic price for a Corvette jumped $434 to $32,479. New for 1990 convertibles was an optional removable hardtop.

During the 1987-1990 period, Chevrolet Motor Div. operated as a branch of General Motors Corp., with its headquarters in Warren, Mich. Robert D. Burger was general manager through mid-1989, when Jim C. Perkins — an enthusiast and Classic Chevy collector — took over the command post.

1987 CORVETTE

1987 Corvette convertible

1987 CORVETTE — SERIES Y — V-8 —
Except for the addition of roller hydraulic lifters to the Corvette's 350 cu. in. (5.7-liter) V-8, little changed this year. Horsepower got a boost to 240 (from the former 230), and gas mileage rated a trifle higher. Joining the option list was an electronic tire-pressure monitor, which signaled a dashboard light to warn of low pressure in any tire. Two four-speed transmissions were available: manual or automatic. Standard equipment included power steering, power four-wheel disc brakes (with anti-locking), air conditioning, a theft-deterrent system, tinted glass, twin remote-control mirrors, power windows, intermittent wipers, tilt/telescope steering column, and AM/FM seek/scan radio.

I.D. DATA: Coding of the 17-symbol Vehicle Identification Number (VIN) was similar to 1984-86. Model year code changed to 'H' for 1987.

CORVETTE

Model Number	Body/Style Number	Body Type & Seating	Factory Price	Shipping Weight	Production Total
1Y	Y-07	2-dr. Hatch Cpe-2P	27999	3216	20,007
1Y	Y67	2-dr. Conv. Cpe-2P	33172	3279	10,625

ENGINE DATA: BASE V-8: 90-degree, overhead valve V-8. Cast iron block and head. Displacement: 350 cu. in. (5.7 liters). Bore & stroke: 4.00 x 3.48 in. Compression ratio: 9.0:1 Brake horsepower: 240 at 4000 RPM. Torque: 345 lbs.-ft. at 3200 RPM. Five main bearings. Hydraulic valve lifters. Tuned-port fuel injection.

CHASSIS DATA: Wheelbase: 96.2 in. Overall length: 176.5 in. Height: (hatch) 46.7 in.; (conv) 46.4 in. Width: 71.0 in. Front Tread: 59.6 in. Rear Tread: 60.4 in. Standard Tires: P245/60VR15 Goodyear Eagle GT.

TECHNICAL: Transmission: four-speed overdrive manual or automatic. **Standard final drive ratio:** 3.07:1 w/manual, 2.59:1 or 3.07:1 w/auto. **Steering:** rack and pinion (power assisted). **Suspension (front):** unequal-length control arms, single-leaf transverse spring and stabilizer bar. **Suspension (rear):** upper/lower control arms with five links, single-leaf transverse spring, stabilizer bar. **Brakes:** Anti-lock; power four-wheel disc. **Body construction:** fiberglass; separate ladder frame with cross-members. **Fuel tank:** 20.0 gal.

CORVETTE OPTIONS:
Automatic air conditioning ($150). Performance axle ratio ($22). Engine oil cooler ($110). Rear defogger & heated outside mirrors ($165). power door locks ($190). Calif emissions system ($99). Radiator cooling boost fan ($75). Dual heated power mirrors ($35). Illuminated left visor mirror ($58). Performance Handling Pkg ($795). Heavy-duty radiator ($40). AM/FM cassette ($132). Delco-GM/Bose music stereo electronic-tuning cassette system ($905). AM/FM delete ($256 credit). Removable roof panel ($615). Dual removable roof panels ($915). 6-way power driver's seat ($240). Delco-Bilstein shock absorbers ($189). Cruise control ($185). Tire low pressure indicator ($325). Leather seats ($400). Leather sport seats ($1025). Custom two-tone paint ($428).

HISTORY: Introduced: October 9, 1986. Model year production: 30,632. Calendar year production (U.S.): 28,514. Model year sales by U.S. dealers: 25,266.

1988 CORVETTE

1988 CORVETTE — SERIES Y — V-8 —
Little changed in Corvette's appearance this year, except for restyled six-slot wheels. Optional 17-wheels looked similar to the standard 16-inchers, but held massive P275/40ZR17 Goodyear Eagle GT tires. Suspension modifications were intended to improve control during hard braking, while brake components were toughened, including the use of thicker rotors. Under the hood, the standard 350 cu. in. (5.7-liter) V-8 could breathe more easily with a pair of modified aluminum cylinder heads. Performance also got a boost via a new camshaft, though horsepower only rose by five. Both a convertible and a hatchback coupe were offered.

I.D. DATA: Coding of the 17-symbol Vehicle Identification Number (VIN) was similar to 1984-87. Model year code changed to 'J' for 1988.

1988 Corvette coupe

CORVETTE

Model Number	Body/Style Number	Body Type & Seating	Factory Price	Shipping Weight	Production Total
1Y	Y07	2-dr. hatch Cpe-2P	29480	3229	15,382
1Y	Y67	2-dr. Conv. Cpe-2P	34820	3299	7,407

ENGINE DATA: BASE V-8: 90-degree, overhead valve V-8. Cast iron block and head. Displacement: 350 cu. in. (5.7 liters). Bore & stroke: 4.00 x 3.48 in. Compression ratio: 9.5:1 Brake horsepower: 245 at 4000 RPM. Torque: 345 lbs.-ft. at 3200 RPM. Five main bearings. Hydraulic valve lifters. Tuned-port fuel injection.

CHASSIS DATA: Wheelbase: 96.2 in. Overall length: 176.5 in. Height: (hatch) 46.7 in.; (conv) 46.4 in. Width: 71.0 in. Front Tread: 59.6 in. Rear Tread: 60.4 in. Standard Tires: P255/50ZR16 Goodyear Eagle GT (Z-rated).

1988 Corvette convertible

TECHNICAL: Transmission: four-speed overdrive manual or automatic. **Steering:** rack and pinion (power assisted). **Suspension (front):** unequal-length control arms, single-leaf transverse spring and stablilizer bar. **Suspension (rear):** upper/lower control arms with five links, single-leaf transverse spring, stabilizer bar. **Brakes:** Anti-lock; power four-wheel disc. **Body construction:** fiberglass; separate ladder frame with cross-members. **Fuel tank:** 20.0 gal.

1988 Corvette coupe

CORVETTE OPTIONS:
Leather Bucket Seats ($400). A8 Leather Adjust. Spt Bucket Seats ($1025). Solid Exterior Color Paint (NC). Electronic Control Air cond ($150). Performance ratio axle ($22). Engine oil cooler ($110). Rear Window Defogger System & Outside Rearview Mirrors ($165). Calif Emission System ($99). Radiator cooling boost fan ($75). Performance Handling Pkg; H.D. Radiator; Radiator Cooling Boost Fan; Eng. Oil Cooler; Pwr Strg oil cooler; FG3 Delco Bilstein Shock Absorbers; H.D. F&R Springs, H.D. Frame; 17" x 9.5" Alum Wheels, P275/40ZR 17 blackwall tires; H.D. frt & rear Stabilizers ($1295). (Z52) Sports Handling Pkg Incls H.D. Radiator; Radiator Cooling Boost Fan; Eng. Oil Cooler; FG3 Delco Bilstein Shock Absorbers; H.D. F&R Springs, 17" x 9.5" Alum Wheels P275/40ZR-17 blackwall tires; H.D. frt & rear Stabilizers ($970). Eng. Block Heater ($20). Twin Remote Heated Mirrors ($35). Lighted Visor Mirrors, Driver ($58). H.D. Radiator ($40); ($40). Elect Tuned Delco/Bose Music System, Incl AM/FM Stereo w/Seek & Scan, Stereo Cass Tape & Digital Clock, special tone & balance control 4 speakers and Pwr Antenna ($773). Removable Roof Panels, Transparent, blue tint or bronze tint ($615). Dual body color-keyed roof panel & blue or bronze transparent roof panel ($915). Pwr 6-way Seats, Driver's Side only ($240). Pass. Side only ($240). Delco/Bilstein Shock Absorbers ($189).

HISTORY: Introduced: October 1, 1987. Model year production: 22,789. Calendar year production: 22,878. Model year sales by U.S. dealers: 25,425.

1989 CORVETTE

1989 Corvette convertible

1989 CORVETTE — SERIES Y — V-8 — Most of the Corvette publicity this year centered on the eagerly-awaited ZR-1, claimed to be the world's fastest production automobile. After several announcements proved premature, the ZR-1 was delayed until the 1990 model year. Meanwhile, the "ordinary" Corvette added a new ZF six-speed manual gearbox with two overdrive ratios. To meet fuel-economy standards, the ingenious transmission was designed so a computer sent a signal that prevented shifts from first to second gear unless the gas pedal hit the floor. Instead, a blocking pin forced the shifter directly into fourth gear, for improved economy during light-throttle operation. Joining the option list was a new FX3 Delco-Bilstein Selective Ride Control system, with a switch to select the desired degree of shock-absorber damping for Touring, Sport or Competition driving. Only coupes with manual shift and the Z51 performance Handling package could get the ride control option. For the first time since 1975, a removable fiberglass hardtop became available for the convertible, but later in the model year.

I.D. DATA: Coding of the 17-symbol Vehicle Identification Number (VIN) was similar to 1984-88. Model year code changed to 'K' for 1989.

CORVETTE

Model Number	Body/Style Number	Body Type & Seating	Factory Price	Shipping Weight	Production Total
1Y	Y07	2-dr. Hatch Cpe-2P	31545	3229	
1Y	Y67	2-dr. Conv. Cpe-2P	36785	3269	

ENGINE DATA: BASE V-8: 90-degree, overhead valve V-8. Cast iron block and head. Displacement: 350 cu. in. (5.7 liters). Bore & stroke: 4.00 x 3.48 in. Compression ratio: 9.5:1 Brake horsepower: 245 at 4300 RPM. Torque: 340 lbs.-ft. at 3200 RPM. Five main bearings. Hydraulic valve lifters. Tuned-port fuel injection.

CHASSIS DATA: Wheelbase: 96.2 in. Overall length: 176.5 in. Height: (hatch) 46.7 in.; (conv) 46.4 in. Width: 71.0 in. Front Tread: 59.6 in. Rear Tread: 60:4 in. Standard Tires: P275/40VR17 Goodyear Eagle GT (Z-rated).

TECHNICAL: Transmission: four-speed overdrive manual or automatic. **Steering:** rack and pinion (power assisted). **Suspension (front);** unequal-length control arms, single-leaf transverse spring and stablilizer bar. **Suspension (rear):** upper/lower control arms with five links, single-leaf transverse spring, stabilizer bar. **Brakes:** Anti-lock; power four-wheel disc. **Body construction:** fiberglass; separate ladder frame with cross-members. **Fuel tank:** 20.0 gal.

CORVETTE OPTIONS:
Preferred Equipment Group Incl Electronic Air Cond; Elect Tuned Delco/Bose Music System; (AM/FM Stereo Radio w/Seek & Scan, Stereo Cas Tape & Digital Clock, special tone & balance control & 4 spkrs)l power Six-Way Driver's Seat ($1193). Corvette Convertible Base Equip Grp Incl w/Mld (NC). Elect Tuned Delco/Bose Music System (AM/FM Stereo w/Seek & Scan, Stereo Cass Tape & Digital Clock, special tone & balance control & 4 spkrs ($773). Leather bucket seats ($425). Leather Adjustable Sport Bucket seats ($1050). Solid Exterior Paint (NC). Electronic Control Air Cond ($170). Performance Ratio Axle ($22). Luggage Carrier ($140). Eng Oil Cooler ($110). Calif Emission System ($100). Radiator Cooling Boost Fan ($75). (Z51) Peformance (Eng Oil Cooler Radiator Fan & H.D. Radiator) ($575). (FX3) Electronic Selective Ride ($1695). Eng Block Heater ($20). Low Tire Pressure Warning Indicator ($325). Lighted Visor Mirror, Driver ($58). H.D. Radiator ($40). Roof Panels Removable, Blue or Bronze Tint ($615). Dual body color-keyed Roof Panel & Blue or Bronze Transparent Roof Panel ($915). Removable Hardtop ($1995). Six-way power seats Driver's Side only ($250). Pass. Side only ($250).

1990 CORVETTE

1990 CORVETTE — SERIES Y — V-8 —
Finally, after months of hoopla and a few false starts, the super-performance ZR-1 Corvette arrived. Intended for production in limited quantity, with a price tag higher than any General Motors product, the ZR-1 became a collectible long before anyone ever saw one "in the flesh," with customers eager to pay far above the suggested retail price for the few examples that became available. Under the ZR-1 hood was a Lotus-designed 32-valve, dual-overhead-cam, 350 cu. in. (5.7-liter) V-8, built by Mercury

1990 Corvette ZR1 coupe

Marine in Oklahoma. Although the displacement was identical to the standard Corvette V-8, this was an all-new powerplant with different bore and stroke dimensions. Wider at the rear than a standard model, partly to contain the huge 315/35ZR17 back tires, the ZR-1 was easy to spot because of its convex back end and rectangular taillamps. Ordinary Corvettes continued to display a concave rear end with round taillamps, Standard ZR-1 equipment included an FX3 Selective Ride adjustable suspension, which was also available on standard Corvettes with the six-speed manual gearbox. Four-speed overdrive automatic was available (at no cost) only on the regular Corvette. New standard equipment included an engine oil cooler, 17-inch alloy wheels, and improved ABS II-S anti-lock braking. The convertible added a new backlight made of flexible "Ultrashield" for improved scratch resistance and visibility. An air bag was installed in the new steering wheel on all Corvettes, and a revised dashboard mixed digital and analog instruments.

I.D. DATA: Coding of the 17-symbol Vehicle Identification Number (VIN) was similar to 1984-89. Model year code changed to 'L' for 1989.

CORVETTE

Model Number	Body/Style Number	Body Type & Seating	Factory Price	Shipping Weight	Production Total
1Y	Y07	2-dr. Hatch Cpe-2P	31979	3223	
1Y	Y67	2-dr. Conv. Cpe-2P	37264	3263	
1Y		2-dr. ZR1 Cpe-2P	58995	3465	

ENGINE DATA: BASE V-8: 90-degree, overhead valve V-8. Cast iron block and head. Displacement: 350 cu. in. (5.7 liters). Bore & stroke: 4.00 x 3.48 in. Compression ratio: 9.5:1 Brake horsepower: 245 at 4000 RPM. Torque: 340 lbs.-ft. at 3200 RPM. Five main bearings. Hydraulic valve lifters. Tuned-port fuel injection. ZR-1 V-8: 90-degree dual, overhead cam V-8. Cast aluminum block and head. Displacement: 350 cu. in. (5.7 liters). Bore & stroke: 3.90 x 3.66 in. Compression ratio: 11.0:1 Brake horsepower: 370 at 5800 RPM. Torque: 370 lbs.-ft. at 5600 RPM. Five main bearings. Hydraulic valve lifters. Tuned-port fuel injection.

CHASSIS DATA: Wheelbase: 96.2 in. Overall length: 176.5 in.; (ZR-1) 177.4 in. Height: (hatch) 46.7 in.; (conv) 46.4 in. Width: 71.0 in.; (ZR-1) 74.0 in. Front Tread: 59.6 in.; (ZR-1) 59.6 in. Rear Tread: 60.4 in.; (ZR-1) 61.9 in. Standard Tires: P275/40ZR17 Goodyear Eagle GT (ZR-1, 315/35ZR17 in rear).

1990 Corvette ZR1 coupe

TECHNICAL: Transmission: four-speed overdrive manual or automatic. **Steering:** rack and pinion (power assisted). **Suspension (front);** unequal-length control arms, single-leaf transverse spring and stablilizer bar. **Suspension (rear):** upper/lower control arms with five links, single-leaf transverse spring, stabilizer bar. **Brakes:** Anti-lock; power four-wheel disc. **Body construction:** fiberglass; separate ladder frame with cross-members. **Fuel tank:** 20.0 gal.

CORVETTE OPTIONS:
Preferred Equip. Grp. Incl Electronic Air cond; Elect Tuned Delco/Bose Music System (AM/FM Stereo w/Seek & Scan, Stereo Cass Tape & Digital Clock, special tone & balance control & 4 spkrs); Pwr 6-way, Driver's Seat ($1273). Pkg w/U1F Radio, Add ($396). Leather Bucket Seats ($425). Leather Adjustable Spt Bucket Seat ($1050). Solid Exterior Color, Paint (NC). Electronic Air Cond ($180). Performance Ratio Axle ($22). Luggage Carrier ($140). Eng Oil Cooler ($110). Calif Emission system ($100). Z51) Performance Handling Pkg Incl Engl Oil Cooler & H.D. Brakes ($460). (FX3) Electronic Selective Ride ($1695). Eng. Block Heater ($20). Low Tire Pressure Warning Indicator ($325). (UU8) Electronically Tuned Delco/Bose Music System (AM/FM Stereo w/Seek & Scan, Stereo Cass Tape & Digital Clock, special tone & balance control & 4 spkrs) ($823). (U1F) Elect tuned Delco-Bose Music System, (AM/FM Stereo w/Seek & Scan, Stereo Cass Tape, Compact Disc Player, Digital Clock special tone & balance control & 4 spkrs) ($1219). Roof Panels, Blue Tint or Bronze Tint ($615). Dual body color-keyed roof panel & Blue or Bronze Transparent Roof Panel ($915). Removable Hard Top ($1995). Pwr 6-way Seats, Driver's Side only ($270). Passenger side only ($270).

A WORD ABOUT OLD CHEVROLETS...

The market for cars more than 10 years is strong. Some buyers of pre-1980 cars are collectors who invest in vehicles likely to increase in value the older they get. Other buyers prefer the looks, size, performance and reliability of yesterday's better-built automobiles.

With a typical 1990 model selling for $12,000 or more, some Americans find themselves priced out of the new-car market. Late-model used cars are pricey too, although short on distinctive looks and roominess. The old cars may use a little more gas, but they cost a lot less.

New cars and late-model used cars depreciate rapidly in value. They can't tow large trailers or mobile homes. Their high-tech engineering is expensive to maintain or repair. In contrast, well-kept old cars are mechanically simpler, but very powerful. They appreciate in value as they grow more scarce and collectible. Insuring them is cheaper too.

Selecting a car and paying the right price for it are two considerations old car buyers face. What models did Chevrolet offer in 1958? Which '63 Chevy is worth the most today? What should one pay for a 1970 Impala convertible?

The Standard Catalog of Chevrolet 1912-1990 answers such questions. The Price Guide section shows most models made between 1912 and 1983. It helps to gauge what they sell for in six different, graded conditions. Models built since 1983 are generally considered "used cars" of which few, as yet, have achieved collectible status.

The price estimates contained in this book are current as of the reprint date, June 1991. After that date, more current prices may be obtained by referring to *Old Cars price Guide* which is available from Krause Publications, 700 E. State St., Iola, WI 54990, telephone (715) 445-2214.

HOW TO USE THE CHEVROLET PRICE GUIDE

On the following pages is a **CHEVROLET PRICE GUIDE.** The worth of an old car is a "ballpark" estimate at best. The estimates contained in this book are based upon national and regional data compiled by the editors of *Old Cars News & Marketplace* and *Old Cars Price Guide*. These data include actual bids and prices at collector car auctions and sales, classified and display advertising of such vehicles, verified reports of private sales and input from experts.

Price estimates are listed for cars in six different states of condition. These conditions (1-to-6) are illustrated and explained in the **VEHICLE CONDITION SCALE** on the following pages. Values are for complete vehicles — not parts cars — except as noted. Modified car values are not included, but can be estimated by figuring the cost of restoring the subject vehicle to original condition and adjusting the figures shown here accordingly.

Appearing below is a section of chart taken from the **CHEVROLET PRICE GUIDE** to illustrate the following elements:

A. MAKE The make of car, or marque name, appears in large, boldface type at the beginning of each value section.

B. DESCRIPTION The extreme left-hand column indicates vehicle year, model name, body type, engine configuration and, in some cases, wheelbase.

C. CONDITION CODE The six columns to the right are headed by the numbers one through six (1-6) which correspond to the conditions described in the **VEHICLE CONDITION SCALE** on the following page.

D. PRICE. The price estimates, in dollars, appear below their respective condition code headings and across from the vehicle descriptions.

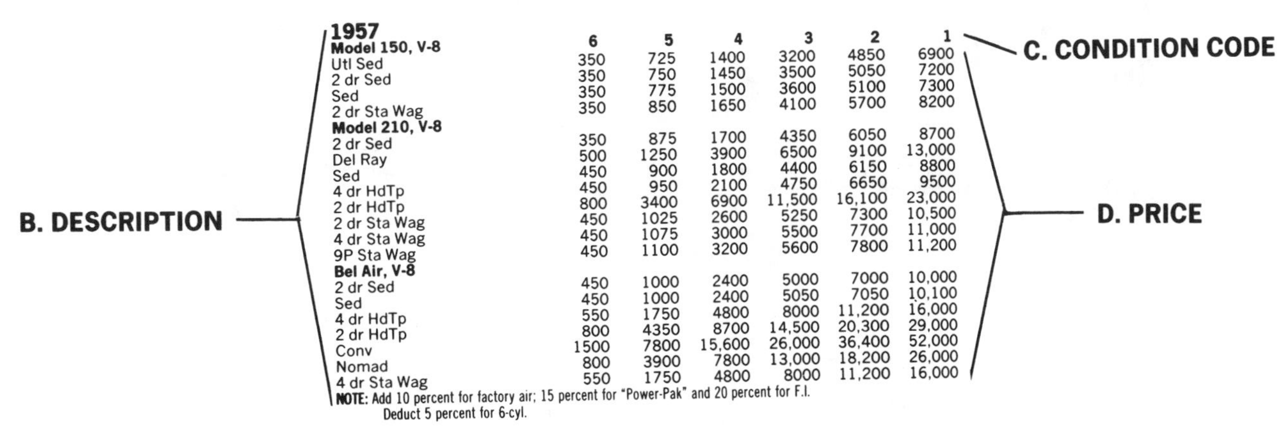

1957	6	5	4	3	2	1
Model 150, V-8						
Utl Sed	350	725	1400	3200	4850	6900
2 dr Sed	350	750	1450	3500	5050	7200
Sed	350	775	1500	3600	5100	7300
2 dr Sta Wag	350	850	1650	4100	5700	8200
Model 210, V-8						
2 dr Sed	350	875	1700	4350	6050	8700
Del Ray	500	1250	3900	6500	9100	13,000
Sed	450	900	1800	4400	6150	8800
4 dr HdTp	450	950	2100	4750	6650	9500
2 dr HdTp	800	3400	6900	11,500	16,100	23,000
2 dr Sta Wag	450	1025	2600	5250	7300	10,500
4 dr Sta Wag	450	1075	3000	5500	7700	11,000
9P Sta Wag	450	1100	3200	5600	7800	11,200
Bel Air, V-8						
2 dr Sed	450	1000	2400	5000	7000	10,000
Sed	450	1000	2400	5050	7050	10,100
4 dr HdTp	550	1750	4800	8000	11,200	16,000
2 dr HdTp	800	4350	8700	14,500	20,300	29,000
Conv	1500	7800	15,600	26,000	36,400	52,000
Nomad	800	3900	7800	13,000	18,200	26,000
4 dr Sta Wag	550	1750	4800	8000	11,200	16,000

NOTE: Add 10 percent for factory air; 15 percent for "Power-Pak" and 20 percent for F.I. Deduct 5 percent for 6-cyl.

VEHICLE CONDITION SCALE

1) EXCELLENT: Restored to current maxiumum professional standards of quality in every area, or perfect original with components operating and appearing as new. A 95-plus point show vehicle that is not driven.

2) FINE: Well-restored, or a combination of superior restoration and excellent original. Also, an *extremely* well-maintained original showing very minimal wear.

3) VERY GOOD: Completely operable original or "older restoration" showing wear. Also, a good amateur restoration, all presentable and serviceable inside and out. Plus, combinations of well-done restoration and good operable components or a partially restored vehicle with all parts necessary to complete and/or valuable NOS parts.

4) GOOD: A driveable vehicle needing no or only minor work to be functional. Also, a deteriorated restoration or a very poor amateur restoration. All components may need restoration to be "excellent," but the vehicle is mostly useable "as is."

5) RESTORABLE: Needs *complete* restoration of body, chassis and interior. May or may not be running, but isn't weathered, wrecked or stripped to the point of being useful only for parts.

6) PARTS VEHICLE: May or may not be running, but is weathered, wrecked and/or stripped to the point of being useful primarily for parts.

CHEVROLET PRICE GUIDE

CHEVROLET

	6	5	4	3	2	1
1912						
Classic Series, 6-cyl.						
Tr	1150	3700	6200	12,400	21,700	31,000
1913						
Classic Series, 6-cyl.						
Tr	1050	3400	5700	11,400	20,000	28,500
1914						
Series H2 & H4, 4-cyl.						
Rds	700	2150	3600	7200	12,600	18,000
Tr	700	2200	3700	7400	13,000	18,500
Series C, 6-cyl.						
Tr	850	2650	4400	8800	15,400	22,000
Series L, 6-cyl.						
Tr	800	2500	4200	8400	14,700	21,000
1915						
Series H2 & H4, 4-cyl.						
Rds	600	1900	3200	6400	11,200	16,000
Tr	700	2150	3600	7200	12,600	18,000
Series H3, 4-cyl.						
2P Rds	700	2300	3800	7600	13,300	19,000
Series L, 6-cyl.						
Tr	750	2400	4000	8000	14,000	20,000
1916						
Series 490, 4-cyl.						
Tr	650	2050	3400	6800	11,900	17,000
Series H2, 4-cyl.						
Rds	600	2000	3300	6600	11,600	16,500
Torp Rds	700	2150	3600	7200	12,600	18,000
Series H4, 4-cyl.						
Tr	700	2300	3800	7600	13,300	19,000
1917						
Series F2 & F5, 4-cyl.						
Rds	650	2050	3400	6800	11,900	17,000
Tr	700	2150	3600	7200	12,600	18,000
Series 490, 4-cyl.						
Rds	600	1900	3200	6400	11,200	16,000
Tr	600	1900	3200	6400	11,200	16,000
HT Tr	650	2050	3400	6800	11,900	17,000
Series D2 & D5, V-8						
Rds	750	2400	4000	8000	14,000	20,000
Tr	800	2500	4200	8400	14,700	21,000
1918						
Series 490, 4-cyl.						
Tr	650	2050	3400	6800	11,900	17,000
Rds	600	1900	3200	6400	11,200	16,000
Cpe	350	840	1400	2800	4900	7000
Sed	200	720	1200	2400	4200	6000
Series FA, 4-cyl.						
Rds	650	2050	3400	6800	11,900	17,000
Tr	700	2150	3600	7200	12,600	18,000
Sed	350	840	1400	2800	4900	7000
Series D, V-8						
4P Rds	800	2500	4200	8400	14,700	21,000
Tr	850	2650	4400	8800	15,400	22,000
1919						
Series 490, 4-cyl.						
Rds	500	1550	2600	5200	9100	13,000
Tr	550	1700	2800	5600	9800	14,000
Sed	200	720	1200	2400	4200	6000
Cpe	350	780	1300	2600	4550	6500
Series FB, 4-cyl.						
Rds	550	1800	3000	6000	10,500	15,000
Tr	600	1900	3200	6400	11,200	16,000
Cpe	350	975	1600	3200	5600	8000
2d Sed	350	900	1500	3000	5250	7500
4d Sed	350	840	1400	2800	4900	7000
1920						
Series 490, 4-cyl.						
Rds	500	1550	2600	5200	9100	13,000
Tr	550	1700	2800	5600	9800	14,000
Sed	350	900	1500	3000	5250	7500
Cpe	350	975	1600	3200	5600	8000
Series FB, 4-cyl.						
Rds	550	1800	3000	6000	10,500	15,000
Tr	600	1900	3200	6400	11,200	16,000
Sed	350	1020	1700	3400	5950	8500
Cpe	450	1080	1800	3600	6300	9000
Cpe	100	300	500	1000	1750	2500
1921						
Series 490, 4-cyl.						
Rds	650	2050	3400	6800	11,900	17,000
Tr	650	2050	3400	6800	11,900	17,000
Cpe	350	975	1600	3200	5600	8000
C-D Sed	350	1020	1700	3400	5950	8500
Series FB, 4-cyl.						
Rds	650	2100	3500	7000	12,300	17,500
Tr	700	2150	3600	7200	12,600	18,000
Cpe	350	1020	1700	3400	5950	8500
4d Sed	350	1020	1700	3400	5950	8500
1922						
Series 490, 4-cyl.						
Rds	650	2050	3400	6800	11,900	17,000
Tr	700	2150	3600	7200	12,600	18,000
Cpe	350	975	1600	3200	5600	8000
Utl Cpe	200	660	1100	2200	3850	5500
Sed	350	1020	1700	3400	5950	8500
Series FB, 4-cyl.						
Rds	650	2050	3400	6800	11,900	17,000
Tr	700	2150	3600	7200	12,600	18,000

	6	5	4	3	2	1
Sed	350	1020	1700	3400	5950	8500
Cpe	450	1080	1800	3600	6300	9000
1923						
Superior B, 4-cyl.						
Rds	650	2050	3400	6800	11,900	17,000
Tr	700	2150	3600	7200	12,600	18,000
Sed	350	840	1400	2800	4900	7000
2d Sed	350	840	1400	2800	4900	7000
Utl Cpe	350	900	1500	3000	5250	7500
DeL Tr	400	1300	2200	4400	7700	11,000
1924						
Superior, 4-cyl.						
Rds	650	2050	3400	6800	11,900	17,000
Tr	700	2150	3600	7200	12,600	18,000
DeL Tr	700	2200	3700	7400	13,000	18,500
Sed	200	720	1200	2400	4200	6000
DeL Sed	200	750	1275	2500	4400	6300
2P Cpe	350	780	1300	2600	4550	6500
4P Cpe	200	720	1200	2400	4200	6000
DeL Cpe	350	800	1350	2700	4700	6700
2d Sed	200	720	1200	2400	4200	6000
1925						
Superior K, 4-cyl.						
Rds	800	2500	4200	8400	14,700	21,000
Tr	850	2650	4400	8800	15,400	22,000
Cpe	350	840	1400	2800	4900	7000
Sed	350	780	1300	2600	4550	6500
2d Sed	350	770	1300	2550	4480	6400
1926						
Superior V, 4-cyl.						
Rds	800	2500	4200	8400	14,700	21,000
Tr	850	2650	4400	8800	15,400	22,000
Cpe	350	840	1400	2800	4900	7000
Sed	350	780	1300	2600	4550	6500
2d Sed	350	770	1300	2550	4480	6400
Lan Sed	350	975	1600	3200	5600	8000
1927						
Model AA, 4-cyl.						
Rds	800	2500	4200	8400	14,700	21,000
Tr	850	2650	4400	8800	15,400	22,000
Utl Cpe	350	800	1350	2700	4700	6700
2d Sed	350	820	1400	2700	4760	6800
Sed	350	840	1400	2800	4900	7000
Lan Sed	350	870	1450	2900	5100	7300
Cabr	650	2050	3400	6800	11,900	17,000
Imp Lan	550	1800	3000	6000	10,500	15,000
1928						
Model AB, 4-cyl.						
Rds	800	2500	4200	8400	14,700	21,000
Tr	850	2650	4400	8800	15,400	22,000
Utl Cpe	350	870	1450	2900	5100	7300
Sed	350	900	1500	3000	5250	7500
2d Sed	350	840	1400	2800	4900	7000
Cabr	700	2150	3600	7200	12,600	18,000
Imp Lan	550	1800	3000	6000	10,500	15,000
Conv Cabr	700	2300	3800	7600	13,300	19,000
1929						
Model AC, 6-cyl.						
Rds	850	2650	4400	8800	15,400	22,000
Tr	850	2750	4600	9200	16,100	23,000
Cpe	500	1550	2600	5200	9100	13,000
Spt Cpe	550	1700	2800	5600	9800	14,000
Sed	400	1300	2200	4400	7700	11,000
Imp Sed	450	1450	2400	4800	8400	12,000
Conv Lan	700	2300	3800	7600	13,300	19,000
2d Sed	400	1300	2200	4400	7700	11,000
Conv Cabr	750	2400	4000	8000	14,000	20,000
1930						
Model AD, 6-cyl.						
Rds	850	2750	4600	9200	16,100	23,000
Spt Rds	900	2900	4800	9600	16,800	24,000
Phae	900	2900	4800	9600	16,800	24,000
2d Sed	400	1300	2200	4400	7700	11,000
Cpe	500	1550	2600	5200	9100	13,000
Spt Cpe	550	1700	2800	5600	9800	14,000
Clb Sed	450	1500	2500	5000	8800	12,500
Spec Sed	450	1450	2400	4800	8400	12,000
Sed	450	1400	2300	4600	8100	11,500
Con Lan	700	2300	3800	7600	13,300	19,000
1931						
Model AE, 6-cyl.						
Rds	900	2900	4800	9600	16,800	24,000
Spt Rds	1000	3100	5200	10,400	18,200	26,000
Cabr	850	2750	4600	9200	16,100	23,000
Phae	900	2900	4800	9600	16,800	24,000
2d Sed	450	1450	2400	4800	8400	12,000
5P Cpe	550	1700	2800	5600	9800	14,000
5W Cpe	550	1800	3000	6000	10,500	15,000
Spt Cpe	650	2050	3400	6800	11,900	17,000
Cpe	600	1900	3200	6400	11,200	16,000
2d DeL Sed	550	1700	2800	5600	9800	14,000
Sed	450	1500	2500	5000	8800	12,500
Spl Sed	500	1600	2700	5400	9500	13,500
Lan Phae	950	3000	5000	10,000	17,500	25,000
1932						
Model BA Standard, 6-cyl.						
Rds	1000	3100	5200	10,400	18,200	26,000
Phae	1000	3100	5200	10,400	18,200	26,000
Lan Phae	950	3000	5000	10,000	17,500	25,000
3W Cpe	650	2050	3400	6800	11,900	17,000
5W Cpe	700	2150	3600	7200	12,600	18,000

	6	5	4	3	2	1
Spt Cpe	700	2300	3800	7600	13,300	19,000
2d Sed	500	1550	2600	5200	9100	13,000
Sed	550	1700	2800	5600	9800	14,000
5P Cpe	700	2150	3600	7200	12,600	18,000
Model BA DeLuxe, 6-cyl.						
Spt Rds	1000	3250	5400	10,800	18,900	27,000
Lan Phae	1000	3100	5200	10,400	18,200	26,000
Cabr	950	3000	5000	10,000	17,500	25,000
3W Bus Cpe	700	2150	3600	7200	12,600	18,000
5W Cpe	700	2300	3800	7600	13,300	19,000
Spt Cpe	750	2400	4000	8000	14,000	20,000
2d Sed	550	1700	2800	5600	9800	14,000
Sed	550	1800	3000	6000	10,500	15,000
Spl Sed	600	1900	3200	6400	11,200	16,000
5P Cpe	700	2300	3800	7600	13,300	19,000
1933						
Mercury, 6-cyl.						
2P Cpe	400	1200	2000	4000	7000	10,000
RS Cpe	400	1300	2200	4400	7700	11,000
2d Sed	350	1020	1700	3400	5950	8500
Master Eagle, 6-cyl.						
Spt Rds	900	2900	4800	9600	16,800	24,000
Phae	950	3000	5000	10,000	17,500	25,000
2P Cpe	400	1200	2000	4000	7000	10,000
Spt Cpe	400	1300	2200	4400	7700	11,000
2d Sed	450	1050	1750	3550	6150	8800
2d Trk Sed	450	1080	1800	3600	6300	9000
Sed	450	1080	1800	3600	6300	9000
Conv	700	2200	3700	7400	13,000	18,500
1934						
Standard, 6-cyl.						
Sed	350	1020	1700	3400	5950	8500
Spt Rds	800	2500	4200	8400	14,700	21,000
Phae	850	2650	4400	8800	15,400	22,000
Cpe	400	1200	2000	4000	7000	10,000
2d Sed	350	1020	1700	3400	5900	8400
Master, 6-cyl.						
Spt Rds	850	2650	4400	8800	15,400	22,000
Bus Cpe	400	1200	2000	4000	7000	10,000
Spt Cpe	400	1250	2100	4200	7400	10,500
2d Sed	450	1090	1800	3650	6400	9100
Twn Sed	950	1100	1850	3700	6450	9200
Sed	450	1130	1900	3800	6600	9400
Conv	750	2400	4000	8000	14,000	20,000
1935						
Standard, 6-cyl.						
Rds	650	2050	3400	6800	11,900	17,000
Phae	700	2300	3800	7600	13,300	19,000
Cpe	450	1140	1900	3800	6650	9500
2d Sed	350	1020	1700	3400	5950	8500
Sed	450	1050	1750	3550	6150	8800
Master, 6-cyl.						
5W Cpe	400	1200	2000	4000	7000	10,000
Spt Cpe	400	1250	2100	4200	7400	10,500
2d Sed	350	1040	1750	3500	6100	8700
Sed	450	1080	1800	3600	6300	9000
Spt Sed	950	1100	1850	3700	6450	9200
Twn Sed	450	1050	1750	3550	6150	8800
1936						
Standard, 6-cyl.						
Cpe	450	1140	1900	3800	6650	9500
Sed	350	1020	1700	3400	5950	8500
Spt Sed	450	1050	1750	3550	6150	8800
2d Sed	350	1020	1700	3400	5900	8400
Cpe PU	450	1170	1975	3900	6850	9800
Conv	450	1450	2400	4800	8400	12,000
Master, 6-cyl.						
5W Cpe	400	1200	2000	4000	7000	10,000
Spt Cpe	400	1250	2100	4200	7400	10,500
2d Sed	350	1040	1750	3500	6100	8700
Twn Sed	450	1050	1750	3550	6150	8800
Sed	450	1050	1800	3600	6200	8900
Spt Sed	450	1080	1800	3600	6300	9000
1937						
Master, 6-cyl.						
Conv	900	2900	4800	9600	16,800	24,000
Cpe	450	1160	1950	3900	6800	9700
Cpe PU	400	1250	2050	4100	7200	10,300
2d Sed	450	1050	1800	3600	6200	8900
2d Twn Sed	450	1080	1800	3600	6300	9000
4d Trk Sed	450	1050	1800	3600	6200	8900
4d Spt Sed	450	1080	1800	3600	6300	9000
Master DeLuxe, 6-cyl.						
Cpe	400	1250	2050	4100	7200	10,300
Spt Cpe	400	1250	2100	4200	7400	10,500
2d Sed	450	1080	1800	3600	6300	9000
2d Twn Sed	450	1090	1800	3650	6400	9100
4d Trk Sed	450	1080	1800	3600	6300	9000
4d Spt Sed	450	1090	1800	3650	6400	9100
1938						
Master, 6-cyl.						
Conv	950	3000	5000	10,000	17,500	25,000
Cpe	450	1160	1950	3900	6800	9700
Cpe PU	400	1250	2050	4100	7200	10,300
2d Sed	450	1080	1800	3600	6300	9000
2d Twn Sed	450	1090	1800	3650	6400	9100
4d Sed	450	1080	1800	3600	6300	9000
4d Spt Sed	450	1090	1800	3650	6400	9100
Master DeLuxe, 6-cyl.						
Cpe	400	1250	2100	4200	7400	10,500
Spt Cpe	400	1300	2150	4300	7500	10,700
2d Sed	450	1090	1800	3650	6400	9100
2d Twn Sed	950	1100	1850	3700	6450	9200
4d Sed	450	1090	1800	3650	6400	9100
4d Spt Sed	950	1100	1850	3700	6450	9200
1939						
Master 85, 6-cyl.						
Cpe	450	1170	1975	3900	6850	9800
2d Sed	450	1120	1875	3750	6500	9300
2d Twn Sed	450	1130	1900	3800	6600	9400
4d Sed	450	1120	1875	3750	6500	9300
4d Spt Sed	450	1130	1900	3800	6600	9400
Sta Wag	850	2650	4400	8800	15,400	22,000
Master DeLuxe, 6-cyl.						
Cpe	400	1250	2050	4100	7200	10,300
Spt Cpe	400	1250	2100	4200	7400	10,600
2d Sed	400	1250	2050	4100	7200	10,300

	6	5	4	3	2	1
2d Twn Sed	400	1250	2100	4200	7300	10,400
4d Sed	400	1250	2050	4100	7200	10,300
4d Spt Sed	400	1250	2100	4200	7300	10,400
Sta Wag	750	2400	4000	8000	14,000	20,000
1940						
Master 85, 6-cyl.						
Cpe	400	1200	2000	4000	7000	10,000
2d Twn Sed	450	1150	1900	3850	6700	9600
4d Spt Sed	450	1140	1900	3800	6650	9500
Sta Wag	950	3000	5000	10,000	17,500	25,000
Master DeLuxe, 6-cyl.						
Cpe	400	1250	2100	4200	7400	10,500
Spt Cpe	400	1300	2200	4400	7700	11,000
2d Twn Sed	400	1200	2000	4000	7000	10,000
4d Spt Sed	400	1200	2000	4000	7000	10,000
Special DeLuxe, 6-cyl.						
Cpe	400	1300	2200	4400	7700	11,000
Spt Cpe	450	1400	2300	4600	8100	11,500
2d Twn Sed	400	1250	2100	4200	7400	10,500
4d Spt Sed	400	1250	2100	4200	7300	10,400
Conv	800	2500	4200	8400	14,700	21,000
Sta Wag	1000	3100	5200	10,400	18,200	26,000
1941						
Master DeLuxe, 6-cyl.						
2P Cpe	400	1200	2000	4000	7000	10,000
4P Cpe	400	1250	2100	4200	7400	10,500
2d Twn Sed	450	1130	1900	3800	6600	9400
4d Spt Sed	450	1120	1875	3750	6500	9300
Special DeLuxe, 6-cyl.						
2P Cpe	400	1300	2200	4400	7700	11,000
4P Cpe	450	1450	2400	4800	8400	12,000
2d Sed	400	1250	2100	4200	7400	10,600
4d Spt Sed	400	1250	2100	4200	7400	10,500
4d Flt Sed	400	1300	2200	4400	7700	11,000
Conv	850	2750	4600	9200	16,100	23,000
Sta Wag	1050	3350	5600	11,200	19,600	28,000
Cpe PU	450	1450	2400	4800	8400	12,000
1942						
Master DeLuxe, 6-cyl.						
2P Cpe	400	1200	2000	4000	7000	10,000
4P Cpe	400	1200	2050	4100	7100	10,200
Cpe PU	400	1250	2100	4200	7400	10,500
2d Twn Sed	450	1050	1750	3550	6150	8800
4d Twn Sed	450	1050	1750	3550	6150	8800
Special DeLuxe, 6-cyl.						
2P Cpe	400	1250	2100	4200	7400	10,500
5P Cpe	400	1300	2150	4300	7500	10,700
2d Twn Sed	450	1090	1800	3650	6400	9100
4d Spt Sed	450	1080	1800	3600	6300	9000
Conv	850	2650	4400	8800	15,400	22,000
Sta Wag	1000	3100	5200	10,400	18,200	26,000
Fleetline, 6-cyl.						
2d Aero	400	1250	2100	4200	7400	10,500
4d Spt Mstr	400	1200	2050	4100	7100	10,200
1946-1948						
Stylemaster, 6-cyl.						
Bus Cpe	450	1140	1900	3800	6650	9500
Spt Cpe	450	1160	1950	3900	6800	9700
2d Twn Sed	450	1050	1800	3600	6200	8900
4d Spt Sed	450	1050	1750	3550	6150	8800
Fleetmaster, 6-cyl.						
Spt Cpe	400	1200	2000	4000	7000	10,000
2d Twn Sed	450	1090	1800	3650	6400	9100
4d Spt Sed	450	1080	1800	3600	6300	9000
Conv	1000	3250	5400	10,800	18,900	27,000
Sta Wag	950	3000	5000	10,000	17,500	25,000
Fleetline, 6-cyl.						
2d Aero	400	1200	2000	4000	7000	10,000
4d Spt Mstr	450	1170	1975	3900	6850	9800
1949-1950						
Styleline Special, 6-cyl.						
Bus Cpe	450	1080	1800	3600	6300	9000
Spt Cpe	450	1130	1900	3800	6600	9400
2d Sed	350	1000	1650	3300	5750	8200
4d Sed	350	975	1600	3250	5700	8100
Fleetline Special, 6-cyl.						
2d Sed	350	1000	1650	3350	5800	8300
4d Sed	350	1000	1650	3300	5750	8200
Styleline DeLuxe, 6-cyl.						
Spt Cpe	400	1200	2000	4000	7000	10,000
2d Sed	350	1040	1750	3500	6100	8700
4d Sed	350	1040	1700	3450	6000	8600
2d HT Bel Air (1950 only)	550	1700	2800	5600	9800	14,000
Conv	850	2750	4600	9200	16,100	23,000
Woodie Wag (1949 only)	650	2050	3400	6800	11,900	17,000
Mtl Sta Wag	450	1450	2400	4800	8400	12,000
Fleetline DeLuxe, 6-cyl.						
2d Sed	450	1050	1750	3550	6150	8800
4d Sed	350	1040	1750	3500	6100	8700
1951-1952						
Styleline Special, 6-cyl.						
Bus Cpe	450	1090	1800	3650	6400	9100
Spt Cpe	450	1140	1900	3800	6650	9500
2d Sed	350	1000	1650	3350	5800	8300
4d Sed	350	1000	1650	3300	5750	8200
Styleline DeLuxe, 6-cyl.						
Spt Cpe	400	1200	2000	4000	7000	10,000
2d Sed	450	1050	1750	3550	6150	8800
4d Sed	350	1040	1750	3500	6100	8700
2d HT Bel Air	550	1700	2800	5600	9800	14,000
Conv	850	2750	4600	9200	16,100	23,000
Fleetline Special, 6-cyl						
2d Sed (1951 only)	350	1020	1700	3400	5900	8400
4d Sed (1951 only)	350	1000	1650	3350	5800	8300
Sta Wag	450	1450	2400	4800	8400	12,000
Fleetline DeLuxe, 6-cyl.						
2d Sed	450	1090	1800	3650	6400	9100
4d Sed (1951 only)	450	1050	1800	3600	6200	8900
1953						
Special 150, 6-cyl.						
Bus Cpe	350	880	1500	2950	5180	7400
Clb Cpe	350	950	1500	3050	5300	7600
2d Sed	350	860	1450	2900	5050	7200
4d Sed	350	850	1450	2850	4970	7100
Sta Wag	400	1200	2000	4000	7000	10,000

	6	5	4	3	2	1
DeLuxe 210, 6-cyl.						
Clb Cpe	450	1140	1900	3800	6650	9500
2d Sed	350	1020	1700	3400	5950	8500
4d Sed	350	1020	1700	3400	5900	8400
2d HT	550	1700	2800	5600	9800	14,000
Conv	950	3000	5000	10,000	17,500	25,000
Sta Wag	400	1250	2100	4200	7400	10,500
210 Townsman Sta Wag	400	1300	2150	4300	7500	10,700
Bel Air						
2d Sed	450	1150	1900	3850	6700	9600
4d Sed	450	1140	1900	3800	6650	9500
2d HT	550	1700	2800	5600	9800	14,000
Conv	1050	3350	5600	11,200	19,600	28,000

1954

	6	5	4	3	2	1
Special 150, 6-cyl.						
2d Utl Sed	350	840	1400	2800	4900	7000
2d Sed	350	860	1450	2900	5050	7200
4d Sed	350	850	1450	2850	4970	7100
Sta Wag	400	1200	2000	4000	7000	10,000
Special 210, 6-cyl.						
2d Sed	350	1020	1700	3400	5950	8500
2d Sed Delray	400	1200	2000	4000	7000	10,000
4d Sed	350	1020	1700	3400	5900	8400
Sta Wag	400	1250	2100	4200	7400	10,500
Bel Air, 6-cyl.						
2d Sed	450	1140	1900	3800	6650	9500
4d Sed	450	1130	1900	3800	6600	9400
2d HT	650	2050	3400	6800	11,900	17,000
Conv	1100	3500	5800	11,600	20,300	29,000
Sta Wag	500	1550	2600	5200	9100	13,000

1955

	6	5	4	3	2	1
Model 150, V-8						
2d Utl Sed	350	900	1500	3000	5250	7500
2d Sed	350	975	1600	3250	5700	8100
4d Sed	350	975	1600	3200	5600	8000
Sta Wag	400	1200	2000	4000	7000	10,000
Model 210, V-8						
2d Sed	450	1140	1900	3800	6650	9500
2d Sed Delray	400	1300	2200	4400	7700	11,000
4d Sed	450	1080	1800	3600	6300	9000
2d HT	550	1800	3000	6000	10,500	15,000
2d Sta Wag	400	1350	2250	4500	7800	11,200
4d Sta Wag	400	1300	2200	4400	7700	11,000
Bel Air, V-8						
2d Sed	450	1450	2450	4900	8500	12,200
4d Sed	450	1450	2400	4800	8400	12,000
2d HT	950	3000	5000	10,000	17,500	25,000
Conv	1350	4300	7200	14,400	25,200	36,000
Nomad	700	2300	3800	7600	13,300	19,000
4d Sta Wag	500	1550	2600	5200	9100	13,000

NOTE: Add 10 percent for A/C; 15 percent for "Power-Pak".
Deduct 10 percent for 6-cyl.

1956

	6	5	4	3	2	1
Model 150, V-8						
2d Utl Sed	350	975	1600	3200	5600	8000
2d Sed	350	1020	1700	3400	5950	8500
4d Sed	350	1000	1650	3350	5800	8300
Sta Wag	400	1200	2000	4000	7000	10,000
Model 210, V-8						
2d Sed	450	1140	1900	3800	6650	9500
2d Sed Delray	450	1400	2300	4600	8100	11,500
4d Sed	450	1140	1900	3800	6650	9500
4d HT	400	1200	2050	4100	7100	10,200
2d HT	550	1800	3000	6000	10,500	15,000
2 dr Sta Wag	400	1250	2050	4100	7200	10,300
4d Sta Wag	400	1200	2000	4000	7000	10,000
9P Sta Wag	400	1200	2000	4000	7100	10,100
Bel Air, V-8						
2d Sed	400	1300	2200	4400	7700	11,000
4d Sed	400	1300	2200	4400	7700	11,000
4d HT	450	1450	2400	4800	8400	12,000
2d HT	900	2900	4800	9600	16,800	24,000
Conv	1300	4200	7000	14,000	24,500	35,000
Nomad	600	1900	3200	6400	11,200	16,000
4d Sta Wag	450	1500	2500	5000	8800	12,500

NOTE: Add 10 percent for A/C; 15 percent for "Power-Pak".
Deduct 10 percent for 6-cyl.

1957

	6	5	4	3	2	1
Model 150, V-8						
2d Utl Sed	350	975	1600	3200	5600	8000
2d Sed	350	1000	1650	3350	5800	8300
4d Sed	350	1000	1650	3350	5800	8300
2d Sta Wag	450	1140	1900	3800	6650	9500
Model 210, V-8						
2d Sed	400	1200	2000	4000	7000	10,000
2d Sed Delray	450	1400	2300	4600	8100	11,500
4d Sed	450	1140	1900	3800	6650	9500
4d HT	400	1200	2000	4000	7000	10,000
2d HT	500	1550	2600	5200	9100	13,000
2d Sta Wag	450	1400	2300	4600	8100	11,500
4d Sta Wag	400	1300	2200	4400	7700	11,000
9P Sta Wag	400	1350	2200	4400	7800	11,100
Bel Air, V-8						
2d Sed	450	1450	2400	4800	8400	12,000
4d Sed	450	1400	2350	4700	8300	11,800
4d HT	500	1550	2600	5200	9100	13,000
2d HT	1050	3350	5600	11,200	19,600	28,000
Conv	1600	5150	8600	17,200	30,100	43,000
Nomad	700	2150	3600	7200	12,600	18,000
4d Sta Wag	500	1500	2550	5100	8900	12,700

NOTE: Add 10 percent for A/C; 15 percent for "Power-Pak" and 20 percent for F.I.
Deduct 10 percent for 6-cyl.

1958

	6	5	4	3	2	1
Delray, V-8						
2d Utl Sed	200	750	1275	2500	4400	6300
2d Sed	350	780	1300	2600	4550	6500
4d Sed	350	780	1300	2600	4550	6500
Biscayne, V-8						
2d Sed	350	800	1350	2700	4700	6700
4d Sed	350	790	1350	2650	4620	6600
Bel Air, V-8						
2d Sed	450	1140	1900	3800	6650	9500
4d Sed	450	1150	1900	3850	6700	9600
4d HT	400	1200	2000	4000	7000	10,000
2d HT	500	1550	2600	5200	9100	13,000
Impala	1050	3350	5600	11,200	19,600	28,000
Imp Conv	1600	5150	8600	17,200	30,100	43,000
Station Wagons, V-8						
2d Yeo	450	1090	1800	3650	6400	9100
4d Yeo	450	1080	1800	3600	6300	9000
6P Brookwood	450	1120	1875	3750	6500	9300
9P Brookwood	450	1130	1900	3800	6600	9400
4d Nomad	400	1300	2200	4400	7700	11,000

NOTE: Add 10 percent for Power-Pak & dual exhaust on 283 V-8.
Add 20 percent for 348.
Add 30 percent for 348 Tri-Power set up.
Add 15 percent for A/C.
Deduct 10 percent for 6-cyl.

1959

	6	5	4	3	2	1
Biscayne, V-8						
2d Utl Sed	200	720	1200	2400	4200	6000
2d Sed	200	745	1250	2500	4340	6200
4d Sed	200	750	1275	2500	4400	6300
Bel Air, V-8						
2d Sed	350	800	1350	2700	4700	6700
4d Sed	350	820	1400	2700	4760	6800
4d HT	350	840	1400	2800	4900	7000
Impala, V-8						
4d Sed	350	840	1400	2800	4900	7000
4d HT	450	1120	1875	3750	6500	9300
2d HT	650	2050	3400	6800	11,900	17,000
Conv	950	3000	5000	10,000	17,500	25,000
Station Wagons, V-8						
Brookwood	350	975	1600	3200	5600	8000
Parkwood	350	1020	1700	3400	5900	8400
Kingswood	450	1080	1800	3600	6300	9000
4d Nomad	450	1140	1900	3800	6650	9500

NOTE: Add 20 percent for speed options and 10 percent for A/C.
Add 5 percent for 4-speed transmission.
Deduct 10 percent for 6-cyl.
Add 30 percent for 348 Tri-Power set up.

1960

	6	5	4	3	2	1
Biscayne, V-8						
2d Utl Sed	200	670	1200	2300	4060	5800
2d Sed	200	730	1250	2450	4270	6100
4d Sed	200	745	1250	2500	4340	6200
Biscayne Fleetmaster, V-8						
2d Sed	200	750	1275	2500	4400	6300
4d Sed	350	770	1300	2550	4480	6400
Bel Air, V-8						
2d Sed	350	820	1400	2700	4760	6800
4d Sed	350	830	1400	2950	4830	6900
4d HT	350	870	1450	2900	5100	7300
2d HT	450	1080	1800	3600	6300	9000
Impala, V-8						
4d Sed	350	870	1450	2900	5100	7300
4d HT	450	1050	1750	3550	6150	8800
2d HT	600	1900	3200	6400	11,200	16,000
Conv	900	2900	4800	9600	16,800	24,000
Station Wagons, V-8						
Brookwood	350	975	1600	3200	5600	8000
4d Kingswood	350	1000	1650	3350	5800	8300
4d Parkwood	350	1020	1700	3400	5950	8500
4d Nomad	450	1080	1800	3600	6300	9000

NOTE: Add 20 percent for speed options and 10 percent for A/C.
Deduct 10 percent for 6-cyl.
Add 30 percent for 348 Tri-Power set up.

1961

	6	5	4	3	2	1
Biscayne, V-8						
2d Utl Sed	200	700	1200	2350	4130	5900
2d Sed	350	780	1300	2600	4550	6500
4d Sed	200	730	1250	2450	4270	6100
Bel Air, V-8						
2d Sed	350	800	1350	2700	4700	6700
4d Sed	350	790	1350	2650	4620	6600
4d HT	350	975	1600	3200	5600	8000
2d HT	500	1550	2600	5200	9100	13,000
Impala, V-8						
2d Sed	350	840	1400	2800	4900	7000
4d Sed	350	850	1450	2850	4970	7100
4d HT	350	1020	1700	3400	5950	8500
2d HT*	550	1700	2800	5600	9800	14,000
Conv*	800	2500	4200	8400	14,700	21,000
Station Wagons, V-8						
Brookwood	350	900	1500	3000	5250	7500
Parkwood	350	975	1600	3200	5600	8000
Nomad	450	1080	1800	3600	6300	9000

NOTE: Add 10 percent for Power-Pak & dual exhaust on 283 V-8.
Add 15 percent for A/C.
Add 35 percent for 348 CID.
*Add 20 percent for Super Sport option.
Add 50 percent for 409 V-8.
Deduct 10 percent for 6-cyl.

1962

	6	5	4	3	2	1
Chevy II, 4 & 6-cyl.						
2d Sed	200	730	1250	2450	4270	6100
4d Sed	200	720	1200	2400	4200	6000
2d HT	400	1200	2000	4000	7000	10,000
Conv	450	1450	2400	4800	8400	12,000
Sta Wag	350	900	1500	3000	5250	7500
Biscayne, V-8						
2d Sed	350	770	1300	2550	4480	6400
4d Sed	350	780	1300	2600	4550	6500
Sta Wag	350	870	1450	2900	5100	7300
Bel Air, V-8						
2d Sed	350	790	1350	2650	4620	6600
4d Sed	350	800	1350	2700	4700	6700
2d HT	500	1550	2600	5200	9100	13,000
Sta Wag	450	1080	1800	3600	6300	9000
Bel Air 409 muscle car						
2d Sed (380 HP)	550	1700	2800	5600	9800	14,000
2d HT (380 HP)	900	2900	4800	9600	16,800	24,000
2d Sed (409 HP)	600	1900	3200	6400	11,200	16,000
2d HT (409 HP)	1000	3100	5200	10,400	18,200	26,000
Impala, V-8						
4d Sed	350	840	1400	2800	4900	7000
4d HT	450	1080	1800	3600	6300	9000
2d HT*	600	1900	3200	6400	11,200	16,000
Conv*	850	2650	4400	8800	15,400	22,000
Sta Wag	400	1200	2000	4000	7000	10,000

***NOTE:** Add 15 percent for Super Sport option.
Add 15 percent for Power-Pak & dual exhaust.
Add 15 percent for A/C.
Add 35 percent for 409 CID.
Deduct 10 percent for 6-cyl except Chevy II.

1963

	6	5	4	3	2	1
Chevy II and Nova, 4 & 6-cyl.						
4d Sed	200	660	1100	2200	3850	5500
2d HT*	450	1080	1800	3600	6300	9000
Conv*	450	1450	2400	4800	8400	12,000
Sta Wag	350	840	1400	2800	4900	7000

***NOTE:** Add 15 percent for Super Sport option.

	6	5	4	3	2	1
Biscayne, V-8						
2d Sed	200	660	1100	2200	3850	5500
4d Sed	200	670	1150	2250	3920	5600
Sta Wag	350	780	1300	2600	4550	6500
Bel Air, V-8						
2d Sed	200	670	1150	2250	3920	5600
4d Sed	200	685	1150	2300	3990	5700
Sta Wag	350	840	1400	2800	4900	7000
Impala, V-8						
4d Sed	350	840	1400	2800	4900	7000
4d HT	450	1080	1800	3600	6300	9000
2d HT*	650	2050	3400	6800	11,900	17,000
Conv*	750	2400	4000	8000	14,000	20,000
Sta Wag	450	1080	1800	3600	6300	9000

NOTE: Add 15 percent for Power-Pak & dual exhaust.
Add 15 percent for A/C.
Add 35 percent for 409 CID.
Add 15 percent for Super Sport option.
Deduct 10 percent for 6-cyl except Chevy II.

1964

	6	5	4	3	2	1
Chevy II and Nova, 4 & 6-cyl.						
2d Sed	200	660	1100	2200	3850	5500
4d Sed	200	670	1150	2250	3920	5600
2d HT	950	1100	1850	3700	6450	9200
Sta Wag	350	860	1450	2900	5050	7200

NOTE: Add 10 percent for 6-cyl.

	6	5	4	3	2	1
Nova Super Sport Series, 6-cyl.						
2d HT	500	1550	2600	5200	9100	13,000

NOTE: Add 25 percent for V8.
Add 10 percent for 4 speed trans.

	6	5	4	3	2	1
Chevelle						
2d Sed	200	660	1100	2200	3850	5500
4d Sed	200	670	1150	2250	3920	5600
2d Sta Wag	350	770	1300	2550	4480	6400
4d Sta Wag	200	745	1250	2500	4340	6200
Malibu Series, V-8						
4d Sed	200	670	1150	2250	3920	5600
2d HT*	550	1700	2800	5600	9800	14,000
Conv*	750	2400	4000	8000	14,000	20,000
4d Sta Wag	350	840	1400	2800	4900	7000

NOTE: Add 15 percent for Super Sport option.
Deduct 10 percent for 6-cyl.

	6	5	4	3	2	1
Biscayne, V-8						
2d Sed	200	660	1100	2200	3850	5500
4d Sed	200	670	1150	2250	3920	5600
Sta Wag	350	780	1300	2600	4550	6500
Bel Air, V-8						
2d Sed	200	670	1150	2250	3920	5600
4d Sed	200	685	1150	2300	3990	5700
Sta Wag	350	840	1400	2800	4900	7000
Impala, V-8						
4d Sed	350	780	1300	2600	4550	6500
4d HT	350	1020	1700	3400	5950	8500
2d HT*	600	1900	3200	6400	11,200	16,000
Conv*	800	2500	4200	8400	14,700	21,000
Sta Wag	450	1140	1900	3800	6650	9500

***NOTE:** Add 15 percent for Super Sport option.
Add 15 percent for Power-Pak & dual exhaust.
Add 15 percent for A/C.
Add 35 percent for 409 CID.
Deduct 10 percent for 6-cyl.

1965

	6	5	4	3	2	1
Chevy II, V-8						
4d Sed	200	670	1150	2250	3920	5600
2d Sed	200	670	1150	2250	3920	5600
Sta Wag	200	670	1200	2300	4060	5800
Nova Series, V-8						
4d Sed	200	685	1150	2300	3990	5700
2d HT	450	1140	1900	3800	6650	9500
Sta Wag	200	720	1200	2400	4200	6000
Nova Super Sport, V-8						
Spt Cpe	450	1450	2400	4800	8400	12,000
Chevelle						
2d Sed	200	650	1100	2150	3780	5400
4d Sed	200	660	1100	2200	3850	5500
2d Sta Wag	200	720	1200	2400	4200	6000
Sta Wag	200	700	1200	2350	4130	5900
Malibu, V-8						
4d Sed	200	670	1200	2300	4060	5800
2d HT	450	1450	2400	4800	8400	12,000
Conv	600	1900	3200	6400	11,200	16,000
Sta Wag	200	730	1250	2450	4270	6100
Malibu Super Sport, V-8						
2d HT	650	2050	3400	6800	11,900	17,000
Conv	850	2650	4400	8800	15,400	22,000

NOTE: Add 50 percent for RPO Z16 SS-396 option.

	6	5	4	3	2	1
Biscayne, V-8						
2d Sed	200	650	1100	2150	3780	5400
4d Sed	200	660	1100	2200	3850	5500
Sta Wag	200	685	1150	2300	3990	5700
Bel Air, V-8						
2d Sed	200	670	1200	2300	4060	5800
4d Sed	200	700	1200	2350	4130	5900
Sta Wag	200	720	1200	2400	4200	6000
Impala, V-8						
4d Sed	350	840	1400	2800	4900	7000
4d HT*	350	1020	1700	3400	5950	8500
2d HT	450	1450	2400	4800	8400	12,000
Conv	700	2150	3600	7200	12,600	18,000
Sta Wag	350	840	1400	2800	4900	7000
Impala Super Sport, V-8						
2d HT	500	1550	2600	5200	9100	13,000
Conv	700	2300	3800	7600	13,300	19,000

NOTE: Add 20 percent for Power-Pak & dual exhaust.
Add 15 percent for A/C.
Add 35 percent for 409 CID.
Add 35 percent for 396 CID.
Deduct 10 percent for 6-cyl.
Add 15 percent for Caprice models.

1966

	6	5	4	3	2	1
Chevy II Series 100						
2d Sed	200	670	1150	2250	3920	5600
4d Sed	200	685	1150	2300	3990	5700
Sta Wag	200	700	1200	2350	4130	5900
Nova Series, V-8						
2d HT	350	975	1600	3200	5600	8000
4d Sed	200	670	1200	2300	4060	5800
Sta Wag	200	720	1200	2400	4200	6000
Nova Super Sport						
2d HT	400	1200	2000	4000	7000	10,000

NOTE: Add 60 percent for High Performance pkg.

	6	5	4	3	2	1
Chevelle						
2d Sed	200	650	1100	2150	3780	5400
4d Sed	200	660	1100	2200	3850	5500
Sta Wag	200	685	1150	2300	3990	5700
Malibu, V-8						
4d Sed	200	670	1200	2300	4060	5800
4d HT	200	720	1200	2400	4200	6000
2d HT	500	1550	2600	5200	9100	13,000
Conv	700	2150	3600	7200	12,600	18,000
Sta Wag	200	720	1200	2400	4200	6000
Super Sport, '396' V-8						
2d HT	800	2500	4200	8400	14,700	21,000
Conv	1000	3100	5200	10,400	18,200	26,000

NOTE: Deduct 10 percent for 6-cyl. Chevelle.

	6	5	4	3	2	1
Biscayne, V-8						
2d Sed	200	660	1100	2200	3850	5500
4d Sed	200	670	1150	2250	3920	5600
Sta Wag	200	670	1200	2300	4060	5800
Bel Air, V-8						
2d Sed	200	720	1200	2400	4200	6000
4d Sed	200	730	1250	2450	4270	6100
3S Wag	200	750	1275	2500	4400	6300
Impala, V-8						
4d Sed	350	780	1300	2600	4550	6500
4d HT	350	975	1600	3200	5600	8000
2d HT	500	1550	2600	5200	9100	13,000
Conv	700	2300	3800	7600	13,300	19,000
Sta Wag	350	840	1400	2800	4900	7000
Impala Super Sport, V-8						
2d HT	600	1900	3200	6400	11,200	16,000
Conv	800	2500	4200	8400	14,700	21,000
Caprice, V-8						
4d HT	450	1140	1900	3800	6650	9500
2d HT	500	1550	2600	5200	9100	13,000
Sta Wag	350	900	1500	3000	5250	7500

NOTE: Add 40 percent for 396 CID.
Add approx. 40 percent for 427 CID engine when available.
Add 15 percent for A/C.

1967

	6	5	4	3	2	1
Chevy II, 100, V-8, 110" wb						
2d Sed	200	700	1075	2150	3700	5300
4d Sed	200	650	1100	2150	3780	5400
Sta Wag	200	670	1150	2250	3920	5600
Chevy II Nova, V-8, 110" wb						
4d Sed	200	660	1100	2200	3850	5500
2d HT	450	1140	1900	3800	6650	9500
Sta Wag	200	670	1200	2300	4060	5800
Chevy II Nova SS, V-8, 110" wb						
2d HT	400	1250	2100	4200	7400	10,500

NOTE: Add 60 percent for High Performance pkg.

	6	5	4	3	2	1
Chevelle 300, V-8, 115" wb						
2d Sed	200	650	1100	2150	3780	5400
4d Sed	200	660	1100	2200	3850	5500
Chevelle 300 DeLuxe, V-8, 115" wb						
2d Sed	200	685	1150	2300	3990	5700
4d Sed	200	670	1200	2300	4060	5800
Sta Wag	200	720	1200	2400	4200	6000
Chevelle Malibu, V-8, 115" wb						
4d Sed	200	720	1200	2400	4200	6000
4d HT	350	840	1400	2800	4900	7000
2d HT	400	1300	2200	4400	7700	11,000
Conv	550	1700	2800	5600	9800	14,000
Sta Wag	350	780	1300	2600	4550	6500
Chevelle Concours, V-8, 115" wb						
Sta Wag	350	800	1350	2700	4700	6700
Chevelle Super Sport 396, 115" wb						
2d HT	750	2400	4000	8000	14,000	20,000
Conv	850	2650	4400	8800	15,400	22,000
Biscayne, V-8, 119" wb						
2d Sed	200	660	1100	2200	3850	5500
4d Sed	200	670	1150	2250	3920	5600
Sta Wag	200	670	1200	2300	4060	5800
Bel Air, V-8, 119" wb						
2d Sed	200	745	1250	2500	4340	6200
4d Sed	200	750	1275	2500	4400	6300
3S Sta Wag	200	720	1200	2400	4200	6000
Impala, V-8, 119" wb						
4d Sed	350	780	1300	2600	4550	6500
4d HT	350	840	1400	2800	4900	7000
2d HT	400	1300	2200	4400	7700	11,000
Conv	650	2050	3400	6800	11,900	17,000
3S Sta Wag	350	780	1300	2600	4550	6500
Impala SS, V-8, 119" wb						
2d HT	450	1450	2400	4800	8400	12,000
Conv	700	2150	3600	7200	12,600	18,000
Caprice, V-8, 119" wb						
2d HT	450	1500	2500	5000	8800	12,500
4d HT	450	1080	1800	3600	6300	9000
3S Sta Wag	350	900	1500	3000	5250	7500

NOTES: Add approximately 40 percent for SS-427 engine options when available in all series.
Add 40 percent for SS-396 option.
Add 15 percent for A/C.

	6	5	4	3	2	1
Camaro						
IPC	900	2900	4800	9600	16,800	24,000
Cpe	500	1550	2600	5200	9100	13,000
Conv	650	2050	3400	6800	11,900	17,000
Z28 Cpe	1250	3950	6600	13,200	23,100	33,000
Yenko Cpe	2800	8900	14,800	29,600	51,800	74,000

NOTES: Deduct 5 percent for Six, (when available).
Add 10 percent for Rally Sport Package (when available; except incl. w/Indy Pace Car).
Add 5 percent for SS-350 (when available; except incl. w/Indy Pace Car).
Add 15 percent for SS-396 (L-35/325 hp; when available).
Add 35 percent for SS-396 (L-78/375 hp; when available).
Add 10 percent for A/C.

1968

	6	5	4	3	2	1
Nova 307 V8						
Cpe	200	670	1200	2300	4060	5800
Sed	200	675	1000	2000	3500	5000

NOTE: Deduct 5 percent for 4 or 6-cyl.
Add 10 percent for SS package.
Add 25 percent for 327 CID.
Add 30 percent for 350 CID.
Add 35 percent for 396 CID engine.

	6	5	4	3	2	1
Chevelle 300						
2d Sed	150	575	900	1750	3100	4400
Sta Wag	150	600	900	1800	3150	4500
Chevelle 300 DeLuxe						
4d Sed	150	575	900	1750	3100	4400
4d HT	150	650	950	1900	3300	4700
Cpe	150	575	900	1750	3100	4400
Sta Wag	150	600	950	1850	3200	4600
Chevelle Malibu						
4d Sed	150	600	900	1800	3150	4500
4d HT	200	675	1000	1950	3400	4900
2d HT	450	1140	1900	3800	6650	9500
Conv	500	1550	2600	5200	9100	13,000
Sta Wag	200	700	1050	2050	3600	5100
Chevelle Concours Estate						
Sta Wag	200	700	1075	2150	3700	5300
Chevelle SS-396						
2d HT	700	2300	3800	7600	13,300	19,000
Conv	750	2400	4000	8000	14,000	20,000
Biscayne						
2d Sed	150	575	900	1750	3100	4400
4d Sed	150	600	900	1800	3150	4500
Sta Wag	150	650	975	1950	3350	4800
Bel Air						
2d Sed	150	600	900	1800	3150	4500
4d Sed	150	600	950	1850	3200	4600
2S Sta Wag	150	650	975	1950	3350	4800
3S Sta Wag	200	675	1000	2000	3500	5000
Impala						
4d Sed	200	675	1000	1950	3400	4900
4d HT	200	700	1200	2350	4130	5900
2d HT	350	975	1600	3200	5600	8000
Cus Cpe	350	1000	1650	3300	5750	8200
Conv	600	1900	3200	6400	11,200	16,000
2S Sta Wag	200	675	1000	2000	3500	5000
3S Sta Wag	200	700	1050	2050	3600	5100
Caprice						
4d HT	350	780	1300	2600	4550	6500
2d HT	450	1080	1800	3600	6300	9000
2S Sta Wag	200	660	1100	2200	3850	5500
3S Sta Wag	200	720	1200	2400	4200	6000

Chevelle 300
NOTE: Only 1,270 Nova 4's were built in 1968.

	6	5	4	3	2	1
Camaro						
Cpe	450	1450	2400	4800	8400	12,000
Conv	600	1900	3200	6400	11,200	16,000
Z28	700	2300	3800	7600	13,300	19,000
Yenko Cpe	2100	6700	11,200	22,400	39,200	56,000

NOTES: Deduct 5 percent for Six, (when available).
Add 10 percent for A/C.
Add 10 percent for Rally Sport Package (when available).
Add 10 percent for SS package.
Add 10 percent for SS-350 (when available; except Z-28).
Add 15 percent for SS-396 (L35/325 hp; when available).
Add 35 percent for SS-396 (L78/375 hp; when available).
Add 40 percent for SS-396 (L89; when available).
Add approx. 40 percent for 427 engine options when availble.

1969

	6	5	4	3	2	1
Nova Four						
Cpe	150	575	875	1700	3000	4300
4d Sed	150	550	850	1675	2950	4200
Nova Six						
Cpe	150	575	900	1750	3100	4400
4d Sed	150	575	875	1700	3000	4300
Chevy II, Nova V-8						
Cpe	150	600	900	1800	3150	4500
4d Sed	150	575	900	1750	3100	4400
Yenko Cpe	2100	6700	11,200	22,400	39,200	56,000

NOTES: Add 25 percent for Nova SS.
Add 30 percent for 350 CID.
Add 35 percent for 396 CID.
Add 10 percent for Impala "SS".
Add 25 percent for other "SS" equipment pkgs.

	6	5	4	3	2	1
Chevelle 300 DeLuxe						
4d Sed	150	500	800	1600	2800	4000
2d HT	350	780	1300	2600	4550	6500
Cpe	150	600	900	1800	3150	4500
Nomad	150	650	950	1900	3300	4700
Dual Nomad	200	675	1000	2000	3500	5000
GB Wag	150	600	900	1800	3150	4500
6P GB Dual Wag	150	600	900	1800	3150	4500
9P GB Dual Wag	150	600	950	1850	3200	4600
Chevelle Malibu, V-8						
4d Sed	150	600	900	1800	3150	4500
4d HT	200	675	1000	2000	3500	5000
2d HT	400	1300	2200	4400	7700	11,000
Conv	450	1450	2400	4800	8400	12,000
9P Estate	150	550	850	1650	2900	4100
6P Estate	150	500	800	1600	2800	4000

NOTE: Add 10 percent for Concours 4-dr hardtop.

	6	5	4	3	2	1
Chevelle Malibu SS-396						
2d HT	700	2300	3800	7600	13,300	19,000
Conv	800	2500	4200	8400	14,700	21,000

NOTE: Add 60 percent for Yenko Hardtop.

	6	5	4	3	2	1
Biscayne						
2d Sed	150	500	800	1600	2800	4000
4d Sed	150	500	800	1550	2700	3900
Sta Wag	150	500	800	1550	2700	3900
Bel Air						
2d Sed	150	600	900	1800	3150	4500
4d Sed	150	500	800	1600	2800	4000
6P Sta Wag	150	500	800	1600	2800	4000
9P Sta Wag	150	550	850	1650	2900	4100
Impala, V-8						
4d Sed	150	600	900	1800	3150	4500
4d HT	200	660	1100	2200	3850	5500
2d HT	350	840	1400	2800	4900	7000
2d Cus Cpe	350	860	1450	2900	5050	7200
Conv	500	1550	2600	5200	9100	13,000
6P Sta Wag	150	550	850	1650	2900	4100
9P Sta Wag	150	550	850	1675	2950	4200

NOTE: Add 35 percent for Impala SS 427 option.

	6	5	4	3	2	1
Caprice, V-8						
4d HT	350	780	1300	2600	4550	6500
Cus Cpe	350	975	1600	3200	5600	8000
6P Sta Wag	150	600	900	1800	3150	4500
9P Sta Wag	150	650	950	1900	3300	4700
Camaro						
Spt Cpe	550	1700	2800	5600	9800	14,000
Conv	700	2300	3800	7600	13,300	19,000
Z28	700	2300	3800	7600	13,300	19,000
IPC	600	1900	3200	6400	11,200	16,000
ZL-1*	1700	5400	9000	18,000	31,500	45,000
RS Yenko	1700	5400	9000	18,000	31,500	45,000

NOTES: Deduct 5 percent for Six, (when available).
Add 5 percent for Rally Sport (except incl. w/Indy Pace Car).
Add 10 percent for SS-350 (when avail.; except incl. w/Indy Pace Car)
Add 15 percent for SS-396 (L78/375 hp; when available).
Add 35 percent for SS-396 (L89/375 hp, alum. heads; when available).
Add approx. 40 percent for 427 engine options when available.
*The specially trimmed coupe with the aluminum 427 block.

1970

	6	5	4	3	2	1
Nova Four						
Cpe	150	500	800	1600	2800	4000
4d Sed	150	500	800	1550	2700	3900
Nova Six						
Cpe	150	550	850	1650	2900	4100
4d Sed	150	500	800	1600	2800	4000
Nova, V-8						
Cpe	150	550	850	1675	2950	4200
4d Sed	150	550	850	1650	2900	4100
Yenko Cpe	2100	6700	11,200	22,400	39,200	56,000
Chevelle						
Cpe	200	670	1200	2300	4060	5800
4d Sed	150	600	900	1800	3150	4500
Nomad	200	675	1000	2000	3500	5000
Greenbrier						
6P Sta Wag	150	600	900	1800	3150	4500
8P Sta Wag	150	600	900	1800	3150	4500
Malibu, V-8						
Sed	150	600	950	1850	3200	4600
4d HT	200	675	1000	2000	3500	5000
2d HT	400	1200	2000	4000	7000	10,000
Conv	450	1450	2400	4800	8400	12,000
Concours	200	660	1100	2200	3850	5500
Est	200	670	1150	2250	3920	5600
Chevelle Malibu SS 396						
2d HT	500	1550	2600	5200	9100	13,000
Conv	900	2900	4800	9600	16,800	24,000
Chevelle Malibu SS 454						
2d HT	900	2900	4800	9600	16,800	24,000
Conv	1000	3250	5400	10,800	18,900	27,000

NOTE: Add 30 percent for SS 396 engine option.
Add 35 percent for SS 454-LS6 engine option.

	6	5	4	3	2	1
Monte Carlo						
2d HT	400	1300	2200	4400	7700	11,000

NOTE: Add 35 percent for SS 454.

	6	5	4	3	2	1
Biscayne						
4d Sed	150	475	750	1475	2600	3700
Sta Wag	150	475	775	1500	2650	3800
Bel Air						
4d Sed	150	550	850	1650	2900	4100
6P Sta Wag	150	500	800	1600	2800	4000
9P Sta Wag	150	550	850	1650	2900	4100
Impala, V-8						
4d Sed	150	600	900	1800	3150	4500
4d HT	200	660	1100	2200	3850	5500
Spt Cpe	350	780	1300	2600	4550	6500
Cus Cpe	350	840	1400	2800	4900	7000
Conv	400	1200	2000	4000	7000	10,000
6P Sta Wag	150	600	900	1800	3150	4500
9P Sta Wag	150	600	950	1850	3200	4600
Caprice, V-8						
4d HT	350	780	1300	2600	4550	6500
Cus Cpe	350	975	1600	3200	5600	8000
6P Sta Wag	150	650	975	1950	3350	4800
9P Sta Wag	200	675	1000	1950	3400	4900

NOTE: Add 35 percent for SS 454 option.
Add 25 percent for Rally Sport and/or Super Sport options.

	6	5	4	3	2	1
Camaro						
Cpe	400	1300	2200	4400	7700	11,000
Z28	550	1800	3000	6000	10,500	15,000
SS	500	1550	2600	5200	9100	13,000
RS	500	1550	2600	5200	9100	13,000

NOTE: Deduct 5 percent for Six, (except Z-28).
Add 35 percent for the 375 horsepower 396, (L78 option).

1971

	6	5	4	3	2	1
Vega						
2d	125	450	700	1400	2450	3500
HBk	125	450	750	1450	2500	3600
Kammback	150	475	750	1475	2600	3700

NOTE: Add 5 percent for GT.

	6	5	4	3	2	1
Nova, V-8						
4d Sed	125	450	700	1400	2450	3500
2d Sed	150	475	750	1475	2600	3700
2d SS	450	1080	1800	3600	6300	9000
Chevelle						
2d HT	450	1080	1800	3600	6300	9000
2d Malibu HT	500	1550	2600	5200	9100	13,000
Malibu Conv	600	1900	3200	6400	11,200	16,000
4d HT	200	720	1200	2400	4200	6000
4d Sed	150	600	900	1800	3150	4500
Est Wag	200	675	1000	2000	3500	5000
Chevelle Malibu SS-350						
2d HT	550	1800	3000	6000	10,500	15,000
Conv	700	2300	3800	7600	13,300	19,000
Chevelle Malibu SS-454						
2d HT	700	2150	3600	7200	12,600	18,000
Conv	800	2500	4200	8400	14,700	21,000
Monte Carlo						
2d HT	450	1450	2400	4800	8400	12,000

NOTE: Add 35 percent for SS 454.

Biscayne, V-8, 121" wb	6	5	4	3	2	1
4d Sed	125	400	675	1350	2300	3300
Bel Air, V-8, 121" wb						
4d Sed	150	500	800	1600	2800	4000
Impala, V-8, 121" wb						
4d Sed	150	550	850	1675	2950	4200
4d HT	200	675	1000	2000	3500	5000
2d HT	200	660	1100	2200	3850	5500
2d HT Cus	200	685	1150	2300	3990	5700
Conv	400	1300	2200	4400	7700	11,000
Caprice, V-8, 121" wb						
4d HT	200	720	1200	2400	4200	6000
2d HT	350	840	1400	2800	4900	7000
Station Wags, V-8, 125" wb						
Brookwood 2-S	125	400	700	1375	2400	3400
Townsman 3-S	150	475	750	1475	2600	3700
Kingswood 3-S	150	500	800	1550	2700	3900
Est 3-S	150	500	800	1600	2800	4000

NOTE: Add 35 percent for SS 454 option.

Camaro	6	5	4	3	2	1
Cpe	400	1200	2000	4000	7000	10,000
Z28	500	1550	2600	5200	9100	13,000

NOTE: Add 15 percent for V-8, (except Z-28).
Add 35 percent for Rally Sport and/or Super Sport options.

1972

Vega	6	5	4	3	2	1
2d Sed	125	450	700	1400	2450	3500
HBk	125	450	750	1450	2500	3600
Kammback	150	475	750	1475	2600	3700

NOTE: Add 15 percent for GT.

Nova	6	5	4	3	2	1
4d Sed	150	475	750	1475	2600	3700
2d Sed	150	475	775	1500	2650	3800

NOTE: Add 25 percent for SS.

Chevelle	6	5	4	3	2	1
Malibu Spt Cpe	450	1450	2400	4800	8400	12,000
Malibu Conv	600	1900	3200	6400	11,200	16,000
4d HT	200	720	1200	2400	4200	6000
4d Sed	150	600	900	1800	3150	4500
Est Wag	150	600	950	1850	3200	4600
Chevelle Malibu SS-350						
2d HT	550	1800	3000	6000	10,500	15,000
Conv	700	2300	3800	7600	13,300	19,000
Chevelle Malibu SS-454						
2d HT	650	2050	3400	6800	11,900	17,000
Conv	800	2500	4200	8400	14,700	21,000
Monte Carlo						
2d HT	450	1450	2400	4800	8400	12,000

NOTE: Add 35 percent for 454 CID engine.
Add 25 percent for 402 LT CID engine.

Biscayne, V-8, 121" wb	6	5	4	3	2	1
4d Sed	125	400	675	1350	2300	3300
Bel Air, V-8, 121" wb						
4d Sed	125	400	700	1375	2400	3400
Impala, V-8, 121" wb						
4d Sed	150	500	800	1600	2800	4000
4d HT	200	675	1000	2000	3500	5000
2d HT Cus	200	700	1050	2100	3650	5200
2d HT	150	650	975	1950	3350	4800
Conv	400	1250	2100	4200	7400	10,500
Caprice, V-8, 121" wb						
4d Sed	150	550	850	1675	2950	4200
4d HT	200	660	1100	2200	3850	5500
2d HT	200	720	1200	2400	4200	6000
Station Wagons, V-8, 125" wb						
Brookwood 2-S	125	400	700	1375	2400	3400
Townsman 3-S	150	475	750	1475	2600	3700
Kingswood 3-S	150	500	800	1600	2800	4000
Est 3-S	150	600	900	1800	3150	4500

NOTE: Add 35 percent for 454 option.
Add 30 percent for 402 option.

Camaro	6	5	4	3	2	1
Cpe	400	1200	2000	4000	7000	10,000
Z28	500	1550	2600	5200	9100	13,000

NOTE: Add 20 percent for V-8, (except Z-28).
Add 35 percent for Rally Sport and/or Super Sport options.

1973

Vega	6	5	4	3	2	1
2d Sed	125	450	700	1400	2450	3500
HBk	125	450	750	1450	2500	3600
Sta Wag	150	475	750	1475	2600	3700
Nova Custom V8						
Cpe	150	500	800	1550	2700	3900
4d Sed	150	475	775	1500	2650	3800
HBk	150	500	800	1600	2800	4000
Chevelle Malibu V8						
Cpe	150	550	850	1650	2900	4100
4d Sed	150	500	800	1600	2800	4000

NOTE: Add 15 percent for SS option.

Laguna V8	6	5	4	3	2	1
4d Sed	150	550	850	1650	2900	4100
Cpe	350	780	1300	2600	4550	6500
3S DeL Sta Wag	125	450	700	1400	2450	3500
3S Malibu Sta Wag	125	450	750	1450	2500	3600
3S Malibu Est	150	475	750	1475	2600	3700
3S Laguna	150	500	800	1600	2800	4000
3S Laguna Est	150	550	850	1675	2950	4200
Monte Carlo V8						
Cpe	200	720	1200	2400	4200	6000
Cpe Lan	350	780	1300	2600	4550	6500
Bel Air						
4d	150	550	850	1650	2900	4100
2S Bel Air	150	500	800	1550	2700	3900
3S Bel Air	150	500	800	1600	2800	4000
Impala V8						
Cpe Spt	200	675	1000	2000	3500	5000
Cpe Cus	200	700	1050	2100	3650	5200
4d Sed	150	550	850	1675	2950	4200
4d HT	150	600	900	1800	3150	4500
3S Impala Wag	150	575	900	1750	3100	4400
Caprice Classic V8						
Cpe	200	660	1100	2200	3850	5500
4d Sed	150	575	875	1700	3000	4300
4d HT	150	650	950	1900	3300	4700
Conv	400	1250	2100	4200	7400	10,500
3S Caprice Est	150	650	975	1950	3350	4800
Camaro						
Cpe	400	1200	2000	4000	7000	10,000
Z28	450	1450	2400	4800	8400	12,000

NOTE: Add 20 percent for V-8, (except Z-28).
Add 35 percent for Rally Sport and/or Super Sport options.

1974

Vega	6	5	4	3	2	1
Cpe	125	450	700	1400	2450	3500
HBk	125	450	750	1450	2500	3600
Sta Wag	150	475	750	1475	2600	3700
Nova						
Cpe	150	500	800	1550	2700	3900
HBk	150	550	850	1650	2900	4100
4d Sed	150	500	800	1550	2700	3900
Nova Custom						
Cpe	150	500	800	1600	2800	4000
HBk	150	550	850	1650	2900	4100
4d Sed	150	500	800	1600	2800	4000

NOTE: Add 10 percent for Spirit of America option where applied.

Malibu	6	5	4	3	2	1
Col Cpe	150	600	900	1800	3150	4500
Col Sed	150	550	850	1650	2900	4100
Sta Wag	150	475	750	1475	2600	3700
Malibu Classic						
Col Cpe	150	650	950	1900	3300	4700
Lan Cpe	150	575	900	1750	3100	4400
Col Sed	150	550	850	1650	2900	4100
Sta Wag	125	450	750	1450	2500	3600
Malibu Classic Estate						
Sta Wag	150	550	850	1650	2900	4100
Laguna Type S-3, V-8						
Cpe	350	900	1500	3000	5250	7500
Monte Carlo						
'S' Cpe	200	660	1100	2200	3850	5500
Lan	200	720	1200	2400	4200	6000
Bel Air						
4d Sed	150	500	800	1600	2800	4000
Sta Wag	150	500	800	1600	2800	4000
Impala						
4d Sed	150	575	875	1700	3000	4300
HT Sed	150	575	900	1750	3100	4400
Spt Cpe	200	675	1000	2000	3500	5000
Cus Cpe	200	685	1150	2300	3990	5700
Sta Wag	150	550	850	1650	2900	4100
Caprice Classic						
4d Sed	150	575	900	1750	3100	4400
HT Sed	150	650	950	1900	3300	4700
Cus Cpe	200	720	1200	2400	4200	6000
Conv	400	1250	2100	4200	7400	10,500
Sta Wag	150	600	900	1800	3150	4500

NOTES: Add 20 percent for Nova SS package.
Add 12 percent for Malibu with canopy roof.
Add 20 percent for 454 V-8.
Add 15 percent for Nova with 185 horsepower V-8.
Add 25 percent for Impala 'Spirit of America' Sport Coupe.

Camaro	6	5	4	3	2	1
Cpe	450	1140	1900	3800	6650	9500
LT Cpe	400	1200	2000	4000	7000	10,000

NOTE: Add 10 percent for Z28 option.

1975

Vega	6	5	4	3	2	1
Cpe	125	450	700	1400	2450	3500
HBk	125	450	750	1450	2500	3600
Lux Cpe	125	450	750	1450	2500	3600
Sta Wag	150	475	750	1475	2600	3700
Est	150	475	775	1500	2650	3800
Cosworth	350	975	1600	3200	5600	8000
Nova						
'S' Cpe	125	450	750	1450	2500	3600
Cpe	125	450	750	1450	2500	3600
HBk	150	475	750	1475	2600	3700
4d Sed	150	475	750	1475	2600	3700
Nova Custom						
Cpe	150	475	750	1475	2600	3700
HBk	150	475	775	1500	2650	3800
4d Sed	150	475	750	1475	2600	3700
Nova LN, V-8						
4d Sed	150	475	775	1500	2650	3800
Cpe	150	500	800	1550	2700	3900
Monza						
2 plus 2	150	500	800	1600	2800	4000
Twn Cpe	150	475	750	1475	2600	3700
Malibu						
Col Cpe	150	500	800	1600	2800	4000
Col Sed	125	450	700	1400	2450	3500
Sta Wag	125	450	750	1450	2500	3600
Malibu Classic						
Col Cpe	150	600	900	1800	3150	4500
Lan	150	650	950	1900	3300	4700
Col Sed	150	475	750	1475	2600	3700
Sta Wag	125	450	750	1450	2500	3600
Est Wag	150	475	750	1475	2600	3700
Laguna Type S-3, V-8						
Cpe	350	900	1500	3000	5250	7500
Monte Carlo						
'S' Cpe	200	660	1100	2200	3850	5500
Lan	200	720	1200	2400	4200	6000
Bel Air						
Sed	125	450	750	1450	2500	3600
Sta Wag	125	450	700	1400	2450	3500
Impala						
Sed	150	475	775	1500	2650	3800
4d HT	150	500	800	1550	2700	3900
Spt Cpe	150	600	900	1800	3150	4500
Cus Cpe	150	600	950	1850	3200	4600
Lan	200	675	1000	2000	3500	5000
Sta Wag	150	500	800	1550	2700	3900
Caprice Classic						
4d Sed	150	500	800	1550	2700	3900
4d HT	150	500	800	1600	2800	4000
Cus Cpe	200	675	1000	2000	3500	5000
Lan	200	660	1100	2200	3850	5500
Conv	450	1450	2400	4800	8400	12,000
Sta Wag	150	500	800	1600	2800	4000

NOTES: Add 10 percent for Nova SS.
Add 15 percent for SS option on Chevelle wagon.
Add 20 percent for Monte Carlo or Laguna 454.
Add 15 percent for 454 Caprice.
Add 15 percent for canopy top options.
Add 10 percent for Monza V-8.

Camaro	6	5	4	3	2	1
Cpe	350	840	1400	2800	4900	7000

	6	5	4	3	2	1
Type LT	350	975	1600	3200	5600	8000

NOTE: Add 30 percent for Camero R/S.

1976

	6	5	4	3	2	1
Chevette, 4-cyl.						
2d Scooter	125	380	650	1300	2250	3200
2d HBk	125	400	700	1375	2400	3400
Vega, 4-cyl.						
2d Sed	125	450	700	1400	2450	3500
2d HBk	125	450	750	1450	2500	3600
Cosworth HBk	350	975	1600	3200	5600	8000
Sta Wag	150	475	750	1475	2600	3700
Est Sta Wag	150	475	775	1500	2650	3800
Nova, V-8						
Cpe	125	450	750	1450	2500	3600
2d HBk	150	475	750	1475	2600	3700
4d Sed	125	450	700	1400	2450	3500
Nova Concours, V-8						
Cpe	150	475	750	1475	2600	3700
2d HBk	150	475	775	1500	2650	3800
4d Sed	125	450	750	1450	2500	3600
Monza, 4-cyl.						
Twn Cpe	125	400	700	1375	2400	3400
2d HBk	125	400	700	1375	2400	3400
Malibu, V-8						
2d Sed	125	450	750	1450	2500	3600
4d Sed	125	450	700	1400	2450	3500
2S Sta Wag ES	125	450	700	1400	2450	3500
3S Sta Wag ES	125	450	700	1400	2450	3500
Malibu Classic, V-8						
2d Sed	150	500	800	1600	2800	4000
Lan Cpe	150	550	850	1675	2950	4200
4d Sed	125	450	700	1400	2450	3500
Laguna Type S-3, V-8						
Cpe	350	900	1500	3000	5250	7500
Monte Carlo, V-8						
Cpe	200	660	1100	2200	3850	5500
Lan Cpe	200	720	1200	2400	4200	6000
Impala, V-8						
4d Sed	125	400	675	1350	2300	3300
4d Spt Sed	125	400	700	1375	2400	3400
Cus Cpe	150	500	800	1600	2800	4000
2S Sta Wag	125	400	700	1375	2400	3400
3S Sta Wag	125	450	700	1400	2450	3500
Caprice Classic, V-8						
4d Sed	125	450	700	1400	2450	3500
4d Spt Sed	125	450	750	1450	2500	3600
Cpe	150	550	850	1675	2950	4200
Lan Cpe	150	600	900	1800	3150	4500
2S Sta Wag	125	450	700	1400	2450	3500
3S Sta Wag	125	450	750	1450	2500	3600
Camaro						
Cpe	200	720	1200	2400	4200	6000
Cpe LT	350	840	1400	2800	4900	7000

1977

	6	5	4	3	2	1
Chevette, 4-cyl.						
2d HBk	100	350	600	1150	2000	2900
Vega, 4-cyl.						
Spt Cpe	125	400	675	1350	2300	3300
2d HBk	125	400	700	1375	2400	3400
Sta Wag	125	450	700	1400	2450	3500
Est Wag	125	450	750	1450	2500	3600
Nova, V-8						
Cpe	125	450	700	1400	2450	3500
2d HBk	125	450	750	1450	2500	3600
4d Sed	125	400	700	1375	2400	3400
Nova Concours, V-8						
Cpe	125	450	750	1450	2500	3600
2d HBk	150	475	750	1475	2600	3700
4d Sed	125	450	700	1400	2450	3500
Monza, 4-cyl.						
Twn Cpe	125	450	700	1400	2450	3500
2d HBk	125	450	700	1400	2450	3500
Malibu, V-8						
Cpe	125	400	700	1375	2400	3400
4d Sed	125	450	700	1400	2450	3500
2S Sta Wag	125	370	650	1250	2200	3100
3S Sta Wag	125	380	650	1300	2250	3200
Malibu Classic, V-8						
Cpe	125	450	700	1400	2450	3500
Lan Cpe	150	500	800	1600	2800	4000
4d Sed	125	450	750	1450	2500	3600
2S Sta Wag	125	400	675	1350	2300	3300
3S Sta Wag	125	400	700	1375	2400	3400
Monte Carlo, V-8						
Cpe	200	675	1000	2000	3500	5000
Lan Cpe	200	660	1100	2200	3850	5500
Impala, V-8						
Cpe	150	500	800	1600	2800	4000
4d Sed	125	450	700	1400	2450	3500
2S Sta Wag	125	450	700	1400	2450	3500
3S Sta Wag	125	450	750	1450	2500	3600
Caprice Classic, V-8						
Cpe	150	550	850	1675	2950	4200
4d Sed	150	475	750	1475	2600	3700
2S Sta Wag	125	450	750	1450	2500	3600
3S Sta Wag	150	475	750	1475	2600	3700
Camaro						
Spt Cpe	350	840	1400	2800	4900	7000
Spt Cpe LT	350	900	1500	3000	5250	7500
Spt Cpe Z28	350	975	1600	3200	5600	8000

1978

	6	5	4	3	2	1
Chevette						
2d Scooter	100	330	575	1150	1950	2800
2d HBk	100	330	575	1150	1950	2800
4d HBk	100	350	600	1150	2000	2900
Nova						
Cpe	125	400	700	1375	2400	3400
2d HBk	125	400	700	1375	2400	3400
4d Sed	125	400	675	1350	2300	3300
Nova Custom						
Cpe	125	450	700	1400	2450	3500
4d Sed	125	400	700	1375	2400	3400
Monza						
Cpe 2 plus 2	125	450	750	1450	2500	3600
'S' Cpe	125	450	700	1400	2450	3500
Cpe	125	400	700	1375	2400	3400
Sta Wag	125	370	650	1250	2200	3100
Est Wag	125	380	650	1300	2250	3200
Spt Cpe 2 plus 2	150	500	800	1600	2800	4000
Spt Cpe	150	475	775	1500	2650	3800
Malibu						
Spt Cpe	125	450	750	1450	2500	3600
4d Sed	125	450	700	1400	2450	3500
Sta Wag	125	450	700	1400	2450	3500
Malibu Classic						
Spt Cpe	150	475	750	1475	2600	3700
4d Sed	125	450	750	1450	2500	3600
Sta Wag	125	450	750	1450	2500	3600
Monte Carlo						
Cpe	150	650	950	1900	3300	4700
Impala						
Cpe	150	500	800	1600	2800	4000
4d Sed	150	475	750	1475	2600	3700
Sta Wag	150	475	750	1475	2600	3700
Caprice Classic						
Cpe	150	575	875	1700	3000	4300
4d Sed	150	500	800	1600	2800	4000
Sta Wag	150	500	800	1600	2800	4000
Camaro						
Cpe	200	720	1200	2400	4200	6000
LT Cpe	350	780	1300	2600	4550	6500
Z28 Cpe	350	840	1400	2800	4900	7000

1979

	6	5	4	3	2	1
Chevette, 4-cyl.						
4d HBk	100	350	600	1150	2000	2900
2d HBk	100	350	600	1150	2000	2900
2d Scooter	100	330	575	1150	1950	2800
Nova, V-8						
4d Sed	125	400	700	1375	2400	3400
2d Sed	125	400	675	1350	2300	3300
2d HBk	125	450	700	1400	2450	3500
Nova Custom, V-8						
4d Sed	125	450	700	1400	2450	3500
2d Sed	125	400	700	1375	2400	3400
NOTE: Deduct 5 percent for 6-cyl.						
Monza, 4-cyl.						
2d 2 plus 2 HBk	150	475	750	1475	2600	3700
2d	125	450	750	1450	2500	3600
Sta Wag	125	380	650	1300	2250	3200
2d Spt 2 plus 2 HBk	150	475	775	1500	2650	3800
Malibu, V-8						
4d Sed	125	450	750	1450	2500	3600
Spt Cpe	150	475	775	1500	2650	3800
Sta Wag	150	475	750	1475	2600	3700
Malibu Classic, V-8						
4d Sed	150	475	750	1475	2600	3700
Spt Cpe	150	500	800	1550	2700	3900
Lan Cpe	150	500	800	1600	2800	4000
Sta Wag	150	475	775	1500	2650	3800
NOTE: Deduct 5 percent for 6-cyl.						
Monte Carlo, V-8						
Spt Cpe	200	675	1000	2000	3500	5000
Lan Cpe	200	660	1100	2200	3850	5500
NOTE: Deduct 10 percent for 6-cyl.						
Impala, V-8						
4d Sed	150	475	775	1500	2650	3800
2d Sed	150	475	750	1475	2600	3700
Lan Cpe	150	500	800	1550	2700	3900
2S Sta Wag	150	475	750	1475	2600	3700
3S Sta Wag	150	475	775	1500	2650	3800
Caprice Classic, V-8						
4d Sed	150	500	800	1600	2800	4000
2d Sed	150	550	850	1650	2900	4100
Lan Cpe	150	550	850	1675	2950	4200
2S Sta Wag	150	550	850	1650	2900	4100
3S Sta Wag	150	550	850	1675	2950	4200
NOTE: Deduct 15 percent for 6-cyl.						
Camaro, V-8						
Spt Cpe	200	670	1200	2300	4060	5800
Rally Cpe	350	770	1300	2550	4480	6400
Berlinetta Cpe	350	790	1350	2650	4620	6600
Z28 Cpe	350	830	1400	2950	4830	6900
NOTE: Deduct 20 percent for 6-cyl.						

1980

	6	5	4	3	2	1
Chevette, 4-cyl.						
2d HBk Scooter	100	360	600	1200	2100	3000
2d HBk	125	370	650	1250	2200	3100
4d HBk	125	380	650	1300	2250	3200
Citation, 6-cyl.						
4d HBk	125	450	700	1400	2450	3500
2d HBk	125	400	700	1375	2400	3400
2d Cpe	125	450	750	1450	2500	3600
2d Cpe Clb	150	475	750	1475	2600	3700
NOTE: Deduct 10 percent for 4-cyl.						
Monza, 4-cyl.						
2d HBk 2 plus 2	125	400	700	1375	2400	3400
2d HBk Spt 2 plus 2	125	450	750	1450	2500	3600
2d Cpe	125	450	700	1400	2450	3500
NOTE: Add 10 percent for V-6.						
Malibu, V-8						
4d Sed	125	450	750	1450	2500	3600
2d Cpe Spt	150	475	775	1500	2650	3800
4d Sta Wag	150	475	750	1475	2600	3700
NOTE: Deduct 10 percent for V-6.						
Malibu Classic, V-8						
4d Sed	150	475	750	1475	2600	3700
2d Cpe Spt	150	500	800	1550	2700	3900
2d Cpe Lan	150	500	800	1600	2800	4000
4d Sta Wag	150	475	775	1500	2650	3800
NOTE: Deduct 10 percent for 6-cyl.						
Camaro, 6-cyl.						
2d Cpe Spt	200	730	1250	2450	4270	6100
2d Cpe RS	200	750	1275	2500	4400	6300
2d Cpe Berlinetta	350	770	1300	2550	4480	6400
Camaro, V-8						
2d Cpe Spt	350	780	1300	2600	4550	6500
2d Cpe RS	350	800	1350	2700	4700	6700
2d Cpe Berlinetta	350	820	1400	2700	4760	6800
2d Cpe Z28	350	840	1400	2800	4900	7000
Monte Carlo, 6-cyl.						
2d Cpe Spt	200	650	1100	2150	3780	5400
2d Cpe Lan	200	660	1100	2200	3850	5500
Monte Carlo, V-8						
2d Cpe Spt	200	670	1200	2300	4060	5800
2d Cpe Lan	200	700	1200	2350	4130	5900
Impala, V-8						

	6	5	4	3	2	1
4d Sed	150	500	800	1550	2700	3900
2d Cpe	150	500	800	1600	2800	4000
4d 2S Sta Wag	150	500	800	1600	2800	4000
4d 3S Sta Wag	150	550	850	1650	2900	4100
NOTE: Deduct 12 percent for 6-cyl. sedan and coupe only.						
Caprice Classic, V-8						
4d Sed	150	500	800	1600	2800	4000
2d Cpe	150	550	850	1675	2950	4200
2d Cpe Lan	150	575	900	1750	3100	4400
4d 2S Sta Wag	150	550	850	1650	2900	4100
4d 3S Sta Wag	150	550	850	1675	2950	4200

1981

	6	5	4	3	2	1
Chevette, 4-cyl.						
2d HBk Scooter	125	370	650	1250	2200	3100
2d HBk	125	380	650	1300	2250	3200
4d HBk	125	400	675	1350	2300	3300
Citation, 6-cyl.						
4d HBk	125	450	750	1450	2500	3600
2d HBk	125	450	700	1400	2450	3500
NOTE: Deduct 10 percent for 4-cyl.						
Malibu, V-8						
4d Sed Spt	150	475	750	1475	2600	3700
2d Cpe Spt	150	475	775	1500	2650	3800
4d Sta Wag	150	475	775	1500	2650	3800
NOTE: Deduct 10 percent for 6-cyl.						
Malibu Classic, V-8						
4d Sed Spt	150	475	775	1500	2650	3800
2d Cpe Spt	150	500	800	1550	2700	3900
2d Cpe Lan	150	500	800	1600	2800	4000
4d Sta Wag	150	500	800	1550	2700	3900
Camaro, 6-cyl.						
2d Cpe Spt	200	745	1250	2500	4340	6200
2d Cpe Berlinetta	350	770	1300	2550	4480	6400
Camaro, V-8						
2d Cpe Spt	350	790	1350	2650	4620	6600
2d Cpe Berlinetta	350	820	1400	2700	4760	6800
2d Cpe Z28	350	860	1450	2900	5050	7200
Monte Carlo, 6-cyl.						
2d Cpe Spt	200	660	1100	2200	3850	5500
2d Cpe Lan	200	670	1150	2250	3920	5600
Monte Carlo, V-8						
2d Cpe Spt	200	700	1200	2350	4130	5900
2d Cpe Lan	200	720	1200	2400	4200	6000
Impala, V-8						
4d Sed	150	500	800	1600	2800	4000
2d Cpe	150	550	850	1650	2900	4100
4d 2S Sta Wag	150	550	850	1650	2900	4100
4d 3S Sta Wag	150	550	850	1675	2950	4200
NOTE: Deduct 12 percent for 6-cyl. on sedan and coupe only.						
Caprice Classic, V-8						
4d Sed	150	550	850	1675	2950	4200
2d Cpe	150	575	875	1700	3000	4300
2d Cpe Lan	150	600	900	1800	3150	4500
4d 2S Sta Wag	150	575	875	1700	3000	4300
4d 3S Sta Wag	150	575	900	1750	3100	4400
NOTE: Deduct 15 percent for 6-cyl. coupe and sedan only.						

1982

	6	5	4	3	2	1
Chevette, 4-cyl.						
2d HBk	125	400	700	1375	2400	3400
4d HBk	125	450	700	1400	2450	3500
NOTE: Deduct 5 percent for lesser models.						
Cavalier, 4-cyl.						
4d Sed CL	150	500	800	1600	2800	4000
2d Cpe CL	150	550	850	1650	2900	4100
2d Hatch CL	150	550	850	1675	2950	4200
4d Sta Wag CL	150	550	850	1675	2950	4200
NOTE: Deduct 5 percent for lesser models.						
Citation, 6-cyl.						
4d HBk	150	475	775	1500	2650	3800
2d HBk	150	475	750	1475	2600	3700
2d Cpe	150	475	775	1500	2650	3800
NOTE: Deduct 10 percent for 4-cyl.						
Malibu, V-8						
4d Sed	150	550	850	1650	2900	4100
4d Sta Wag	150	550	850	1675	2950	4200
NOTE: Deduct 10 percent for 6-cyl.						
Celebrity, 6-cyl.						
4d Sed	150	550	850	1675	2950	4200
2d Cpe	150	575	875	1700	3000	4300
NOTE: Deduct 10 percent for 6-cyl.						
Camaro, 6-cyl.						
2d Cpe Spt	200	750	1275	2500	4400	6300
2d Cpe Berlinetta	350	780	1300	2600	4550	6500
Camaro, V-8						
2d Cpe Spt	350	800	1350	2700	4700	6700
2d Cpe Berlinetta	350	830	1400	2950	4830	6900
2d Cpe Z28	350	880	1500	2950	5180	7400
NOTE: Add 20 percent for Indy pace car.						
Monte Carlo, 6-cyl.						
2d Cpe Spt	200	685	1150	2300	3990	5700
Monte Carlo, V-8						
2d Cpe Spt	200	730	1250	2450	4270	6100
Impala, V-8						
4d Sed	150	575	900	1750	3100	4400
4d 2S Sta Wag	150	575	900	1750	3100	4400
4d 3S Sta Wag	150	600	900	1800	3150	4500
NOTE: Deduct 12 percent for 6-cyl. on sedan only.						
Caprice Classic, V-8						
4d Sed	150	600	950	1850	3200	4600
2d Spt Cpe	150	650	950	1900	3300	4700
4d 3S Sta Wag	150	650	950	1900	3300	4700
NOTE: Deduct 15 percent for 6-cyl. coupe and sedan only.						

1983

	6	5	4	3	2	1
Chevette, 4-cyl.						
2d HBk	125	450	700	1400	2450	3500
4d HBk	125	450	750	1450	2500	3600
NOTE: Deduct 5 percent for lesser models.						
Cavalier, 4-cyl.						
4d Sed CS	150	500	800	1550	2700	3900
2d Cpe CS	150	500	800	1600	2800	4000
2d HBk CS	150	550	850	1650	2900	4100
4d Sta Wag CS	150	550	850	1650	2900	4100
NOTE: Deduct 5 percent for lesser models.						
Citation, 6-cyl.						
4d HBk	150	475	775	1500	2650	3800
2d HBk	150	475	750	1475	2600	3700
2d Cpe	150	475	775	1500	2650	3800
NOTE: Deduct 10 percent for 4-cyl.						
Malibu, V-8						
4d Sed	150	550	850	1675	2950	4200
4d Sta Wag	150	575	875	1700	3000	4300
NOTE: Deduct 10 percent for 6-cyl.						
Celebrity, V-6						
4d Sed	150	575	875	1700	3000	4300
2d Cpe	150	575	900	1750	3100	4400
NOTE: Deduct 10 percent for 4-cyl.						
Camaro, 6-cyl.						
2d Cpe Spt	350	770	1300	2550	4480	6400
2d Cpe Berlinetta	350	790	1350	2650	4620	6600
Camaro, V-8						
2d Cpe Spt	350	820	1400	2700	4760	6800
2d Cpe Berlinetta	350	840	1400	2800	4900	7000
2d Cpe Z28	350	900	1500	3000	5250	7500
Monte Carlo, 6-cyl.						
2d Cpe Spt	200	670	1200	2300	4060	5800
Monte Carlo, V-8						
2d Cpe Spt SS	350	820	1400	2700	4760	6800
2d Cpe Spt	200	745	1250	2500	4340	6200
Impala, V-8						
4d Sed	150	600	900	1800	3150	4500
NOTE: Deduct 12 percent for 6-cyl.						
Caprice Classic, V-8						
4d Sed	150	650	950	1900	3300	4700
4d Sta Wag	150	650	950	1900	3300	4700
NOTE: Deduct 15 percent for 6-cyl.						

1984

	6	5	4	3	2	1
Chevette CS, 4-cyl.						
NOTE: Deduct 10 percent for V6 cyl.						
2d HBk	125	450	750	1450	2500	3600
NOTE: Deduct 5 percent for lesser models.						
Cavalier, 4-cyl.						
4d Sed	150	475	750	1475	2600	3700
4d Sta Wag	150	500	800	1600	2800	4000
Cavalier Type 10, 4-cyl.						
2d Sed	150	475	775	1500	2650	3800
2d HBk	150	500	800	1550	2700	3900
2d Conv	200	660	1100	2200	3850	5500
Cavalier CS, 4-cyl.						
4d Sed	150	500	800	1550	2700	3900
4d Sta Wag	150	500	800	1600	2800	4000
Citation, V-6						
4d HBk	150	550	850	1650	2900	4100
2d HBk	150	550	850	1650	2900	4100
2d Cpe	150	550	850	1675	2950	4200
NOTE: Deduct 5 percent for 4-cyl.						
Celebrity, V-6						
4d Sed	150	500	800	1600	2800	4000
2d Sed	150	500	800	1600	2800	4000
4d Sta Wag	150	550	850	1650	2900	4100
NOTE: Deduct 5 percent for 4-cyl.						
Camaro, V-8						
2d Cpe	350	790	1350	2650	4620	6600
2d Cpe Berlinetta	350	820	1400	2700	4760	6800
2d Cpe Z28	350	850	1450	2850	4970	7100
NOTE: Deduct 10 percent for V-6 cyl.						
Monte Carlo, V-8						
2d Cpe	200	720	1200	2400	4200	6000
2d Cpe SS	350	800	1350	2700	4700	6700
NOTE: Deduct 15 percent for V-6 cyl.						
Impala, V-8						
4d Sed	150	650	950	1900	3300	4700
NOTE: Deduct 10 percent for V6 cyl.						
Caprice Classic, V-8						
4d Sed	200	675	1000	1950	3400	4900
2d Sed	200	675	1000	2000	3500	5000
4d Sta Wag	200	675	1000	1950	3400	4900
NOTE: Deduct 10 percent for V-6 cyl.						

1985

	6	5	4	3	2	1
Sprint, 3-cyl.						
2d HBk	125	450	700	1400	2450	3500
Chevette, 4-cyl.						
4d HBk	125	450	750	1450	2500	3600
2d HBk	125	450	700	1400	2450	3500
NOTE: Deduct 20 percent for diesel.						
Spectrum, 4-cyl.						
4d HBk	125	450	750	1450	2500	3600
2d HBk	125	450	750	1450	2500	3600
Nova, 4-cyl.						
4d HBk	125	450	750	1450	2500	3600
Cavalier						
2d T Type Cpe	150	550	850	1675	2950	4200
2d T Type HBk	150	575	875	1700	3000	4300
T Type Conv	200	660	1100	2200	3850	5500
NOTE: Deduct 10 percent for 4-cyl.						
NOTE: Deduct 5 percent for lesser models.						
Citation, V-6						
4d HBk	150	550	850	1675	2950	4200
2d HBk	150	550	850	1675	2950	4200
NOTE: Deduct 10 percent for 4-cyl.						
Celebrity, V-6						
4d Sed	150	575	875	1700	3000	4300
2d Cpe	150	575	875	1700	3000	4300
4d Sta Wag	150	575	900	1750	3100	4400
NOTE: Deduct 10 percent for 4-cyl. Deduct 30 percent for diesel.						
Camaro, V-8						
2d Cpe Spt	350	800	1350	2700	4700	6700
2d Cpe Berlinetta	350	830	1400	2950	4830	6900
2d Cpe Z28	350	860	1450	2900	5050	7200
2d Cpe IROC-Z	350	950	1500	3050	5300	7600
NOTE: Deduct 30 percent for 4-cyl. Deduct 20 percent for V-6.						
Monte Carlo, V-8						
2d Cpe Spt	200	730	1250	2450	4270	6100
2d Cpe SS	350	820	1400	2700	4760	6800
NOTE: Deduct 20 percent for V-6 where available.						
Impala, V-8						
4d Sed	150	650	975	1950	3350	4800
NOTE: Deduct 20 percent for V-6.						
Caprice Classic, V-8						
4d Sed	200	675	1000	2000	3500	5000
2d Cpe	200	675	1000	2000	3500	5000
4d Sta Wag	200	700	1050	2100	3650	5200
NOTE: Deduct 20 percent for V-6. Deduct 30 percent for diesel.						

1986	6	5	4	3	2	1
Chevette						
2d Cpe	125	450	750	1450	2500	3600
4d Sed	150	475	750	1475	2600	3700
Nova						
4d Sed	150	475	750	1475	2600	3700
4d HBk	150	475	775	1500	2650	3800
Cavalier						
2d Cpe	150	500	800	1600	2800	4000
4d Sed	150	550	850	1650	2900	4100
4d Sta Wag	150	550	850	1675	2950	4200
2d Conv	200	720	1200	2400	4200	6000
Cavalier Z24						
2d Cpe	200	670	1200	2300	4060	5800
2d HBk	200	685	1150	2300	3990	5700
Camaro						
2d Cpe	350	820	1400	2700	4760	6800
2d Cpe Berlinetta	350	840	1400	2800	4900	7000
2d Cpe Z28	350	900	1500	3000	5250	7500
2d Cpe IROC-Z	350	975	1600	3200	5600	8000
Celebrity						
2d Cpe	150	575	900	1750	3100	4400
4d Sed	150	600	900	1800	3150	4500
4d Sta Wag	150	600	950	1850	3200	4600
Monte Carlo						
2d Cpe	350	780	1300	2600	4550	6500
2d Cpe LS	350	840	1400	2800	4900	7000
Monte Carlo SS						
2d Cpe	350	975	1600	3200	5600	8000
2d Cpe Aero	450	1050	1750	3550	6150	8800
Caprice						
4d Sed	200	660	1100	2200	3850	5500
Caprice Classic						
2d Cpe	200	685	1150	2300	3990	5700
4d Sed	200	670	1150	2250	3920	5600
4d Sta Wag	200	720	1200	2400	4200	6000
Caprice Classic Brougham						
4d Sed	200	700	1200	2350	4130	5900
4d Sed LS	200	720	1200	2400	4200	6000

1987	6	5	4	3	2	1
Sprint, 3-cyl.						
2d HBk	125	450	750	1450	2500	3600
4d HBk	150	475	750	1475	2600	3700
2d HBk ER	150	475	750	1475	2600	3700
2d HBk Turbo	150	475	775	1500	2650	3800
Chevette, 4-cyl.						
2d HBk	125	450	750	1450	2500	3600
4d HBk	150	475	750	1475	2600	3700
Spectrum, 4-cyl.						
2d HBk	150	500	800	1550	2700	3900
4d HBk	150	500	800	1550	2700	3900
2d HBk EX	150	475	775	1500	2650	3800
4d HBk Turbo	150	500	800	1600	2800	4000
Nova, 4-cyl.						
4d HBk	150	475	775	1500	2650	3800
4d Sed	150	500	800	1550	2700	3900
Cavalier, 4-cyl.						
4d Sed	150	500	800	1600	2800	4000
2d Cpe	150	500	800	1550	2700	3900
4d Sta Wag	150	550	850	1650	2900	4100
4d Sed GS	150	550	850	1650	2900	4100
2d HBk GS	150	500	800	1600	2800	4000
4d Sta Wag GS	150	550	850	1675	2950	4200
4d Sed RS	150	550	850	1675	2950	4200
2d Cpe RS	150	550	850	1650	2900	4100
2d HBk RS	150	550	850	1650	2900	4100
2d Conv RS	200	745	1250	2500	4340	6200
4d Sta Wag	150	550	850	1675	2950	4200
NOTE: Add 10 percent for V-6.						
Cavalier Z24 V-6						
2d Spt Cpe	200	700	1200	2350	4130	5900
2d Spt HBk	200	670	1200	2300	4060	5800
Beretta						
2d Cpe 4-cyl.	150	650	950	1900	3300	4700
2d Cpe V-6	200	675	1000	2000	3500	5000
Corsica						
4d Sed 4-cyl.	150	650	975	1950	3350	4800
4d Sed V-6	200	700	1050	2050	3600	5100
Celebrity						
4d Sed 4-cyl.	150	600	950	1850	3200	4600
2d Cpe 4-cyl.	150	600	900	1800	3150	4500
4d Sta Wag 4-cyl.	150	650	950	1900	3300	4700
4d Sed V-6	150	650	975	1950	3350	4800
2d Cpe V-6	150	650	950	1900	3300	4700
4d Sta Wag V-6	200	675	1000	1950	3400	4900
Camaro						
2d Cpe V-6	350	830	1400	2950	4830	6900
2d Cpe LT V-6	350	840	1400	2800	4900	7000
2d Cpe V-8	350	860	1450	2900	5050	7200
2d Cpe LT V-8	350	870	1450	2900	5100	7300
2d Cpe Z28 V-8	350	950	1550	3100	5400	7700
2d Cpe IROC-Z V-8	350	1000	1650	3300	5750	8200
NOTE: Add 20 percent for 350 V-8 where available.						
Monte Carlo						
2d Cpe LS V-6	350	790	1350	2650	4620	6600
2d Cpe LS V-8	350	820	1400	2700	4760	6800
2d Cpe SS V-8	350	975	1600	3250	5700	8100
Caprice, V-6						
4d Sed	200	670	1150	2250	3920	5600
Caprice Classic V-6						
4d Sed	200	670	1200	2300	4060	5800
2d Cpe	200	685	1150	2300	3990	5700
4d Sed Brgm	200	700	1200	2350	4130	5900
2d Cpe Brgm	200	670	1200	2300	4060	5800
Caprice, V-8						
4d Sed	200	670	1200	2300	4060	5800
4d Sta Wag	200	730	1250	2450	4270	6100
Caprice Classic V-8						
4d Sed	200	720	1200	2400	4200	6000
2d Cpe	200	700	1200	2350	4130	5900
4d Sta Wag	200	750	1275	2500	4400	6300
4d Sed Brgm	200	730	1250	2450	4270	6100
2d Cpe Brgm	200	720	1200	2400	4200	6000

1988	6	5	4	3	2	1
Sprint, 3-cyl.						
2d HBk	100	360	600	1200	2100	3000
4d HBk	125	380	650	1300	2250	3200
2d Metro	100	330	575	1150	1950	2800
2d Turbo	100	350	600	1150	2000	2900
Spectrum, 4-cyl.						
2d HBk Express	100	325	550	1100	1900	2700
4d Sed	100	350	600	1150	2000	2900
2d HBk	100	330	575	1150	1950	2800
4d Turbo Sed	125	370	650	1250	2200	3100
Nova, 4-cyl.						
5d HBk	125	450	700	1400	2450	3500
4d Sed	125	400	700	1375	2400	3400
4d Sed Twin Cam	150	550	850	1650	2900	4100
Cavalier						
4d Sed	125	400	700	1375	2400	3400
2d Cpe	125	450	750	1450	2500	3600
4d Sta Wag	125	400	700	1375	2400	3400
4d RS Sed	150	500	800	1550	2700	3900
2d RS Cpe	150	500	800	1600	2800	4000
2d Z24 Cpe V-6	200	675	1000	2000	3500	5000
2d Z24 Conv V-6	200	720	1200	2400	4200	6000
Beretta, 4-cyl.						
2d Cpe	150	550	850	1675	2950	4200
2d Cpe V-6	150	600	900	1800	3150	4500
Corsica, V-4						
4d Sed	150	500	800	1600	2800	4000
4d Sed V-6	150	575	875	1700	3000	4300
Celebrity, 4-cyl.						
4d Sed	125	450	750	1450	2500	3600
2d Cpe	125	450	700	1400	2450	3500
4d Sta Wag	150	500	800	1550	2700	3900
4d Sed V-6	150	500	800	1550	2700	3900
2d Cpe V-6	150	475	775	1500	2650	3800
4d Sta Wag V-6	150	550	850	1650	2900	4100
Monte Carlo						
2d Cpe V-6	200	660	1100	2200	3850	5500
2d Cpe V-8	200	720	1200	2400	4200	6000
2d SS Cpe V-8	350	975	1600	3200	5600	8000
Caprice, V-6						
4d Sed	200	675	1000	2000	3500	5000
4d Classic Sed	200	660	1100	2200	3850	5500
4d Brgm Sed	200	720	1200	2400	4200	6000
4d LS Brgm Sed	350	780	1300	2600	4550	6500
Caprice, V-8						
4d Sed	200	720	1200	2400	4200	6000
4d Classic Sed	350	780	1300	2600	4550	6500
4d Sta Wag	350	840	1400	2800	4900	7000
4d Brgm Sed	350	840	1400	2800	4900	7000
4d LS Brgm Sed	350	900	1500	3000	5250	7500
Camaro						
V-6						
2d Cpe	200	660	1100	2200	3850	5500
V-8						
2d Cpe	200	720	1200	2400	4200	6000
2d Conv	400	1200	2000	4000	7000	10,000
2d IROC-Z Cpe	350	1020	1700	3400	5950	8500
2d IROC-Z Conv	500	1550	2600	5200	9100	13,000

CORVAIR

1960	6	5	4	3	2	1
Standard, 6-cyl.						
Sed	200	720	1200	2400	4200	6000
Cpe	350	780	1300	2600	4550	6500
DeLuxe, 6-cyl.						
Sed	200	730	1250	2450	4270	6100
Cpe	350	800	1350	2700	4700	6700
Monza, 6-cyl.						
Cpe	950	1100	1850	3700	6450	9200

1961	6	5	4	3	2	1
Series 500, 6-cyl.						
Sed	200	720	1200	2400	4200	6000
Cpe	350	780	1300	2600	4550	6500
Sta Wag	200	750	1275	2500	4400	6300
Series 700, 6-cyl.						
Sed	350	770	1300	2550	4480	6400
Cpe	350	840	1400	2800	4900	7000
Sta Wag	350	800	1350	2700	4700	6700
Monza, 6-cyl.						
Sed	350	790	1350	2650	4620	6600
Cpe	350	1000	1650	3300	5750	8200
Greenbrier, 6-cyl.						
Spt Wag	350	840	1400	2800	4900	7000
NOTE: Add $1,200. for A/C.						

1962-1963	6	5	4	3	2	1
Series 500, 6-cyl.						
Cpe	350	790	1350	2650	4620	6600
Series 700, 6-cyl.						
Sed	350	790	1350	2650	4620	6600
Cpe	350	850	1450	2850	4970	7100
Sta Wag (1962 only)	350	820	1400	2700	4760	6800
Series 900 Monza, 6-cyl.						
Sed	350	850	1450	2850	4970	7100
Cpe	350	1040	1700	3450	6000	8600
Conv	400	1250	2100	4200	7400	10,500
Sta Wag (1962 only)	350	860	1450	2900	5050	7200
Monza Spyder, 6-cyl.						
Cpe	450	1090	1800	3650	6400	9100
Conv	400	1300	2200	4400	7700	11,000
Greenbrier, 6-cyl.						
Spt Wag	350	820	1400	2700	4760	6800
NOTE: Add $1,600. for K.O. wire wheels. Add $800. for A/C.						

1964	6	5	4	3	2	1
Series 500, 6-cyl.						
Cpe	350	820	1400	2700	4760	6800
Series 700, 6-cyl.						
Sed	350	790	1350	2650	4620	6600

Series 900 Monza, 6-cyl.	6	5	4	3	2	1
Sed	350	840	1400	2800	4900	7000
Cpe	350	1040	1700	3450	6000	8600
Conv	450	1140	1900	3800	6650	9500
Monza Spyder, 6-cyl.						
Cpe	450	1090	1800	3650	6400	9100
Conv	400	1300	2200	4400	7700	11,000
Greenbrier, 6-cyl.						
Spt Wag	350	850	1450	2850	4970	7100

NOTE: Add $1,600. for K.O. wire wheels.
Add $800. for A/C except Spyder.

1965

Series 500, 6-cyl.	6	5	4	3	2	1
4d HT	200	700	1075	2150	3700	5300
2d HT	200	720	1200	2400	4200	6000
Monza Series, 6-cyl.						
4d HT	200	720	1200	2400	4200	6000
2d HT	350	975	1600	3200	5600	8000
Conv	400	1250	2100	4200	7400	10,500

NOTES: Add 20 percent for 140 hp engine.
Add 30 percent for 180 hp engine.

Corsa Series, 6-cyl.	6	5	4	3	2	1
2d HT	350	975	1600	3200	5600	8000
Conv	400	1300	2200	4400	7700	11,000
Greenbrier, 6-cyl.						
Spt Wag	350	780	1300	2600	4550	6500

NOTE: Add $1,000. for A/C.

1966

Series 500, 6-cyl.	6	5	4	3	2	1
4d HT	200	660	1100	2200	3850	5500
2d HT	200	730	1250	2450	4270	6100
Monza Series, 6-cyl.						
4d HT	200	745	1250	2500	4340	6200
2d HT	350	975	1600	3200	5600	8000
Conv	400	1300	2200	4400	7700	11,000

NOTES: Add 20 percent for 140 hp engine.
Add 30 percent for 180 hp engine.

Corsa Series, 6-cyl.	6	5	4	3	2	1
2d HT	350	1040	1700	3450	6000	8600
Conv	450	1400	2300	4600	8100	11,500

NOTE: Add $1,000. for A/C.

1967

Series 500, 6-cyl.	6	5	4	3	2	1
2d HT	200	720	1200	2400	4200	6000
4d HT	200	660	1100	2200	3850	5500
Monza, 6-cyl.						
4d HT	200	745	1250	2500	4340	6200
2d HT	350	975	1600	3200	5600	8000
Conv	400	1250	2100	4200	7400	10,500

NOTES: Add $1,000. for A/C.
Add 20 percent for 140 hp engine.

1968

Series 500, 6-cyl.	6	5	4	3	2	1
2d HT	200	720	1200	2400	4200	6000
Monza, 6-cyl.						
2d HT	350	975	1600	3200	5600	8000
Conv	400	1250	2100	4200	7400	10,500

NOTE: Add 20 percent for 140 hp engine.

1969

Series 500, 6-cyl.	6	5	4	3	2	1
2d HT	350	840	1400	2800	4900	7000
Monza						
2d HT	450	1140	1900	3800	6650	9500
Conv	400	1300	2200	4400	7700	11,000

NOTE: Add 20 percent for 140 hp engine.

CORVETTE

1953

	6	5	4	3	2	1
6-cyl. Conv	3600	11,500	19,200	38,400	67,200	96,000

NOTE: Add $1,800. & up for access. hardtop.

1954

	6	5	4	3	2	1
6-cyl Conv	1950	6250	10,400	20,800	36,400	52,000

NOTE: Add $1,800. & up for access. hardtop.

1955

	6	5	4	3	2	1
6-cyl Conv	2650	8400	14,000	28,000	49,000	70,000
8-cyl Conv	2650	8400	14,000	28,000	49,000	70,000

NOTE: Add $1,800. & up for access. hardtop.

1956

	6	5	4	3	2	1
Conv	1900	6000	10,000	20,000	35,000	50,000

NOTE: All post-1955 Corvettes are V-8 powered.
Add $1,800. & up for removable hardtop.
Add 20 percent for two 4 barrel carbs.

1957

	6	5	4	3	2	1
Conv	2050	6600	11,000	22,000	38,500	55,000

NOTES: Add $1,800. for hardtop; 30 percent for F.I.
Add 25 percent for two 4 barrel carbs.

1958

	6	5	4	3	2	1
Conv	1700	5400	9000	18,000	31,500	45,000

NOTES: Add $1,800. for hardtop; 30 percent for F.I.
Add 25 percent for two 4 barrel carbs.

1959

	6	5	4	3	2	1
Conv	1600	5050	8400	16,800	29,400	42,000

NOTES: Add $1,800. for hardtop; 30 percent for F.I.
Add 20 percent for two 4 barrel carbs.

1960

	6	5	4	3	2	1
Conv	1600	5050	8400	16,800	29,400	42,000

NOTES: Add $1,800. for hardtop; 30 percent for F.I.
Add 20 percent for two 4 barrel carbs.

1961

	6	5	4	3	2	1
Conv	1650	5300	8800	17,600	30,800	44,000

NOTES: Add $1,800. for hardtop; 30 percent for F.I.
Add 20 percent for two 4 barrel carbs.

1962

	6	5	4	3	2	1
Conv	1700	5400	9000	18,000	31,500	45,000

NOTE: Add $1,800. for hardtop; 30 percent for F.I.

1963

	6	5	4	3	2	1
Spt Cpe	1450	4550	7600	15,200	26,600	38,000
Conv	1350	4300	7200	14,400	25,200	36,000
GS					value not estimable	

NOTES: Add 20 percent for F.I.; $4,500. for A/C.
Add $1,800. for hardtop; $3,000. for knock off wheels.
Z06 option, value not estimable.

1964

	6	5	4	3	2	1
Spt Cpe	1050	3350	5600	11,200	19,600	28,000
Conv	1100	3500	5800	11,600	20,300	29,000

NOTES: Add 20 percent for F.I.; $4,500. for A/C.
Add $1,800. for hardtop; $3,000. for knock off wheels.

1965

	6	5	4	3	2	1
Spt Cpe	1250	3950	6600	13,200	23,100	33,000
Conv	1300	4100	6800	13,600	23,800	34,000

NOTES: Add 30 percent for F.I.; $4,500. for A/C.
Add $3,000. for knock off wheels; 50 percent for 396 engine.
Add $1,800. for hardtop.

1966

	6	5	4	3	2	1
Spt Cpe	1250	3950	6600	13,200	23,100	33,000
Conv	1300	4100	6800	13,600	23,800	34,000

NOTES: Add $4,500. for A/C; 20 percent for 427 engine - 390 hp.
Add 50 percent for 427 engine - 425 hp.
Add $3,000. for knock off wheels; $1200. for hardtop.

1967

	6	5	4	3	2	1
Spt Cpe	1300	4200	7000	14,000	24,500	35,000
Conv	1350	4300	7200	14,400	25,200	36,000

NOTES: Add $4,500. for A/C. L88 & L89 option not estimable. 20 percent for 427 engine - 390 hp. Add 40 percent for 427 engine - 400 hp, 60 percent for 427 engine - 435 hp; $4,000. for aluminum wheels; $1800. for hardtop.

1968

	6	5	4	3	2	1
Spt Cpe	950	3000	5000	10,000	17,500	25,000
Conv	1050	3350	5600	11,200	19,600	28,000

NOTES: Add 40 percent for L89 427 - 435 hp aluminum head option. L88 engine option not estimable.

1969

	6	5	4	3	2	1
Spt Cpe	1000	3100	5200	10,400	18,200	26,000
Conv	1100	3500	5800	11,600	20,300	29,000

NOTES: Add 50 percent for 427 - 435 hp aluminum head option. L88 engine option not estimable.

1970

	6	5	4	3	2	1
Spt Cpe	900	2900	4800	9600	16,800	24,000
Conv	1000	3250	5400	10,800	18,900	27,000

NOTES: Add 20 percent for LT-1 option. ZR1 option not estimable.

1971

	6	5	4	3	2	1
Spt Cpe	850	2750	4600	9200	16,100	23,000
Conv	1000	3100	5200	10,400	18,200	26,000

NOTES: Add 20 percent for LT-1 option; 20 percent for LS 6 option; ZR1 and ZR2 options not estimable.

1972

	6	5	4	3	2	1
Spt Cpe	850	2750	4600	9200	16,100	23,000
Conv	1000	3100	5200	10,400	18,200	26,000

NOTES: Add 20 percent for LT-1 option; ZR1 option not estimable.

1973

	6	5	4	3	2	1
Spt Cpe	800	2500	4200	8400	14,700	21,000
Conv	1000	3100	5200	10,400	18,200	26,000

1974

	6	5	4	3	2	1
Spt Cpe	650	2050	3400	6800	11,900	17,000
Conv	900	2900	4800	9600	16,800	24,000

1975

	6	5	4	3	2	1
Spt Cpe	700	2150	3600	7200	12,600	18,000
Conv	1000	3100	5200	10,400	18,200	26,000

1976

	6	5	4	3	2	1
Cpe	650	2050	3400	6800	11,900	17,000

1977

	6	5	4	3	2	1
Cpe	650	2050	3400	6800	11,900	17,000

1978

	6	5	4	3	2	1
Cpe	700	2300	3800	7600	13,300	19,000

Note: Add 10 percent for pace car or anniversary model.
Add 10 percent for L82 engine option.

1979

	6	5	4	3	2	1
Cpe	700	2150	3600	7200	12,600	18,000

NOTE: Add 10 percent for L82 engine option.

1980

Corvette, V-8	6	5	4	3	2	1
Cpe	700	2150	3600	7200	12,600	18,000

NOTE: Add 10 percent for L82 engine option.

1981

Corvette, V-8	6	5	4	3	2	1
Cpe	700	2150	3600	7200	12,600	18,000

1982

Corvette, V-8	6	5	4	3	2	1
2d HBk	700	2300	3800	7600	13,300	19,000

NOTE: Add 20 percent for Collector Edition.

1983

NOTE: None manufactured.

1984

Corvette, V-8	6	5	4	3	2	1
2d HBk	700	2150	3600	7200	12,600	18,000

1985

Corvette, V-8	6	5	4	3	2	1
2d HBk	700	2150	3600	7200	12,600	18,000

1986

Corvette, V-8	6	5	4	3	2	1
2d HBk	700	2300	3800	7600	13,300	19,000
Conv	850	2750	4600	9200	16,100	23,000

NOTE: Add 10 percent for pace car.

1987

Corvette, V-8	6	5	4	3	2	1
2d HBk	700	2300	3800	7600	13,300	19,000
Conv	850	2750	4600	9200	16,100	23,000

1988

Corvette, V-8	6	5	4	3	2	1
2d Cpe	600	1850	3100	6200	10,900	15,500
Conv	800	2500	4200	8400	14,700	21,000

1989

Corvette, V-8	6	5	4	3	2	1
2d HBk	800	2500	4200	8400	14,700	21,000
Conv	950	3000	5000	10,000	17,500	25,000

1990

Corvette, V-8	6	5	4	3	2	1
2d HBk	850	2750	4600	9200	16,100	23,000
Conv	1000	3250	5400	10,800	18,900	27,000
2d HBk ZRI	1700	5400	9000	18,000	31,500	45,000

1991

Corvette, V-8	6	5	4	3	2	1
2d HBk	1100	3500	5800	11,600	20,300	29,000
Conv	1200	3850	6400	12,800	22,400	32,000
2d HBk ZRI	1800	5750	9600	19,200	33,600	48,000

Speaking of Great Automotive Books, Read What These Six Have to Say!

"**1995 Standard Guide to Cars & Prices** - The accurate price information found in this updated guide can help you avoid overpaying for that car of your dreams. If you have one stored away, the updated values can also help you decide if it's the smart time to sell, or not. 608 pages packed with over 220,000 price listings, 150 B&W photos, 6x9, $15.95, **code CG07**"

"**Chevrolet High Performance** - Chronicles four decades of hard charging, revved up Chevy high performance, from 1955 to present day. Includes the "hot" Corvettes, Corvairs, Chevelles, Camaros, Monte Carlos and many more. 304 pages, over 200 photos, 8-1/2x11, $24.95, **code CH01**"

"**Race Car Flashback** - Reads like back issues of the classic racing magazine, "Speed Age." Filled with true stories and blow-by-blow rundowns of motorsports racing from the early days on the sands of Daytona to today's super speedways. 304 pages, over 300 photos, 8-1/2x11, $19.95 **code RC01**"

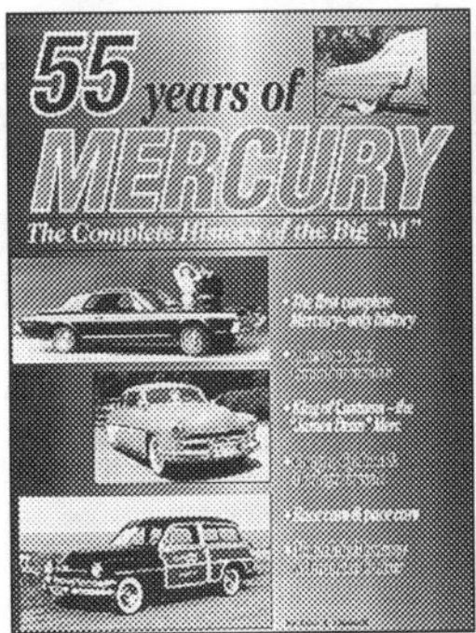

"**Mustang: The Affordable Sportscar** - Take a joy ride in America's favorite "pony." A must read for anyone who has ever owned one, has one... loves these special, sporty cars. A 30th anniversary tribute that makes a great gift! 304 pages, over 300 photos, 8-1/2x11, $16.95, **code MS01**"

"**55 Years of Mercury** - The "big M" hot performers come to life in this special, first-time edition filled with marvelous Mercury facts and trivia. Details the 55-year history of Mercury, and corrects many misconceptions and inaccuracies. 256 pages, over 500 photos, 8-1/2x11, $16.95, **code ME01**"

"**Automobilia** - Almost anything you want to know about automotive memorabilia, is conveniently collected and compiled in this special volume. You'll find accurate values for a myriad of items, including gas globes, hood ornaments, pedal cars, and much more! 275 pages, 300 photos, 8-1/2x11, $19.95, **code AO01**"

❑ ***YES**, please rush me the following book(s).*

❑ *Plus also send me your FREE, complete automotive listing.*

Qty	Code	Price	Subtotal
	CG07	$15.95	$
	RC01	19.95	
	CHO1	24.95	
	MS01	16.95	
	ME01	16.95	
	AO01	19.95	
Subtotal			$
Shipping (add $2.50 first book, $1.50 each add'l. Addresses outside U.S. add $5 per book, U.S. funds.)			$
WI residents add 5.5% sales tax			$
TOTAL AMOUNT ENCLOSED			$

Name ______________________

Address ______________________

City ______________________

State ____________ Zip ________

❑ Check or money order (to Krause Publications)

❑ MasterCard ❑ VISA

Credit Card No. ______________________

Expires: Mo. ____________ Yr. ________

Signature ______________________

MasterCard & VISA Customers
Dial Toll-Free

800-258-0929

Dept YZB2

Mon. - Fri. 6:30 am - 8:00 pm,
Sat. 8:00 am - 2:00 pm, CT

MAIL TO:

KRAUSE PUBLICATIONS

700 E. State Street
Dept. YZB2
Iola, WI 54990-0001

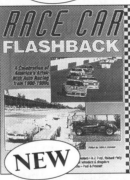

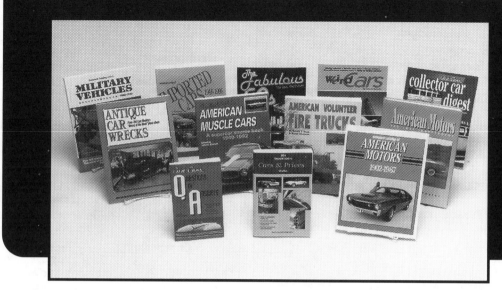